CHEMICAL INSTRUMENTATION: A SYSTEMATIC APPROACH SECOND EDITION

HOWARD A. STROBEL
Duke University

CHEMICAL INSTRUMENTATION: A SYSTEMATIC APPROACH
SECOND EDITION

ADDISON-WESLEY PUBLISHING COMPANY
Reading, Massachusetts · Menlo Park, California
London · Amsterdam · Don Mills, Ontario · Sydney

This book is in the
ADDISON-WESLEY SERIES IN CHEMISTRY

Consulting Editor
Francis T. Bonner

ISBN 0-201-07301-3
DEFGHIJKL-MA-798765

To Shirley, Gary, Lynn, and Paul

PREFACE to Second Edition

Twelve years have passed since the appearance of the first edition of *Chemical Instrumentation*. Since the second edition represents a substantial rewriting, its main aspects deserve comment; its scope and aims, the ways in which the book has changed in response to developments in techniques and instrumentation, and some of the possibilities foreseen for use of this edition in courses.

Though a major revision has been carried out, the scope and aims of the book remain essentially the same. The volume treats a large number of the spectrometric, electrometric, and other physical methods that are important to chemists. What is lost by the omission of certain techniques (the book is long already) has—it is hoped—been compensated by the adoption of a consistent point of view.

The basic goal of the book is to offer a broad coverage of physical methods. The text reflects the conviction that such methods can best be mastered if the instrumentation necessary to measurement is studied in its own right. Thus equal emphasis is given to measurement principles and instrument design on the one hand and to techniques and their underlying theory on the other. The basic aim has also seemed best served by a semiquantitative approach, that is, by introducing mathematical expressions where necessary for good understanding but omitting most derivations of equations.

The other major goal is the development of a working mastery of the measurement process itself. It is easiest to describe the goal by suggesting criteria by which a working grasp can be recognized. Some of them are (a) facility in using instruments similar to or related to those one has studied; (b) an ability to devise and apply appropriate criteria for choosing an instrument (or a technique) for measurements on a given system; (c) facility in appreciating and mastering kinds of measurements that are unfamiliar. This aim has seemed best achieved by use of a modular approach* to instrumentation, a point that will be discussed below.

The second aim is actually also related to the time dimension of chemical measurement. One's grasp of physical methods must be sufficient to allow him to cope with the stream of new or modified instruments and techniques that appears. The questions that one must answer satisfactorily are: "What advantage(s) does the new instrument or technique offer over the present one?" and "How can the new device best be utilized in determinations of interest to me?" Answering the queries should be a straightforward process, though not always an easy one, given a good grounding in measurement and techniques.

---

* A module is a subassembly or part that performs a particular function. Some examples are dc power supplies, monochromators, detectors, and amplifiers. When a modular point of view is taken, an instrument is represented by a block diagram.

How does the second edition differ from the first? In the years that have elapsed since the publication of the first edition, there have been major changes in the field of measurement and analysis. Three of the most visible are (a) the well-nigh complete shift of electronics from vacuum tubes to semiconductor devices, (b) the increasing development of automatic instruments and tie-ins between instruments and computers, and (c) a growing acceptance of a modular or a "systems" view of instruments. All of these changes are reflected in this edition. Several chapters are given over to solid state electronics, and the older tube electronics is virtually excluded. Both automation and computer control are treated briefly and generally as they relate to instrument design. This discussion will be found in the parts of Chapters 1, 3, 9, and 17 that deal with the systems aspects of instruments. For reasons of brevity and because of rapid development in the field, little attempt is made to deal with automation and computer control in the discussion of individual instruments.

As noted above, a modular view of instrument design and function has been adopted. Its advantages deserve fuller comment. One is that it effects an economy both for the author and the reader. Modules are treated separately in early chapters where their characteristics can be explored with appropriate rigor and the most important different forms can be described and compared. Later, in chapters on techniques block diagrams are used for a particular instrument to show the modules that make it up and the pattern in which they are linked. For example, monochromators, optical sources, and detectors are discussed in Chapters 11 and 12, and the building up of spectrometers of various types is treated in Chapters 13–18, which deal with various spectroscopic methods. When an instrument is discussed, suitable choices of modules for it are suggested through examples and sometimes also through exercises at the ends of chapters. A very few modules that are peculiar to a single technique, such as burner-nebulizers in flame spectrometry, are discussed in chapters on techniques.

Some other advantages of a modular approach accrue to the instrument user. The most important is that he can understand an instrument on a "macroscopic" level. The types of components that make it up and their function can be perceived without the necessity of mastering a mass of detail. Further, manufacturer's specifications tend to become more intelligible since many aspects of the performance of an instrument are determined by the quality of particular modules. For example, the resolution of a spectrophotometer is mainly determined by the quality of its wavelength isolation device. A third advantage is that a "systems" approach is feasible. As a result, it becomes a fairly straightforward process to propose ways to optimize one or another aspect of instrument behavior, e.g., sensitivity, or to adapt it to new measurement situations.

The reader familiar with the first edition will observe other changes as well. He will find that the treatment of several topics has been expanded to chapter length (fluorometry, flame spectrometry, Raman spectrometry, and chromatography) and several new topics are included (NMR spectrometry, single sweep and pulse polarography, mass spectrometry, operational amplifiers, signal-to-noise optimization, digital electronics, and monochromators). Further, the theoretical background of most measurement techniques is presented in greater depth. Finally, SI notation and units have been generally adopted (see Appendix C).

As a result of the way the book has been revised, the second edition can be used in at least three kinds of courses:

1) A junior-senior analytical chemistry course emphasizing physical methods. An appropriate selection of material would be Chapter 1, followed by chapters selected from the blocks 13 through 16 and 18 through 31. The index should prove helpful in locating pertinent analytical information. In such a course it is recommended that a problem book appropriate to the aims of the particular course be used also.

2) A senior or first-year graduate course in instrumentation that stresses electronics and electrical methods. Appropriate material would be Chapters 1 through 9, 23, and chapters selected from the block 24 through 28. Chapter 19 and perhaps also Chapter 17 could be included.

3) A senior or first-year graduate course in instrumentation that treats optical and spectral methods. Appropriate material would be Chapters 1 and 8, 10 through 12, 17, and chapters selected from the blocks 13 through 16 and 20 through 22. Selected sections from Chapter 2 through 7 could be included.

When used in courses the book will need to be supplemented by a laboratory manual. Since courses in modern analysis and instrumentation differ appreciably in aim and scope from school to school, it seemed wise to omit laboratory experiments from this edition. The teacher is accordingly referred to the many fine laboratory manuals that have appeared in the past several years. Some are the following:

1. C. N. Reilley and D. T. Sawyer, *Experiments for Instrumental Methods.* New York: McGraw-Hill, 1961.

2. L. P. Morgenthaler, *Basic Operational Amplifier Circuits for Analytical Chemical Instrumentation*, 2nd ed. Danville, Calif.: McKee-Pedersen Instruments, 1968.

3. G. G. Guilbault and L. G. Hargis, *Instrumental Analysis Manual.* New York: Marcel Dekker, 1970.

4. A. James Diefenderfer, *Basic Techniques of Electronic Instrumentation.* Philadelphia: Saunders, 1972.

5. C. E. Meloan and R. W. Kiser, *Problems and Experiments in Instrumental Analysis.* Columbus, Ohio: C. E. Merrill, 1963.

6. R. W. Hannah and J. S. Swinehart, *Experiments in Techniques of Infrared Spectroscopy*, rev. ed. Norwalk, Conn.: Perkin-Elmer, 1968.

7. Issues of *Journal of Chemical Education* (this journal publishes suitable experiments from time to time).

The teacher will also wish to know that names of manufacturers of a particular type of instrument have been omitted in this edition. Now there is at least one instrument listing that appears annually, an August issue of *Analytical Chemistry*, entitled "Laboratory Guide." Usually a late fall issue of *Science*, "Guide to Scientific Instruments," is also published. These compilations are up-to-date and inclusive, and instruments appear to be classified with care.

An annotated bibliography of important references appears at the end of each chapter. An additional collection of references too recent to be listed there has been organized in the same way and appears in Appendix D. Both listings should be consulted. References to each chapter bibliography within a chapter are denoted by brackets. Thus [12] means "see Reference 12, which will be found at the end of this chapter." Where reference is made to literature at the end of another chapter, the number of that chapter is given, following the reference number. Thus [12, Chap. 10] means "See Reference 12, listed at the end of Chapter 10." A reference to the tenth chapter of Reference 12 would be [Chap. 10 of 12].

Acknowledgments

I especially thank two colleagues—Dr. Maurice Bursey and Dr. Charles H. Lochmüller—for writing Chapters 30 and 31 on mass spectrometry and chromatography, respectively. Their share in this enterprise is considerable.

In addition, I am grateful to the host of authors from whose works I have learned. The group numbers too many to name, but they are acknowledged in the many references at the ends of chapters.

I thank sincerely Drs. Leon N. Klatt and John T. Bowman for reading and commenting on the entire manuscript. Warm appreciation is also due to Dr. Marvin M. Crutchfield, who performed the same function for the chapter on nuclear magnetic resonance spectrometry, to Gray F. Crouse, who assisted greatly in the preparation of illustrations, to many students, who after using some of these chapters in preliminary draft, offered criticism and thoughtful suggestions, to Cathy Penny, Gloria Powers, and Sandy Parker for typing the numerous drafts and the final manuscript, and to Scott A. Miller for his generous assistance in reading proof.

Finally, I solicit the assistance of readers of this book in identifying errors and in offering suggestions.

Leicester, England   H.A.S.
March 1972

PREFACE to First Edition

This text has grown out of the teaching of two one-semester advanced courses in instrumental analysis, one emphasizing optical methods, the other emphasizing electrical techniques. Its level is therefore appropriate both to the advanced chemistry major and to the first-year graduate student who has not been exposed to a systematic coverage of chemical instrumentation.

While writing this text, I was guided by the conviction that the instrumental techniques that are used in analysis and research can best be mastered if chemical instrumentation is studied in its own right. Accordingly, after beginning with a critical examination of the process of measurement, this book turns to a systematic treatment of instrument *design* and instrumental *methods*. The adequate consideration of the first theme has dictated the strong undercurrent of physics, engineering, and physical chemistry that is evident on inspection of this book. These disciplines provide the fundamentals that are needed to understand design and function. The pursuit of the second theme, laboratory procedures for the use of instruments, has required a running discussion of physical properties and behavior throughout. Above all, I have aimed for a good balance between physical theory and design on the one hand, and chemical theory and procedure on the other.

Because one focus is on instrumentation, a substantial amount of physical theory has been introduced. Chapters 2, 3, and 4 deal respectively with errors, the interaction of electromagnetic radiation and matter, and physical optics. These chapters set the stage for the consideration, in following chapters, of several basic optical techniques. Similarly, in the second half of the book, Chapters 11, 12, and 13 respectively treat electrical phenomena and electrochemistry, basic electronics, and somewhat more advanced electronics. These chapters furnish background for the discussion of electrical methods of analysis. Where desirable, additional theory has been introduced in some of the chapters on methods.

Although the chapters on specific techniques and analyses are largely complete in themselves, it is not intended that they be studied without the collateral or prior reading of the appropriate theoretical sections, or without some accompanying laboratory experiments. A concerted attempt has been made to integrate the physical theory with the discussion of particular techniques and kinds of instrumentation. It is hoped that the cross referencing ensures that the reader who begins his study with any one of the methods is promptly directed to the pertinent background theory. Likewise, the representative laboratory experiments in the appendix are grouped according to type of instrumentation to facilitate reference to the chapters on methods.

In all parts, as complete an understanding of the subject matter as possible has been sought. This aim has seemed best served by treating theory qualitatively, i.e., by introducing mathematical expressions when necessary for good understanding, with appropriate definition of symbols but with few derivations of equations. This aim has required also that careful attention be given to the adequate statement and explanation of all major aspects of instrument design and operational and analytical procedures by placing them in their proper theoretical perspective.

This approach has justification. For instance, methods that are characteristic of instrumental analysis are applied as often in research, where one must have a basic appreciation of what he is measuring, as they are in routine analysis. Again, in colleges and universities, "instrumental" and some advanced analytical courses are as useful in introducing students to the tools of the many varied applications of chemical research as such courses are in acquainting students with analytical methods *per se*. The problems of identification, quantitative analysis, and measurement are common to all chemical pursuits.

The "research" approach also serves well by allowing a suggestive coverage of commercial instruments. Because a text cannot examine more than one or two representative instruments of a type without becoming a reference work or catalog, it must seek instead to develop the student's perspective and basic understanding. Success will result in the student's ability to appreciate the design and performance of other instruments of the same, or related, type as the representative instrument with which he has had contact. Actually, a problem with a time dimension presents itself, for new instruments or modifications of old ones are appearing on the market with increasing frequency. Ready adaptation to developments and, indeed, anticipation of some of the developments require the student to have a sound grasp of fundamentals. At the minimum, he should be able to examine new types of instruments with discernment and understanding, and he should know how to make simple modifications to his own instruments when such modifications are desirable.

A bibliography is listed at the end of each chapter, and references to the bibliography are denoted by brackets. Thus, [12] means "See Reference 12, which will be found at the end of this chapter." Where reference is made to literature that is listed at the end of another chapter, the number of that chapter is given following the reference number. Thus [12, Chap. 10] means "See Reference 12, listed at the end of Chapter 10"; a reference to the tenth chapter of Reference 12 would be [Chap. 10 of 12].

Acknowledgments are due to many colleagues and the host of authors of basic texts from whom I have learned. The latter group are too numerous to list, but they comprise many of the references at the ends of chapters. I am particularly grateful to Dean Marcus E. Hobbs for the point of view that he has contributed as my predecessor in the instrumental courses at Duke University and for starting me in this venture of authorship by agreeing initially to serve as co-author. We both regretted that he had to withdraw because of the pressures of his administrative duties after he had prepared a first draft of but a single chapter, Chapter 3. His criticism of some of the other early chapters and helpful counsel have also been highly valued. I also wish to thank most sincerely Dr. L. B. Rogers for reading and commenting on the entire manuscript.

Others to whom I am in debt for reading portions of chapters and making useful suggestions are Drs. William R. Krigbaum, Louis D. Quin, and Dewey K. Carpenter. Finally, the unstinting efforts of my wife in typing the several drafts of the manuscript are most heartily acknowledged. Without her encouragement and assistance, this book would never have been undertaken.

October 1959   H.A.S.

CONTENTS

SOME SPECTROMETRIC METHODS

Chapter 13   Emission Spectrometry

Chapter 14   Flame Spectrometry

Chapter 15   Fluorometry

Chapter 16   Absorption Spectrometry

SOME ELECTROANALYTICAL METHODS

Chapter 26   Single-Sweep and Pulse Polarography

Chapter 27   Coulometric Methods

Chapter 28   Conductometric Methods

OTHER METHODS

Chapter 29   Methods Using Radioisotopes

Chapter 1

MEASUREMENT AND INSTRUMENTATION

1.1 INTRODUCTION

All chemical determinations are basically measurements of physical properties of substances. For example, characteristic wavelengths are measured in infrared spectrometry, the mass of a precipitate in a gravimetric determination, and cell potential differences in potentiometry. It is true that separations and one or more chemical reactions may also be inherent to a determination. Separations remove interferences from samples, and quantitative chemical reactions are indispensable to procedures such as gravimetric and titrimetric methods. In general, the importance attached to measuring the physical property lessens as the number of steps preliminary to it increases. Yet the determination of the property is a crucial step. Both the complexity of a measurement (whether preliminary separations, reactions, or other operations are indicated) and its precision usually depend on the property selected and the mode of measurement used.

A list of possible measurements may be developed by recalling the many physical properties materials possess: light absorption, refractive index, specific resistance, magnetic susceptibility, solubility, temperature coefficient of expansion, etc. As the list is considered, it becomes obvious that most properties are of interest only in their own right. Only a few like light absorption find wide application in the identification of substances, estimation of amounts, and study of behavior. Two important questions can be raised.

1. How do chemists and instrument makers decide that the potentialities of a property are sufficient to warrant the development of convenient methods of measurement and appropriate instrumentation?
2. How can we determine the physical property most suitable for analytical or research measurements on a particular type of sample?

The interrelationship of these questions should be evident. The decision to develop a new measurement surely is spurred by insights developed in answer to the second question. Still other queries might be added.

Although a full answer to the first question is beyond the scope of this book, the question is relevant. For example, as a result of just this kind of decision, in the 1960s nmr, esr, and atomic absorption spectrometry were developed into common techniques. You will also find the question useful as one basis around which to organize ideas about measurement. Some aspects of an answer will be implied in this chapter, and others will be offered in Chapter 8 and in the chapters on particular methods.*

---

* After perusing major parts of the book you may be tempted to frame your own answer.

1

The search for an answer to the second question will call for a comparison of physical properties, their methods of measurement, and available instrumentation. Such a search will be implicit through most of the book. Each later chapter on a particular technique like nmr spectrometry will provide data helpful in assessing the relative merits of the property. Similarly, chapters on instrument modules or systems will contribute general information useful in evaluating instrumentation. In the chapters on techniques a few comparisons of properties will be made to stimulate you to develop your own. The process of choosing the best property to determine can be really understood, however, only if the measurement process itself and the connection between instrument design and quality of measurement are appreciated. This relationship must now be examined.

1.2 THE NATURE OF A MEASUREMENT

To what degree does every measurement resemble all others? The question is helpful because it leads to an analysis of the steps involved in a chemical determination. They are:

1. Generation of signal,

2. Detecting and/or transducing the signal after its interaction with (or generation by) a sample of interest,

3. Amplification,

4. Processing or modification (conversion of the signal into a form suitable to operate a readout device), and

5. Output or readout (as a line on a chart, pointer deflection on a meter, digital reading, etc.).

Not all steps are required in every measurement. Nor is every step necessarily associated with a separate entity; instrument modules or subassemblies that perform two or more functions are common.

Generation of signal.   The majority of physical measurements are records of a response of a substance to an imposed signal. Examples are abundant. A refractive index measurement requires a light beam as well as the apparatus for observing the effect, a conductance determination requires an electrical current, and an absorption measurement a beam of light. By convention, optical signals originate from a "source," electrical ones from a "generator."

Transducing or detecting. Usually the "information" (the altered or self-generated signal) is detected and transformed into a useful form of output by a single component. It is called a *detector* or an *input transducer*. A phototube, for example, not only detects light signals but transduces them into electrical currents. If a multiplier phototube is substituted, it will provide three types of action: It will (a) detect the light, (b) transform it into a current, and (c) amplify it by as much as 10^7 times. Still another example is an electrode, which, on being immersed in a suitable solution, produces a voltage that varies with activity.

Amplification; transmission. In general, detectors that respond by transducing the original information into an electrical signal, either a current or a voltage, are preferred above all others. The value of this kind of output arises mainly from the remarkable degree of amplification and signal modification possible by use of electronics. Amplification in an instrument is usually indispensable. For instance, the maximum current that may be drawn in most pH measurements amounts to about 10^{-12} A. The meter that presents the result, however, requires currents of the order of 10^{-3} A to operate. Amplification of the detector-transducer output by a factor of 10^9 is necessary and can be accomplished electronically. Another reason for preferring an electrical output is that of general convenience; this type of output is more easily handled under nearly all conditions.

Processing. The step of processing or modification of the signal to a useful form is an increasingly common one in instruments. For example, signals may be differentiated and integrated with ease, and in modern instrumentation it is not uncommon to have a computation stage sufficiently elaborate to calculate concentrations automatically from the raw data of signals. For example, direct-reading atomic absorption spectrophotometers and automatic analyzers make this kind of computation.

Readout. After any processing a signal is read out or presented. Meter deflections, digital readouts, and wiper locations along slidewires (reported as a pen position on a chart) are common instrument "outputs," and they have the advantage of great simplicity. A disadvantage is their restriction of data-taking to isolated points. If an absorption curve is to be found as a function of wavelength, a recorder that produces a pen tracing of the curve is much to be preferred as a means of presentation. On the other hand, the measurement of very rapidly varying properties cannot be handled by these arrangements. Here the data may best be presented by use of an oscilloscope and/or recording optically or magnetically.

All the steps will be treated fully, though perhaps not explicitly, as the text progresses.

Quality requirements. It is important to appreciate that there are also subjective expectations with regard to the quality of measurements, which set the process of their determination somewhat apart from other operations. All measurements must be valid, reproducible, accurate, and sensitive, although the specifications vary in degree. A brief treatment of some of these quality requirements will be given in Section 1.5 and the following sections.

1.3 CHOICE OF A METHOD OF MEASUREMENT

A measurement begins with an examination of the chemical system of interest. Kinds of information that must be learned about available samples are: (a) physical state, (b) expected constituents and percentage ranges, (c) amounts, (d) whether a measurement of a property of one constituent will be affected by the presence of other constituents; (e) whether samples can be consumed in measurement, and (f) time and cost limitations. In order to establish an appropriate level of precision and accuracy, you must know the way the results of measurement will be used. As suggested in the following example, a consideration of these factors will lead to a choice of:

1. The physical property to be determined and a method of measurement,
2. Appropriate instrumentation, and
3. Specifics of procedure.

Example How the emission spectrum of a sample is observed depends on the kind of sample and the information sought. Since different spectral regions may be examined, procedure and instrumentation tend to vary from determination to determination.

If a sample contains a few elements that are easily excited, flame excitation and a low-resolution spectrometer may suffice for the determination. On the other hand, the identification of trace-level components in a steel sample requires a source of energy, a carefully designed excitation routine, and a precise spectrometer of high resolution.

The choice of *physical property* to be measured usually requires comparing the merits of several properties, in order to assess which is best suited to the kind of sample(s) available and the type of information sought. Some properties are highly specific and characteristic, like a mass spectrum, and will allow a direct identification and quantitative determination of a substance as well as yield other information, in this case about molecular structure and gas-phase reactions. Other properties such as refractive index are characteristic but essentially nonspecific. They are of limited value for a direct identification but are useful for corroboration of identity. This type of property is also well suited to use for quantitative determination in many simple systems. Refractive index and density are good examples of nonspecific but characteristic properties that are frequently measured to determine the composition of binary liquid mixtures. Finally, even noncharacteristic but *extensive* properties like mass must be considered. Not only is this measurement the basis of classical gravimetry, but the thermal decomposition of compounds is commonly followed by changes in sample weight.

The selection of a *method of measurement* is equally important. A poor method will limit reliability, sensitivity, and usefulness of the measurement as much as awkward techniques. An example will illustrate the importance of this step.

Example The refractive index may be used as an indication of the purity of transparent liquids. It may be found in a variety of ways:

1. By microscopic determination of both the real depth of an empty container and its apparent depth when filled with the liquid,

2. By ascertaining the apparent bending of an opaque rod immersed in the liquid,

3. By interferometry, which depends on the change of the wavelength of light with refractive index, or

4. By a determination of the critical angle of refraction of light in the medium.

The last is certainly the most straightforward. It usually requires only an observation of the angle that the boundary between bright and dark areas makes with the light ray entering the liquid at grazing incidence. An illustration is given in Fig. 1.1.

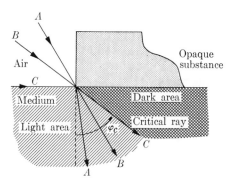

Fig. 1.1 Observation of the critical angle in a liquid. The refractive index of the liquid is a function of the critical angle φ_c.

1.4 CONTROL OF VARIABLES

For successful measurement, it is likewise essential that the factors that will influence projected measurements be kept in view. Under what conditions will determinations be made? What variables are known to influence the measurements? Which variables must be regulated and which can be left uncontrolled? In seeking answers to these questions, both factors that appear to influence (a) the property to be observed or its measurement and (b) the reliable functioning of the instrument must be considered.

All variables that affect the value of physical properties or their observation must be regulated or somehow allowed for during a measurement. Temperature changes alter most properties; ordinary pressure fluctuations influence measurements on gases; aging and mechanical shock will affect alignment; and sound waves, radioactive emanations, electric or magnetic fields, and other influences should in most cases be considered in designing. To ignore even a seemingly "remote" variable without checking the extent of fluctuation likely to be encountered and the consequent effect is hazardous. Insulation and regulation are general techniques for holding one or more critical variables constant.

Example Temperature is found to introduce differences of the order of 2% per degree in the electrical conductivity of liquids. The closeness of control required will be dictated by the precision sought, and the method of control by the flexibility of procedure desired. *Insulation* will smooth temperature changes and allow measurements at the prevailing temperature, but it severely restricts flexibility. It is more general to use *regulation* in conjunction with insulation by circulating thermostated fluid around the sample holder.

The host of other factors influencing a property or its determination are best controlled by the use of other stratagems. Really there are two basic and complementary approaches at this point. One is procedural, the other substantive, i.e., it involves attention to design. A discussion of design possibilities will be taken up later. Here three procedural stratagems will be considered. Note that these effect control of determinate error.

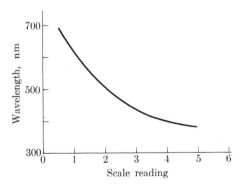

Fig. 1.2 Calibration or dispersion curve for a prism spectrograph.

The use of *calibration curves* prepared by carrying out measurements on standards is a common procedural arrangement to compensate for variables whose magnitude cannot easily be estimated or whose drift cannot be conveniently regulated. The method is routine in research and analysis. *Calibrations* or standardizations of balances, pipets, chemicals, and instruments by test or comparison with reference compounds or standards furnish corrections that may be applied to actual measurements.

Calibrations are most useful if organized in tabular or graphic form. In Fig. 1.2 such a curve is given for a prism spectrograph. These scale readings were plotted when known wavelengths were observed with a particular spectrograph in a particular room. Assuming the room is maintained at constant temperature, the influence of temperature, aging, previous mechanical shock, irregular scale graduation, shifts in alignment caused by temperature changes, the untheoretical response of the instrument, and mechanical and optical errors in the instrument should be minimized when the calibration curve is used.

Example In flame photometric analysis of alkali metal salt solutions, continual *recalibration* is valuable. Vaporization rates, flame temperatures, and excitation efficiencies depend on many variables that cannot easily be controlled. By calibrating the instrument response with known samples just before and just after analyzing an unknown, one can make allowance for actual operating conditions. (A large deviation will probably suggest resetting controls.)

Variables may also differ in magnitude from measurement to measurement. In this case a second procedural stratagem, the use of *blanks*, is frequently effective. A blank is a sample identical in makeup with an unknown, except that the constituent of interest is omitted. A measurement is made first on a blank and then on an unknown. If blank and unknown are affected alike by determinate errors, a comparison of results should produce data free from systematic effects by minor variables. A prime example may be drawn from spectrophotometric analysis.

Example The intensity of monochromatic light transmitted by a dissolved sample may be related in simple fashion to its concentration. When the solution is placed in a transmission cell, however, the cell walls further reduce the intensity by reflecting and absorbing light (see Fig. 16.1).

These effects may be eliminated by a measurement procedure making use of a blank. With the arrangement shown in Fig. 1.3, a ratio is taken of the meter deflection with the sample solution in the beam to that when the blank is substituted. The ratio represents the transmittance of the sample alone. The effect of the cell is canceled. Note the other variables controlled at the same time. Solvent absorption and drift in source intensity or in the performance of other modules is also canceled.

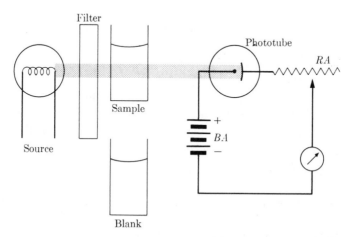

Fig. 1.3 Single-beam, direct-reading filter photometer. Readings are taken of the transmittance of the sample and blank. Battery BA supplies power to the phototube. The tap on resistor RA is varied to adjust the meter deflection to 100% when the blank is in the beam.

Controls are a third procedural method. They are probably more commonly used in complex noninstrumental systems where some variables cannot conveniently be identified. When they are used in analytical work, they are samples of known concentration in "x" as much like the unknown as possible, and are used as a "running" reference. For example, in testing the corrosion resistance of a new alloy, one designates a few samples as controls and treats them each time in the same way, while varying the treatment of the others.

1.5 BASIC DESIGN PATTERNS

Let us now investigate some of the good designs for laying out an instrument. From this overall perspective, an instrument is a system (a) whose parts or modules may be arranged in various patterns, e.g. in a single channel, and (b) whose operation may be controlled in appropriate ways, e.g. manually or automatically. An orderly approach is to consider design patterns first and to defer the question of control. It will be taken up in a general way in Section 1.10.

Since a pattern is made up of parts, a question immediately arises as to what are the elements of an instrument. Is a UV-VIS spectrophotometer made up of fuses, slits, diffraction grating, chopper, a photomultiplier tube, transistors, and other components? Or is it better described as composed of a continuous source, monochromator, detector-transducer, amplifier, etc.? The latter approach, which identifies *modules* or subassemblies that perform needed functions, proves preferable. It lends itself to the identification and formulation of design patterns.

Example A few illustrations may clarify the concept of a module. Sometimes a module is a subassembly like an amplifier that performs one of the basic steps involved in measurement. Or more than one module may be necessary to a step. Providing variable wavelength, monochromatic light is a good illustration. No simple source presently known meets the specifications and two modules must be used: a continuous source and a monochromator. A module may also be an element like a power supply that furnishes dc electrical power to all parts of an instrument.

How may an instrument be described to make clear its general design and operation? A *block diagram* appears to provide the picture sought. The diagram sacrifices details but displays modules that comprise an instrument and the patterns of coupling. The latter is indicated by arrows connecting module blocks that show the flow of the signal and energy in the instrument. An example is the line "block" diagram of a single-beam absorption spectrophotometer in Fig. 1.4.

Continuous $\Rightarrow$ Monochromator $\Rightarrow$ Sample $\rightarrow$ Detector $\rightarrow$ Amplifier $\rightarrow$ Readout
source

Fig. 1.4 Line block diagram of a single-beam spectrophotometer.

What design patterns are useful in providing the accuracy, dynamic range, and other kinds of performance desired in a measurement? How closely do maintenance and cost relate to basic layout? Answers to these queries and related ones are central in developing an instrument, or in selecting a particular instrument from those available for an analysis. The first consideration ought to be identification of the main patterns of design that appear feasible. Some designs are:

1. Single channel,
2. Modified single channel with feedback control of source intensity,
3. Modified single channel with phase-sensitive detection,
4. Double channel.*

In single-channel or single-beam design, modules are arranged in a sequence. The signal moves from module to module. In a double-channel design the flow of energy is divided. A blank (or reference) is inserted in one channel and the sample in the other channel. Even with double-channel design, as small a section of an instrument as possible is made dual channel to ensure reliability of performance and reduce cost.

Since the steps in making a measurement can be satisfactorily performed in sequence, what reasons are there for ever using a double-channel arrangement?

In a figurative sense the second channel is present, of course, whenever a procedure calls for a blank. As was discussed in the previous section, in this case the instrument

---

* The modifications indicated for single-beam design can also be used in double-channel instruments.

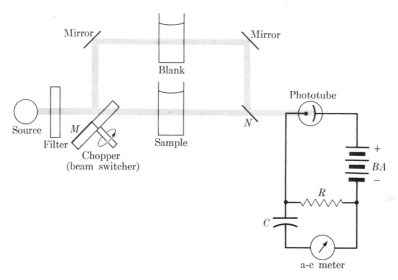

Fig. 1.5 One type of double-channel, direct-ratio absorption photometer. Mirror N is half-silvered and both transmits and reflects light. One half of the rotating chopper wheel is cut away entirely. The other half is covered by a front-surface mirror M.

is used *twice* to obtain a single piece of information. When the measurement is made on the blank, *the instrument is adjusted so that its response is some standard value*, e.g., 100%. This operation constitutes a calibration, since the effect of drift or fluctuation in the behavior of any component is eliminated by bringing the overall response up to the standard value each time.

The same desirable results are achieved in a double-channel instrument, which has a reference (or standardizing) channel and a measuring channel. Its design may be like that shown schematically in Fig. 1.5. Under what circumstances are the added complexity and cost of double-channel design merited? It is clear that precision single-channel instruments can usually be designed at lower cost and since they have fewer parts, they offer fewer potential sources of trouble. Nevertheless, the double-channel design represents a definite advance over a single-channel arrangement when

1. The many variables that affect a measurement are under only partial control and fluctuate in magnitude at a rate somewhat faster than can be accommodated by a procedure using blanks or standards [as is true, e.g., in flame photometry (Section 14.6)],

2. Measurement variables are under reasonable control and fluctuate in magnitude at a slow rate, but automatic operation and recording are sought, or

3. A differential measurement appears desirable.

When these conditions hold, the double-channel design provides a degree of accuracy and sensitivity unobtainable any other way. Further discussion of double-channel operation will be reserved for Section 17.5, when the topic will be explored as a part of the discussion of spectrophotometers.

1.6 GENERAL PROPERTIES OF MODULES

Before we discuss design any further, it will be helpful to characterize in a general way the dynamic behavior of modules. A good description requires specification of input, "transfer," and output characteristics. When individual modules such as monochromators and amplifiers are treated in later chapters, these factors will be dealt with. Basically, the energy or signal entering a module must result in a predictable level of energy or signal, often of different form, at its output.

Input. The input characteristics of a module must always be specified. The *type* of input such as an infrared beam, gamma ray, or voltage will ordinarily be self-evident. The useful *range* of input must also be known. An input whose magnitude falls below a threshold will produce no effect; an input that exceeds a maximum level will result in a distorted output or damage to the module. Finally, a quantity such as the input *impedance* must be given. When one knows the impedance, one can assess conditions for effective coupling. The input impedance also enables one to estimate the influence of a module on preceding modules.

Transfer characteristic. It is the ability of a module to change the signal at its input that justifies its inclusion in an instrument. This effect can be described generally in terms of a transfer function, which relates output to input. If I_i is the input quantity, the transfer function f is defined by the expression:

$$I_o = f(I_i),$$

where I_o is the output. The rate of change of output with input, termed the sensitivity S of the module, is expressed as follows:

$$\frac{dI_o}{dI_i} = S. \tag{1.1}$$

Sensitivity is defined here in its precise meaning, which is the magnitude of response.* There are many synonyms for sensitivity; some are, gain (for an amplifier), response (for a photometric detector), and attenuation factor (for a filter). Where sensitivity varies with I_i, distortion occurs in transfer. Some error of this type is inevitable, but the sensitivity of a module should ideally be constant.

Output. As with input, the type, dynamic range, and output impedance are of interest. The input and output may be different forms of signal. For example, the input of a photomultiplier tube is light and its output is an electrical current. The range of output will be defined at the lower end by random fluctuations that arise in the module, i.e. by its noise. The upper level may be defined by the power available or by the level at which distortion becomes appreciable. Finally, an output impedance helps define the best coupling to transfer signal and energy effectively to the next module.

---

* Sensitivity, as applied to a whole instrument, may also effectively determine the minimum input for which observable response occurs. This minimum level of response is called the *limit of detectability*. Although a sensitive module is likely to have a low level of detectability, sensitivity properly relates to response at all levels and should not be used as a synonym for detectability.

1.7 PROPAGATION OF UNCERTAINTY

As functioning parts of an instrument, each component contributes some error to the measurement of the property of interest. Viewed as a dynamic system, a measuring device can be no more reliable than its least accurate part. Under some conditions it may actually be much less accurate. Considerations of the origin and propagation of error become acute in the design, modification, or repair of instruments. They are also important in the analogous case in which data from many instruments enter the calculation of a derived quantity. In the first case each component will contribute error; in the second each operation will do so.

The propagation of error may be traced mathematically by drawing on a knowledge of the dynamics of the system. The general case will be taken up first. Let R indicate the property being determined. It will depend in some known manner on several variables, x, y, z, which are the outputs of instrumental components, that is, $R = f(x, y, z)$. The error or uncertainty in R may then be found by taking the total differential:

$$dR = \frac{\partial R}{\partial x}\bigg|_{y,z} dx + \frac{\partial R}{\partial y}\bigg|_{x,z} dy + \frac{\partial R}{\partial z}\bigg|_{x,y} dz. \tag{1.2}$$

In Eq. (1.2), the differentials dx, dy, and dz are to be regarded as fluctuations in the response of components that combine to produce dR, the error in R. Note that the fluctuations in the response of components do not add directly but are first modified by their functional relationship to R. For example, dx is multiplied by $\partial R/\partial x$ before addition.

Equation (1.2) must be altered before it can be applied conveniently to experimental situations. This involves transforming the differentials dx, dy, and dz into standard deviations or other measurement of the uncertainty (or scatter) in measured values. By definition, $\sigma_x^2 = \Sigma(dx)^2/n$*. To make the transformation, Eq. (1.2) must first be squared:

$$(dR)^2 = \left(\frac{\partial R}{\partial x} dx + \frac{\partial R}{\partial y} dy + \frac{\partial R}{\partial z} dz\right)^2. \tag{1.3}$$

Inspection reveals that terms of type I, $(\partial R/\partial x)^2(dx)^2$, and type II, $(\partial R/\partial x)(\partial R/\partial y)\,dx\,dy$, are formed.

Step two is the summation of Eq. (1.3) over all measurements. In this operation, type II terms will tend to vanish, since it has been assumed that

1. dx and dy behave independently of each other, and

2. Positive and negative values of dx and dy are equally probable.

Then, on addition, positive terms of type II will cancel the negative ones and Eq. (1.3) becomes

---

* This definition of standard deviation assumes that the scatter in an infinite number of replicate performances has been observed. Where only a few observations have been made (at least five), a small-set standard deviation s is defined as $s^2 = \Sigma(dx)^2/(n - 1)$. It serves as an estimate of the standard deviation. [15,17]

$$\sum_i (dR_i)^2 = \left(\frac{\partial R}{\partial x}\right)^2 \sum_i (dx_i)^2 + \left(\frac{\partial R}{\partial y}\right)^2 \sum_i (dy_i)^2 + \left(\frac{\partial R}{\partial z}\right)^2 \sum_i (dz_i)^2. \qquad (1.4)$$

All terms may now be divided by n, giving

$$\frac{\sum_i (dR_i)^2}{n} = \left(\frac{\partial R}{\partial x}\right)^2 \frac{\sum_i (dx_i)^2}{n} + \cdots,$$

or, equivalently,

$$\sigma_R^2 = \left(\frac{\partial R}{\partial x}\right)^2 \sigma_x^2 + \left(\frac{\partial R}{\partial y}\right)^2 \sigma_y^2 + \left(\frac{\partial R}{\partial z}\right)^2 \sigma_z^2. \qquad (1.5)$$

Equation (1.5) for the propagation of error is the expression sought. The quantity σ^2, which is termed the variance, is often used in comparing experimental procedures. However, it is not as useful as σ in situations where bounds are to be reported for measurements, as is the case here. An illustration of the application of Eq. (1.5) follows.

Example It is desired to know the relative error in the measurement of the electrical power P expended in a resistance. In this case the voltage drop V across the resistance and the current I in it are measured, and the power consumed is found by calculation from the expression $P = VI$. Using Eq. (1.5),

$$\sigma_P^2 = \left(\frac{\partial P}{\partial I}\right)^2 \sigma_I^2 + \left(\frac{\partial P}{\partial V}\right)^2 \sigma_V^2.$$

Now

$$\left(\frac{\partial P}{\partial I}\right) = V \qquad \text{and} \qquad \left(\frac{\partial P}{\partial V}\right) = I.$$

On substitution of these partial derivatives, we obtain

$$\sigma_P^2 = V^2 \sigma_I^2 + I^2 \sigma_V^2. \qquad (1.6)$$

The relative error in the power is simply σ_P/P. One must divide through Eq. (1.6) by P^2 or its equivalent:

$$\frac{\sigma_P^2}{P^2} = \frac{V^2}{V^2 I^2} \sigma_I^2 + \frac{I^2}{V^2 I^2} \sigma_V^2,$$

and then simplify:

$$\frac{\sigma_P^2}{P^2} = \frac{\sigma_I^2}{I^2} + \frac{\sigma_V^2}{V^2}. \qquad (1.7)$$

For the case of interest, assume the measured values are $I = 0.55 \pm 0.02$ A and $V = 115 \pm 1$ V, where the limits given for each is the standard deviation. Then Eq. (1.7) becomes

$$\frac{\sigma_P^2}{P^2} = \frac{(0.02)^2}{(0.55)^2} + \frac{(1)^2}{(115)^2} = 133 \times 10^{-5} + 8 \times 10^{-5},$$

and $\sigma_P/P = 0.038$.

Even if it was not evident earlier, it is now clear that a large fraction of the uncertainty in the power is contributed by the current measurement. If that determination could be made as precisely as the voltage measurement, the relative error would be only $\sqrt{16 \times 10^{-5}} = 0.013$, a value of relative standard deviation three times smaller.

From the example just given and a host of others that could be cited, it can be concluded that in the design, construction, modification, or selection of an instrument, a preliminary analysis of the uncertainty likely to be contributed to a measurement by each module can be valuable. Usually the reproducibility of modules is known from previous experience or can be calculated from available data on its components. If a preliminary estimate shows that the precision of measurement is likely to be less than desired, any module contributing a great deal of uncertainty must be altered or replaced. If this is not possible, a new design may be required. Costly changes in a system can frequently be avoided by advance analysis of this type.

1.8 SINGLE-CHANNEL DESIGN

In this basic, widely used instrument design there is a single path along which energy passes from source to sample, and measurement information moves from detector-transducer to output. The single chain of modules suggests that to secure a given quality of output:

1. Generally, all modules should perform at least at the quality level desired. A determination precise to $\pm 1\%$ can no more be obtained with a source that fluctuates badly than with a detector-transducer whose response is nonlinear.
2. Modules must be appropriately coupled or interfaced. If coupling distorts a signal or causes a serious loss of energy, an inferior instrument output is secured quite as certainly as when one or more modules function badly.
3. Drift with time (aging) or with change in environmental conditions like temperature must be minimized. Any increment in signal that results from drift in a module will simply be passed from one module to the next.

Given these understandings, the precision of measurement with a single-channel device is seen to depend largely upon whether (a) quality parts are used to construct modules, (b) parts are operated at a fraction of their rated values, (c) effective coupling is used, (d) due design measures are taken to minimize drift and (e) calibration is made at appropriate intervals to compensate for residual drift and other sources of error. The cost of an instrument will of course rise as this kind of stability is built in. The kinds of considerations raised will be treated in subsequent chapters as modules and instruments are discussed. Yet it will be helpful here to distinguish two general areas of instrumentation, general-purpose and precision, and then to illustrate some ways precision is secured by extension of the simple single-channel design.

General-purpose instrumentation. A single-channel instrument intended to operate at ordinary levels of concentration and precision can be designed with considerable simplicity and ruggedness. Ordinary concentrations are taken as those at which changes in the measured property are easily detectable, and ordinary precision is assumed 1–3%. Such an instrument needs only a simple detector-transducer and a sturdy but sensitive output meter. Cost will be low to moderate and maintenance minimal. Whenever a simple instrument of this type is adequate for measurements of interest and there are only occasional samples to be analyzed, it is to be preferred over more complex devices; a simplified illustration of an instrument of this kind has already been given in Fig. 1.3. Other examples are refractometers, pH meters, and radioactivity counters.

How can a readout allow for fluctuations too rapid to be compensated? Usually the fluctuations can be smoothed by registering only the average value during a given interval. Alternatively, a total or integrated reading can be recorded. This subject will be dealt with at length in Chapter 8.

Precision instrumentation. If a single-channel device is to be used for precise measurements (precision $\pm 0.1\%$ or better), it will have to be more complex than a general-purpose instrument. Usually ruggedness will be sacrificed first. At the very least, a stable source, a sensitive detector of wide dynamic range, a stable, high-gain amplifier, and a precision readout module (see below) will have to be incorporated. What is equally important is that the performance of all components will be critical, since most of them will be operating closer to their limits. If such a device is to be used at the trace concentration level, the detector and preamplifier will also have to have low noise characteristics.

Detailed attention will be given only to the precision readout device. There are at least two forms in use, potentiometric and digital. Both operate on a null-balance principle, e.g., vary a known voltage until it equals the unknown one. Only the potentiometric type will be considered here; a discussion of the digital type is deferred to Section 9.7.

In Fig. 1.6a, b direct and null methods of voltage determination are illustrated. The precision of a meter readout (the direct method) is dependent on the linearity and reproducibility of a meter. By contrast, in the potentiometric device the burden of measurement is shifted to a slidewire, whose stability and linearity can be made far superior to that of a meter. Ordinarily the wiper (contact) on a long slidewire can be positioned with an accuracy of $\pm 0.01\%$. If a meter is used to find the point of

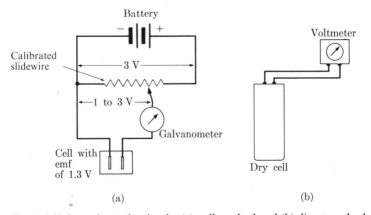

Fig. 1.6 Voltage determination by (a) null method and (b) direct method.

balance as in the figure it need have only short-term stability. It must be sensitive but need not be accurate. Null-balance readouts are more complex and more expensive.

It should be noted that the precision of a potentiometric readout is often latent. The usual potentiometric readout device, a recording potentiometer, has a chart that can be read to only $\pm 1\%$. When used with a general-purpose instrument, this precision is entirely adequate. The same device can be used in precision instrumentation by arranging for scale expansion when needed. One way to do so is to switch precision resistors in series with the slidewire. For example, after a $10\times$ expansion, the entire slidewire represents only 10% of the basic scale. In terms of readout, precision over that 10% of the output range is increased tenfold (to $\pm 0.1\%$). Whether the reliability of measurement is $10\times$ greater will depend on the performance of the other modules and the system.

Some modifications of single-channel design. The two extensions of single-channel design mentioned in Section 1.5 illustrate kinds of pattern modification useful in enhancing precision. The modification achieving *feedback stabilization of a source* is especially important for highly refined optical measurements (precision better than $\pm 0.1\%$). Other changes in an instrument may also be necessary.

Where a source whose output is constant to $\pm 0.1\%$ or better is required, reliance solely on regulation or stabilization of the incoming power is usually inadequate. It becomes advisable to arrange negative feedback control if greater constancy is desired. Such an arrangement is shown for an optical source as a line diagram in Fig. 1.7.

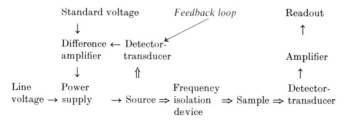

Fig. 1.7 Line block diagram of a single-channel absorption photometer with feedback stabilization of the source. A second detector is added to monitor the source. The output of this detector is converted to a voltage and compared with a standard voltage. Any difference (error signal) is amplified and used to change the energy input of the source in the proper direction.

It is the need to push measurement down toward the level of detectability that makes still another modification, namely the use of *phase-sensitive detection*, attractive. The method calls for the operation of several of the modules of an instrument in close relationship, again indicating the power of a change in the basic design. A line diagram of the arrangement for a generalized instrument is shown in Fig. 1.8. The basic signal is modulated, i.e., caused to fluctuate in amplitude, in this case by modulating the source itself. An amplifier that selectively amplifies only frequencies close to those of modulation is used. The amplified signal is then demodulated (detected) in synchronism with the original modulation. In this way, noise is greatly minimized. This arrangement is treated in detail in Section 8.7.

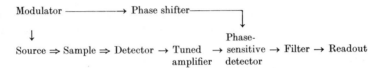

Fig. 1.8 Line block diagram of a single-channel instrument with phase-sensitive detection.

1.9 LIMIT OF DETECTION AND AMPLIFICATION

The quest for increased sensitivity in measurement is a relentless one. In large part the search is the direct result of new scientific endeavors in chemistry and physics. For example, the existence of new transuranium elements is sometimes first determined by work on an ultramicro scale with only 50 to 1000 atoms! In analyses of transistor materials, sensitivity is also the byword, for impurities present at the level of one part per billion must be quantitatively determined.

The full sensitivity of measurement may be realized, in general, only by using a sensitive detector and electronic amplification. Actually, both components produce and amplify not only the signal, but also noise, that is, random electrical fluctuations (of small amplitude). The two are superimposed in the output. In Fig. 1.9 a hypothetical signal with and without superimposed noise is illustrated. The limit of detectability usually depends on the amplitude of the noise, as will be discussed at length in Section 8.2.

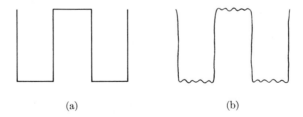

Fig. 1.9 Square-wave signal (a) without and (b) with superimposed noise.

In most cases the frequency of the useful signal differs from that of most of the noise, and selective amplification may be used to enhance the signal. If desirable, a difference in frequency may be deliberately introduced. For example, in the device of Fig. 1.5 the useful signal will fluctuate at whatever rate the chopper turns. An amplifier selectively tuned to that frequency will enhance the signal but not the bulk of the noise. Some noise cannot be excluded, of course, and indeed some will be generated in the amplifier. As a result, the meaningful amplification of very faint signals and the very great amplification of ordinary signals will be impossible.

1.10 AUTOMATIC OPERATION AND COMPUTER CONTROL

As suggested in the earlier discussion of basic design patterns, both the layout of modules and the mode of control of their operation are involved in a complete design for an instrument. Some design patterns have been discussed; in this section the concern will be with modes of control. Three general types of control can be identified. They are:

1. Manual, in which an operator controls the instrument and often performs essential steps, such as zeroing and setting of the 100% reading;

2. Automatic, in which most control is provided by built-in negative feedback loops that are associated with servomotors. Self-standardizing and unattended operation are ensured once an operator has selected the mode of operation and started the device; and

3. Computer control, in which a digital computer is linked to an instrument to fix conditions for data acquisition and to process information obtained.

Table 1.1 Effect of Instrument Control on Analysis Requirements

	Type of Control		
Requirement	Manual	Automatic	Computer-Control
Size of sample	Basically dependent on method, design of modules		
Detection limit	Basically dependent on method, design of modules*		
Kind of sample and breadth of concentration range	Basically dependent on method, design of modules		
Scan over range of values of a variable	Difficult	Easy	Easy
Time for single-point analysis			
a. of single sample;	Moderate	Moderate	Moderate
b. of many samples or process stream	Long	Moderate; limited by method, design of modules	Potentially short; limited by method, design of modules
Precision	Good	Good	Excellent
Freedom from interferences	Basically dependent on method		Independent of method to degree overlapping effects can be resolved by computation

* In some cases computer procedures such as time-averaging may lower the limit of detectability an order of magnitude or two.

A crude assessment of the potentialities of these kinds of control is made in Table 1.1. From the table it is evident that the three methods of control have little impact on the size and kind of sample required, the detection limit, and the concentration range that may be examined. These particular factors depend mainly on the method of measurement chosen and the design and coupling of modules in the instrument used. The table also notes several factors for which the type of control can affect results significantly. In general, the more assistance the instrument or a computer provides in the control of operation, the better the processes of *data acquisition* and *data processing*. It is these two categories that cause automatic or computer control to be definitely superior. What is lost in some cases is sturdiness in construction, and there is a much greater need for maintenance and a higher investment, both initially and on a continuing basis.

Automatic operation. Appreciable redesigning is necessary before most manual instruments will control their own operation according to given instructions. An illustration of the type of modification required will make this point clearer. In automatic operation, energy, usually electrical, must be tapped off at appropriate stages to run motors. An example is the system diagramed in Fig. 1.10. The servomotor is used to adjust the width of an optical slit to supply light of constant intensity. In the arrangement pictured, the signal from a phototube detector, which receives a fraction of the light from the slit, is amplified and compared with a standard voltage. The difference or unbalance signal is used to drive the servomotor, which opens or closes the slit, depending on the direction of unbalance. When the light coming through increases, a larger signal is received and the motor closes the slit until no further unbalance signal reaches it; the slit jaws narrow just enough to cancel the increase. In this case the instruction given is the constant voltage, which is to be matched against the amplifier output.

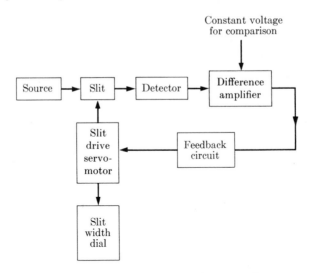

Fig. 1.10 Slit control system for automatic spectrophotometer.

The requirement of calibration stability for automatic operation is such that only null-reading devices are well suited for it. If in addition to null balance, the double-channel feature can be included in the design, calibration problems are considerably eased (Section 17.5).

Computer control. As Table 1.1 suggests, the gains from computer control of an instrument are basically speed, precision, and versatility in measurement. A block diagram illustrating the essential interrelationships among modules when computer control is used is shown in Fig. 1.11. It should be emphasized that this is a design for complete control, i.e. there is a complete feedback loop involving the computer. A less comprehensive scheme would remove the topmost module, the digital-to-analog converter, and simply let the computer function as data acquirer and processer.

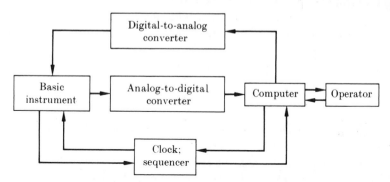

Fig. 1.11 Block diagram of a computer-controlled instrument. The operator may assume control or modify the control exercised by the computer. Basically, the computer operates the instrument according to the instructions given it at the outset.

On the highest level of sophistication the topmost module would be left intact. The computer would be programed to intercede in the actual operation of the instrument in order to optimize its performance in any desired way. In this way more precise measurements might be taken, interferences might be reduced in their effect, noise might be reduced, or other optimization effected. Some of these possibilities are detailed for particular techniques in Table 9.4.

1.11 CONCLUSIONS

Any instrument may be classified according to its functions, usefulness, limitations, and possibilities of modification. These qualities become all-important for a measuring instrument whose indications are to be accepted as "true." It is obvious that the manipulations and operating procedures prescribed by the manufacturer will ordinarily produce the specified results under stipulated conditions. But in all nonroutine operations or in devising new routines, a category that includes most analytical and research problems, the horizon of the user of the instrument must be wider. For these operations it is important that the instruments be understood in terms of (a) their theoretical basis, (b) the influence of changing conditions, (c) the basic design pattern, (d) the function and response of components and their dynamic interaction, and finally (e) the type of control.

It has been implied that a distinctive feature of instrumental procedures is that all call for some sort of initial or continuous calibration. For this reason a given analysis performed instrumentally on one or two samples may prove more time-consuming and may yield no more information than when done by a classical chemical method. Where a routine may be set up, as for example in the titration of several solutions or in the quality control of steel from an open-hearth furnace, the instrumental procedures are faster.

Finally, a cardinal concept in good design—and therefore in the selection of the instrument most appropriate for a given study—is that of simplicity. Ordinarily, the simplest instrument that has the desired sensitivity, accuracy, and operating features will be the best choice. Its operation will be less involved, there will be fewer components to give trouble, spurious responses of the instrument will be more easily noted and traced to their source, maintenance will be simplified, and often the cost will be less. In the use and design of instruments, as in research, elegance of measurement is best attained by emphasis on simplicity.

REFERENCES

Theory as well as practical information on good design, materials, and methods of construction (with emphasis on optical instruments) is given by:

1. H. J. Cooper, *Scientific Instruments.* New York: Chemical Publishing, 1946
2. A. Elliott and J. H. Dickson, *Laboratory Instruments, Their Design and Application.* New York: Chemical Publishing, 1953
3. T. N. Whitehead, *The Design and Use of Instruments and Accurate Mechanism.* New York: Dover, 1954

Some basic aspects of modules and of working with instruments as systems are discussed in:

4. S. Z. Lewin, "Proper Utilization of Analytical Instrumentation," *Anal. Chem.* **33** (3), 23A (1961)
5. K. S. Lion, *Instrumentation in Scientific Research—Electrical Input Transducers.* New York: McGraw-Hill, 1959
6. R. G. McKee, "A Modular Approach to Chemical Instrumentation," *Anal. Chem.* **42** (11), 81A (1970)
7. McKee Pederson, *McKee Pederson Applications Notes.* Danville, Calif.: McKee Pederson, (Volume 1 appeared in 1966)

Much theory and many practical suggestions for research instrumentation are given by:

8. H. J. J. Braddick, *The Physics of Experimental Method.* 2d ed. New York: Reinhold, 1963
9. Eric B. Pearson, *Technology of Instrumentation.* Princeton: Van Nostrand, 1958
10. E. B. Wilson, *An Introduction to Scientific Research.* New York: McGraw-Hill, 1952

Emphasizing engineering and industrial as well as systems aspects of instrumentation are:

11. Douglas M. Considine, ed., *Process Instruments and Controls Handbook.* New York: McGraw-Hill, 1957
12. D. R. Coughanowr and L. B. Koppel, *Process Systems Analysis and Control.* New York: McGraw-Hill, 1965
13. E. M. Grabbe, S. Ramo, and D. E. Wooldridge, eds., *Handbook of Automation, Computation, and Control.* Vol. 1: Control Fundamentals. New York: Wiley, 1958

Statistical aspects of measurement and instrument design are treated in:

14. K. A. Brownlee, *Statistical Theory and Methodology in Science and Engineering.* New York: Wiley, 1960
15. R. B. Dean and W. J. Dixon, "Simplified Statistics for Small Numbers of Observations," *Anal. Chem.* **23**, 636 (1951)
16. K. Eckschlager, *Errors, Measurement and Results in Chemical Analysis.* New York: Van Nostrand Reinhold, 1969
17. H. Kaiser, "Quantitation in Elemental Analysis," *Anal. Chem.* **42** (2), 24A and (4), 26A (1970)

18. John Mandel, *The Statistical Analysis of Experimental Data*. New York: Interscience, 1964
19. V. V. Nalimov, *The Application of Mathematical Statistics to Chemical Analysis*. Reading, Mass.: Addison-Wesley, 1963

The basic principles, design, functioning, and construction of commercially available chemical instrumentation are discussed in a continuing feature published monthly in the *Journal of Chemical Education*:

20. G. W. Ewing, ed., "Topics in Chemical Instrumentation," 1967–present
21. S. Z. Lewin, ed., "Chemical Instrumentation," 1959–66

Listings of instruments by type and manufacturer are collated and published annually as:

22. "Laboratory Guide to Instruments, Equipment, and Chemicals," *Analytical Chemistry*, August issue
23. "Guide to Scientific Instruments," *Science*, fall issue

Comprehensive discussions of advances in selected areas of chemical instrumentation appear annually or less frequently in the following continuing series:

24. *Analysis Instrumentation*, Vol. 1 (1963). New York: Plenum
25. *Advances in Analytical Chemistry and Instrumentation*, Vol. 1 (1962). New York: Wiley-Interscience
26. *Proceedings of the Instrument Society of America*

EXERCISES

1.1 a) Comment on the following statement: All analytical procedures properly fall under the heading *instrumental* analysis, even gravimetric and volumetric methods.

b) What essential difference is there between a manual titration with a visual end point, a manual potentiometric titration, and an automatic potentiometric titration, all of the same sample? Consider your answer in the light of the steps involved in making a measurement.

1.2 What difference is there between viewing an instrument as a "black box" and treating it on a modular basis? Since modules are in a sense "black boxes", wherein does the greater power of the latter approach lie?

1.3 a) What factors determine the frequency with which an instrument should be calibrated? How should the standards used in calibration compare with samples to be run? Explain.

b) With some calibrated instruments like flame photometers it is desirable to intersperse standard samples with unknowns. What purpose does this procedure serve?

1.4 Tabulate the more important advantages and disadvantages of a double-channel spectrophotometer (or other double-channel device). Indicate whether these attributes or liabilities are inherent in the double-channel design itself.

1.5 Examine the spectrophotometers shown in Figs. 17.6, 17.10, and 17.17. Develop a table of the modules used in each. Assign each component shown to a module. Indicate whether any of these assignments seems arbitrary.

1.6 The capillary rise method is to be evaluated as a method for obtaining reliable values of the surface tension of a series of liquids. In this method the surface tension γ is given by $\gamma = \frac{1}{2} hgdr$, where h is the height to which the liquid rises in the capillary, g is the acceleration due to gravity, d is the density of the liquid, and r is the radius of the capillary. If the relative standard deviations for these quantities are $\sigma_d = 0.2\%$, $\sigma_h = 0.4\%$, $\sigma_r = 0.5\%$, and $\sigma_g = 0.01\%$, will the method yield surface tensions with an uncertainty (relative standard deviation) not greater than 0.5%?

[*Ans.*: No, here $\sigma_{surf.\,tens.} = 0.7\%$.]

BASIC ELECTRONICS

Chapter 2

BASIC ELECTRICAL VARIABLES

Electrical circuitry enters the field of chemical instrumentation at two main points. First, electrical or magnetic properties of interest to chemists require appropriate circuits in their measurement. Nuclear magnetic resonance, cell electrode potential, dielectric constant, and many other properties fall into this category. Second, optical, mechanical, and indeed most other properties of substances are ordinarily sensed by detector-transducers like phototubes and thermocouples that produce an electrical current or voltage. With this type of output, use can be made of the striking advantages associated with electronics. These include the possibility of signal amplification, signal processing to enhance results, and computation of related quantities. Accordingly, the chapters comprising this section (Chapters 2 through 9) examine in some detail electrical and electronic circuitry as they relate to chemical instrumentation. Specific electrical measurement techniques such as potentiometry and polarography are taken up in later chapters treating particular methods.

2.1 INTRODUCTION

Electric currents that energize circuits are either unidirectional, i.e. direct-current (dc), or they are alternating-current (ac) and are characterized by a frequency anywhere from a fraction of one hertz (Hz) or cycle per second to about 50 gigahertz (GHz). The behavior of circuits carrying currents requires the use of fundamental electrical parameters such as resistance R, inductance L, and capacitance C. Interest will focus on their relation to circuit design, i.e. on their dependence on frequency, and any other behavior that affects their use in instrumentation. In other words, the control and usefulness of electrical signals will be considered as important as their behavior. The general scheme of electrical notation used in this volume is summarized in Table 2.1.* Also, throughout the text V is used instead of E in referring to voltages, unless otherwise noted. That way E is reserved for electric fields.

2.2 OHM'S LAW

Whenever a source of electromotive force (emf), such as a battery or contact potential, is incorporated in a closed circuit a current is observed. The potential difference introduced by the source accelerates charged particles in the circuit, whether its parts are metal, semiconductor, gas, or electrolytic solution. The current i is defined

---

* This scheme has been recommended by the IEEE, *IEEE Trans. Electron Devices* **ED-11**, 392 (1964).

Table 2.1 Electrical Conventions

Type of Variable	Identifying Symbol	Subscript
Direct current	Capital	Capital
AC or variational	Lower case	Lower case
AC rms or effective	Capital	Lower case
Instantaneous total value	Lower case	Capital
Supply voltage	Capital	Double capital

Examples:

The dc current in a resistor	I_R
The ac voltage drop across a capacitor	v_c
Total instantaneous collector current	i_C
Collector supply voltage for a transistor	V_{CC}

as the rate of movement of charge Q through the circuit path and has the units of coulombs per second $(C\ s^{-1})$ or amperes (A). While there is a current, charge carriers such as electrons are accelerated until they suffer inelastic "collision" and dissipate their kinetic energy as heat. After collision they are again accelerated with the result that an average velocity may be determined.

It is more convenient, however, to deal with a circuit on a macroscopic level by beginning with Ohm's law, which describes the voltage–current characteristics of most materials. On this level it is conventional to follow a net *positive current*, one which moves from a point of positive potential to a point of negative potential. Though such a convention is arbitrary, it is desirable for simplicity, since charge carriers are actually sometimes negative (electrons and negative ions) and sometimes positive (holes and positive ions). At times the convention will be put aside in order to follow specific kinds of charge carriers. With proper definition of terms, Ohm's law holds for both dc and ac currents. When the law does not hold for a subspace, e.g., for a thermistor, the behavior must be specially considered. For a simple dc circuit having a resistance in series with a source of voltage, Ohm's law may be written as

$$I = V/R \qquad \text{or} \qquad V = IR \tag{2.1}$$

where V is the potential difference or emf of the source in volts, R the resistance of the circuit in ohms, and I the current in amperes at all points in the circuit. A representative application of the law may be made using the circuit of Fig. 2.1. For example, the right-hand statement of Ohm's law above suggests that

1. The passage of charge at the rate I through a resistance produces a voltage drop of magnitude IR across the resistance. Often this is termed an IR drop.

2. The voltage drop developed across R just equals the voltage of the source. This idea leads to Kirchhoff's second law (Section 3.1).

Energy dissipation.   The electrical energy furnished by a source, i.e., the kinetic energy acquired by charge carriers as a result of acceleration, is dissipated as heat to the

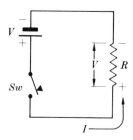

Fig. 2.1 Schematic representation of a simple resistive dc circuit. The voltage drop across R is equal, and of opposite sign, to that across the battery V.

degree that the charge carriers suffer inelastic collisions. The rate at which energy J is consumed in sustaining a current is defined by the expression

$$P = \frac{dJ}{dt} = VI, \tag{2.2}$$

where P is the power, or energy converted to heat per unit time. When V is in volts and I in amperes, P is in watts. Equation (2.2) may be rearranged using Ohm's law so that the resistance appears explicitly as

$$P = I^2R = V^2/R. \tag{2.3}$$

On the basis of this relation the power transformed into heat in a resistance is often termed the "I-squared-R" loss.

AC circuits. If a dc source V is replaced by an ac "generator," the direction of current will reverse periodically. The period T of each cycle is by definition the reciprocal of the frequency f. In an ac circuit the current may be represented as a sine wave (note the analogous treatment of electromagnetic optical radiation in Chapter 10) whose instantaneous value i is given by

$$i = I_p \sin \omega t. \tag{2.4}$$

Here I_p is the peak value of the current and ω is the angular frequency ($\omega = 2\pi f$) whose units are radians per second (rad s^{-1}). In a circuit containing only resistance the instantaneous voltage v is in phase with the current and may be expressed by a similar relation:

$$v = V_p \sin \omega t. \tag{2.5}$$

To provide consistency in calculating power expenditure in ac and dc circuits, an *effective* or "average" current must be defined for an ac system. As seen from Eq. (2.3), an average of the square of i over a cycle is required to calculate the average power dissipation. The effective current is thus a root-mean-square (rms) value and can be shown to be $I = I_p/\sqrt{2} = 0.707\, I_p$.

By definition, the effective current in an ac circuit is the equivalent dc value I that gives an equal power dissipation. Eq. (2.3) gives the dc power expended; substituting for I the ac expression of

Eq. (2.4) gives the ac equivalent. Equating these expressions and averaging yields the result:

$$I^2 R = R I_p^2 \overline{\sin^2 \omega t}.$$

The average called for can be obtained by integrating $\sin^2 \omega t$ over a half-cycle (or more) and dividing by the increase in ωt during this interval. One obtains:

$$\overline{\sin^2 \omega t} = \frac{1}{\pi} \int_0^\pi \sin^2 \omega t \, d(\omega t) = \tfrac{1}{2}.$$

Thus, $I^2 = I_p^2/2$ and the effective current I is $I_p/\sqrt{2}$.

The effective or rms voltage V for an ac circuit has a parallel definition:

$$V = 0.707 V_p. \tag{2.6}$$

It is interesting to note that the instantaneous voltage in an ac line rated at 115 volts (its effective voltage) peaks at $1.414 \times V = 162.6$ volts.

2.3 RESISTANCE

A variety of commercial resistors is shown in Fig. 2.2. Many are composition resistors fabricated by molding graphite powder and resin. Not shown are the type of circular-wound variable resistors commonly known as potentiometers or pots (see also Section 3.2). This type has leads to the ends of winding and a third connection to a wiper that can be moved along the winding. There is little precision of setting with a

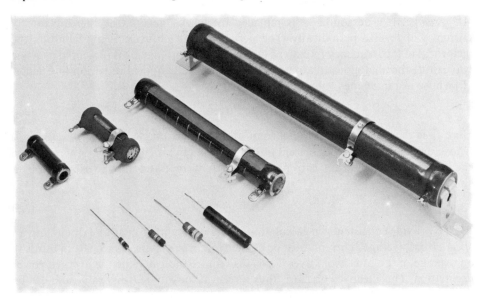

Fig. 2.2 Several types of commercial resistors. Those in the front row are of the carbon type and range in size and ability to dissipate power from the $\tfrac{1}{4}$W resistor at the left to the 2W at the right. The larger resistors contain resistance wire wound on ceramic forms. Three of these have adjustable metal taps that may be moved to any desired position. (Courtesy of American Radio Relay League, Inc.)

single-turn potentiometer; greater precision can be achieved by increasing the length of winding and coiling it into a helix that the wiper must follow. Carefully wound ten-turn potentiometers are in effect modern slidewires (see Section 3.2).

In what ways do the resistors of Fig. 2.2 differ? A resistor is described not only by its resistance, but also by power rating, design tolerance, and temperature coefficient. Common power ratings are 0.25, 0.5, 1, or 2 watts and common design tolerances, ± 5, ± 10,* or $\pm 20\%$. Clearly, in precision applications such as a Wheatstone bridge special resistors accurate to at least $\pm 1\%$, and often to $\pm 0.1\%$ or better, will be required.

Example A 5 kΩ resistor specified for an amplifier must carry effective currents up to 10 mA. What preferred value ($\pm 10\%$ tolerance) and power rating should be specified for the resistor?

The closest preferred value is 4.7 kΩ. This value will approximate to 5 kΩ sufficiently in most cases. The power dissipation I^2R is $(0.01)^2 \times 5 \times 10^3 = 0.5$ W. A 2 W resistor would be a good choice to provide a margin of safety.

The realization that all circuits must dissipate heat during use suggests the importance of (a) designing for adequate dissipation by radiation or convection and (b) allowing a preliminary warm-up of any sensitive instrument. Only after attainment of constant temperature will resistors, capacitors, and other components have constant values. Then dependable, relatively drift-free operation can be expected.

Temperature coefficient of resistance. Since any resistor heats during use, its temperature coefficient of resistance must also be taken into account in precision applications. Resistors fabricated from wire have the positive coefficients characteristic of electrical *conductors.* An average temperature coefficient for metals, e.g., is $+0.003\,\Omega\Omega^{-1}{}^{\circ}\mathrm{C}^{-1}$ (0.3 % per °C) near room temperature. By special alloying it is possible to develop wire with a very low coefficient for use in bridges, etc. For example, manganin alloys (Cu–Mn–Ni) have coefficients as small as $1 \times 10^{-7}\ \Omega\,\Omega^{-1}{}^{\circ}\mathrm{C}^{-1}$ over a short range of temperature.

Any property with a temperature coefficient also deserves consideration as a basis for thermometry. Thus, a number of metals are used as *resistance thermometers.*

Example The great reproducibility of the resistance of pure platinum wire with temperature and time has led to its selection as a secondary temperature standard from $-183°$ to $+630°\mathrm{C}$. Nichrome and other alloys are used to make wire for the thermal conductivity devices frequently used as detectors in gas–liquid chromatographs and some types of vacuum gages. In these devices the wire is heated by current flow. The denser or more conducting the gas surrounding the hot wire, the lower the wire temperature and resistance. The wire functions basically as a resistance thermometer.

---

* Wide-tolerance resistors such as are used in electronic circuits are supplied only in certain *preferred values.* For resistors with a $\pm 10\%$ (silver band) tolerance the preferred values are multiples of the factors 1.0, 1.2, 1.5, 1.8, 2.2, 2.7, 3.3, 3.9, 4.7, 5.6, 6.8, and 8.2. These values provide adequate coverage of the range and yet secure the advantage of standardization. Intermediate resistance values are available in the series with $\pm 5\%$ (gold band) tolerance; still fewer values are available in the $\pm 20\%$ (no band) tolerance group.

On the other hand, the temperature coefficient of resistance of semiconductors like silicon, germanium, and metal oxides, is negative (Section 4.2). A particular class of semiconductors, thermistors, that is useful in temperature measurement will be considered further below.

Specifications of resistance thermometer devices usually include the temperature coefficient, maximum operating temperature, resistance at room temperature, thermal time constant, and dissipation constant. The last two require definition. The thermal time constant τ defines the rate at which a resistance device equilibrates with its surroundings. Its response is "exponential" and τ is simply the time required for its temperature to change through 63% of the interval between its initial temperature and that of the surroundings. In general, devices with smaller resistances have smaller time constants. The *dissipation constant* is defined as the power required to raise the temperature of the device one degree above the surroundings. This constant suggests a safe power level for operation. For example, representative specifications for a thermistor (see below) might be: $R = 1000\ \Omega$ at $0\,°C$, $1\ \Omega$ at $200\ °C$; $t_{max} = 200\,°C$; $\tau = 3\,s$; and $C = 3\,mW°C^{-1}$.

Thermistors. The temperature coefficient of resistance of some semiconductor mixtures is so large as to suggest particular usefulness in temperature measurement. For example, mixtures of the oxides of manganese, nickel, copper, and uranium fall in this category and are widely used in bead or rod form as *resistance thermometers*. The generic name thermistor has been given them. Interestingly, germanium and silicon are unattractive in this application since their resistance is strongly dependent on impurity content. A comparison of the temperature–resistance characteristics of a representative metal and a thermistor is given in Fig. 2.3.

Thermistors are usually fabricated by pressing powdered oxide mixtures onto wire leads, followed by sintering to give a hard ceramic bead or disk of perhaps 1–3 mm size. Some are also prepared by low-energy sputtering of a 0.05 to 0.1 μm oxide layer directly onto a surface whose temperature is to be measured. Thin gold leads are added.

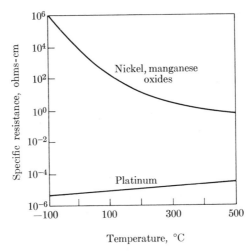

Fig. 2.3 Comparison of common metal and thermistor temperature coefficients of resistance.

Maximum useful temperature ranges of thermistors are about 100 to 200°C. Relative temperature coefficients as large as -7% per °C have been achieved.

The resistance of thermistor materials also changes with voltage and they may properly be called nonohmic. At a fixed temperature, however, there is little dependence on voltage.

Thermistors to be used in applications where good reproducibility ($\pm 0.1°$ or better) is required must be used with proper precautions. Only when indicated by a manufacturer should thermistors with similar specifications be interchanged without recalibration of a device. Due allowance must also be made for dependence of resistance on previous history. Commercial thermistors are usually artificially aged to minimize this variability. Stability is improved also by passage of a small current at all times, avoiding thermal and mechanical shock, and limiting the temperature range over which the thermistor is used.

Series and parallel resistances. The study of electrical circuits may be greatly simplified by using Ohm's law to sum the several resistances in a practical circuit. By so doing one obtains a single *equivalent* resistor. The process is analogous to the development of a model. If two or more resistors are in *series* as in Fig. 2.4a, the equivalent resistor is determined as follows. There is a single current I in the circuit giving voltage drops IR_1 across R_1 and IR_2 across R_2. The total voltage drop occurring is $V = IR_1 + IR_2 = I(R_1 + R_2) = IR_{eq}$. Thus, for the general case

$$R_{eq} = R_1 + R_2 + \cdots, \tag{2.7}$$

i.e., resistances in series add.

In the case of resistances in parallel, shown in Fig. 2.4b, the current I in the main part of the circuit divides at the junction. The voltage drops across all resistors are identical, however, since there can be only one voltage between two points. From Ohm's law the total current I is the sum of the currents in each separate resistance,

$$I = I_1 + I_2 = \frac{V}{R_1} + \frac{V}{R_2} = V\left(\frac{1}{R_1} + \frac{1}{R_2}\right). \tag{2.8}$$

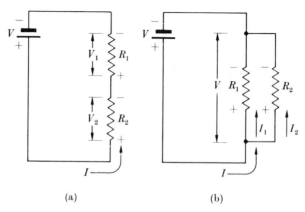

          (a)   (b)

Fig. 2.4 (a) Resistances in series. (b) Resistances in parallel.

The resistance equivalent to the sum of resistances in parallel is seen to be

$$\frac{1}{R_{eq}} = \frac{1}{R_1} + \frac{1}{R_2} + \cdots, \tag{2.9}$$

i.e., the reciprocals add to give the reciprocal of the sum.

2.4 MEASUREMENT OF V, I, AND R BY METER

The basic parameters, voltage, current, and resistance, can all be measured by use of a d'Arsonval meter. This moving-coil meter converts current in a circuit to a physical displacement of a pointer along a scale. In the meter the current flows through a coil of fine wire between the poles of a permanent magnet, causing the coil to be subjected to a torque proportional to the current in the wire. This torque is opposed by the "restoring" torque of suspension springs. The deflection of the coil is registered by an attached pointer. A deflection proportional to the current results since the restoring torque increases with twisting, and movement stops when a balance is attained. In general, moving-coil meters are designed to yield full-scale deflections for currents from 50 μA to 1 mA.* Though such a meter responds to current, Ohm's law indicates that it should also be able to measure voltage or resistance. These possibilities will be discussed below.

Ammeters. As a current-registering device, a moving-coil meter is designated an *ammeter*. The sensitivity of the meter will determine the smallest magnitude of current to which it responds; however, its range may be increased by shunting a known fraction of the total current around it.

    A representative circuit for an extended-range meter is shown in Fig. 2.5. The sum of the current in the meter I_m and that in the shunt I_s must equal the total current in the circuit, that is $I = I_m + I_s$. Since the voltage drop between points A and B is across each branch, it follows that $I_m R_m = I_s R_s$. Combining the equations, the scale multiplication factor I/I_m can be found. First,

$$I = I_m + I_m R_m/R_s.$$

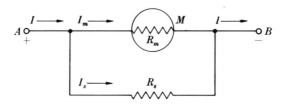

Fig. 2.5 Use of parallel resistor R_s to increase the range of meter M as an ammeter. By use of the shunt (R_s) only a fraction of current I, which is to be measured, exists in the meter itself. The range is extended by the factor I/I_m.

---

* Greater sensitivity is obtained by increasing the strength of the magnet, the coil area, or the number of turns of wire in coil, or by decreasing the stiffness of the springs. A balance must, of course, be struck between sensitivity and the ability of the suspension to withstand mechanical shock and vibration.

Then, rearranging,

$$I/I_m = 1 + R_m/R_s. \tag{2.10}$$

Example What shunt resistance R_s must be used to increase by a factor of 100 the range of an ammeter whose internal resistance is 50 Ω? From Eq. (2.10), $I/I_m = 100$ and $R_m/R_s = (100 - 1) = 99$. Substituting $R_m = 50$, $R_s = 50/99 = 0.505$ Ω. The *ratio* of current in the meter to that in the shunt will then be $1/99$ but its *range* will have increased 100 times.

Shunt resistors in general need be accurate only to $\pm 1\%$, since most moving-coil meters have about this accuracy. The commonly used Ayrton shunt is described in Exercise 2.7.

Voltmeter. A moving-coil meter can also serve as a voltmeter. According to Ohm's law, when the meter registers current I_m, there must be a voltage V_m across its resistance R_m. If R_m is unknown, it can best be determined by employing a potentiometer (Section 3.2).*

To extend the *voltage range* of a meter it is necessary to add resistance in series as shown in Fig. 2.6. As for current measurement, meter sensitivity determines the smallest voltage measurable. The scale multiplication factor for the arrangement of Fig. 2.6 is simply R_{total}/R_m. Doubling the resistance in the circuit doubles the voltage range, etc. Since I_m is constant, the new full-scale voltage reading is just $V_{\text{new}} = I_m R_{\text{total}}$.

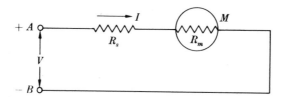

Fig. 2.6 Use of a series resistor R_s to increase the range of meter *M* as a voltmeter. This resistor permits a much higher voltage to be measured between points *A* and *B* by reducing the current produced by a given voltage.

Example What series resistance is necessary to adapt a 50 μA meter for use as a 0–50 V voltmeter? According to the relation $V_{\text{new}} = I_m R_{\text{total}}$ the total resistance in the circuit must be 50 V/50 × 10⁻⁶ A = 1 MΩ.

The resistance of the meter R_m will probably be about 500 Ω. In selecting a series resistor the meter resistance may be neglected since its contribution to the total is only 0.05%, and the meter itself is probably accurate only to 1%. This meter is said to have a resistance of 20 000 Ω V⁻¹ since its resistance is the full-scale reading × 20 000.

---

* Use of a potentiometer ensures that a reliable measurement is made and that the coil of the meter is not damaged by the comparatively large current a conventional test meter or volt-ohm-milliammeter (VOM) would produce in it.

Ohmmeter. A convenient method of adapting a moving-coil meter to serve as an ohmmeter also exists. A representative ohmmeter circuit is shown in Fig. 2.7. Measuring a resistance involves a two-step process. First, leads A and B are connected and resistance R_1 is varied until a full-scale deflection is obtained. The meter is registering battery voltage V. This scale value corresponds to zero ohms. Second, leads A and B are connected to unknown resistor R_x, which is thereby placed in series with R_2. The meter now registers voltage drop V'. Application of Ohm's law shows that V' is just

$$V' = V \times \frac{R_2}{R_2 + R_x},$$

which can be rearranged to give R_x,

$$R_x = R_2 \left[\frac{V}{V'} - 1 \right]. \tag{2.11}$$

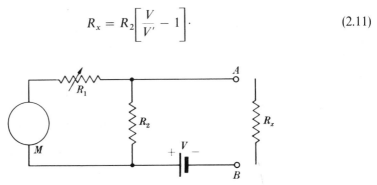

Fig. 2.7 A simple ohmmeter. Test leads extend from A and B. In operation, R_1 is first adjusted until meter M gives a full-scale deflection. This operation is accomplished by short-circuiting points A and B. Then R_x is inserted and the meter now registers voltage $VR_2/(R_2 + R_x)$. The meter can be calibrated so that the second reading is the unknown resistance.

When used as an ohmmeter, the meter scale is no longer linear. For that reason it is usually inscribed directly in ohms. According to Eq. (2.11), a half-scale deflection corresponds to $R_x = R_2$; a fourth-scale deflection to $R_x = 3R_2$, etc. Different resistance ranges are secured by varying R_2.

Two precautions should be noted. First, measurements should be made with an ohmmeter only when a circuit is unenergized. Otherwise, circuit operation may be distorted or unexpected voltages may appear across the ohmmeter! Second, the resistance of some devices cannot safely be determined with an ordinary ohmmeter; they may draw a damaging amount of current. Meters, semiconductor devices, electron tube filaments, relays, and other low-current components fall into this category.

Multimeter. A test meter usually incorporates the functions of voltmeter, ammeter, and ohmmeter in one instrument, and often is designated a volt-ohm-milliammeter (VOM). It provides a series of resistances for changing the ranges of a moving-coil meter, and a source of voltage such as a mercury cell or dry cell for the ohmmeter function. In addition, low-cost semiconductor diodes (Section 4.4) may be used in parallel with the meter to protect it against accidental overloads. Such devices begin conducting heavily when the voltage across them exceeds 0.5 volt, shunting possible overload currents around the meter. At the normal operating potentials such diodes introduce less than 1 % error.

Errors. The reliable measurement of voltages in "sources" of appreciable internal resistance (1 kΩ or more) poses a special problem. Because a voltmeter has a finite resistance, connecting it across a voltage source causes current to flow. Any source has some internal resistance, which can be considered in series with its voltage as shown in Fig. 2.8 (see Section 3.1). When current flows, there is an IR drop across the internal resistance. This voltage drop opposes the source voltage and the apparent voltage measured will be less than the true value. As a rule of thumb, the error reaches 1 % when the meter resistance is only 100 times the source resistance.

Where the measurement error is too large to be tolerated, a vacuum tube voltmeter or other device of very high input resistance (10 MΩ or greater) should be used. An estimate of the minimum voltmeter resistance needed to permit a measurement of desired accuracy can be made in straightforward fashion using Ohm's law and an equivalent circuit as shown in Fig. 2.8.

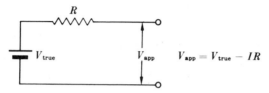

Fig. 2.8 Thévenin equivalent circuit model of a voltage source. R is its internal resistance and V_{true} its open-circuit voltage.

Example The voltage of a 10 V dc source whose internal resistance is 10 kΩ is to be measured. A 1000 ohms per volt, 30 V meter is available. What will be the error in the measurement?

The voltmeter will put 1000 ohms per volt × 30 V (the full-scale deflection) or 30 kΩ resistance across the source terminals. In terms of Fig. 2.8, V = 10 V and R = 10 kΩ. Applying Ohm's law, the current in the circuit is 10 V ÷ (10 + 30) kΩ = 2.5×10^{-4} A. This gives an internal IR drop of $2.5 \times 10^{-4} \times 10 \times 10^3$ = 2.5 V. The apparent measured source voltage will be 10 − 2.5 = 7.5 V. The error will be (2.5/10) × 100 = 25 %.

Similarly, current measurements will be in error, depending on the fractional increase in circuit resistance contributed by the meter. Exercise 2.6 provides an example.

AC measurement. Though a moving-coil meter is a dc device, it can be used to measure ac if semiconductor diodes (Section 4.4) are added in series with it.*

One suitable combination is shown in Fig. 2.9a. The addition of shunt or series resistance permits range extension as for a dc meter. This type of ac meter responds to the *average current*, which equals $0.637 \, I_p$ for sine wave ac. The factor 0.637 also applies if the meter is used in measurements of ac voltage. Often each marking on

---

* Meters that permit coil movement in a single direction regardless of current direction are also used.

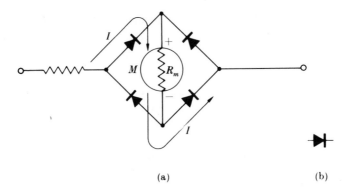

(a)   (b)

Fig. 2.9 A full-wave ac voltmeter. (a) Circuit diagram. (b) Diode symbol. The diodes pass positive current only in the direction of the arrowhead. The circuit permits only the direction of current shown in the meter branch. The path of current in the circuit external to it is shown for the half-cycle when the left-hand terminal is positive.

the scale is increased by the factor 0.707/0.637 so that the meter reads in rms or "effective" units (Section 2.2).

Digital voltmeter. Unknown voltages can be measured with still higher precision (± 0.1 to $\pm 0.01\%$) if a null-type instrument is used. The potentiometer (Section 3.2) is one such device. Another is the digital voltmeter, technically an analog-to-digital converter (Section 9.7). Both types function by determining the exact value of a variable, known voltage V_s, that matches the voltage V_x under measurement. The difference voltage ΔV, where

$$\Delta V = V_x - V_s \tag{2.12}$$

is followed precisely; when it is zero, the value of the known voltage is read out.

Example In the ramp type of digital voltmeter unknown voltage V_x is compared with a ramp, which is a voltage increasing or decreasing at a known steady rate from zero volts. The comparison process is shown in Fig. 2.10. A measurement is begun by producing a pulse or gate that starts the ramp generator and an oscillator producing a series of square pulses.

The pulses are counted electronically. Since they are of uniform duration and spacing, the count at any time will be proportional to the value attained by the ramp. This count is converted to voltage and displayed digitally.

Simultaneously, the difference voltage $\Delta V = V_x - V_{ramp}$, is monitored by a comparator circuit. When $\Delta V = 0$, the oscillator is stopped, and digital display indicates the unknown voltage.

2.5 CAPACITANCE

When a potential difference V exists between two points of a circuit not connected by a conductor, these points have a *capacitance* between them. The formation of the potential difference can be pictured as the result of the work done per unit charge in effecting the separation. Thus capacitance C, which is defined by the equation

$$C = Q/V, \tag{2.13}$$

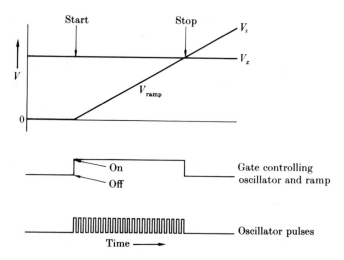

Fig. 2.10 Waveforms in a digital voltmeter of the ramp type.

basically represents energy stored in the capacitor. For a particular device, capacitance depends both on *geometry*, i.e., shape, area, and spacing of its conducting plates (or sheets), and on the *dielectric constant** of the insulator layer between them.

Formulas have been worked out for many geometries. The unit of capacitance is the farad, one coulomb per volt. Most circuit capacitances are much smaller, of the order of microfarads or picofarads.

Table 2.2 Some Properties of Insulators

	Dielectric constant	Breakdown strength (kV mm^{-1})	Power factor
Air	1.0	—	0.0
Mica and glass	4.0–7.0	20–40	0.0015
Nylon	5.0	19	0.03
Polystyrene	2.5	24	0.0005
Mylar	3.2	160	0.003
Ceramic (high-ϵ)	1000 upward	4	0.01
Teflon	2.0	19	<0.0001

To select a capacitor for a particular application one must take into account not only capacitance, but also its maximum operating voltage (often termed working voltage) and design tolerance. The latter may be treated by the considerations discussed for resistors (Section 2.3). Properties of some of the insulators used in capacitors are listed in Table 2.2. Voltage rating is determined by the breakdown

---

* The dielectric constant ϵ of a filling substance is defined as the ratio of capacitance C when it is present to that when there is a vacuum between plates: $\epsilon = C/C_{vac}$. Dielectric constant is also known as permittivity or specific inductive capacity.

strength and thickness of the dielectric layer. The thinner the layer, the higher the capacitance, yet the lower the voltage at which breakdown occurs. Thus, working voltage and capacitance vary inversely for a fixed-size capacitor. At high frequencies, 50 MHz or above, the *power factor* of a capacitor also becomes significant. This quantity is defined as the ratio of power dissipated to that stored and is determined largely by the dielectric. Polystyrene and Teflon have especially low power factors.

Capacitors are usually fabricated by interleaving "sheets" of conductor and dielectric material, though in high-voltage capacitors a liquid dielectric is customary. Ceramic and plastic-film capacitors usually have their metal layer vacuum-deposited. Units are sealed to exclude the atmosphere.

When large capacitances are required in a dc circuit where polarity remains fixed, as in dc power supplies, relatively inexpensive *electrolytic* capacitors are commonly used. These ingenious devices employ an aluminum or tantalum foil that has been electrolyzed to develop a thin oxide (dielectric) coating on one side. A low-conductance paste electrolyte is added between layers. Fixed polarity is essential, for if polarity reverses accidentally, the oxide layer erodes and the capacitor shorts.

DC behavior. A capacitance blocks a steady dc current but permits charge to flow in or out of it when the dc is turned on or off or whenever there is a change in current. In the circuit of Fig. 2.11, when the switch is turned to position (1), electrons flow from the negative side of the voltage source, charging the bottom capacitor plate negatively and are withdrawn from the upper plate, leaving an excess of positive charge. A transient current flows that finally ends when the capacitor voltage equals and opposes in sign the battery potential. A current exists in the capacitor as well because of the changing flux of the electrostatic field between the plates. If the switch is now opened, the charge on C remains until it leaks off by some indirect high-impedance path.

Values of the transient current and instantaneous capacitor voltage can be found by the following process. According to Kirchhoff's voltage law (Section 3.1), battery potential V_{BB} is equal to the potential drops iR (across R) and $v_C = Q/C$ (across C), that is

$$V_{BB} = iR + Q/C. \tag{2.14}$$

By differentiation of Eq. (2.14) with respect to time one obtains $0 = R\,di/dt + i/C$. Rearranging to separate variables gives

$$\frac{di}{i} = -\frac{dt}{RC}. \tag{2.15}$$

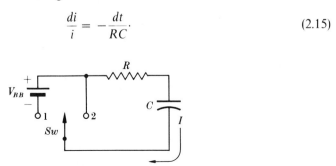

Fig. 2.11 Schematic of a dc circuit with resistance and capacitance.

The solution of Eq. (2.15) is the expression desired:

$$i = \frac{V_{BB}}{R} \exp - \frac{t}{RC}. \tag{2.16}$$

The exponential decrease of i with time predicted by Eq. (2.16) is shown graphically in Fig. 2.12. A time constant for the process will be defined below.

The instantaneous voltage v_C across the capacitor may be found by rewriting Eq. (2.14) as $V_{BB} = Ri + v_C$ and substituting for i from Eq. (2.16). The result is

$$v_C = V_{BB} (1 - e^{-t/RC}). \tag{2.17}$$

The time-dependence of v_C is also shown in Fig. 2.12.

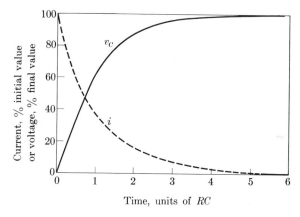

Fig. 2.12 Variation of current and capacitor voltage with time during charging of the capacitor in the circuit of Fig. 2.11.

If in Fig. 2.11 the switch is shifted to position (2) at any time, the capacitor will discharge through resistance R. The initial current will be extremely large if R is minute. This phenomenon is the basis for exploding wire techniques for vaporizing solids.

The transient current is again defined by Eq. (2.16) and the voltage falls exponentially according to an analogous relation.

Time constant. According to Eq. (2.16), charging and discharging are infinite processes. For that reason it is useful to define a time constant τ_c as a measure of the rate. Customarily, τ_c is taken as the time at which the exponent in Eq. (2.16) is unity. Thus, $\tau_c = RC$. When $t = \tau_c$, $i = V_{BB}/Re$ and the current has fallen to $1/e$ or 37% of its initial value V_{BB}/R. τ_c has the dimensions of seconds when R is in ohms and C in farads. Note that there will always be resistance in leads or the voltage source and a capacitor may never be charged or discharged instantaneously.

Example The time constant for a circuit in which $R = 300\ k\Omega$ and $C = 10\ pF$ is $3 \times 10^5\ \Omega \times 10 \times 10^{-12}\ F = 3\ \mu s$.

Series and parallel capacitors. Circuits containing two or more capacitances are usually simplified by calculation of an equivalent capacitance that represents the sum of the separate ones. The summing may be done as follows. If capacitors are in series as in Fig. 2.13a, the voltage across the set must be the sum of the potential differences across each one,

$$V = \frac{Q_1}{C_1} + \frac{Q_2}{C_2} + \frac{Q_3}{C_3}. \tag{2.18}$$

Since the charge for the right-hand plate of C_1 must have come from the left-hand plate of C_2, etc., the charge on each capacitor must be the same, $Q_1 = Q_2 = Q_3$. The sum of voltages becomes

$$V = Q\left(\frac{1}{C_1} + \frac{1}{C_2} + \frac{1}{C_3}\right) = \frac{Q}{C_{eq}}. \tag{2.19}$$

Thus for capacitances in series the reciprocal of the total capacitance is equal to the sum of the reciprocals of the individual capacitances.

On the other hand, if capacitances are in parallel, as in Fig. 2.13b, the voltage across each is the same and the individual charges add. In this case, the total capacitance is

$$\frac{Q_1}{V} + \frac{Q_2}{V} + \frac{Q_3}{V} = C_1 + C_2 + C_3 = C_{eq}. \tag{2.20}$$

Thus, capacitances in parallel add.

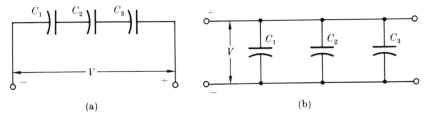

(a)   (b)

Fig 2.13 Capacitances in series and in parallel.

AC behavior. In an ac circuit a capacitor stores and releases charge continuously. This process is accompanied by two effects; a phase difference ϕ is introduced between the current flowing and the voltage across the capacitor and current is impeded.

The magnitude of phase difference produced in a pure capacitance can be easily defined for sine wave ac. Equation (2.13) is rewritten as $Q = Cv$ and $V_p \sin \omega t$ is substituted for v. The resulting expression is then differentiated with respect to time. One obtains

$$\frac{dQ}{dt} = i = C\frac{d}{dt}(V_p \sin \omega t) = \omega C V_p \cos \omega t = I_p \cos \omega t. \tag{2.21}$$

In the right-hand expression I_p has been substituted for $\omega C V_p$ because this product must be the peak value of the current. Since voltage depends on a sine function and the current on a cosine function, there is a 90° phase difference between them. The current is said to "lead" the voltage. In a practical capacitor circuit, resistance and some inductance would also be present, if only in the leads, and a smaller phase difference would be observed (Section 2.7).

A second effect of capacitance is that it impedes an ac current. The effect is the consequence of the storage of charge. There is no energy dissipation as there is in the case of a resistor.

Ohm's law is easily extended to capacitive circuits by defining *reactance* X_c as the measure of the impeding effect of capacitance. Just as $R = V/I$, X_c can be defined as ratio of peak capacitor voltage V_p to peak capacitor current I_p. According to Eq. (2.21) the ratio is

$$\left(\frac{V_p}{I_p}\right)_{cap} = \frac{V_p}{\omega C V_p} = \frac{1}{\omega C} = \frac{1}{2\pi f C} = X_c. \tag{2.22}$$

Example 1   A 20 pF capacitor at a frequency of 10 MHz will offer a reactance of

$$\frac{1}{6.28 \times 10 \times 10^6 \text{ (Hz)} \times 20 \times 10^{-12} \text{ (farads)}} = 800\ \Omega.$$

Example 2   If 250 V at 4 kHz is applied to a 0.1 μF capacitor, the effective (rms) current that will flow will be

$$I = \frac{V}{X_c} = V 2\pi f C = 0.62 \text{ A}.$$

Note that capacitive reactance varies inversely as frequency and capacitance. Since only small reactances are ordinarily sought in a circuit, it can be anticipated that small capacitances will be most useful at high frequencies where their reactance is low, whereas large capacitances will be needed at low frequencies. For this reason also the small *distributed* or stray capacitances of wires are usually of consequence only at high frequencies.

Example   The stray capacitance between a set of lead wires and a metal chassis is found to be about 10 pF. Assume a 10 kΩ resistor in the circuit is shunted by this capacitance. Can the reactance of the stray capacitance be neglected if the circuit is energized by a 10 kHz signal? If energized by a 100 MHz signal?

At 10 kHz, the reactance is

$$X_c = \frac{1}{6.28 \times 10^4 \times 10^{-11}} = 1 \text{ M}\Omega.$$

So large a shunting reactance can certainly be neglected in comparison with 10 kΩ. At 100 MHz, however, the reactance is 10^4 times less, 100 Ω, and shunts the 10 kΩ resistor extensively.

When an ac voltage is imposed on a circuit with some capacitance, a transient current associated with initial charging is superposed on the steady ac. Fortunately, the transient current may usually be neglected.*

---

* If the capacitive time constant is less than the period of the ac, the amplitude of the transient current is negligible after a fraction of a cycle. However, if the time constant is longer than one period, the amplitude of the transient current is small, though it persists over an interval corresponding to many cycles.

2.6 INDUCTANCE

When there is current in a conductor, a magnetic field exists around it. Work is required to establish the field at the outset. The interaction between field and current is conventionally described by stating that when a dc circuit is first made and current increases in a conductor, the actual voltage drop along its length is smaller than the value predicted by Ohm's law. An opposing voltage v_L that is induced in the conductor by the developing magnetic field reduces the instantaneous voltage. Voltage v_L is defined by the expression

$$v_L = -L\frac{di}{dt} \tag{2.23}$$

where L is a constant termed the self-inductance, and di/dt is the rate of increase of current.* A component of high inductance termed an inductor is made by coiling a low-resistance wire. Its magnetic field is the sum of the fields contributed by individual loops.**

The way in which current varies with time in a dc circuit with an inductor L in series with voltage source V_{BB} and a resistor R is given by the expression

$$i = \frac{V_{BB}}{R}[1 - e^{-(R/L)t}], \tag{2.24}$$

where i is the instantaneous current and t the time. The dependence of current on time in an inductive circuit is exponential. Note the similarity of Eq. (2.24) and Eq. (2.17). In an RL circuit the current rise parallels the voltage rise across a capacitor in an RC circuit.†

Reactance. The process of withdrawal of energy for storage in a magnetic field when current is increasing, or returning it to a circuit as current decreases, causes an inductance to retard or impede current in an ac circuit. The retarding effect is termed inductive reactance, and its magnitude is defined as

$$X_L = \omega L = 2\pi f L. \tag{2.25}$$

Ohm's law is also applicable to inductance. For example, the magnitude of the voltage drop across an inductor is just $V_L = IX_L$. Note that rms values of current and voltage apply.

---

* The negative sign indicates the opposition of the induced potential to that provided by some voltage source in the circuit.

** An inductor for high-frequency use, called a choke, has a core of air. An inductor for low-frequency use is usually wound on a core of soft iron to concentrate its magnetic field still more and thereby enhance its inductance.

† The analogy suggests the merit of defining a time constant τ_L for an inductive circuit. It should be the interval over which the exponential in Eq. (2.24) becomes unity. This yields $\tau_L = L/R$. If L is in henries and R is in ohms, τ_L is given in seconds. In an interval corresponding to τ_L, the current will build up to 63% of its final value.

Example   What is the voltage drop across an inductor of reactance of $100\,\Omega$ at 5 MHz for a current of 50 mA? $V = IX_L = 50 \times 10^{-3} \times 100 = 5$ V.

It is clear from Eq. (2.25) that inductive reactance increases linearly with frequency. At ultra-high frequencies even the very small *distributed* inductance in wires leads to appreciable reactance. To minimize this effect leads are all but eliminated in such circuits.

Inductors see much less application in electronic circuits than capacitors. Where reactance is needed, capacitors are ordinarily used for one or more reasons. Inductors are often bulky (especially those for low frequencies) in comparison with capacitors; they cannot be successfully designed into integrated circuits; and their dissipation of power is greater because they have appreciable resistance. It is fortunate that capacitance-resistance networks can perform with ease the functions desired.

Transformers.   If a magnetic field set up by a primary coil is caused to couple efficiently with a secondary coil, usually by winding both on an iron core that links the coils, the device serves as a transformer in an ac circuit. The magnetic flux in the transformer is proportional to the number of turns n_1 in the primary coil; because all the flux loops through the secondary coil, the voltage induced is proportional to the turns ratio n_2/n_1 where n_2 is the number of secondary turns. The voltage V_2 that appears across the terminals of the secondary coil is given by

$$V_2 = V_1(n_2/n_1) \tag{2.26}$$

where V_1 is the voltage imposed across the primary coil. Clearly it is possible to step up or step down voltages (and inversely, currents) in ac circuits by use of transformers of different turns ratios. A further discussion of transformers will be found in Section 3.8 where impedance matching is considered.

2.7 IMPEDANCE

Any practical circuit contains resistance, capacitance, and inductance. In discussing components individually it is convenient to consider dissipative effects (arising from resistance) separately from "storage" effects (arising from reactance). Both current and voltage are best represented vectorially because of phase differences that obtain. The power expended is then defined as a product,

$$W = I \cdot V = IV \cos\phi, \tag{2.27}$$

where ϕ is the phase difference between them. For resistance the product becomes $IV_R = I^2R$, but for a pure capacitor or inductor $\phi = 90°$ and the product is zero. As a result $\cos \phi$ is defined as the *power factor*.

To calculate the overall retarding effect on current of components with R, L, or C the impedance Z is defined. Its magnitude will be of central interest here though its phase relative to the current vector will also be important. Since no power is dissipated in a pure reactance, it is convenient to assign it the phase angle corresponding to the phase of the voltage in it. For example, since voltage lags current in a pure capacitance by $90°$, X_c is assigned $\phi = -90°$. Similarly, voltage leads current by $90°$

in a pure inductance and $\phi = 90°$ for X_L. For a pure resistance, $\phi = 0$, of course.

Accordingly, reactances and resistance are ordinarily represented vectorially as in the example illustrated in Fig. 2.14.* The magnitude of Z as obtained vectorially is given by the expression

$$Z = \sqrt{R^2 + (X_L - X_C)^2} \tag{2.28}$$

and the phase angle ϕ is defined by its tangent,

$$\tan \phi = \frac{X_L - X_C}{R}. \tag{2.29}$$

In terms of Fig. 2.14 the power factor, $\cos \phi$, is R/Z. Note that the apparent power supplied, $I^2 Z$, is always larger than that expended, which is $I^2 R$.

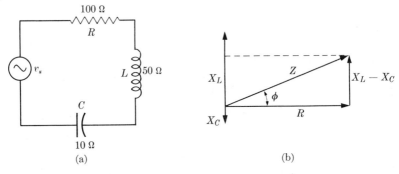

Fig. 2.14 Vector representation of the capacitive and inductive reactances X_L and X_C and resistance R for a series connection. (a) The circuit. Values of the reactance of each component are given for a particular frequency. (b) Vector diagram indicating a means by which impedance Z can be obtained.

Example For the circuit of Fig. 2.14a, what is (a) the impedance and (b) the voltage drop in each component; (c) what must the applied voltage v_s be? Take $I = 10$ mA.

a) First, the impedance is

$$Z = \sqrt{R^2 + (X_L - X_C)^2} = \sqrt{(100)^2 + (50 - 10)^2} = 107.8 \ \Omega.$$

b) Second, the voltage drops can be deduced by applying Ohm's law. The voltage drop across the resistance is

$$IR = 10 \times 10^{-3} \times 100 = 1 \text{ V}.$$

The voltage drop across the inductance is

$$IX_L = 10 \times 10^{-3} \times 50 = 0.50 \text{ V},$$

---

* The magnitude and phase angle of reactances may be handled mathematically by representing reactance and impedance as complex numbers. The real part of each is associated with resistance, the imaginary part with reactance. In the complex plane, imaginary quantities are plotted along the y-axis, corresponding to the 90° phase differences that obtain here. For example, a series combination of a capacitance and a resistance gives a complex impedance $Z = R + jX_C$, where $j = \sqrt{-1}$. The imaginary part X_C is graphed at right angles to the real part R as in Fig. 2.14b.

and that across the capacitance is

$$IX_C = 10 \times 10^{-3} \times 10 = 0.10 \text{ V}.$$

c) Finally, the applied voltage v_s must be

$$IZ = 10 \times 10^{-3} \cdot 107.8 = 1.078 \text{ V}.$$

Note that the sum of voltage drops $(1 + 0.50 + 0.10 = 1.60 \text{ V})$ exceeds the applied voltage because the voltages in the components are out of phase.

2.8 RESONANCE

The behavior of ac circuits is, in general, strongly frequency-dependent. Both inductive reactance and capacitive reactance vary with frequency. As might be expected, the sensitivity to frequency is greater, the smaller the resistance of the circuit and the larger the reactance.

It is apparent from Eq. (2.28) that under certain conditions the reactances of the capacitors and inductors cancel because of their inverse phase dependence. For a given circuit, the frequency at which $X_L - X_C$ vanishes and *only resistance opposes the current* may be found by equating capacitive and inductive reactances and solving for the frequency. The result is

$$f = (2\pi \sqrt{LC})^{-1}. \tag{2.30}$$

The circuit is said to be *in resonance* at this frequency, i.e., the apparent power I^2Z that must be supplied is a minimum.

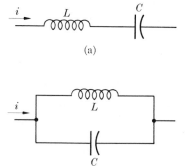

Fig. 2.15 Resonant circuits. (a) Series-resonant *LC* combination. (b) Parallel-resonant *LC* combination.

In Fig. 2.15 the two types of conventional resonant circuits, the series and parallel combinations, are illustrated. Their properties are quite different although both resonate at essentially the frequency defined by Eq. (2.30). The series-resonant circuit is the less interesting and needs only be described as having a minimum impedance and maximum current at its resonant frequency. By contrast, the impedance of a parallel *LC* circuit is a maximum at resonance as indicated in Fig. 2.16 and current i

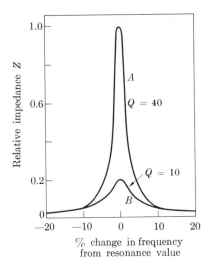

Fig. 2.16 Impedance of a parallel resonant circuit as a function of frequency. Curve A is for a high-Q circuit, curve B for a low-Q circuit.

is a minimum.* By regarding the value along the ordinate as $1/Z$, the figure can also represent the behavior of a series LC circuit. In this case, as inferred, $1/Z$ is a maximum at resonance.

Example If $L = 1.0 \times 10^{-3}$ henries, $C = 0.44 \ \mu\text{F}$, and $R = 150 \ \Omega$ in a series LC circuit, what is its resonant frequency? If a 20 V signal of this frequency is applied to the circuit, what are the voltage drops across each component (assume no distributed resistance in the coil or leads) and the current?

First, the resonant frequency

$$f_0 = \frac{1}{2\pi\sqrt{LC}} = \frac{1}{6.28\sqrt{1.0 \times 10^{-3} \times 4.4 \times 10^{-7}}} = 7.16 \ \text{kHz}.$$

Second, $Z = R$ at resonance and application of 20 V rms will give $I = V/R = 0.20 \ \text{A}$.

The currents and voltages in the inductance and capacitance are much greater, but cancel. Ohm's law gives a drop of

$$IX_C = 0.2 \times 1/2\pi f_0 C = 0.2/6.28 \times 7.6 \times 10^3 \times 4.4 \times 10^{-7} = 95 \ \text{V (rms)}$$

across C. Across L there is a drop of ‚

$$IX_L = 0.2 \times 6.28 \times 7.6 \times 10^3 \times 1.0 \times 10^{-3} = 95 \ \text{V (rms)}$$

also.

---

* The parallel LC circuit is sometimes termed a tank circuit, because it "stores" energy. At the resonant frequency energy is stored in its capacitor during one part of a cycle, only to be *transferred to the magnetic field of its inductance* during the next part of the cycle as capacitor recharges with opposite polarity. Once the tank circuit is "charged," energy need be supplied only to offset that lost as heat in the resistance of the circuit.

As seen in the example, the voltages across the reactive components cannot be zero. The instantaneous values of these voltages cancel, however, since they are 180° out of phase. As in the example below, even though the voltage applied to the circuit is small, the capacitor and inductor in the series resonant circuit must be capable of withstanding the much higher voltages that exist across them.

For an LC combination the sharpness of the resonance peak is usually described by the Q or *quality factor* of its circuit. Two alternative but equivalent definitions are useful. First, Q is the ratio of the energy stored to that dissipated during a cycle. Alternatively, Q is defined as $f_0/\Delta f$ where Δf is the width of the curve when its amplitude has fallen to half the maximum value. Both lead to the expression

$$Q = 2\pi f_0 \, L/R. \qquad (2.31)$$

In Fig. 2.16 curves are given for two different values of Q.

The impedance characteristics of LC circuits give them many applications in electronics as frequency-selective circuits. For example, a particular band of frequencies can be selectively removed by a series LC circuit that is grounded. The use of these combinations as filters will be further considered in Section 3.5.

2.9 THE OSCILLOSCOPE

The oscilloscope finds ready use as a device for displaying voltage and current waveforms. For that reason it is appropriate that the oscilloscope be described in this chapter. It also finds special use as an *x-y* recorder, e.g. in nuclear decoupling in nmr spectrometry and in presenting rapidly changing instrument outputs, such as are obtained in single-sweep polarography and certain kinetic studies.

Cathode ray tube. The heart of the oscilloscope is a cathode ray tube, a device using a focused electron beam to trace signals on a fluorescent screen. Since electrons have negligible mass yet are charged they make an ideal beam for this purpose, for they can be moved or stopped almost instantly in response to electric fields. The signals are visually displayed because fluorescence produced when the beam strikes the screen persists from 0.5 to perhaps 5 s, depending on the phosphor with which the screen is coated and its preparation.

Of particular interest is the design of the electron gun, pictured in Fig. 2.17. The path and focusing of the electron beam are shown. Note that the positive terminal of the dc supply is grounded. The most negative point in the gun is the grid, which controls the beam intensity. The more negative the grid, the smaller is the number of electrons that escape through the opening, and the fainter is the image on the screen.

The electrons that do pass the grid are accelerated and focused by the electrostatic field between cathode and grid. Closer to the screen a more sensitive stage of focusing is provided by splitting the anode and inserting an electrode whose potential can be varied smoothly over a relatively small range. The control of the voltage of this electrode allows the electron beam to be brought to a focus precisely at the screen. The general features of an electrostatic cathode ray* tube are clearly shown in the

---

* Magnetic fields are also used for focusing and deflection, particularly in the large cathode ray tubes used in TV and radar sets. [9]

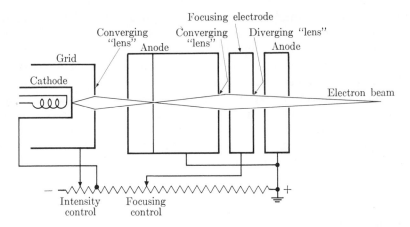

Fig. 2.17 The electron gun in an electrostatic cathode ray tube. The actions of the electrical fields at different points along the path of the beam are suggested in terms of the optical analogies. The focal length of the two "lenses" at the right is varied by adjusting the potential of the focusing electrode.

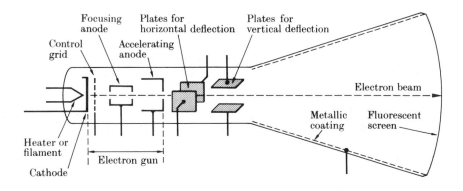

Fig. 2.18 Schematic diagram of a cathode ray tube with electrostatic focusing.

schematic diagram in Fig. 2.18. The screen itself is curved so that the distance from the final anode will be constant regardless of the angle through which the beam is deflected.

Signals are displayed on the screen, after conversion to a voltage, by causing them to deflect the electron beam. Ordinarily a signal is imposed across the vertical plates. To accommodate a wide range of input amplitudes, a stage of attenuation and one or more stages of amplification are also provided. As the electron beam passes between the plates, it is deflected to an extent proportional to the dc potential difference across them. The height of the pattern is therefore a measure of signal amplitude. Usually the screen is ruled so that wave height can be read in divisions and multiplied by a calibration factor to give the true amplitude.

Time base. Most signals are presented as a function of time. Both periodic and transient signals can be usefully observed in this way. To secure a time display, a steadily increasing electrostatic field is imposed across the horizontal plates. It sweeps the electron beam across the face of the tube while the field on the vertical plates is producing a deflection proportional to signal amplitude. At the end of a sweep the field on the horizontal plates must suddenly be "canceled" to return the beam to its start.*

If a periodic signal is being displayed, an appropriate time base is one that sweeps the signal across once every period, every two periods, or every n periods. A "stroboscopic" picture of one period, two periods, or n periods of the signal is obtained. In research instruments the time base may be set precisely.

Example One cycle of a 5 kHz sine wave is to be displayed on an oscilloscope. Its period is $1/5000 = 200\,\mu s$. A 5 kHz sawtooth wave is generated as a time base. Assume that its ramp (rising) portion is 190 μs long and the return portion 10 μs. Then only the last 5% of the cycle of the signal, which occurs during the beam return, will not be seen. To view two cycles of the wave, the sweep frequency should be cut in half.

Each sweep must also be *synchronized* to start at the same point in the cycle of a periodic signal to secure a stable display. To accomplish this result, a fraction of the signal to be displayed is mixed with the time base in a circuit that generates a voltage spike, which triggers the start of the sweep.

x-y plotting. A variable other than time can easily be displayed along the *x*-axis. An oscilloscope is a good *x-y* plotter. A basic example is the comparison of a sine wave of unknown frequency with the output of a calibrated sine wave oscillator. The oscillator frequency is varied until a simple Lissajous figure appears. From the pattern the frequency ratio can be determined and the unknown frequency calculated.

Display of high-frequency signals. The high-frequency limit of an oscilloscope is determined by its amplifier frequency limits and fastest sweep rate. Most oscilloscopes have amplifiers that handle dc to a few megahertz. By convention, the upper limit is the frequency at which the voltage gain is down 30% (the 3 dB point).

The frequency restriction on signal display is most evident when a square wave is imposed. The side of the pattern, a composite containing very high frequencies, should ideally be vertical. In practice an oscilloscope can display it only with a finite slope. Its maximum rate of deflection is measured by its *rise time* t_r. If a step input or square wave is imposed, t_r is the interval required for beam deflection to increase from 10% to 90% of its final value. It can be shown to be approximately the reciprocal of the amplifier bandwidth Δf. Specifically, $t_r = 0.35/\Delta f$, where Δf is the stated frequency range.

Example What apparent rise time will be observed on a dc to 5 MHz oscilloscope for a step function whose true rise time is 1 ns? The oscilloscope bandwidth can be taken as 5 MHz. Its

---

* The voltage pattern needed is termed a sawtooth wave and has the outline ⌁⌁⌁⌁.

rise time will be $t_r = 0.35 \div 5 \times 10^6 = 70$ ns. Since this is the limiting factor, the step function will appear with a 70 ns rise time.

Sweep rates are a second limiting factor in display of very-high-frequency signals. A way around this difficulty is suggested below.

Special-purpose oscilloscopes. The *sampling oscilloscope* is an ingenious modification that permits display of a periodic signal even of microwave (1–30 GHz) frequency. A signal that appears at the input is sampled at a slightly later point in the cycle each time it repeats. This point-by-point presentation continues until in a matter of perhaps 100 μs one complete cycle has been displayed. Then sampling begins again.

Some of the other special types of oscilloscope available are: *storage*, a kind that permits an operator to keep a waveform or trace on the screen for a long period, and in some instruments until he wishes to erase it; *digital readout*, a modification that reads out the amplitude difference between two spots that can be moved at will along a curve being displayed; and *dual trace*, a type that simultaneously displays two signals as a function of time to allow the time relation between them to be made clear.

REFERENCES

Electrical measurements are discussed on an introductory level in:

1. A. C. J. Beerens, *Measurement Methods and Devices in Electronics.* London: Cleaver-Hume, 1966

A lucid presentation of basic electrical measurements on the intermediate to advanced level is to be found in:

2. Ernest Frank, *Electrical Measurement Analysis.* New York: McGraw-Hill, 1959
3. Forest K. Harris, *Electrical Measurements.* New York: Wiley, 1952
4. B. E. F. Karsa, *Electrical Measuring Instruments and Measurements.* Budapest: Akademiai Kiado, 1967

Special attention is given to precise measurements in electronics in:

5. G. Klein and J. J. Zaalberg Van Zelst, *Precision Electronics.* New York: Springer-Verlag, 1967
6. F. G. Spreadbury, *Electronic Measurements and Measuring Instruments.* London: Constable, 1956

Other publications of interest are:

7. E. A. Boucher, "Theory and Application of Thermistors," *J. Chem. Educ.* **44**, A935 (1967)
7a. R. Harruff and C. Kimball, "Temperature Compensation Using Thermistor Networks," *Anal. Chem.* **42** (7), 73A (1970)
8. E. A. Loew, *Direct and Alternating Currents, Theory and Machinery.* 4th ed. New York: McGraw-Hill, 1954
9. J. E. Nelson, "Oscilloscopes in Chemistry," *J. Chem. Educ.* **45**, A635, A787 (1968)
10. G. Parr and O. H. Davie, *The Cathode Ray Tube and Its Applications.* 3rd ed. New York: Reinhold, 1959

EXERCISES

2.1 Derive the expression for average power dissipation $P_{av} = \frac{1}{2}RI_p^2$ for ac current in a resistance.

2.2 After standing for a year, a 1.5 V dry cell proves able to furnish only 5 mA of current. What is its internal resistance?

[*Ans.*: 300 Ω.]

2.3 How may several 10 kΩ, 2 W resistors be connected to obtain an equivalent resistance of 1 kΩ with 20 W "capacity"? How many are required?

[*Ans.*: Connect in parallel; 10 required.]

2.4 An electric arc has a negative resistance characteristic, i.e., its current increases as the voltage drop across it decreases. It may be brought into a condition of stable operation by placing a resistor R of proper value in series. Discuss the self-controlling features of this combination, which provides regulation when the current momentarily decreases or increases.

2.5 A voltmeter has a resistance of 300 Ω and gives a quarter-scale deflection when 0.15 V is applied across it. What is its full-scale current sensitivity?

[*Ans.*: 2 mA.]

2.6 The extended-range ammeter of Fig. 2.5 is used to measure current in a circuit consisting of a 10 V battery shorted by a 5 kΩ resistor. Assume the meter resistance is 50 Ω. What current exists in the circuit

    a) Before the meter is inserted?

    b) After the meter is inserted?

    c) What is the error in the current measurement?

[*Ans.*: (a) 2 mA; (b) 1.98 mA; (c) 1 %.]

2.7 A schematic diagram of an Ayrton shunt is given below. By proper choice of R_1, R_2, and R_3 meter M can be given three desired current ranges. If the meter is a 100 µA device with an internal resistance R_m of 2 kΩ, and is to be given current ranges of 10 mA, 100 mA, and 1 A, what values must be chosen for the shunt resistors?

[*Ans.*: $R_1 = 18.2\ \Omega$, $R_2 = 1.8\ \Omega$, $R_3 = 0.2\ \Omega$.]

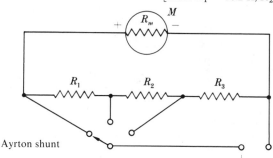

Ayrton shunt

2.8 a) Draw a schematic diagram for an ac ammeter of the full-wave type that is based on a moving-coil meter. Show how a shunting resistor can be added.

    b) What fraction of the peak current does such a meter register?

[*Ans.*: (b) Assuming negligible voltage drop across the diodes, $I_m = 0.637\ I_p$ (it measures the average current).]

2.9 Suppose for the ohmmeter shown in Fig. 2.7 that the meter is a 1 mA device with an internal resistance of 50 Ω, that $R_2 = 1$ kΩ, and that $V = 20$ V. What value of R_1 is needed? What would be the value of a resistance which gave a one-fifth scale deflection when connected across AB?

[*Ans.*: 20 kΩ, 4 kΩ.]

2.10 Two capacitors of 1.0 μF and 0.01 μF capacity are connected in series across a 45 V battery. What is the voltage drop across each?

[*Ans.*: 0.446 and 44.6 V.]

2.11 The charging of a capacitor is to be used to obtain an approximately linear rate of voltage increase. For this purpose a 0.05 μF capacitor is to be charged to only 20% of the applied voltage. What value of resistance must be used in series with it if the charging time desired is 10 μs?

[*Ans.*: 895 Ω.]

2.12 What time is theoretically required to discharge a 0.001 μF capacitor to 10% of its original value in a circuit with a resistance of 10 kΩ?

[*Ans.*: 23 μs.]

2.13 After 0.10 s, what will be the current in a dc circuit with a total resistance of 700 Ω and a capacitance of 20 μF in series, when 50 V is applied across the elements?

[*Ans.*: 56 μs.]

2.14 There is an effective current of 40 mA at 50 kHz in an ac circuit. The total series resistance is 25 kΩ, and the impedance 30 kΩ. What is the power dissipated?

[*Ans.*: 40 W.]

2.15 An ac voltage defined by the equation $v = V_p \sin \omega t$ is imposed in sequence across a pure resistance R, a pure capacitance C, and a pure inductance L.

a) Sketch a current-time curve for each case.
b) Derive an expression for the current in each case that shows its magnitude and phase.

[*Ans.*: Capacitance current $i = V_p \omega C \sin(\omega t + \pi/2)$.]

2.16 A 20 kΩ resistor and 0.15 H inductor with a resistance of 11 Ω are connected in series. What value capacitor must be added in series to achieve resonance at 240 kHz? What is the equivalent impedance at resonance? What is the value of Q for this circuit?

[*Ans.*: 2.9 pF; 20 kΩ; 11.3.]

Chapter 3

ELECTRICAL NETWORKS

3.1 KIRCHHOFF'S LAWS AND EQUIVALENT CIRCUITS

To analyze the many electrical networks that figure in instrumentation, procedures for systematic attack and simplification are valuable. Where it is not possible to reduce resistances or impedances to simple series and parallel combinations, Kirchhoff's two laws are especially important. They are:

1. The algebraic sum of the currents at any junction in a circuit is zero, $\Sigma_i I_i = 0$. This law has already been used implicitly in dealing with parallel resistors (Section 2.3) when it was assumed that current is continuous; the law may be equally well regarded as a statement that electrical charge is conserved. It should be noted that a junction may also be called a *node* or *branch point*. This law is illustrated by application to the circuit of Fig. 3.1.

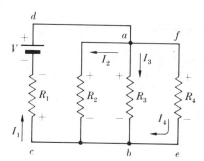

Fig. 3.1 Application of Kirchhoff's laws to a branched circuit. The first law applied to node a gives $\Sigma I = I_1 - I_2 - I_3 - I_4 = 0$. The second law applied to the loop $abcd$ gives $\Sigma V = V - I_3 R_3 - I_1 R_1 = 0$ and applied to loop $abef$ gives $\Sigma V = I_4 R_4 - I_3 R_3 = 0$.

2. The algebraic sum of the potential differences around any complete loop of a circuit is zero, $\Sigma_i V_i = 0$. In Fig. 3.1 the law is applied to both loops $abcd$ and $abef$. This law was also used implicitly earlier: it was assumed in dealing with series resistors (Section 2.3). Essentially, the law is a statement of the conservation of energy.

To apply Kirchhoff's two laws to a network is a straightforward process. One begins by assigning a current of arbitrary but reasonable direction in terms of the polarity of any dc source to each resistance or impedance in the network. Then the sign of the potential drop across each resistor is marked according to the convention that the current enters the positive end of a resistance. The laws are applied node by node and loop by loop to obtain a sufficient number of simultaneous equations to allow solution for all the unknown currents.* If an assigned current proves to be negative, it in fact has the opposite direction to that chosen. When the currents have been found, voltage drops, power dissipated in components, etc., can be readily calculated.

Unfortunately, networks with three or more nodes yield a great many equations in terms of just as many variables. These simultaneous equations yield to standard determinant methods but the determinants become progressively more cumbersome as the number of branches grows. For example, the equations for a Wheatstone bridge require the evaluation of two sixth-order determinants (six rows and six columns) to determine each current.

Often a simpler approach to the analysis of complex networks is the use of Kirchhoff's laws to state *loop currents*. In this case one need solve directly only for the one or two currents of real interest. This method will be illustrated for the Wheatstone bridge in Section 3.3.

Equivalent circuits. Another extremely useful tool in circuit analysis is the replacement of part or all of a circuit by an equivalent circuit, which is, in effect, a simple

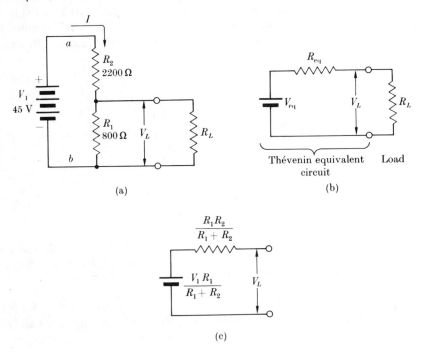

(a)

(b)

(c)

Fig. 3.2 Determination of a Thévenin equivalent circuit. (a) A voltage divider circuit. (b) The Thévenin equivalent circuit. (c) Thévenin equivalent circuit for the divider output across R_1.

---

* It may be shown that if there are n unknown currents, n independent equations can be written so that solution is always possible.

model of the original that behaves like it in so far as the quantity of interest is concerned. For example, this approach was employed in treating series and parallel combinations of resistances (Section 2.3). In that case a set of resistors was replaced by a single element of equivalent resistance. Similarly, in Section 2.5 an equivalent capacitor was used in lieu of a set of capacitors. In each instance the equivalent circuit made it easier to calculate a circuit current. In the analysis of electronic circuits, active devices such as transistors can also be replaced by equivalent resistances and voltage sources to simplify an analysis of circuit behavior.

The *Thévenin equivalent circuit* is one of the two or three most useful models for simplifying a more complex circuit. Thévenin's theorem states that any network can be replaced by an equivalent circuit containing only one voltage source and one series resistor. This equivalent circuit is shown in Fig. 3.2b. The Thévenin circuit will deliver a voltage and current identical to those furnished at the terminals of the original circuit. The *voltage divider* pictured in Fig. 3.2a provides a simple case to illustrate how a circuit is reduced to a Thévenin equivalent circuit. What is sought is the output voltage V_L available to load R_L.

The Thévenin equivalent battery V_{eq} is the *open circuit potential* at the output terminals. It is simply the voltage drop IR_1 that appears across R_1 before load R_L is connected. Consider R_L disconnected. Applying Ohm's law to the voltage divider circuit yields $V_1 = IR_1 + IR_2$. The current in the voltage divider is $I = V_1/(R_1 + R_2)$ and the open-circuit voltage drop across R_1 is $IR_1 = V_1R_1/(R_1 + R_2) = V_{eq}$.

What is the value of the series resistance R_{eq} for the Thévenin circuit? To calculate it, consider the battery short-circuited (or replaced by its internal resistance, if not negligible). In the circuit of Fig. 3.2a points a and b are now joined, putting R_1 and R_2 in parallel. This combination, whose resistance is $R_2R_1/(R_2 + R_1)$, is the desired resistance R_{eq}. In Fig. 3.2c the completed equivalent circuit is shown. Another application of the theorem will be made in the discussion of the Wheatstone bridge in Section 3.3.

Example   Derive an equation for the V_L for the voltage divider of Fig. 3.2a. What is the value of V_L if $R_L = 1$ kΩ? if $R_L = 10$ kΩ?

From the Thévenin equivalent circuit of Fig. 3.2b it is evident that the fraction of V_{eq} that will appear across R_L is $R_L/(R_L + R_{eq})$. Thus, $V_L = V_{eq}R_L/(R_L + R_{eq})$.

To obtain values of V_L, first calculate V_{eq} and R_{eq}:

$$V_{eq} = 45 \times 800/(800 + 2200) = 12 \text{ V}.$$

$$R_{eq} = 800 \times 2200/(800 + 2200) = 587 \ \Omega.$$

Now, when $R_L = 1$ kΩ,

$$V_L = 12 \times 1000/(1000 + 587) = 7.6 \text{ V}.$$

When $R_L = 10$ kΩ,

$$V_L = 12 \times 10\,000/(10\,000 + 587) = 11.3 \text{ V}.$$

3.2 THE POTENTIOMETER

This simple, fundamental device consists of (a) a precision variable voltage divider*
and (b) a difference detector. A potentiometer is used to determine an unknown dc
potential by precise comparison with a known dc potential. No simple circuit is
more important in measurement: a determination with a potentiometer is *the*
classical null procedure (Section 1.8).

A simple type of potentiometer is illustrated in Fig. 3.3. Circuit A consists of a
stable but adjustable source of dc current I_A, working battery V_{BB}, variable resistor
R_v, and precision slidewire R whose resistance increases linearly along its length. A
tap or wiper moves along R to divide the total voltage drop I_AR into two parts
I_AR_B and I_AR_A. Resistance R may be a single wire, a tightly wound wire helix, one
side of which is contacted by a wiper, or a series of known resistances connected to
the terminals of a rotary switch (or some combination as in Fig. 3.4). Even if V_{BB} is
a dry cell, over a short period of time the combination of V_{BB} and R_v yields a stable
current that can be varied by adjustment of R_v.

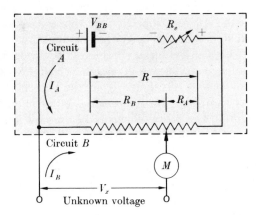

Fig. 3.3 Schematic of a simple potentiometer. V_x is an unknown voltage smaller than V_{BB}. R is
a resistor (slidewire) whose resistance varies uniformly along its length. R_v is an adjustable resistor
that permits the current in circuit A to be varied so that the voltage drop across R can be
calibrated.

Circuit B includes R_B, unknown voltage V_x, and difference or null detector M,
often a galvanometer. Once the voltage across R has been accurately fixed by standardization, the wiper is moved until detector M registers zero current (in circuit B).
When $I_B = 0$, $I_AR_B = V_x$. The unknown voltage has been determined by a null
procedure. The readout is the position of the wiper on the slidewire.

A practical potentiometer is shown schematically in Fig. 3.4. It differs from the
circuit of Fig. 3.3 in the addition of a standard cell circuit to facilitate calibration of
the slidewire voltage drop, and a second wiper or tap on the slidewire to provide
greater precision in reading. To calibrate the slidewire, switch Sw is moved to the
lower position, which places standard cell SC in series with difference detector,

---

* In electronics a variable voltage divider is itself often called a potentiometer or a "pot."

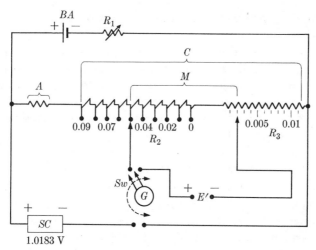

Fig. 3.4 Circuit of a semiprecision potentiometer with a range of from 0.0002 V to 0.11 V. Resistance $A = 91.73\ \Omega$, $R_2 = 9.00\ \Omega$, and $R_3 = 1.10\ \Omega$; thus, $A + R_2 + R_3 = 101.83\ \Omega$, and the instrument will be direct-reading in volts when the standard cell, SC, furnishes 1.0183 V. (After Andress, P. M., "Semi-Precision Potentiometers." Rubicon Notes, No. 1. Philadelphia: Rubicon.)

galvanometer G. The wipers on the slidewire are set to tap off an indicated voltage equal to that of SC. Current from battery BA is varied by adjusting R_1 until the galvanometer shows no deflection. If the slidewire scale has been marked with precision, the voltage along the entire slidewire now conforms to its scale.

The potentiometer of Fig. 3.4 gains an order of magnitude in precision by incorporating a second wiper on its "slidewire." The reason is that one wiper may select among relatively large resistances, and the other among small resistances, as shown in Fig. 3.4. The range of the instrument illustrated is 0 to 0.11 V; its sensitivity is 5×10^{-5} V.

A more versatile precision potentiometer may be devised by two further changes. An extra slidewire can be incorporated in series with AC to alter the total resistance so that standard cells of different voltages can be accommodated without the need to change calibration marks on AC. Other resistors can also be substituted for A to provide ranges of emf measurement. Both adjustments are possible on high-precision instruments such as the Leeds and Northrup type-K potentiometers. These potentiometers permit use of standard cell potentials varying from 1.0174 to 1.0205 V, and the use of potential ranges of 0–0.01611 V, 0–0.1611 V, and 0–1.611 V.

Accuracy. The accuracy of potentiometers depends on several factors:

1. The accuracy of the fixed resistors, the linearity of the slidewire, and the degree of mechanical stability in the wiping of the slidewire. The accuracy of these factors may be 99.99 % or better in a precision potentiometer.

2. The stability of the ratio of total resistance AC to that part tapped off, which depends on the time stability of the resistances and on the similarities of the characteristics of different parts. If alloys of comparable electrical characteristics are used

throughout for the windings, the ratio will ordinarily be constant with time and with moderate temperature changes.

3.   The reliability with which the comparison can be made between the voltage drop along the slidewire and both the standard cell emf and unknown voltages. This comparison is actually a function of the sensitivity of the difference detector as well as the fineness of setting possible for (a) the variable resistor in the battery circuit and (b) the slider on the precision variable resistor. The standard cell comparison may usually be made to within 0.01 %.

4.   The constancy of the standard cell voltage, which is a function of the age and temperature of the cell. Often the unsaturated Weston cell is used because its temperature coefficient is so small as to be negligible in most measurements.

5.   The constancy of the emf of the battery during the measuring period. With dry cells frequent restandardization of current is necessary. Mercury cells have a much greater life and an output that is steady at 1.34 V over most of their life. Zener diode circuits (Section 4.5) are still more constant in output (0.1 to 0.01 %), and if used may nearly eliminate the need for recalibration of the precision divider.

As in a Wheatstone bridge (see below), the contact resistance at wipers does not ordinarily affect the precision of measurements since it is not part of the voltage divider. Only when the contact resistance is so large as to reduce the sensitivity of the difference detector is precision affected. For example, when a moving-coil galvanometer is used, an upper limit of one megohm may be set as the sum of contact and other resistances in the comparison circuit. Good precision and reasonable speed of measurement, however, require that the resistance be 10 kΩ or less.

Measurement of voltages in high-resistance circuits calls for a difference detector of very high sensitivity. Eminently suitable are electronic amplifiers that respond to "unbalance" currents as small as 10^{-11} to 10^{-13} A coupled to a readout device. For example, such amplifier-readout combinations are used in pH meters, since glass electrodes characteristically have resistances of 100 MΩ.

Example   What error is associated with the use of a galvanometer of sensitivity 10^{-9} A mm^{-1} to determine an IR drop of one volt across a resistance of (a) 10^4 Ω, and (b) 10^6 Ω? For a detectable deflection of 0.2 mm, a 2×10^{-10} A current will be necessary. The minimum voltage change detectable will thus be 2×10^{-10} A $\times 10^4$ $\Omega = 10^{-6}$ V, which would introduce an error of $(10^{-6}/1) \times 100 = 10^{-4}$ %. For the 10^6 Ω resistor the uncertainty is 10^2 greater or 0.01 %.

Had only 0.01 V been measured, the error would in both instances have been 100 times larger: 10^{-2} % and 1 %.

Current and resistance measurements.   A potentiometer can also be used to measure dc current precisely. A small precision resistor is inserted in the circuit and the voltage drop across it observed. The current is calculated from Ohm's law. Likewise, an unknown resistance R_x may be determined by placing it in series with a standard resistor R_s and a mercury battery. The voltage drop across each resistance is measured and the ratio IR_x/IR_s gives R_x in terms of the standard R_s.*

---

* The advantage of the potentiometer method over a Wheatstone bridge procedure (Section 3.3) is that an unknown resistance is determined in terms of a single standard resistor rather than the several resistances of a bridge.

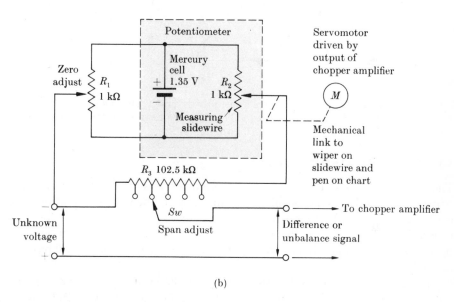

(a)

(b)

Fig. 3.5 Recording potentiometer. (a) Line diagram. (b) Simplified schematic of Heath Servo Recorder (Courtesy of Heath Co.).

Recording potentiometer. Self-balancing potentiometers make good dc voltage recorders. As discussed in Section 1.8, they are used as readout devices for many instruments such as pH meters or UV-VIS spectrometers. A line block diagram of a potentiometric recorder is shown in Fig. 3.5a. In Fig. 3.5b a simplified schematic diagram of a recorder is given. The basic potentiometer is identified as a constant current source (mercury cell) and a 1 kΩ slidewire. The zero adjustment control provides independent control of the zero position on the chart.

If the wiper on R_1 is at the bottom and the slidewire wiper is at the top of R_2, 1.35 V appears across R_3, the recorder span control. Taps on R_3 ensure that set fractions, e.g. 10 and 25 mV voltage drops, can be "picked off" as the range of the recorder. In operation the voltage to be measured is compared frequently with the voltage across the portion of R_3 tapped off. If they differ, the chopper difference amplifier produces a proportional output. This signal drives a servomotor, which moves the wiper on the measuring slidewire in the direction that reduces the difference. Simultaneously it drives a pen on the recorder chart. When balance is attained, there is no error signal and the pen position is a measure of the unknown potential.

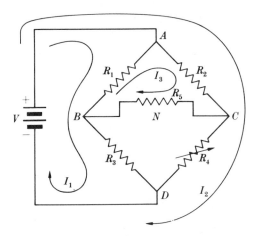

Fig. 3.6 Wheatstone bridge circuit. Source V energizes the bridge. The null detector is represented by R_5. Ratio arms are R_1 and R_2. R_3 is an unknown resistance inserted for measurement. Loop currents for analysis of the circuit are also shown.

3.3 THE DC WHEATSTONE BRIDGE

This well-known bridge is a simple network for determination of unknown resistances or conductances. The precision inherent in the design of the Wheatstone bridge derives from the fact that, like the potentiometer just discussed, it relies on a comparison procedure. Thus, a measurement is a null determination. In this section the dc operation of the bridge will be taken up; a discussion of ac operation will be deferred to Section 28.5.

The basic circuit of a Wheatstone bridge is shown in Fig. 3.6. Two resistance arms, $R_1 + R_3$ and $R_2 + R_4$, are connected by a shunt BC in which a null detector N (of resistance R_5) is located. Measurements are made by balancing, i.e., varying the resistance of at least one arm, for example R_4, until there is no current in the shunt. In other words, at balance the potential of points B and C must be equal.

To find the relative values of the bridge resistances at balance is a straightforward process. First, voltage V appears across both arms $R_1 + R_3$ and $R_2 + R_4$. Second, points B and C can be at equal potential only when the drop across R_1 equals R_4, that is $I_1 R_1 = I_2 R_2$ and $I_1 R_3 = I_2 R_4$. Substituting for I_2 in the first equation gives

$$I_1 R_1 = R_2(I_1 R_3/R_4).$$

Canceling I_1 and rearranging gives

$$R_1/R_2 = R_3/R_4.$$

This equation is the condition of balance.

Design. Because of its wide use, the design of the Wheatstone bridge deserves examination. In any application values of three of the bridge resistances must be known. (In Fig. 3.6, R_3 may be taken as unknown.) A much greater range of unknown resistance values can be handled by the bridge if the ratio R_1/R_2 is varied as well as R_4. In most semiprecision designs fixed ratios of R_1/R_2 from perhaps 0.001 to 1000.0 may be selected by a switch. Such bridges are versatile but seldom accurate to better than $\pm 1\%$. A current-indicating device is ordinarily used as the null detector, often with some amplification.

What factors must be controlled to ensure high precision, reliability, and sensitivity in a dc Wheatstone bridge? Precision resistors (maximum accuracy about $\pm 0.01\%$) should be used. They should be designed for high stability and have small temperature coefficients. For best precision R_1 and R_2 should be identical in value and construction so that they will drift in like fashion with time and temperature and maintain their resistance ratio of unity. The null detector must have sufficient sensitivity for the precision of balance required.

An important advantage of the Wheatstone bridge is that within reasonable limits its balance point is independent of both energizing voltage and resistance in either the power branch or the detector branch. As a result, a possible major source of error, contact resistance in switches and in connections to the unknown resistor, can be minimized by arranging that such contacts be in series with the power circuit. In the detector branch the resistance should be whatever value will allow best sensitivity of detection.

Other methods of resistance comparison are possible [2] and direct types of measurement employing a galvanometer and dc sources are sometimes devised, particularly for resistances of high value (another method was discussed at the end of the last section). Unfortunately, most other procedures require circuits either less accurate or inherently more complicated.

3.4 NETWORK ANALYSIS

After taking up some basic networks, it is desirable to introduce two powerful methods of network analysis. They are best illustrated by application to the already familiar case of the Wheatstone bridge.

Loop current method. This procedure is sometimes termed Maxwell's method. Its effectiveness derives from a simultaneous use of both of Kirchhoff's laws. Even complex networks can ordinarily be simplified. In essence the method calls for establishing any set of current loops (each must be a complete loop) that includes every resistance or other such passive element in at least one loop.

A set of current loops for the Wheatstone bridge that meets the basic requirement of the method is shown in Fig. 3.6. By intention only one loop includes the null detector resistance R_5. The voltage sum around each loop in turn is

1. $\Sigma V = 0 = -V + (I_1 - I_3)R_1 + I_1 R_3$
2. $\Sigma V = 0 = -V + (I_2 + I_3)R_2 + I_2 R_4$
3. $\Sigma V = 0 = (I_3 - I_1)R_1 + (I_2 + I_3)R_2 + I_3 R_5$

These simultaneous equations may best be solved by rearranging in terms of the three loop currents I_1, I_2, and I_3 to give

$$
\begin{array}{lll}
1.\ I_1(R_1 + R_3) & -I_3 R_1 & = V \\
2.\ & I_2(R_2 + R_4) + I_3 R_2 & = V \\
3.\ -I_1 R_1 + I_2 R_2 & + I_3(R_1 + R_2 + R_5) = 0 &
\end{array} \qquad (3.1)
$$

What is the current I_3 in the null detector? While the other currents may also be found, I_3 is of primary interest. The method of solution by determinants defines I_3 in terms of the ratio of two determinants. The resulting expression is stated in Eq. (3.2).*

$$I_3 = \frac{\begin{vmatrix} R_1 + R_3 & 0 & V \\ 0 & R_2 + R_4 & V \\ -R_1 & R_2 & 0 \end{vmatrix}}{\begin{vmatrix} R_1 + R_3 & 0 & -R_1 \\ 0 & R_2 + R_4 & R_2 \\ -R_1 & R_2 & R_1 + R_2 + R_5 \end{vmatrix}} = \frac{V(R_1 R_4 - R_2 R_3)}{\begin{vmatrix} & & \\ & & \\ & & \end{vmatrix}}. \tag{3.2}$$

The reduction of the determinants is straightforward.

At the moment, however, it is of interest to demonstrate that the condition of balance obtained is identical with that from Section 3.3. Accordingly, let I_3 be zero. For this condition to be true, the numerator of Eq. (3.2) must vanish. In other words, $V(R_1 R_4 - R_2 R_3) = 0$. Since V is nonzero, the parenthetical expression must be. Thus $R_1 R_4 - R_2 R_3 = 0$. On rearranging, the familiar equation for the Wheatstone bridge is obtained:

$$\frac{R_1}{R_2} = \frac{R_3}{R_4}. \tag{3.3}$$

Note that where the bridge unbalance current itself is of interest, it can be expressed by completing the solution of Eq. (3.2).

Thévenin equivalent circuit method. An equally effective method of analysis of a network is to replace part or all of it by an equivalent circuit such as a Thévenin equivalent circuit (Section 3.1). As long as the current and voltage to be delivered to a load, like the null detector of the Wheatstone bridge, are of interest the approach is useful. Recall that the Thévenin circuit consists of an open-circuit voltage in series with an equivalent resistance. In Fig. 3.7a the Wheatstone bridge is shown again, and in Fig. 3.7b the battery is short-circuited to begin the development of the Thévenin equivalent circuit. Since points A and D are now connected, R_1 and R_3 appear in parallel as do R_2 and R_4. Further, these two parallel combinations are in series. Note that R_5, which will be regarded as the load resistor, will be across the output terminals. The Thévenin resistance equivalent to the total set of resistors is just

$$R_{eq} = \frac{R_1 R_3}{R_1 + R_3} + \frac{R_2 R_4}{R_2 + R_4}. \tag{3.4}$$

What is the equivalent "battery" of the circuit? It is just the open-circuit potential V_{eq} at the output terminals of Fig. 3.7a. In other words, it is the voltage difference

---

* By convention, in the solution of three simultaneous equations the determinant in the numerator lists in its first two columns the coefficients of the variables not being solved for and its third column, the constants on the right side of the equations. The determinant in the denominator lists in its columns the coefficients of all three variables.

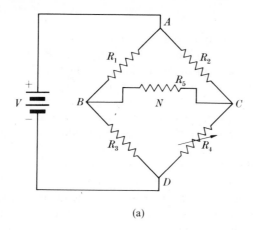

(a)

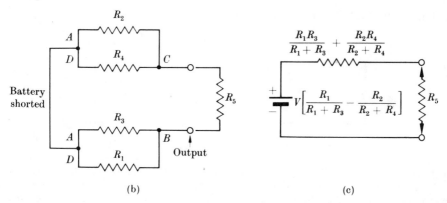

(b)   (c)

Fig. 3.7 A Thévenin equivalent representation of a Wheatstone bridge. (a) Wheatstone bridge. (b) Bridge circuit after shorting battery. (c) The final equivalent circuit with the resistance of the null detector appearing as the load.

between points B and C. Since the voltage at B is $VR_1/(R_1 + R_3)$ and that at C is $VR_2/(R_2 + R_4)$, V_{eq} is

$$V_{eq} = V\left[\frac{R_1}{R_1 + R_3} - \frac{R_2}{R_2 + R_4}\right]. \tag{3.5}$$

If a null detector of resistance R_5 is connected to the terminals of this Thévenin equivalent circuit, the current in it will be

$$I_{null\ det} = \frac{V_{eq}}{R_{eq} + R_5}. \tag{3.6}$$

It is left as Exercise 3.3 to show that, when the numerator of Eq. (3.6) goes to zero, Eq. (3.3) is again obtained. When the equivalent circuit approach is familiar, its simplicity compared with more elaborate methods of network analysis is often striking.

3.5 FILTERS

All networks composed only of passive components like resistors, capacitors, and inductances attenuate signals, i.e. reduce their amplitude. But networks that attenuate certain frequencies more than others make useful filters. One type is the *bandpass filter* that provides a "window" for a narrow range of frequencies and strongly attenuates others. A parallel *LC* resonant circuit (Section 2.8) is a good example. Those signals whose frequency lies in a narrow band around the resonant frequency are passed and others rejected. The higher the quality factor Q of the circuit the narrower is its bandwidth. Much more commonly, band filters discriminate *against* a narrow band centered about a characteristic frequency f_0. The networks providing this kind of selective attenuation are discussed toward the end of this section.

A second type is the *cutoff filter* that strongly attenuates frequencies either below or above a selected value. For example, the simple *RC* circuits illustrated in Fig. 3.8 perform in this way. If the output is taken across the resistor, as in Fig. 3.8a, the circuit is a *high-pass filter*. It attenuates low frequencies severely since the series capacitor has its greatest reactance at those values. The low-pass *RC* filter, in Fig. 3.8b, in which the output is taken across the capacitor, is discussed later.

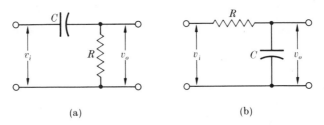

(a)   (b)

Fig. 3.8 Cutoff filters. (a) High-pass *RC* filter. (b) Low-pass *RC* filter. In each the capacitor acts to impede low frequencies. They are selectively attenuated in (a) and selectively passed in (b). Frequencies badly attenuated by (a) are also differentiated and those badly attenuated by (b) are also integrated.

To describe attenuation as a function of frequency, input and output voltages must be known. It is convenient to concentrate on peak values since Ohm's law may be applied to simplify formulation. Recall that peak values are directly related to rms values of current and voltage. The peak current in the *RC* circuit of Fig. 3.8a can be determined from the peak input voltage $(V_p)_i$ and the impedance of the *RC* combination, which is $Z = \sqrt{R^2 + (1/\omega C)^2}$. Assume that the current in capacitor C continues through R. This condition will be valid as long as very little current is taken from the output. Then, using Ohm's law, $I_p = (V_p)_i/Z$, or

$$I_p = (V_p)_i/\sqrt{R^2 + (1/\omega C)^2}. \tag{3.7}$$

Similarly, the peak value of output voltage $(V_p)_o = I_p R$. Finally, the rms voltage ratio V_o/V_i can be expressed. The value of the ratio is

$$\frac{V_o}{V_i} = \frac{R(V_p)_i/\sqrt{R^2 + (1/\omega C)^2}}{(V_p)_i} = \frac{1}{\sqrt{1 + (1/\omega RC)^2}}. \tag{3.8}$$

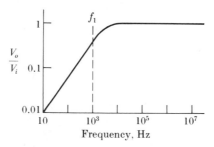

Fig. 3.9 Frequency response of a high-pass filter. The frequency f_1 is called the half-power frequency and is defined by the relationship $2\pi f_1 RC = 1$. At f_1, $V_o^2/V_i^2 = \frac{1}{2}$ and the power, which is proportional to V^2, has been halved.

A graph of this ratio is shown in Fig. 3.9.

It is useful to mark the boundary of the range of frequencies passed. For this purpose a *half-power frequency* f_1, the frequency at which $V_o/V_i = 1/\sqrt{2}$, is defined.* From Eq. (3.8) it follows that $\omega RC = 1$ at this frequency. Since $\omega = 2\pi f$, the frequency itself is defined as well:

$$f_1 = (2\pi RC)^{-1}.$$

The configuration and behavior of a high-pass filter are compared with those of other types in Table 3.1.

What happens to phase angle when a signal passes through this filter? It can be shown that the phase angle of current relative to voltage is given by

$$\phi = \arctan \frac{1}{\omega RC}. \tag{3.9}$$

For example, at frequency f_1, Eq. (3.9) gives an angle $\phi = +45°$, which means that current leads as would be expected in a capacitive circuit. When $f \gg f_1$, however, $1/\omega RC \to 0$, and $\phi \to 0$. In other words, for frequencies passed with little attenuation, the filter has little effect on the phase angle.

Actually a high-pass filter has two distinctive applications. Its common use is as a *coupling network* between two stages of an ac amplifier (Section 6.1). Interestingly, the circuit also serves as a differentiator of signals whose frequencies are well below f_1, as will be discussed in the next section. It is apparent that the magnitude of R and C must be selected with care for a particular application.

Conversely, taking the output of an RC circuit across the capacitor, as in Fig. 3.8b, yields a *low-pass filter*. The capacitor blocks low frequencies but provides a "shunt path" for high frequencies. Again, the frequency at which $\omega RC = 1$ is a useful index of cutoff. At this frequency, conveniently designated f_2, half the power in the signal fails to appear in the output, and at higher frequencies the attenuation becomes progressively larger. While the phase angle is again 45° at the half-power frequency, it approaches 90° for those frequencies transmitted well, since $1/\omega RC \to \infty$.

---

* Since the power expenditure in a circuit is V^2/R, if the resistive impedance of the input and output circuits is equal (a common assumption) $P_o/P_i = V_o^2/V_i^2$. When $P_o/P_i = 1/2$, $V_o/V_i = 1/\sqrt{2}$.

Table 3.1 Characteristics of Several Types of Filters

Filter type Characteristic frequency f_0	Circuit diagram	Voltage ratio (V_o/V_i) at f_0	Filter behavior
Parallel LC (Band pass) $f_0 = 1/2\pi\sqrt{LC}$		Max.	Passes narrow band centered around f_0. At f_0, $\phi = 0°$, Z_{LC} has max. value, and nearly all the voltage drop is across LC
Series LC (Band discrimination) $f_0 = 1/2\pi\sqrt{LC}$		Min.	Passes all frequencies but those centered around f_0. At f_0, $\phi = 0°$, Z_{LC} has min. value
High-pass RC (Cutoff at low freq.) $f_0 = 1/2\pi RC$		$1/\sqrt{2}$	Passes frequencies f, where $f > f_0$ with $\phi \approx 0°$. At f_0, half the power is passed and $\phi = 45°$
Low-pass RC (Cutoff at high freq.) $f_0 = 1/2\pi RC$		$1/\sqrt{2}$	Passes frequencies f, where $f < f_0$ with $\phi \approx 90°$. At f_0, half the power is passed and $\phi = 45°$

Wien bridge
(Band discrimination)
$f_0 = 1/2\pi RC$

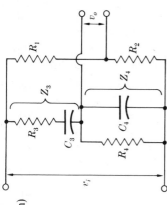

0 if $R_1 = 2R_2$; otherwise min.

Rejects narrow band centered around f_0. At f_0, $\phi = 0°$. For $f \ll f_0$, $\phi = 90°$; for $f \gg f_0$, $\phi = -90°$

Bridged-T
(Band discrimination)
$f_0 = 1/2\pi \sqrt{R_1 C_1 R_2 C_2}$

Same as for Wien bridge

Twin-T
(Band discrimination)
$f_0 = 1/2\pi RC$

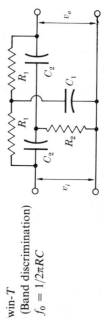

0 if $R_2 = 2R_1$; otherwise min.

Same as for Wien bridge

Band filters that selectively attenuate a narrow band of frequencies are represented by the *series LC circuit* (Section 2.8) as well as a number of more complex *RC* networks. As summarized in Table 3.1, the series *LC* arrangement has minimum impedance at its characteristic or resonant frequency f_0. Consequently, it has maximum current at resonance and all the voltage drop occurs across *R*, giving a minimum output voltage.

Wien bridge. An important example of an *RC* band discrimination filter is the Wien bridge shown schematically in Fig. 3.10. This kind of filter network is especially advantageous at frequencies below 5000 Hz, where an equivalent *LC* resonant circuit would require a very large inductor.

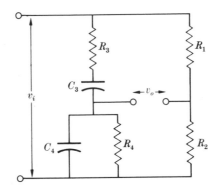

Fig. 3.10 Schematic circuit diagram of a Wien bridge. When used as a frequency-selective filter, often $C_3 = C_4$ and $R_3 = R_4$.

The Wien bridge can be recognized by its two resistance arms, a parallel *RC* combination in the third arm, and a series *RC* combination in the fourth. Note that in Fig. 3.10 V_i is the energizing voltage and V_o the output, which will go to a null detector if the network is used as a bridge. The conditions of balance for the bridge can be shown to be twofold:

$$\frac{R_3}{R_4} + \frac{C_4}{C_3} = \frac{R_1}{R_2} \tag{3.10a}$$

and

$$\omega^2 R_3 R_4 C_3 C_4 = 1. \tag{3.10b}$$

It is the appearance of the frequency in the balance conditions that distinguishes this bridge from many other ac bridges and, of course, makes possible its filtering action. If a Wien bridge filter is to be sensitive to some frequency f_0 at least the second equation must be satisfied for f_0, e.g., by adjusting C_3 and R_3. For use at a fixed frequency, a Wien bridge is often designed with $R_3 = R_4$ and $C_3 = C_4$.

Example A Wien bridge filter is to be incorporated in a frequency-selective amplifier. What is its characteristic frequency f_0 if $R_3 = R_4 = 1$ kΩ and $C_3 = C_4 = 1$ μF? What must the ratio R_2/R_1 be for (complete balance) maximum sensitivity at this frequency?

From Eq. (3.10b) and the values given, f_0 is just $f_0 = 1/2\pi R_3 C_3 = 1/10^3 \times 10^{-6} \times 6.28 = 159$ Hz. According to Eq. (3.10a), the bridge is completely balanced when $R_1 = 2R_2$.

The sharpness of frequency selectivity is shown for this case in Fig. 3.11. Here the voltage ratio V_o/V_i is graphed against the frequency ratio f/f_0. Both the ratio for a partially balanced bridge (Eq. (3.10a) not satisfied) and that for a balanced bridge are shown. When a true balance obtains, the characteristic frequency is infinitely attenuated. The Wien bridge can thus select a single frequency even more precisely than a parallel LC circuit, as is clear from Table 3.1.

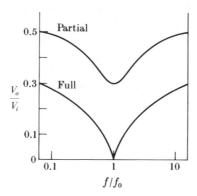

Fig. 3.11 Frequency response of a Wien bridge filter circuit. The upper curve shows the dependence of V_o/V_i when only Eq. (3.10b) is satisfied. The characteristic frequency f_o is completely blocked by the bridge at full or true balance (lower curve).

Two other commonly used frequency-selective networks based on RC combinations are the *twin-T* and *bridged-T* filters. Both are shown in Table 3.1. A variety of applications of filter networks is illustrated in subsequent chapters.

Piezoelectric filters. Thin slabs of piezoelectric substances such as crystalline quartz or lead zirconate-titanate ceramic make very efficient band-pass filters. Shape, thickness, and angle of cut (where a section of a crystal is used) determine the characteristic frequency of vibration under ac excitation and thus the frequency band passed. In most cases these rugged miniature components behave like a series LC resonant circuit that is shunted by additional capacitance though altering the design of the electrodes used permits some variation. For example, use of a ring and center electrode on one side allows achievement of impedance matching behavior as well as filtering, making the element useful for coupling ac circuits efficiently (Section 3.8).

3.6 DIFFERENTIATING CIRCUIT

The high-pass filter of Fig. 3.8a also differentiates some signals with respect to time. Since the circuit passes frequencies larger than f_1, it is clear that its differentiating action must be restricted to frequencies less than f_1. What accounts for the development of differentiation at lower frequencies? The answer may be found by comparing expressions for the input voltage, its time derivative, and the output voltage of the circuit of Fig. 3.8a.

Consider a sinusoidal ac input, $v_i = (V_p)_i \sin \omega t$. The circuit output will be the voltage drop across R, that is, v_o will be given by

$$v_o = Ri = RI_p \sin(\omega t + \phi), \tag{3.11}$$

where ϕ is the phase angle between current and output voltage produced by the circuit. Further, the time derivative of the input voltage is just

$$\frac{dv_i}{dt} = \omega(V_p)_i \cos \omega t. \tag{3.12}$$

To compare Eqs. (3.11) and (3.12), substitutions for ϕ and I_p are required. A value for ϕ may be deduced from Eq. (3.9). When $f \ll f_1$, $\omega RC \to 0$ and according to Eq. (3.9), $\phi \to 90°$. When this value is inserted in Eq. (3.11), the equation becomes

$$v_o = RI_p \cos \omega t.$$

Second, I_p can be found from Eq. (3.7). When $\omega RC \to 0$, $I_p = \omega C(V_p)_i$.* Now Eq. (3.11) becomes

$$v_o = \omega RC(V_p)_i \cos \omega t. \tag{3.13}$$

A comparison of Eqs. (3.12) and (3.13) shows that the output voltage can be expressed as

$$v_o = RC\frac{dv_i}{dt}, \tag{3.14}$$

which establishes that a time derivative is obtained for frequencies much less than f_1.

How can a "high-pass" RC circuit serve under some conditions as a filter (Section 3.5) and under others as a differentiator? Its dynamics are illustrated in column A of Table 3.2. The process occurring is the charging or discharging of capacitor C. Current from this activity produces the iR drop that corresponds to v_o. As would be expected, output curves look like typical dc capacitor charging curves (Section 2.5) except in limiting cases. In particular the form of the output in relation to an input signal depends on the relative magnitude of time constant RC and period of signal T. It is the limiting cases that yield either coupling or differentiation. Note the necessary conditions for each as stated in the table.†

Applications. In chemical instrumentation it is valuable to use such a differentiating circuit when a derivative

1. Is a more sensitive measure of a quantity of interest than the variable itself;

2. Is required, as in measurement of a reaction rate;

---

* Multiply through the numerator and denominator of Eq. (3.7) by ωC to put it in a form where ωRC can be allowed to approach zero without creating difficulties.

† As may be observed, with a square-wave input neither differentiation (which should yield alternating positive and negative spikes) nor coupling is accomplished without distortion. Allowance would have to be made for the very high frequencies present in such a signal to secure better performance.

Table 3.2 Output Waveforms of *RC* Circuits as a Function of Circuit Time Constant τ for Square
Wave Input

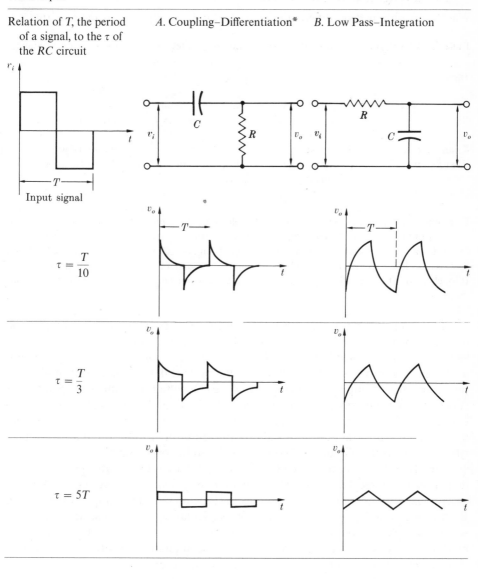

Relation of *T*, the period   *A.* Coupling–Differentiation*   *B.* Low Pass–Integration
  of a signal, to the τ of
  the *RC* circuit

$\tau = \dfrac{T}{10}$

$\tau = \dfrac{T}{3}$

$\tau = 5T$

Condition for coupling: *Condition for low-pass filter*:
$\tau > 5T$ (capacitor never more $\tau < T/10$ (capacitor always
  than partially charged)   nearly fully charged)
Condition for differentiation: *Condition for integration*:
$\tau < T/10$ (capacitor always $\tau > 5T$ (capacitor never more
  nearly fully charged)   than partially charged)

* A high-pass filter is basically a coupling circuit for ac signals whose frequencies are greater than f_1.

3. Has a shape that lends itself better to actuating a control device or counting circuit better than that of the variable itself.

Waveforms obtained on differentiating a few kinds of signal are listed in Table 3.3.

Table 3.3 Waveforms Obtained on Differentiation and Integration of Three Types of Signals

Input	Output	
	Differentiation	*Integration*
Square wave	Alternate + and − pulses at each change of polarity	Triangular wave
Triangular wave	Square wave	Parabolic wave
Sawtooth wave	Constant + or − signal with abrupt switching back and forth	Parabolic wave

Example In a potentiometric titration the cell voltage contains the information about the progress of the reaction. Its slow change with added titrant provides no signal for triggering a "shut down" device to stop the titration at the end point. A second derivative of the cell voltage, however, yields a sharp voltage spike just before the point of inflection followed by passage through zero. This type of output can easily be used to terminate a titration at the end point (Section 24.9).

Three important points about the use of RC circuits in instrumentation must be noted. First, even if the independent variable in a measurement is not time, as long as *the actual independent variable is changing at a steady rate*, the time differentiation an RC circuit provides is proportional to the desired derivative. For example, in a potentiometric titration a *time* derivative of the cell voltage is useful as long as titrant is added at a steady rate. Second, since an RC circuit attenuates badly the very frequencies it differentiates, at least one stage of amplification ordinarily accompanies it. For that reason, practical details about differentiators will be found in Section 7.5 where the use of RC circuits with operational amplifiers is discussed.

Finally, a differentiating circuit can be expected to approximate closely the time derivative of a typical instrumental signal (a slowly changing dc voltage or current) except where it undergoes discontinuities in slope or very large slopes are involved. Even though ωRC may be too large for a particular signal, modest departures (up to 20 to 40%) of the output from proportionality to the derivative can be eliminated by using an amplifier with negative feedback in conjunction with the circuit. This is another advantage gained by use of an operational amplifier.

3.7 INTEGRATING CIRCUIT

The other simple RC circuit, the *low-pass configuration* (see Fig. 3.8b) can be used to obtain a time integral of a signal. The necessary condition in this case is that any frequency to be integrated be larger than filter cutoff frequency f_2 ($f_2 = 1/2\pi RC$). This limitation has the effect of requiring that the time constant RC of the circuit be large compared with the period of the signal to be integrated. The variation in output of this circuit as its time constant is varied relative to the period of the incoming signal is illustrated in column B of Table 3.2. It can be shown for the frequency conditions stated that an output taken across capacitor C equals

$$v_C = \frac{1}{RC}\int v_i\, dt,\tag{3.15}$$

which is the desired proportionality.

Amplification is nearly always required to secure a useful output. To avoid shunting the capacitor of the network, and altering the conditions for integrating, the network is best used in conjunction with an operational amplifier, whose negative feedback provides an essentially infinite input resistance. Accordingly, a detailed discussion of integration is reserved to Section 7.6. Waveforms secured on integrating a few types of signals are listed in Table 3.3.

3.8 POWER TRANSFER; IMPEDANCE MATCHING

In many circuits it is of interest that maximum power be developed in an output device or other load. In others it is more desirable that an efficient transfer of power to a load be arranged. The question asked is what percentage of the total power expended is developed in the load. The interrelation of the quantities may be studied in terms of Fig. 3.12, where three different loads are available. Each is assumed to be connected in turn to the output terminals of a circuit. This circuit, as is characteristic of the output of a device, is represented by its Thévenin equivalent circuit (Section 3.1).

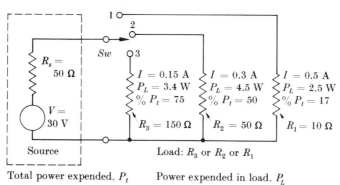

Total power expended, P_t Power expended in load, P_L
$P_t = I^2 R_s + I^2 R_L$ $P_L = I^2 R_L$

Fig. 3.12 Circuit for consideration of effectiveness of power transfer. Maximum transfer occurs when the load resistance $R_L = R_s$, that is, when load R_2 is inserted. The most efficient use of power, i.e., expending it in the load, occurs when $R_L > R_s$, as for R_3.

The power P_L expended in a load will always be smaller than the total power P_t developed because of internal resistance associated with the source of voltage. From Fig. 3.12, the power delivered to the load is

$$P_L = I^2 R_L = \left[\frac{V}{R_s + R_L}\right]^2 R_L.\tag{3.16}$$

The relationship of R_L and R_s for developing maximum power in the load can be shown (by differentiating Eq. (3.16)) to be $R_s = R_L$. The data in the figure confirm the result. The load is said under these conditions to be matched to the output circuit.

The efficiency of power used when load and circuit resistances are matched must of course be 50%, for half the power is expended uselessly in the internal resistance. Efficiency can be improved by using a higher resistance load. For example, if R_3 in Fig. 3.12 is substituted, 75% of the total power developed is expended in the load. Although more efficient, less power has been developed in the load than before, and it is apparent that a compromise between power transfer and efficiency must be struck. Usually, power transfer is more important and only where the amount of power involved is large, as in a municipal electrical system, is efficiency a major concern.

AC circuits. In the case of ac circuits the result just developed also applies but the magnitude of impedances must now be matched. Account must also be taken of the phase angle ϕ between current and voltage. It will be recalled that cos ϕ, the *power factor* (Section 2.7), defines the fraction of the voltage in phase with the current, and thus the true power developed. For maximum power transfer cos ϕ should be nearly unity. In most *electronic* circuits it proves sufficient to match impedances without regard to phase angle. Where high power is involved, the angle becomes important and the desired condition is often achieved by offsetting the phase shift in the basic circuit by an equal and opposite shift in the load.

Since the impedance of a load is ordinarily fixed, an electrical strategem can be used to match impedances in an ac circuit. It is only necessary to couple the load to the output by a transformer of proper turns ratio and power capacity. If the load is too great, a step-up transformer must be used, and vice versa. The *turns ratio* t is defined by $t = n_2/n_1$, where the n_2 is the number of turns in the secondary winding, and n_1 is that in the primary.

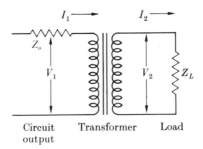

Circuit   Transformer   Load
output

Fig. 3.13 Use of a transformer to match a load impedance Z_L to the output impedance Z_o of an ac circuit.

The effect of an impedance Z_L in the secondary circuit on the primary circuit can be seen in terms of the transformer circuit of Fig. 3.13. Consider that load impedance Z_L establishes the effective current I_2 in the secondary, i.e., $I_2 = V_2/Z_L$, where V_2 is the effective voltage across the secondary winding. The turns ratio then establishes the ratio of secondary and primary voltages $t = n_2/n_1 = V_2/V_1$. But the current ratio is inversely related to t, $t = I_1/I_2$. Combining these three equations gives

$$I_2 = \frac{V_1 t}{Z_L} = \frac{I_1}{t}$$

$$I_1 = \frac{t^2 V_1}{Z_L} = \frac{V_1}{Z_L/t^2} = \frac{V_1}{Z_{eq}}. \tag{3.17}$$

The transformer has produced in the primary circuit an equivalent impedance $Z_{eq} = Z_L/t^2$. If the output impedance is Z_o, impedance will be matched when $Z_o = Z_{eq}$ or

$$Z_o = Z_L/t^2. \tag{3.18}$$

Example What turns ratio transformer must be selected to transfer maximum power from a 10 kΩ impedance output to a 100 Ω load? To achieve a match, $Z_o = Z_L/t^2$, and the turns ratio $N = \sqrt{Z_L/Z_o} = \sqrt{10^2/10^4} = 0.10$. A step-down transformer with one secondary turn to each 10 primary turns is needed.

Power ratings. Changes in power levels are ordinarily stated in decibels (dB). By definition this unit is:

$$1 \text{ decibel} = 10 \log_{10} \frac{P_2}{P_1}, \tag{3.19}$$

where the ratio P_2/P_1 is the ratio of power at point 2 to that at point 1. If amplitudes of voltages appearing across two *equal-size* resistors, one at point 1 and the other at point 2, are known instead, V^2/R may be substituted for P to give the expression:

$$1 \text{ decibel} = 20 \log_{10} \frac{V_2}{V_1}. \tag{3.20}$$

Example 1 A doubling of the power level corresponds to a gain of $10 \log_{10}(2/1) = 3.03$ dB.

Example 2 The output voltage of a transistor amplifier is 200 times the input signal voltage, and the output current 50 times the signal current. What is the power gain? Equation (3.19) is applicable: gain in dB = $10 \log_{10}(200 \times 50)/1 = 10 \log 10\,000 = 40$ dB.

REFERENCES

The titles at the end of Chapter 2 should also be consulted. Volumes providing a basic, detailed coverage of fundamental circuits are:

1. National Bureau of Standards, *Precision Measurements and Calibration, Electricity and Electronics*. Handbook 77, Vol. 1. Washington: U.S. Government Printing Office, 1961
2. M. B. Stout, *Basic Electrical Measurements*. Englewood Cliffs, N.J.: Prentice-Hall, 1960

A more advanced treatment of basic circuits is provided by:

3. Donald P. Leach, *Basic Electric Circuits*. New York: Wiley, 1969

Some papers relating to potentiometers that are of interest are:

4. Rubin Battino, "Several Designs for Constructing Potentiometers," *J. Chem. Educ.* **42**, 211 (1965)
5. S. Z. Lewin, "Recording Devices," *J. Chem. Educ.* **36**, A729 (1959); **37**, A7, A65, A129 (1960)

EXERCISES

3.1 Apply Kirchhoff's laws to reduce the circuit shown in Fig. 3.14 to a single resistor R_{eq} in series with the 10 V dc source. What is R_{eq}?

[*Ans.*: 27 Ω.]

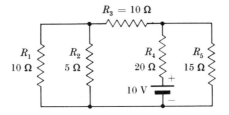

Figure 3.14

3.2 Use the Thévenin equivalent circuit developed for the voltage divider of Fig. 3.2a to calculate values for equivalent voltage V and resistance R.

  a) What current will flow if a 2.5 kΩ load resistor R_L is across the output?
  b) Apply Kirchhoff's laws to the circuit of Fig. 3.2a, with R_L attached, and develop an expression for the current in R_L. Show that it is identical to the expression we obtain when we use the Thévenin equivalent circuit.

[*Ans.*: a) 3.9 mA; b) $I = V_1 R_1 / [R_1 R_2 + R_L (R_1 + R_2)]$.]

3.3 Use Eq. (3.6) to obtain the condition of balance for the Wheatstone bridge. Assume $V_{eq} = 0$.

3.4 Draw a schematic diagram of a recording type of Wheatstone bridge that can measure a resistance which is changing with time.

3.5 Show how a Wheatstone bridge might be modified to measure impedances. Define the condition of balance for the modified bridge.

3.6 How can contact resistances be placed in series with the power circuit of a Wheatstone bridge? Why is the resistance error in a measurement minimized by this procedure?

3.7 Assume values for resistances for the Wheatstone bridge of Fig. 3.6 as follows: $R_1 = R_3 = 1$ kΩ, $R_2 = 2$ kΩ, $R_4 = 3$ kΩ, $R_5 = 800$ Ω and $V = 10$ V. What current flows in the null detector?

[*Ans.*: 0.4 mA.]

3.8 What similarities are there between a Wheatstone bridge and a Wien bridge? Can conductance measurements be made with a Wien bridge by substituting a conductance cell for arm R_3-C_3? Can conductance measurements be made with a Wien bridge if energized by dc? by ac?

3.9 For the potentiometer circuit shown in Fig. 3.15, find an expression for the unbalance current flowing through the meter M. V_{unk} is the voltage being measured by the potentiometer.

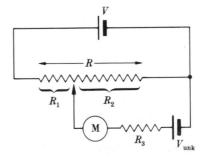

Figure 3.15

3.10 In the servo recorder (self-balancing potentiometer) shown in Fig. 3.5b the potentiometer serves as a variable reference voltage. Because a zero-adjust circuit has been added, the voltage output is referenced to the zero-adjust setting. Part of the circuit has been redrawn in Fig. 3.16 to make this point. Let R_1 and R_2 be resistances above and below the wiper of the zero adjust and R_3 and R_4 be the resistances above and below the wiper of the slidewire. When no unknown voltage is applied and the zero-adjust variable resistor is adjusted, the motor of the servo recorder adjusts the slidewire until $V_{ref} = 0$. What relationship must hold between R_1, R_2, R_3, and R_4? (*Hint*: Use Thevenin's theorem.)

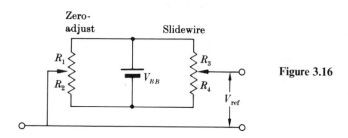

Figure 3.16

3.11 Draw a schematic diagram of a simple "scratch filter" for a stereo amplifier, i.e., a filter which will reduce high-frequency noise. Be sure to justify the magnitude of the components used and predict the filter performance. Remember that the human audible range extends as high as 12 to 15 kHz.

3.12 In electrical instruments 60 Hz noise from line current is very common. Design a filter that will specifically attenuate this frequency. What other circuits might also be used?

3.13 What is the cuton frequency f_1 for the circuit of Fig. 3.8a if values of components are $C = 0.10\ \mu F$ and $R = 1\ k\Omega$?

[*Ans.*: 1590 Hz.]

3.14 Construct a differentiating circuit that has an output of 2 V when the input voltage is changing at a rate of 5 V min^{-1}.

3.15 A 10 μA ac signal appears in a 5Ω resistor. It is desired to achieve as efficient a voltage transfer to the input of an amplifier as possible. Discuss whether a 100 Ω input impedance or a 1 MΩ input impedance would be preferable. (See Section 5.1 for additional information.)

3.16 A Student's potentiometer (see Fig. 3.17) is designed to provide two voltage ranges for measurement. The potentiometer is standardized by turning switch 1 to a and wipers x_1 and x_2 to positions that "tap off" exactly 101.78 Ω of resistance between them. A Weston cell of 1.0178 V serves as the reference voltage marked "Std." Switch 2 is turned to "Std." Resistance R_1 is next adjusted until galvanometer G gives no deflection. Now the voltage drop across $R_5 + R_6$, which is the range of the potentiometer, is 2.000 V.

a) When switch 1 is turned to a, what is the current in branch $R_5 + R_6$? In branch $R_2 + R_3$?
b) What is the value of R_1? The second voltage range becomes available when switch 1 is turned to b and switch 2 is set at the neutral position.
c) What is the new potentiometer range? How does the new range compare with the previous one?

[*Ans.*: a) 10.0 mA in R_4, 0.100 mA in $R_2 + R_3$; b) 99.1 Ω; c) 20.0 mV range.]

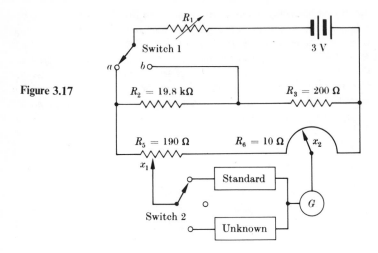

Figure 3.17

Chapter 4

SEMICONDUCTOR DEVICES

4.1 INTRODUCTION

Electronics is concerned with the sensitive control of electric power in response to signals. It is the flow of charge carriers—electrons, holes (centers of positive charge), and, sometimes, ions—that must be governed. Electronics makes valuable use of networks of passive components like capacitors and resistors, such as were discussed in Chapter 3, but they are insufficient in themselves. An important reason is that networks attenuate, often severely, any signal on which they operate; their output is smaller than the input power. Networks are merely electrical; only with the addition of *active devices* such as transistors or electron tubes do they become *electronic* circuitry.

The central role of an active component is illustrated in the generalized electronic circuit of Fig. 4.1. The circuit basically comprises an active device and a power supply that it controls. Upon receipt of an input signal, the active element lets a predictable amount of energy "move" from power supply to a load. The load may be virtually any kind of device from a motor to a meter.

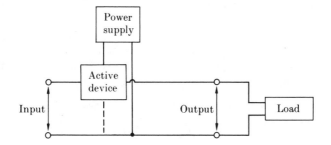

Fig. 4.1 Simplified block diagram of a generalized electronic circuit.

Several critical functions performed by electronic circuits can be listed. Those of primary importance are:

1. Transmission of information over a distance (as in telemetry of data from satellites);

2. Generation of electromagnetic radiation of any frequency up to the optical region (as in producing 60 MHz ac for a nuclear magnetic resonance spectrometer);

3. Amplification of a weak signal;

4. Performance of mathematical operations (such as integration of the area under a peak in a gas chromatogram).

The third function is especially important. The limits of instrumental detection and the precision of measurement are greatly extended by electronic amplification.

Active devices are vital to the performance of these functions. Among other things, they provide the power to stabilize systems, determine null or balance conditions, achieve reliable functioning, and give a desired amplitude output.

In this text emphasis is given to semiconductor devices as the most important class of active devices. Limitations of space preclude treating electron tubes, though a brief comparison of the relative advantages of solid-state and electron tube devices will be made in Section 4.11. While virtually all new instrumentation incorporates semiconductor devices, refined and proved tube circuits are to be found in many older instruments.

4.2 SEMICONDUCTORS

Semiconductors are crystalline materials that have an electrical resistivity intermediate between conductors and insulators. The class includes elements such as silicon and germanium that are in the region of transition between metals and nonmetals and compounds such as indium antimonide and silicon carbide. Their conductivity is a result of the continuous freeing of a tiny fraction of the bonding electrons and positive centers by virtue of thermal agitation or absorption of light. The process of recombination of electrons and positive centers is continuous also, and an equilibrium is quickly reached. Pure substances* of this type are classed as *intrinsic* semiconductors.

From an electronic point of view, two attributes of semiconductor single crystals are of special importance. First, electrical conductivity can easily be controlled by adding traces of other substances, a process termed *doping*. Second, precisely defined junctions separating regions with different types of conductivity can be formed. Potential gradients imposed across these junctions can be altered by signals and in that way sensitive control of current flow in the crystal realized. It is by selecting the type, concentration (about 1 part in 10^8), and physical location of impurities in a single crystal that semiconductors are tailored to a wide variety of electronic uses.

Impurity effects.   In semiconductors conduction is increased by the addition of foreign substances that behave as either donors or acceptors of electrons. In pure germanium or silicon the four valence electrons per atom are localized in covalent bonds. Consider the effect of introducing atoms of a Group V element, e.g., antimony. Wherever an antimony atom with its five valence electrons substitutes in the lattice for a semiconductor atom a local region with an "excess" electron results. The fifth electron, though localized, needs only a small amount of energy to break away if the energy of the semiconductor crystal conduction band is near its energy. It may then serve as a charge carrier for electrical conduction. There are still intrinsically produced electrons and holes (see below), but the donated electrons outnumber them. A semiconductor doped this way is termed an *n-type* semiconductor. The letter signifies

---

* Zone refining, a widely used purification method, reduces impurities to the level of about 1 to 10 parts per billion.

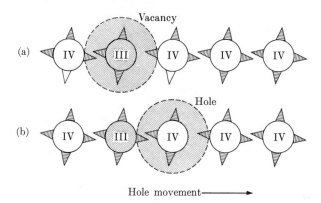

Fig. 4.2 Schematic illustration of hole formation in a semiconductor. A single plane of atoms in a crystal is shown. Bonding electrons are pictured as solid triangles protruding from the atomic kernel. (a) A low-lying electron level or "vacancy" located at the Group III atom. Other atoms are Group IV (Ge or Si) atoms. (b) Hole formed at Group IV atom, by loss of a bonding electron.

that the *majority carrier* of charge is negative. The much less abundant holes are the *minority charge* carrier.

Conversely, introducing atoms of an element of Group III, such as gallium, results in the appearance of centers of electron deficiency in the electronic "pattern," for there are three valence electrons where ordinarily four would be. Each substituent atom is a potential electron acceptor, and if its valence level is close to that of the semiconductor atoms it can attract an electron from one of them to fill the "vacancy." This movement of charge leaves a *hole* or local positive charge centered at the donating semiconductor atom. Since the hole can accept a valence electron from a neighboring semiconductor atom, the hole can move. The process is illustrated in Fig. 4.2. Hole movement also constitutes electrical conduction. The process can continue easily with the result that holes can move through the crystal until they undergo recombination with a free electron. Materials in which holes are the majority carriers, i.e., are in excess, are labeled *p-type* semiconductors. Free electrons are still present and function as minority carriers, but their number is reduced through recombinations with holes.

Though the mechanism of hole conduction really involves electron movement, the process can easily be distinguished from normal electron conduction. Holes have a much lower mobility, and this type of conduction shows a different temperature dependence. These characteristics are summarized in Table 4.1 for the two semiconductors most widely used in solid-state devices, germanium and silicon.

The relative height of different electron energy levels in semiconductors is illustrated in Fig. 4.3. As in all solids, the levels exist in bands. In an intrinsic semiconductor there is a wide "forbidden" gap between the valence band (occupied by the bonding electrons) and the conduction band (corresponding to levels occupied by delocalized electrons). At room temperature ($kT \sim 0.03$ eV) very few electrons are distributed across the gap. As a result, conduction is small since only electrons with energies that place them in the conduction band can respond to an imposed external electric field.

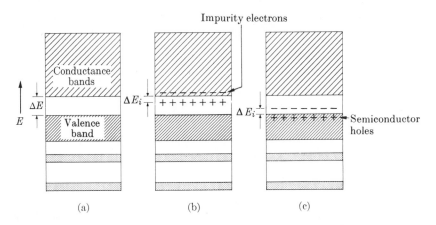

Fig. 4.3 Energy levels for electrons in semiconductors. (a) Energy bands in pure semiconductor. (b) Bands in *n*-type impurity semiconductor. $+ +$, donor impurity level; $- -$ conduction by impurity electrons. (c) Bands in *p*-type semiconductor. $- -$, acceptor impurity level; $+ +$ conduction by holes in valence band. The relative magnitude of energy differences are $\Delta E \sim 1$ eV, $\Delta E_i \sim 0.01$ eV.

Table 4.1 Some Characteristics of Germanium and Silicon Semiconductors

	n-type	*p-type*
Impurity introduced	Group V element, such as P, As, Sb	Group III element such as B, Al, Ga, In
Type of impurity	Donor	Acceptor
Majority carrier	Electron	Hole
Mobilities of majority carrier, cm s^{-1} for field of 1 V cm^{-1} at 25 °C	Ge: 3800 Si: 1300	Ge: 1800 Si: 480
Excitation energy for conduction	Ge: 0.01 eV Si: 0.05 eV	Ge: 0.01 eV Si: 0.05 eV

Note, however, in Fig. 4.3 the effect of properly selected impurities. When an intrinsic semiconductor is doped with an donor-type (Group V) impurity, a new energy level appears that is due to the "extra" impurity electrons. It is just below the sparsely occupied conduction band of the base semiconductor. Because the gap between new and conduction levels is much less than kT, the statistical distribution of "extra" electrons from the impurity places most of them in the crystal conduction band. Thus even at trace levels of doping conduction is substantially larger in the doped crystal.

An analogous result is secured on doping with acceptor-type (Group III) atoms. This time, as shown in Fig. 4.3c, a new but unoccupied level appears just above the valence band. Because the gap is small, at 25 °C many semiconductor electrons will be distributed into the new level. Their departure creates vacancies or holes within the valence band. Conduction *in the valence band* becomes possible: the holes can move as bound electrons transfer to them. A schematic illustration of the process was given in Fig. 4.2.

Effect of temperature. The width of the band gap (Fig. 4.3) is critical in determining the useful temperature range for a semiconductor electronic device. Such a device is useful only up to the temperature at which intrinsic charge carriers become so numerous that impurity doping no longer governs electrical properties. The larger the energy gap for a substance, the smaller the rate at which intrinsic carriers increase with temperature, and the lower the conductivity at a given temperature. The best balance between these conflicting trends is achieved when the gap is about 1 eV. Pure germanium and silicon, with gaps of 0.72 and 1.03 eV, respectively, meet the requirement well. If the gap is too small, the thermal energy level will be sufficiently high at room temperature ($kT \sim 0.03$ eV) to excite large numbers of bonding electrons to the conduction level. If the gap is too great, as is true for carbon in the diamond form ($\Delta E \sim 7$ eV), the substance is an insulator! The temperature coefficients of conductivity of germanium and silicon are sufficiently large for these substances to be no longer useful electronically above about 85 °C and 150 °C, respectively. Since some heat is dissipated in all semiconductor devices, it may be anticipated that special design provisions to ensure temperature stability will be routine in circuits using them.

Diffusion and drift. In semiconductors, charge carriers move by the mechanisms of diffusion and drift. Diffusion originates in the random thermal motion of all species in a substance and results in a net flux from regions of higher concentration to regions of lower concentration.

Charge carriers that are diffusing have a certain average lifetime before they suffer collision with oppositely charged species and are bound or trapped in the process termed *recombination.* Any damage to the crystalline structure induced by nuclear radiation, excessive heating, or mechanical shock or stress will shorten lifetimes.

Drift is a more orderly process that results when an external electric field is imposed. This type of movement of charge carriers is responsible for current in a semiconductor when a voltage is applied. In either process mobility of charge carriers is a function of doping, the character of the lattice, and temperature.

4.3 THE *p-n* JUNCTION

As suggested earlier, control of the movement of charge carriers in a semiconductor is achieved by applying appropriate potentials across *p-n* junctions formed in a single crystal. There are many ways to create such a junction. For example, it is usually formed by the diffusion of appropriate impurities into selected regions of a crystal.

In the manufacture of both a single diode and an integrated circuit the processes of forming a junction are basically similar. Access of an impurity to the crystal is limited by some appropriate means to the small region(s) to be doped. The concentration of doping agent, time, and temperature are regulated to control the depth and concentration of doping atom. In general different types of doping are done in successive operations. Since technological developments occur rapidly, the reader is referred to other sources for details. [1, 2]

An understanding of the electrical character of a *p-n* junction begins with an examination of charge distribution and local potential *in the absence of an applied external voltage.* When the junction is not at thermal equilibrium, charge carriers diffuse across the boundary. As shown in Fig. 4.4a, there is a net flow of holes from the *p*-side where they are abundant into the *n*-region where their concentration is low. Similarly, electrons diffuse from the *n*-region into the *p*-region. As a result, positive charge accumulates on the right side of the boundary and negative charge on the left. The potential difference produced opposes the further diffusion of majority charge carriers from either side, though it promotes the movement of minority carriers. The electrical gradient at the boundary is illustrated schematically in Fig. 4.4b. When the gradient is constant, thermal equilibrium is attained, and the net current at the junction from diffusion of all kinds is zero.

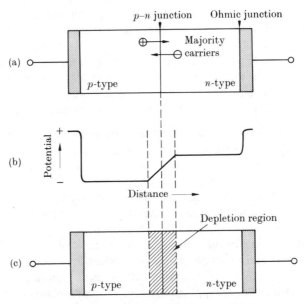

Fig. 4.4 A *p-n* junction in a semiconductor crystal when no field is applied externally. (a) Pre-equilibrium condition. Majority charge carriers diffuse across *p-n* junction from regions in which they are in excess. (b) Equilibrium condition. The local potential gradient caused by diffusion of charge carriers. Once this steady potential difference exists at the *p-n* junction there is no further net current. Potential differences (contact potentials) also exist at the ohmic junctions where semiconductor layers are bonded to metal to attach external leads. Note that there is no net potential difference across the crystal. (c) Depletion region at *p-n* junction at equilibrium. In this region the concentration of majority charge carriers is greatly reduced.

How has the junction's character been altered in the process? On the *n*-side of a boundary the entering holes have tended to combine with electrons, reducing the population of charge carriers. Here atomic cores predominate, which accounts for the net positive charge. Similarly on the *p*-side, the net number of electrons that have entered have combined with holes. The result is the appearance of a boundary region on either side of the junction termed a *depletion region,* since the concentration of charge carriers in it is smaller than elsewhere in the crystal. This situation is pictured in Fig. 4.4c.

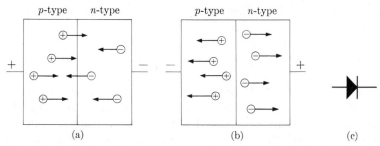

Fig. 4.5 Schematic illustration of current in a *p-n* diode. (a) Forward biasing: appreciable flow. (b) Reverse biasing: minute flow. (c) Diode symbol. The arrowhead points in the direction of conventional positive current (hole flow).

If an external potential difference is now applied, the junction acts as a unidirectional valve. In Fig. 4.5 are shown the currents that result. If the *p*-region is made positive relative to the *n*-region, a step termed *forward biasing*, a positive current moves in the conventional direction. The applied voltage reduces the junction potential, permitting majority carriers to drift across easily. Holes drift into the *n*-region under the applied field, electrons into the *p*-region. Note that the polarity of the external voltage directs majority carriers toward the *p-n* junction. There is a considerable forward current. At the same time a reverse (leakage) current exists but is minute, since the potential difference at the *p-n* junction is much less favorable to the crossing of the minority carriers responsible for it.

Under *reverse biasing* a negative voltage is applied externally to the *p*-area, giving a larger junction potential than the thermal one shown in Fig. 4.4b. Now the applied potential favors movement of minority carriers and opposes that of majority carriers. The result is that only a minimal current, termed a reverse or leakage current, flows. Note also that the depletion layer becomes wider, since majority carriers tend to suffer recombination over a greater volume on either side of the junction. The possibility for sensitive control of current by applying small voltages is clear and will be pursued below in connection with specific devices.

Junction capacity. A *p-n* junction also acts as a capacitor. The charge separation that builds up has already been described and the depletion region serves as the dielectric. Since the width of this layer and the magnitude of potential across it vary with external biasing, capacitance is dependent on the applied voltage. In fact, capacitance decreases with increasing reverse bias, since the layer widens rapidly. Usual *p-n* junction capacitances are of the order of 1–15 pF. Commercial capacitors based on *p-n* junctions (often between aluminium and silicon) are available and are often used for voltage control of frequency in resonant circuits. Their capacitance varies essentially as $1/\sqrt{V + 0.65}$ where V is the applied voltage.

4.4 THE DIODE

Any semiconductor device with a single *p-n* junction belongs to the class of diodes.*

---

* Many of these devices may be identified by the "1N" in their designation, for example 1N91 or 1N1615.

As just discussed, such devices inherently conduct in a single direction, i.e., are *rectifiers*. In practice this term is reserved for the type of device which handles large currents and others are simply called diodes.

The conduction of a representative diode is shown in Fig. 4.6. Since its forward resistance is only a few hundred ohms, substantial current flows when it is biased a few tenths of a volt (about 0.2 V for Ge, 0.7 V for Si) in the forward direction. When reverse-biased, however, such a diode has about a megohm resistance and a leakage current of only a few microamperes. If the reverse bias is increased sufficiently (5 to 200 V), the junction will "break down," giving rise to excessive conduction. Unless the current is limited externally, strong heating and junction damage will result. The relationship of the leakage region to the breakdown region is illustrated clearly in Fig. 4.6.

In most instances an *avalanche mechanism* is operative in the breakdown phenomenon. As noted before, under reverse biasing the depletion region broadens. When it has a relatively high field across it, conduction electrons gain sufficient energy in crossing to produce electron-hole pairs by collision. Holes are also accelerated across the depletion layer and produce further ionization. The process spreads in chain reaction fashion, increasing conduction rapidly.

A second mechanism predominates if breakdown occurs at voltages below about 6 V, as it does in diodes that have thin depletion regions (a result of heavy doping). This so-called *Zener breakdown* is a field-emission effect believed to result from quantum-mechanical tunneling of electrons across the junction. They are presumed to tunnel from valence levels in the *p*-region to available conduction levels in the *n*-region.

4.5 ZENER DIODE

A diode specially designed to operate under breakdown conditions is termed a Zener diode. As is evident from the current–voltage curve of Fig. 4.6, the voltage across a

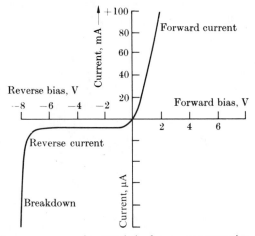

Fig. 4.6 Current–voltage curve or characteristic for a representative semiconductor diode. Note that the current scale for reverse bias is in *micro*amperes, but that for forward bias is in *milli*amperes. The breakdown voltage may be greater or smaller than shown.

p-n junction operated under these conditions is nearly independent of current. For example, the voltage drop for a 653C4 Zener diode increases only from 7.00 V to about 7.15 V at 25 °C as the (reverse) current rises from 5 mA to 20 mA. By appropriate doping, breakdown can be arranged to occur at a desired voltage in highly repro-ducible fashion. Zener diodes are thus widely useful both as voltage standards and as devices that ensure nearly constant voltage even though the current is varying somewhat.

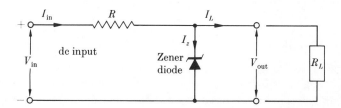

Fig. 4.7 Circuit incorporating a Zener diode to achieve a regulated or constant output voltage.

A representative Zener diode circuit is illustrated in Fig. 4.7. Note that the diode is used with a current-limiting resistor R and that the input voltage must always be higher than the diode breakdown value for the circuit to operate. If the input voltage rises, more current will flow through the diode without appreciably affecting the voltage across it or the load. Virtually all the voltage increase is reflected in a greater voltage drop across R. The maximum current that the diode has to carry, occurring when the source voltage is at a maximum and the load is disconnected, must, of course, not exceed the maximum rated value, $I_{z\,max}$.

Example How can a suitable value of "dropping resistor" R for the Zener diode circuit of Fig. 4.7 be determined? First, note that $I_i = I_z + I_L$ and that $V_i = V_R + V_z$. Assume V_z is constant.

It is easiest to proceed by use of limiting cases. Taking the smallest value of V_i and the largest value of I_L, R must be small enough to permit at least the minimum Zener current $I_{z\,min}$ (one that ensures operation in the linear breakdown region) to exist. Ohm's law gives $I_{L\,max} = V_z/R_{L\,min}$. Then

$$R = (V_{i\,min} - V_z)/(I_{z\,min} + I_{L\,max}).$$

In addition, the resistor must ensure that at maximum input voltage and no load the maximum diode current is not exceeded. Thus the equation

$$R = (V_{i\,max} - V_z)/I_{z\,max}$$

must also be satisfied.

The degree to which a Zener diode approximates a constant voltage source is dependent both on its *incremental resistance* r_z, where $r_z = \Delta V_z/\Delta I_z$, and on its temperature coefficient of voltage. Representative values of r_z are from 10 to 100 Ω. Temperature coefficients relate closely to the mechanism of breakdown. Diodes that depend mainly on the Zener mechanism (breakdown below 6 V) have a negative coefficient of about $-0.1\,\%$ per degree and those that depend mainly on an avalanche mechanism (breakdown above 7 V) have a positive temperature coefficient of about

$+0.1\%$ per degree. To ensure precise reproducibility of breakdown voltage, Zener diodes are often placed in a temperature-controlled oven.

Example The incremental resistance of the Zener diode in the regulator circuit of Fig. 4.7 is $20\ \Omega$. If its current increases by 10 mA during regulation, what increase will be noted in its voltage drop V_z? Since $V_z = V_{z\,\text{initial}} + I_z r_z$, the increase will be

$$\Delta V_z = I_z r_z = 0.010 \times 20 = 0.20\ \text{V}.$$

4.6 THE TRANSISTOR

A semiconductor device with three sections of alternating "polarity," i.e., with two *p-n* junctions back to back, is a transistor. Two sequences fit this definition, *p-n-p* and *n-p-n*; transistors of both types are common. The devices are said to be bipolar. Transistors are made from a thin section of a single crystal by appropriate doping; a variety of methods of fabrication is used. A schematic cross section of one type of transistor is given in Fig. 4.8a.

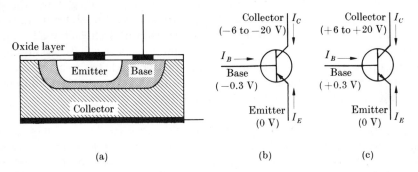

(a)   (b)   (c)

Fig. 4.8 (a) Double-diffused planar transistor. An oxide layer is first grown on the surface of a wafer. A portion of the layer is etched away and an appropriate impurity is diffused in to form the base. The process is repeated for the emitter layer. (b) Symbol for *p-n-p* transistor. Approximate dc voltages (biases) applied to electrodes are shown for a Ge transistor. The emitter-base junction is forward-biased. The emitter is identified by the arrow, which always points in the direction of conventional current flow. By convention, electrode currents I_C, I_B, and I_E are considered to flow toward the transistors. Since I_C and I_B actually flow outward, they are reported as negative. (c) Symbol for *n-p-n* transistor.

Symbols for the *n-p-n* and *p-n-p* types of transistors are also given in Fig. 4.8. The three sections or electrodes are labeled *emitter, base*, and *collector*. The type of transistor is identifiable by the direction of the emitter arrow, which always points the direction of conventional positive current. Recall that the arrow convention is also used for a diode. The origin of electrode names relates to the "generation" of majority charge carriers in the emitter and their "collection" in the collector region. These charge carriers must pass through the base, where they are minority carriers. The base is a thin (about 0.05 mm thick) intermediate layer. Charge carriers that leave the emitter are said to be injected into the base.

Example In a *p-n-p* transistor, holes are the majority carrier originating in the *p*-type emitter. They are injected into the *n*-type base, and collected by the *p*-type collector. According to the current conventions of Fig. 4.8, current signs will be: I_E, $+$; I_B, $-$; and I_C, $-$.

In the following paragraphs discussion will center on the *p-n-p* type of device, but all ideas can be extended to its *n-p-n* counterpart by simply switching to electrons as majority charge carriers, reversing electrode polarities, and accounting for current directions.

To control charge flow in a transistor requires that dc voltages be applied to its electrodes, a process called *biasing*. The effect of biasing is illustrated in Fig. 4.9. When no external voltages are applied (Fig. 4.9a) internal potential gradients in the *p-n-p* device are such that the base is equally positive with respect to emitter and collector. In most applications transistor junctions are biased as shown in Fig. 4.8b: the base is negative and the collector quite negative relative to the emitter. As a result, the emitter-base junction is forward-biased and the base-collector junction reverse-biased. One effect, as is evident in Fig. 4.9b, is to lower the potential barrier at the emitter-base junction. The consequence is that holes are injected into the base. The base is thin and the majority of the holes (97 to 99.5%) that enter diffuse across it and are captured by the collector. As seen in Fig. 4.9b, the relatively high negative potential of the collector creates a steep potential gradient at its boundary that causes holes to be strongly attracted.

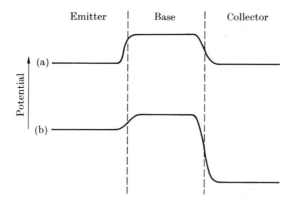

Fig. 4.9 Junction potentials in a *p-n-p* transistor. (a) No external bias. (b) External biases applied as in Fig. 4.8b. Now the base-emitter potential barrier is lowered (the junction is forward-biased) and the collector-base potential drop is increased (reverse-biased).

Some holes recombine with electrons while traversing the base. These carriers are lost to the collector current. The process of recombination gives rise to an external base current I_B as electrons flow in to compensate for those lost. The reduced potential barrier at the emitter-base junction also permits some electrons from the base to enter the emitter. This flow enhances the emitter current I_E but the flow can have no effect on I_C since crossings of the collector junction are not affected.

Three important things are accomplished by making the collector quite negative.

Holes are collected, leakage of holes from the collector back to the base is minimized, and a very-high-resistance junction is secured.*

How do currents originate in the emitter and collector leads, since one cannot have "holes" in a conductor? The concentration of holes in the emitter must, of course, be sustained as some move into the base. Their formation, a process also termed *injection*, occurs at the junction of the emitter and its external lead. The lead is slightly positive relative to the base (see Fig. 4.8b), and electrons are constantly attracted from the emitter as external current I_E, leaving holes behind. At the other end of the transistor, as holes enter the collector from the base, electrons move in from the collector lead to maintain electrical neutrality. This flow constitutes current I_C.

One good way to show the behavior of a transistor in a circuit is by means of graphs. If a transistor is to provide effective control of charge flow, there must be evidence that one or more of its currents or interelectrode voltages is strongly dependent on another of them. In Figs. 4.10 and 4.11 some interrelationships are examined for two modes of biasing.

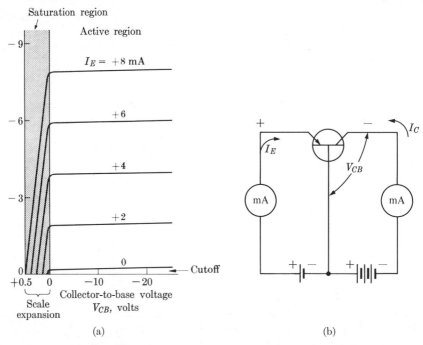

(a)   (b)

Fig. 4.10 Current-voltage curves for a transistor in the common-base design. (a) The family of collector current *vs* collector-to-base voltage curves with emitter current as a variable. A simplified schematic of the measuring circuit is shown in (b).

---

* It is the resistance of this boundary that ensures the control desired, since it provides that charge is transferred from a region of low resistance (emitter-base boundary) to one of high resistance (fundamentally to a load resistor as will be seen later). Indeed, the term transistor is a contraction of "transfer resistor."

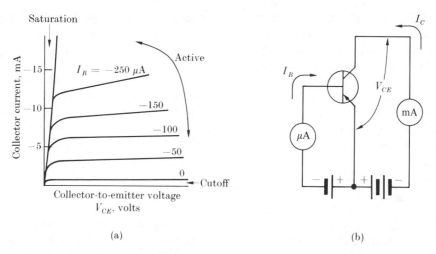

Fig. 4.11 Current-voltage behavior of the common-emitter transistor design. (a) The family of collector current vs collector-to-emitter voltage curves with base current as a variable. (b) Circuit.

In Fig. 4.10b the common-base circuit configuration is shown for a p-n-p transistor. The name derives from the fact that the base lead is common to input (emitter) and output (collector) circuits. The collector current derived for a representative transistor in this configuration is plotted versus collector-base voltage in Fig. 4.10a. There are several curves, each obtained for one value of emitter current. The family of curves is called a set of common-base characteristics.

When the emitter lead is common to input and output circuits, the family of collector characteristics obtained for a representative transistor is that shown in Fig. 4.11a. Now the base current I_B is the parameter, each value of which gives rise to one curve in the family. Note the simplified common-emitter configuration circuit in Fig. 4.11b. These circuits are amplifier stages. The reason is especially evident for the common-emitter circuit since a small change in base current I_B can bring about a large change in collector current I_C. Both configurations of amplifier are discussed in Chapter 5, with detailed attention to the common-emitter type.

Further examination of the families of collector characteristics (Figs. 4.10a and 4.11a) shows that the collector-base voltage exercises relatively little control over behavior when the transistor operates in the *active region*. In this region the emitter junction is forward-biased and the collector junction reverse-biased as noted before. Raising the potential V_{CB} does increase the width of the collector junction depletion layer and therefore gives the current curves a finite slope. The resistance of this layer is roughly I_C/V_{CB}, the slope. Actually, V_{CB} can be said to control the working width of the base, since any hole that reaches the edge of the collector depletion region is effectively collected.

Both Figs. 4.10a and 4.11a show that I_C falls greatly when the collector bias is drastically reduced. As V_C becomes less negative, the collector-base junction eventually also becomes forward-biased. When both emitter and collector-junctions are so biased, the transistor is said to have *saturated*. It is operating in the shaded region of the graph.

Contrast that region with the region of *cutoff*, when both junctions are reverse-biased. In the case of cutoff, the reversal of base current brings about the change in bias. In both saturation and cutoff regions the collector current has the value I_{CO} and is very much smaller than in the active region.

The families of collector current curves also provide information about the responsiveness of a transistor. Two dimensionless current-ratio parameters are useful in making the analysis. One is α, the common-base forward short-circuit current transfer ratio, also symbolized as h_{fb}. Alpha is defined as $\alpha = -h_{fb} = \partial i_C / \partial i_E$ and varies somewhat with v_{CB}, the collector-base potential.* The parameter α is seen to define the fraction of charge carriers injected into the base that are captured by the collector. Practical values of α range from 0.97 to 0.995. It can be shown that

$$i_C = I_{CBO}(1 - e^{v_C/kT}) - \alpha i_E, \tag{4.1}$$

where I_{CBO} is the reverse saturation current or leakage current of the base-collector junction. Only when $i_E \simeq 0$, or the temperature rises, does the first term contribute appreciably. When a transistor operates in the active region, Eq. (4.1) reduces to the useful approximate expression

$$\alpha \simeq -i_C/i_E. \tag{4.2}$$

The other parameter, β, is the analog for the common-emitter circuit. It is called the common-emitter forward short-circuit current transfer ratio and also symbolized by h_{fe}. It is defined as $\beta = h_{fe} = (\partial i_C / \partial i_B)$ and varies somewhat with collector-emitter bias. Practical values range from 30 to 250, indicating the potency of base current in controlling collector current. When the collector-base potential is large compared with the emitter-base potential, it can be shown that

$$i_C = \frac{I_{CBO}}{1 - \alpha} + \frac{\alpha i_B}{1 - \alpha}. \tag{4.3}$$

At reasonable values of i_C, Eq. (4.3) reduces to the second useful approximate expression

$$i_C \simeq \frac{\alpha i_B}{1 - \alpha} = \beta i_B.\dagger \tag{4.4}$$

Small-signal performance. In order to analyze or describe the operation of transistors more fully a physical model is needed that leads to the definition of quantities like α and β which characterize performance. For chemical instrumentation the linear or small-signal operation of transistors as amplifiers is of central concern. Accordingly the *hybrid model*, which is simple and suitable to this use, will be discussed here. It allows the insights and modes of analysis of network theory to be applied. Many other models are in use. One of the most attractive is the hybrid-π model, which gives good agreement with experiment from dc to frequencies where performance is

---

* Changing values of variables are now involved, and lower-case letters are used hereafter in accord with conventions noted in Table 2.1.

† Since $i_E = -i_C - i_B$, by application of Kirchhoff's law to either Fig. 4.10b or 4.11b, it can be shown that $\beta = \alpha/(1 - \alpha)$.

impaired [8, Chap. 5]. Since it is somewhat more complex, it is usually employed only at higher frequencies.

The hybrid model of an active device is shown in Fig. 4.12 as a "black box" with two input and two output terminals.* Input and output currents and voltages are shown. To illustrate the approach used with the hybrid model, it will be applied in a preliminary way to the most widely used transistor configuration, the common-emitter arrangement. In Section 5.4 the model will be taken up again and applied to amplifier circuits generally.

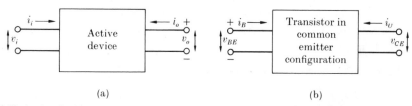

(a)   (b)

Fig. 4.12 Active device represented as a network or black box with two input terminals and two output terminals. Since a transistor is a three-lead device, one electrode must always be *common* to input and output circuits. This model of a transistor leads to the definition and measurement of hybrid parameters. (a) General model. (b) Model applied to one-stage of amplifier with transistor in common emitter configuration. Both leads marked minus go to the emitter.

To adapt the hybrid model to a transistor in this configuration the question to be asked is: What two external currents and voltages are of greatest interest? The usefulness of presenting some collector characteristics is now clear. From Fig. 4.11a it appears that base and collector currents and base-emitter and collector-emitter potentials will be the appropriate set of four variables.

With this kind of network model, any two variables can be considered independent; the other two will be dependent variables. Since the choice is an arbitrary one, it has been decided on the basis of convenience. Usually v_{CE}, which is fairly easily controlled, and i_B, which can be an input current, are taken as independent. Then v_{BE} and i_C are dependent variables. In other words, $i_C = f_1(i_B, v_{CE})$ and $v_{BE} = f_2(i_B, v_{CE})$. What is now needed mathematically is a statement of how small changes di_B and dv_{CE} (in the independent variables) affect the magnitude of the dependent variables. The desired relationships can be found by differentiating and are

$$di_C = \frac{\partial i_C}{\partial i_B}\bigg]_{v_{CE}} di_B + \frac{\partial i_C}{\partial v_{CE}}\bigg]_{i_B} dv_{CE}, \tag{4.5}$$

$$dv_{BE} = \frac{\partial v_{BE}}{\partial i_B}\bigg]_{v_{CE}} di_B + \frac{\partial v_{BE}}{\partial v_{CE}}\bigg]_{i_B} dv_{CE}. \tag{4.6}$$

Several comments may be made about these equations. First, note that each partial derivative is the slope of a curve. For example, $\partial i_C / \partial v_{CE}$ is the slope of the collector curves of Fig. 4.11a. The partial derivatives are therefore characteristic of a given transistor, in a given configuration amplifier circuit. As will be seen below,

---

* It is the "black box" aspect that is the main disadvantage of the model. No quantitatively valuable model of the transistor provides a satisfying internal picture of its operation.

they are specified by manufacturers for each kind of transistor. Second, as is evident from the curves of Fig. 4.11a, and confirmed by Eq. (4.5), slopes $\partial i_C/\partial v_{CE}$ vary with the value of i_B. A transistor parameter (partial derivative) is not a true constant. Yet such parameters provide a basis for intercomparing transistors and for elementary circuit design. Third, Eqs. (4.5) and (4.6) basically describe the effect of *small* changes in variables.

Values of the partial derivatives of Eqs. (4.5) and (4.6) for a given transistor characterize its operation in a common-emitter amplifier configuration. They are termed *small-signal parameters*. These hybrid parameters are collected in Table 4.2 and conditions under which they are measured are indicated briefly. An advantage of the hybrid model is that the parameters that result have *real* values at low frequencies and are easily measured.

Table 4.2 Hybrid Parameters for Common-Emitter Configuration

Partial derivative	Hybrid designation	Name	Measurement requirement	Representative values and units
$\dfrac{\partial i_C}{\partial i_B}$	h_{fe}* (f = forward)	Forward transfer current ratio	Output must be a short circuit for ac	50 to 200 (dimensionless)
$\dfrac{\partial i_C}{\partial v_{CE}}$	h_{oe} (o = output)	Output admittance†	Input must be an open circuit for ac	$2 \times 10^{-5}\,\Omega^{-1}$
$\dfrac{\partial v_{BE}}{\partial i_B}$	h_{ie} (i = input)	Base input impedance	Output must be a short circuit for ac	1 to 2 kΩ
$\dfrac{\partial v_{BE}}{\partial v_{CE}}$	h_{re} (r = reverse)	Reverse transfer voltage ratio	Input must be an open circuit for ac	10^{-3} to 10^{-4} (dimensionless)

* The second subscript defines the circuit configuration; e.g., the subscript e designated the common-emitter arrangement.

† An admittance is the reciprocal of an impedance. Here h_{oe} is the reciprocal of the collector impedance.

Some further words of caution must be given about the use of small-signal parameters. The fabrication of individual transistors by present methods yields similar units but not identical ones. All transistors of a given type, e.g., those designated 2N2049, will behave similarly but their values of β (h_{fe}) may vary from 60 to 100, and other parameters will show similar range. Further, as mentioned above, small-signal parameters are fairly constant only for small changes in current (and voltage). An idea of the variability encountered is given in Fig. 4.13. Third, all parameters are temperature-dependent. A conclusion to be drawn from such words of caution is that circuit design will have as one of its chief objectives the minimizing of the dependence of performance on the exact value of parameters.

Manufacturers' specifications. Manufacturers give specifications of small-signal and other parameters for transistors in considerable detail. The usual range of properties

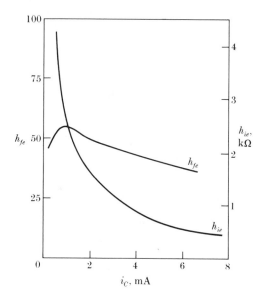

Fig. 4.13 Representative dependence of two small-signal parameters on collector current. Note differing ordinate scales at right and left.

is specified as an aid to designers. In addition, a host of maximum ratings is given. The strong temperature dependence of transistor properties is responsible for specifications such as the maximum voltages, currents, and power dissipation that can be allowed. The change of such ratings with operating temperature is also stated. Further, the frequency dependence of a transistor is noted. Usually given is a cutoff frequency f_α, the frequency at which the parameter falls to 0.707 of its audiofrequency value. Finally, they usually also include a second basic type of performance curve, the *current transfer characteristic*, a plot of i_C against i_B. The transfer curve may be replotted at several temperatures. Both the degree of nonlinearity in "current transfer" and a reasonable operating temperature may be deduced.

Switching performance. Though it may seem surprising, transistors are used most widely in switching. This application reflects the importance of digital electronics (Chapter 9) and the extensive use of transistors (in integrated circuit form) to perform switching in computers. The possibility of a transistor acting as a switch is inherent in the control that the base exercises over the collector current. At very small base currents the collector current is small, as shown in Fig. 4.11, indicating an apparently large collector-emitter resistance. On the other hand, for a larger (though comparatively small) base current, the collector current will be very much greater. In this case, the resistance offered by the collector-emitter circuit will be small. The two situations correspond to the open (high-resistance) and closed (low-resistance) positions of a switch, respectively. A simple transistor switch circuit is shown in Fig. 4.14. From the description of performance in the caption it may be deduced that a transistor active as a switch is likely to be in either the cutoff or the saturation region. It goes into saturation because a high i_C causes a large iR drop in the load resistor R_L (see Fig. 4.14) and thus reduces V_{CE} to less than 1 V.

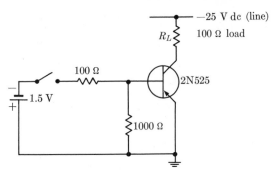

Fig. 4.14 A single-transistor switching circuit. The 100 Ω resistor is the load to which the 25 V line is to deliver about 6 W of power (250 mA current) when the switch is closed. The 1000 Ω resistor between base and ground is used to reduce leakage current, which ordinarily exists when the switch is in the "open" position. Note that the *p-n-p* transistor uses a common emitter arrangement.

Of more interest is the speed of switching, important in most high-speed operations. What charge redistributions at junctions are necessary to take a transistor from cutoff to active region to saturation (turning on) and vice versa (switching off)? The distribution of charge carriers at junctions proves the critical factor and is shown in Table 4.3. In terms of charge movement, the slowest operation would appear to be going from saturation to cutoff. Large concentrations of minority charge carriers in the base must be removed. For example, in a *p-n-p* transistor, holes would be the minority carrier in the base. When such a transistor is in the active region, hole concentration is high where they have just been injected from the emitter and low on the far side of the base because of the favorable collecting gradient. In saturation both junctions are forward-biased and holes injected by the emitter move only slowly across the base.

Table 4.3 Transistor Junction Potentials and Base Charge Distribution

			Minority carrier* concentration in base at junction with	
Region	*Junction biasing*		*Emitter*	*Collector*
	Emitter–base	*Base–collector*		
Active	Forward	Reverse	Moderate	Nearly zero
Cutoff	Reverse	Reverse	Nearly zero	Nearly zero
Saturation	Forward	Forward	High	Moderate

* Minority carriers *in the base* have been injected from either emitter (during operation in the active region) or both emitter and collector (during operation in saturation region). In a *p-n-p* base minority carriers are holes, the majority carrier of the emitter and collector.

Specifications of importance in switching are time intervals. The intervals of major interest are shown graphically and in tabular form in Fig. 4.15. The square switching pulse imposed on the base is drawn in Fig. 4.15a. The response in terms of collector current is drawn in Fig. 4.15b and the transient regions are identified by symbol. These regions are listed and names given them in Fig. 4.15c.

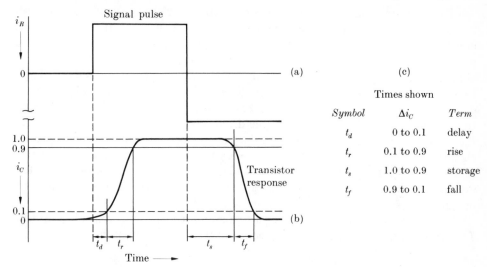

Symbol	Δi_C	Term
t_d	0 to 0.1	delay
t_r	0.1 to 0.9	rise
t_s	1.0 to 0.9	storage
t_f	0.9 to 0.1	fall

Fig. 4.15 Switching transients in a *p-n-p* transistor. (a) Negative-going switching pulse imposed on base current. (b) Collector current waveform during same interval. (c) Identification of characteristic intervals of transistor response.

4.7 THE FIELD-EFFECT TRANSISTOR

This semiconductor device is often called *unipolar* to distinguish it from the regular transistor, which is *bipolar*. The operation of a regular transistor is based on the sensitive control of the injection of minority carriers into a base layer. By contrast, the operation of a field-effect transistor depends on the flow of majority charge carriers in a channel. Flow in the channel is controlled by imposed fields.

There are two basic forms of the field-effect transistor; the junction and insulated-gate types. The first has one or more *p-n* junctions on either side of the conducting channel. The second type has an insulating oxide layer between input and conducting channel. Both varieties are fabricated from a single crystal of semiconductor.

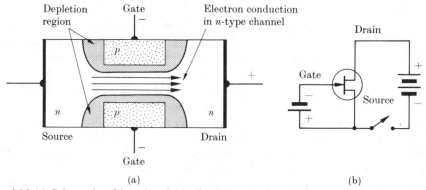

Fig. 4.16 (a) Schematic of junction field-effect transistor. The channel is *n*-type and relies on electron movement for conduction. (b) Symbol for *n*-channel FET. The arrowhead points the direction of positive current at the gate. Biasing is also shown. Electrons, as majority charge carrier, must be attracted from source to drain.

The junction *field-effect transistor* (FET) must be biased to develop a reverse-biased junction. The channel may be either *n*- or *p*-type. A two-sided FET is shown in side view in Fig. 4.16a. The device is simply a bar of *n*-type semiconductor with ohmic contacts at either end, one termed the *source*, the other the *drain*. Midway along the bar a *p*-type *gate* was formed on each side by doping. One-sided or planar FETs are common. Biasing for an *n*-channel FET is shown in the Fig. 4.16b. A drain-source potential difference V_{DS} causes majority carriers, in this case electrons, to move through the channel toward the drain. This flow constitutes drain current I_{DS}. At the reverse-biased junction with the gate, the depletion layer extends into the channel, effectively reducing its width, or increasing its resistance so far as conduction is concerned. Thus, the gate voltage determines the drain current through its effect on the channel resistance. Usually the gate potential is referred to the source and designated V_{GS}.

A set of current characteristics for a representative FET is graphed in Fig. 4.17. The active region for the device corresponds to the flat portion of the curves. In any

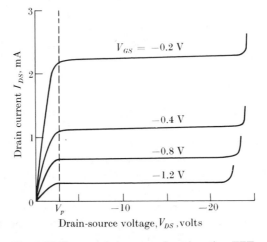

Fig. 4.17 Characteristic curves for a junction FET.

event, V_{DS} must be smaller than the value at which the current suddenly begins to rise steeply. This effect shows the onset of ionization breakdown in the semiconductor.

Two other distinctive features of the curves deserve comment. First, the initial portion of each drain characteristic has a different slope, denoting that the FET has a different resistance at each value of gate voltage. As suggested above, the channel does behave like a resistor whose magnitude is determined by V_{GS}.* Thus, an FET should be useful as a voltage-controlled resistor when operated in this range.

The second noteworthy aspect is that the curves imply nearly constant resistance for a FET at values of V_{GS} higher than the "knee" in the curves. The loss of the earlier characteristic resistance is attributed to the extension of the depletion layer between gate and drain. As this junction becomes reverse-biased, the depletion layer "pinches

---

* Recall that a regular transistor gave current characteristics (Fig. 4.11) with essentially the same slope in the saturation region, indicating a fixed resistance in this range.

off" the channel (see Fig. 4.16a). Appropriately, the knee of the curves is identified as the pinch-off voltage V_p. Above V_p only the electrostatic field of the moving electrons keeps open a small channel section. The current is prevented from rising appreciably even though the voltage is increased.

In addition to the possibility of its application as a voltage-controlled resistor, the FET is superior to a regular transistor in more important ways. Because an input signal appears at a reverse-biased junction, the FET has a very high input resistance (about 10^9 Ω). For a representative silicon FET, input currents are of the order of 10^{-8} to 10^{-10} A. Practically, however, a resistor of perhaps 10^7 Ω must be inserted in parallel with the input to establish a potential (bias) on the gate relative to the source and also to furnish a path for the gate (leakage) current, thus substantially reducing the circuit input resistance. A second advantage of the FET is the absence of any offset voltage [9, Chap. 5] since the entire length of the conduction channel is uni-polar. If very slowly fluctuating signals are being "chopped," an FET can be used successfully with signals of lower amplitude than can a transistor (Section 8.6). Other advantages are low internal noise and an outstanding ability to withstand high-energy radiation, since there is no current-carrying junction to be destroyed.

Insulated-gate FET. In this type of field-effect transistor either a *p*- or *n*-type channel is used, but the gate is metallic and is separated from the channel by a thin (0.15 μm) insulated film of oxide. For a silicon device, the film is silicon dioxide. Both enhance-ment and depletion types are available (see below). Because of their construction, these devices are often identified as MOS (metal-oxide-semiconductor) transistors or MOSFET devices.

In Fig. 4.18 a representative design for a *depletion* type of *n*-channel MOS tran-sistor is shown. To control conduction the formation of a depletion region that extends outward from the oxide layer under the gate is used. If a positive bias is applied to the gate relative to the source (V_{GS} positive), free electrons in the *n*-type channel are de-pleted, reducing channel conduction between source and drain. If a negative bias V_{GS} is applied, electrons are repelled from the oxide, concentrating them in the channel, causing conduction to increase. The depletion type of MOS transistor behaves in a fashion analogous to a regular FET and has a family of drain characteristics like that in Fig. 4.17.

Enhancement-type MOS transistors. These are also common, especially in switching. In such devices the source and drain regions are initially of opposite polarity to the channel. In terms of Fig. 4.18a, they would be *p*-type with the channel *n*-type. There is no source-drain conductivity in the absence of a gate bias. When a negative bias is applied to the gate, free electrons in the *n*-type channel region are repelled and a depletion layer forms next to the oxide layer. But increasing the negative bias causes a widening of the layer, and with application of sufficient bias, "free" holes from the *p*-type source begin to enter the layer. The layer soon changes to a hole-dominated channel and there is conduction. It is now a *p*-channel device. Clearly, conduction occurs above a threshold gate bias. The phenomenon is described as inversion. Such a transistor represents an open circuit when the gate is unbiased, but a circuit of finite resistance when *forward-biasing* of the gate-source junction inverts the channel. Drain current curves are similar to those in Fig. 4.17. The difference in behavior of

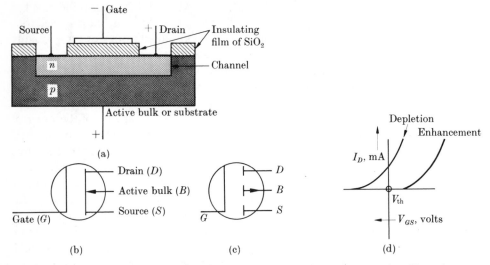

Fig. 4.18 (a) Structure of an MOS field-effect transistor of the depletion type. It utilizes electron conduction in a lightly doped *n*-type channel. (b) Symbol for *n*-channel depletion-type MOS FET. Arrow pointing toward channel identifies *n*-type and direction of positive current; solid channel line indicates depletion (normally on) device. (c) Symbol for *p*-channel (arrow pointing away) enhancement type (dashed channel line, i.e., off unless forward bias applied to gate). (d) Transfer curves for two types of MOS (insulated gate) transistors. Note that gate voltage increases to the left.

the two kinds of MOS transistor is better illustrated by the transfer curves (I_D against V_{GS}) in Fig. 4.18d. As the figure shows, when $V_{GS} = 0$, the enhancement type is normally off, the depletion type normally on.

The insulated gate of the MOS transistor offers a very high input resistance—up to $10^{15}\,\Omega$—and does not really require any gate leakage resistor. Other distinctive possibilities arise by virtue of the insulating layer. As Fig. 4.18d shows, a MOS transistor, when $V_{GS} = 0$, can operate as a normally open switch (enhancement type) or normally closed switch (depletion type) and be changed to the other state by applying a gate voltage.

4.8 THYRISTORS

There also exists a family of semiconductor devices known as thyristors, with four layers that alternate in the sequence *p-n-p-n*. Of the many types possible the present discussion will cover only the silicon controlled rectifier and the silicon controlled switch. Information about four thyristors is given in Table 4.4. Nearly all these devices find major application in switching, voltage phase control, ac power regulation, and other uses involving control of large amounts of power. For example, silicon controlled rectifiers are presently available with ratings of 1800 V and 550 A (average)!

Silicon controlled rectifier (SCR). This rectifier is a *p-n-p-n* device that conducts in only one direction but whose operation is triggered or fired by the application of a pulse of current. A schematic diagram and symbol for the SCR is shown in Table 4.4. Note that its circuit symbol suggests its unidirectional character, the arrow once

Table 4.4 Characteristics of Some Thyristors

Number of leads	Device name	Symbol	Equivalent cross section*	Triggering signal	Applications
3	Silicon controlled rectifier (SCR) [Reverse blocking triode thyristor]			Gate signal	Inverters, phase controls, choppers
3	Light-activated SCR (LASCR) [Reverse blocking triode thyristor]		(Same as SCR)	Gate signal or radiation	Position monitors, limit switches, trigger circuits, photoelectric controls
4	Silicon controlled switch (SCS) [Reverse blocking tetrode thyristor]			Gate signal on either gate lead	Logic circuits, counters, control circuits
3	Triac [Bidirectional triode thyristor]			Gate signal or exceeding breakover voltage	Switching, phase control of ac

again pointing in the direction of conventional positive current. One of its layers has no external lead.

Two states may be distinguished for the SCR. If the voltage applied across it leaves the cathode positive and anode negative, i.e., polarities are opposite those shown in Table 4.4, the SCR behaves like two reverse-biased diodes in series, and only a small leakage current flows. This state will exist during half of each cycle if ac is applied. When biased in the (forward) direction indicated in the table, it has both an ON state, which is equivalent to normal forward conduction across a *p-n* junction, and a zero-current OFF state. It is the gate potential that determines the state, a pulse of current as low as 1 mA being sufficient to trigger the ON condition. Once the SCR is conducting, it can be turned off only by reducing the anode potential to zero.

A good model for the device is the two-transistor equivalent circuit sketched in Fig. 4.19. Here the gate is simultaneously the base of Q_2 and the collector of Q_1. Note that the two transistors are a complementary pair, i.e., one is a p-n-p, the other an n-p-n type. When there is no gate signal, only leakage current flows. Even this would result in causing the transistors to conduct were not the large signal current gain h_{FE} much less than unity at low currents. If a positive pulse is now applied to the gate, the base of Q_2 will be favorably biased, and its collector current will actuate the base of Q_1; both h_{FE} and conduction will increase rapidly as the current increases until the normal ON state is attained.

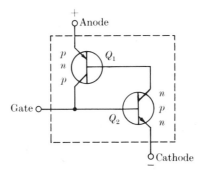

Fig. 4.19 Two-transistor model of a silicon controlled rectifier (SCR).

Three additional points about its operation are important to note. First, even without a gate signal, application of a sufficiently high voltage of "forward polarity" will turn an SCR on. This kind of breakdown results when accelerated minority carriers liberate majority carriers in the gate region. The minimum potential at which it occurs is termed the *breakover voltage*. Second, a minimum "holding current" must flow in the cathode layer for the device to be stable in the ON condition. If the current is very small, carriers will be lost by recombination, causing h_{FE} to fall, and the SCR will turn itself off. Third, the SCR is a negative resistance device (as will be discussed below) and an external resistor must be used in series to limit current to allowable values.

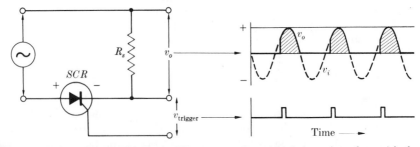

Fig. 4.20 A representative SCR circuit. The output voltage (shaded portion of curve) is that fraction input voltage V_i for which the polarity across the SCR is as shown following its "turning on" by application of a triggering pulse (generated by an auxiliary circuit). By varying the timing of the triggering pulses, the power at the output can be adjusted.

The chief advantage of an SCR lies in the ease with which it can conduct any desired fraction of a positive half-cycle of an ac wave, thus allowing power output to be precisely controlled. An illustration of the operation of an SCR is given in Fig. 4.20.

The silicon controlled switch (SCS). This is a four-layer device similar to the SCR and is also described in Table 4.4. It has additional versatility because gates are provided for both anode and cathode. The advantage gained is that it can be switched off as well as on by means of signal.

4.9 NEGATIVE-RESISTANCE DEVICES

Active devices that exhibit *negative resistance* over part of their active range should also be included in this discussion. The significance of the term negative resistance can be best illustrated in terms of the current–voltage graph presented in Fig. 4.21. According to Ohm's law, the slope of such a plot, $\partial i/\partial v$, is proportional to $1/R$. If the slope is negative, as is true for one voltage range in the figure, the system behaves as if its resistance were negative. In this range current is actually decreasing as voltage increases. Devices with negative resistance characteristics over part of their ranges are useful in switching, generation of signals (as oscillators), and in many other applications [3, Chap. 9]. Two negative-resistance active devices will now be examined briefly.

Tunnel diode. This tiny semiconductor diode has very high concentrations of doping impurities and a behavior conditioned by the ease with which quantum-mechanical tunneling can occur, as in a low-voltage Zener diode. The characteristic of a representative tunnel diode and its circuit symbol are shown in Fig. 4.21. Both the high reverse current (when its junction bias is negative) and the current peak at small forward voltages are the result of tunneling.

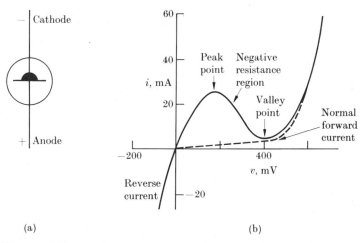

(a)   (b)

Fig. 4.21 The tunnel diode. (a) Circuit symbol, (b) Current–voltage characteristic. The negative resistance region lies between about 100 and 400 mV, where an increase in v causes the current to fall.

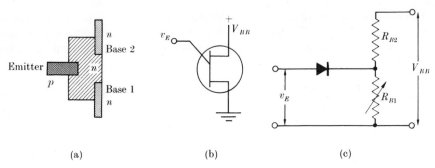

Fig. 4.22 The unijunction transistor. (a) Schematic of construction. (b) Circuit symbol. (c) Equivalent circuit.

While the negative resistance portion of the current–voltage characteristic gives the tunnel diode its particular importance, it lies at too low voltages (100 to 400 mV) to permit the device to be used easily with other semiconductor components. Almost all other devices operate under higher voltage drops. The tunnel diode operates with great rapidity, however, since its depletion layer is extremely thin and is used in very-high-frequency applications such as switching.

Unijunction transistor. A single *p-n* junction may be used in still another way, as is illustrated by the unijunction transistor. This three-terminal device has two ohmic leads, called base-1 and base-2, at opposite ends of an *n*-type silicon bar. A rectifying contact which serves as an *emitter* is also made to an area between the bases. In Fig. 4.22 the schematic design of the device, its symbol, and a simplified model or equivalent circuit are shown.

In essence, as suggested in the equivalent circuit, the length of bar between bases acts as a voltage divider, $R_{B1} + R_{B2}$, whose total resistance is about 5–10 kΩ. A fraction η of this resistance is effective between the emitter and base-1.

If the emitter voltage V_E is less than the voltage across R_{B1}, which is ηV_{BB}, the emitter-base "diode" shown is reverse-biased. However, if V_E is increased until it exceeds ηV_{BB}, current flows. The voltage across the unijunction transistor now falls, since the resistance offered to the current is only that of a forward-biased diode. The characteristic of a unijunction transistor is much like that illustrated in Fig. 4.21 for the tunnel diode. An advantage possessed by the unijunction transistor is that the negative-resistance portion of its operation can be designed to begin at significantly higher voltages (3 to 20 V). As a result, it is often used with other semiconductor devices. This advantage is gained at the cost of speed, however, and its applications are limited to moderate to high frequencies. For example, it can supply current pulses to a silicon controlled rectifier.

4.10 THE INTEGRATED CIRCUIT

Entire circuits can also be formed in the surface of a single semiconductor crystal by appropriate etching and doping techniques. Where active components like diodes and transistors are required, *p*- and *n*-layers are introduced at appropriate spacings. MOS leaving undoped portions of appropriate length. While capacitances can be introduced by forming an oxide (dielectric) film between semiconductor layers or, less often, by use of *p-n* junctions, they are commonly omitted unless really essential. Inductances cannot be incorporated, but there is no difficulty in substituting *RC* networks to secure a desired reactance or frequency dependence. For example, a Wien bridge (Section 3.5) is a convenient alternative to an *LC* network for obtaining frequency selectivity. The relative location of components in a crystal must, of course, be planned judiciously to eliminate unwanted low-resistance paths or capacitances.

Many examples of integrated circuits are given in the following chapters. The appearance and application of integrated-circuit versions of common modules such as difference amplifiers and logic circuits (Sections 7.1 and 9.3) are steadily accelerating. In redesigning circuits for fabrication as integrated circuits striking advantages in cost, size, and stability are often secured.

4.11 A COMPARISON OF SEMICONDUCTOR DEVICES AND TUBES

Since decisions as to whether semiconductor devices or electron tubes are to be employed sometimes arise in instrument design, a brief consideration of relative merits is desirable. A qualitative comparison of several properties is made in Table 4.5. The chief disadvantages of semiconductor devices are seen to be temperature sensitivity, higher noise level (Section 8.3), and susceptibility to radiation damage. For most applications semiconductor devices are more attractive than electron tubes, and indeed are used in nearly all new instrumentation.

Table 4.5 Comparison of Some Properties of Semiconductor Devices and Electron Tubes

	Semiconductor devices	*Electron tubes*
1. Power consumption	Low	Moderate to high
2. Heat generation	Very small	Moderate
3. Ruggedness	High	Low to moderate
4. Life	Long	Moderate
5. Noise	Moderate	Low
6. Frequency response	Good	Good
7. Temperature sensitivity	Great	Small
8. Electromagnetic pickup	Low	Moderate
9. Size	Very small	Moderate to large
10. Cost	Low to moderate	Moderate
11. Damage by radiation	Moderate	Low

In the following chapters semiconductor circuits will be emphasized but a few important tube circuits will be presented since relatively few instruments manufactured before 1965 employed solid-state circuitry.

4.12 BASIC DC POWER SUPPLY

It is appropriate to conclude the chapter by discussion of an electronic module basic to all systems. Virtually all active devices require dc power to function. In most instances it is convenient to derive this power from ac power lines.* A line diagram of a representative dc power supply is shown in Fig. 4.23. Here attention will be given mainly to the stages devoted to rectification and filtering, and regulation will be discussed in the next section.

ac line → Transformer → Rectifier → Filter → Regulator → dc output

Fig. 4.23 Line block diagram of a regulated dc power supply.

Some representative circuits that include an ac step-up or step-down transformer (Section 2.6) and rectifier stages are shown in Fig. 4.24. For most semiconductor circuitry the transformer would be of the step-down variety; 15–30 V dc supplies are the most common. The *halfwave* rectifier in Fig. 4.24a is the simplest possibility. Since the diode conducts only when forward-biased, current will appear in the diode circuit only during half of each ac cycle, as illustrated in Fig. 4.24d. This circuit has several disadvantages relative to other rectifiers: (a) it uses half the available power; (b) its output requires more smoothing; and (c) its diode must have a high-peak inverse voltage rating. †Its important advantage is its low cost.

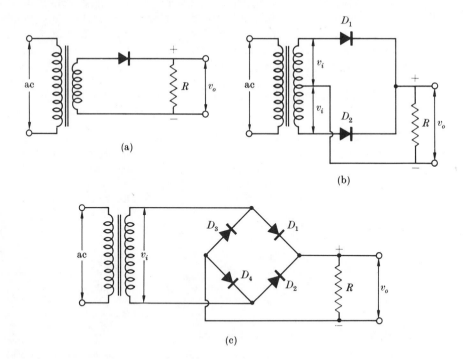

(a)

(b)

(c)

---

* In the U.S.A. power lines furnish 115 V or 230 V, 60 Hz; in other countries 220 V, 50 or 60 Hz is commonly supplied.

† When reverse-biased, the diode has the entire peak secondary voltage across it. The peak voltage is just 1.41 times the quoted or rms figure. The requirement on one diode may be lessened by using two in series.

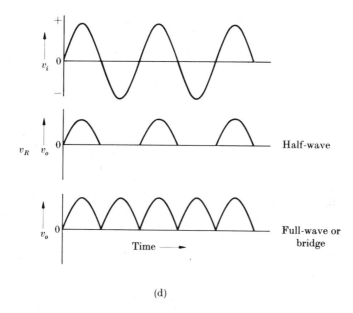

(d)

Fig. 4.24 Rectifiers. (a) Half-wave. (b) Full-wave. (c) Bridge. (d) Input waveform in transformer secondary and output waveform across resistor.

A more satisfactory though more expensive arrangement is the use of a center-tapped transformer and the double diode pattern depicted in Fig. 4.24b. This *full-wave* rectifier conducts during each half cycle, the diodes being alternately forward-biased. Note that the current through output resistor R is unidirectional and that the top of the resistor is at a positive potential. The current waveforms are shown in Fig. 4.24d. A minor performance disadvantage relative to the half-wave rectifier circuit is that only half the transformer secondary is employed at a time. Advantages are that its output is more easily smoothed and that is uses power more efficiently.

A still more effective arrangement is the bridge rectifier shown in Fig. 4.24c. Recall that this design was employed to convert a moving-coil meter to ac use (see Fig. 2.8). A less expensive transformer can be used since no center tap is needed. The transformer is also efficiently used. A possible disadvantage is that two diodes are always in series with the output load, but this drawback is minimal since the voltage drop is small (0.2 to 0.6 V across each). In addition, each diode has only half the inverse voltage applied across it, allowing use of lower-rated diodes.

Example In the bridge rectifier of Fig. 4.24c, what is the current path during the half-cycle when the voltage across the secondary of the transformer is such that the top of the winding is positive? It is through D_1, R, and D_4. Note that D_3 and D_4 are reverse-biased since their anodes (arrowhead) are at a voltage v_i-iR while their cathodes (bar) are at nearly v_i. Trace the current path on the other half-cycle.

Filtering. Shunt capacitors, i.e., capacitors placed across the output of a rectifier circuit, are used for smoothing its pulsating dc output. A simple filter of this type is shown in Fig. 4.25. For it to be effective the time constant RC must be as long as

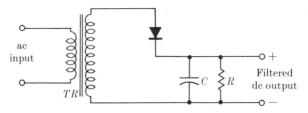

Fig. 4.25 Simple capacitor filter with half-wave rectifier.

practicable compared with a period T of the output. When the diode is non-conducting, capacitor C discharges through R (and any load); unless $RC \gg T$, the amount of discharge is too substantial and poor smoothing is secured.

The output waveform is shown as curve v_C in Fig. 4.26a. Note that if neither R_L nor a load were present, capacitor C would charge to the peak secondary voltage V_p and remain there. When current is drawn, however, $V_o < V_p$. Now the output voltage can be represented as a dc component V_{dc} plus an ac component called *ripple*. From Fig. 4.26b the dc output is seen to be roughly $V_p - V_r/2$, where V_r is the largest amplitude of the ripple. There are two approximations in this expression for V_{dc}: (a) the output waveform is only roughly triangular and (b) there is also a small voltage drop in the secondary winding and in the diode. To develop an expression for V_o, the largest magnitude of ripple must be found. Let this be V_r.

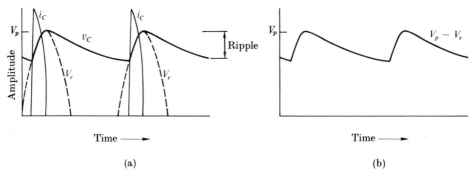

(a)   (b)

Fig. 4.26 Waveforms in smoothing the output of a half-wave rectifier. The output voltage is v_C. also shown are capacitor charging current i_C, and the output V_r that would appear across R if C were not present. (a) Actual waveforms. (b) Assumed triangular output waveform $V_p - V_r$.

Example What is the largest magnitude of the ripple voltage for a simple RC filter of the type shown in Fig. 4.25? Assume that $RC \gg T$, when T is the period of the output waveform. It follows that the drop in capacitor voltage v_C can be assumed linear over the interval during which it discharges. If the dc discharge current I is constant, $I = \Delta Q/T$, where ΔQ is the loss of capacitor charge during period T. Since $C = Q/V$ and $T = 1/f$, where f is the frequency, $I = fC\Delta V$, or $\Delta V = V_r = I/fC$. Note that $I = V_{dc}/R_L$. The value of V_r is just $V_r = V_{dc}/fR_LC$.

From the value of V_r worked out in the example, V_{dc} can be found:

$$V_{dc} = V_p - \frac{V_r}{2} = \frac{V_p}{1 + 1/2fR_LC}. \tag{4.7}$$

This equation can also be applied to a full-wave rectifier. In this case $f = 120$ Hz since pulses occur every half-cycle and smoothing for a given R and C is twice as good.

Clearly, in a smoothing circuit of the type shown, the greater C and R, the smaller is the ripple. Yet if R is made large, the mean voltage obtainable at the output will depend very greatly on the current drawn by the load. An additional factor that must be allowed for is suggested in Fig. 4.26a. If the capacitor has discharged appreciably, it may draw very substantial currents i_C as it recharges. Excessive currents that would damage diode or transformer must be avoided.

4.13 REGULATED POWER SUPPLY

The more current drawn from a power supply of the type just described, i.e. the greater the demands of a load, the lower the output voltage. Where this dependence is objectionable, regulation or stabilization of voltage is added to achieve a constant output. One or more stages of regulation also simultaneously insulate the output against line voltage fluctuations and further reduce ripple. Specifications used to describe the quality of voltage regulation usually include: the load "regulation," the % fluctuation in V_o, or load stability factor $\Delta V/\Delta I_L$, where ΔV is the change in output voltage with a change ΔI_L in load current; the temperature stability factor $\Delta V/\Delta T$; and the amplitude of the remaining ac ripple and noise.

A simple method of regulation is the series resistor-shunt Zener diode arrangement described earlier in Section 4.5. About 2–4% regulation is secured.

Many instruments require more stable supplies. Figure 4.27 is a block diagram of a generalized regulated power supply. Note the part marked "control" in the upper side of the output line. Such a device is termed a series regulator and acts as if it were a variable resistor. Its "resistance" is adjusted by the amplified output of the comparator in the direction needed to provide a constant current through $R_1 + R_2$ and thus insure a constant output voltage. The comparator determines any difference between the voltage of a stable reference voltage device and the IR drop across resistor R_2. For example, if IR_2 is smaller than V_{ref}, the comparator output, after amplification, causes the control device to pass more current.

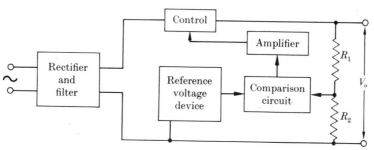

Fig. 4.27 Block diagram of a feedback-stabilized regulated power supply. V_o is the regulated output.

Figure 4.28 is a schematic diagram of a simple form of series regulator employing a transistor. Its transistor is in the emitter-follower configuration (Section 5.5), a circuit that insures a minimal output impedance. More importantly, the voltage across R_L follows or nearly equals the voltage across the Zener diode Z, which is the input signal to the base of transistor Q.*

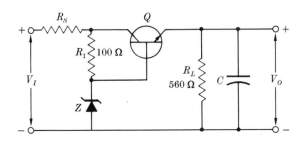

Fig. 4.28 Simple series regulator to regulate a dc power supply. Zener diode Z supplies a reference potential. Transistor Q serves both as comparator and control device to adjust current flow to R_L and the output.

Note. Among other purposes, resistor R_L serves to insure that the current through the transistor does not decrease so much that its β begins to fall off seriously. It is also essential to keep the base potential higher than that of the emitter. Resistor R_S may be omitted entirely, but not resistor R_L. The circuit of Fig. 4.28 has the disadvantage that whatever ripple voltage remains from the rectifier circuit is supplied to the output through the base-emitter junction of the transistor. Finally, it is important to insure temperature stability by achieving as good a match as possible between the temperature coefficients of the Zener diode and the base-emitter junction.

Better regulation can be secured by increasing the gain of the control device and stabilizing the amplification of the signal that arises when reference and sample voltages (here the voltage drop IR_L) are different [9, Chap. 5]. A more sophisticated circuit designed to accomplish this goal will be discussed in Section 5.7, where it will serve also to illustrate a basic transistor amplifier configuration. A discussion of the special problems of high-power or high-voltage supplies is beyond the scope of this text.

Protection of transistors and rectifier diodes against sudden overloads is always desirable in a power supply that is to be used for a variety of purposes. Often tunnel diodes or thyristors are used in this way. Fusing is also desirable but it provides protection of a slower-acting type.

REFERENCES

Some general resources are:

1. GE *Transistor Manual*. 7th ed. Syracuse, N.Y.: General Electric Co., 1964
2. RCA *Transistor Manual*. Harrison, N.J.: Radio Corporation of America, 1967

* Another way of interpreting the constant output voltage is to observe that it is just the sum of the voltage across the Zener diode and the base-emitter junction of the transistor. These voltages are nearly independent of current.

Introductions to the transistor in electronics are provided by:

3. Hendrik DeWaard and David Lazarus, *Modern Electronics*. Reading, Mass.: Addison-Wesley, 1966
4. J. Dosse, *The Transistor, Basic Theory and Application*. Princeton: D. Van Nostrand, 1964
5. R. G. Hibberd, *Transistors: Principles and Applications*. New York: Hart, 1965
6. E. Norman Lurch, *Fundamentals of Electronics*. New York: Wiley, 1960

Treatments, on an intermediate to advanced level, of the theory and functioning of semiconductor devices are available in:

7. F. E. Gentry, *et al.*, *Semiconductor Controlled Rectifiers: Principles and Applications of p-n-p-n Devices*. Englewood Cliffs, N.J.: Prentice-Hall, 1964
8. A. K. Jonscher, *Principles of Semiconductor Device Operation*. New York: Wiley, 1960
9. John P. McKelvey, *Solid-State and Semiconductor Physics*. New York: Harper and Row, 1966
10. Leonce J. Sevin, Jr, *Field-Effect Transistors*. New York: McGraw-Hill, 1965
11. R. R. Wright and M. R. Skutt, *Electronics, Circuits and Devices*. New York: Ronald, 1965

The physics of semiconductors is well discussed on an advanced level in:

12. John L. Moll, *Physics of Semiconductors*. New York: McGraw-Hill, 1964

EXERCISES

4.1 In the circuit of Fig. 4.7 assume the Zener diode provides 50 V at diode currents from 5 to 40 mA. The supply voltage V_i is 200 V.

   a) What value of R will provide voltage regulation from $I_L = 0$ to I_{max}? What is I_{max}?

   b) Let R have the value just found. If $I_L = 20$ mA, over what range of V_i will the circuit provide voltage regulation?

4.2 In a Zener-regulated supply like that of Fig. 4.7, the incremental resistance is 20 Ω (V A^{-1}). If the voltage is to be regulated to ± 0.05 V, what is the tolerable range of diode current?

$$[Ans.: \pm 2.5 \text{ mA.}]$$

4.3 A germanium diode begins to conduct strongly when forward biased 0.2 V. Often such a diode is wired across the terminals of a sensitive meter to protect it against an overload.

   a) Draw a circuit that will protect a 50 μA meter of 2 kΩ resistance against both forward and reverse overloads.

   b) Calculate the current at which diode protection begins. Is this protection sufficient?

$$[Ans.: \text{b) } 100 \ \mu\text{A.}]$$

4.4 Look up characteristics of several types of transistors and interpret the values as fully as possible. How do characteristics of low-level and power transistors differ?

4.5 Compare Eqs. (4.4) and (4.5). What can you conclude about the value of $(\partial i_C / \partial v_{CE})$? Is your conclusion confirmed by the collector characteristic of Fig. 4.11a?

4.6 In the bridge rectifier circuit of Fig. 4.24c, a pair of diodes is always in series. In selecting suitable diodes for a particular rectifier, what diode ratings can be relaxed as a result, if any?

4.7 Assume the transformer secondary of Fig. 4.24b is tapped at the lower end instead of the middle.

   a) Draw waveforms of the currents in the diodes and in R.

   b) What effect does the position of the tap have on ripple?

4.8 Discuss the operation of the circuit of Fig. 4.27.

4.9 Two power supplies are shown schematically in Fig. 4.29. Briefly describe the function of the diodes, resistors, and capacitors in each.

  a) The power supply in Fig. 4.29a is for an AM-FM tuner. Which of the positive voltages, $+14$ or $+9$, is better regulated? Suggest an approximate turns ratio for the transformer. Consider that its input is to be 115 V ac line voltage.
  b) The regulated power supply in Fig. 4.29b is intended for constant-current coulometry (see J. T. Stock, *J. Chem. Educ.* **46**, 858 (1969)). In what configuration are the transistors used? How is temperature stabilization provided by use of a complementary pair of transistors? How might one determine precisely the current provided?

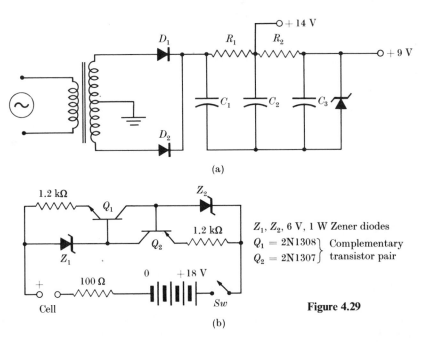

(a)

(b)

Z_1, Z_2, 6 V, 1 W Zener diodes
$Q_1 = 2N1308$ ⎱ Complementary
$Q_2 = 2N1307$ ⎰ transistor pair

Figure 4.29

4.10 The ac line voltage available in laboratories is usually constant to no more than $\pm 5\%$. Assume that an ac voltage regulator is installed to ensure a more constant source. Its specifications state that its output is constant to $\pm 0.1\%$ (rms) but suffers a 3% distortion (in waveform). Estimate roughly the constancy of voltage experienced by the following types of lab instrumentation:

  a) one whose load is mainly thermal;
  b) one built around a dc power supply of the capacitive-input type that the device loads only lightly; and
  c) one built around a dc power supply that is heavily loaded and that responds generally to the average value of voltage.

Chapter 5

BASIC AMPLIFIER CONFIGURATIONS

In this chapter the discussion of the linear or small-signal behavior of transistors which was introduced in Section 4.6 will be continued. By definition, small-signal behavior characterizes transistors operating in their active region, a region defined by the families of collector current curves for the transistor.*

The terms linear and small-signal are synonymous with *amplification*. When a transistor is operating in its active region, the device plus supporting circuit that furnishes necessary dc voltages or biases is termed an *amplifier*. If a varying or incremental voltage or current, i.e., a *signal*, is applied to one or the other of its inputs, its current and voltages will shift from the values produced by the biases alone. These changes constitute the output of the amplifier.

One transistor in general makes a single *stage* or unit of an amplifier possible. Pairs of transistors are however required for certain kinds of stages such as the input of a differential amplifier. Several basic types of amplifier stages will be examined in this chapter.

As noted earlier, transistor parameters vary from device to device even among transistors of the same type. Further, these quantities are functions of temperature, current and other operating variables, age, and signal frequency. A primary goal of circuit design therefore is to lessen dependence on exact values of parameters. As will be seen, one way to achieve independence is by external control of biasing. It can be expected that simple descriptions of transistor amplifiers are often not possible. Because of the considerable interdependence of variables, it will prove convenient to rely on equivalent circuits and graphical analysis.

5.1 THE AMPLIFIER MODULE

At the outset the relation of an amplifier to the rest of an instrument must be described. Once these relationships are understood, detail about amplifier design and performance will be more meaningful. As shown in Fig. 5.1, the amplifier follows the detector in the instrument channel.† The diagram recalls that the modular or general aspects of an amplifier (Section 1.6) will determine how well it fits into an overall device.

From this perspective a host of questions arises. How efficiently can energy and information be transferred from the detector into the amplifier and then transferred

---

* See Figs. 4.10 and 4.11 for a definition of this region under two sets of conditions.
† Other amplifiers may be used, e.g., in supplying energy to drive a monochromator slit, but the amplifier in the signal channel is located here.

Source → Sample → Detector-   → Amplifier → Processing → Readout
transducer   stage

Fig. 5.1 Line block diagram of a generalized instrument.

from amplifier to the next module? What amplification does it provide? Is amplification frequency-dependent? Will all magnitudes of signal be amplified equally well? These questions may be summarized as, "What are the input, transfer, and output characteristics of an amplifier?"

To deal with an amplifier as a module, it will suffice to represent input and output circuits in some simplified way. Thévenin equivalent circuits (Section 3.1) are fine for this purpose. In Fig. 5.2 the amplifier module has been redrawn to show these circuits. One Thévenin circuit represents the detector or input transducer. It appears as open-circuit voltage V_s in series with detector output impedance Z_s. The amplifier input is shown as input impedance Z_i "loading" the detector. Note that the pattern is repeated in representing the amplifier output and its load.

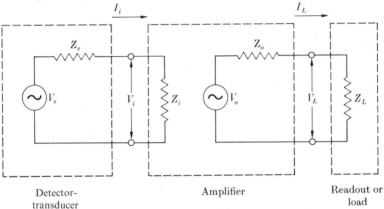

Detector-   Amplifier   Readout or
transducer   load

Fig. 5.2 Input-output model of an amplifier. Thévenin equivalent circuits are used to represent outputs of preceding module (shown as detector-transducer) and the amplifier. The input and output impedances of the amplifier, Z_i and Z_o, may be determined by first disconnecting the other modules and then applying varying values of V_i and V_{rev} to input and output while measuring currents and voltages required by the following expressions: $Z_i = (\partial V_i/\partial I_i)V_{rev}$ and $Z_o = (\partial V_{rev}/\partial I_o)V_i$. (For a definition of V_{rev}, see reference 4 or 8.)

How can amplifier input and output impedances Z_i and Z_o be found? A method is suggested in the legend for the figure. Once these impedances are known, amplifier input and output voltages can be calculated. Note that only part of the detector output voltage V_s can appear across the amplifier input; part is "lost" across Z_s, which comprises the rest of a voltage divider, $Z_s + Z_i$. The amplifier input must be simply $V_s Z_i/(Z_s + Z_i)$.

Whether an amplifier should be designed to have a high input impedance or a low one will depend on the type of transfer of greatest importance, power transfer, voltage transfer, or current transfer. The conditions for optimizing each will now be examined. In practice, one may have to "trade off" or sacrifice part of transfer to secure another desired result.

1. Maximum power will be transferred when Z_s and Z_i are matched (Section 3.8). This condition will be sought in general when a powerful signal is involved. A good example is the need to transfer as much power as possible from a stereo tuner to a pair of speakers.

2. Maximum voltage transfer will occur when Z_i is made as large as feasible. This condition prevails if the output from the preceding stage is to be furnished as a voltage, and a minimum of current (or power) is to be transferred. A representative application would be the transfer of a thermocouple emf to an amplifier.

3. Maximum current transfer calls for Z_i to be as small as possible. For example, this condition should be met in coupling a current source like a photoconductive detector to an amplifier.

All these considerations also apply to the relationship between the output of an amplifier and the module that follows it. Even more important, they are useful in describing the transfer between stages of an amplifier (as will be seen in Section 6.1).

It is obvious the diagram in Fig. 5.2 gives no clue about the transfer operation, i.e., the amplification achieved by the amplifier. In part the omission is deliberate, for the subject is complex enough for this chapter and the following one to be devoted to it. It is also true no detail is required to define amplifier gain. It is only necessary to measure the currents and voltages designated in Fig. 5.2. Then a current gain A_I, a voltage gain A_V, and a power gain A_P can de defined. They are expressed as follows:

$$A_I = \frac{I_L}{I_i}; \ A_V = \frac{V_L}{V_i}; \ A_P = \frac{I_L V_L}{I_i V_i}. \tag{5.1}$$

These gains are closed-circuit magnitudes that are valid when load L is imposed.*

Open-circuit or no-load values of gain may also be given. For example, the open-circuit voltage gain A_V' for the module in Fig. 5.2 is just $A_V' = V_o/V_i$, where V_o is the output voltage when the load is disconnected.

5.2 BASIC AMPLIFIER CONFIGURATIONS

The properties and behavior of an amplifier are essentially determined by the configuration used for each active component, e.g., a transistor. In the majority of cases each semiconductor device and associated circuitry will comprise a stage of an amplifier. This chapter will deal with the design and behavior of individual stages. As noted in Section 4.6, transistor configurations are classified by the lead that is common to input and output circuits or is at signal ground. The three basic design patterns are pictured in simplified form in Fig. 5.3. It is striking that they differ only slightly.

Which transistor lead is at signal or ac ground in each case? In Fig. 5.3 it is clear that in the common-emitter amplifier as drawn the emitter is at both dc and ac ground. There is also no question that the base is grounded in the common-base design. In the common-collector design, however, the collector is at a negative dc potential but is at ac ground (connected through the dc voltage source).

---

* Closed-circuit values are especially useful for most transistor amplifiers and stages of such amplifiers. Each stage "loads" other stages.

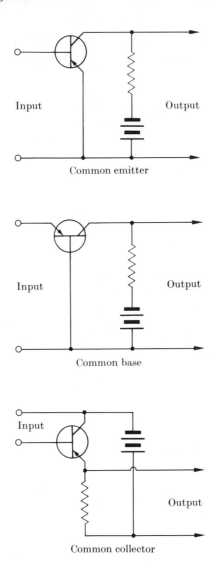

Fig. 5.3 Basic transistor configurations.

In the circuits of Fig. 5.3 a resistance represents the passive component across which an output voltage appears. Often the output voltage (dc or ac) is in series with a fixed dc supply voltage. Actual electrode biasing arrangements and other resistors or capacitors in the amplifier circuit have been omitted.

Different configurations yield surprisingly different performances, as may be seen from the data listed in Table 5.1. Stages built along the lines of these basic designs can be combined in many ways to make a multistage amplifier. If advantage is taken of differences that can be obtained by varying configuration as well as differences realizable through use of many types of transistors, amplifiers can be constructed to meet a wide variety of needs.

Table 5.1 Characteristics of Basic Transistor Amplifier Configurations*

Configuration†	Impedance		Open-circuit gain		
	Z_i	Z_o	A_V	A_I	A_P
Common-emitter	Moderate	Moderate	High	High	High
	1.5 kΩ	50 kΩ	−200	+35	40 dB
Common-collector	High	Low	~1	High	Low
(emitter-follower)	350 kΩ	450 Ω		−35	15 dB
Common-base	Low	High	High	~1	Moderate
	35 Ω	1 MΩ	300		25 dB

* Based on data of J. Watson. [9]

†Occasionally the term "grounded" is substituted for "common," as in grounded-emitter, grounded-base.

5.3 COMMON-EMITTER AMPLIFIER

The most widely used transistor configuration by far is the common-emitter (*CE*) design. Its attractiveness as an amplifier stage lies in its combination of high gain and moderate impedances (Table 5.1). As shown in Fig. 5.3, the design calls for the input signal to be applied at the base (in series with a base-emitter bias voltage that is not shown). The output is taken from the collector circuit. Note that the output is the sum of collector supply voltage V_{CC} and the voltage drop across a resistor. A single *CE* stage like this is basically a building block; it will ordinarily be found in series with other stages.

How are suitable bias voltages provided for the electrodes of a transistor in an amplifier stage? When should passive components such as capacitors be introduced

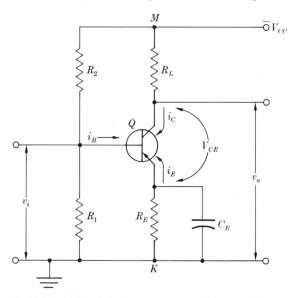

Fig. 5.4 A well-stablized ac common-emitter amplifier.

to make the stage functional? A good way to seek answers is by study of a well-designed stage. It is instructive to go through the process of selecting resistors and capacitors to build it and for the purpose the representative audiofrequency common-emitter amplifier circuit of Fig. 5.4 will be used. A simple procedure that involves transistor specifications, general principles relating to transistor operation, and Ohm's law will be followed.

Consider that a 2N2614 transistor, a high-quality germanium p-n-p type, is to be used in the amplifier.* The specifications listed by the manufacturer are given in Appendix A. The maximum operating values are of major interest since the circuit should be set up so that they cannot under any conceivable circumstances be exceeded. The rated maximum value for collector-emitter voltage V_{CE} is -35 V† and that for collector current I_C is -50 mA. These data permit trial values of collector supply voltage V_{CC} and collector current to be picked. A generous safety margin is desirable for a long life; therefore, let V_{CC} be -15 V (a voltage available from many dc power supplies) and let an average value for I_C be -5 mA.

Before proceeding further, it is important to select a suitable operating point for the transistor. By definition, the *operating point* is the set of static or average values of transistor currents and voltages that result from biases alone. The concept will be discussed below. To choose the operating value of V_{CE}, the criterion of the *half supply voltage principle* will be used. Basically, the principle states that thermal runaway, i.e. destruction because of failure to control thermal effects, of a transistor is unlikely as long as (a) there is resistance in both its collector and emitter circuits and (b) the average voltage drop across the transistor is less than half the supply voltage (in this case -15 V). This gives an upper bound of -7.5 V for V_{CE}. A lower bound is set by the I_C against V_{CE} curve, since it indicates the active region ends at about -0.5 V. A good choice for V_{CE} is -6 V.

These data provide a place to begin with the circuit of Fig. 5.4, which represents an ac common-emitter amplifier. Values of components will be worked out initially for the branch that extends from point M, which is at voltage V_{CC} (-15 V) through R_L, transistor Q, and R_E to point K, which is at ground potential. The 15 V potential difference is concentrated in the voltage drops, $I_C R_L$, V_{CE}, and $I_E R_E$.

Ohm's law can be applied to define R_L and R_E. From Eq. (4.2), $-I_C = I_E$ to a first approximation. With $V_{CE} = -6$ V, there must be a 9 V drop in $R_L + R_E$. From Ohm's law, $R_L + R_E = 9 \div 5 \times 10^{-3} = 1.8$ kΩ.

How should 1.8 kΩ be divided between R_L and R_E? The matter can be resolved by recognizing the need to secure as high an output voltage (or power) from the amplifier as possible. Only the voltage drop in R_L is going to appear in the output since the emitter is at ac ground (ac bypasses R_E). Observe from Fig. 5.4 that $V_o = V_{CC} - I_C R_L$. Accordingly, R_L should have as large a fraction of the 1.8 kΩ as possible. On the other hand, R_E cannot be made too small without losing the protection against

---

* In general, the desired power level, amplification, operating currents and voltages, frequency range, and noise figure will be the basis for choosing a transistor. A study of manufacturer's specifications for transistors should allow a choice of one or more appropriate devices.
† Measured with a 10 kΩ resistor between base and emitter.

thermal runaway that an emitter resistor provides. Arbitrarily, let $R_L = 1.2$ kΩ and $R_E = 600$ Ω.

Before other components of the circuit can be selected rationally, the average (quiescent) value of transistor base current I_B must be identified. Its value can be found by a general graphical procedure, the load line method.

Load lines. A load line is a plot of values of output current *vs* output voltage when a given load is inserted in the type of circuit of interest. The idea will be developed in general terms in order not to restrict conclusions to the present case.

Consider the amplifier circuit of Fig. 5.5a that shows only the output circuit with any detail. In Fig. 5.5b a generalized family of output characteristics for the transistor is plotted. To determine the effect of load R_L on these parameters note that output values of the circuit obey the equation

$$I_o = \frac{V_{\text{supply}} - V_o}{R_L}. \tag{5.2}$$

This expression defines the dc or *static load line* of the circuit and is shown in Fig. 5.5b. Observe that it has an intercept on the V_o axis of V_{supply}. When the load is resistive and ohmic in behavior, as in this case, the load line is linear as shown. If an output circuit offers an ac impedance significantly different from its dc resistance, a dynamic load line should also be plotted. The importance of the load line is that every point along it which is within the active region of the transistor represents a possible *operating point* for the amplifier. A value toward the center of the line is preferable for the operating point so that the output voltage V_o can "swing" with maximum amplitude on either side of it.

We can now determine a dc load line for the present case. Recall that the output characteristics for a *CE* amplifier (Fig. 4.11a) are plots of I_C against V_{CE} with I_B as a variable, *not* of I_C against V_o, as shown in Fig. 5.5. Further, emitter resistor R_E must

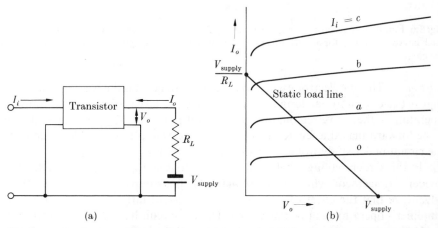

Fig. 5.5 Generalized representation of a transistor circuit. (a) Circuit without bias arrangements but with simple load, resistance R_L. (b) Graphical representation of transistor behavior. The static load line for the circuit is superposed on a family of output characteristics (current–voltage curves).

be included in the analysis since V_{CE} is affected by dc drops in both R_L and R_E. The dc load line is defined by the equation

$$V_{CE} = V_{CC} - I_C(R_L + R_E) \tag{5.3}$$

using the approximation $-I_C = I_E$ made earlier. Since load line Eq. (5.3) represents a straight line, it may be graphed by solving for intercepts. The intercept on the voltage axis corresponds to $V_{CE} = V_{CC} = -15$ V. The other intercept corresponds to

$$I_C = V_{CC}/(R_L + R_E) = -15/1800 = -8.3 \text{ mA}.$$

Use of the intercepts locates the dc load line in Fig. 5.6.* From Fig. 5.6, the value of I_B corresponding to the operating point is about -0.04 mA.

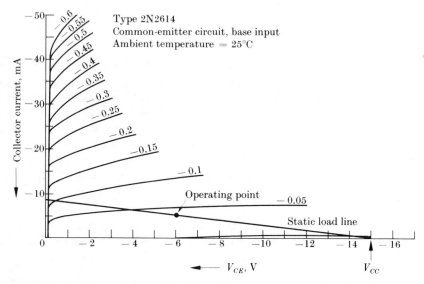

Fig. 5.6 Family of collector characteristics for a 2N2614 transistor with dc load line superposed. Each curve is graphed for a constant-base current. The base current (in mA) is given at the end of the curve.

Base bias. The one electrode whose bias remains to be set is the base. It is not essential that it be set exactly; as long as V_{CE} is sufficiently large to ensure the transistor is operating in the active region, the base-emitter potential, V_{BE}, automatically adjusts to be forward-biased a few tenths of a volt. For example, a suitable value of V_B for the circuit under study would be $V_B = I_E R_E - 0.6$ V $= -3.6$ V.

In this circuit, voltage divider $R_2 + R_1$ (between V_{CC} and ground) fixes V_B. The divider arrangement, which is one of many methods of base biasing, [4, 9] offers the advantage that the effect of changes in base current (arising from heating) on the amplifier's operation can be minimized. The CE circuit has been redrawn in Fig. 5.7 to show currents in R_2 and R_1. The current in R_2 is $I + I_B$, while that in R_1 is only

---

* The situation corresponding to the current intercept cannot actually be attained. According to Fig. 5.6, the transistor will saturate whenever V_{CE} becomes smaller than about -0.5 V.

I. If values of R_1 and R_2 make $I \gg I_B$, changes in I_B will have little effect on the bias V_B. By divorcing the bias from dependence on a particular transistor at a particular temperature, protection is provided against change in performance on substitution of new transistors of the same type or with temperature fluctuations. If I is set at 0.3 mA, a value six times I_B, even if I_B increases by 10 % for any reason, the current in R_2 increases relative to that in R_1 by less than 2.0 %. Thus, V_B remains essentially constant. Still larger values of I can be used as long as power dissipation in the resistors is tolerable. Suitable values for R_1 and R_2 are 12 kΩ and 33 kΩ, respectively.

Example   Determine values for R_1 and R_2 in Fig. 5.6. The value of R_1 must set potential V_B at a value slightly more negative (say -3.6 V) than V_E, which has a value of -3 V. This value must correspond to the voltage drop IR_1. Let $I = 3 \times 10^{-4}$ A (see above); then

$$R_1 = 3.6 \text{ V} \div 3 \times 10^{-4} \text{ A} = 12 \text{ k}\Omega.$$

Resistor R_2 must be substantially larger. Here

$$(I + I_B)R_2 = V_{CC} - IR_1 = -15 \text{ V} + 3.6 \text{ V} = -11.4 \text{ V}.$$

Substituting values of the currents and solving for R_2 gives

$$R_2 = 11.4 \text{ V} \div 3.4 \times 10^{-4} \text{ A} = 33 \text{ k}\Omega.$$

Capacitor C_E must still be specified. It provides an ac path from emitter to ground and ensures a steady emitter bias V_E relative to ground. Without the bypass capacitor the voltage drop $I_E R_E$ will cause a fluctuation in V_E that largely offsets the effects of an input signal, as will be discussed in Section 5.5. A 100 μF ceramic capacitor is a reasonable choice for C_E. Its adequacy in bypassing ac is the subject for Exercise 5.6.

Figure 5.7 also specifies 4 μF input and output capacitors. They are valuable in coupling stages since they pass ac but block the dc necessary to biasing. Coupling will be examined in Section 6.1.

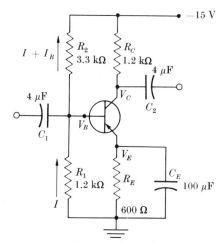

Fig. 5.7 A well-stabilized common-emitter amplifier showing currents in voltage divider $R_2 + R_1$. Input and output capacitors have been added also.

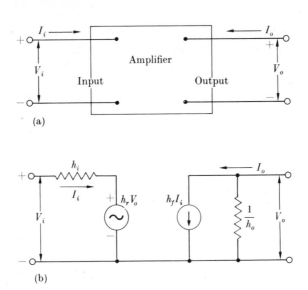

Fig. 5.8 The hybrid model of a transistor used as amplifier. (a) External connections and voltages. (b) Hybrid equivalent circuit or model for a transistor in any configuration. The model differs from one configuration to another only in the changing values of h-parameters. A second subscript is added to each h-parameter to designate the particular configuration, for example, h_i becomes h_{ie} for the common-emitter mode. Other resistors and capacitors actually used in a circuit must be added.

5.4 MODEL FOR A TRANSISTOR AMPLIFIER

A straightforward way to predict the performance of an amplifier stage is much needed. Presumably, the prediction would take into account the circuit design or configuration, small-signal parameters such as α and β that characterize its transistor(s), and the values of passive components that complete the circuit. The hybrid or h-parameter equivalent circuit discussed in Section 4.6 permits such predictions.* The basic model and the equivalent circuit it leads to for a transistor amplifier (regardless of configuration) are presented in Fig. 5.8.

In developing an equivalent circuit of a transistor, all parameters that appear in descriptive equations such as Eqs. (4.5) and (4.6) must be represented. For this reason the equivalent circuit in Fig. 5.8b shows an *internal voltage source* $h_r V_o$ and an *internal current source* $h_f I_i$. The former reflects the manner in which output voltage V_o tends to leak back or offset the input voltage, and the latter indicates the manner in which the transistor seems to generate the output current.

Characteristics of transistor amplifier stages such as current and voltage gains A_I and A_V defined in Eqs. (5.1) and input and output impedances Z_i and Z_o can be expressed in terms of the circuit of Fig. 5.8b. It can be shown that

---

* Other models are widely used also, especially for design purposes. The hybrid model is employed here because of its simplicity, its reliability at low frequencies, and the ease with which its small-signal parameters can be measured.

$$A_I = I_o/I_i = -h_f/(1 + h_o Z_L)$$
$$A_V = V_o/V_i = A_I Z_L/Z_i$$
$$Z_i = V_i/I_i = h_i + h_r A_I Z_L \tag{5.4}$$
$$Z_o = (h_i + Z_s)/[(h_i + Z_s)h_o - h_f h_r].$$

To use the equations a second letter subscript, e, b, or c, that designates the amplifier configuration is added to the symbols for the h-parameters. For example, for the common-emitter configuration, h_f, h_o, h_i, and h_r become h_{fe}, h_{oe}, h_{ie}, and h_{re}. If their values are known, Eqs. (5.4) can be solved. If only values in another configuration are available, they may be converted to values for the desired configuration by use of tables [6, 7, 9]. CE and common-collector parameters are especially easily interrelated. The following almost exact relations hold:

$$h_{fc} = -(h_{fe} + 1) = -(\beta + 1), \qquad h_{oc} = h_{oe}, \qquad h_{ic} = h_{ie}, \qquad h_{rc} = 1. \tag{5.5}$$

Table 5.2 Representative Values of Transistor Parameters for Single-Stage Amplifiers (at $I_E = 1.3$ mA)

Parameter	Common-emitter	Common-collector	Common-base
h_i	1.1 kΩ	1.1 kΩ	22 Ω
h_f*	50†	−51	−0.98
h_r*	2.5×10^{-4}	1	2.9×10^{-4}
$1/h_o$	40 kΩ	40 kΩ	2 MΩ

* These parameters are pure numbers. See Eqs. (4.5) and (4.6).
† Values as high as 200 are common for some types.

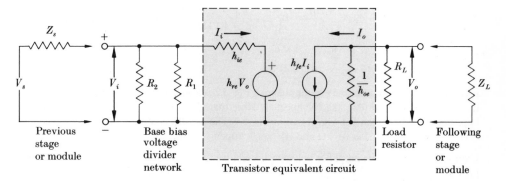

Fig. 5.9 Hybrid-parameter equivalent circuit of the ac common-emitter amplifier of Fig. 5.7. The section in gray is the equivalent circuit of the transistor itself (cf. Fig. 5.8b). The only components of Fig. 5.7 omitted in drawing the equivalent circuit are coupling capacitors C_1 and C_2, by-pass capacitor C_E, and emitter resistor R_E. The reactance of the capacitors is small compared with that of other components and may be neglected. Since C_E by-passes ac around R_E, it may be neglected also. The parallel resistance combination of the voltage divider network $R_1 + R_2$ can usually be neglected also.

Representative values of the parameters are given in Table 5.2. They should be understood as *rough* approximations in so far as a particular transistor is concerned.

How does the hybrid model apply to a particular amplifier? Consider the ac amplifier of Fig. 5.7. The hybrid equivalent circuit for it is shown in Fig. 5.9. First, the equivalent circuit for a transistor given in Fig. 5.8 forms the heart of the amplifier circuit. Next, R_1 and R_2, which establish the bias for the transistor base, appear in parallel at the input. Since the bottom line can be considered the common or ground lead, this representation means the ac input to the amplifier can "leak" to ground through either R_1 or R_2. A reason for choosing large values for R_1 and R_2 aside from minimizing power loss from V_{CC} is now evident. In practice, both resistances are large compared with the resistance equivalent to h_{ie} and most of the ac appears across the base-emitter junction of the transistor as desired. Third, R_L appears in the equivalent circuit shunting $1/h_{oe}$, the "collector" resistance. Since $R_L \ll 1/h_{oe}$, the open-circuit output impedance of the device is determined by R_L. Note that the module across the output, the load, will shunt R_L.

Conspicuous by their absence in the equivalent circuit are C_1, C_2, C_E, and R_E. All would be necessary in a dc equivalent circuit. None are in an ac circuit. The capacitances are chosen to have little reactance for ac of the frequencies being handled, and R_E is effectively bypassed for ac. In other words, the emitter is at ac ground, a necessary characteristic of the common-emitter configuration.

Example 1 Apply Eqs. (5.4) to the common-emitter amplifier of Fig. 5.7 to deduce its voltage gain and input impedance. Consider that a 2N2614 transistor is used in the circuit. For a rough calculation it will be satisfactory to use the approximate transistor specifications of Table 5.2, except for h_{fe}, which is the most crucial parameter. The manufacturers' specifications give for h_{fe} the range 100 to 250; a value of 150 will be used. It will be necessary to calculate A_I also (see equation for A_V). Assume Z_L in the equations is just R_L. The desired values are found to be

$$A_I \simeq -h_{fe} \simeq -150$$

$$A_V = \frac{A_I Z_L}{Z_i} \simeq \frac{h_{fe} R_L}{h_{ie}} = \frac{-150 \times 1.2 \text{ k}\Omega}{1.1 \text{ k}\Omega} \simeq -150$$

$$Z_i \simeq h_{ie} \simeq 1.1 \text{ k}\Omega.$$

The power gain is $A_I \cdot A_V \simeq 2 \times 10^4$ or 43 dB.

Example 2 If the load of the CE amplifier of Fig. 5.7 is a second CE amplifier stage, how will the voltage gain of the first stage be affected? Note that Z_i for such a stage is 1.1 kΩ. Now this impedance will be in parallel with R_L, as in Fig. 5.9. The parallel combination has an impedance of $(1.1 \times 1.2)/(1.1 + 1.2) = 0.6$ kΩ and $A'_V = \frac{1}{2} A_V$ (open-circuit).

Example 3 Assume an amplifier voltage gain relative to signal voltage V_s is desired. How must Eq. (5.4) be modified?

The source impedance must be included in the calculation. Refer to Fig. 5.2. The gain relative to V_s is given by $A''_V = V_o/V_s$. Since $V_i = V_s Z_i/(Z_i + Z_s)$, A''_V is

$$\frac{A_V \times Z_i}{(Z_i + Z_s)} = \frac{A_I Z_L}{(Z_i + Z_s)}.$$

Shunting by $R_1 + R_2$ is still neglected, which is a valid approximation in most cases.

Three further notes are in order. First, any dependence of gain and impedances on frequency has been neglected. Suffice it to say that the coupling capacitors will reduce the gain at quite low frequencies, and capacitances internal to the transistor (interelectrode capacitances) will reduce gain at relatively high frequencies. This subject will be discussed in Section 6.3. Second, the impedance of the load, or next stage, will also shunt the output, as observed in Example 2 above, reducing gain. If desired, shunting can be avoided by use of a transformer *in place of* R_L to couple the circuit to the load (Section 6.2).

A third note has to do with the phase shift produced by a CE amplifier. The output voltage is 180° out of phase with the input signal. A simple analysis suggests this must be true. For example, for the circuit of Fig. 5.7, trace the effect of applying a positive-going signal to the base of the p-n-p transistor. Its effect will be to decrease V_{BE}, force I_C to diminish, and cause the voltage drop $I_C R_L$ to fall. Since $V_o = V_{CC} - I_C R_L$, and V_{CC} is negative, the output voltage becomes *more negative*. Similarly, a negative-going input to the base of the transistor will make V_o more positive. In each case the output signal is shifted 180° in phase relative to the input, i.e., inverted. The matter will be considered further in Section 6.3 since phase shift is somewhat frequency-dependent.

5.5 EMITTER-FOLLOWER

Another widely used basic configuration is the common-collector arrangement or as it is generally known, the emitter-follower. This descriptive name emphasizes the synchronism between the emitter potential (the output) and the input signal. A representative emitter-follower amplifier is shown schematically in Fig. 5.10. Note that

1. The collector is at ac ground (though at a dc potential of V_{CC} volts) since there is no resistor in the collector circuit,
2. The output is taken across emitter resistor R_E, and
3. There is no emitter bypass capacitor.

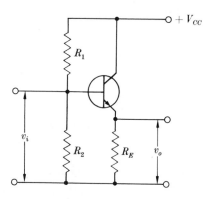

Fig. 5.10 Emitter-follower (or common-collector) transistor amplifier. An *n-p-n* transistor is used.

As reported in Table 5.1, the emitter-follower features the highest input impedance and lowest output impedance of the several amplifier arrangements. These properties are often sufficiently attractive that the characteristic slight attenuation in signal voltage ($A_V \simeq 0.98$) is a small price to pay. There is, of course, still a good current gain in the emitter follower.

What is the mode of operation of the amplifier? Its essentials can be seen by use of the circuit in Fig. 5.10. As a signal makes the base of the n-p-n transistor more positive, emitter current I_E increases. Simultaneously, the emitter itself becomes more positive because of the larger IR drop in resistor R_E. Since the output, v_o, is taken from the "top" of R_E, its polarity has "followed" that of the signal: they are in phase. Clearly, the rise in emitter potential must be slightly less than that in the potential of the base. Otherwise there will be no increase in forward bias V_{BE} to produce the rise in emitter current. Two conclusions follow from this simple analysis.

From what has just been stated, it is evident that the configuration must produce a slight voltage attenuation. Second, since any input signal to the base is largely "offset" by the rise in emitter potential, this configuration can accommodate large amplitude input signals (see below).

Application of Eqs. (5.4) and (5.5) yields Eqs. (5.6) for gains and impedances of an emitter follower stage.

$$Z_i = h_{ic} + A_I R_E \simeq (\beta + 1)R_E$$

$$Z_o = \frac{h_{ic} + Z_s}{(h_{ic} + Z_s)h_{oc} + (\beta + 1)} \simeq \frac{h_{ic} + Z_s}{\beta + 1} \tag{5.6}$$

$$A_I = \frac{-(\beta + 1)}{1 + h_{oe}R_E} \simeq -(\beta + 1)$$

$$A_V = \frac{A_I R_E}{Z_i} \simeq 1.$$

Several points about this set of equations should be noted. First, load impedance Z_L was replaced by R_E. Second, the equation for Z_i is valid if the transistor resistance from base to collector is large. Third, the approximate expressions follow from the exact ones on considering the relative magnitudes of emitter-follower parameters.

Example What values of gain and impedance can be realized for a representative emitter-follower such as that in Fig. 5.10? Assume $R_E = 2k\Omega$, $z_s = 10 \ k\Omega$, and use of a transistor for which $h_{ic} = 1 \ k\Omega$ and $\beta = 50$. From the above equations there results

$$A_I = -51, \qquad A_V \simeq 1,$$

$$Z_i \simeq (\beta + 1)R_E = 51 \times 2 = 102 \ k\Omega,$$

and

$$Z_o \simeq \frac{(h_{ic} + Z_s)}{(\beta + 1)} = \frac{(1000 + 10\,000)}{51} = 200 \ \Omega.$$

It is important to keep in mind that resistors R_1 and R_2 shown in Fig. 5.10 are effectively in parallel with the input impedance of the transistor. If they are smaller than Z_i, which is large for this configuration, they will determine input impedance.

How can this dilemma be resolved? One answer is to use a transistor with as high a maximum voltage rating V_{CE} as possible. The higher this value, the larger V_{CC} can be and therefore the greater the values permitted for R_1 and R_2 if they are to pass a given current (a value large compared with the base current). Maximum V_{CE} ratings at present extend up to 200 V, and input impedances up to 1 MΩ are thereby realizable for an emitter-follower. A disadvantage of the arrangement is the requirement of a high-voltage dc supply. The output impedance of the previous stage, of course, also affects the input impedance and in a multistage device would need to be taken into account.

An alternative means of achieving a high input impedance that requires only a low-voltage dc supply utilizes the principle of *bootstrapping*. A representative circuit based on the idea is shown schematically in Fig. 5.11.

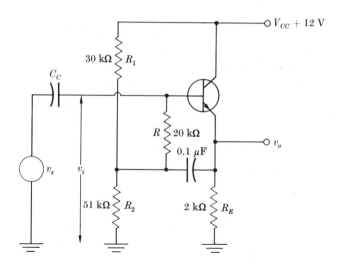

Fig. 5.11 Bootstrap circuit to provide high input impedance for an emitter-follower stage.

In this amplifier R_1 and R_2 are no longer part of the input circuit. The circuit input impedance Z_i is seen to be the parallel combination of impedance Z_R associated with the path containing resistor R and transistor input impedance Z_i. Both impedances will be enhanced by feedback. Impedance Z_R is just v_i/i_R, where i_R is the current in resistor R. Since the voltage drop across R and C is fixed at the value $v_i - v_o$, the current in R is $i_R = (v_i - v_o)/R$.* Further, v_o is just $v_o = Av_i$. Combining this expression with the previous equation for current i_R and the definition $Z_R = v_i/i_R$ gives $Z_R = R/(1 - A)$. Impedance Z_R must be very large since A is almost unity.

---

* This expression neglects the reactance of capacitor C. As long as $X_C \ll R$, the approximation is not serious.

Example What is the input impedance of the emitter-follower of Fig. 5.11? It will be the parallel combination of $R/(1 - A)$ and $Z_i = (\beta + 1)R_E$.

Assume parameters for the transistor are $\beta = 50$ and $h_{ic} = 1$ kΩ. Then $Z_i = 51 \times 2$ k$\Omega = 102$ kΩ (as before). Now

$$A = \frac{1 - h_{ic}}{Z_i} = 1 - 0.01 = 0.99.$$

Accordingly,

$$Z_R = \frac{20 \text{ k}\Omega}{(1 - 0.99)} = 100 \times 20 \text{ k}\Omega = 2 \text{ M}\Omega.$$

It is clear that Z_i will determine the input impedance, since it is much smaller. Note also that increasing R_E by a factor of 5 would raise Z_i to 500 kΩ.

A second problem in an emitter-follower circuit is associated with the use of large input signals. Signals of considerable magnitude can be tolerated (nearly as large as $V_{CC}/2$) since they are almost completely offset by the opposing voltage across R_E. Unfortunately, the output impedance will change substantially as a result of the large change in emitter current. If a large capacitor is used in the output circuit, waveforms are likely to be "clipped." [8]

The property of high input and low output impedance causes emitter-follower circuits to be useful as intermediate stages to

1. Isolate a load from a signal source, as in an oscilloscope, or

2. Match a high-impedance source to a low-impedance load.

In such applications they are often called buffers.

5.6 DIFFERENTIAL AMPLIFIER

The differential or difference amplifier is an important configuration consisting of an emitter-coupled pair of matched transistors or a cathode-coupled pair of matched electron tubes.* In Fig. 5.12 schematic diagrams for representative transistor and tube differential amplifiers are given. Emphasis will be given to the semiconductor type though the analysis can readily be extended to tube versions. [6, 7]

It is the bridgelike character of the differential amplifier that gives the configuration its importance. To emphasize this point, the circuit of Fig. 5.12b has been redrawn as a bridge in Fig. 5.13. Electron tubes form two arms and their load resistors the other two arms. What is the condition of balance of the amplifier bridge? If matched tubes and equal load resistances are used, meter M should show no deflection when the input signals to the grids of the tubes are equal.† Unbalance may be described in

---

* Because of the usefulness of this circuit brief mention will be made of the electron tube version also.

† For a transistor differential amplifier the condition of balance would be use of matched transistors and resistors and appearance of equal signals at the transistor inputs.

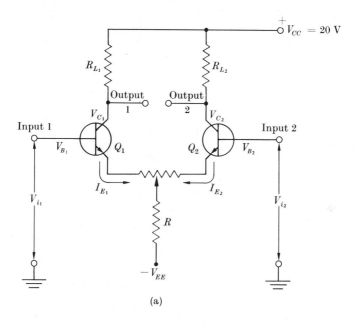

(a)

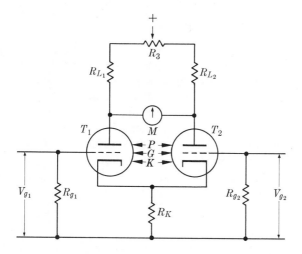

Fig. 5.12 A basic differential amplifier circuit. In (a) two *n-p-n* transistors are used and in (b) two triodes. For best operation R is made as large as possible. An arrangement for biasing the bases or grids is omitted. Tube elements are K = thermionically emitting cathode, G = grid, P = plate or anode.

terms of an equivalent dc offset at the input (Section 7.2) and must be corrected before an amplifier is used. In the circuits of Fig. 5.12, unbalance can be corrected to some degree at least by moving the tap on the variable resistor indicated.

The many uses of a difference amplifier grow out of its distinctive properties.

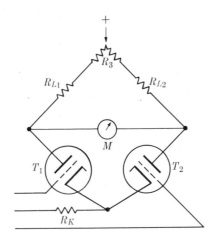

Fig. 5.13 Bridge circuit equivalent of the amplifier circuit of Fig. 5.12b.

For a perfectly balanced circuit, one with identical transistors and passive components:

1. An output is secured that is proportional to the difference between the two inputs;
2. The output drifts very little with temperature changes or with the passage of time;
3. Either a positive-going or negative-going output can be obtained from a positive-going input signal.

When emitters of a pair of transistors are coupled, the devices become strongly interdependent. Indeed, the controlling principle of a differential amplifier is that the current in resistor R be essentially constant. To the degree this condition is met, the current in one transistor can increase only as much as that in the other falls.

In many designs a constant current is achieved by using as large a value for R as is feasible. Since an appreciable voltage drop results, the lower end of resistor R is usually not grounded, but connected instead to a supply voltage opposite in polarity to V_{CC} (see Fig. 5.12a). In integrated-circuit versions of a differential amplifier, however, a constant current source is substituted for R (Section 6.1).

Example In the circuit of Fig. 5.12a consider $I_{E_1} + I_{E_2} = 1$ mA, $R_L = 10$ kΩ, $R = 10$ kΩ, and $V_{CC} = +20$ V. What should the value of V_{EE} be? The voltage drop across R is 1 mA × 10 kΩ = 10 V. A reasonable choice of V_{EE} is −10 V.

What response does a differential amplifier make to a signal? Consider the circuit of Fig. 5.12a. Assume the base of Q_2 is at $+1$ V. If a positive-going signal is applied to the base of its twin, Q_1, the forward bias V_{BE} of Q_1 will increase, and its emitter and collector currents will increase. Since the sum $I_{E_1} + I_{E_2}$ is nearly constant, the emitter and collector currents in Q_2 must decrease by an equal amount. If $R_{L_1} = R_{L_2}$, the voltage drop across R_{L_2} will decrease. Thus, V_{o_1} will ideally become more negative by the same amount that V_{o_2} becomes more positive. This situation is described by stating that the outputs at V_{o_1} and V_{o_2} are *balanced* with respect to each other.

Before considering expressions for gain and impedance for the differential amplifier, account needs to be taken of two very different modes of use. In most of the circuit configurations discussed earlier, transistors were operated linearly, i.e., biased to function in their active regions (Section 4.6). The differential configuration is also employed principally in this way. Sometimes, however, it is used as a comparator or voltage level indicator (or as the input stage of a comparator), an application in which only a yes-no answer is sought. Such an application depends on the switching properties of transistors, as will be discussed in Chapter 9.

The behavior of a differential configuration as a comparator is illustrated in Table 5.3. The table presents rough data for a circuit like Fig. 5.12a, in which $V_{CC} = 20$ V. A dc signal, 1 V, is applied to be base of transistor Q_2 and voltages from 0 to 2 V are applied to the base of Q_1. The differential output ($V_{C_1} - V_{C_2}$) has an initial value of $+11$ V, falls to zero when the signals applied to the bases are equal, and attains a final value of -11 V. Rather abruptly (the data in the table are too coarse to specify exactly) the comparator output changes sign when V_{B_1} goes from less than 1 V to more than 1 V.

Table 5.3 Signal and Output Voltages of a Differential Amplifier Used as a Voltage Level Detector

V_{B_1}	V_{B_2}	V_{C_1}	V_{C_2}	$V_o = V_{C_1} - V_{C_2}$
0.0	$+1.0$	$+20$	$+9$	$+11$
0.5	$+1.0$	$+20$	$+9$	$+11$
1.0	$+1.0$	$+15$	$+15$	0
1.5	$+1.0$	$+9$	$+20$	-11
2.0	$+1.0$	$+8$	$+20$	-12

When used as a comparator, the differential configuration offers mainly its limiting values. Much smaller differences in signal must be used at the inputs it is to amplify. These matters will be further discussed in connection with operation amplifiers with differential inputs in Section 7.3.

With the differential configuration an input may be made to one base or to both and an output may be taken from one collector only or from both. It can be shown that the output voltage at V_{o_1} is given by

$$V_{o_1} = \frac{\beta R_L}{2(h_{ie} + R_s)} (V_{i_2} - V_{i_1}), \tag{5.7}$$

where R_s is the (Thévenin) resistance assumed connected in series with the signal at each input. Note that this output is taken relative to ground. Similarly, the output at the collector of Q_2 is

$$V_{o_2} = \frac{\beta R_L}{2(h_{ie} + R_s)} (V_{i_1} - V_{i_2}). \tag{5.8}$$

Finally,

$$V_{o_1} - V_{o_2} = \frac{\beta R_L}{(h_{ie} + R_s)} \Delta V_i. \tag{5.9}$$

Note that resistance R, which is common to both emitter circuits, fails to appear in these expressions: since it behaves as a constant current source, it has essentially a constant voltage drop across it.

Voltage gains can be calculated as follows. For a *single-ended output*, e.g., from the collector of Q_1,

$$A_{V\text{single}} = \frac{V_{o_1}}{V_{i_1} - V_{i_2}} = \frac{\beta R_L}{2(R_s + h_{ie})}. \tag{5.10}$$

For a *differential output*, i.e., one taken between V_{o_1} and V_{o_2}, the gain is doubled:

$$A_V = \frac{V_{o_1} - V_{o_2}}{V_{i_1} - V_{i_2}} = \frac{\beta R_L}{R_s + h_{ie}}. \tag{5.11}$$

For a *triode difference amplifier* such as the one sketched in Fig. 5.12b quite similar equations are obtained for voltage gain. For a differential output the defining expression is

$$A_V = -\frac{\mu R_L}{R_L + r_p} \tag{5.12}$$

where μ and r_p are tube parameters termed the amplification factor and plate resistance, respectively. For a single-ended output the voltage gain is half that in Eq. (5.12). In this case no source resistance is assumed.

In the paragraphs that follow several types of applications of difference amplifiers will be described. For further information Sections 7.2 and 7.3 and the references at the end of the chapter should be consulted.

Example 1 A representative triode dc difference amplifier is used in the Bausch and Lomb Spectronic 20 Spectrophotometer. The optical features of this instrument will be shown in Fig. 17.6. It uses the difference amplifier shown schematically in Fig. 5.12b to amplify the output of its photocell. The values of the various parameters of the circuit are the following: R_{g_1} and $R_{g_2} =$ 10 MΩ; $R_K = 1000\ \Omega$; $R_{L_1} = R_{L_2} = 0.1$ MΩ. A twin triode with a μ of 70 and r_p of $6 \times 10^4\ \Omega$ (the values are identical for the two triodes) is used. The grid of tube T_1 is attached directly to the cathode of the photocell detector.

In operation, light striking the photocathode will cause the ejection of electrons. A corresponding number will be drawn from the grid of tube T_1, making it more positive and increasing the output voltage of the tube. The meter indication will be directly proportional to the intensity of the signal on grid 1 and thus to the light incident on the phototube.

From Eq. (5.12) it appears that the gain of this amplifier is approximately half the amplification factor. It should be remembered, however, that the small current from the phototube has already been "amplified" considerably by impressing it across a 10 MΩ resistor. For example, if 10^{-10} A flows through the resistor, a grid signal of 1 mV is available for amplification. The actual amplification (current driving the meter M versus the current i_{g_1}) is probably of the order of 10^4 to 10^5.

The initial balance of dark currents (the current in each plate circuit when no light falls on the phototube) is obtained by varying the position of the tap on resistor R_3 (50 kΩ), which alters the relative value of the voltage furnished to the two plates from the power supply. Though not shown, further stabilization against the effect of transients is provided in the Spectronic 20 amplifier by placing a low capacitance 500 pF directly across each grid. A regulated version of the Spectronic 20 is also available in which a second phototube–differential amplifier unit monitors the source and feeds back correction signals.

Example 2 Voltage measurements between two points in a high-frequency or high-impedance circuit are conveniently made with a difference amplifier. Use of a regular amplifier is rarely feasible since one side of its circuit is ordinarily grounded to the chassis. (If a regular amplifier is used without such grounding, the whole circuit will "float" in terms of voltage, and unnecessary leakage paths to ground may be introduced.) On the other hand, a difference amplifier can easily "handle" a potential difference in a high-voltage or high-frequency circuit since the only paths to ground in this case are through large resistances.

Example 3 In an oscilloscope a difference amplifier ordinarily provides the means of centering a display on the screen. A dc centering voltage is applied to one input of the "vertical" amplifier and the signal to be displayed to the other. The effect is analogous to that observable in Table 5.3 where only the small portion of the signal to Q_1 centered around 1 V, which may be considered the centering voltage applied to the input to transistor Q_2, would have been displayed. If a different centering voltage is applied, the pattern displayed by the oscilloscope shifts up or down. Usually the last stage or two of amplification for both vertical and horizontal sets of plates of an oscilloscope is a difference amplifier.

Example 4 A difference amplifier can function as a *phase splitter*. To achieve high power gain with minimum distortion in an ac amplifier, pairs of transistors are often operated push-pull (Section 6.2). To drive such a pair, an input signal must be split into two portions identical except for being 180° out of phase. The outputs of a difference amplifier furnish two such signals, one positive-going and the other negative-going. The term phase inverter is also applied to this type of circuit.

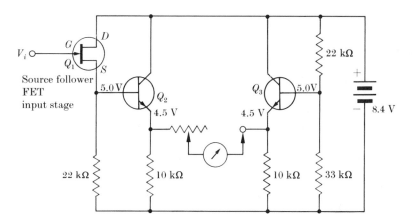

Fig. 5.14 Simplified schematic of Heathkit Solid State Volt-Ohm Meter IM-17. A high-input impedance (11 MΩ) is secured by use of an FET in a source-follower configuration. Note the voltage divider biasing of the base of Q_3. A comparable dc biasing of the base of Q_2 must be secured by the series combination of Q_1 and the 22 kΩ resistor. (Courtesy of Heath Co.)

Emitter-follower difference amplifier. Still greater stability·can be secured from an emitter- or cathode-follower [2] type of difference amplifier. In this case collector circuits are coupled. A representative circuit of this type used in a solid-state volt-ohmmeter is shown in Fig. 5.14. An ordinary moving-coil meter is connected across the output, which is taken between the separate emitter circuits. One input of the differential pair (the base of Q_3) is at 5 V, the dc bias established; the other input (the base of Q_2) is biased at 5 V but also receives the voltage to be measured, after any desired attenuation (network not shown) and amplification by FET Q_1. Note that a high input impedance is ensured by the use of the FET.

Common-mode rejection ratio. According to the equations defining the gain of a difference amplifier, when an identical signal is applied to both inputs, the output signal should be zero. Because of slight mismatching of components, this is never exactly true. While an output is mainly the amplified difference signal, $(V_{i_1} - V_{i_2})$, to the degree that mismatching has occurred, there will also be a small component originating from any identical part of the input signal. This fraction is termed a *common-mode signal* and is defined as $(V_{i_1} + V_{i_2})/2$.

The differential output is thus expressible as $V_{o_1} - V_{o_2} = A_d v_d + A_c v_c$ where A_d is the gain for the difference signal and A_c that for the common-mode signal. The common-mode rejection ratio (CMRR) of an amplifier is defined as CMRR $= A_d/A_c$. For a high-quality difference amplifier values of the CMRR usually are of the order of 10^4.

How may the rejection of common-mode signals be improved? One important way is by improving matching. Most circuits of this type are made by integrated circuit techniques to ensure as nearly identical characteristics of the pair of transistors, resistors, and the rest of the circuit as possible. Another is to ensure a constant total emitter current. Doing so by increasing the shared emitter resistor indefinitely is impractical. In general, it is more attractive to substitute a constant current source. An integrated circuit version of a differential amplifier, so stabilized, will be shown in Fig. 6.1. It is worth noting that this procedure also provides a way to stabilize the circuit against the effect of temperature changes.

5.7 DARLINGTON CONFIGURATION AMPLIFIER

The Darlington configuration also features a pair of transistors coupled in such a way that they behave as a super emitter-follower. The circuit is especially useful where large, regulated currents are needed. As shown in Fig. 5.15, one emitter-follower stage (based on transistor Q_2) becomes the emitter load or emitter impedance of transistor Q_1. This cascading effect is accomplished by the direct connection of the emitter of transistor Q_1 to the base of Q_2. A demanding requirement of the configuration is now evident. Since the emitter current of Q_1 flows through the base of Q_2, the latter must have considerable current-carrying capacity. Actually, it is advantageous to have a matched transistor pair that meets this specification.

In Fig. 5.15 the current at various points is shown. The formulas can be deduced by working back from the emitter current of transistor Q_2. For example, the collector current of Q_2 is $\alpha_2 i_E$ and the base current $(1 - \alpha_2)i_E$. Across the pair of transistors the current gain (as seen from the base of Q_1) is

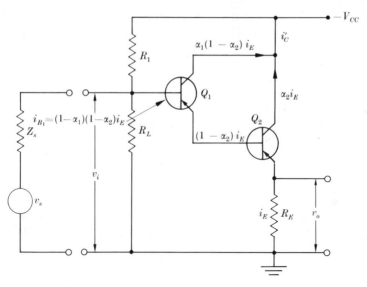

Fig. 5.15 Darlington configuration amplifier. The interrelation of currents is shown.

$$A_I = i_C'/i_{B_1} = \frac{\alpha_1(1 - \alpha_2)i_E + \alpha_2 i_E}{(1 - \alpha_1)(1 - \alpha_2)i_E} \approx \beta_1\beta_2. \tag{5.13}$$

This is just the product of the current gain of two emitter-followers. As a cascaded pair of emitter-followers, the voltage gain is predictably just $\alpha_1\alpha_2$, nearly unity. For example, for a transistor whose $\beta = 50$ ($\alpha = 0.98$), the current gain is about 2500, the voltage gain about 0.96. It should also be noted that the configuration has a very low output impedance.

In Darlington amplifiers, especially if more than two transistors are cascaded, adequate care must be taken to minimize the cumulative effect of leakage current and drift. For example, drift in the output voltage produced by changes in V_{BE} with temperature is multiplied by the number of transistors in the configuration. Therefore

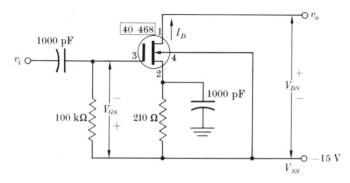

Fig. 5.16 A very-high-frequency (100 MHz) amplifier based on an *n*-channel depletion type of MOS (metal-oxide semiconductor) transistor. Electrodes are (1) drain, (2) source, (3) insulated gate (insulated by a silicon dioxide layer from the bulk of the transistor), (4) bulk (substrate).

it is important that (a) at least the first transistor in a Darlington series have low-leakage current, e.g., be a silicon device, and (b) temperature stability be ensured, preferably by the use of an emitter resistor for the first transistor.

5.8 COMMON-SOURCE FET AMPLIFIER

The special features of field-effect transistors (FETs) are used to advantage in a number of types of amplifiers. In Fig. 5.16 a very-high-frequency amplifier that operates efficiently at 100 MHz and might be useful in telemetry or FM amplification is shown in a common-source configuration. In the circuit the bias for the gate V_{GS} is fixed by use of a 210 Ω source resistor. The operating point is established in a linear portion of the drain current characteristic at $V_{GS} = -1$ V and $I_D = 5$ mA. The input impedance is the gate-to-source resistance of 4.5 kΩ shunted by 5.5 pF interelectrode capacitance (about 300 Ω reactance at 100 MHz). A power gain of 14–20 dB is realized. The output impedance is 4.2 kΩ shunted by 1.4 pF (about 1 kΩ reactance at 100 MHz).

REFERENCES

An introduction to amplifiers and electronics is provided by:

1. John D. Ryder, *Electronic Engineering Principles*. 3d ed. Englewood Cliffs: Prentice-Hall, 1961

Well-written volumes on an intermediate level that emphasize circuitry of interest in instrumentation are:

2. J. J. Brophy, *Basic Electronics for Scientists*. New York: McGraw-Hill, 1966
3. H. V. Malmstadt, C. G. Enke, and E. C. Toren, *Electronics for Scientists*. New York: Benjamin, 1962
4. Leon F. Phillips, *Electronics for Experimenters*. New York: Wiley, 1966

Clear discussions of semiconductor electronics on an intermediate level are available in:

5. James F. Gibbons, *Semiconductor Electronics*. New York: McGraw-Hill, 1967
6. J. Millman and C. C. Halkias, *Electronic Devices and Circuits*. New York: McGraw-Hill, 1967
7. H. J. Reich, J. G. Skalnik, and H. L. Krauss, *Theory and Applications of Active Devices*. Princeton: Van Nostrand, 1966

Well-written volumes on an intermediate level that emphasize circuit design are:

8. David J. Comer, *Introduction to Semiconductor Circuit Design*. Reading, Mass.: Addison-Wesley, 1968
9. J. Watson, *Semiconductor Circuit Design*. Princeton: Van Nostrand, 1966

EXERCISES

5.1 How well does the model shown in Fig. 4.1 fit a transistor amplifier like the one pictured in Fig. 5.4?

5.2 Show how the hybrid model of Fig. 5.8 can be developed from Eqs. (4.5) and (4.6).

5.3 Describe the manner in which a common-emitter amplifier based on an *n-p-n* transistor introduces a 180° phase shift in the output relative to its input.

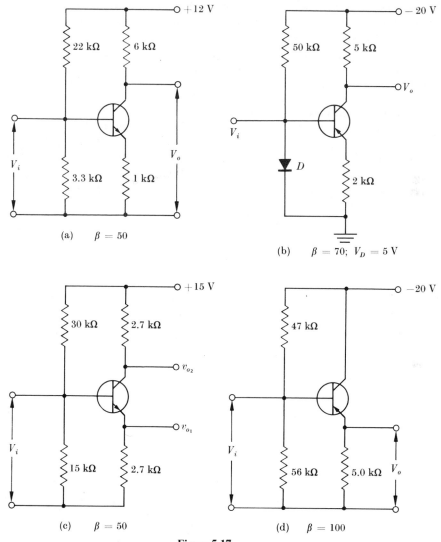

Figure 5.17

5.4 Determine as much as possible about the operating points of the transistors in the linear circuits drawn in Fig. 5.17. In each case identify the transistor configuration or type of circuit. (*Hint*: Begin by considering voltage drops in the divider circuit related to the base bias.)

5.5 Assume that a 2N2953 transistor is to be used in the one-stage common-emitter amplifier of Fig. 5.4. Using transistor specifications given in Appendix B, set a reasonably conservative operating point for the transistor and calculate an appropriate resistance, power dissipation, and tolerance for each resistor and capacitor. Write the load line equation for this circuit.

5.6 In the *CE* amplifier of Fig. 5.7, by-pass capacitor C_E is intended to shunt ac around R_E. Consider that the circuit is to amplify signals in the 100 to 10,000 Hz range. What fraction of the ac component of emitter current exists in the path including R_E at 10,000 Hz? at 100 Hz?

[*Ans.*: About 0.01%; less than 3%.]

5.7 Consider an amplifier whose input signal comes from a source that furnishes 0.50 mV ac in series with 300 Ω. The following characteristics are known for the amplifier: $R_i = 1.50$ kΩ, $R_o = 2.5$ kΩ, open-circuit output voltage, 42 mV.

a) What is the open-circuit voltage gain relative to the source? relative to the amplifier input voltage?

b) A 2.5 kΩ load is attached. What is the voltage supplied to the load? What is the voltage gain relative to the source now?

c) What is the current gain with load attached?

d) With load connected, what is the power gain in decibels relative to the source?

[*Ans.*: a) 84, 100; b) 21 mV, 42; c) 30.]

5.8 Why is a differential amplifier relatively unaffected by temperature changes?

5.9 On the basis of the bridge analogy, what role does an input signal play in the differential amplifier?

Chapter 6

MULTISTAGE AMPLIFIERS

6.1 COUPLING OF STAGES

To achieve substantial gain several stages of amplification must invariably be coupled or cascaded. How is efficient coupling arranged? When the subject was considered in Section 5.1, only the possibility of a *direct* connection of modules was discussed. Since voltages and impedances at the inputs and outputs of amplifier stages may be very different, it is important that other types of coupling be available also. Ideally, a coupling "circuit" must

1. Secure optimum transfer of voltage and/or power;
2. Introduce little distortion in signal;
3. Allow dc voltages to be different at the points coupled.

To some degree these requirements are mutually exclusive, and practical coupling circuits usually optimize performance with respect to no more than two of them. In the following discussion these criteria will be applied to three widely used types of coupling, *direct, transformer,* and *resistance-capacitance coupling.*

Direct coupling. This has two outstanding advantages, simplicity and freedom from signal distortion. It involves only a connection; it requires no passive components, e.g., capacitors. Accordingly, it transmits all frequencies without attenuation. Its limitations are serious also: It fails to block dc (thus dc potentials at output and input must be equal) and it can do nothing to facilitate voltage or power transfer. An additional disadvantage of direct coupling is that drift in one stage is passed on to the next and amplified by it.

Example When common-emitter stages based on *p-n-p* transistors are operated in a conventional way, the collector of the first transistor may be at -10 V, while the base of the next is at -3 V. (See Fig. 6.2.) Clearly, the stages can be coupled directly only if the base of the second stage can operate at -10 V. While dc biases can be altered to effect the necessary changes in the second stage, its collector might well have to operate at -17 V. To avoid this kind of steady rise in bias from one stage to the next, a different design must be worked out.

In spite of its disadvantages direct coupling is nearly always used in integrated circuits. Actually, some redesigning of circuits is necessary anyway to take advantage of integrated circuit technology.* Extra transistors and diodes can be economically

---

* In such circuits it is desirable to minimize the number of resistors and capacitors, which are precisely the elements required in most coupling networks. These components occupy a great deal of space in a semiconductor chip.

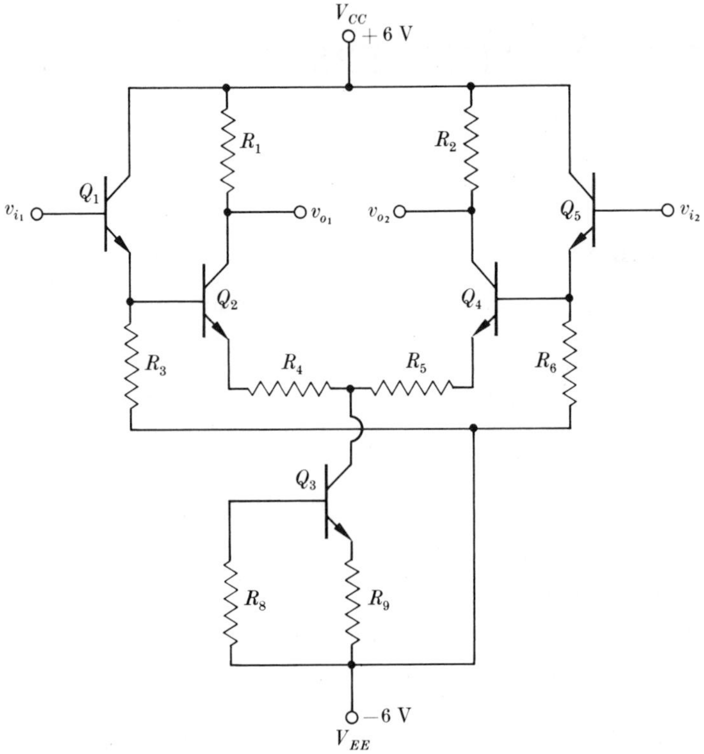

Fig. 6.1 Simplified schematic of RCA CA3000 integrated-circuit difference amplifier. Direct coupling is used throughout. Q_1 and Q_5 are used as emitter-followers to provide high (0.1 MΩ) input impedance and a wide range of linear operation. Q_3 is a constant-current source for the difference amplifier, which consists of transistor pair Q_2 and Q_4. Emitter resistors R_4 and R_5 provide negative feedback to stabilize and improve the linearity of the amplification. (Courtesy of RCA.)

added to a silicon chip to offset power lost because of direct coupling and also to assist in establishing dc biases and to stabilize against drift. Excellent frequency response and lower cost are secured in the completed amplifier.

Example An example of effective use of direct coupling is illustrated in the integrated circuit of Fig. 6.1. Emitter-follower input stages built around transistors Q_1 and Q_5 provide high input impedance. The low output impedance of these stages matches the moderate input impedance of the difference amplifier which used transistors Q_2 and Q_4. There is no problem in establishing biases, since the dc potential at the top of R_3 and R_6 is appropriate to the biasing of the bases of Q_2 and Q_4.

Transformer coupling. Transformer coupling of stages has many advantages and some marked disadvantages. Among its strong points are excellent dc "isolation" of stages, less power dissipation per amplifier stage (no load resistor is necessary), and good impedance matching. Among its drawbacks are that efficient transformers are bulky, often expensive and, in general, operate well only over a limited frequency range. Transformers for low-frequency use are especially large and thus susceptible to "pick up" of stray fields. In general, transformer coupling is limited either to cases where especially efficient coupling is required, as in high-fidelity amplifiers or power amplifiers. It is also used in instances where the winding serves as the inductance in an inductance-capacitance band-pass filter, as in the first stage of an amplifier receiving a chopped signal.

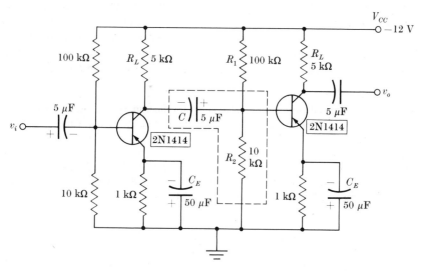

Fig. 6.2 A two-stage *RC*-coupled audio amplifier. The coupling circuit is encircled by a dashed line.

Resistance-capacitance (RC) *coupling.* This type of coupling is commonly used except in integrated circuits. A two-stage *CE* amplifier with *RC* coupling is illustrated in Fig. 6.2. Basically, the *RC* coupling network is a high-pass filter (Section 3.5). It blocks dc and severely attenuates frequencies below its cut-on frequency.* Appropriate values of *R* and *C* for coupling can be chosen by identifying the lowest frequency of interest f_L and applying the following criteria:

1. *C* must have a relatively small reactance for f_L, and
2. The time constant of the filter ($\tau = RC$) must be long compared with the period of f_L.

Example How well does the *RC* combination shown in Fig. 6.2 meet the criteria above if it is to amplify signals from 100 to 10,000 Hz? The first one is met since

$$X_C = 1 \div 6.28 \times 100 \times 5 \times 10^{-6} \simeq 320 \ \Omega,$$

---

* Signals whose frequencies are below the cut-on or half-power frequency are differentiated by the circuit. See Section 3.6.

which is small compared with the value of R_L, 5 kΩ. The second is also met. The time constant

$$RC = 10 \times 10^3 \times 5 \times 10^{-6} = 0.05 \text{ s}$$

which is large compared with the period for this frequency, 0.01 s. Ideally, it should be 10 times larger.

In multistage CE amplifiers both RC coupling and direct coupling put the low input impedance of a following stage in parallel with the load of the previous stage, reducing voltage gain. To achieve a given gain, therefore, extra stages are required. Often these are additional CE stages. Alternatively, an emitter-follower may be inserted between pairs of CE stages as a *buffer*. The high input impedance of an emitter-follower does not load a previous stage appreciably and its low output impedance more nearly matches the small input impedance of the following CE stage.

Example What is the voltage gain of the two-stage amplifier in Fig. 6.2? Assume the transistors have identical values of parameters. If coupling were neglected, the voltage gain of the first stage, as calculated from Eq. (5.5), would be $-\beta R_L/Z_i$ or $-\beta R_L/(Z_i + Z_s)$ where Z_s is the impedance of the signal source.

With coupling, the greatest effect will be on Z_L for stage 1. Coupling puts Z_i of the second stage (essentially h_{ie}) in parallel with load resistor R_L, further reducing the equivalent impedance Z_L of stage 1 and the gain. The complete expression defining Z_L is

$$\frac{1}{Z_L} = h_{oe} + \frac{1}{R_L} + \frac{1}{R_1} + \frac{1}{R_2} + \frac{1}{h_{ie}}.$$

Since $h_{ie} \simeq 1$ kΩ and the other resistances are five or more times that value the equation reduces to $Z_L \simeq h_{ie}$. With the coupling shown the gain of the first stage is $-\beta h_{ie}/(h_{ie} + Z_s)$. If Z_s is about 1 kΩ while $h_{ie} \simeq 1$ kΩ, the gain is just -0.5β.

For the second stage the voltage gain is $-\beta R_L/h_{ie}$. This value is an open-circuit figure, which is valid if the amplifier load does not shunt R_L seriously. The combined voltage gain is $A_V \cdot A_V = A_V'$ and $A_V' \simeq 0.5\beta^2 R_L/h_{ie} \simeq -2.5\beta^2$. If $\beta = 80$, $A_V \simeq 1600$.

In the RC coupling of transistor stages resistor R_2 can seldom be larger than about 10 kΩ. If very low frequencies are to be passed without great attenuation, it is necessary that coupling capacitor C be large, in general 10–25 µF. An electrolytic or ceramic capacitor is suitable since the working voltage required is no more than 12 V. Finally, it should be noted that the operating point of the second transistor will usually be different from that of the first in order to make the most of amplification possibilities.

Decoupling. For stability, a single power supply is generally the source of all operating voltages. Since some of the ac current from each stage goes through the power supply, small ac voltage drops appear across its internal resistance. The result is undesired interactions between stages, as ac will appear in bias voltages. This positive feedback (Section 6.4) is avoided by "decoupling" earlier stages from each other by appropriate use of low-pass RC filters. (See Exercise 6.11.)

Attenuator. Can a particular amplifier handle signals of widely varying amplitudes? It is true that gain can be altered by a factor of 10–100 by use of a voltage divider at the input to the (power) stage of an amplifier. If one amplifier is to handle a wide range of amplitudes, it is customary to use a high-gain circuit with a variable attenuator at its input. Large signals can then be reduced appropriately before amplification, yet there is sufficient gain to handle small signals. A versatile dc-ac attenuator is illustrated in Fig. 6.3. It is a dc voltage divider to which capacitor C_1 has been added. The need for C_1 becomes evident at high frequencies where amplifier input capacitance C_i shunts R_2 seriously. Without C_1 the higher frequencies in a wide-band signal are badly attenuated compared with lower frequencies. For constant attenuation at all frequencies it can be deduced that $C_1 = C_i R_2 / R_1$.

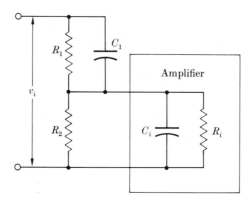

Fig. 6.3 Frequency-compensated attenuator used at amplifier input. Capacitor C_1 is usually adjustable to compensate for amplifier changes on aging.

6.2 POWER AMPLIFIERS

When an amplifier must deliver signals at power levels of a watt or more, a somewhat different type of output stage is involved. One or more power transistors must be used. These active devices are designed for sustained operation under conditions of large excursions in voltage V_{CE} and current I_C, and are capable of dissipating large amounts of power.* Such amplifiers often have transformer coupling to loads, as illustrated in Fig. 6.4a. The power stage in this case is simply a CE configuration whose components can handle the power. An advantage of the circuit is its low dc power dissipation. Naturally, operating values V_{CE}, I_C, and P must not surpass the maxima specified for the active device. It is useful to plot these values when dc and ac load lines are worked out for a circuit. In Fig. 6.4b such curves are shown for the circuit of Fig. 6.4a.

---

* The collector of a power transistor is bonded to its metal case, which is attached to a heat sink, e.g., a finned radiator. The maximum power specification is ordinarily determined by the quality of the heat sink.

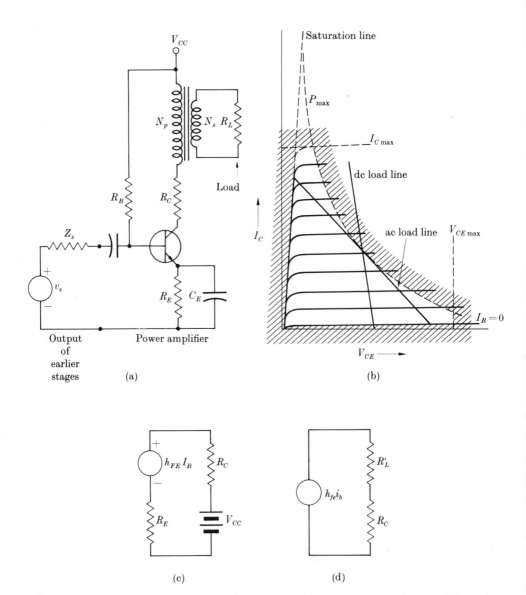

Fig. 6.4 Power amplifier with transformer coupling to load. (a) Schematic of the amplifier. To minimize dissipation in the transistor circuit, R_C and R_E are small. The ac component of i_C bypasses R_E but experiences resistance R_L' (load R_L reflected into the collector circuit by the transformer). (b) Characteristic curves with ac (dynamic) load line tangent to the maximum power hyperbola for maximum power delivery. (c) Equivalent dc output circuit. The transistor is replaced by voltage generator $I_B h_{FE}$, where h_{FE} is the large signal parameter. The small dc resistance of the transformer primary is neglected. (d) Equivalent ac circuit.

Example The power expended in a transistor can be identified with the product $I_C V_{CE}$. A maximum power hyperbola ($P_{max} = I_C V_{CE}$) can then be estimated. The hyperbola for the transistor of Fig. 6.4a is shown superposed on the family of collector characteristics. Both dc (static) and ac (dynamic) load lines are also drawn. The equivalent circuits of Figs. 6.4c and 6.4d aid in understanding the origin of these lines. It is clear that the transistor is operated as near maximum power as possible since the ac load line is tangent to the maximum power hyperbola at one point.

Input signal amplitudes in power amplifiers must be sufficiently limited to prevent loss of the tops and bottoms of the output signal, a form of distortion termed *clipping*. At high values of I_C (the top of a signal) severe decreases in β (h_{fe}) are responsible for clipping. At the bottom of a signal clipping results from a stage being driven to cutoff. When collector current falls, V_{CE} becomes large, I_B reverses sign, and a transistor ceases to conduct. An input signal i_B sufficiently large to cause V_{CE} to traverse the length of the dynamic load line will produce an output clipped at both extremes.

Still another limitation is the likely introduction of more subtle forms of distortion (Section 6.5). Only one distortion, a nonlinear one, will be mentioned here. This distortion arises from a nonlinear "transfer" of signal from input to output. The waveform of output is not a faithful reproduction of the input signal. Since for a power transistor I_C often varies more linearly with V_{BE} than with i_B, a voltage input to a power stage is usually preferable.

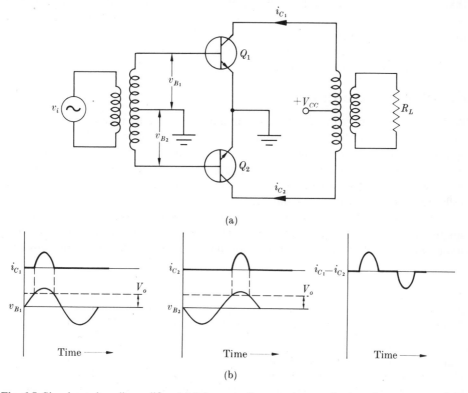

(a)

(b)

Fig. 6.5 Simple push-pull amplifier. (a) Schematic diagram that emphasizes the symmetry of the circuit. A transformer input ensures the necessary out-of-phase signals to the bases of Q_1 and Q_2. When there is no signal, each is biased at cutoff. (b) Current and voltage waveforms (see (a) for identification). The curve at the right gives the current in the output transformer primary.

Push-pull amplifier. A highly efficient power amplifier can be developed by use of a pair of transistors "back to back" in *CE* configurations. The design, termed a push-pull amplifier, is illustrated schematically in Fig. 6.5. Its efficiency stems from its low quiescent power dissipation.* The transistors operate alternately, each being cut off except when the input signal v_i exceeds the minimum forward bias V_o necessary for conduction. Little power is dissipated except when a signal is received.

For push-pull operation, each transistor must

1. Operate just above cutoff ($I_C \simeq 0$ and $V_{CE} \simeq V_{CC}$) and
2. Receive the input signal 180° out of phase from the other.

The phase relationships for a push-pull amplifier are illustrated in Fig. 6.5b. For example, for transistor Q_1 in Fig. 6.5a, only during the positive-going portion of signal v_{B1} to its base will there be an output signal, i_{C1}. Transistor Q_2 "conducts" during the next half-cycle.

To provide the phased inputs a device termed a *phase inverter* or *phase splitter* is required. It must divide the signal from the preceding stage and produce equal parts 180° out of phase. In Fig. 6.5a a center-tapped transformer serves this purpose. Relative to the center tap, the voltage at one end of the secondary winding is equal to that at the other end and is 180° out of phase with it. Each end drives the base of one transistor. Alternatively, a differential amplifier or an emitter-resistor phase inverter could be used.†

Finally, Fig. 6.6 shows a method of biasing push-pull transistors that secures amplification with minimum distortion.

6.3 AMPLIFIER BANDWIDTH

As has been implied from time to time, an amplifier actually responds satisfactorily only to signals that fall within a certain range of frequencies termed its "bandwidth." The previous discussion of gain has related to mid-band behavior, i.e., optimum amplifier behavior. Since actual response can be determined easily enough, e.g., with a sine wave generator and an oscilloscope, what is needed is an ability to predict the influence of design factors on bandwidth.

The relation of design to bandwidth is best seen by considering a two-stage amplifier and developing models of it. Three models suffice, one for mid-band, another for low frequencies, and a third for high frequencies. In Fig. 6.7 an equivalent

---

* Efficiency in a power amplifier is defined as the ratio of power in the output signal to the total power delivered to the collector from power supply V_{CC}. If a collector current flows at all times, a great deal of power is dissipated in the (necessarily) large quiescent current I_C. An amplifier for which this condition holds is termed *class A*, since it usually also follows that its output is nearly free from distortion. If greater efficiency is desired, a transistor may be biased at cutoff. Now the transistor conducts roughly only half the time a signal is received. This type of amplifier is called *class B*. An amplifier whose power transistor(s) is (are) cut off more than half the time is termed *class C*. It is apparent that class B and class C amplifiers produce a distorted output. Yet designs such as the push-pull configuration can be devised to accommodate such behavior.

† The emitter-resistor phase inverter is simply a *CE* amplifier with an unbypassed emitter resistor. One output is taken at the collector and the other at the emitter.

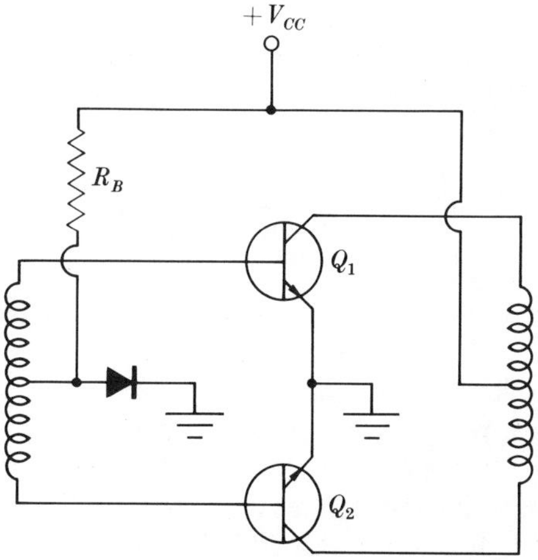

$+V_{CC}$

Fig. 6.6 Push-pull amplifier with diode bias to ensure that the bases of the transistor are forward-biased when $v_i = 0$ (see Fig. 6.5a). In this way distortion (see Fig. 6.5b) is minimized.

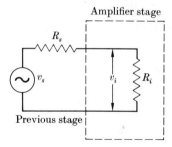

Amplifier stage

Previous stage

Fig. 6.7 Mid-band equivalent circuit for an amplifier.

circuit for *mid-band frequencies* is sketched. Its simplicity is striking. Thévenin equivalent circuit $V_s + R_s$ represents the output of the first stage, e.g. the first stage of the amplifier in Fig. 6.2. Similarly, R_i represents a set of parallel resistances, R_1, R_2, and the h_{ie} associated with the input of a second stage. But the model shows a direct connection of stages. Coupling capacitor C does not appear since it has minimal impedance at mid-band frequencies relative to R_i. Further, bypass capacitors C_E have been omitted for the same reason. The model stresses that mid-band gain voltage A_m is essentially independent of frequency.

Low-frequency performance. At low frequencies gain is limited by elements such as series capacitors (see Section 2.5). Both interstage coupling capacitors and bypass capacitors will reduce gain as frequency falls toward zero. How well do standard types of coupling perform? If direct coupling is used, and there are no emitter-resistor bypass capacitors, there should be no loss of gain even at dc. With RC coupling, however, gain will fall badly at low frequencies. Transformer coupling also introduces frequency dependence, but its consideration is beyond the scope of the book.

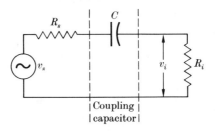

Fig. 6.8 Low-frequency equivalent circuit for an amplifier.

A low-frequency model of an amplifier is sketched in Fig. 6.8. It differs from the circuit of Fig. 6.7 in the appearance of coupling capacitor C in series with R_i.* Since the combination CR_i is a high-pass filter (Section 3.5), the frequency response of the circuit is predictable. The essential question is the fraction of signal voltage V_s developed across R_i. Since R_i and C function as an ac voltage divider, the fraction is just $R_i/(R_i + X_C)$. Substituting the reactance of the capacitor ($X_C = 1/j\omega C$) and dividing numerator and denominator by R_i, the fraction becomes $[1 + 1/j\omega CR_i]^{-1}$. Accordingly, it can be assumed that the voltage gain at low frequencies A_f relative to the gain at mid-band equals this fraction. Thus A_f/A_m is just[†] $(1 + 1/\omega^2 R_i^2 C_C^2)^{-1/2}$, which can be rewritten in terms of the filter cut-on frequency f_1 (Section 3.5) as

$$A_f/A_m = (1 + f_1^2/f^2)^{-1/2}. \tag{6.1}$$

Example What is the voltage gain of an amplifier at frequency f_1 relative to its gain at mid-band? Substituting in Eq. (6.1) gives $A_f/A_m = (1 + 1)^{-1/2} = 1/\sqrt{2} = 0.707$. The voltage gain is down 29.3% from mid-band.

The decrease in power gain is given by dB $= 20 \log V_m/V_f$ and found to be $20 \log 1.414 = 20 \times 0.15 = 3$ dB. As expected from the high-pass filter model used, at frequency f_1 the power gain is half that at mid-band.

Interestingly, the relative power gain (A_f^2/A_m^2) falls off with frequency at a nearly constant rate of 6 dB per octave or 20 dB per decade of frequency. The pattern may be seen in Fig. 6.10. At very low frequencies where the reactance of C_E is significant a still more rapid decline occurs. [8, Chap. 5]

Example A capacitor of 1 μF is used to couple two amplifier stages whose input resistances are 1 kΩ. What is the equivalent half-power frequency of the resulting amplifier? If its mid-band voltage gain is 10^3, what is the voltage gain at 100 Hz?

Use Eq. (6.1). Half-power frequency

$$f_1 = 1/6.23 \times 10^3 \times 10^{-6} = 160 \text{ Hz}.$$

---

* Only at very low frequencies must bypass capacitors C_E be added. Their capacitance is usually several times that of C.
[†] Since reactance is a complex quantity, to obtain the magnitude of the ratio it is necessary to take the square root of the sum of squares of real and imaginary parts.

The relative gain at 100 Hz is

$$A_f/A_m = [1 + (1.6)^2]^{-1/2} = 0.53.$$

The absolute voltage gain at 100 Hz is

$$0.53 \times 10^3 = 530.$$

How might mid-band response be extended on the low-frequency side? The most direct methods are the obvious ones, to increase the size of the coupling capacitor or omit it entirely. Alternatively, RC compensating networks can be introduced in the emitter or collector circuit. [3, Chap. 9] Negative feedback is also widely used (Section 6.4).

High-frequency response. The gain of an amplifier falls off in similar fashion at high frequencies (usually above 1 MHz). In this range an amplifier appears to be a low-pass filter, i.e., a resistance shunted by capacitance. It is capacitances within the active devices (interelectrode capacitances) and stray circuit capacitances that affect high-frequency operation.* In Fig. 6.9 capacitances of this type are represented schematically for a CE amplifier stage. The greater the frequency, the greater the shunting (to ground) of load resistor R_L.

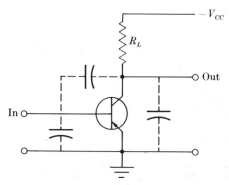

Fig. 6.9 Parasitic and stray capacitances (dashed lines) in a common-emitter transistor amplifier stage. Their magnitude is minute but causes high-frequency performance to fall off steadily.

Example How may the high-frequency response of a transistor amplifier stage be estimated? In general, manufacturers specify a half-power value for the best high-frequency configuration, the common-base arrangement. The value given is the frequency f_{hfb} at which parameter α (also h_{fb}), the forward current transfer ratio, has 0.707 its mid-band magnitude.

For a CE configuration amplifier the half-power frequency f_2 is given to a good approximation by $f_2 = (1 - \alpha)f_{hfb}$. Since $\alpha \simeq 0.98$, it is clear that the high-frequency response of a CE amplifier is worse by a factor of 50 or more.

---

* The rate of drift of charge carriers across a transistor base also soon becomes limiting. As the frequency is increased, the rate of change of signal eventually exceeds the drift rate and leads to a reduction in response much like that attributable to interelectrode capacitances.

It can be shown that the analog of Eq. (6.1) that expresses voltage gain at high frequency f in relation to the mid-band gain A_m is

$$A_f/A_m = [1 + 1/\omega^2 C^2 R^2]^{-1/2} = [1 + f^2/f_2^2]^{-1/2}, \qquad (6.2)$$

where f_2 is the filter cutoff frequency defined by $f_2 = 1/2\pi RC$ (Section 3.5). The "roll-off" in power gain at high frequencies is like that observed at low frequencies, 20 dB per decade of frequency.

How may mid-band response be extended to higher frequencies? The simplest method is to decrease the load resistance. Since the major contributor to the resistance in the expression for the half-power frequency above is R_L, a decrease in this value will perforce increase f_2. A greater bandwidth is secured but at the cost of voltage gain at all frequencies! In designing wide-band or *video* amplifiers this stratagem is widely used. Thus, to achieve a fixed total gain in a video amplifier, additional stages are required.

Overall frequency response. The bandwidth of an amplifier is defined as extending from cut-on (lower half-power frequency) f_1 to cutoff (upper half-power frequency) f_2. In Fig. 6.10 the overall response of an amplifier is shown in terms of voltage gain. Since a log-log scale is used, the "roll off" on each side of the mid-band range is linear.

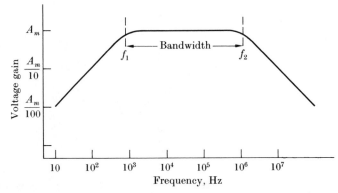

Fig. 6.10 Response of an RC-coupled amplifier as a function of frequency. Half-power or cutoff frequencies are f_1 and f_2. The voltage gain plotted falls off by a factor of 10 per decade of frequency.

Each additional stage of limited bandwidth causes bandwidth to deteriorate further. The gain of one stage is multiplied by that of every other in determining overall gain. Exercise 6.10 gives an expression for the change.

Phase angle and frequency. Earlier it was noted that there is a 180° phase shift for a *CE* configuration amplifier, and 0° shift for an emitter-follower configuration. There is also no phase shift for a common-base arrangement. The relationship holds strictly, however, only at the center of an amplifier band.

At other frequencies the phase of the output signal relative to that of the input can be predicted from the angular or imaginary part of capacitor reactance. It can be shown that the shift θ (relative to the phase at mid-band) is expressed by the equation $\tan \theta = f_1/f = f/f_2$. For example, at the lower half-power frequency f_1, $\tan \theta = 1/2$

and the phase shift relative to mid-band is 45°. Similarly, at the higher half-power frequency f_2, θ is $-45°$. All these values must be added to the mid-band phase characteristic of the amplifier. Over the mid-band range, which may be defined as extending approximately from $10f_1$ to $0.1f_2$, θ varies from about $+6°$ to $-6°$.

6.4 FEEDBACK

Feedback is a process in which a portion of the output of an amplifier is added to the signal at its input. The addition may also occur within a single stage or within two or more stages. The characteristics of an amplifier are modified substantially by feedback, though the effect secured depends greatly on the phase of the returned signal relative to the incoming signal. Some feedback occurs naturally; most is arranged deliberately to achieve desired amplifier behavior.

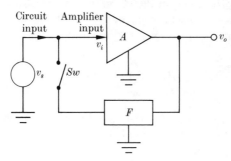

Fig. 6.11 Amplifier (shown as triangle) of gain A with feedback network. The fraction "fed back" is F. The output voltage v_o is taken relative to ground.

An amplifier with feedback is pictured in block diagram form in Fig. 6.11. The distinction between the circuit input v_s and the amplifier input v_i is important. The latter is the input to the amplifier itself. When the feedback loop is open (switch Sw_1 open), the *open-loop* gain* A describes the amplifier output:

$$A = v_o/v_i = v_o/v_s. \tag{6.3}$$

But when a fraction F of the output voltage is fed back, the voltage appearing at the amplifier input is

$$v_i = v_s + Fv_o. \tag{6.4}$$

Under conditions of feedback it becomes desirable to define a *closed-loop* or circuit gain G as well: $G = v_o/v_s$. Since v_s and v_i are no longer equal, $G \neq A$. Eliminating v_i from Eq. (6.4) gives an expression for G in terms of A:

$$G = \frac{A}{1 - FA}. \tag{6.5}$$

Basically, the loop has altered the original gain by the factor FA, which is commonly labelled the *loop gain*. Note that the sign of the feedback fraction F has not been fixed.

---

* Only absolute values of gains will be considered.

Negative feedback. This will correspond to adding to the incoming signal a portion of the output 180° out of phase with it, i.e., to giving F a negative sign. Because of feedback $v_i < v_s$ and $G < A$. This drop in circuit gain is clearly evident in terms of Eq. (6.5). Its denominator is greater than unity when F is negative. Though overall gain is sacrificed, the advantages secured are impressive. In general, negative feedback brings about *greater stability, broader bandwidth*, and *reduction of the distortion and noise* that always arise *in* an amplifier.*

A case of particular importance is the limiting situation in which negative feedback fraction F is comparatively large. Then $|FA| \gg 1$ and $1 - FA \simeq |FA|$. Equation (6.5) reduces to $G \simeq -1/F$. With substantial negative feedback the amplifier no longer affects the circuit! Circuit parameters external to the amplifier will determine both gain and performance. This valuable result is the basis for the applications of operational amplifiers, which will be discussed in the next chapter.

How great an improvement in the stability of a transistor circuit is secured by use of negative feedback? A useful measure can be obtained by modifying Eq. (6.5). Differentiating it, rearranging terms, and substituting for G, eventually yields the expression

$$\frac{dG}{G} = \frac{dA}{A} \times \frac{1}{1 - FA}. \tag{6.6}$$

Since F is negative, $(1 - FA) > 1$. According to Eq. (6.6), any fluctuation dA in amplifier gain causes a change in circuit gain dG that is $1/(1 - FA)$ times smaller.

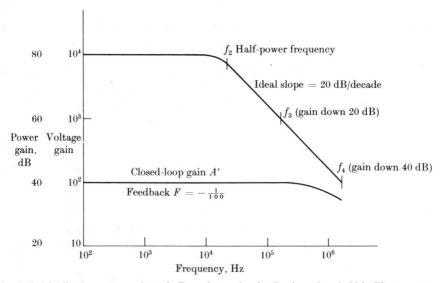

Fig. 6.12 Idealized representation of effect of negative feedback on bandwidth. The upper curve represents the gain without feedback or open-loop gain. The lower curve represents the gain when the feedback loop is closed and the fraction of v_o fed back is F.

---

* The general concepts relating to feedback are widely applicable. Most self-regulatory arrangements employ negative feedback to control their behavior. The term cybernetics is applied to the detailed study of such systems.

Example 1   For an amplifier of gain $A = 10^3$, consider that a feedback loop with $F = -0.01$ is arranged. The factor $1 - FA = 11$. With this amount of negative feedback, a 10% change in A causes less than 1% change in circuit gain G.

Example 2   How is bandwidth increased by negative feedback? Consider an amplifier of voltage gain $A_m = 1 \times 10^4$ (80 dB), whose normal response curve is that depicted in Fig. 6.12. If a loop that feeds back 0.010 v_o out of phase is added, the mid-band circuit gain G_m according to Eq. (6.5) will be $10^4/(1 + 100) = 99$.

At the half-power frequency f_2, the open-loop voltage gain A_f is 7.07×10^3. From Eq. (6.5) G_f will be

$$\frac{7.07 \times 10^3}{(1 + 70.7)} = 98.6.$$

Thus, at f_2 the value of G is down only 0.4% from its mid-band value. Contrast this small loss with the roughly 30% drop in gain of the open-loop amplifier. Consider a still higher frequency f_3 at which $A = 1 \times 10^3$, i.e., open-loop gain is down 90% from the mid-band value. In this case $G_f = 90$, a 9% drop from mid-band.

Positive feedback. This occurs whenever a fraction of the output is added to the input *in phase*. Some positive feedback occurs naturally in amplifiers. For this type of feedback F is positive in sign and the denominator of Eq. (6.5) will approach zero. Since the circuit gain is greatly increased, instability may follow. Yet a narrower bandwidth is secured and positive feedback is often introduced in a circuit to make it frequency-selective. A good example is the use of positive feedback in the input stage of a radio to enhance its selectivity to the carrier wave of the station to which it is tuned.

In the limit, as $FA \to 1$, G tends toward infinity. Now any internal or external fluctuation in the circuit will produce an amplifier output, and whether there is even an input signal is largely irrelevant. Under such extensive positive feedback, the output consists only of these frequencies amplified with least loss. The phenomenon is described by stating that the amplifier "has broken into oscillation." A familiar example is experienced in an auditorium when a squeal indicates that too much sound from a loudspeaker has been returned through a microphone to the PA system. Circuits with large positive feedback are useful for the generation of sine wave or other periodic signals (Chapter 9).

Example   When $AF = 1$, what actually occurs since infinite gain is not possible is that the smallest circuit fluctuation produces so much feedback that it drives transistors in the circuit to saturation. When they are saturated, gain falls to zero, and the amplifier quickly "recovers." Each random fluctuation causes a repetition of this cycle. The output of the amplifier consists of a series of pulses, a pattern characteristic of a relaxation oscillator.

It is difficult to eliminate all positive feedback in an amplifier. For that reason, amplifiers are seldom built with more than three CE stages coupled. The output of a fourth stage is always in phase with the input signal to the first, and even a minute amount of positive feedback could be disastrous. Very careful design is required to achieve stability in any high-gain amplifier.

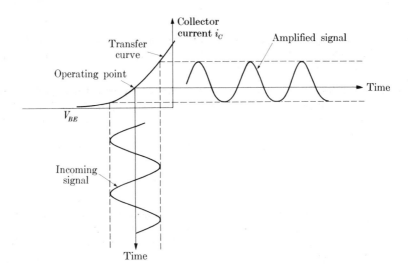

Fig. 6.13 Nonlinear distortion produced by a transistor. The operation extends over a nonlinear portion of its transfer characteristic.

6.5 DISTORTION

Since negative feedback also provides a means of reducing amplifier distortion, we should now consider this important subject. The output waveform of an amplifier is seldom a linear reproduction of the input signal. For example, Fig. 6.13 shows distortion attributable to operation of a transistor in a nonlinear portion of its transfer curve. In addition to such evident waveform distortion all outputs contain random unwanted fluctuations collectively described as noise. This topic is of sufficient importance to be treated separately in Chapter 8.

From an operational point of view a satisfactory analysis of distortion can be made by taking into account known limitations in the performance of circuit components. The three commonly identified types of distortion are *nonlinear, frequency,* and *phase* distortion. The first is undoubtedly the most common and was just illustrated. In nonlinear distortion, what occurs, as shown by a Fourier analysis of the output, is the introduction of harmonics, i.e. multiples of the fundamental frequencies in the signal. For a simple amplifier, harmonics beyond the third are seldom generated.

Frequency and phase distortion result from the frequency-dependent behavior of components such as capacitors and semiconductor devices. They occur when frequencies in a signal are unevenly amplified. A broad-band signal would suffer frequency distortion in a narrow-bandwidth amplifier. Phase distortion describes the tendency of an amplifier to affect the phase of frequencies present in a signal to different extents. It will be serious only for frequencies outside the bandwidth of an amplifier.

Fortunately, both distortion and the noise that originates within an amplifier can be reduced by negative feedback. The effect of negative feedback is to add an out-of-phase precursor of distortion and noise to the input. On amplification, this precursor will substantially cancel the distortion the amplifier generates.

Example Consider that the output of an amplifier contains the amplified input signal Av_s plus components D that represent noise and distortion: $v_o = Av_s + D$. The effect of feedback can be best seen by estimating a rough signal-to-noise ratio. Loosely, this ratio at the output is $S/N = Av_s/D$.

Now allow negative feedback. Consider that the input signal is increased until even with feedback of fraction F the output returns to v_o. While the amplifier will again inherently produce distortion of magnitude D, only a smaller magnitude D_F will appear. How can D_F be calculated? Consider that the feedback signal now amounts to FD_F. This signal appears in the output in amplified form AFD_F. The expression for D_F must be $D_F = D + AFD_F$, which may be rearranged to give $D_F = D/(1 - AF)$. Since the sign of F is negative, $D_F < D$. The signal-to-noise ratio is now

$$\frac{S}{N} = \frac{Av_s}{D_F} = \frac{Av_s}{D}(1 - AF).$$

With feedback the ratio is enhanced by the feedback factor $1 - AF$. For example, if $F = -0.01$ and $A = 10^4$, distortion and noise produced *within the amplifier* are reduced by the factor $1 - (-0.01 \times 10^4) = 101$.

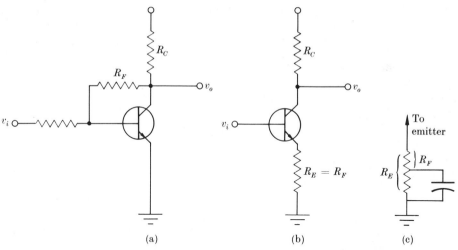

Fig. 6.14 Negative feedback circuits. In each circuit resistor R_F is the principal source of feedback. (a) Circuit providing shunt voltage feedback. In this CE circuit, the voltage fed back is proportional to output *voltage*. The feedback resistor shunts the input and reduces the input impedance of the circuit. Since the voltage fed back is taken from the collector of a CE amplifier, it will be 180° out of phase with the input and will constitute negative feedback. (b) Circuit providing series current feedback. In this emitter-follower circuit, voltage fed back is proportional to the output *current*. Since the feedback is in series with the input loop, the input current is reduced and the circuit input impedance increased. (c) An emitter resistor partly by-passed to provide partial negative feedback in an ac amplifier.

6.6 AMPLIFIERS WITH FEEDBACK

Providing negative feedback in an amplifier circuit may be as simple as omitting a by-pass capacitor around an emitter resistor. Figure 6.14 shows two feedback arrangements, one utilizing a voltage proportional to the output voltage and the other a voltage proportional to the output current. Note the modes of classification of type of feedback as explained in the figure legend. Arrangements may also be complex, as in the integrated circuit of Fig. 7.1 where a fraction of the output voltage of a late stage of an amplifier is fed back to an appropriate point in an early stage.

Regardless of whether negative feedback is classified as of current or voltage type, if the feedback circuit shunts the input, the input impedance is reduced, as Fig. 6.14a illustrates. If the feedback circuit is in series with the input "loop" as in the circuit in Fig. 6.14b, input impedance is increased.

From Fig. 6.14b it may be concluded that any ac amplifier that incorporates an unbypassed emitter resistor has internal negative feedback. To regulate the fraction of feedback, it can be arranged to by-pass all but a portion of the emitter resistor. An emitter resistor modified in this way is shown in Fig. 6.14c. The ac voltage across portion R_F offsets part of the input signal to the base (accompanying transistor not shown) by raising the voltage of the emitter relative to ground. Note that the feedback fraction F is $R_F/(R_C + R_F)$.

Example 1 If the open loop voltage gain A_v of the CE stage shown in Fig. 6.14c is 150 and R_L is 10 kΩ what must the value of R_F be for 10 dB of negative feedback? This specification may be translated, "With feedback the gain is 10 dB down from the intrinsic gain." First, voltage gain G may be found from the definition of a decibel, dB $= 20 \log G/A_v$. Accordingly, dB $= -10 = 20 \log G/A_v$. This gives $G/A_v = 0.316$ and $G = 48$. The value of F may be found from $G = A/(1 - FA)$. Substitution of the values given yields $48 = 150/(1 - 150F)$. Thus $F = -0.014 = R_F/(R_L + R_F)$. Since $R_L \gg R_F/R_L = 0.014$, $R_F = 0.014$, $R_L = 140\,\Omega$. Throughout, only the absolute values of G and A have been used.

Example 2 How does series voltage feedback such as occurs in the circuit of Fig. 6.11 affect its input impedance? If switch Sw is open and there is no feedback, the circuit input impedance is that provided by the amplifier. Call it Z_i. Then $Z_i = v_i/i_i = v_s/i_i$. If switch Sw is closed, a new circuit input impedance Z_i' is observed. It is $Z_i' = v_s/i_i$. The values of the two impedances can be compared. With feedback,

$$v_i = v_s + Fv_o = v_s + FAv_i$$

since $v_o = Av_i$. Solving for v_s gives $v_s = (1 - FA)v_i$. If this expression is substituted in the equation for Z_i' and the definition $Z_i = v_i/i_i$ is used, we obtain

$$Z_i' = \frac{(1 - FA)v_i}{i_i} = (1 - FA)Z_i.$$

Negative feedback of this type increases the circuit impedance since the factor $1 - FA$ is positive; positive feedback decreases it.

Ingenious control of the feedback loop provides additional possibilities. By selecting the frequency fed back through use of a filter such as the twin-T arrangement (Section 3.5), it is possible to have an amplifier *tuned* to the frequency at which the voltage fed back is a minimum. The relative gain will then be very many times greater at this frequency, and the device will behave essentially as a generator of sine waves of this frequency.

In *operational* amplifiers shunt negative feedback is employed. These amplifiers are high-gain dc amplifiers, arranged so that the shunt feedback circuit is external to the amplifier and can be varied at will. Chapter 7 will be devoted to a consideration of the properties and applications of operational amplifiers.

Finally, it must be noted that two kinds of phase considerations are important in circuits with negative feedback. First, there must be assurance that the phase of the signal fed back differs by 180° *over the frequency range* of the signal. Second, it is important that feedback circuits be analyzed to ensure that the phase shift does not exceed 180° at frequencies well outside the bandwidth of the amplifier. Though the amplifier has little gain at such frequencies, such feedback would ordinarily be partially regenerative (see Section 7.2) and a possible source of instability.

6.7 DC AMPLIFIER

A wide variety of detectors and transducers have a dc output. The group comprises phototubes, electrodes, thermocouples, some bridge circuits, current detectors (used in mass spectrometry), flame ionization detectors (used in gas chromatography), and many others. In general use nearly all those detectors must be followed by one or more stages of amplification to obtain a readout of reasonable amplitude.

A dc amplifier is simply a semiconductor circuit that responds linearly to signals of zero frequency. Its bandwidth ordinarily extends upward through the audiofrequency range and often beyond. Several types of dc amplifiers may be usefully identified. An amplifier with a very high input impedance (100 MΩ or greater) is often called an *electrometer*. Its input stage is distinctive and generally incorporates an electrometer tube [4, Chap. 5], an appropriate field-effect transistor, or a dynamic capacitor (Section 8.6). Whether of the electrometer type or not, an amplifier may be a true dc amplifier or, alternatively, may involve initial conversion of a signal to ac (by modulation) and ac amplification, followed by synchronous reconversion to dc.

A true dc amplifier can be distinguished mainly by the fact that it requires direct coupling of stages. Consequently, it must be designed to resolve problems such as drift that are inevitable with direct coupling (Section 6.1). To combat these tendencies a differential amplifier stage (Section 5.6) is commonly used as the input circuit. Such a stage operates with minimal drift and dc offset. Another characteristic of stable dc amplifiers is extensive use of negative feedback.

It proves convenient to deal with true dc amplifiers in the following chapter. Most modern devices of this type are operational amplifiers, i.e. have high gain and great stability, and have applications that extend well beyond any routine use for dc signals. The discussion of the type of dc amplifier that employs modulation and ac amplification will be deferred until Chapter 8. This type lends itself particularly well to the improvement of the signal-to-noise ratio of an instrument. Actually, modulation may also be employed with an operational amplifier and appropriate portions of both chapters should be examined to obtain a full account of possibilities for enhancing performance at low signal amplitudes.

REFERENCES

The titles at the end of Chapter 5 serve this chapter also. In addition, the following volumes may be of interest:

1. H. N. Bode, *Network Analysis and Feedback Amplifier Design.* Princeton: Van Nostrand, 1951
2. R. G. Hibberd, *Integrated Circuits, A Basic Course for Engineers and Technicians.* New York: McGraw-Hill, 1969
3. W. A. Lynch and J. G. Truxal, *Principles of Electronic Instrumentation.* New York: McGraw-Hill, 1962
4. RCA, *RCA Linear Integrated Circuit Fundamentals.* Harrison, N.J.: RCA, 1966

EXERCISES

6.1 Why must the time constant of an *RC* coupling circuit be long compared with the period of the lowest frequency of interest? How does the circuit behave if the time constant is considerably shorter than the period?

6.2 In a multistage amplifier to be used with high-resistance signal sources, what configuration of input stage would be the best choice? Explain.

6.3 A large-amplitude ac signal is to be displayed on an oscilloscope whose input impedance is 3.6 MΩ shunted by 35 pF.

    a) What size compensating capacitor is required for a $20\times$ input attenuating circuit (see Fig. 6.3)?

    b) What is the input impedance of the oscilloscope at 100 kHz?

6.4 When an ac power amplifier has a transformer output circuit, it has low dc dissipation. Explain. How does the ac dissipation in the output circuit compare with that in the load?

6.5 Explain the role of R_B and the diode in the circuit of Fig. 6.6. If a germanium diode and silicon transistors are used, will the biasing be as desired? Explain.

6.6 A resistor may be used in place of the diode in the push-pull amplifier of Fig. 6.6 to secure an appropriate forward bias for the bases of the transistors. Explain.

6.7 In a push-pull circuit it is also possible to use a transistor pair with complementary symmetry, one *n-p-n* and the other *p-n-p*. Such an amplifier requires no preceding phase inverter stage. The principal difficulty lies in matching transistor characteristics exactly; if there is an unbalance in behavior, considerable distortion results.

    a) Draw a schematic diagram of this type of push-pull circuit without providing for dc biasing.

    b) Redraw with provision for biases.

    c) Why is a transformer output unnecessary? Might it still be desirable?

6.8 Draw a schematic circuit diagram for an emitter resistor phase splitter (described in the footnote on p.146). Show that its two outputs are 180° out of phase. What values of emitter and load resistance will guarantee approximately equal amplitude outputs?

6.9 In Section 6.3 coupling capacitors were treated as mainly responsible for falloff of amplifier gain at low frequencies. Assume the low-frequency model of Fig. 6.8 applies to the second stage of the CE amplifier of Fig. 6.2 and that $C_E \simeq C_C$. Extend the model to include this by-pass capacitor C_E. Develop an equation to show the additional reduction in gain that results.

6.10 When several identical stages are coupled, the resulting amplifier has a narrower bandwidth than any one stage. For n identical stages, the effect is given by:

$$\frac{f_1}{f_1'} = \frac{f_2'}{f_2} = (2^{1/n} - 1)^{1/2},$$

where f_1 and f_2 are the half-power frequencies of a single stage and f_1' and f_2' are the half-power points for the whole amplifier. Assume that four CE stages whose half-power frequencies are 20 and 2×10^5 Hz and whose mid-band frequency is 2000 Hz are RC-coupled. What is the bandwidth ($f_1' - f_2'$) of the resulting amplifier neglecting any coupling loss?

[*Ans.*: 0.045 to 87 kHz.]

6.11 In Section 6.1 it was indicated that a low-pass RC filter can be used to divert ac signal from the collector voltage supply. In effect the filter decouples the power supply by by-passing the ac to the chassis ground.

a) Sketch an RC low-pass filter and also redraw the two-stage CE amplifier of Fig. 6.2 to include it.

b) Given that the high-frequency cutoff (half-power frequency) of such a filter is just $f_2 = 1/2\pi RC$, select values of R and C for decoupling the power supply of a circuit that amplifies in the 10^3 to 10^4 Hz range.

Chapter 7

OPERATIONAL AMPLIFIERS

7.1 INTRODUCTION

The operational amplifier is so versatile a device that discussing it encourages a re-examination of the steps in making a measurement. The sequence of steps was listed in Section 1.2 and is shown again in block diagram form in Fig. 7.1. One reason for reconsideration is that use of an operational amplifier often makes it feasible to accomplish amplification and modification simultaneously. To do this we link an appropriate passive network, e.g., a differentiation or integration circuit (Chapter 3), to an operational amplifier.*

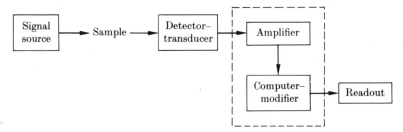

Fig. 7.1 Generalized single-channel instrument. An operational amplifier with its associated feedback network combines the modules within the dashed box.

What is the role of amplifier as distinguished from that of network? When employed separately, the amplifier produces an enlarged version of the signal from the detector or input transducer and the network performs the desired operation on it. There is a productive way to combine them: incorporate the network, or appropriate parts of it, into a negative feedback loop for the amplifier. With this design, the amplifier output is essentially determined by the network and both operations are accomplished more efficiently than by use of separate modules. Some major advantages of the combination are:

1. Substantial power may be drawn before an operation is performed inaccurately;

2. The useful frequency range of a network is often extended;

3. The accuracy of the operation is usually better; and

4. An operation can be carried out reliably over a longer time interval.

---

* Usage of the term varies. Often the term includes amplifier and associated network, but this implication will be avoided here for reasons of clarity.

The first result follows from harnessing the amplifier to the network and the others mainly from use of a highly stable amplifier and the tendency of negative feedback to broaden frequency response and minimize distortion.

Another reason for reexamining the steps in measurement is that an operational amplifier, or several of them with different characteristics, make it possible for us to develop our own instrumentation. As long as most components are delicate, single-purpose elements, it is appropriate that instruments be assembled by a manufacturer. The advent of small-size, low-to-moderate-cost, quality operational amplifiers alters the situation. Now a modular approach can be taken by the individual in assembling many kinds of instruments. [3, 4, and 8, Chap. 1; 6, Chap. 9] Where there is a desire to test design ideas, to make a special instrument for one or two measurements, or to modify a given instrument, it is now often feasible to do so.

7.2 THE OPERATIONAL AMPLIFIER

An operational amplifier is recognized by its performance, not its design. It is basically a very stable, wide-frequency-band (dc to high audiofrequencies), direct-coupled, high-gain (A_V usually greater than 10^4) amplifier. Further, it has a minute input current (usually 10^{-8} to 10^{-13}A) and a low output impedance (about 1 to 10 Ω). Ideally, it also gives zero output when no signal is received. These credentials are impressive and brief attention to its design seems suggested.

The first stage of an amplifier is the most critical one, as will be discussed in Section 8.4. Any instability or drift that it contributes will be amplified by all succeeding stages. In a direct-coupled device like an operational amplifier, the susceptibility to drift is at a maximum. In this situation, the differential or difference amplifier (Section 5.6) proves the best input stage. The simplified diagram of an operational amplifier in Fig. 7.2 suggests this arrangement.* Not only does the input stage respond

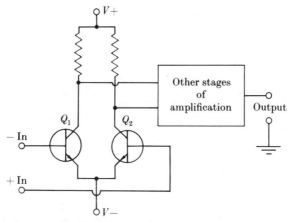

Fig. 7.2 Simplified diagram of a representative operational amplifier. Inputs are to the bases of transistor pair Q_1-Q_2 comprising a differential amplifier. The inverting input ($-$ designation) leads to an amplified output 180° out of phase with the input signal. The $+$ or noninverting input yields an in-phase output.

---

* Only differential input operational amplifiers will be discussed.

chiefly to the difference in signals at its dual inputs, therefore cancelling drift, but the dual inputs themselves provide great flexibility in use. They are not identical: one is "inverting" and the other "noninverting." A signal at the *inverting* input gives an amplified output of opposite polarity. For a signal introduced at the *noninverting* input, there is a virtually identical gain but no sign change.

Even with a well-matched pair of transistors in the input stage, however, temperature effects are not completely eliminated. There is also a relatively large steady input or *bias current*. As a result, two additional types of input stage have been developed for certain kinds of application. One is the FET differential pair, which has a much smaller bias current. Even MOS transistor pairs are used to reduce input currents still more. The second type is the chopper-stabilized amplifier, whose dc input is through a chopper amplifier. While the bias current tends to be the same order of magnitude as that of the FET, drift with temperature is very much less. Operational amplifiers based on discrete components, a monolithic integrated circuit, and combination (hybrid) devices are widely available commercially.*

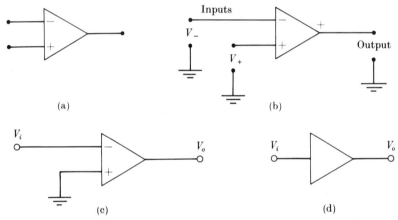

Fig. 7.3 Operational amplifier symbols and inputs. The amplifier is identified by a triangle with inverting ($-$) and noninverting ($+$) inputs and the output taken from the apex. Occasionally the input side is shown curved. (a) General three-terminal symbol. (b) Operational amplifier with differential input. Here the grounded sides of leads are shown. (c) Operational amplifier with input to inverting terminal. The noninverting terminal is grounded in this case. Neither the grounded side of the input and output leads nor the usual resistance between the noninverting and ground are shown. (d) Representation of (c) by a two-terminal symbol.

Figure 7.3 shows symbols for operational amplifiers. Note that the inverting terminal is identified by a minus sign, the other by a plus sign. The common (grounded) lead wire is shown in Fig. 7.3a, but is ordinarily omitted as in Fig. 7.3b, where only the "high" side of lines is shown. In many applications the noninverting terminal is grounded (Fig. 7.3c). When this is the case, the two-terminal symbol of Fig. 7.3d is

---

* Discrete component and hybrid operational amplifiers seem likely to continue to hold a performance advantage over monolithic operational amplifiers as development continues, since performance tradeoffs must be made in the design of the latter.

also used. The three-terminal symbol will be used until it is familiar; later in the chapter the two-terminal symbol will be employed where it applies.

A distinctive property of a high-gain, differential-input amplifier is that *its input terminals must be essentially at the same potential* for it to operate normally. The tolerable difference will depend on the gain A and the limiting output voltage V_o (see next section). With a differential input stage, they are related by the expression $V_o = A(V_+ - V_-)$. Since V_o is of the order of 10 V and A is very large, $V_+ - V_- \simeq 0$.

Example An operational amplifier has a gain of 5×10^4. Its limiting output voltage is $|10|$ V, that is, no larger output voltage is possible, no matter how great the input signal. What is the maximum potential difference that can exist between input terminals if it is to operate within its limits? Since $V_+ - V_- = V_o/A$, the difference can be calculated. It is just $10/5 \times 10^4 = 0.2$ mV.

Feedback networks. It was suggested earlier that an electrical network (often some combination of resistors and capacitors) would determine the behavior of an operational amplifier if appropriately used as a negative feedback loop. How is this result brought about? Actually, negative feedback is associated in two ways with operational amplifiers. Internal feedback is a necessity. A direct-coupled device (Section 6.1) can be highly stable only with generous negative feedback as an intrinsic part of the circuit.

The second type of negative feedback is arranged *externally*, usually through a network selected to perform an operation of interest. A fraction of the amplifier output is simply returned through the network to the *inverting* input. The noninverting input is grounded. The requisite 180° phase change is assured unless altered by a network component like a capacitor. This configuration is shown schematically in Fig. 7.4. The shunt feedback (Section 6.6) used is termed *operational feedback*. What must be stressed is that the feedback fraction is made large enough for the input network impedance and the feedback impedance to determine the behavior of the circuit. The possibility of achieving this kind of behavior was discussed in Section 6.4.

In Fig. 7.4 currents in most branches are labeled. From Kirchhoff's current law it is evident that $i_i = i_f + i_a$. Further, from Ohm's law the current in the input impedance Z_i is just $i_i = (v_i - v_s)/Z_i$ and the current in the feedback impedance Z_f is $i_f = (v_s - v_o)/$

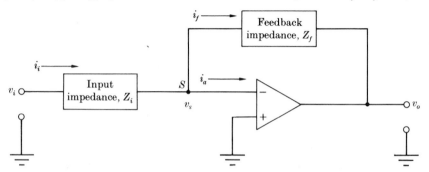

Fig. 7.4 Operational amplifier in normal operating configuration. The positive (noninverting) input is grounded.

Z_f. Note that voltage v_s is just the voltage at the inverting input of the amplifier. From these equations an expression for output voltage v_o under conditions of operational feedback can be developed:

$$v_o = -v_i \frac{Z_f}{Z_i} + v_s \left[1 + \frac{Z_f}{Z_i} \right] + i_a Z_f. \tag{7.1}$$

No approximations have been made in formulating Eq. (7.1). By combining it with the amplifier gain expression $v_o = A(v_+ - v_s)$, a general equation for a system with operational feedback in which neither input terminal is grounded can be obtained:

$$v_o = -v_i \frac{Z_f}{Z_i} - \frac{v_o}{A} \left[1 + \frac{Z_f}{Z_i} \right] + v_+ \left[1 + \frac{Z_f}{Z_i} \right] + i_a Z_f. \tag{7.2}$$

For all those cases in which the operational feedback system of Fig. (7.4) is used, $v_+ = 0$, and the expression reduces to

$$v_o = \frac{-v_i Z_f/Z_i + i_a Z_f}{1 + (1 + Z_f/Z_i)/A}. \tag{7.3}$$

Can Eq. (7.3) be simplified for ordinary use? Two approximations are worthwhile. First, the bias current i_a is very small.* Thus, the term $i_a Z_f$ can ordinarily be neglected with little error. Second, the voltage gain is large enough (10^4 or greater) for the term $(1 + Z_f/Z_i)/A$ in the denominator to be ordinarily small compared with unity. With these approximations Eq. (7.3) becomes

$$v_o = -(Z_f/Z_i)v_i. \tag{7.4}$$

What is striking about Eq. (7.4) is the disappearance of any dependence on the properties of the operational amplifier itself, the condition assumed earlier. It is now evident why a very high gain is essential; only under these conditions is the feedback performance of the system independent of the amplifier.

Example 1 What is the error in using Eq. (7.4) if $A = 1 \times 10^4$, $i_a = 1 \times 10^{-8} A$, $v_i = 2.0$ V, $R_f = 100$ kΩ, $R_i = 10$ kΩ? Consider first the error caused by dropping the term $i_a Z_f$ from the numerator of Eq. (7.3). The term $v_i Z_f/Z_i$ is just $2 \times 10^5/10^4 = 20$; the term

$$i_a Z_f = 1 \times 10^{-8} \times 10^5 = 1 \times 10^{-3}.$$

The neglected term is no more than 0.01 % of the term retained.

The error in v_o arising from the approximation in the denominator is usually larger. In this case it is just

$$1 - \left(1 + \frac{1 + Z_f/Z_i}{A} \right)^{-1} = \frac{Z_i + Z_f}{(A+1)Z_i + Z_f}.$$

---

* Some maximum values in 1970 are, for monolithic IC op amps, $i_a \sim 400$ to 500 nA; for discrete transistor op amps, $i_a \sim 10$ to 40 nA; for an FET pair, 10 to 100 pA; for a chopper-stabilized op amp, 50 to 100 pA.

This error is

$$\frac{1 \times 10^4 + 10 \times 10^4}{10^4 \times 10^4 + 10^5} = \frac{11 \times 10^4}{1 \times 10^8} = 1.1 \times 10^{-3} \quad \text{or} \quad 0.1\%.$$

Example 2   Show that Eq. (7.4) can also be written $v_o = -i_f Z_f$.
  The demonstration is as follows. Applying Ohm's law to the input circuit of Fig. 7.4 gives

$$-v_i/Z_i = i_i.$$

Kirchhoff's current law gives

$$-i_i = -i_a - i_f.$$

Since $i_a \simeq 0$, Eq. (7.4) becomes $v_o = -i_f Z_f$.

In describing the circuit of Fig. 7.4, recall that since $v_+ = 0$, the amplifier gain expression requires that the potential at the inverting input must be essentially at ground also. Point S is termed a *virtual ground*. It is of course the feedback that allows the amplifier to enforce this condition. When the circuit is used for mathematical operations the terminal is also called the *summing point* since currents may be added here from a variety of sources without interference between them because the terminal is poised or maintained at ground.

7.3 LIMITATIONS ON AMPLIFIER PERFORMANCE

Before examining applications of operational amplifiers, some factors that affect their reliability and performance need attention. To be precise, all amplifiers are subject to these limitations. They are treated here because of their central importance when high accuracy is sought in performance, as in most applications of operational amplifiers. The important restrictions on performance are the existence of

1. Output limits (output voltage and current can reach but not exceed limiting values for a given amplifier);
2. DC offset (appearance of an output voltage even with no input signal) and bias current;
3. *Drift* (gradual shift with time and temperature of offset voltage, bias current i_a, and output signal);
4. Finite frequency response and resulting instability;
5. Finite input impedance; and
6. Noise.

The last factor will be considered in Chapter 8.

Limits.   It is characteristic of an amplifier that its output voltage can be no greater than its supply voltages. If V_{CC} is 15 V and V_{EE} is -15 V, or vice versa, the output voltage can approach but never exceed one or both of these limits. An amplifier is said to "limit" when its output is driven to such a boundary.

   How do limits affect the useful range of amplitude of input signal? The range can be calculated by dividing the limiting voltage by the amplifier gain. For example, if gain A_v is 10^4 and the limiting voltage is $+10$ V, the maximum useful input signal is $1.0\,\text{mV}$ (assuming for a differential input device that the other input is at 0 V). The range of linear response will depend, of course, on the characteristics of a particular amplifier.

   A definite current limit exists for an amplifier also. Further, the current that can be furnished nearly always falls as the output voltage increases. Whenever current is limiting, a booster amplifier can be used in series with an operational amplifier inside the feedback loop. An example will be shown in Fig. 7.20. In this case the operational amplifier will compensate for any instabilities in the system and the "booster" need not be especially stable.

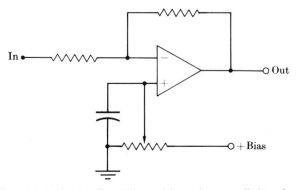

Fig. 7.5 Circuit for minimizing dc offset. The positive voltage applied to the noninverting lead is varied until there is no output voltage for zero signal.

dc offset. Even when no signal appears at the inverting input of an operational amplifier and the other input is grounded, there is still ordinarily an output voltage. Voltage offset is traceable to unequal base-emitter potentials in the differential input pair of active devices. Conventionally, this voltage is "balanced out" by application of a small dc voltage to the input terminal serving as a reference. For example, in

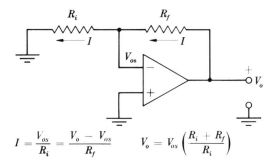

$$I = \frac{V_{os}}{R_i} = \frac{V_o - V_{os}}{R_f} \qquad V_o = V_{os}\left(\frac{R_i + R_f}{R_i}\right)$$

Fig. 7.6 Calculation of dc or voltage offset. The dc output V_o that appears when the inverting input is grounded through input resistor R_i is termed the voltage offset. It is conventional to refer V_o to the input terminal as indicated in specifying V_{os}. A formula for calculating it from V_o is given.

the circuit of Fig. 7.4, a compensating bias would be applied to the noninverting terminal. One circuit by which this may be accomplished is shown in Fig. 7.5. The bias applied is adjusted by moving the resistor tap until the output is zero with no signal at the other input. In general there is an internal circuit for balancing.

For a particular amplifier the magnitude of voltage offset is usually stated in terms of the input correction required. A basis by which the offset may be calculated is shown in Fig. 7.6. As stated, the dc offset V_{os} is just $V_o R_i/(R_i + R_f)$ or the output voltage times the feedback fraction.

Often it is desired to reduce the equivalent voltage offset attributable to bias current. In Fig. 7.6 it is evident that bias current from the inverting terminal through R_i to ground will produce an apparent voltage offset also. To compensate for this effect of bias current and thus lower further the signal input currents that may be used with the operational amplifier, a resistance is inserted between the noninverting terminal and ground. It can be shown that its value should be $R_i R_f/(R_i + R_f)$. When this compensation is used, only the difference in bias currents affects V_o.

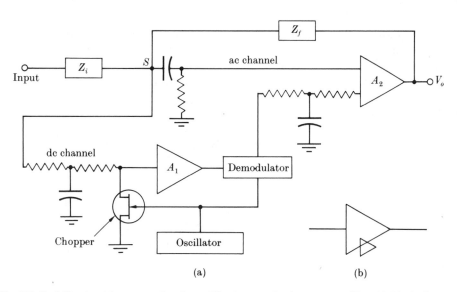

(a)   (b)

Fig. 7.7 Stabilization of an operational amplifier by use of a chopper amplifier. (a) Block diagram. A_1 is an amplifier of gain about 1000, A_2 the operational amplifier being stabilized. The FET switch chops or modulates the dc voltage at the summing point S. After amplification, demodulation, and filtering out the chopper frequency, a correction is obtained that can be applied to the noninverting operational amplifier input. (b) Symbolic representation of chopper-stabilized operational amplifier.

Amplifier drift. As we would expect, the voltage offset and bias current are subject to drift. Temperature changes, power supply variations, humidity, and ageing are some of the causes, listed in order of decreasing importance. Solid-state operational amplifiers at present show drifts in dc offset of a few $\mu V\,°C^{-1}$ and in bias current of about 1 nA $°C^{-1}$.

Where very low dc offset and drift are required, chopper stabilization may be employed.*A chopper-stabilized operational amplifier is shown in block diagram form in Fig. 7.7. The FET chopper converts any dc signal at the summing point to ac, amplifies it, and then demodulates and filters it to obtain a dc correction voltage.

The control of drift in the operational amplifier comes when this compensating potential is directed to the noninverting terminal of the operational amplifier. In the circuit of Fig. 7.7 the final value of V_s is the intrinsic dc offset of the chopper amplifier (only a few μV) plus the offset of the operational amplifier at its input divided by the gain of the chopper amplifier. In general, it is of the order of a few tens of microvolts.

While the problem of dc offset is greatly reduced by use of a chopper amplifier, some frequency discrimination is introduced. Both the rate of chopping and the necessity of filtering to remove internally generated noise cause loss of signal frequencies much greater than the rate of chopping. With an FET chopper, as in Fig. 7.7, chopping is not really limiting. Because of the capacitor in the lead to the operational amplifier itself, the higher-frequency components of signal V_i are principally amplified by the main amplifier. Note that signal V_i appears at the inputs of both amplifiers. The dc and low-frequency gain is the product of the two gains and is usually greater than 10^7. The bias current is now very low indeed (50 to 100 pA).

Frequency response and stability. Since operational amplifiers are direct-coupled, their amplification is excellent for dc and low-frequency signals. For transistor devices at about 10 kHz and for FET and chopper amplifiers at about 100 to 500 kHz, response begins to fall off. A representative response curve is shown as a dashed line in Fig. 7.8. The decrease in gain is attributable mainly to the steady rise with increasing frequency of the shunting effect of small interelectrode capacitances in transistors or other semiconductor devices. Once response begins to fall, it decreases at about 20 dB per decade of frequency, but at high frequencies the rate of decrease is usually steeper as additional sources of capacitance begin to shunt.

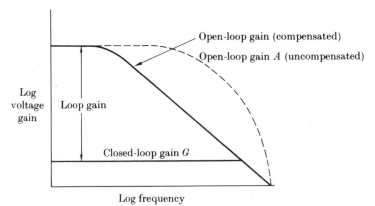

Fig. 7.8 Bode plot of amplifier response. The broken line represents the amplification of a normal high gain amplifier. The full line represents the case in which gain at higher frequencies has been arbitrarily reduced by a compensating *RC* circuit to attain an ideal slope of 6 dB per octave or 20 dB per decade of frequency.

---

* Instability in the power supply should, of course, be dealt with directly.

While the loss of gain at high frequencies is not a problem in most applications of operational amplifiers, the accompanying phase shift is (Section 6.3). Recall the feedback loop. If the amplifier introduces an additional phase shift (beyond the normal 180°), the feedback may become positive and create instability. As discussed in Section 6.4, such instability manifests itself as a tendency for the amplifier to break into oscillation and generate a single frequency.

The prospects for instability may be diagnosed from Fig. 7.8. This type of log voltage gain–log frequency graph is termed a Bode diagram. The slope of the curve is related to the intrinsic amplifier phase shift. For a slope of zero (at mid-band), there is only the basic inversion (180° shift). For a slope of unity (a power slope of 20 dB per decade), the extra phase shift is 90°; for a slope of two (40 dB per decade), the extra phase shift is 180°. Note that the dashed curve has a slope of two at high frequencies. For any signal of these frequencies the total phase shift is the sum of the feedback phase shift of 180° (output to inverting input) and the internal phase shift of 180°. If they are returned to the input, there will be positive feedback. Filtering such frequencies from the input signal is not a satisfactory solution, since they will exist in the internal amplifier noise in sufficient amplitude to make the amplifier unstable.

How may the system be stabilized? The answer is straightforward. Internal compensation in the form of an appropriate RC network can be used to reduce the amplifier response in the manner suggested in the solid curve in Fig. 7.8. Its smaller rate of decrease implies that the internal phase shift is only an extra 90° across the entire range.

Actually, capacity in the input or in the load may also increase the phase shift and induce stability. These extra phase shifts are predictable and are most often compensated by introducing capacitance in the feedback loop, either across the feedback resistor or as a series RC shunt around it. The compensating capacitance should be small so that the amplifier will still respond rapidly to changes in input or output conditions.

Example A coaxial cable input (capacitance about 100 pF m^{-1}) to an operational amplifier can easily introduce a 90° phase shift beyond that of the amplifier. Unstable operation is quite likely if the feedback network is solely resistive. The difficulty can be avoided by shunting the feedback resistor by a small capacitor.

Speed of response. The finite time rate of response of an operational amplifier should be kept in view if a fast response is desired. When a chopper stabilizer is used, or when inputs or loads are strongly capacitive, speed of response is further limited. In general the speed of response of an amplifier to a steady input signal is termed its *slewing rate* and is presently of the order of volts per microsecond. In addition, delay in response may be encountered because an amplifier will limit when a load or feedback network is switched in. Often this problem can be alleviated by using a shorting switch that avoids the necessity of breaking a circuit.

Input impedance. Basically, the input to an operational amplifier is a voltage input. For this reason it becomes important that the circuit input impedance Z_i be smaller than the amplifier input impedance Z_d (termed a differential impedance if neither input is grounded). Otherwise, since impedance Z_d is essentially in parallel with Z_i, the effective open loop gain of the amplifier is reduced. In turn, the accuracy of circuit performance is lessened because a reduction in gain affects the fraction of gain that can go to feedback. Differential impedance ranges from about 200 kΩ (transistor input) to $10^{11}\,\Omega$ (FET input). The value for a given amplifier can be estimated from V_s, the dc offset referred to the input, and i_a, the amplifier input current. For example, if the dc offset is 2 mV and $i_a = 10^{-8}$ A, $Z_d = 2\,\text{mV}/10^{-8}\,\text{A} = 200\,\text{k}\Omega$.

7.4 MATHEMATICAL OPERATIONS

It is possible to carry out a variety of "mathematical" operations on a signal simply by linking an appropriate network of passive elements like resistors to an operational amplifier. With such a combination, signals can easily be added, multiplied, integrated, or otherwise modified. The possibilities for instrumentation are attractive. By incorporating one or more operational amplifiers and networks, the output of a detector-transducer can be converted to an electrical form in which it more nearly represents the information sought. For example, it is worthwhile to perform the operation "$-\log$" on the optical transmittance of a solution to obtain an output proportional to the concentration of the absorbing species. Accordingly, several basic operations will be suggested here and in the two sections that follow.

Addition and subtraction. In Fig. 7.9 the network necessary for addition of signals is shown. As indicated, it is really input currents (V_i/R_i) that are summed. When resistances R_1 and R_2 are equal, V_1 and V_2 are simply added.

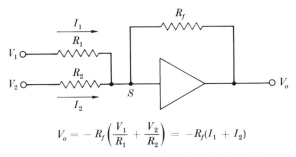

$$V_o = -R_f\left(\frac{V_1}{R_1} + \frac{V_2}{R_2}\right) = -R_f(I_1 + I_2)$$

Fig. 7.9 Addition by use of an operational amplifier. For simple addition all resistances should be equal. If desired, a weighted sum may also be taken by multiplying each voltage V_i by a different factor $(1/R_i)$ by simply selecting appropriate values of input resistors R_i.

Example   In the circuit of Fig. 7.9, assume $V_1 = 0.50$ V, $V_2 = 0.30$ V, $R_1 = R_2 = R_f = 100$ kΩ. What are I_1, I_f, and V_o?
   Since $I_1 = (V_1 - V_s)/R_1$ and $V_s \simeq 0$,

$$I_1 = 0.50/1 \times 10^5 = 5.0 \times 10^{-6}\,\text{A}.$$

Further,

$$I_f = I_1 + I_2 = 5.0 \times 10^{-6}\,\text{A} + \frac{(0.30 - 0)}{1 \times 10^5} = 8.0 \times 10^{-6}\,\text{A}.$$

Thus,

$$V_o = -R_f I_f = -1 \times 10^5 \times 8 \times 10^{-6} = -0.80 \text{ V},$$

the sum of V_1 and V_2.

How precise is the addition if the open-loop gain of the amplifier is 5×10^4? According to Eq. (7.1), the fractional error will be $(1 + Z_f/Z_i)/A$. The error is thus

$$\frac{(1 + 1)}{5 \times 10^4} = 0.4 \times 10^{-4} = 4 \times 10^{-5} \qquad \text{or} \quad 0.004\%.$$

If resistances with a $\pm 1\%$ tolerance were used in the network, they would introduce a far greater error and would effectively determine the accuracy of the operation. If the bias current is 10 nA, the error from this source might also be estimated.

Should a weighted sum be desired, appropriate values of the input resistances should be selected. The weighting of each input is just R_f/R_i. To subtract a signal, it is only necessary to change its sign and then "add" it.

A necessary condition for addition and subtraction that needs to be made explicit is that signals do not interfere. Interference will occur only if current flows from point S back to signal sources. With a balanced operational amplifier, S is at virtual ground, the inputs are isolated from each other, and the requirement is met.

Sign inversion. Use of an operational amplifier with a feedback network in which $R_i = R_f$ yields $v_o = -v_i$. The output is identical to the input but of opposite polarity. The circuit is often called an *inverter*.

Change of scale. A signal amplitude may be multiplied by a constant factor k by using a network in which $R_f/R_i = k$. Clearly, if signal polarity is not to be changed, an inverter must be used in series with the multiplier.

Logarithmic amplifier. The logarithm of a positive input signal can be taken by the circuit of Fig. 7.10. The desired logarithmic response is provided by transistor Q in the feedback circuit. With its base grounded the collector-emitter voltage, which is

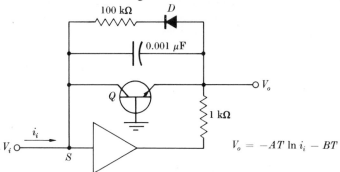

Fig. 7.10 Logarithmic amplifier for positive input signals. A and B are constants for a given transistor and T is the absolute temperature. The operational amplifier should have $i_a \ll i_i$. The 0.001 μF capacitor is necessary for stability. The diode-resistor combination ensures that application of a signal of incorrect polarity will not cause "lock up" and a steady spurious output regardless of subsequent input.

the amplifier output voltage, is the logarithm of the collector current. Clearly, the accurate operation of this circuit will require $i_i = i_C$, a condition that will be met if the amplifier input current i_a meets the requirement $i_a \ll i_i$. A further necessary condition is that the leakage current of the transistor be small compared with the input current. When these conditions are satisfied, it is ideally possible to obtain an accurate response for input currents from 10^{-11} to 10^{-2} A.

Note that an *n-p-n* transistor is used in Fig. 7.10, since it provides appropriate polarities if the input current is positive. To take the logarithm of a negative signal it is only necessary to substitute a *p-n-p* transistor and reverse the diode in the parallel branch.

Some form of temperature compensation is also needed to make the circuit of Fig. 7.10 generally usable. It may best be provided by use of a second, identical logarithmic circuit to which a reference current i_z is directed. If the two circuit outputs are directed to the terminals of a third operational amplifier this device will respond to the difference. Its output will accordingly be given by $v_o = C \log i_1/i_2$. Exercise 7.3 is based on such a circuit.

Laplace transforms. It has been straightforward to deduce the role of the impedances in networks considered up to this point. Only Ohm's and Kirchhoff's laws have been required to deduce output voltages. When two or more passive elements comprise an impedance, however, the complexity of mathematics increases rapidly. In these situations the Laplace transformational method can effect a great simplification. References provide a good exposition of the method. [7, 8]

Example Consider the application of the Laplace transformational method to the simple integrator network of Fig. 7.14a. First, the basic operational amplifier expression, Eq. (7.3), becomes

$$v_o(p) = - [Z_f(p)/Z_i(p)]v_i(p), \qquad (7.5)$$

where $v(p)$ and $Z(p)$ are voltage transforms and impedance transforms, respectively. For the integrator circuit, $Z_f(p)/Z_i(p)$ is just $1/RCp$, where p is the Laplace parameter. Substitution of this expression in Eq. (7.5) gives $v_o(p) = -v_i(p)/RCp$. If there is no charge on capacitor C (of Fig. 7.9a) initially, $1/p$ corresponds to the operation $\int dt$. Substituting this value for p and returning Eq. (7.5) to the time domain gives

$$v_o = -\frac{1}{RC} \int v_i \, dt,$$

the normal "integrator" equation.

7.5 DIFFERENTIATION

The *RC* differentiating circuit treated in Section 3.6 can be adapted for use with an operational amplifier. The essential element is the series capacitance. It also appears as a series input to the operational amplifier. In Fig. 7.11 the circuit is repeated and then shown connected to an amplifier. Unfortunately, while the *RC* circuit differentiates, it fails to provide more than minimal output and is limited in frequency range. By contrast, the network-amplifier combination of Fig. 7.11b differentiates, furnishes

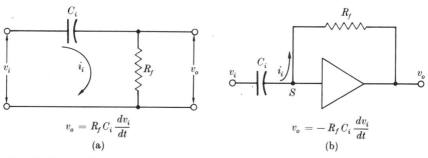

$$v_o = R_f C_i \frac{dv_i}{dt}$$

(a)

$$v_o = - R_f C_i \frac{dv_i}{dt}$$

(b)

Fig. 7.11 A simple differentiator. (a) Basic *RC* circuit. As current is drawn from the output, erroneous results are secured. (b) A simple operational amplifier differentiator. The usable frequency range is extended over that of (a), since point *S* can be kept at virtual ground over a broad range of frequency by negative feedback through R_f. Current can now be drawn to the extent the amplifier can supply it.

moderate current (2 to 20 mA), and has an extended frequency range now limited mainly by the amplifier.

The differentiating action of the latter circuit can be verified quickly. Recall that $v_o = -i_i R_f$. Taking the defining equation for the capacitor $C = Q/V$, rearranging it to $Q = C_i v_i$, and differentiating it gives $dQ/dt = i_i = C_i \, dv_i/dt$. This value of input current can be substituted in the output expression. One obtains $v_o = -R_f C_i \, dv_i/dt$.

In fact, this simple operational amplifier differentiator proves inadequate for what is at first a surprising reason. High-frequency noise, always present, yields a derivative with a very large value, dv_i/dt. Though the noise amplitude is minute, its derivative proves an appreciable fraction of most instrument signal derivatives. Recall that such signals are likely to be slowly varying dc.

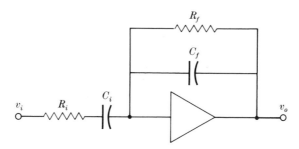

Fig. 7.12 Practical differentiator circuit. At low frequencies $v_o = -R_f C_i(dv_i/dt)$. High frequencies contribute little to v_o since they appear mainly across R_i in the input circuit and are shunted through C_f (around R_f) in the feedback circuit.

How can the noise error be minimized? The obvious strategy is use of filters since they can be designed around R_f and C_i. Two such filters have been included in the practical differentiator circuit shown in Fig. 7.12. One is *high-pass* filter $R_i C_i$ in the input circuit, the other *low-pass* filter $R_f C_f$ in the feedback circuit. Each may be given the same time constant τ'. If the highest signal frequency expected is f, components for the input filter should be selected to give a characteristic frequency f_1 that equals

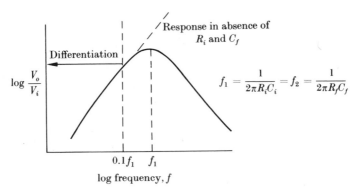

Fig. 7.13 Response of practical differentiator of Fig. 7.9.

or exceeds $10f$. This requirement ensures that frequency f be differentiated with an accuracy of $\pm 1\,\%$, which is sufficient accuracy for many applications. Since $f_1 = 1/2\pi\tau'$, and $f_1 = 10f$, the desired time constant $\tau' = R_iC_i = 1/20\pi f$. Further, $\tau' = R_fC_f = 1/20\pi f$.

In Fig. 7.13 the response curve for the practical differentiator is drawn. Note that the device has its greatest output at characteristic frequency f_1. At higher frequencies low-pass filter R_fC_f rapidly reduces the gain and ensures minimal response to noise.

Example A potentiometric titration curve is to be differentiated. A full-scale response time of 1 s, which corresponds to a frequency of about 1 Hz, will be adequate. Then $f_1 \geqslant 20f$ and $\tau' = 0.008$ s. Actually, a value of 0.01 s will probably be satisfactory.

First, a value for $R_fC_i = \tau$ that is relatively large, perhaps 10 s, can be selected. To secure this value, let $R_f = 1$ MΩ and $C_i = 10\ \mu$F. The values of the other components are fixed by the time constant τ' ($\tau' = R_iC_i = R_fC_f$). Since $\tau' = 0.01$ s,

$$R_i = 0.01/10 \times 10^{-6} = 1\ \text{k}\Omega \qquad \text{and} \qquad C_f = \frac{0.01}{1 \times 10^6} = 0.01\ \mu\text{F}.$$

A second derivative can be taken if desired by placing a second practical differentiator in series with the first one. In this case, additional filtering is needed. Usually it takes the form of a low-pass filter inserted after both the first and second differentiators. The filter time constant may be as much as $100\ \tau'$.

7.6 INTEGRATION

To integrate an electrical signal with respect to time, advantage may be taken of the ability of a capacitor to store charge. If the signal is unaffected by the circuit used, the total charge stored will equal the integral $\int i\,dt$. When this relation holds, the voltage across the capacitor v_c will equal Q/C, where C is the capacitance, or $v_c = \int i\,dt/C$.

What is the role of an operational amplifier in this operation? As in other cases, it ensures that the signal source is unaffected by the measuring circuit. In Fig. 7.14a a network-amplifier combination suitable for integration is shown schematically. Resistor R yields current i_i from the input signal V_i, and capacitor C stores charge

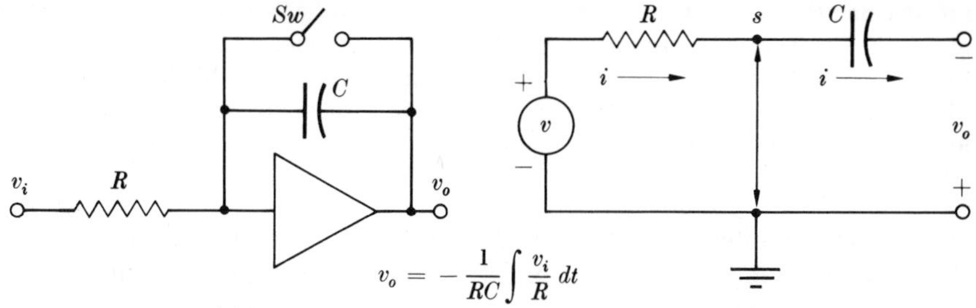

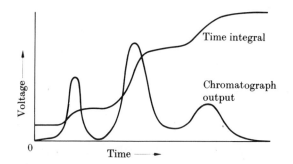

$$v_o = -\frac{1}{RC}\int \frac{v_i}{R}\,dt$$

(a)   (b)

Fig. 7.14 Integrator. The output voltage v_o is proportional to the time integral of input signal v_i. (a) Operational amplifier integrator. Integration occurs during the interval of time t that switch Sw is open. (b) Equivalent circuit. The heavy double-headed arrow represents the virtual ground at point s.

until limited by the maximum output voltage of the amplifier. A shorting switch across C is a desirable addition to permit integration over desired time intervals. At any time the output can be reset to zero. Since point S in the circuit is at virtual ground, the output voltage will reflect the potential difference across the capacitor. This point is emphasized in the equivalent circuit of Fig. 7.14b.

Fig. 7.15 Gas chromatograph output signal and its time integral.

Example 1 What is the relationship between input signal and output voltage in the circuit of Fig. 7.14a? First, since $V_s \simeq 0$, $i_i = V_i/R$. On the same basis, $v_o = Q/C$. Further, $Q = \int i_f\,dt$ and thus

$$v_o = \frac{1}{C}\int i_f dt.$$

If $i_i \gg i_a$ (operational amplifier input current), $i_i = i_f$. Substituting for i_f and adding a negative sign to mark the inverting effect of the operational amplifier,

$$v_o = -\frac{1}{RC}\int i\,dt.$$

Example 2 A portion of a chromatogram from a gas-liquid chromatograph is given in Fig. 7.15, together with its time integral obtained with the circuit of Fig. 7.14. Integration was started at

$t = 0$ by opening the reset switch Sw. Note that the output voltage (integral) increases steadily during a peak. The increase is proportional to the area ($v \times t$) under the peak. When the signal again returns to the base line ($v_i = 0$), the output voltage is constant. If the signal fails to return to the base line, v_o continues to rise, introducing error. The output of the integrator can be reset to zero at any point by shorting the capacitor.

How precise is integration by this method? Several electrical sources of error may be noted. Their magnitude must be estimated for a particular circuit. All may be successfully minimized. They are:

1. Capacitor leakage, i.e., loss of charge by conductance through the integrating capacitor. Leakage causes the value of the integral to drift downward. It may be minimized by use of a polystyrene capacitor or other high-quality type. Clearly, the leakage resistance will establish a minimum value of current that can be integrated with a given accuracy.

2. dc offset. This error will yield an apparent input signal and lead to spurious integration. Use of an operational amplifier with low drift and careful initial balancing will minimize the error. Integration over a long interval requires a highly stable amplifier.

3. Circuit leakage to the summing point. All signals, whether legitimate or stray, will be integrated, and it is essential that proper insulation be provided around the input lead and that it be shielded against magnetic fields.

Example An integrator with a 1 μF capacitor whose leakage resistance is $1 \times 10^{11} \, \Omega$ is charged to 1 V. Its leakage current near the end of integration is 1×10^{-11} A. Thus, the input current to the integrator circuit should be at least 1×10^{-9} A for 1% accuracy of integration.

Analog computers. It is only a step from single mathematical operations to the development of an analog computer. Basically, this consists of many operational amplifiers and banks of precision variable and fixed capacitors, resistors, and voltage sources. A wide variety of mathematical equations can be simulated electrically by setting up appropriate networks. Each term in an equation is represented by a small network. Then all terms (networks) that must add to zero are connected to the summing point of another operational amplifier. Finally, a voltage proportional to the constant in the equation is fed in from a voltage source. Values of the variable or variables that are solutions to the equation are then read as circuit voltages by measurement of potentials at appropriate points.

Since instrument design increasingly calls for the addition of computation stages to relieve an operator of the need to perform calculations, analog computers are useful in instrumentation. In general, digital computers offer advantages in accuracy and speed and are likely to be used instead since instrument control may also be effected (Sections 1.10 and 9.8). Nevertheless, simple analog computers may be more attractive where versatility and the possibility of trying out new configurations may be at a premium. A discussion of analog computers is beyond the scope of the book. They are well described in some of the references listed at the end of this chapter.

7.7 MEASUREMENT OF CURRENT AND VOLTAGE

Operational amplifiers also have general application in the precise measurement of currents and voltages from detectors or input transducers. As feedback-stabilized amplifiers, they raise the amplitude of a signal until it can be registered by a readout device or digitized for input to a computer. Of special importance in this application is that the operational amplifier can provide a virtual ground at its inverting input. As a result, its interaction with a detector is negligible; it is said to be an *isolation* or *buffer amplifier*. The response of the detector is therefore more ideal and less error is introduced into the measurement of current or voltage.

For *current measurement* a multiplier configuration like that in Fig. 7.4 is ordinarily used. An accurate determination of current is possible since the input is to a virtual ground. In this case the detector itself provides input impedance Z_i. All its output signal continues into Z_f (assuming $i_i \gg i_a$) and the output is given by $V_o = -i_i Z_f$.

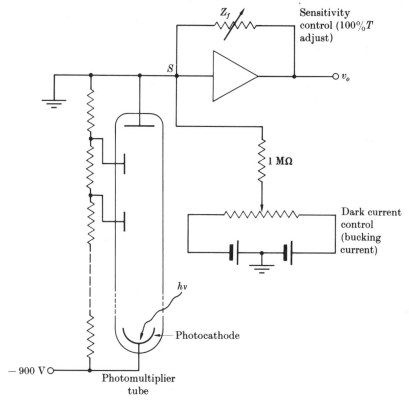

Fig. 7.16 Operational amplifier circuit for measurement of current from photomultiplier tube.

Example A circuit for amplification of the output of a photomultiplier tube is sketched in Fig. 7.16. By use of a variable feedback impedance Z_f one can select a multiplication factor appropriate to each level of incident illumination.

For instance, if the output registers on a recorder whose full scale voltage span is 10 mV the input current for full scale deflection will be 1×10^{-6} A if $Z_i = 10$ kΩ (internal resistance in photomultiplier tube) and 1×10^{-7} A if $Z_i = 100$ kΩ.

Note that the circuit also provides for cancellation (subtraction) of the photomultiplier dark current. A current equal to the dark current but of opposite sign is "added" to the photomultiplier output at the amplifier summing point. This compensating current can be set when the photomultiplier shutter is closed. At this time the voltage divider is adjusted until the amplifier output v_o is zero.

How large a multiplication factor may be reliably used in this type of circuit? Assuming that noise is not limiting, the feasible multiplication (largest useful value of Z_f) may be fixed by amplifier characteristics such as gain, input current, differential impedance, and by the accuracy of measurement desired. It is not difficult to develop an expression that interrelates these several variables and yields an answer. (In general, the use of larger values of Z_f also means greater stray capacitance and more likelihood of instability.)

In first approximation, current i_a entering the amplifier is defined by the potential across the input terminals $V_s - V_+ = V_s$ and the differential impedance Z_d* of the amplifier according to Ohm's law: $i_a = V_s/Z_d$. Since $V_o = i_i Z_f$, these equations can be combined to derive a value for Z_f related to amplifier parameters:

$$Z_f = (i_a/i_i)AZ_d. \qquad (7.6)$$

A maximum value for Z_f can now be deduced and thus the greatest current multiplication factor determined. It remains only to state the accuracy sought in a measurement. This accuracy will fix the ratio i_a/i_i in Eq. (7.6), since bias current i_a is the background current. For 1% accuracy, $i_a/i_i \leq 0.01$; for 0.1% accuracy $i_a/i_i \leqslant 0.001$.

Example What is the maximum value of Z_f that can be used with an FET operational amplifier whose $i_a = 1 \times 10^{-10}$ A, $Z_d = 10^{11}$ Ω, and $A = 5 \times 10^4$, if it is to measure current with 0.1% accuracy?

To attain this accuracy, $i_a/i_i \leqslant 0.001$. Substituting this value and the others in Eq. (7.6) gives

$$Z_f = 10^{-3} \times 5 \times 10^4 \times 10^{11} = 5 \times 10^{12} \; \Omega.$$

Interestingly, with this amplifier the limitation on input current is more restrictive than the value of Z_f. Even with the smallest current (1×10^{-7} A) that can be measured with the specified accuracy, R_f need be only 1 MΩ to obtain a satisfactory output voltage of 100 mV.

To determine very small currents an *electrometer* or other preamplifier of high input impedance and low noise level is inserted between the source and a standard operational amplifier. Often a device with a chopper input will still further reduce the minimum current that can be measured. [9]

In a *voltage measurement* the same considerations apply. The signal v_i yields a current when connected to input impedance Z_i. Since minimal current must be

---

* It should be emphasized that the differential impedance is the impedance *between* the input terminals. Often a common mode input impedance, which is always very much higher, is also quoted.

drawn for a precise measurement, it is necessary first to select a Z_i such that $Z_i \gg Z_{source}$. Further, the operational amplifier must have a differential impedance Z_d sufficiently high to permit the desired gain Z_f/Z_i. Again, Eq. (7.6) expresses the interrelationship.

In view of the requirement $Z_i \gg Z_{source}$, how can signals from high-impedance sources be determined? One operational amplifier circuit used for this purpose is the *voltage follower*, shown schematically in Fig. 7.17. It is strikingly different in two respects. The voltage to be measured is directed to the noninverting input and its entire output is returned to the inverting input. In this instance, neither input is grounded. Since the feedback fraction F is -1, the closed circuit gain of the amplifier is unity. In this case, $v_o = v_i$.

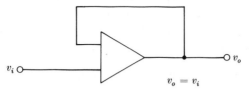

$$v_o = v_i$$

Fig. 7.17 Voltage follower. The circuit is valuable with high-impedance sources.

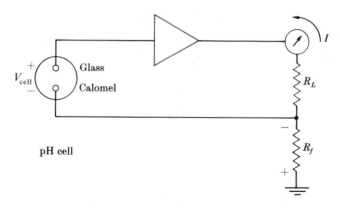

Fig. 7.18 Voltage-measuring circuit using series current feedback to the inverting input. A very high impedance is developed at the input of the operational amplifier. In this circuit only the error signal ($V_{cell} - V_{R_f}$) reaches the input and is amplified by the operational amplifier. Output meter I (calibrated in pH or millivolts) registers the current I needed to develop a voltage in feedback resistor R_f that is equal and opposite to that developed by the pH cell. Alternatively, a voltmeter V can be employed in lieu of I as the readout device. Various modifications of this circuit are used in commercial pH meters (Section 24–5).

With this series (not operational) feedback in the voltage follower, input impedance becomes tens of megohms. Thus it is possible to draw a current as small as 1 pA from a source connected in this way. A further consequence of the feedback is a very low output impedance (about 1 Ω) and an output current nearly independent of voltage.

Another circuit used with high-impedance sources is illustrated in Fig. 7.18. Note that the emf of a pH cell with a glass electrode (high resistance) is to be determined.

Again there are major differences between this arrangement and the usual operational amplifier circuit. First, an MOS transistor pair or other device with very high input impedance is required for the operational amplifier input. Second, the voltage source is part of the negative feedback loop from output to inverting input. Third, output current exists in part of the feedback loop and then flows to ground through resistor R_f. By intent, the voltage drop in R_f is opposite in sign to the cell voltage. Since $V_i = V_{cell} - V_{R_f}$, only the voltage difference appears at the inverting input. Though V_i will not be zero when the source is first connected, the amplifier will drive the difference to zero, since the noninverting terminal is grounded. The amplifier will do so by adjusting its output current appropriately.

The basic circuit of Fig. 7.18 is used in several pH meters (Section 24.5). Either the output current, which is proportional to the cell voltage, or the voltage drop across R_f can be registered as the readout. In general, the high-impedance electrode is connected to the inverting input as shown to simplify shielding of both these high-impedance elements.

7.8 PRECISE CONTROL OF CURRENT AND VOLTAGE

As might be expected, the circuits described in the last section can also be used as sources of constant, precisely known current or voltage. For this purpose, a standard voltage source is used as V_i and the operational amplifier circuit is designed to draw minimum current.

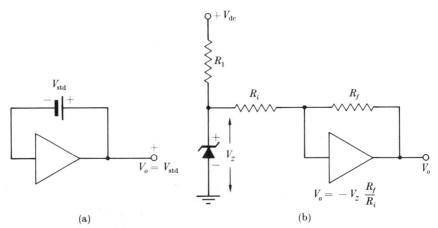

(a)   (b)

Fig. 7.19 Standard voltage sources based on an operational amplifier and a known voltage. Considerable current can be drawn from the output of either source without affecting the known voltage. (a) Standard cell or other voltage reference across output and inverting input. The noninverting input is grounded and the output taken relative to ground. (b) Voltage multiplying circuit with a Zener diode reference. R_i is chosen so that the current in the Zener diode is controlled by the operational amplifier and therefore is constant.

In Fig. 7.19 two *potentiostats*, or constant voltage sources, based on an operational amplifier and a voltage reference like a Weston cell are illustrated. The first is especially simple since the feedback loop consists only of V_{ref}. The amplifier output voltage equals the reference voltage. Since the noninverting input is at ground, the output voltage must just offset the reference and be of opposite polarity in order that the inverting input can be driven to ground potential. The operational amplifier can provide considerable current while maintaining this output value, though it cannot exceed the usual maximum (about 5 to 20 mA). It should be reemphasized that this current does not flow through the cell: the amplifier input current is minute.

The schematic of a more versatile Zener reference source is pictured in Fig. 7.19b. The current through the Zener diode is provided essentially entirely by the amplifier. Thus it operates at constant current and furnishes a voltage constant to 0.01 %. If more current is needed (the Zener diode uses part of the operational amplifier output), a booster amplifier can be used inside the feedback loop.

Example   The circuit of Fig. 7.18 is often applied to constant-potential electrolysis. It is redrawn in Fig. 7.20 as it might be used with a three-electrode cell. The most evident difference is that resistances R_L and R_f are now solution resistances between pairs of electrodes. A booster amplifier has been added to increase the current available for electrolysis. This amplifier is a standard noninverting type that allows a much larger current to flow in the electrolytic cell than could be furnished by the operational amplifier.

Since the booster amplifier is in the feedback loop, the potential drop between the reference electrode and the working electrode at which electrolysis occurs is still maintained constant (at V_{ref}). Usually V_{std} is set by adjustment of a potentiometer (not shown).

During electrolysis the current through the cell may vary through several orders of magnitude, but as long as it does not exceed the output of the booster amplifier the potential of the working electrode relative to the reference will be maintained equal to V_{std}. Precise control of the species being electrolyzed can thus be achieved.

A generalized version of a constant current source or *amperostat* is shown in Fig. 7.21a. A constant current is developed in the feedback loop. To achieve this condition, advantage is taken of equality of the current in an operational feedback

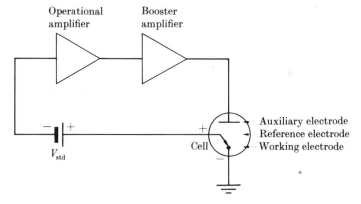

Fig. 7.20 Potentiostat for controlled potential electrolysis. The circuit holds the voltage difference $V_{reference} - V_{working}$ constant at V_{std}. Usually V_{std} is supplied by a potentiometer circuit and can be set to a desired value. The booster amplifier ensures that much larger currents are available than the operational amplifier alone can supply.

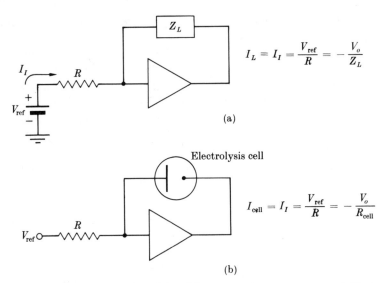

$$I_L = I_I = \frac{V_{ref}}{R} = -\frac{V_o}{Z_L}$$

(a)

$$I_{cell} = I_I = \frac{V_{ref}}{R} = -\frac{V_o}{R_{cell}}$$

(b)

Fig. 7.21 Application of an operational amplifier to supply constant current. Current in load Z_L or the electrolysis cell is that in the input circuit V_{ref}/R, but cannot exceed the maximum output of the amplifier. (a) A general circuit. (b) An electrolysis cell circuit.

loop with that in the input. A known current is developed at the summing point S and continued through the desired circuit, which is symbolized by feedback impedance Z_L.

A practical application of the circuit to control of current in electrolysis is shown in Fig. 7.21b. The two limitations of placing the electrolysis cell in the feedback loop are that neither current I_i nor voltage V_{cell} can exceed the rated output values of the amplifier.

In Fig. 7.22 a more versatile amperostat is sketched. No current is drawn from the reference voltage source and currents as large as those a booster amplifier can supply will be held constant. Neither load terminal needs to be grounded.

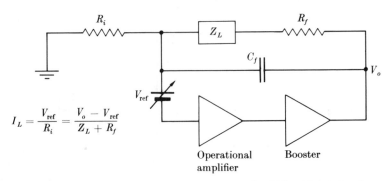

$$I_L = \frac{V_{ref}}{R_i} = \frac{V_o - V_{ref}}{Z_L + R_f}$$

Operational   Booster
amplifier

Fig. 7.22 Amperostat that furnishes constant current to load Z_L without drawing current from the reference voltage source. The current may be adjusted to any level available from the booster amplifier as long as the voltage output of the operational amplifier is not exceeded. C_f and R_f should be inserted only if needed for stability.

REFERENCES

Operational amplifier theory and applications are treated on an introductory to intermediate level in:

1. Burr-Brown, *Handbook and Catalog of Operational Amplifiers*. Tuscon, Ariz.: Burr-Brown Research Corp., 1969
2. H. V. Malmstadt, C. G. Enke, and E. C. Toren, *Electronics for Scientists*. Chapter 8. New York: 1962
3. R. G. McKee, "A Modular Approach to Instrumentation," *Anal. Chem.* **42** (11), 91A (1970)
4. *McKee-Pedersen Applications Notes*, a bimonthly company publication of McKee-Pedersen Instruments, Danville, Calif.: Vol. 1 appeared in 1966
5. Philbrick, *Applications Manual for Computing Amplifiers*. Philbrick Researches, Inc., Dedham, Mass., 1966
6. C. N. Reilley, "Instrumentation Based on Operational Amplifiers," *J. Chem. Educ.* **39**, A853, A933 (1962)

Also of interest are:

7. R. W. Landee, D. C. Davis, and A. P. Albrecht, *Electronic Designer's Handbook*. New York: McGraw-Hill, 1957
8. B. J. Ley, A. G. Lutz, and C. F. Rehberg, *Linear Circuit Analysis*. New York: McGraw-Hill, 1959
9. H. V. Malmstadt, "A Versatile and Inexpensive pH Recording Electrometer," *J. Chem. Educ.* **41**, 148 (1964)
10. C. F. Morrison, Jr.,*Generalized Instrumentation for Research and Teaching*. Pullman, Wash.: Wash. State University, 1964

EXERCISES

7.1 Develop an expression for the output voltage in each of the circuits of Fig. 7.23 in terms of the input voltage(s).

$$[Ans.:\ a)\ V_o = (1 + R_f/R_i)V_i;\ b)\ V_o = V_2 - V_1;$$

$$c)\ V_o = \frac{R_4}{R_3 + R_4}\left(1 + \frac{R_2}{R_1}\right)V_2 - \frac{R_2}{R_1}V_1.]$$

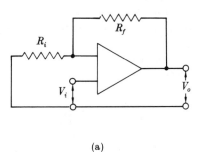

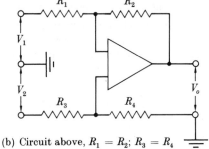

(a)

(b) Circuit above, $R_1 = R_2$; $R_3 = R_4$

(c) Circuit above, $R_1 \neq R_2$; $R_3 \neq R_4$

Figure 7.23

7.2 Draw a schematic diagram of an operational amplifier circuit that will provide precision variable multiplication of an input voltage.

7.3 a) Draw a schematic diagram of a multioperational amplifier network combination suitable for obtaining an output proportional to $\log(i_1/i_2)$ where i_1 and i_2 are two input currents. Assume both are positive, i.e., are directed into the system.

b) Show by block diagram how this system can be used as part of a double-beam spectrophotometer.

7.4 For the practical differentiator circuit of Fig. 7.12 assume $C_f = 100$ pF and $R_i = 10^5$ Ω. Using the criterion given in Section 7.5 for 1% accuracy in differentiation, calculate possible values for C_i and R_f if signals below 1 kHz comprise the input.

7.5 Draw a schematic diagram of an operational amplifier circuit that will find the area under the peaks registered by a gas chromatograph with a flame ionization detector. The chromatograph output is a current. What are the units of the areas reported?

7.6 Show that the output voltage of the circuit in Fig. 7.24 is given by the expression: $V_o = (1 + R_1/R_2)V_{\text{ref}}$.

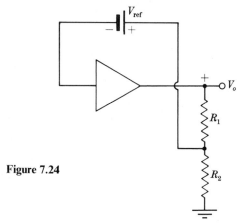

Figure 7.24

7.7 Discuss the usefulness of the circuit of Fig. 7.4 as a constant voltage generator if a reference (standard) voltage source is substituted for v_i. How much current can the generator furnish if v_o is to be constant? To what extent is the choice of a value for Z_i limited?

7.8 Redraw Fig. 7.18 with a potentiometer in place of R_f. How can the potentiometer serve as the readout? What is the magnitude of amplifier current I in this case?

7.9 The operational amplifier circuit of Fig. 7.25 serves as a readout for the thermocouple which provides its input voltage. Assume the thermocouple has a resistance of 20 Ω.

a) Does the circuit successfully treat it as a voltage source? That is, does it transfer voltage without drawing current? Explain very briefly.

b) Develop an equation for v_o in terms of the thermocouple emf.

c) What advantage is gained by use of the potentiometer?

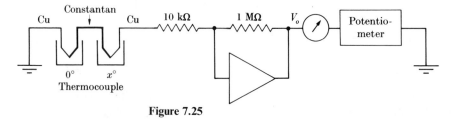

Figure 7.25

7.10 a) Develop an equation for the output voltage of the circuit of Fig. 7.26a in terms of the cell resistance R. What advantage does this circuit have over a Wheatstone bridge in monitoring a conductometric titration?

  b) The oscillator can be represented by the Thévenin equivalent circuit in Fig. 7.26b. How will oscillator voltage v_i vary if R_{cell} varies from 1000 to 700 Ω during a titration? What relative error in v_o will result?

  c) Sketch another circuit in which the error discussed in (b) is minimized by using an additional operational amplifier. [See *MPI Applications Notes* **2** (6), 25 (1967).]

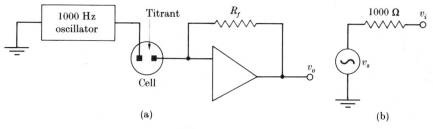

(a)   (b)

Figure 7.26

Chapter 8

SIGNAL-TO-NOISE OPTIMIZATION

8.1 INTRODUCTION

The demand for sensitivity in measurement, i.e., lower detection limits for analytical methods and greater precision in routine analysis, increases steadily. As a result, it has become increasingly necessary to develop ways to deal with the random background present in all measurements. While noise is only one of the factors that may limit accuracy, its peculiar importance is that it is *the* limiting factor in fixing the possible precision of measurements. Noise ultimately establishes the lowest concentration of a species that can be quantitatively estimated, just as it fixes the precision of determinations at higher levels. In this chapter attention will be given to a variety of instrumental procedures devised to optimize the quality of measurements.

Basically, *noise* originates in the kinds of motions of atoms and molecules associated with temperature and with the necessary randomness of events on the atomic level. A more detailed analysis will be undertaken in the next section. Noise may appear in any module in an instrument, signal source, sample cell, detector, amplifier, processing stage, or readout device. In this chapter attention will be focused on noise in the detector and amplifier, for these are usually the crucial modules in terms of extending the sensitivity of a measurement.

Over against noise stands the signal, the information for which a measurement was made. In spectrophotometry the signal is the change in intensity of light of a given wavelength as a result of sample absorption. Or in Raman spectrometry it is an alteration in frequency attributable to a vibration in a molecule under study. Again, in dc polarography it is the diffusion current and halfwave potential associated with electrolysis of an analytical species.

How do these definitions of signal and noise relate to a more general discussion of the quality of measurement? It will be helpful to distinguish the ways factors contributing to poor precision whether on the macroscopic level or at the limit of detection are analyzed and controlled. Most measurements are carried out on a macroscopic level where uncertainty in a determination is analyzable as determinate and/or indeterminate error. In these procedures the indeterminate error is attributable directly not to molecular fluctuations but to random variation in temperature, humidity, pressure, line voltage, and a dozen other parameters. Closer control of environmental variables, more stable instruments, or a different method of measurement will improve the precision of determination. These macroscopic approaches were discussed systematically in Chapter 1.

At or near the limit of dectability noise is interpreted somewhat differently. The role of the instrument or its modules is of concern. We distinguish *signal*, taken as the analytical information in the output, from the *noise* also present. All the variable, unwanted part of the response of the module is usually subsumed under the label "noise" and an analysis of its origins is undertaken. A module is then described as operating with a given *signal-to-noise ratio* (*S/N*). This measure of quality has been generally accepted.

Confusion may arise in considering the output of modules that generate an appreciable background response. For example, a gamma-ray detector produces a background count and a photomultiplier tube a dark current even when sample is not present. This "baseline" response is not the result of indeterminate error or noise but of the nature of the device. It must be subtracted or allowed for. The true signal is a difference between total response and background. This situation will be taken up as each method of measurement is discussed in later chapters. The importance of a clear understanding becomes apparent when it is appreciated that both the signal and background "count" of such a module will be subject to uncertainty, i.e. contain noise. For both signal and background the noise is usually specified by calculating the standard deviation of the fluctuations observed.

Example In flame emission spectrometry (Chapter 14) the intensity of a characteristic atomic emission line is measured to determine an element quantitatively. The observed intensity I_{obs} is the sum of the true emission intensity for the line I_l and the background emission of flame and other elements in the sample I_b.

How is I_l determined? The spectrometer wavelength is set at the characteristic wavelength and adjusted until maximum intensity is indicated. With an appropriately narrow slit, intensity is then measured by observation over a brief period to average out some noise. The wavelength setting is next changed very slightly until only background radiation is incident on the detector and background intensity is observed over a brief interval. The line intensity is $I_l = I_{obs} - I_b$.

What strategies exist for improving the quality of sensitive measurements? One is certainly to enhance the signal by all possible means, a type of approach that will be of interest in treating each technique. A second is to reduce noise, a topic that will be explored at some length in this chapter and in Section 19.9. A third is to optimize *S/N* by techniques that discriminate between signal and noise, an approach that will be considered in the last section of this chapter.

Since the concern in instrumentation is with the final result of a measurement, attention must be given not only to noise originating in a particular module but also to its transfer from one module to the next. For that reason we must not lose sight of the influence of a given module upon the preceding and succeeding one. Questions of transfer of voltage, current, and power are thus relevant. Often, by judicious arrangement of transfer conditions, noise that has originated in a module may be selectively discriminated against in transfer of "signal" to the next module.

8.2 SENSITIVITY AND DETECTION LIMITS

Because the detection limit for a technique defines its value to a considerable degree it is worthwhile to define this concept as precisely as possible. At the outset, however, it must be differentiated from the idea of sensitivity. Sensitivity has been used in two different ways in much of the literature. Basically, sensitivity identifies the response of a module to an input as indicated in Section 1.6. For an instrument as a whole this concept may be expanded to include its response to a sample. This type of sensitivity S' is defined by the differential quotient

$$S' = dI_o/dQ, \tag{8.1}$$

where I_o is the output of the instrument and Q is the quantity of substance whose property is measured.

Sensitivity is there a measure of degree of response and represents a function that will be defined over the entire range in which a response is possible. The limiting sensitivity, i.e., the value of S' as $Q \to 0$, will be related to the detection limit. It is precisely at this concentration level that noise looms large and may completely overwhelm the signal that represents a legitimate response. How is the detector input I_i to be separated into signal and noise? Or more appropriately, by what factor must I_i exceed the estimated random fluctuation in I_i for the indication to be taken as detection of the property sought?

Limit of detection.   From a measurement perspective, the limit of detection represents the least concentration of amount of a substance that can with any confidence be said to be present when a particular technique is used. It depends on both statistical fluctuations in background and the limiting sensitivity of the measurement. Neither will appear explicitly.

The defining equation for the limit of detection D is

$$D = c = \bar{c} + ks, \tag{8.2}$$

where c is the minimum concentration a particular measurement can establish, $\bar{c}$ is the amount of c that would be assumed present if measurements on a blank were converted to concentration using the limiting value of S', and s is the estimated standard deviation of the fluctuations observed in measurements on the blank.* To use Eq. (8.2) with any confidence in a practical situation, it has been recommended that measurements be made on as many as twenty blanks. Though this is often an insufficient sample to approximate an infinite set, which would be required for an exact value of standard deviation, it does at least provide a good estimate. There can be no knowledge that the distribution of results follows a normal pattern (Gaussian distribution), but in most cases this assumption is reasonable. There is finally a question about the magnitude of k in Eq. (8.2). Since the statement is a definition, its value is to a degree arbitrary. While a convincing argument has been made that $k = 3$ is the best choice [8] many workers have proposed $k = 2$. The intent in any case is to provide a statement of the limit of detection that holds at the 95% confidence level. By definition, at this level of confidence only once in 20 times would a larger readout be the result of chance; 95% of the time it would represent detection of the species sought.

---

* For Eq. (8.2) to be applied successfully, the *least measure*, the smallest increment in readout that can be recognized, must be small enough for statistical fluctuations that are valid to be observed. Use of too large a least measure will result in establishing a meaningless lower limit to the detectability.

In many instances the limit of detectability will be estimated from a calibration curve rather than by measurements on blanks. External standards are used. How may such results be used to fix a detection limit? Both the number of standards and the range of concentration they represent will critically affect the ability to make such a decision. It is of course necessary that the series extend to the lowest concentration that can be made up with any reliability. With a range of six or more samples whose largest concentration is at least four times the smallest, satisfactory precision is obtained. [7] Relatively little additional precision is secured by increasing the range or the number of samples.

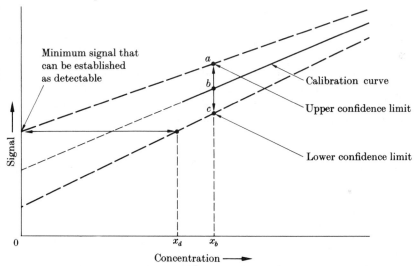

Fig. 8.1 A proposed method [7] for defining limit of detectability and a decision limit in terms of a calibration curve. The calibration curve is a least-squares best curve (regression curve) determined with external standards. The upper and lower confidence limits represent the probable range of signal, e.g., when known concentration x_b is present. The signal observed is likely to exceed or fall short of these limits only a few percent of the time. The detection limit x_d is defined as the highest likely concentration corresponding to the minimum signal that can be established as detectable.

It has been suggested that a more appropriate set of concepts includes both a minimum signal that can be accepted as different from background, termed a *decision limit*, and a limit of detectability, the minimum concentration relating to this signal. The concentration would be the lowest value that could be distinguished from zero. The proposed interrelation of these terms is shown in Fig. 8.1. Note that the calibration curve is flanked by an upper curve indicating the upper range for values with 95 % confidence, and a lower curve indicating the same idea for results on the low side. Finally, a determination limit may also be defined if there is sufficient information. It is to be regarded as the minimum concentration that can be determined at an acceptable level (arbitrarily defined) of precision.

8.3 NOISE

All extraneous and essentially random fluctuations added to a signal are termed noise. Such random variations have their ultimate origin in the particulate or discrete nature of matter, charge, and energy. Noise has a statistical origin and may therefore be minimized but not eliminated. As a consequence, noise establishes both the limiting sensitivity of a module and the limit of detection of a technique or instrument. For convenience the present discussion will be restricted to electrical signals. The treatment is therefore directly applicable to most modules used in instruments. In other instances, as in treating lamp emission, an adaptation can be made.[1]

Environmental noise. Surroundings are always one source of noise. Light reflected by objects in a room, energy radiated by 60 Hz electrical lines in walls, and mechanical vibrations transmitted through a floor are three very common examples. The "pick-up" of such random energy from surroundings may be minimized by techniques like shielding, thermostatting, and filtering.

Satisfactory electrical shielding is perhaps hardest to devise, especially protection against the 60 Hz power distribution system in a building. Two steps should be taken. First, all shielding for an instrument should be grounded to the same *spot*, whether it is a pipe or ground "terminal." It can be shown that there are differences of hundreds of millivolts between different places on most grounds. A spurious input signal through leads to ground can be avoided when a single connection is used. Second, for work at very low noise levels, differential-input amplifiers that have a high common-mode rejection ratio (Section 5.6) should be used. Any 60 Hz pickup will be common to both inputs of the circuit and will cancel when only the difference in signals at the two inputs is amplified.

Example In a sensitive amplifier or oscilloscope, leads should be kept short and the input to the first stage should be well shielded, especially if the source of the signal has a high impedance. These steps will minimize pickup of 60 Hz radiation. Adequate insulation or thermostatting must be incorporated to protect against temperature and humidity changes.

Johnson noise. It is possible to classify noise roughly according to its origin. One very basic type is noise that originates in a resistor (or conductor). Recall that all electrical signals are an ordered drift of electrons superposed on a basic random fluctuation. The noise associated with such fluctuations is called Johnson noise or resistor noise, since its magnitude is proportional to $R^{1/2}$. It has a root-mean-square voltage component given by the expression

$$v_{rms} = \sqrt{4kTR\Delta f}, \tag{8.3}$$

where k is the Boltzmann factor, T is the absolute temperature, R is the resistance, and Δf the frequency bandwidth in hertz over which a measurement is made. Since the dependence is on Δf and not on frequency, Johnson noise may be called "white" noise: the contribution per $Hz^{1/2}$ is constant across the spectrum. Note that this noise exists whether there is a flow of current or not.

Example A resistance of 300 kΩ at 300 °K (about room temperature) in the input of an amplifier whose bandwidth is 10^5 Hz contributes an rms noise voltage of

$$7.4 \times 10^{-12} \sqrt{RT\Delta f} = 7.4 \times 10^{-12} \sqrt{3 \times 10^5 \times 300 \times 10^5} = 20 \times 10^{-6} \text{ V} \quad \text{or} \quad 20\,\mu\text{V}.$$

The resistance in the first stage of an amplifier will, of course, be the most important: All its Johnson noise will be amplified by succeeding stages. For example, if the first stage has a voltage gain of 50, noise that originates at its input will be 50 times more important than even the noise in the second stage. For this reason designing for high gain in the initial stage is also wise.

Ways to minimize Johnson noise are implicit in Eq. (8.3). It will be worthwhile in some instances to lower the temperature; in others, to narrow the amplifier bandwidth. For example, photomultipliers and other radiation detectors are often cooled to minimize Johnson noise.

Shot noise.   This is associated with variations in number of charged particles crossing a boundary or arriving at an electrode.* It arises from the essential randomness of such events. Shot noise originates in transistors as electrons or holes cross the depletion later to the collector and in vacuum and photomultiplier tubes when electrons arrive at the anode. Such shot noise can be described by the following formula:

$$i_{rms} = \sqrt{2Ie\Delta f},\qquad (8.4)$$

where e is the charge on the electron, and I is the collector current or other current due to some "single-event" type of process. Clearly, shot noise is also white noise since it depends only on bandwidth Δf. Ordinarily, shot noise is small in magnitude, and may be neglected in comparison with Johnson noise.

Flicker noise.   A third major type of noise is that termed flicker or excess noise. It is also called $1/f$ noise since it contributes an rms voltage proportional to $1/f^n$ where f is the frequency and n is a constant near unity. The mechanism by which it originates is not well established. In general it arises where granular material is present, as in certain types of carbon resistors, or where clusters of atoms may be involved, as in photocathode emission. What is clear is that flicker noise is likely to predominate at frequencies somewhere below 300 Hz. In this regard electron tubes are "quieter" than transistors; among tubes, triodes are less noisy than pentodes; and among transistors, FETs are quieter than regular (bipolar) transistors. Flicker noise is a serious source of uncertainty in small signals of dc or very low frequency such as a spectrophotometer signal.

8.4 MINIMIZING NOISE IN A SYSTEM

Under many conditions the magnitude of the signal (information) from a module or instrument is large compared with that of the noise, and the noise may be ignored. For most macroscopic measurements this situation holds. Yet the greater the noise component, the greater is the uncertainty or error in a measurement. As a result, every reasonable means of reducing noise is ordinarily employed in instrument design.

There are three common situations in which noise may be a significant factor. First, it will be of concern whenever source energy is limited and environmental noise is high, as in IR and NMR spectrometry. Since the signal cannot be large, noise

---

* The name is meant to suggest its resemblance to the discreteness of a stream of small shot. While it was first described by Schottky, it is not named for him.

from the surroundings together with instrumental noise can introduce serious error even at ordinary levels of sample concentration. Second, noise will be of interest whenever there is a desire to increase the precision of a measurement. Finally, noise will actually be the limiting factor in measurements near the limit of detectability as discussed in the last section.

The signal-to-noise ratio in a particular system is defined as the ratio of *power* in the signal relative to that in the noise:

$$S/N = 10 \log_{10} (V_s^2/V_n^2), \tag{8.5}$$

where V_s is the signal voltage and V_n the noise voltage.*

When noise signals from independent sources combine, the resultant noise is the sum of the squares of rms noise voltages. If each noise source is designated by a letter subscript, the observed total rms noise V_N is given by

$$V_N^2 = V_a^2 + V_b^2 + \cdots + V_n^2.$$

The contributions to V_N^2 can also be analyzed into component frequencies. On this basis V_N^2 becomes

$$V_N^2 = \sum V_{Ni}^2 \delta f_i = V_{N1}^2 \delta f_1 + V_{N2}^2 \delta f_2 + \cdots,$$

where V_{Ni} is the noise associated with each small bandwidth δf_i. If the noise is white and all bandwidths δf_i are one Hz, $V_{N1} = V_{N2} = \cdots$, and

$$V_N^2 = V_{Ni}^2 \sum \delta f_i = V_{Ni}^2 \Delta F,$$

where ΔF is the system bandwidth and V_{Ni}^2 is the noise power per hertz.

Consider now a representative instrument in which modules are connected in sequence. Only the detector furnishes signal, but each subsequent module adds noise. It appears crucial that the detector yields a large S/N and that modules which follow do not diminish the ratio seriously. The *noise figure* (NF) of a module is a convenient measure of the degree to which a module degrades S/N. The definition is

$$NF = \frac{S_i/N_i}{S_o/N_o}, \tag{8.6}$$

where the subscripts i and o refer to module input and output, respectively.

Example 1 What should the noise figure be for an ideal amplifier? Since the amplifier should contribute no additional noise and should amplify the signal and noise voltages at its input equally, it should have a NF of unity (0 dB).

Example 2 The S/N ratio at the input of an amplifier is 50 and at the output 25. Its noise figure in decibels is 10 log 50/25 = 10 log 2 = 3 dB.

---

* Voltages are squared since the power developed in a resistance or impedance is just V^2/R or V^2/Z. In Eq. (8.5) R or Z cancels since it can be assumed that both voltages are developed in the same resistance or impedance.

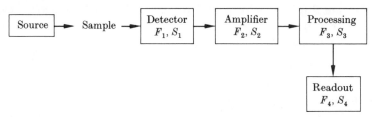

Fig. 8.2 Modules comprising a single-channel instrument. Symbols are: sensitivity, S_i, and noise figure, F_i.

When noise figures are known for modules that are coupled as shown in Fig. 8.2 to form a single-channel instrument, an overall noise figure can be calculated. If the modules are of sensitivity or gain $S_1, S_2, \ldots$ (Section 1.6) and noise figure $F_1, F_2, \ldots$, the system will have a noise figure [1]

$$F = F_1 + \frac{F_2 - 1}{S_1} + \frac{F_3 - 1}{S_1 S_2} + \cdots. \tag{8.7}$$

Equation (8.7) confirms that noise in modules becomes progressively less critical toward the readout end of an instrument. Note that the denominator of each term is the product of all preceding sensitivities or gains. This is the result noted earlier for the first stage of an amplifier.

How may an input signal be transmitted through a system, the proper operations performed, and its S/N optimized as much as possible? An important consideration will of course be the nature of the signal, but to a large extent it will be characteristics such as signal frequency, system bandwidth, and drift that establish the overall quality of the measurement. Each of these factors will now be considered briefly.

Signal frequency. The energy beam falling on a detector in a chemical instrument is often dc, i.e. zero-frequency, or at most slowly varying dc. It is evident that this is the case in instruments such as pH meters, dc polarographs, mass spectrometers, and gas chromatographs. But does this description hold when light (frequency 10^{14} to 10^{16} Hz) is used in spectrophotometry or when high-frequency electrical energy (10^8 to 10^{10} Hz) is used in NMR and ESR spectrometry? What quantity is measured in the latter techniques? In all these instances the quantity sensed is the rate or number of quanta or photons (of a given frequency) arriving at a detector. The detectors used are relatively insensitive to differences in the frequency of the radiation.*

Since flicker effect or $1/f$ noise dominates at these low frequencies, it is advantageous to shift the measuring frequency if noise is a problem at all. For this purpose, the instrument channel is modulated by imposing a sine or square wave, or chopped, i.e. interrupted periodically. The process will be described in Section 8.6.

Drift. The tendency of the output of a system to vary slowly with time creates a form of low-frequency noise. Sometimes it is termed baseline drift. In an instrument it is often a major factor in defining sensitivity of measurement and the detection limit. Drift can seriously affect the precision and accuracy of results. It may be noted that

---

* In dispersive instruments one frequency band at a time is brought to the detector.

dc offset (Section 7.3) is an error related to that of drift, in that it too is capable of amplification as a signal passes through a system. Both drift and dc offset may also be minimized by modulation techniques (Section 8.6).

Bandwidth. By using as narrow a system bandwidth Δf as possible, both Johnson and shot noise can be greatly reduced. Equations (8.3) and (8.4) make this clear. How much can the bandwidth be narrowed for a given measurement without introducing other problems? The most straightforward answer is found by examining the time interval a module or an instrument requires to respond to an abrupt change in its input called a *step*. For example, a very-low-frequency square wave might be directed to an input. Its height is not critical as long as the module or instrument is not over-loaded. What is sought by this process is an estimate of the rate of response of the instrument. How long a time is required for the response to rise to $x\%$ of its final value? This interval, t_r, will be the *measurement time* of the instrument. It can be shown that the effective instrument bandwidth Δf is related to t_r by the expression

$$\Delta f = \frac{1}{2} \int_0^\infty [a(t)^2] \ dt \simeq \frac{1}{t_r}, \tag{8.8}$$

where $a(t)$ is the slope of the relative time-response curve. Bandwidth is in hertz and time in seconds. The approximate relation stated in Eq. (8.8), $\Delta f \propto 1/t_r$, is quite ade-quate for present purposes. When t_r is defined as the rise time, it is the time required for a signal to increase from 10% to 90% of its final value.

Example 1 What is the approximate bandwidth of a system whose response to a step change in input requires 10^{-2} s? It should be $1/t_r$ or $1/0.01 = 100$ Hz.

Example 2 In any instrument, the measurement time is fixed by the slowest module. In an infrared spectrometer that uses a thermocouple detector (35 ms response time) this module has the slowest response. Consider that the spectrometer radiation beam is chopped at 13 Hz and frequencies of 13 ± 1 Hz are passed by the amplifier that handles the detector output. A recorder with a 1 sec full-scale response time is used. Two useful kinds of questions can be asked.

a) Are the parts compatible in terms of bandwidth and frequency? If it is assumed that the rotating sector chopper produces one square pulse of light with every revolution, each pulse will have a length of $(1/2) \times (1/13) = 39$ ms. The reason for the slow rate of chopping is seen to be the need to match pulse lengths to the thermocouple response. The longer response times of modules that follow should provide some averaging of noise toward zero.

b) If the sharpest absorption peak to be determined is likely to be 5 cm^{-1} wide, how fast a spectral scan can be made without losing precision? The 1 s response time of the recorder is limiting. It appears that the scan rate cannot be faster than 5 cm^{-1} s^{-1}. (See Section 17.7.)

Example 3 Will noise be a greater problem in a system with a short or a long response time? A short response time corresponds to a broad bandwidth. Both Johnson and shot noise are proportional to $(\Delta f)^{1/2}$. For this reason a system with a fast response is more likely to be noisy.

8.5 SIGNAL AVERAGING

In many modern instruments it is possible to select the system time constant or interval used for measurement, at least within prescribed limits. This constitutes a choice of bandwidth in the light of Eq. (8.8). How is such a choice related to time-averaging or *ensemble-averaging techniques* in which repeated measurements of a given property are averaged? It proves to be the case that at a given setting of the independent variable of measurement, e.g., wavenumber for an IR absorption curve, averaging minimizes noise with an effectiveness proportional to the square root of the time of averaging. If a system is sufficiently steady a long interval may be used for one measurement. The requirement is seldom met, however, and it is more common to average many short scans until an equivalent total time has elapsed. Averaging is carried out by both digital and analog devices.

Example It is desired to obtain a precise intensity reading of an NMR absorption peak at $-7.10\,\delta$ units relative to TMS. To reduce the noise background is it better to use a 2 s time constant during measurement and an appropriately slow scan or use several fast scans (at lower rf field strength to avoid saturation) with 0.1 s time constant and then average 20 scans? In terms of minimizing noise the results should be identical, for noise occurring over a 2 s interval is averaged.

To the degree that a set of N repeated traces corresponds to a normal distribution, the average of an ensemble will have a precision $(N)^{1/2}$ times better than a single trace. The signal-to-noise ratio will improve by the same factor.

Modes of averaging. Regular ensemble averaging calls for summing N measurements and then dividing the total by N. An arithmetic mean is calculated. Alternatively, as long as N is selected in advance, each value can be divided by N initially and the quotients summed directly to secure the mean.

If the latter type of calculation is used, *exponential averaging* can be substituted at will with a possible significant saving of time. The procedure is also known as a *running average*. The running average A_i is the average up to and including point i and is given by

$$A_i = A_{i-1} + \frac{(\text{new value} - A_{i-1})}{N}, \tag{8.9}$$

where A_{i-1} is the running average just prior to i and N is the total number of results to be averaged. A simultaneous oscilloscopic readout allows one to determine when a desired clarity of result has been attained. Often an exponential average may be terminated when as few as one fourth of the total number of results that are initially assumed necessary have been averaged.

Curve recovery. Most averaging programs for chemical instruments are used to elucidate features of a curve such as absorption peaks. The instrument with which they are used need be stable only for the period of one trace. Each trace is added to those accumulated only after the independent variable has reached a magnitude that signifies the beginning of the portion of interest, or after an external "trigger" or gating pulse is sensed.

In order to recover a curve when $S/N \ll 1$, special strategies are necessary. No longer is it sufficient to deal with an entire curve. Features can be recovered by dividing the region to be averaged into M equal-width channels and averaging the desired number of times within each channel independently. Resolution of features comparable to the least measure, the channel width, is attained after sufficient averaging.* For example, when $S/N \approx 0.1$, an average of 30,000 samples may be required to recover a curve.

8.6 MODULATION; CHOPPING

To minimize $1/f$ noise, the central frequency of measurement is frequently shifted from zero (direct current) to a high frequency by modulating the signal, as discussed in Section 8.4. The rationale for modulation is set forth clearly in Fig. 8.3. By shifting the signal frequency to a region where background or noise is lower, the signal can be perceived more reliably. In the next section the extraction of the signal by demodulation will be discussed.

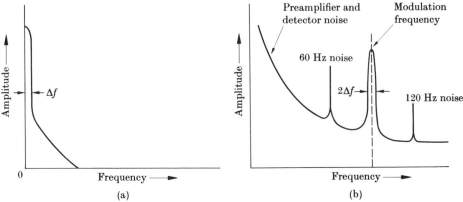

Fig. 8.3 Use of chopping or modulation to shift the frequency of a dc signal away from the region where $1/f$ noise is large. (a) The signal. Its information is centered in a narrow band at nearly zero frequency. (b) The signal after chopping at about 80 Hz and passage through a preamplifier. Note the high $1/f$ noise level from the detector and amplifier stage and the 60 Hz and harmonic 120 Hz power line pickup.

One very effective type of chopper was shown in Fig. 7.7. Others are in evidence throughout the text. Accordingly, only a modulator that represents a type of optimum development for low-noise work, the dynamic capacitor, will be treated here.

The dynamic capacitor. In this conversion device, mechanical energy supplied by an ac-actuated solenoid is used to modulate an imposed dc signal from a detector. The dc input is fed to a fixed metal plate of a capacitor, the other plate of which is vibrated at a frequency of perhaps 450 Hz. The arrangement used and the associated circuit

---

* The device employed is sometimes called a "box car" integrator.

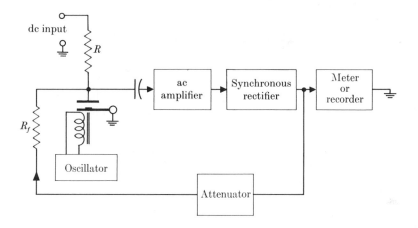

Fig. 8.4 A schematic of a dynamic capacitor (vibrating reed) electrometer circuit.

that gives an output voltage proportional to the input signal are depicted in a block diagram in Fig. 8.4. The ac output of the capacitor is proportional to the charge collected, thus to the dc input.

Noise introduced by the dynamic capacitor, drift in its response, and instability in the associated amplifier are special problems in this type of design. To minimize these factors, negative feedback to the dc (non-grounded) side of the vibrating capacitor is also ordinarily provided in the circuit, as shown. Where stability is of paramount importance, feedback sufficient to "cancel" the dc input is common. The detection limit of such an electrometer is 10^{-17} A.

The dynamic capacitor finds particular use wherever a detector furnishing extremely small direct currents, such as a glass electrode (Section 24.3) or an ionization chamber (Section 31.5), is employed. Its design and construction are critical. [14, 15]

Frequency response. What rate of chopping should be used in a system? As noted in the preceding section, the frequency selected should, if possible, shift the signal beyond the region of intense $1/f$ noise, which ends at about 300 Hz. It will not be possible, e.g., when a detector has a long response time. In addition, the frequency should be compatible with the general bandwidth desired for the system. In effect, chopping averages a signal over one complete chopping cycle and defines the highest frequency that can be present. Upper frequency limits available at present are about 1000 Hz for an electromechanical chopper and several hundred kHz for a semiconductor chopper. As we will see in the next section, subsequent filtering ordinarily reduces the frequency range substantially again. Where a steep slope, which requires high frequencies for its expression, is being followed, the only alternative is to use a very slow scan speed (Section 17.7).

8.7 DEMODULATION; PHASE-SENSITIVE DETECTION

After the output of a transducer or detector has been modulated and amplified to a level where it is no longer likely that noise will degrade the signal, the amplified information must be separated from the modulating signal and as much of the noise

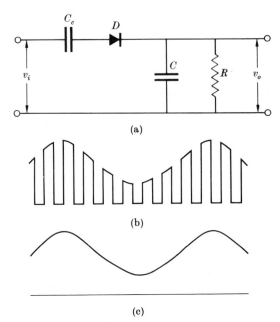

(a)

(b)

(c)

Fig. 8.5 Diode peak detector used to rectify or demodulate a chopped signal (a) Schematic diagram. Capacitor C_c couples the detector circuit to a preceding stage. (b) Modulated input signal v_i. The dashed outline is the signal prior to modulation. (c) Output signal v_o after smoothing by the RC filter.

present as possible. The process of *demodulation* is also called detection or rectification. It is a procedure analogous to the rectification of ac line voltage (Section 4.13).

An electronic switch is a suitable demodulator. For example, the diode peak detector shown schematically in Fig. 8.5 can be used. The input signal is the modulated simple waveform shown in Fig. 8.5b. Noise is not shown in the illustration. Diode D transmits essentially the top half of each pulse. Since it is only the waveform defined by the peaks of the pulses that is of interest, the low-pass RC filter following the diode is essential. It transmits only low frequencies and recovers the original input signal. The output of the circuit is seen in Fig. 8.5c.

The type of rectification just described is a satisfactory way to recover information from a modulated signal whose $S/N \gg 1$. When the ratio is about unity or is less, the method fails. This difficulty is illustrated in Fig. 8.6 where two amplified, chopped signals that differ greatly in their values of S/N are shown. In the first case, where

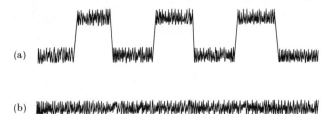

(a)

(b)

Fig. 8.6 Chopped signals plus noise. (a) $S/N \gg 1$ (b) $S/N < 1$.

$S/N \gg 1$, the contribution of the signal is quite evident, and the detector will respond easily to it, producing an output proportional to the recovered information. In the second instance, there is only a noise output since the detector responds to the dominant component, the noise.

Phase-sensitive demodulation. When $S/N < 1$ information can still be gleaned from an output if demodulation is carried out *in phase* with the original chopping signal. In other words, the detector is "turned on" only when the instrument channel is known to be open. This important procedure is known variously as *synchronous demodulation* and *phase-sensitive detection* and the amplifier whose output is de-modulated is said to be "phase-locked" or is called a *lock-in amplifier.* A classic circuit used for this purpose is illustrated schematically in Fig. 8.7. It is a full-wave rectifier in which diodes D_1 and D_2 can pass a signal only when they receive enabling pulses v_r. These pulses are phased to correspond to the arrival of the modulated signal at this point in the circuit.* A further low-pass filter (not shown) always follows the phase-sensitive detector.

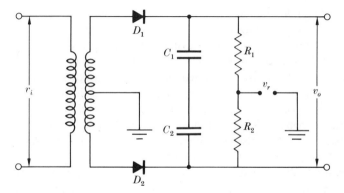

Fig. 8.7 Phase-sensitive demodulator. The input v_i is the instrument signal after modulation and amplification. A portion of the modulating signal is fed in as v_r to bias diodes D_1 and D_2. The diodes pass v_i only when they are forward-biased, i.e., when v_i is in phase with the modulating signal.

A simpler demodulating circuit that is useful when high-frequency modulation has been employed is shown in Fig. 8.8. A *p*-channel field-effect transistor (FET) serves as rectifier. In this case the demodulating signal is directed to gate *G* of the FET through a diode. When the demodulating signal is negative, the diode is forward-biased, and the gate becomes negative relative to source *S*. The FET transmits; its transmission is blocked when the diode receives a positive pulse and is nonconducting, in which case *G* and *S* are at the same potential.

Basically, this technique is a type of *correlation analysis.* In information theory it is shown that the mixing of a reference signal of phase related to the signal of interest

---

* Before reaching this point, the modulated signal has certainly been shifted in phase. Accordingly, v_r is obtained by passing a portion of the modulating signal through an active phase-shifting network to achieve a comparable shift.

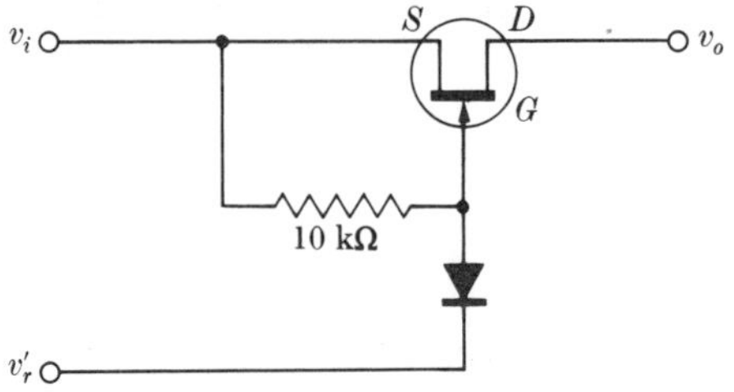

Fig. 8.8 A field-effect transistor phase-senstive demodulator.

will yield a product greater than zero, while the mixing of the reference signal with noise will yield a product that tends toward zero with increasing time interval.

Indeed, the cross-correlation of the amplifier output (chopping signal plus information from the detector) with "pure" chopping signal will yield a constant that reflects the signal plus some residual noise. Following detection, a low-pass RC filter is used to increase further the time interval and the noise correlation goes nearly to zero. An output of very narrow bandwidth is achieved.

An illustration of a generalized instrument with a lock-in amplifier system is given in Fig. 8.9. Note that a wide-band preamplifier will pass the modulated signal and a generous band of noise. The tuned amplifier that follows should raise the amplitude of signal plus noise to a point where it is larger than the inherent drift of the next stage, the phase-sensitive detector. The tuned amplifier excludes a substantial amount of noise, since its band pass is very much narrower than that of the preamplifier. Since noise has been amplified also, the narrowing of bandwidth ensures that noise does not overload the phase-sensitive detector.*

The low-pass filter is essential to the system. Usually it is an active filter, that is, an operational amplifier with a feedback network consisting in the simplest case of a resistor and capacitor in parallel. The extra amplification helps offset attenuation in the circuit. The time constant should be variable, by switching in different capacitors, from 0.01 to 10 s. In establishing the overall system bandwidth this filter further narrows the bandwidth. More important, it excludes harmonics produced by the phase-sensitive detector. The "mixing" of frequencies of f_0 (reference) and $f_0 \pm \Delta f$ (channel) during detection gives not only an output Δf but also bands at $2f_0 + \Delta f$ and other frequencies. These extraneous frequencies are rejected.

In general, the components needed for signal optimization may be obtained as separate units that contain all of the modules enclosed within the dashed line.

---

* In a double-channel spectrophotometer phase-sensitive detection is integral to the comparison of the transmittance of sample and blank. The radiation beam is chopped not only to enhance S/N by shifting the frequency from zero but also to allow a time-sharing mode of employment of detector and amplifier. The signal from each channel falls alternately on the detector. In such a case, since $S/N \gg 1$ at the outset, regular detection produces adequate output pulses. However, the channel connected at a given time must be known to obtain $\log (P_{\text{blank}}/P_{\text{sample}})$ as a readout. If the instrument does not transmit the phase information from the chopper, the operator must supply it by observing that the recorder is tracking in the wrong direction!

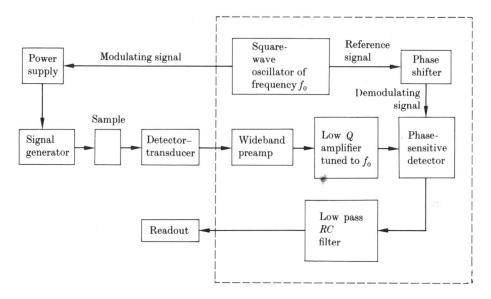

Fig. 8.9 Simplified block diagram of an instrument employing lock-in or synchronous detection techniques. The output of the signal generator is modulated at frequency f_0. The tuned amplifier selectively amplifies ac of $f_0 \pm f$. The phase-sensitive detector responds only when "enabled" by a signal from the modulator. The demodulator output is a narrow frequency band, further narrowed by the RC filter. The portion of the system within the broken line includes the components essential to phase-sensitive detection.

8.8 OTHER METHODS OF OPTIMIZING S/N

In the preceding three sections several methods were described for reducing noise and therefore of improving the S/N of a system. In this section attention is given to some other modifications of instrument systems that enhance measurement near the limit of detection.

Coupling of detector to amplifier. Earlier the importance of ensuring that each module, especially the amplifier, does not degrade S/N was stressed. It follows that degradation of S/N may also occur in the coupling of modules. The most critical connection is that between detector and the first stage of the amplifier. Two considerations are of importance.

First, if the detector is a current source and its signal is small, its output is directed into a large resistance in order to develop as great an amplifier input voltage as possible. This type of situation is pictured later in Fig. 8.10. Here V_i is proportional to R. This resistor, of course, introduces noise, but Eq. (8.3) makes clear that its noise voltage is proportional to $R^{1/2}$. Accordingly, the use of a coupling resistor ensures, with respect to new noise, a S/N proportional to $R^{1/2}$. While it is advantageous to use a very large value of dropping resistor R, several factors act to limit it. One is the need for the IR drop to be below the voltage that will saturate, i.e., cause a nonlinear response of either the source or the amplifier input. A second is a need to avoid this magnitude resistor with its tendency toward pickup and stray capacitances to ground.

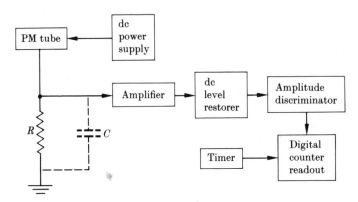

Fig. 8.10 Block diagram of a photon counting system. The time constant RC of the amplifier input circuit must be kept small (less than 1 μs). An amplifier capable of amplifying pulses arriving at rates as high as 10^6 s^{-1} must be used.

Another limiting factor is the requirement that the RC circuit it forms with the (inevitable) stray capacitances have a time constant commensurate with the response time desired.

Example Devise a rough diagram and select a practical value of R for a photomultiplier to be connected to a dropping resistor R to generate an input voltage for an amplifier. The circuit is to have a measurement or response time of 10^{-4} s or less. It is known that the photomultiplier output current will not exceed 10^{-7} A, that the amplifier input capacitance is 20 pF, and that its input voltage must be no greater than 1 mV to avoid saturation.

A suitable circuit is shown in Fig. 8.10. The lead from the photomultiplier tube to the amplifier input must be kept short to avoid additional stray capacitance. Assume the total capacitance across R is 20 pF (from the amplifier) and 20 pF (stray). Since the response time is to be 10^{-4} s or less, the decay time (time constant) of the RC circuit must be less than 10^{-4} s. Thus

$$RC < 10^{-4}\,\text{s}$$

and

$$R < \frac{10^{-4}\,\text{s}}{(20+20) \times 10^{-12}\,\text{F}} = 2.5 \times 10^6\,\Omega.$$

What value of R will give a maximum allowed input pulse? Since $V_i < 1 \times 10^{-3}$ V and $I_{PM} \sim 10^{-7}$ A,

$$R < \frac{1 \times 10^{-3}\,\text{V}}{1 \times 10^{-7}\,\text{A}} \approx 1 \times 10^4\,\Omega.$$

This value of R appears a reasonable choice rather than $2.5 \times 10^6\,\Omega$, since the current cited is an upper limit.

The second factor of interest in coupling relates to the noise voltage v_n and noise current i_n generated by the preamplifier (or amplifier first stage). Recall that a good performance in this stage is critical. For a minimum preamplifier noise figure it can be shown that there is an optimum relationship between source resistance R_s and equivalent Johnson noise resistance of the preamplifier, which is v_n/i_n, where these values are the noise voltage and current in the preamplifier. The appropriate expression is

$$R_s' = v_n/i_n. \tag{8.10}$$

Since the actual value of R_s is ordinarily not this optimum figure, transformer coupling provides the needed matching (Section 3.8).

Example A preamplifier gives rise to a noise voltage $v_s = 10^{-8}$ V Hz$^{-1/2}$ and noise current $i_n = 10^{-13}$ A Hz$^{-1/2}$. What is the optimum resistance for a detector that is to be coupled to it?
According to Eq. (8.10), $R_s' = 10^{-8}$ V$/10^{-13}$ A $= 10^5$ Ω. Assume the actual detector resistance $R_s = 10$ Ω. A step-up transformer can be used between detector and preamplifier input. Let $t = n_s/n_p$, the secondary-to-primary turns ratio in the transformer. Then $R_s t^2 = 10^5$ Ω. Solving, $t^2 = 10^4$ and $t = 100$. It can be shown that in this instance matching improves S/N by a factor of 500 over direct coupling.

Photon counting. This technique is perhaps the most sensitive of all for optimizing S/N in optical systems at low radiation levels where the discreteness of quanta dominate the picture. In Fig. 8.10 a block diagram of the basic instrumentation is given. At low light levels, a photomultiplier tube output consists of individual current pulses that can be counted. These photon-induced pulses must be distinguished from dark-current pulses that originate within the tube from other causes (Section 11.7). As may be seen in Fig. 11.17, their amplitude is substantially less. A pulse amplitude discriminator, which may be simply an operational amplifier with differential input, can be set to pass only pulses whose height exceeds a minimum figure. The number of pulses that pass is counted as the readout of the device.

The counting of photons is subject to a statistical analysis similar to that used in radioactivity determinations. Noise is basically the variation in rate of arrival of photons. Since this is a random process, the probability of fluctuations is proportional to the square root of the number of counts (Section 31.11). If measurements successfully exclude most unwanted counts, S/N proves to be simply

$$\frac{S}{N} = \frac{\text{total counts}}{(\text{total counts})^{1/2}} = (\text{total counts})^{1/2}. \tag{8.11}$$

Equation (8.11) can be expected to hold when the counting rate is high.

Where measurements are made at very low light levels, the number of spurious nonphoton-induced pulses counted at the discriminator level set may be a significant fraction (greater than 1%) of the total. It can be shown [6] in this case that

$$\frac{S}{N} = \frac{(r_s T)^{1/2}}{(1 + 2r_b/r_s)^{1/2}}, \tag{8.12}$$

where r_s and R_b are total and background (dark) counting rates, respectively, at a given discriminator voltage and T is the counting interval. Note that this expression reduces to Eq. (8.11) when $1 \gg 2r_b/r_s$.

Some experimental considerations involved in securing good results may be cited. [6] See Section 11.7 for further details about photomultipliers.

1. The photomultiplier gain must be stable at the level of precision desired, say 0.1%. How stringent the requirement proves to be may be seen by estimating the likely fluctuation in gain. It will be approximately the product of the number of dynode stages and the degree of constancy of the voltage furnished by the power supply. For example, for a 10-dynode photomultiplier tube the regulation must be 0.01% to secure the desired precision in gain. Gain will affect the amplitude of pulses.

2. The time constant of the *RC* (amplifier input) circuit and amplifier must be sufficiently small that closely spaced pulses are distinguishable. If the system is to be used to a rate as high as 10^6 current pulses per second, a time constant of the order of $0.2\,\mu s$ is appropriate. Similarly, an amplifier capable of operating at frequencies up to at least 10 MHz is needed. Whenever the coincidence rate of pulses becomes too high, a shift must be made from photon counting to a regular dc measurement techniques.

3. At higher counting rates the amplifier base line tends to shift. The dc level restorer, which is a diode clamp circuit (Section 9.6), restores the reference line. In this way the correct referencing of pulse heights is ensured.

REFERENCES

Noise in electrical circuits is discussed on an intermediate level in:

1. W. R. Bennett, *Electrical Noise.* New York: McGraw-Hill, 1960
2. F. N. H. Robinson, *Noise in Electrical Circuits.* New York: Oxford University Press, 1962
3. H. E. Rowe, *Signals and Noise in Communication Systems.* Princeton: Van Nostrand, 1965

Other references of interest are:

4. R. R. Alfano and N. Ockman, "Methods for Detecting Weak Light Signals," *J. Opt. Soc. Am.* **58**, 90 (1968)
5. Edward J. Blair, *Introduction to Chemical Instrumentation, Electronic Signals and Operations.* New York: McGraw-Hill, 1962
6. M. L. Franklin, Gary Horlick, and H. V. Malmstadt, "Basic and Practical Considerations in Utilizing Photon Counting for Quantitative Spectro-chemical Methods," *Anal. Chem.* **41**, 2 (1969)
7. Andre Hubaux and Gilbert Vos, "Decision and Detection Limits for Linear Calibration Curves," *Anal. Chem.* **42**, 849 (1970)
8. H. Kaiser, "Quantitation in Elemental Analysis," *Anal. Chem.* **42** (2), 24A (1970); (4), 26A (1970)
9. F. H. Lange, *Correlation Techniques.* Princeton: Van Nostrand, 1967
10. H. V. Malmstadt, R. M. Barnes, and P. A. Rodriguez, "A Multipurpose High Precision Recording Photometer," *J. Chem. Educ.* **41**, 263 (1964)
11. J. Reichert and J. Townsend, "Gated Integrator for Repetitive Signals," *Rev. Sci. Instrum.* **35**, 1692 (1964)
12. M. L. Parsons, "The Definition of Detection Limits," *J. Chem. Educ.* **46**, 290 (1969)
13. H. Kaiser and A. C. Menzies, *The Limit of Detection of a Complete Analytical Procedure.* London: Hilger, 1968

The design of dynamic capacitors is discussed in:

14. H. Palevsky, R. K. Swank, and R. Grenchik, "Design of Dynamic Condenser Electrometers," *Rev. Sci. Instrum.* **18**, 298 (1947)

15. B. M. Tolbert, *Ionization Chamber Assay of Radioactive Gases*. Washington, D.C.: A.E.C. Technical Report UCRL-3499 (1956)

EXERCISES

8.1 What is the rms *current* contributed by Johnson noise? (*Hint*: Use Ohm's law.)

$$[Ans.: (4kT\Delta f/R)^{1/2}.]$$

8.2 In Section 3.2 the servomotor principle was introduced in connection with the self-balancing potentiometer. A servomotor is a phase-sensitive, reversible motor used to drive a balancing device like a potentiometer. The motor responds to an amplified unbalance signal from the device in such a way that the motor drives the signal to zero.

a) Draw a block diagram of the arrangement.
b) Discuss the sense in which this type of circuit utilizes negative feedback.
c) Suggest some ways in which the S/N can be improved for this process.

8.3 What connection is there between the number of stages, modules, and components in an instrument and the S/N of an instrument? In an instrument is it better to use a one-stage amplifier with a microammeter readout or a two-stage amplifier with a milliammeter readout? On what basis would you choose one or the other?

8.4 In Section 1.6 the sensitivity of a module was defined in terms of its transfer function. What is the relation between sensitivity and the S/N of a module?

8.5 Discuss the connection between the S/N of an instrument and the precision and frequency of its calibration. What is the connection between the standard deviation of measurements on a species to which an instrument responds sensitively and its S/N? Consider measurements both at high levels of concentration and at trace levels.

8.6 Draw a block diagram of a lock-in amplifier arrangement for a Wheatstone bridge. Describe it briefly also. What advantage does it offer over the usual energizing and detection arrangements?

8.7 Give examples of factors that contribute to noise in an optical system.

8.8 Discuss the best way to couple a thermocouple detector and preamplifier in an infrared spectrophotometer. The thermocouple has a resistance of 30 Ω. The noise voltage and current of the preamplifier (taken at its input) are 1×10^{-7} V and 1×10^{-11} A.

Chapter 9

DIGITAL ELECTRONICS

9.1 INTRODUCTION

The branch of electronics concerned with pulses and switching has grown steadily in importance in recent years. Chemical instrumentation has been the beneficiary, as well as sometimes the instigator, of this development. Digital or pulse-switching electronics is used on many levels in instrumentation. The most obvious is a direct use in amplifying and shaping of pulses, as, e.g., in a technique like photon counting, which was discussed in Section 8.8. On a slightly higher level, digital electronics provides the techniques for counting pulses and discriminating among them by energy. Further, it produces timing pulses to start and stop operations, sample (measure) a signal over a particular interval, and process data. On perhaps the highest level, it provides the theory and technique for digital computers that can operate an instrument in such a way as to optimize performance. Two brief examples of digital electronic applications in instrumentation provide further illustration.

Example 1 In a determination of radioactivity, the instrument signal itself is a series of pulses. Each alpha-, beta-, or γ-ray "particle" that triggers the detector causes a burst of current. Digital electronics provides the basis for amplifying and counting the pulses. Either the pulses arriving in a fixed time interval are counted, or the time required for a fixed count is determined. The operation requires a digital "clock" to start and time the duration of counting.

Example 2 In pulse polarography, the use of pulses is central to the method and to timing the measurement sequences. Only the timing sequence that involves the dropping mercury electrode will be summarized. A drop dislodger is used to cause a mercury drop to fall from the electrode, starting the sequence. A precise interval after the start of the new drop, a square voltage pulse is imposed on the new drop. Near the end of the pulse, a further pulse leads to measurement of the current for an exact interval. When the pulses terminate, the mercury drop is dislodged and the cycle is repeated.

At the outset of the discussion of digital electronics it will be helpful to distinguish between analog and digital signals. A signal is in *analog form* whenever it exists as an amplitude of a variable capable of a continuous range of values. Some analog signals are the potential of a pH cell, the intensity of an infrared wavelength, and the height of a peak in a gas chromatogram. Often the information contained in a signal is also read out in analog or continuous form as a needle deflection on a meter dial or the position of a pen tracing a curve on a chart.

By contrast, a signal is in *digital form* when it represents a numeral or a "word." It is a series of pulses whose number represents information such as the amplitude of an electrode potential. Thus, in digital electronics one emphasis is on converting the amplitude of a continuous variable into a discrete number. For this purpose, the analog signal is sampled, i.e., measured, at appropriate times and the amplitude converted to a number represented by pulses.

It must also be noted that in order to treat pulse and switching operations as they are realized in practice, what may appear to be an excursion from the topic is necessary. All of digital electronics today is built on simple on-off switching and binary logic concepts. Accordingly, binary logic operations and logic gates are discussed in the next two sections as background essential to the rest of the chapter.

9.2 BINARY LOGIC CONCEPTS

An electrical switch is either *open* or *closed*. Similarly, in the binary number system there are two digits, *0* and *1*. In logic a statement is either *false* or *true*. These three systems are compatible: each has two well-defined states. As a result, the operations of logic (and later, of binary arithmetic) can be carried out electrically if circuits are designed correctly. In this section the basic operations of logic will be discussed and in the following section their electrical implementation will be treated.

Consider the implications of the true-false or 1-0 binary approach. For A, B, and other variables there will be two states, a *true* state and a *false* state. A variable may be in either state but in no other. As many variables will be used as are needed, though in this discussion two, A and B, are sufficient. The state of a variable will be evident from the way a letter is written. A plain capital A, for example, denotes the "true" state of A. It can be equated with the 1 state (binary digits), or closed state (switching). A capital letter with an overbar, such as $\bar{A}$, denotes the "not true" or "false" state of A.

There are three basic ways of combining variables to develop logical statements or logic functions. They are denoted by the fundamental logic operations AND, OR, and NOT and are symbolized as follows:

$$\cdot = \text{AND}, \qquad + = \text{OR}, \qquad \text{and} \quad ^{-} = \text{NOT}.$$

Consider the following examples of the use of these symbols:

$$A \cdot B = T; \qquad A + B = T; \qquad \text{and } \bar{A}.$$

The first two combinations are propositions. The first, $A \cdot B = T$, should be read: "When A is true *and* B is true, then T follows."* The first statement can also be translated into electrical terms: "If switch A is closed *and* switch B is closed, there will be transmission." For example, this result would be realized if A and B are two switches in series with a battery and a light. The light would be on when both were closed.

The OR concept ($A + B = T$) should be read: "When A is true *or* B is true *or* both are true, then T follows." This statement is usually described as the "inclusive OR" concept. How would this be implemented electrically with switches? The possibility

---

* This is seen to be analogous to the series of statements in logic known as a syllogism: major premise, minor premise, and conclusion.

should suggest itself that it corresponds to switches in parallel lines. If either or both is closed, transmissions of current results.

The NOT concept means the inverse of the condition suggested. For instance, $\bar{A}$ means that if A represents a true condition, then $\bar{A}$ represents the opposite. Consider the statement $\bar{A} \cdot \bar{B} = T$. It should be read, "When A is false and B is false, then T follows." Note the clear implication that all other combinations, such as A true and B false, do not yield T.

Truth tables. Logic statements are valuable precisely because of their certain outcome. Yet the outcome or conclusion of statements more complex than those simple examples may not be immediately evident. For this reason, it is the usual practice to draw up a "truth table" that demonstrates the outcome of all possible combinations. To illustrate the idea truth tables are given in Table 9.1 for the AND, OR, and NOT concepts just introduced. Note that a 0 and a 1 are used in place of false and true. These values are termed *logic levels*: a 0 is low and a 1 high. The table also shows the symbol for the electronic circuit called a logic gate (to be discussed in the next section) that will combine variables in the prescribed way.

Table 9.1 Some Logic Statements, Logic Symbols, and Truth Tables

AND	OR	NOT
$A \cdot B = T$	$A + B = T$	$\bar{A} = T$
A AND $B = T$	A OR $B = T$	NOT $A = T$

Truth Table			Truth Table			Truth Table	
A	B	T	A	B	T	A	T
0	0	0	0	0	0	0	1
0	1	0	0	1	1	1	0
1	0	0	1	0	1		
1	1	1	1	1	1		

Some items of interest in the table may be noted. The AND operation causes a true outcome (gives rise to transmission) only under one of four sets of input conditions: only when both A and B are at logic 1 level is the output at a logic 1 level. The opposite situation holds for the OR concept. Its output is at a logic 1 level for three of the four possible input situations, 1 and 0, 0 and 1, and 1 and 1.

Example How can a truth table be constructed for the logic statement $A \cdot B \cdot C \cdot D = Z$? It should have five columns, one for each input variable A, B, C, D and a final one for the output variable Z. Only the combination of input variables for which each is logic 1, should result in a logic 1 at the output.

In order to be sure that all combinations are listed in the table, a systematic approach is needed. We should begin the table by letting each input variable be zero, then let each input variable assume the value 1 in turn, then let two or more assume the value of 1 simultaneously, then three, and finally all.

Table 9.2 Some Theorems of Boolean Algebra*

Association	$(A + B) + C = A + (B + C)$
	$(AB)C = A(BC)$
Distribution	$(A + B)C = AC + BC = C$
	$A + BC = (A + B)(A + C)$
De Morgan's laws	$\overline{A + B} = \overline{A}\overline{B}$
	$\overline{AB} = \overline{A} + \overline{B}$
Absorption	$A + AC = A$
	$B(B + C) = B$

* Whenever two letters are adjacent, as in AB, an AND combination is intended. The dots used earlier are omitted in the table.

Boolean algebra. This branch of algebra allows one to examine logic statements with more power than a truth table allows. Some key theorems are illustrated in Table 9.2. The importance of the theorems may be suggested in straightforward fashion. The association theorems indicate that the order of performance of AND or OR operations is of no consequence. (A Boolean commutation theorem with a similar conclusion was omitted.) The distribution theorem shows that combinations of variables may be treated according to the laws of algebra. The second illustration under "distribution" will be reexamined below. Consider the absorption theorem next. It is not intuitively evident but its implications are obvious: any set of terms in a given variable reduces to that variable. Basically, the absorption theorem allows redundant terms to be identified. Now the second statement under the distribution theorem becomes clearer: when its two parenthetical statements are multiplied, the only term that does not contain A (and therefore reduces to A) is the combination BC.

De Morgan's theorems are particularly important, since NOT functions play a large role in modern binary digital operations. The two statements should be read as follows: first, "Neither A NOR B is the same as NOT A AND NOT B"; second, "NOT $(A$ AND $B)$ is the same as NOT A OR NOT B." Some very useful and important manipulations of logic statements can be made using De Morgan's theorems.

An important example dealing with an application of logic operations to the binary system follows. It is beyond the scope of the text to treat logic operations in more detail.

Example How can binary addition be stated in logic terms? The question becomes important, since logic concepts are the basis for arithmetic operations in digital computers. An answer has several stages.

First, recall that in binary notation only a 0 and a 1 are used. Recall also what each place in a number means. For example, the decimal number

$$7354 \quad \text{stands for} \quad 7 \times 10^3 + 3 \times 10^2 + 5 \times 10^1 + 4 \times 10^0.$$

Similarly, in binary notation, the number

$$1011 \quad \text{stands for} \quad 1 \times 2^3 + 0 \times 2^2 + 1 \times 2^1 + 1 \times 2^0.$$

If one were to translate the binary number given (1011) into decimal notation, the decimal equivalents of the binary terms would simply be added to give $8 + 0 + 2 + 1 = 11$.

Second, the ordinary rules of addition apply to binary addition. Consider the addition of the number used above to itself. We have

$$\begin{array}{r} 1011 \\ + \ 1011 \\ \hline \end{array}$$

and the sum, 10110

The validity of the sum can be verified, if the reader wishes, by conversion to decimal notation. The result is $16 + 0 + 4 + 2 + 0 = 22$.

Third, binary addition may be stated as a series of arithmetic statements as follows:

$$0 + 0 = 0, 0 + 1 = 1, 1 + 1 = 0 \text{ and carry } 1.$$

It can be shown that these four statements relative to addition can be subsumed in logic statements as follows:

$$S = A \cdot \bar{B} + B \cdot \bar{A}$$
$$C = A \cdot B$$

where S is a sum, and C the "carry" to the next column to the left. The validity of the first statement is evident on expressing it in words as, "When A is 1 *and* B is zero *or* when A is 0 *and* B is 1, S is 1."* Statements like these must be made *for each column* in numbers being added. Further, if more than two digits are being added in a column, additional variables, one for each additional digit, will be required.

Fourth, combinations of logic gates that will carry out these operations simply can be worked out using Boolean algebra. The result is the production of basic units known as half-adders and full-adders that can be assembled in more complex circuits. [2]

NAND and NOR concepts. Two further logic concepts or operations that combine AND with NOT and OR with NOT should also be included. The first yields a NAND, the second a NOR. To sense their operation, recall the truth table for AND. There is a 1 output only when all the inputs are 1. The NAND concept provides the opposite possibility. When *all* inputs are high, its output is low. In the logic gate symbol this inversion is shown by placing a small circle at the output. The NAND symbol and truth table are shown in Table 9.3. Similarly, NOT and OR give the NOR concept. It calls for a low output when *any* of its inputs is high. Both its symbol and truth table are given in Table 9.3. It is the combination of two logic concepts in one that makes NAND and NOR operations a versatile basis for digital electronics.

---

* While the symbols 0 and 1 in the previous sentence strictly identify logic levels, the identification with binary notation is valid if *positive logic* is used.

Table 9.3 Additional Logic Statements, Symbols, and Truth Tables*

NAND	NOR

$\overline{A \cdot B \cdot C} = T$

NOT $(A$ AND B AND $C) = T$

$\overline{A + B + C} = T$

NOT $(A$ OR B OR $C) = T$

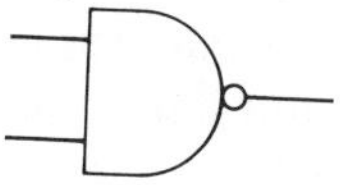

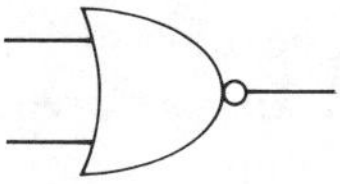

Symbol   Symbol

Truth Table

A	B	C	T
0	0	0	1
0	0	1	1
0	1	0	1
1	0	0	1
0	1	1	1
1	0	1	1
1	1	0	1
1	1	1	0

Truth Table

A	B	C	T
0	0	0	1
0	0	1	0
0	1	0	0
1	0	0	0
0	1	1	0
1	0	1	0
1	1	0	0
1	1	1	0

* The small circle appearing at the output in the symbols denotes inversion.

9.3 LOGIC GATES

The translation of a logic concept into a semiconductor circuit that will accomplish the desired operation is a rapidly advancing technology. A circuit that performs a logic operation is appropriately termed a *gate*: It transmits a signal when the conditions that permit it to switch between its "off" and "on" states are met. One state is a logic low and the other a logic high. The emphasis in design is upon achieving speed (present switching times are a few nanoseconds), low power consumption per gate (presently as little as 1 mW), small size, and low cost. A wide interchangeability among gates is also an objective.

These objectives are best attained by use of integrated-circuit techniques. Commonly many gates are incorporated in a single (monolithic) silicon "chip," a level of fabrication termed medium-scale integration. Historically, the main families of digital integrated circuits have been resistor-transistor logic (RTL), diode-transistor logic (DTL), transistor-transistor logic (T^2 logic or TTL), and emitter-coupled or emitter-clamped logic (ECL). FET gates of the metal-oxide-semiconductor (MOS) type are also made. It appears that T^2 logic is likely to dominate the scene because of its speed (presently 13 ns propagation delay) and greater noise immunity (1 V). Voltage levels and current directions are not identical among all types, which leads to coupling problems. DTL and TTL devices are compatible but cannot be used with RTL gates. A designer must select one or the other at the outset. Since most new devices are being produced from TTL logic circuitry, only this type will be discussed here.

TTL gate. In T^2 logic a NAND gate is the basic type of gate at present. Its schematic circuit design is shown in Fig. 9.1. This gate employs *positive* logic, i.e. its logic 1 state corresponds to a positive voltage (about 3 V). The logic 0 state is located at about $+0.2$ V, as near the other end of the accessible dc range (ground) as feasible. The gate is also *current-sinking*, i.e., requires a flow of current into the output, as in Fig. 9.1 suggests immediately.

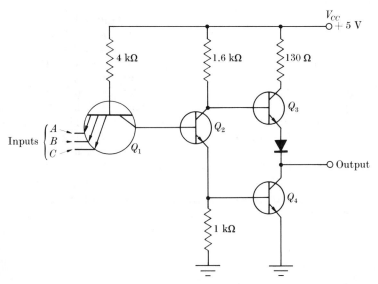

Fig. 9.1 A TTL logic NAND gate. Some specifications are: speed 6 ns; wattage per gate 10 mW; output voltages: logic 0, about $+0.2$ V; logic 1, about $+3.3$ V; noise immunity, 1 V.

The operation of the NAND gate of Fig. 9.1 can be described by asking whether each transistor is cut off or in saturation (Section 4.6). As the gate switches states each transistor makes this type of transition. Two data needed for an analysis are the following: The voltage drop for a forward-biased *p-n* silicon junction is about 0.75 V, and V_{CE} for a saturated transistor is about 0.4 V.

Consider first the case in which at least one input to the gate is logic 0, about 0.2 V. Then V_{BE} for transistor Q_1 will be sufficient to forward-bias this junction. Current will flow from V_{CC} out of each input that is about 0.2 V. Next note that the base of Q_1 cannot be greatly over $+0.75$ V. This potential is the high point in the path to ground that includes potential drops V_{BC} of Q_1, V_{BE} of Q_2, and V_{BE} of Q_4. This series of *p-n* junctions can conduct only if the sum of potentials exceeds $3 \times 0.75 = 2.25$ V; with the small voltage available, they must be cut off. Thus Q_2 and Q_4 must be off. What is the state of transistor Q_3? If Q_4 is off, its collector can rise in potential, toward the 5 V supplied at V_{CC}. In any event it is likely that there will be sufficient drop across Q_3 for it to conduct and saturate. The output will be at about 3.3 V

$(5 - I_C \times 130 - 0.4 - 0.75)$. This is the expected result. Recall that a NAND gate (Table 9.3) has a 1 output when *any* input is 0. The single contrary case holds when all inputs are high (or unconnected). Now there is no conduction from base to emitter of Q_1 and its base will be at a sufficiently high potential for the string of *p-n* junctions, V_{BC} of Q_1, V_{BE} of Q_2, and V_{BE} of Q_4, to conduct. The output will be V_{CE} for Q_4 when it is in saturation, about $+0.4$ V. It is at the 0 logic level.

Example What is the state of transistor Q_3 in the NAND gate of Fig. 9.1 when all inputs are high? Two pieces of information from the paragraph above are that V_{BE} of $Q_4 \simeq 0.75$ V and $V_o \simeq 0.4$ V. The potential at the base of Q_3 can be estimated from these data and the circuit diagram. It must be V_{BE} of Q_4 plus V_{CE} of Q_2 or $0.75 + 0.4 = 1.15$ V. The emitter of Q_3 proves to be at the same potential, that is V_{CE} of Q_4 plus V_{diode}, or 1.15 V. The conclusion is that Q_3 is off.

Integrated-circuit gates are encapsulated in standard types of "containers." The most common is the dual-in-line package (DIP), a 0.75×2 cm rectangle with seven to ten or more sturdy leads protruding downward along each side. Two of the main specifications of gates are *fan out* and *delay time*. Fan out is the number of gates one device can drive or actuate without distortion. For example, a T^2 gate can drive ten other TTL gates.* The delay time or operating time of a gate is of interest because parallel paths to another gate input sometimes contain differing numbers of intermediate gates. Signals directed along the two paths will arrive at the terminal gate at different times. Almost certainly a faulty response by the terminal gate will be the result. For this reason, if excessive time differences are likely the design is altered.

9.4 MULTIVIBRATORS

As the discussion of logic gates in the preceding section implied, in pulse and digital electronics there is a wide need for circuits that have two definite states and can be induced to make a sudden transition between them. In addition to logic gates, another class of electronic devices known as multivibrators shows this behavior. In Fig. 9.2 the three different types of multivibrator are described by their inputs and outputs. At the left are pictured two well-spaced triggering or input pulses, and at the right the output pulses that result. The monostable multivibrator has one indefinitely stable state but may be triggered into a quasi-stable state whose duration depends on circuit parameters. The bistable multivibrator has two indefinitely stable states. A pulse of proper sign can cause an abrupt transition from one to the other. The astable multivibrator has two quasi-stable states and alternates between them as long as it is energized, independent of triggering. These very important circuits are widely used for timing and pulse counting. They are found in instruments, digital computers, and in digital data transmission systems.

In multivibrators two active devices are required. They may be a pair of tubes, a pair of transistors, or a pair of logic gates. The output of one active device is direct-

---

* The input load a gate presents and its output power are specified in unit loads. For example, a gate input might present one unit load and its output be capable of driving ten unit loads. For such devices the fan out is ten.

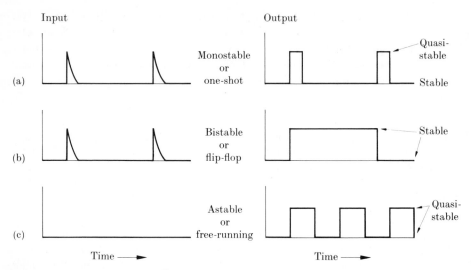

Fig. 9.2 Input and output characteristics of multivibrators. A single timescale is used. (a) Monostable multivibrator or one-shot. Its only stable state is the low state. When triggered, its output goes to a higher quasi-stable state for an interval determined by an RC circuit. (b) Bistable multivibrator or flip-flop. When triggered with a pulse, its output goes from one stable state to the other. (c) Astable or free-running multivibrator. Its lack of stable states causes it to generate output pulses continuously.

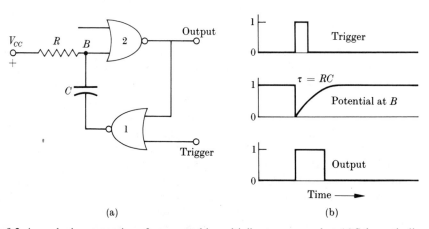

Fig. 9.3 A NOR logic gate version of a monostable multivibrator or one-shot. (a) Schematic diagram. One output is capacitively coupled to the input of the other gate. (b) Waveforms. The duration of a pulse is about RC seconds.

coupled to the input of the other. This arrangement forces one active device to be on (saturated or logic 1), the other to be off (at cutoff or logic 0). The three multivibrators differ only in whether neither, one, or both of the active devices can remain cut off indefinitely. In order to focus attention on the essential nature of the process only logic gate multivibrators will be discussed.

Monostable multivibrator or one-shot. In Fig. 9.3a a one-shot based on coupled NOR gates is shown. Its operation may be best understood in terms of the waveforms pictured in Fig. 9.3b. If a positive-going (trigger) pulse appears at the input of gate 1, it causes the output of this NOR gate to go to the 0 state. (Confirm this with the truth table in Table 9.3.) Since capacitor C cannot change potential instantly, it transmits the 0 to point B and to the input to NOR gate 2. Now its output must become 1, as shown in the lowest of the waveform plots. This is a temporary situation. Capacitor C will gradually recharge to positive voltage V_{CC} through resistor R. When the potential at B crosses the threshold of the logic 1 level again, the output of NOR gate 2 will make the transition to its 0 level.

As shown in Fig. 9.3b, this shift brings the square pulse at the output to an end. Simultaneously, the 0 level signal will appear at the input to NOR gate 1. Its output will return to a logic 1. The monostable multivibrator is indefinitely stable in this state. No further change will occur in the absence of an additional positive trigger. Note that time constant RC effectively determines the rate of recharging of C and therefore the duration of the pulse.

The one-shot is widely used as a reliable ($\pm 1\%$) source of timed pulses in instrumentation. For example, it is used in pulse polarography. Because it generates a rectangular shaped pulse, it can be used to "gate" or open to transmission some other circuit. This application will be discussed later under sampling. Further, it generates a rapid transition at a predictable time after a trigger and is also useful as a delay circuit, e.g. in starting a voltage sweep in polarography a predetermined time after a new mercury drop has begun to grow.

Astable multivibrator. A logic gate version of an astable multivibrator using NAND gates is shown in Fig. 9.4. Note that one input of each gate is unused (and is at logic 1) and the output of each gate is coupled through a capacitor to the input of the other. With capacitive coupling each change in output will be transmitted instantly to the input of the coupled gate. Whenever gate 1 has a logic 1 output, capacitor C_2 transmits this voltage to the input of gate 2, causing its output to assume its low state. Capacitor C_2 will gradually discharge through R_3 and R_1. When the process is sufficiently complete, the input to NAND gate 2 becomes 0, causing its output to become 1. This voltage is transmitted to the input of NAND gate 1. Its output goes to 0. Now capacitor C_1 begins discharging. The output states continue to alternate and a series

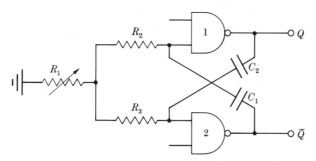

Fig. 9.4 Astable multivibrator based on a pair of NAND gates. Each output is capacitively coupled to the input of the other gate.

of constant duration output pulses occurs. The frequency of the resulting square wave is approximately $\frac{1}{2}RC$ when $R = R_1 + R_2$, $R_1 = R_3$ and $C = C_1 = C_2$. The output is not a pure rectangular wave. If a well-shaped rectangular wave output is desired, the pulses can be used to drive inverters.

Bistable multivibrator or flip-flop. The flip-flop is one of the most widely used digital electronic circuits. It has two stable states and can be triggered from one to the other by the application of a pulse *at an appropriate point.* When operated this way, its output changes logic level with each input pulse and returns to the same level only after the second pulse. For this reason, it is a central element in most binary counting systems. It can also serve as a memory, since its output level reflects the previous input. It is also used to produce gating signals for other circuits and in the processing of pulse-type waveforms. Other names given to a flip-flop are multi, Eccles–Jordan circuit, trigger circuit, and scale-of-two toggle circuit.

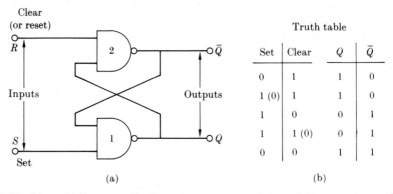

(a)   (b)

Fig. 9.5 Bistable multivibrator or flip-flop using NAND gates. It is an *RS* (reset-set) type. If 0 pulses are applied alternately to the two inputs, the output will flip from one stable state to the other. Logic 1 pulses cause no change. (a) Block diagram. (b) Truth table.

A variety of flip-flops is available in integrated circuit form. One of these, a simple *RS* type, is shown in Fig. 9.5. The device consists of two cross-coupled NAND gates. NOR gates may also be used. Note that coupling is direct. Since no capacitor is present to charge or discharge and thereby bring about a transition between states, it appears that only an external zero pulse can produce a transition. The operation of the flip-flop can be followed from the truth table in Fig. 9.5b. Assume the *set* (*S*) input is initially at level 0 and the clear (*R*) input at level 1. Because one input of gate 1 is 0, output *Q* must be 1. Both inputs of gate 2 are 1; and its output $\bar{Q}$ must be 0. This situation corresponds to the top line of the truth table.

If the set input is now changed to 1, there is no change because the other input to gate 1 is still a 0. (Its two inputs are 0 and 1, still calling for an output 1.) The inputs to gate 2 are 1 and 1, calling for output 0. When $S = 1$, however, the application of a 0 pulse to the clear input *R* (third line of the truth table) does cause the flip-flop to change state. (When the 0 is applied, the inputs to gate 2 are 1 and 0, causing its output to become 1. Since this change makes both inputs of gate 1 unity, its output goes to 0.) If the clear input is next changed to 1 (line four of truth table) the output does not alter. The reader should verify this situation and examine the change on returning to line one when the set input is next made 0.

Aside from the interesting relationship existing because of the cross-coupling of the NAND gates, the flip-flop of Fig. 9.5 shows "memory." The output Q is a fixed level until a 0 pulse is applied to the opposite input. In other words, the flip-flop shows which of the two inputs previously had a 0 pulse.

Nevertheless this simple circuit leaves much to be desired. One problem involves the timing of pulses. In the circuit of Fig. 9.5 an output transition tends to occur so quickly that it alters the effect of an input signal. Some way is needed to hold the output state once it is reached. Further, a way to hold input states briefly is also required. They should be transferred to a flip-flop only after it has responded to a previous signal.

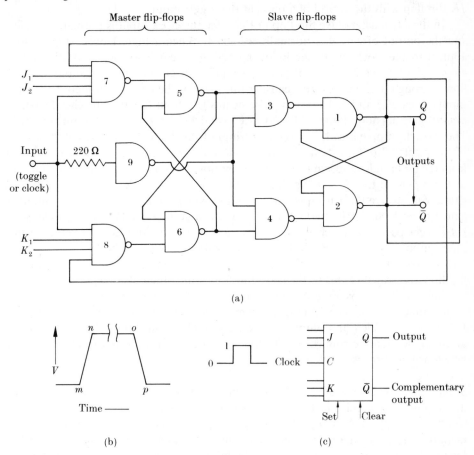

(a)

(b)   (c)

Fig. 9.6 JK flip-flop based on NAND gates. It is a master-slave type of device. (a) Circuit diagram. (b) Input pulse showing finite rise and fall times. (c) Block symbol for a JK flip-flop. Only the inputs (at left) and outputs (at right) needed in a given application are actually used. For counting, the C (clock) or toggle input must receive a "1" pulse and all external J and K inputs must be open or at a 1 level. Set and clear (reset) inputs appear at the bottom. A "0" pulse directed to either overrides all other programs and sets or clears the flip-flop output.

A second problem is that the output does not register the receipt of every pulse. From the truth table in Fig. 9.5 note that the flip-flop will respond to every zero pulse that arrives only when (a) both inputs R and S are at logic 1 and (b) the incoming pulse is directed to the proper input.

In Fig. 9.6a a JK master-slave flip-flop that resolves both the timing and response problems is shown schematically. Several sets of NAND gates have been added to the original flip-flop, which now appears as gates 1 and 2. Note particularly the coupling of outputs Q and $\bar{Q}$ to the input of NAND gates 7 and 8. This interconnection ensures that the device can respond to all pulses. Further, when pulses are to be counted, they are directed to a special input marked *toggle* or *clock* input. The flip-flop is said to toggle or *complement* on the receipt of each pulse at the clock input since its output changes state. A brief description follows of the opening and closing of gates in a JK flip-flop with the arrival of a pulse at the toggle input.

In the JK master-slave flip-flop of Fig. 9.6a, the clock input is normally a logic 0 and the output of gate 9 is normally a logic 1. When a logic 1 pulse (Fig. 9.6b) is applied to the clock input, the following actions occur in sequence. At the outset, current flows from the inputs of gates 7, 8, and 9. The current from the input to gate 9 flows through a 220 Ω resistor, causing this input to be closer to a logic 1 than the inputs to gates 7 and 8. Thus as a pulse begins the input to gate 9 reaches 1 first. As a NAND gate, its output goes to 0, and gates 3 and 4 close (their outputs are at logic 1). The slave flip-flop (gates 1, 2) receives a 1 input from 3 and 4 regardless of the output of the master flip-flop. *As the top of the pulse is reached*, gates 7 and 8 receive a 1 from the input pulse and can transmit information about the state of their other inputs to the inputs of the master flip-flop (gates 5, 6). For example, if Q is 0 and $\bar{Q}$ is 1, gate 7 will receive the 1 from $\bar{Q}$ and its output will go to zero, causing the output of gate 5 to be 1. Similarly, the output of gate 6 will go to 1. *On the trailing edge of the pulse* received at the clock input, gates 7 and 8 eventually receive a zero, causing their outputs to be 1; as the bottom of the trailing edge is reached, gate 9 transmits a 1 to gates 3 and 4, allowing them to respond to the logic level output of the master flip-flop and transmit this to the slave flip-flop, which then also responds.

Since a flip-flop is a module in its own right, it is usually represented in circuits by a simple symbol. The rectangular symbol in common use is drawn in Fig. 9.6c. Inputs are at the left and outputs at the right. Only inputs and outputs needed in a given application are connected. The use of flip-flop symbols is illustrated in Fig. 9.9, which will be discussed below.

Sequencing. When measurements with an instrument are made intermittently or discontinuously, precise instructions must be furnished to one or more modules as to when to respond. Actually, sequencing is required, since each module of an instrument must respond at a proper time. The situation is analogous to that just described for the JK flip-flop. Due account must be taken in such instructions of delay times, etc.

One or more types of multivibrator can be used to generate gating signals useful in timing on-off instructions. Where a succession of timing commands must be given, a set of monostable multivibrators or one-shots can be used. Two useful ways to combine them are shown in Fig. 9.7. When different parts of an instrument must be

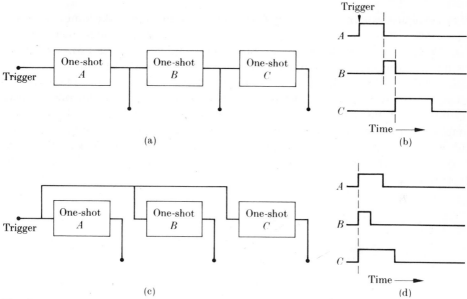

Fig. 9.7 Monostable multivibrators or one-shots used to generate timing or gating sequences. (a) Series arrangement in which each one-shot is triggered by the preceding one. (b) Pulse output of series arrangement. (c) Parallel arrangement. All one-shots trigger simultaneously to give pulse pattern shown in (d).

gated in sequence, the series arrangement is one means of securing the desired control. On the other hand, the parallel combination of one-shots would be useful where several modules must be operated simultaneously but for lengths of time that differ. Since a one-shot has a time reliability of about $\pm 1\%$, the series arrangement of Fig. 9.7 will give poorest reliability for pulse C, and best precision for pulse A. Each pulse from the parallel sequence will be equally reliable.

If highly precise time intervals are required, a crystal oscillator, which is very stable, is usually employed. It provides c..ly a steady series of output pulses and for that reason is sometimes called a clock. It can be employed to generate gating pulses of different lengths. For the purpose, the oscillator pulses are used to drive preset counters (see next section). Each counter is set to a count proportional to the pulse length desired from it. A pulse begins when the counter is started, its output furnishing the pulse. There is no change in the pulse it provides until the input pulses finally tally to the preset figure. When that count is reached, the counter output changes logic level, terminating the pulse.

Example It is desired to generate a 150 μs pulse using a counter and a 1 MHz quartz oscillator. What count must be present on the counter?

It should be set to 150 counts. Whether a pulse of exactly 150 μs is obtained depends on the part of a pulse that causes a change in output state.

Sampling. Pulses of the type that have been described are commonly generated to open and close gates, e.g., in measuring a signal during a prescribed interval. This type of measurement is termed sampling. A type of device that can make a measurement for a prescribed interval and hold the information is shown in simplified form in Fig. 9.8. It is seen to be basically an operational amplifier integrator. (In an actual circuit gates triggered by pulses of the kind just discussed would take the place of the switches shown.) When the switches are in the sample (S) position the input signal v_i charges capacitor C_1 through whatever resistance R the input circuit offers.* The operational amplifier is in the follower configuration and its output will follow the amplitude of the input signal. At the end of sampling both switches are opened and the two capacitors will drift at the same rate, ensuring the output voltage will remain constant. This type of *sample-and-hold* operation can be performed with many other types of circuits.

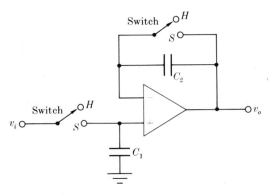

Fig. 9.8 Analog sampling (measuring) circuit of the sample-and-hold type. Capacitor C_1 is charged during sampling and C_2 immediately following. The output voltage is proportional to the total charge received during sampling.

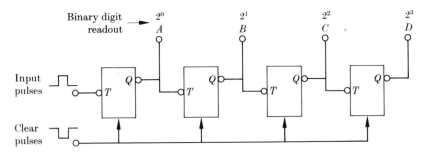

Fig. 9.9 A four-bit binary counter comprising four JK flip-flops. The output state of each flip-flop is registered at A, B, C, and D. Pulses move through the counter by "ripple carry."

---

* The time constant RC must be appropriate to the signal that is to be sampled, i.e., sufficiently short for the sampling to reflect the frequency of the signal but sufficiently long to allow some averaging of high-frequency noise that is inevitably present.

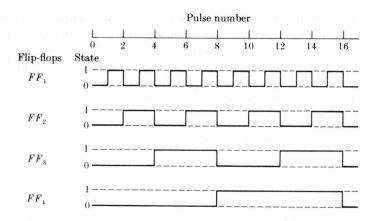

Fig. 9.10 Output waveforms for the flip-flops that comprise the counter of Fig. 9.9. Note that each flip-flop toggles only when the preceding one goes from 1 to 0.

9.5 COUNTERS

Flip-flop devices that will toggle or complement, i.e. register each input pulse by a change in output state, are widely used in counting. It is only necessary to connect the Q output of one flip-flop (see Fig. 9.6c) to the toggle or clock input of the next to develop the basic counter. A set of four JK flip-flops cascaded in this fashion is shown in block symbols in Fig. 9.9. Each application of a positive input pulse to the clock input C will cause a shift in output states. The output is shown taken from terminal Q. Accordingly, flip-flop A will shift its output from 0 to 1 at the first pulse, 1 to 0 at the second, 0 to 1 at the third, and so forth. Recall that response occurs on the trailing edge of a pulse (as it decreases from 1 to 0). Whenever the output of flip-flop A goes from 1 to 0, it will cause the second flip-flop to go from 0 to 1.

A graphical record of all changes that occur during the receipt of sixteen successive input pulses at C is shown in Fig. 9.10. The output state of each flip-flop (FF) is indexed as a function of input pulse number. In every case, a flip-flop toggles when the output of the preceding one drops from 1 to 0. Note that for some pulses a great many flip-flops are affected. For example, on the sixteenth pulse the *successive* changes are: FF_1 goes from 1 to 0, FF_2 from 1 to 0, FF_3 from 1 to 0, and FF_4 from 1 to 0. Each change in output triggers a change in the state of the next flip-flop. This mode of coupling is known as *ripple carry*. The toggling "ripples" through the entire set of flip-flops when an appropriate pulse is received at the input. Since there are many gates in a JK flip-flop, transmission of a pulse is moderately slow (80 ns per flip-flop).

How can counting be speeded? One possibility is to take advantage of the observation that any flip-flop that is to make a transition does so when all previous ones go from 1 to 0. This observation is the basis for wiring a much faster *synchronous counter*. This type of device employs more complex coupling, and what is termed "carry look-ahead logic." [6]

Note in Fig. 9.9 that provision is also made for clearing the counter. It is accomplished by application of a negative-going pulse to the "clear" input. At this input, such a pulse overrides any other operations and returns all outputs Q to the 0 state.

Though it is beyond the scope of this text to develop counters in more detail, several other operations of interest may be suggested. The counter just discussed is an "up" counter, i.e. counts from 0 upward. It is also possible to develop a "down" counter. To make the change it is only necessary in Fig. 9.9 to connect the $\bar{Q}$ output of each flip-flop to the toggle of the next flip-flop. Similarly, flip-flops wired so that they may count either up or down are easily designed.

Readout and decoder. A means of displaying the count reached by a counter is necessary also. The simplest way a count can be read out is to connect miniature incandescent bulbs in an appropriate way to the output of each flip-flop. Each output that is a logic 1 lights its bulb. As is evident from Fig. 9.9, this readout (from right to left) is the binary system count registered.

To simplify reporting it is often desirable to *decode* or translate the output to a number basis other than the binary one. For example, displaying the four-place decimal number 1000 on a binary scale requires a 10-bit output. For this reason, decoders that translate the other number bases are common. The octal (base 8) scale is widely used. If an output is to be reported on this scale, flip-flops are grouped in sets of three.

Binary-coded decimal (BCD) decoders are common also. In them flip-flops are grouped in sets of four, each set geared to the production of a decimal digit. Many decoding arrangements are possible this way since only ten of sixteen counts are to be used. The most common arrangement is the so-called 1-2-4-8 counting in which counting proceeds normally up to nine and on the tenth count all outputs are returned to 0.

Shift registers. If arithmetic operations are to be carried out with a counter it is frequently necessary to be able to shift information from one flip-flop to the next in the set. The type of flip-flop arrangement in which this kind of shift can be made is termed a shift register.* Connections are arranged in such a way that on receipt of a proper pulse each flip-flop shifts its output to the next in the series.

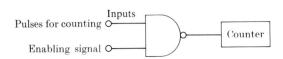

Fig. 9.11 Gating arrangement for a counter. The NAND gate transmits pulses only when the enabling input is at the 1 level.

Gating. In most chemical instrumentation it is desired to start a counter only when a measurement is to be made. Ordinarily this requires an enabling pulse to be sent to the counter at the proper moment in the process of measurement. In Fig. 9.11 a straightforward gating arrangement is depicted. A series NAND gate is used. The pulses to be counted are directed to one input and the enabling pulse to the other. Only when a logic 1 is received at the enabling input does the NAND gate transmit the count pulses. Such a device might be used, for example, to count radioactive dis-integrations of a sample over a prescribed time interval.

---

* A set of flip-flops is called a register.

9.6 WAVE SHAPING

Whenever a pulse moves through an instrument its shape or amplitude is likely to require modification at certain points. There are many reasons why this should be: a square pulse is certain to be distorted after transmission through a circuit with poor high-frequency response and may require restoration to its original form; or, in other situations, the shape of a pulse may be satisfactory but its amplitude so great that it must be reduced to avoid distortion in a module; a third possibility is that a series of pulses may have to be referenced to a given voltage level to permit subsequent dis-crimination among them by amplitude. It is operations of this kind that fall under the general heading of wave shaping and will be discussed in this section.

Clipping circuit. When it is desired to limit the amplitude of, or clip, an incoming signal, reverse-biased diodes may be used. An example of a simple circuit that is suitable is given in Fig. 9.12. In this illustration clipping is arranged at both positive and negative voltage. If only one operation is of interest, one diode and its bias supply may be removed. In the clipper circuit of Fig. 9.12 an input signal will produce a small voltage drop across R but will otherwise appear at the output unchanged unless a diode begins to conduct. Diode D_1 bypasses any portion of a signal whose potential across ab exceeds V_1 ($V_1 = V_i + V_d$, where V_d is the drop across the p-n junction of the diode). For germanium $V_d \simeq 0.2$ V, for silicon $V_d \simeq 0.6$ V. When $V > V_1$ the output will remain at V_1, the rest of the voltage drop appearing across R. Similarly, diode D_2 begins to conduct whenever the negative potential of the signal exceeds V_2, where $V_2 = V_j + V_d$. In this case, the bottoms of the signal peaks are clipped. The effect of clipping is evident in Fig. 9.12b.

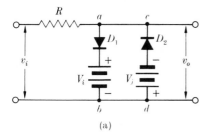 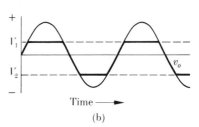

Fig. 9.12 Diode clipper circuit. Diodes D_1 and D_2 are reverse-biased just below the voltages at which the input signal is to be clipped or truncated. When the signal becomes more positive than V_1 ($V_1 = V_i + V_d$, where V_d is the voltage drop across the diode), D_1 conducts and causes any further voltage increment to appear across R. Similarly D_2 clips the negative peaks at V_2.

Clipping circuits are often used to limit the height of pulses prior to counting, where their number and not their amplitude is of interest. Such circuits are also useful prior to a gate or triggering circuit that is easily saturated.

Clamping circuit. Frequently it is necessary to establish a dc reference point for a periodic signal. A circuit of this kind that "references" or clamps a square wave at 0 volts is shown in Fig. 9.13. Its effect is evident in Fig. 9.13b. Where input signal v_i has no defined voltage except with reference to itself, output signal v_o has a definite

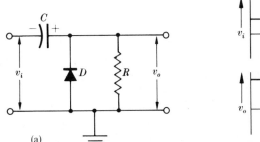

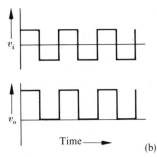

(a)   (b)

Fig. 9.13 Clamping circuit. Diode D conducts on each negative half-cycle (when upper terminal is negative) of the input signal, charging C (polarity shown) to the negative peak potential of the signal. R is selected so that $RC \gg T_{signal}$. The circuit causes the negative peaks to be at zero volts dc. (a) Circuit schematic. (b) Output waveform clamped at zero volts.

dc voltage at all times. Since a dc component has been added to an ac signal, the term *dc restorer* is also applied to this type of circuit.

Its operation may be described as follows. Diode D conducts only on the second half of each cycle when the lower input terminal is positive relative to the upper. If D behaves as an ideal diode, it is a short-circuit when conducting and v_o is 0 V. Internally, however, during successive intervals of conduction of D, capacitor C gradually charges to the peak negative potential V_p of the signal. Note that its right-hand terminal becomes positive. During the other half-cycle when D is nonconducting, v_o is the voltage of the capacitor. While it can discharge through R, assume that $RC \gg T_1$, the period of the signal. Since C cannot respond to sudden fluctuations, its voltage will be nearly constant at V_p. The voltage appearing at the output will be $v_o = v_i + V_p$. The input signal is reproduced at the output with a constant dc voltage added.

By inverting the diode the signal may be clamped so that its maximum positive voltage is zero. Or, if a dc voltage source is inserted in series with the diode, it may be clamped about that value. In a more precise treatment allowance would be made for the diode resistance and voltage drop.

Example What is the relation between peak output voltage and the peak negative input potential V_p in the circuit of Fig. 9.13? When v_o is a maximum, the value is contributed half by v_i and half by the capacitor voltage. Thus, $(v_o)_{peak} = 2V_p$.

Schmitt trigger. An important modification of the basic binary multivibrator discussed in the last section is shown in Fig. 9.14. In this instance, transistors are shown in place of NAND or other logic gates since the circuit, called a Schmitt trigger, is ordinarily fabricated in this way. Note that the output of transistor Q_1 (at its collector) is coupled through C_1 to the base or input of transistor Q_2. While the collector of Q_2 is not so coupled to Q_1, its emitter is coupled through R_4 to the emitter of Q_1. The feedback necessary to stabilize the two states (Q_1 saturated, Q_2 cut off; and vice versa) is present. As in other binary multivibrators, the circuit has two stable states, with the amplitude of the input pulse determining which of the two will be stable.

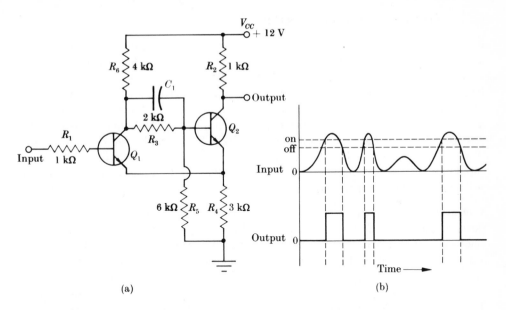

Fig. 9.14 Schmitt trigger circuit. (a) Schematic diagram. (b) Input and output waveforms.

The operation of the circuit may be described by considering the case where transistor Q_2 is initially conducting and Q_1 is cut off. This state is sustained by the substantial voltage drop across R_4, which biases the emitter of Q_1 at a quite positive potential. If an input pulse is received at the base of Q_1, the circuit will continue as before unless the pulse is more positive than the drop across R_4. If this is the case, the circuit will rapidly move to it its other stable state with Q_1 conducting. The collector of Q_1 falls rapidly in potential, and this lower voltage is transmitted by C_1 since it cannot change potential instantly. Because the base of Q_2 becomes negative relative to its emitter, Q_2 is driven to cutoff. It will be sustained at cutoff by the voltage drop that Q_1 creates across R_4. When the input pulse amplitude diminishes sufficiently, the circuit returns to its original state. The voltage at which this change occurs is significantly below the value that triggered the first shift in state. This condition comes about because the base of Q_2 is at a lower potential than it was previously because of feedback from the collector of Q_1. In Fig. 9.14b input and output waveforms demonstrate the action of the Schmitt trigger.

Two interesting applications may be noted for the Schmitt trigger. First, it is possible to utilize the circuit to obtain essentially square waves from assorted pulses of sufficient amplitude. An application of this type would be of value where a square wave had been degraded by successive networks and needed to be restored to its original form. Second, because there is a threshold voltage at which the circuit triggers, it is possible to use a Schmitt trigger as a pulse height discriminator. Close control (to about 0.1 V) is possible by utilizing a dc voltage in series with the input signal. In Fig. 9.14 its ability to discriminate between pulses on the basis of amplitude is illustrated also.

9.7 ANALOG-TO-DIGITAL CONVERTERS

In most instances the output of an instrument is in analog form.* Several questions arise if it is desired to convert such an output to digital form to take advantage of powerful signal processing procedures that digital computers offer. Can conversion be made in real time?† How rapidly and precisely can a conversion be made? The speed of conversion and its accuracy will be of prime importance. To a considerable extent answers to these questions and others are inherent in the conversion process selected. An external factor that is determinative is the rate at which information is presented. A slow analog-to-digital (A-to-D) converter cannot be meaningfully used with a rapid scanning instrument like a mass spectrometer. In the discussion that follows it will be assumed that appropriate matching of instrument to converter will be arranged.

Comparator. An essential module in most A-to-D converters is a comparator, a device capable of indicating whether an unknown signal is larger or smaller than a reference signal. Recall that an operational amplifier should serve this purpose well, since a difference of as little as 1 mV in the signals at its two inputs should produce a change in output of at least -10 to $+10$ V (Section 7.3). Actually, if an operational amplifier is to be used as a comparator, there are two worthwhile modifications. First, it should be designed to recover rapidly after it limits or saturates, and second, its output swing should be reduced to a magnitude more compatible with the 2.5 to 3 V gap between logic levels.

Specifically designed operational amplifiers useful as comparators are readily available commercially, but it is also possible to modify a conventional amplifier. First, a small amount of positive feedback can be provided to speed recovery from saturation. It is only necessary to return a portion of the output to the noninverting input. The cost paid is that some hysteresis is thereby introduced: the voltage at which switching occurs is slightly different when the unknown voltage is increasing and when it is falling. Second, diodes, either conventional or of the Zener type, can be added in a regular operational feedback network to reduce or "bind" the output swings possible. Exercise 9.4 deals with this type of circuit. Two A-to-D converters will now be described.

Frequency A-to-D converter. A very accurate converter (0.005 %) can be developed by translating a voltage input into a proportional frequency. In Fig. 9.15 a simplified block diagram of such a device is shown. The unknown voltage input V_{unk} produces an operational amplifier integrator current of amplitude V_{unk}/R_1. Its ramp output is compared with a reference voltage V_{ref}. When the ramp voltage equals V_{ref}, the com-

---

* Most detector-transducers have voltage or current outputs proportional in amplitude to the physical quantity being represented. It is usually only detectors responding to discrete events, like a photomultiplier receiving individual photons at low light levels or a scintillation counter responding to radioactive events, that produce essentially a digital output.

† Real time refers to ordinary time. The processing of data from an instrument is done in *real time* by a computer when the computer has sufficient speed to perform all necessary calculations while data are being received. When it appears data will arrive at a rate greater than that at which they can be processed, the data are stored on tape or in a computer memory and processed later in machine time.

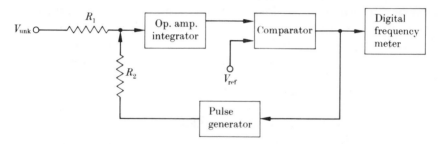

Fig. 9.15 Simplified block diagram of an A-to-D converter of the frequency type.

parator changes logic output, triggering a precision pulse generator. This device produces single pulses of exact charge (coulomb) content. The pulse is opposite in sign to the charge accumulated by the integrator. As a result, the arrival of a pulse at the summing point of the integrator causes the capacitor to discharge rapidly. As soon as the short pulse ends, integration begins again. In the meantime, the comparator output has returned to its original level.

The comparator produces a pulse each time the integrator output equals the reference voltage. These pulses are counted by the digital frequency meter. Since a wide range of counts can be recorded, a digital readout can be obtained over a wide analog input. The coulomb content of the pulses can be adjusted to secure an optimum response.

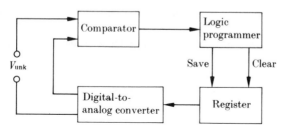

Fig. 9.16 Block diagram of an A-to-D converter based on a successive approximation approach to an unknown voltage V_{unk}. The reference voltage is generated by the digital-to-analog converter on instruction from a program. The value of the unknown voltage is the reading of the register when the comparison is complete.

Successive approximation converter. A very fast and widely used converter is shown in block diagram form in Fig. 9.16. This device is distinctly different from the preceding in that the reference voltage is generated by a digital-to-analog converter.* Its analog output is proportional to the digital number supplied. The logic programmer first instructs the register to deliver to the digital-to-analog converter a logic 1 for the most significant place or bit. The comparison of the reference voltage then generated with the unknown may have either of two outcomes. If the reference voltage is greater than the unknown, the comparator changes output and causes the program-

---

* One of the references should be consulted for details of such a device.

mer to reset that place in the register and to produce a logic 1 in the next most signi-ficant bit. But if the reference voltage generated was smaller than the unknown voltage, the comparator output is unchanged and the programmer instructs the register to save the 1. In quick succession, each bit in the binary register can be tried as a 1 in succession. Some ten to fifty ns are required to complete a conversion of the analog input to a digital output.

9.8 INSTRUMENTS AND DIGITAL COMPUTERS

As suggested in Section 1.10, a link between a computer and an instrument provides a sophisticated mode of control. Both the measurement process (data acquisition) and the processing of data can be enhanced. The possibilities are well illustrated by Table 9.4. As the table suggests, a digital computer can aid in many ways, such as in reducing noise background, performing Beer's-law calculations to obtain concentra-tions, or comparing the spectrum of an unknown substance with stored spectra to identify the unknown. It is beyond the scope of this volume to discuss digital computers and modes of interfacing to instruments.

The ultimate in usage of a computer is to have the device control the entire opera-tion of the instrument. Not only is data acquisition facilitated, but it becomes possible

Table 9.4 Some Applications of Computer Techniques to Absorption Spectrometry and Gas Chromatography*

A. Absorption Spectrometry

1. Smoothing of digitized absorption spectra by a least-squares smoothing procedure.
2. Correction of band shapes for slit width error.
3. Resolution of overlapping bands into individual components.
4. Correction of wavelength errors.
5. Conversion of wavelength to frequency scale and vice versa.
6. Conversion of transmittances to absorbencies and vice versa.
7. Correction for baseline drift.
8. Peak search.
9. Addition and subtraction of spectra to determine components of mixtures or to synthesize the spectra of mixtures for comparison with unknown spectra.
10. Library search and peak matching.
11. Fourier inversion of interferometer scans in infrared interference spectroscopy.
12. Synthesis of theoretical spectra from band intensity and position correlation data for functional groups.

B. Gas Chromatography

1. Determination of integrated peak areas from digitized GC signals.
2. Correction for unsymmetrical peak shapes.
3. Correction for base line drift.
4. Automatic fraction collection.
5. On-line production control analyses.
6. Peak matching and library search.

---

* From *Spex Speaker* **12** (3), 3 (1967). Published by Spex Industries, Metuchen, N.J.

to use the computer in sophisticated fashion to enhance the quality of the data taken. [5] Many further developments along this line will certainly be forthcoming.

Finally, it must be reiterated that it is not necessary to link an instrument to a computer to utilize digital electronics. As indicated in this chapter, modern instruments often incorporate one or more digital electronic modules. Most are associated with gating, providing a time sequence for steps in a measurement, or counting. Such electronic modules are legitimate parts of an instrument.

REFERENCES

The general references of Chaper 5 should also be consulted. Clear treatments of digital electronics on an intermediate level are available in:

1. R. Littauer, *Pulse Electronics*. New York: McGraw-Hill, 1965
2. H. V. Malmstadt and C. G. Enke, *Digital Electronics for Scientists*. New York: Benjamin, 1969
3. J. Millman and H. Taub, *Pulse, Digital, and Switching Waveforms*. New York: McGraw-Hill, 1965

Other publications of value are:

4. J. L. Hughes, *Digital Computer Lab Workbook*. Maynard, Mass.: Digital Equipment Corp., 1968
5. S. P. Perone, D. O. Jones, and W. F. Gutknecht, "Real-Time Computer Optimization of Stationary Electrode Polarographic Measurements," *Anal. Chem.* **41**, 1154 (1969)
6. J. S. Springer, "Using Integrated Circuits in Chemical Instrumentation," *Anal. Chem.* **42** (8), 22A (1970)

EXERCISES

9.1   A half-adder must perform logic operations (a) $A\bar{B} + B\bar{A}$, the sum, and (b) AB, the "carry." Devise a combination of logic gates energized from inputs A and B that will perform these operations.

9.2   In Fig. 9.17 two diode clipping circuits are shown. For a sine wave input, sketch one cycle of the output waveform of each.

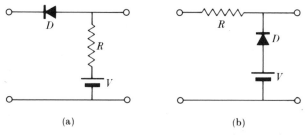

(a)   (b)

Fig.9.17 Two diode clipping circuits. Input is at the left and output at the right.

9.3   In Section 9.4 the possibility of using a crystal oscillator with parallel sets of flip-flops to form precise pulses is described.

   a) Draw a block diagram of such an arrangement.

   b) Assume a 1 MHz crystal oscillator is available and a pair of flip-flops is to be used. How should the flip-flops be set to form a pulse that begins 150 ms after a trigger signal and is 21.5 ms long?

9.4 Draw a schematic circuit diagram for a "bound" operational amplifier that uses a pair of 2 V Zener diodes in a feedback network.

9.5 Demonstrate the JK flip-flop of Fig. 9.6 toggles or complements with each logic 1 pulse received at the clock input. For this purpose assume initial states $Q = 1$ and $\bar{Q} = 0$ and prepare a table that shows the output (when determined) of gates 1 through 9 (a) initially, (b) on the rising edge of an input pulse, (c) at its top, (d) on the falling edge, and (e) at the conclusion of the pulse. Repeat for a second pulse.

9.6 Describe the waveform expected when (a) an astable multivibrator (period A seconds) drives a monostable multivibrator (pulse length B seconds, with $B < A$), (b) an astable multivibrator drives a complementing flip-flop, and (c) a trigger signal starts a monostable vibrator (pulse length A seconds) that drives a second monostable multivibrator (period B seconds). Show waveforms versus time as in Fig. 9.7.

BASIC OPTICS

BASIC OPTICS

Chapter 10

ASPECTS OF PHYSICAL AND GEOMETRICAL OPTICS

10.1 INTRODUCTION

The many types of interaction between matter and electromagnetic radiation in the optical range suggest the importance of this region of the spectrum. As may be seen in Fig. 10.1 the optical range covers essentially six decades of frequency from the far infrared (about 10^{11} Hz) through the vacuum ultraviolet (about 10^{17} Hz). The design of optical instrumentation arises out of a general understanding of the phenomena associated with the propagation of radiation in all types of media.

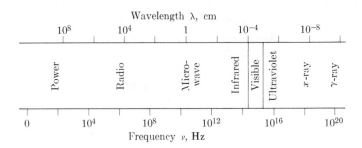

Fig. 10.1 Total spectrum of electromagnetic radiation. The optical region includes frequencies from the microwave range to the X-ray range.

It is useful to classify optical phenomena according to the model employed to treat them. Thus, *physical optics* treats phenomena such as refraction that can be described by using a wave model for radiation. No picture of matter is necessary. *Geometrical optics* includes those phenomena where only the direction of energy transport needs be accounted for, as in focusing a lens. Both these areas will be considered in this chapter. Interactions in which the quantized nature of radiation and atomic systems is essential to a description will, however, be deferred; they will be treated at modest length in the chapters on spectroscopy.

It should be emphasized that a completely rigorous treatment of any optical phenomenon requires quantum mechanics. Yet since wave theory provides a simple, rather elegant, model that yields widely valid equations, this more readily presented and interpreted approach will be employed. The "explanations" provided by this model are, of course, imprecise, as is known from a quantum-mechanical treatment.

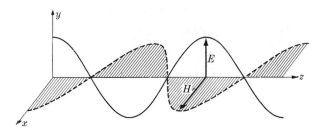

Fig. 10.2 Propagation of a linearly polarized electromagnetic wave train of a single frequency. The electric vector E and magnetic vector H represent the fields established at right angles to the direction of propagation.

10.2 ELECTROMAGNETIC WAVES

The classical model of light that will be used defines radiation as electromagnetic (EM) waves. Figure 10.2 pictures the simplest type of EM wave train, one which is linearly (or plane-) polarized and consists of a single frequency, i.e., is *monochromatic*. Such a beam of radiation is best characterized as a moving force field with indentifiable frequency, velocity, and intensity. Its frequency v is truly constant, i.e. independent of the medium. The radiation, of course, also has a wavelength λ, but it depends on the properties of a medium. It is defined for each case by the fact that the product λv equals the velocity of radiation in the medium.* In a vacuum the product is just the speed of light c (2.998×10^8 m s^{-1}). This limiting case can be related to any other by use of the index of refraction n. By definition n is just the factor by which velocity is reduced if radiation traverses the medium instead of a vacuum. The general expression relating n and λ is

$$v\lambda_i = c/n_i \tag{10.1}$$

where i designates a particular medium. An example of the dependence of wavelength on velocity is illustrated in Fig. 10.3.

As shown in Fig. 10.2, the electric and magnetic aspects of EM waves may be identified with an electric field E and a magnetic field H. For a beam of radiation traveling in, e.g., the z-direction, the variation of the two fields can be described by the expressions

$$E_y \sin 2\pi(vt - z/\lambda)$$
$$H_x \sin 2\pi(vt - z/\lambda). \tag{10.2}$$

Note that the combinations vt and z/λ are dimensionless and define time and distance dependence, respectively. It should be apparent from the form of the equations that either the electric or the magnetic equation can be used in any situation in which *only* the wave character of radiation is important.

By convention, in the rest of the text the electric equation, that is to say, the electric vector, will be used exclusively unless otherwise noted. Since this aspect is

---

* Strictly speaking, the velocity in this case is the phase velocity, not the actual rate of propagation, which is the group velocity. This matter will be examined in more detail in Section 10.6.

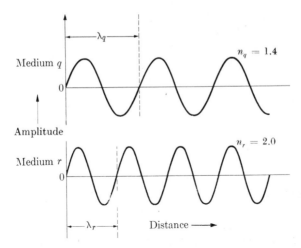

Fig. 10.3 Variation of wavelength of linearly polarized light with the medium through which it passes. Both its phase velocity and its wavelength are smaller in r, the medium of higher refractive index.

the one active in quantum interactions with matter, the convention is especially useful here. It should be stressed that the usage does not in any sense imply that the magnetic aspect of radiation is less real.

The direction of vibration of the electric vector and phase relationships among the waves making up a wave train or beam are also important. In Fig. 10.2 a limiting case with regard to each was shown. The beam was *linearly polarized* since the electric vectors of all component waves were taken as vibrating in a single direction, parallel to the y-axis. Other modes of polarization as well as unpolarized radiation will be treated in Sections 10.12 through 10.16. The beam in Fig. 10.2 also represented a limiting case in that it was *coherent*: the electric vectors of all the waves reached their maxima and minima at the same time and at the same point along the z-axis. In short, all the waves were *in phase*. Commonly, however, as will be discussed below, waves are incoherent and originate either at different times or at different points in space. Thus, they show a phase difference.

Finally, it may be noted that the energy and intensity of an EM wave can be defined without reference to the particulate nature of light. The *intensity* I is a flux defined as the energy streaming through a unit area per second in the direction of wave propagation. Mathematically, it is just $I = E_y^2 c/8\pi$. Note that I is related to the square of wave amplitude and is not directly dependent on frequency or velocity.

10.3 WAVE INTERACTION

In optical systems, often by design, the paths of a great many EM waves intersect or are closely parallel. For example, refraction basically occurs because of the interaction of an incident wavefront with waves emitted by particles of matter that have been distributed by the front. How can nonabsorptive interactions like this be treated? In general, the answer is provided by the *principle of superposition*: Force fields of waves add linearly in the region where waves overlap, whether they cross or actually coincide for a distance. At high intensities, however, linear superposition does not necessarily hold, but this is a topic beyond the scope of this book.

The application of the principle can best be pursued by a combined graphical and descriptive treatment. Again it will be convenient to use monochromatic, linearly polarized waves. For this purpose, Eq. (10.2) can be modified to focus attention on the phase or phase angle α.

$$E = E_y \sin (\omega t + \alpha), \tag{10.3a}$$

or in more general notation

$$y = A \sin (\omega t + \alpha), \tag{10.3b}$$

where y has now been substituted for E and A symbolizes the wave amplitude E_y. In both versions α includes the time aspect of *phase* and the aspect associated with distance and ω is the angular frequency ($\omega = 2\pi v$). Equations (10.3) are a statement of the magnitude of the electric field produced at any point by a passing EM wave train. The significance of the phase angle may be seen by setting t in Eqs. (10.3) equal to 0; then $E = E_y \sin \alpha$. Thus, α is identified as the constant that fixes the part of the cycle in which the wave disturbance is when timing starts.

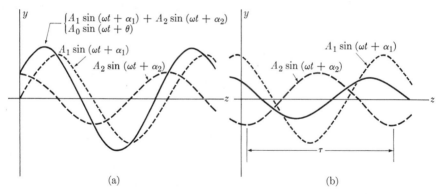

(a)   (b)

Fig. 10.4 Superposition of two linearly polarized wave trains of the same frequency. (a) Phase difference of about 90°. (b) Phase difference of nearly 180°.

In Fig. 10.4 two waves of different amplitude but of the same frequency are plotted as a function of time, first separately and then superposed. Their difference is shown as about 90° in Fig. 10.4a and nearly 180° (or half a wavelength) in Fig. 10.4b. The result of superposition is the wave shown as a solid line. The expression for this result,

$$y = A_1 \sin (\omega t + \alpha_1) + A_2 \sin (\omega t + \alpha_2), \tag{10.4}$$

is obtained by vector addition of two equations like Eq. (10.3). Here A_1 and A_2 are the maximum amplitudes of the two waves. Trigonometric manipulation allows a reduction to

$$y = A_0 \sin (\omega t + \theta),$$

where A_0 is the maximum amplitude of the resultant and θ represents its phase angle.

Although practically it is impossible to produce a monochromatic wave like that described, theoretically it could be done by using an infinitely long train of waves. The short trains available experimentally can be shown to contain a finite spread of wavelengths. The matter is considered below in the discussion of Fourier analysis.

It is clear from Eq. (10.4) and Fig. 10.4 that the amplitude and thus of course the intensity of radiation resulting from interference depend strongly upon the difference in the phase angle of the waves. As $\alpha_1 - \alpha_2$ is increased, the amplitude of the resultant goes through a periodic variation. A maximum in *constructive* interference is secured when $\alpha_1 - \alpha_2$ equals 0°, 360°, 720°, ... Intensity minima, which mark the greatest degree of *destructive* interference, occur when the phase differences have the values of 180°, 450°, ...

An important question is the fate of the energy "lost" when waves interfere, since energy cannot be annihilated without some compensating effect. Clearly, no mass is being generated here, so the energy disappearing from one spot must be appearing elsewhere. This cannot be pictured by wave representation. Quantum mechanics is more successful with its probability function. According to it, the regions of destructive interference are those where there is a very low probability of finding photons. In other areas the probability of their being found is proportionately enhanced.

There is also the question of the *intensity* to be expected when a great many wave trains of the same frequency but of random phasing are superposed. All natural sources emit radiation of this kind in which the amount by which each train of waves is ahead or behind any other (either in time or in space) is purely a matter of chance. Analysis shows that n randomly phased wave trains of the same frequency give an array of waves that on the average has an amplitude increasing as the square root of n. The overall intensity must therefore increase *linearly* with the number of superposed waves, since intensity varies as the square of the amplitude. This result indicates, for example, that the intensity of radiation of 435.8 nm wavelength from a mercury lamp will on the average be the intensity from a single excited atom multiplied by the total number of atoms emitting. It is a somewhat striking result, since the emitting atoms are scattered over a large volume and emit quite randomly.

A more complicated instance is the interference of wave trains of different frequency as well as different amplitudes and phasing. If only two waves are involved, Eq. 10.4 may be modified as follows:

$$y = A_1 \sin(\omega_1 t + \alpha_1) + A_2 \sin(\omega_2 t + \alpha_2). \tag{10.5}$$

Regardless of how many waves are superposed, so long as the velocity of the component waves is the same, the resultant will move with this velocity. This behavior is illustrated in Fig. 10.5. For example, complex wave trains are found in the polychromatic radiation of hot tungsten filaments of incandescent lamps. If the radiation is moving through a vacuum, all the component frequencies will have the same velocity, but in air or any other material dispersion will complicate the superposition.

It is worth stressing that the basic equations of EM wave propagation are *linear* under all common conditions, whether the wave or the quantum character of light is predominant. In other words, two or more light waves can pass at the same time through the same section of a medium, each behaving independently of the others. The possibility of strict superposition of waves need only be abandoned when very

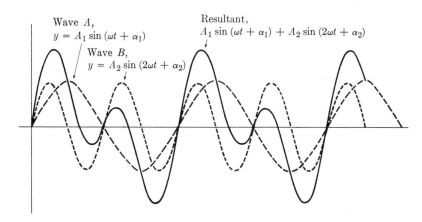

Fig. 10.5 Superposition of wave trains of different frequency and amplitude. Wave B has twice the frequency of wave A.

intense radiation is encountered, as in the use of lasers. Similarly, the probability of absorption or emission involving a photon is independent of the number of other photons present under normal conditions, i.e., there is no dependence on intensity.

The simplicity lent to EM processes by linearity is important, for nonlinear phenomena are well known in electronics (modulation, demodulation, parametric amplification) and in acoustics, where they give rise to beats between waves of differing frequencies. Involved in these nonlinear phenomena are mixing of different waves of distinct phase and frequency by a medium or a device with a nonlinear behavior. Sum and difference frequencies are obtained and harmonics may also be generated.

A further contrast with electronics may be made in applications involving light from ordinary sources. Usually EM wave trains are the result of contributions from very many randomly occurring emission processes and are incoherent. Interactions of light of a particular frequency with a medium are in part hard to define because of such incoherence. It will be recalled that in electronics the phase of a signal is usually well defined.

10.4 FOURIER ANALYSIS

In some cases it is desirable to be able to reverse the process of superposition. Experimentally a prism or a diffraction grating is fairly successful in resolving polychromatic radiation, although neither device can produce wave trains of a single frequency. Only by mathematical analysis can a complex wave train be exhaustively resolved into a set of simple sine waves. The arbitrary nature of the process should be understood. The frequencies obtained in the analysis will depend largely on the assumption made about the constitution of the complex wave train.

In the most widely used method of resolution, Fourier analysis, the components are taken as monochromatic waves, each of an integral frequency. If ω is the basic frequency, then the waves will have the frequencies ω, 2ω, ... The complex wave is represented by an expression with a series of sine terms,

$$y = A_0 + A_1 \sin (\omega t + \alpha_1) + A_2 \sin (2\omega t + \alpha_2) + \cdots, \qquad (10.6)$$

where $A_0, A_1, A_2, \ldots$ are amplitude constants. Note that the terms are of the same form as those in Eq.(10.5).* In general, the coefficients $A_0, A_1, A_2, \ldots$ cannot be evaluated easily, and computers or mechanical devices known as harmonic analyzers are used. For a discussion of Fourier series, Fourier integrals, and Fourier transforms, references should be consulted. [See, e.g., pp. 621–633 of ref. 7.]

The Fourier series representation is limited in that it represents in a satisfactory fashion only essentially infinite waves. When a Fourier analysis is to be performed on ordinary optical and electrical signals of limited duration, a Fourier integral is required. It differs from the series in that an infinite number of component waves that are only infinitesimally different in frequency are assumed. The application of the integral yields a continuous distribution of component waves rather than a series of separate ones, each with a discrete frequency and amplitude. Figure 10.6 shows the distribution of frequencies contributing to a spectral line, which always has a width. For example, the line might be the 435.8 nm mercury wavelength. The length of wave disturbance forming the image is shown at the left, and the amplitude of the components at the right.

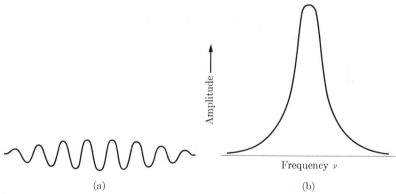

(a)   (b)

Fig. 10.6 The distribution of frequencies in a spectral line of finite width. (a) Wave contour of the "disturbance." (b) Amplitudes of the component frequencies.

10.5 SECONDARY EMISSION

When a matter particle—molecule, atom, or ion—is subjected to the periodically varying electric field of an EM wave, the particle is polarized, i.e., a dipole is induced, usually one oscillating in phase with the incident wave. This process is suggested in Fig. 10.7. Assuming the impinging radiation is not of a frequency characteristically absorbed, the oscillating dipole instantaneously generates a secondary wave of the same frequency. In the wave model it is the interaction or interference of this secondary emission with the incident radiation that is the basis for the phenomena of refraction (transmission), reflection, and scattering. These will be treated in subsequent sections.

In Fig. 10.8 the relation of secondary emission to the oscillating dipole is refined

---

* The most general Fourier series also contains terms in the cosines of the frequencies.

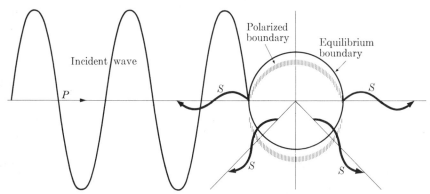

Fig. 10.7 Oscillative dipole induced in an atom by the passage of a monochromatic, polarized wave. The wavelength is assumed long with respect to atomic dimensions. Waves S are secondary waves produced by the oscillating dipole.

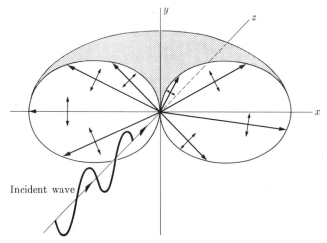

Fig. 10.8 Intensity pattern of the secondary emission of an oscillating dipole. The emitting particle is at the origin. The toroidal or doughnut-shaped evelope represents the intensity of the emission. For example, in the xy cross section shown the intensity of emission in a given direction is proportional to length of the radius vector. All secondary rays are linearly polarized.

to permit graphing of intensities and angular distribution. Note (a) the relative amplitudes, (b) that the secondary waves are linearly polarized, and (c) that there is no emission perpendicular to the direction of travel of the primary wave. The greater the polarizability of a particle, that is, the larger the refractive index of the medium made up of the particles, the greater the amplitude of the secondary waves will be.

In quantum theory the secondary emission of radiation is regarded as a process of excitation to some unstable and unobservable state followed by an immediate reemission (in about 10^{-14} s). The incident light quantum is considered to be absorbed and reemitted.

Usually the excited molecule or other species drops back to the initial state. If the exciting frequency is in the visible or UV, however, molecules sometimes fall to an excited vibrational or rotational level, giving rise to secondary emission of different wavelength, a phenomenon termed the *Raman effect* (Chapter 18).

The materials of greatest interest in physical optics belong to the class designated *dielectrics* or nonconductors. These have no, or at most very few, free electrons or ions and are usually optically transparent. Since electrically conducting solids either absorb radiation or reflect it strongly, they are optically of less interest and will be considered only very briefly in connection with reflection in Section 10.8. In addition, the present discussion will be concerned only with optically *isotropic* media, substances whose optical properties are the same in all directions. Anisotropic substances will be considered later in connection with polarized light in Section 10.13.

Whenever radiation passes from one dielectric material into another, it is partially reflected and partially transmitted. In the new medium it retains its characteristic frequencies but is propagated with a different velocity and thus, with a different wavelength. In general, the radiation also changes direction abruptly at an interface, i.e. is *refracted*.

If the interface is small in extent, a condition that exists whenever a small particle is suspended in some other material, the radiation is scattered rather than reflected. As will be discussed in detail in Section 10.10, the division between reflection and scattering occurs when dimensions become of the order of a wavelength of the incident beam. Absorption may also occur at the interface and in the bulk of the second material, but since it is definitely a quantum effect it is considered separately in the chapters on spectrometry. In Fig. 10.9 the interfacial effects are shown schematically for unpolarized monochromatic radiation incident from air onto a piece of glass.

10.6 REFRACTION

The reader is probably familiar from a general physics course with the use of the Huygens wavefront construction to account for the angular relationships of refraction. [pp. 25ff of 1] This approach is satisfactory for deducing the familiar statement involv-

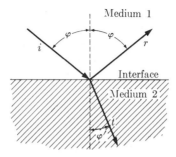

Fig. 10.9 Two interfacial phenomena, reflection and transmission, exhibited by EM waves. ϕ is the angle of incidence and reflection, and ϕ' is the angle of refraction. Incident beam i, reflected beam r, and transmitted beam t are all in the same plane.

ing velocities, Eq. (10.7), and Snell's law, Eq. (10.8).

$$\frac{\sin \phi}{\sin \phi'} = \frac{v_1}{v_2}; \qquad (10.7)$$

$$\frac{\sin \phi}{\sin \phi'} = \frac{n_2}{n_1}. \qquad (10.8)$$

In the expressions, the symbolism is taken from Fig. 10.9, that is ϕ and ϕ' are angles of incidence and refraction measured relative to a perpendicular to the interface. The subscripts refer to the first and second medium respectively, and n is the refractive index. The ratio of sines becomes indeterminate for vertical incidence; in that case, experiment shows that the radiation is not deviated but makes the usual change in velocity.

For the common case of incidence from air, Eq. (10.8) can be simplified. Since n_1 is close to unity, we can use instead the nearly exact relation

$$n_2 = \sin \phi / \sin \phi'.$$

Were it possible to secure and work with truly monochromatic radiation, Eq. (10.7) would define a "true" velocity. But even the narrowest spectral emission line is actually a band of frequencies (Section 13.3), each of which will experience a different n and thus travel at a different velocity, as discussed in the next section. Accordingly, for a so-called monochromatic beam the velocity v of Eq. (10.7) represents a *phase velocity* at which a wavefront of a given frequency moves through a medium. The front is determined by combination of the secondary emission of atoms in the forward direction and the residue of the incident radiation (that propagates at velocity c). Thus v, the phase velocity of the combination wavefront, can exceed c if the phase of the secondary emission leads that of the incident radiation, or be less than c if it lags the incident light. [3]

In contrast to refractive index measurements, direct determinations of light velocities in matter involve observation of the rate of propagation of energy, thus a *group velocity* u. It is a "pulse-travel-time" velocity that makes allowance for the range of wavelengths present in a pulse and is defined relative to v by the expression $u = v - \lambda(dv/d\lambda)$. Differences in u and v may amount to several per cent near an absorption band.

Example Michelson measured the velocity of light in carbon disulfide by a rotating mirror device and found $c/u = 1.77$. He also showed by use of a refractometer that $n_2 = c/v = 1.64$.

A natural restriction on refraction that is of particular interest is the existence of a limit to the angle of refraction in the medium of higher refractive index termed the *critical angle* ϕ_c. If this is the second medium, radiation will be refracted in it at the critical angle when incident from medium 1 on the interface at 90°. Though this case of grazing incidence can be approached only as a limit, it leads to a mathematical definition of ϕ_c since, as $\sin \phi \to 1$, Eq. (10.8) becomes

$$\sin \phi' = \sin \phi_c = n_1/n_2. \qquad (10.9)$$

Conversely, if radiation is incident on the interface from medium 2, total reflection (back into the medium) occurs when the angle of incidence exceeds ϕ_c (Section 10.8).

Two questions may now be posed: (1) if radiation is incident from a vacuum onto a medium, how is the wavelength increased without any loss of energy, and (2) how are a refracted and a reflected beam formed, since secondary emission occurs in all directions in the plane formed by the incident beam and the interface?

The answer to the first may be expressed qualitatively in terms of the fact that the electric vector of a wave induces a dipole of the opposite sign. Consider a wave incident from a vacuum onto an isotropic medium. The positive end of the radiation vector effectively "moves" into an atomic region which has a net negative charge. The interaction will be much the same as if one tries to push a positive charge through a medium of negative charges. The positive charge is slowed until some equilibrium velocity is achieved. The wave is slowed in the same way. Since the number of wavefronts arriving at the interface per second is not changed, it follows that the distance between successive fronts in the medium is smaller. The wavelength of the radiation has been shortened upon entering the medium.

To answer the second question, one must examine the interference or combination of the incident and secondly waves along the wavefront in the medium. In the refracting medium, the particles, whether atoms, molecules, or ions, are fairly regularly spaced in spite of small, random thermal movements. Therefore the lateral secondary radiation from the induced dipole destructively interferes. In the surface, the interference is complete for isotropic media except in the directions of (a) the refracted ray and (b) the reflected ray. If conditions are right for total reflection, only the latter appears.

Dielectric constant and refractive index. It is of interest that the dielectric constant ϵ plays the same role in the electrical range as does the refractive index in the optical range, i.e. serves as a measure of polarization. The quantities are very simply interrelated for substances whose magnetic susceptibility is unity, i.e., for almost all transparent materials, by the equation $\epsilon_v = n_v^2$ where the subscript v indicates that the expression holds when both are measured at the same frequency.

A representative picture of the dependence of n or $\sqrt{\epsilon}$ on frequency from dc through the optical range is shown in Fig. 10.10. Several types of polarization are operative in the radiofrequency range. As the frequency rises, each type in succession is "phased

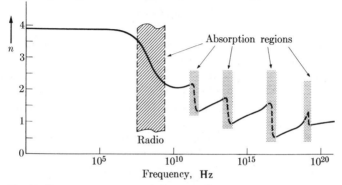

Fig. 10.10 Variation of n or $\epsilon^{\frac{1}{2}}$ with frequency for a polar dielectric.

out." There is less time for it to occur and ϵ falls. For example, the decrease in n in the radiofrequency range is associated with increasing inability of polar molecules to orient in phase with the incident radiation. Across the broad range of frequencies there is a progression toward lower and lower refractive indices until $n \simeq 1$ in the X-ray region. Here there is not even time for electronic polarization.

10.7 OPTICAL DISPERSION

It is a commonly observed phenomenon that the refractive index depends on frequency. For example, it is this dependence that allows a glass prism to spread a beam of white light into a spectrum. Thus the terms in Eqs. (10.7) and (10.8) should actually have a subscript designating the frequency.

The variation of refractive index with frequency is called *dispersion*. In order to describe the phenomenon more precisely, it is necessary to go beyond the wave model to one that will represent the interaction of bound electrons with radiation. For this purpose a simple classical model in which a dielectric is considered as a collection of bound electrons uniformly distributed in a lattice of atomic cores is adequate.

The incidence of light will cause a forced oscillation of each bound electron that will ordinarily be in phase with the periodic EM field. Since a nucleus is comparatively massive, it is reasonable to assume that in the short intervals before field polarity reverses it will not move. If radiation of ordinary intensity is incident, only small displacements of electrons from equilibrium positions need be considered, and a Hooke-law type of restoring force can be employed in developing an equation of motion.

To obtain an exact solution a convenient boundary condition to impose is that the system will have a natural or characteristic frequency, namely one at which it will absorb energy. For each "kind" of bound electron the value of natural frequency will differ. These different oscillations will not interfere, at least not at intensity levels below those of laser beams. The values of displacements obtained by solving the equation for one kind of electron lead to the following expression for polarizability in the y-direction, α_y,

$$\alpha_y = \frac{e^2/m}{4\pi(v_y^2 - v^2)} \tag{10.10}$$

where e is the electronic charge, m is the electron mass, and v_y is the natural frequency for the electron in the y-direction. By introducing the expression for molar refraction, $M(n^2 - 1)/(n^2 + 2)\rho = 4\pi N_0\alpha/3$, the refractive index can be related to the polarizability. Here N_0 is Avogadro's number, M is the molecular weight, and ρ is the density. Since there are usually several electrons that can be moved with some ease, Eq. (10.10) is ordinarily a summation of several terms. Combining such a summation with the expression for the molar refraction yields finally the expression

$$\frac{M}{\rho} \frac{(n^2 - 1)}{(n^2 + 2)} = \frac{N_0 e^2/m}{3\pi} \sum_i \frac{f_i}{v_i^2 - v^2} \tag{10.11}$$

where f_i is the number of electrons of kind i in the atom (frequently termed the oscillator strength), and v_i is the characteristic or natural frequency for the vibration of these electrons in the y-direction. The type of interaction of radiation and matter described by Eq. (10.11) is termed *electronic polarization*.

The relationship between frequency and refractive index may be simplified for gases. It can be shown that for gases $n \simeq 1 + a$ where a is a constant much less than unity. Thus the term $n^2 + 2 \simeq 3$ and the term $n^2 - 1 \simeq 2(n - 1)$. With these approximations, Eq. (10.11) becomes

$$n - 1 = \frac{\rho N_0 e^2/m}{2\pi M} \sum_i \frac{f_i}{v_i^2 - v^2}. \tag{10.12}$$

A quantitative picture of the dependence of n on frequency may now be attempted. At low frequencies, where $v \ll v_i$, it is seen that n remains essentially constant and greater than unity. As v approaches v_i, the refractive index must become larger. Finally, when $v = v_i$, on the basis of this simple model, the refractive index becomes infinite. Because of damping effects that have not been considered the index actually remains finite. Note that the denominator $v_i^2 - v^2$ changes sign when $v > v_i$. Accordingly, as the frequency exceeds a characteristic absorption frequency, n must fall from a high value to less than unity. Here phase velocities will exceed c, the vacuum velocity of light. As v increases further, normal dispersion is again observed. The anomalous behavior of n in the vicinity of absorption frequencies is shown in Fig. 10.11, as predicted by this simple model. It is significant that the behavior of n is intimately related to the existence of characteristic absorption frequencies.

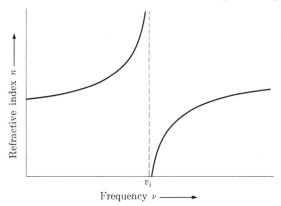

Fig. 10.11 Behavior of the refractive index in the neighborhood of an absorption frequency v_i.

Infrared dispersion. At infrared frequencies the vibration of the electric vector of radiation is sufficiently slow that atomic nuclei can be displaced relative to one another before the direction of the imposed field reverses. In other words, in this spectral range the field perturbs the normal vibrations and rotations of atoms and gives rise to *atomic polarization*. As a result of the greater magnitude of this form of polarization, the index of refraction is proportionately larger in the infrared. Again there is a sudden decrease in n at frequencies just larger than each characteristic vibrational absorption frequency.

10.8 REFLECTION

Reflection occurs whenever radiation is incident upon a boundary between dielectrics across which there is a change in refractive index. The quality of the surface has much to do with the nature of the phenomenon. The usual law of equal angles of incidence and reflection applies only in the case of regular reflection from a smooth surface, called *specular* reflection. Irregular surfaces give rise to diffuse reflection, of little interest in optical work. For most angles of incidence and types of interface, the reflected beam has a different total intensity, state of polarization, and phase from the incident one. In addition, if many frequencies are present there are usually chromatic differences in the reflected radiation as well.

The amount of reflection, that is the ratio of the intensity of the reflected radiation to that incident on the interface, is termed the *reflectance* or reflectivity. Since reflection can be considered as resulting from the secondary radiation of atomic dipoles induced in the surface, it is related to the polarizability of atoms. It seems reasonable to expect that for a given angle of incidence ϕ the reflectance will be greater the larger the refractive index of medium 2. Actually, allowance must be made for the interference of secondary and incident radiation, so that the refractive index of medium 1 is involved as well.

It can be shown for the simplest case, that of normal incidence onto the flat surface of a nonabsorbing medium, that the reflectance R is defined as

$$R = \frac{(n_2 - n_1)^2}{(n_2 + n_1)^2} = \frac{(n_{21} - 1)^2}{(n_{21} + 1)^2}, \tag{10.13}$$

where $n_{21} = n_2/n_1$. Clearly, the greater the difference in refractive index of the media, the larger the reflectance. Note also that the magnitude of reflectance at normal incidence is independent of which medium has the greater n.

Example   According to Eq. (10.13), visible light falling vertically from air onto a plate of ordinary glass of $n = 1.50$ would undergo about 4% reflection ($R = 0.04$). As light emerges from the far surface of the glass plate it will again be normally reflected with $R = 0.04$. The intensity of the transmitted radiation is thus approximately 92% of that incident. It may also be said that the plate has a transmittance of 0.92.

On the other hand, if $n_2 = n_1$ there can be no reflection. For example, X-rays cannot be reflected at all efficiently into air at "ordinary" angles, since $n_{X\text{-ray}} \sim 1$ for most substances. Note also the bearing Eq. (10.13) has on visibility: objects become invisible when surrounded by a medium of identical refractive index. A way to determine approximate refractive indices for glasses and other nonconducting solids such as minerals is suggested by this result (Section 21.8).

When radiation falls obliquely on an interface, the reflectance varies with the angle of incidence. Polarization and phase changes also occur (see Section 10.13) but may be ignored if only the overall reflectance is of interest. It was shown by both Fresnel and Maxwell that the appropriate expression for the reflectance of a non-absorbing medium is

$$R = \frac{1}{2}\left(\frac{\sin^2(\phi - \phi')}{\sin^2(\phi + \phi')} + \frac{\tan^2(\phi - \phi')}{\tan^2(\phi + \phi')}\right). \tag{10.14}$$

To solve the equation, the appropriate angles of refraction ϕ' are calculated from the known index n at the frequency of interest and for selected ϕ's from Eq. (10.8). The squares of the sine and tangent terms should be noted. These enter when amplitudes are converted to intensities. If only the ratio of wave amplitudes were of interest, unsquared trigonometric terms would be involved.

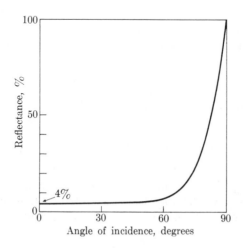

Fig. 10.12 Reflectance as a function of angle of incidence for unpolarized monochromatic light incident from air onto a glass plate of $n = 1.50$.

An illustration of the way reflectance changes with angle of incidence is given in Fig. 10.12. Although the graph plotted is for the reflection of unpolarized monochromatic light incident from air onto a glass of $n = 1.50$, the result is typical of optical cases. It is interesting that the reflectance is (1) approximately constant up to angles of incidence of 60°, and then (2) rises quickly to 100% at 90°, or grazing incidence. The reader may confirm the behavior by looking at this page at a low angle with respect to an overhead light.

Regardless of the angle of incidence, serious intensity losses occur when radiation must traverse many lenses, prisms, cells, etc. For example, there need be only a few plates of lenses of $n = 1.50$ to reduce the transmitted power by 50%, since *each* surface has a reflectance of 0.04. Some ways of cutting reflection loss are suggested below.

Multiple reflection. An intimately associated phenomenon is that of multiple internal reflection. In a slab of dielectric internal reflections cannot be avoided although they may be minimized, allowed for, or utilized. The nature of these reflections may best be seen in the case depicted in Fig. 11.14, p. 303.

Some of the radiation reflected from the far face of the plate (ray 1′) will again be reflected from the front face (ray 2). In magnitude, ray 2 will be about 4% of ray 1′ (as before). The process will, of course, continue indefinitely. The radiation that actually emerges from the far side of the plate is the reduced "primary" beam plus a small supplement of radiation from the multiple reflections.

In the more common case of oblique incidence, the multiply reflected rays deviate, of course, from the primary beam. Together with the initially reflected energy, these rays constitute *stray radiation.* Since they will not undergo the same optical alterations, their reentry into the primary beam at any point will cause spurious results (Section 12.8).

Reducing reflected losses. Two general means are used to reduce reflection when it is undesirable. Optical elements that are in contact, such as those in achromatic lenses, are cemented with a material of similar refractive index (rather than left with air gaps between them). This approach is also a basis for the oil-immersion technique used in microscopy, where a high-refractive-index oil fills the space between sample slide and objective lens.

The second method is the deposition of a low-reflection coating designed to secure destructive interference of light that would otherwise be reflected. The type of deposit and thickness of layer are decided on the basis of the following criteria:

1. The thickness of coating must be just one-fourth the wavelength in the center of the spectral band whose transmission is desired.

2. The intensity of radiation reflected from the outside of the coating must be equal to that reflected from the interface between the coating and the optical element. This condition is met if the refractive index of the coating, n_c, is given by

$$n_c = \sqrt{n_1 n_2},$$

where the subscripts refer to the usual media 1 and 2, and light is vertically incident.

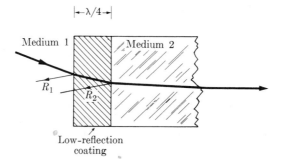

Fig. 10.13 The reduction of reflection by a low-reflectance coating. Although radiation is usually almost normally incident on the coated surface, it is drawn as obliquely incident to allow the reflected rays to be shown. Rays R_2 and R_1 superpose and destructively interfere, since they are nearly one half-wavelength out of phase.

In Fig. 10.13 the manner in which the low-reflection coating reduces losses is shown diagrammatically. Any wave that emerges from the front of the coating after reflection at the coating-medium 2 interface will have traveled one half-wavelength more than a wave of the same frequency reflected directly from the coating.* On superposition, the two rays will destructively interfere: the energy that would appear in reflected rays is shifted to the transmitted beam. If medium 1 is air ($n_1 = 1$) the value of n_c must be about $\sqrt{n_2}$. Thus, glass lenses of $n = 1.50$ to 1.65 require a coating of a transparent layer with n in the range of from 1.22 to 1.28.

Either magnesium or calcium fluoride is commonly used as a coating. Each is applied in layers of the desired thickness by vacuum evaporation techniques. The deposit has too high ($n = 1.35$) a refractive index, but is still quite effective. Most lenses intended for the visible region are coated so as to pass green light (550 nm) well. Even for red and blue light, their reflectance is no more than about 0.6 %.

Total reflection. Under certain conditions, radiation fails entirely to pass through an interface between transparent media and is totally reflected. (The trivial case of grazing incidence may be neglected.) Total reflection occurs when radiation strikes an interface with a medium of *lower* refractive index at an angle greater than the ciritical angle (Section 10.6). A graph of reflectance for this type of incidence is given in Fig. 10.14. Noteworthy is the fact that the reflectance rises very steeply as the angle of incidence approaches the critical.

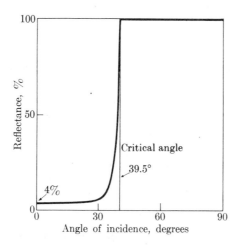

Fig. 10.14 Magnitude of internal reflection at various angles of incidence. Monochromatic radiation incident from a glass of $n_D = 1.57$ into air.

In optical systems total internal reflection enjoys at least two applications that arise from the fact that all the power is reflected if the second medium is nonabsorbing.

1. *Totally reflecting prisms* such as are illustrated in Fig. 10.15 may be used instead of mirrors in situations where losses in intensity would be serious. Here the only losses occur at the entrance and exit faces.

---

* Actually, there is a phase change on reflection from a surface of higher refractive index. It need not be considered here, however, since the change is the same for each of the interfering rays.

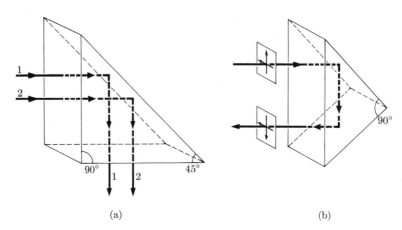

Fig. 10.15 Totally reflecting prisms. (a) Right-angle prism. (b) Porro prism. The orientation of an image on entering and emerging is shown by the arrows.

2. *Fiber optics*, bundles of thousands of fine parallel fibers that are coated, can be used to transmit radiation into places that are difficult of access with very little loss of intensity. Multiple internal reflections will occur within each fiber as it transmits radiation.

If the second medium is absorbing, total internal reflection often represents a useful means of obtaining its absorption spectrum. This application will be considered further in the following section.

Aside from the obvious limitation imposed by a restricted range of transparency, there are other precautions that must be observed in using total internal reflection. Dispersion, polarization effects, and image rearrangements can occur under varying conditions and must be taken into consideration. [3, 10] For example, in the correct use of the prisms shown in Fig. 10.15, radiation is always perpendicularly or nearly perpendicularly incident. Note also that the Porro totally reflecting prism brings about a reorientation of any image transmitted through it.

Reflection from an absorbing medium. If a medium is absorbing, e.g., a red plastic or a metal, the reflectance from its surface at normal incidence can be calculated from Eq. (10.13) by use of the complex refractive index $\hat{n}$. By definition,

$$\hat{n} = n - ik, \tag{10.15}$$

where k is the attenuation index of the medium.* The reflectance equation for normal incidence becomes

---

* Alternative definitions are in use. The other definition is $\hat{n} = n(1 - ik)$; when used, the product nk appears in equations in place of k. The usual absorption coefficient α can also be used in place of k. For example, α appears in the Lambert exponential law for transmission $I/I_0 = e^{-\alpha d}$, where I and I_0 are the transmitted and incident intensities, respectively, and d the thickness of the medium. The substitution of α can be made by use of the expression $k = \alpha c/4\pi v$, where c is the vacuum velocity of light and v its frequency.

$$R = \frac{(n_2 - n_1)^2 + k_2^2}{(n_2 + n_1)^2 + k_2^2}. \tag{10.16}$$

Except for strongly absorbing substances, the product k is small relative to the parenthetical term and can be neglected for normal (external) reflection from an absorbing medium. In the following section this discussion will be extended to internal reflection from an absorbing medium.

Example What is the external reflectance in air of a gray glass plate of $\alpha = 10^4$ and $n_2 = 1.50$ at 500 nm? Since $\lambda = c/v$, $k = \alpha\lambda/4\pi = 10^4 \times 500 \times 10^{-9}$ m/4 $\times$ 3.14 $= 3.98 \times 10^{-3}$. The magnitude of k^2 will be quite negligible. Thus, $R = 0.04$, as for a nonabsorbing plate.

10.9 TOTAL INTERNAL REFLECTION

When radiation undergoes total internal reflection, it actually penetrates a fraction of a wavelength into the medium beyond the reflecting surface. In discussing the phenomenon it will be convenient to use the classical terms "denser," referring to a medium of higher refractive index, and "rarer," referring to one of lower index. Because of the superposition of incident and reflected waves at the boundary, a standing wave is set up normal to the reflecting surface in the two media. [10] In the rarer medium it is termed an *evanescent wave* since its amplitude falls off exponentially to zero within a fraction of a wavelength from the interface.

In Fig. 10.16 the nature of the standing wave is sketched for the case of incidence at an angle greater than the critical angle on a boundary between denser and rarer media where neither medium is absorbing. As the figure suggests, the electric field

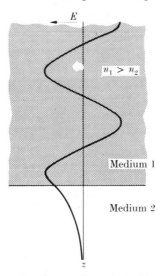

Fig. 10.16 Amplitude of standing electric wave formed on either side of an interface during total internal reflection. The superposition of incident and reflected waves in the upper (denser) medium causes the standing wave. The depth of penetration d_p into the rarer medium is the distance over which the amplitude falls to e^{-1} of its value at the reflecting interface.

amplitude on either side of the interface may be substantial.* Its amplitude is strongly dependent on the angle of incidence, gradually falling to zero as the angle is increased toward 90°. Though not shown in the figure, the evanescent wave has field strength in all *three* directions because of the nature of the interaction.

Frustrated total reflection.   Either a lossless mechanism or an absorption mechanism can be used to withdraw energy from the evanescent wave. Here lossless "coupling" implies withdrawal of energy in optical form. To do so it is only necessary that a second transparent element be positioned not more than a fraction of a wavelength from the interface. Then part of the optical energy is transmitted through the second element, and the rest is still internally reflected. The descriptive name, frustrated total reflection, is applied. A simple arrangement for securing the effect is shown in Fig. 10.17.

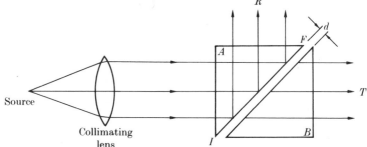

Fig. 10.17 Frustrated total internal reflection. Collimated radiation of wavelength λ (in denser medium) incident on the interface IF between prism A and air is either totally reflected (beam R) or transmitted through adjacent right-angle prism B. The transmission increases steadily as the distance d between prisms is decreased. It is zero for $d/\lambda = 1$, reaches 50% for $d/\lambda = 0.3$, and is 100% for $d/\lambda = 0$.

The intensity of the transmitted beam is strongly dependent on the distance of separation. Accordingly, the technique offers a method of *intensity modulation* of a beam of radiation. For example, with the arrangement in the figure a transmittance of 50% is attained with a separation of $0.3\lambda_1$, where λ_1 is the wavelength in the denser medium. At a separation of $0.8\lambda_1$, the transmission falls to zero. To modulate, the separation is varied at will. The transmitted intensity changes accordingly.

In addition, the intensity varies with the angle of incidence, decreasing steadily the more ϕ exceeds ϕ_c. Parallel polarized light is also favored in transmission relative to vertically polarized radiation (Section 10.13). Finally, since the transmittance T and reflectance R prove to be *smooth functions* of the separation between prisms, it must be concluded that no interference phenomena occur in the gap between them. As will be noted below, their absence is characteristic of internal reflection.†

---

* If reflection occurs from a metallic surface or a metallic mirror, a standing wave also is produced, but a node, i.e., a region of minimum amplitude, occurs at the surface because of the high conductivity of the metal. In this case, the depth of penetration is also smaller (about 10 nm).

† Another useful (lossless) method of frustrating total internal reflection is varying the refractive index of either medium. If incidence is at or just beyond the critical angle, decreasing n_1 or increasing n_2 sufficiently will destroy total internal reflection. An electric field, pressure, or other appropriate variable can be used for this purpose. For example, if the second medium is a polar liquid, refractive index may be altered by application of an electric field.

Attenuated total reflection. Where the rarer medium is absorbing, the intensity of radiation totally reflected also falls below 100%. In this case, energy is only absorbed at characteristic wavelengths and in general is then degraded to heat. The phenomenon is the basis for internal reflection spectroscopy (Section 16.8), a widely used spectrometric technique.

Since the electric field amplitude in the rarer medium decreases exponentially, it is convenient to define a *penetration depth* d_p as the interval over which the field falls to $1/e$ of its value at the surface. This depth is given by the expression

$$d_p = \lambda_1/2\pi(\sin^2 \phi - n_{21}^2)^{1/2}, \tag{10.17}$$

where λ_1 is the wavelength in the denser medium, ϕ the angle of incidence, and n_{21} the ratio of the refractive index of the rarer medium to that of the denser. It can be seen that penetration depth will increase as the angle of incidence increases and as the two media become closer in refractive index. Since the extent of absorption depends on penetration, optimum conditions for attenuation of reflectance are an angle of incidence slightly greater than the critical angle and a small refractive index difference between rarer and denser media. The depth of penetration is not polarization-sensitive.

How great a penetration into the absorbing medium can be expected? Since both the angular and refractive index terms in the denominator of Eq. (10.17) will not differ markedly from unity, the denominator will in general be between 1 and 10. Thus the penetration is a fraction of the wavelength λ_1.

In most cases the rarer medium will be thicker than the depth of penetration. Thus it is also convenient to define an effective depth d_e of penetration in terms of the fraction by which the reflectance R is decreased by the presence of an absorbing medium. The expression used is $R = (1 - \alpha d_e)$ where α is the Lambert-law absorptivity. The expression relates to a single reflection, of course. If the rarer medium is of low absorption, the effective thickness is given by the expression

$$d_e = \frac{E_0^2 n_{21} d_p}{2 \cos \phi}, \tag{10.18}$$

where E_0 is the electric field amplitude at the interface.

Finally, a surprising aspect of absorption in the rarer medium under conditions of internal reflection is that to some degree it occurs in all directions. Because of the nature of the interaction, the evanescent wave has some electric field strength in all three directions. As a result, it is possible for an absorbing dipole in the rarer medium (connected with a quantum transition) to be oriented in virtually any direction and still absorb from the radiation incident on the interface. The intensity of absorption will, of course, vary with the orientation of the dipole.*

10.10 SCATTERING

Like reflection and refraction, scattering has its origin in the induced secondary

---

* This contrasts strongly with regular absorption processes in which a dipole can withdraw energy from the electric field only if perpendicular to the direction of propagation and parallel to the electric vector's vibration.

emission of particles that lie in the path of radiation. Secondary radiation is scattered only if the particles

1. Have dimensions about the order of magnitude or smaller than the incident wavelengths and
2. Are randomly distributed in a medium of refractive index different from their own.

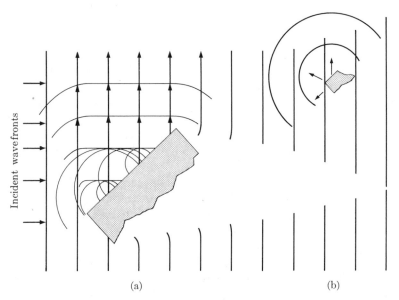

(a)   (b)

Fig. 10.18 Similarity of reflection and scattering of radiation. Monochromatic radiation is incident. (a) Reflection from particle whose dimensions are greater than 2λ. (b) Scattering by particle whose dimensions are smaller than $3\lambda/2$.

In other cases the lateral rays originating from the secondary emission of atoms mutually cancel through destructive interference, leaving only a refracted and a reflected beam. The role of dimensions in causing reflection rather than scattering at a surface is illustrated in Fig. 10.18. In this figure a small particle is seen to give rise to a nearly spherical wavefront. If the radiation that the particle scatters is in the visible, an observer with a microscope or ultramicroscope could "see" the particle, but it would appear only as a point; no surface features would be resolved.

Approximate upper size limits of particles responsible for scattering in various regions of the optical spectrum are given in Table 10.1. Lower limits are more difficult to assign, since scattering efficiency of small particles varies about as the square of the volume at a given wavelength. For visible light, some familiar examples of scattering particles are those in smoke and freshly formed precipitates.

Small particles. The simplest case of scattering is that involving (a) very small, (b) spherical, (c) optically isotropic particles. Their longest dimension must be no more than from 5 to 10% of the wavelength of incident radiation. Their scattering is not essentially different from that of the single atom shown in Fig. 10.8 and is known as

Table 10.1 Structures Producing Scattering

Incident radiation		Maximum particle size (approximate dimensions), μm	Type of aggregate
Wavelength, μm	Spectral region		
10	Infrared	15	Large colloidal particles
0.5	Visible	0.75	Colloidal particles, macromolecules
0.001	X-ray	0.002	Small molecules, atoms

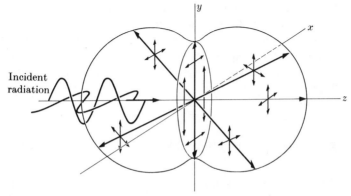

Fig. 10.19 Pattern of scattering of unpolarized monochromatic light by a small, spherical, isotropic particle. The particle is at the origin. The scattered intensity is indicated by the length of the vector. Only two cross sections of the scattering envelope are shown, that in the yz-plane and that in the xy-plane. The state of polarization of the scattered rays in those planes is indicated by the small vibrational vectors. Radiation scattered in either direction along the z-axis (0° and 180° to the direction of propagation) is unpolarized; that scattered at 90° to the direction of propagation is linearly polarized.

Rayleigh scattering. For a single particle, a symmetrical intensity pattern of the sort shown in Fig. 10.19 is obtained with unpolarized radiation. The intensity of scattering, I_s, is given in this case by the following expression:

$$I_s = \frac{8\pi^4\alpha^2}{\lambda^4 r^2}(1 + \cos^2\theta)I_0. \tag{10.19}$$

Here α is the polarizability of the particle, λ the vacuum wavelength, I_0 the incident intensity, θ the angle between the incident and the scattered ray, and r the distance from the center of scattering to the detector. It may also be shown that the polarizability varies roughly as the volume of a particle. Hence Eq. (10.19) predicts that the scattering will increase strongly as the particles become larger. In any collection of particles of different sizes the larger ones will contribute very heavily to the observed scattering.

Note also the inverse dependence of intensity on the fourth power of the wavelength. The intensity increases very strongly as the wavelength becomes shorter, that is, as it approaches the size of the particle. For example, according to Eq. (10.19), violet light of wavelength 400 nm is scattered about 3.8 times better than green light of 550 nm. The blue color of the sky is a familiar result of this kind of discrimination. Dust particles of small dimensions, molecules of water, etc., cause the short wavelengths in sunlight to be scattered so efficiently as to make the predominant color blue. The red color of the sun at sunset and as seen through smoke or fog is confirmation that the long wavelengths (red) are much less effectively scattered and are more completely transmitted.

Liquids and solutions. In pure liquids and in solutions of normal small particles, there is ordinarily a fairly regular array of "molecules." These systems are poor light scatterers, since here also lateral destructive interference ensures that virtually all the incident radiation is transmitted as the refracted beam (or reflected at the surface). There is a possibility, however, for very weak scattering. It originates in the inhomogeneities (small density and concentration fluctuations) constantly generated by thermal forces. Some volume elements will have more particles than the average, others less. Each nonaverage volume region acts briefly as a scattering center of polarizability $\Delta\alpha$, where

$$\Delta\alpha = \alpha_{local} - \alpha_{av}. \tag{10.20}$$

In this case $(\Delta\alpha)^2$, a very small quantity, replaces α^2 in Eq. (10.19), and the scattering is very faint.

Polymer solutions and sols. A markedly different result is obtained if the solute is composed of large molecules (15 A < dimensions < 400 A) of polarizability different from that of the solvent. Note that the scattering in the visible range will still be of the Rayleigh type. There is now a contribution to the scattered light by density fluctuations in the solvent, which is very small, and one due to the "concentration" fluctuations, which will increase with concentration.

Large particle scattering. Some other approach is necessary to handle particles whose dimensions are greater than 10% of λ. One difficulty is the fact that scattering centers in large particles are far enough apart for some interference from the secondary rays emitted from separate areas of the particle to be likely to occur. The situation is pictured for a large spherical particle in Fig 10.20. The rays emitted in backward directions are highly susceptible to interference because of the large path differences possible. For example, compare distances for paths SBA and SCA. In the forward directions the path differences among rays are much less, and the interference is usually constructive. The result is a shift from the symmetrical intensity patterns of Figs. 10.8 and 10.19 to one showing much less scattering for angles greater than 90°. The new intensity pattern plotted in Fig. 10.21 shows the preponderance of forward scattering. Quite qualitatively, it may be seen that further increasing the size or bringing particles closer together so that there is lateral destruction would tend to give rise to a more and more clearly defined forward or transmitted beam. Eventually the ordinary situation of a single refracted beam would be attained.

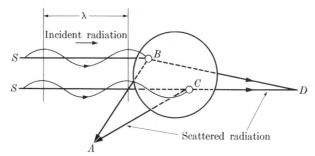

Fig. 10.20 Interference in scattering from a large molecule.

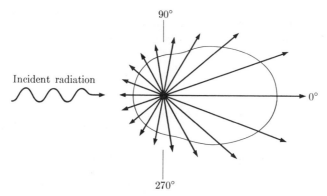

Fig. 10.21 Pattern of scattered intensities for a large molecule. Radiation is incident from 180°. Only a cross section of the scattered distribution is shown.

10.11 DIFFRACTION

Radiation is observed in most instances to travel in straight lines, a property termed *rectilinear propagation*. One exception has already been noted, that of scattering by small particles. Another, which is closely related, is what may be called an *edge-effect diffraction*. For example, the curved wavefront originating from the edges of the larger object in Fig. 10.18 is the result of diffraction. It is found that whenever a ray passes the edge of an obstacle or goes through an aperture it is somewhat "bent." As in Fig. 10.18, some radiation is spread into areas that would be in "shadow" if rectilinear propagation persisted.

To explain diffraction, the Huygens principle may be reintroduced. According to it, each point on a wavefront is potentially a new source of waves. The origin of a single wavelet at a slit is shown schematically in Fig. 10.22.

Diffraction gives rise to very striking effects with narrow optical slits because of interference effects. One is the Fraunhofer pattern of alternating light and dark bands (fringes) produced by passing parallel illumination through a rectangular slit. To observe the pattern, the emergent radiation must be focused onto a distant plane surface. This pattern and its origin are discussed in Section 12.2. A very different result is secured if many narrow, regularly spaced slits are used. The case of greatest interest, that of the diffraction grating, leads to the disposition of the incident radiation

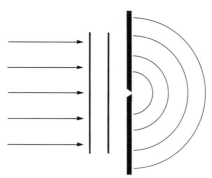

Fig. 10.22 A spherical wavelet spreading from a slit of infinitestimal width. If a very large number of these wavelets are produced side by side, as in a wide gap, the new wavelets interfere so as to give a plane wavefront and apparent rectilinear propagation. The analogy may be made with the production of a reflected image rather than scattered radiation (Fig. 10.18). For an ordinary narrow slit (Fig. 12.2), interference effects are appreciable.

into a spectrum and will be considered in detail in Section 12.6. A second basic type of diffraction, the Fresnel class, covers cases in which the incident radiation is not parallel and the diffracted waves are not brought to a focus; since this is not so important in the optical systems to be encountered it will not be discussed further.

10.12 POLARIZED RADIATION

Most sources produce EM disturbances in which the vibrations of electric and magnetic vectors occur with equal amplitude at all orientations perpendicular to the direction of propagation. Such radiation is said to be unpolarized. End on, a beam of this kind gives a vector picture like that of Fig. 10.23a, where only the electric vibration is shown.*

With few exceptions, contact with an interface between material media causes *preference* to be introduced into the vibrational pattern. The change may best be expressed if the representation of unpolarized radiation is resolved into two mutually perpendicular vibrations, as in Fig. 10.23b, by projection of every component vibration onto one or other of the rectilinear vibrations. Actually, the amplitude of the pair of vectors in (b) is much more enhanced by this process than is indicated in the sketch. The usefulness of this model will be seen shortly.

If a material medium affects the amplitude of these hypothetical wave trains differently, it is said to *polarize* the beam. When one vibration is completely eliminated, the radiation is said to be *linearly polarized*. It is also often described as plane-polarized.† In other cases the electrical vibration may continuously rotate in a

---

* This sketch falls short of a complete representation of the electrical vector. While there is no preferred direction of vibration, the constant changes in phase among the wave trains that make up an unpolarized beam give to it a predominantly elliptical character.

† In order to use the same "principle of projection" to represent all the kinds of preference, namely, that employed in Fig. 10.23a, the term linearly polarized will be used throughout. [13] When the term "plane-polarized" is used, it is necessary to consider the plane formed by the vibration and the direction of propagation.

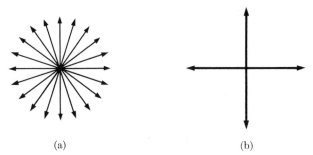

Fig. 10.23 End view of an unpolarized beam of radiation. The vibrations of the electric vector are shown (a) unresolved and (b) resolved into linear vibrations perpendicular to each other.

clockwise sense, i.e., the beam may be right-*circularly polarized*. The locus of the tip of the vector may for this kind of preference be portrayed in projection by a circle. The opposite result is also possible, i.e., one yielding left-circularly polarized light. Finally, if the projection of the tip of the vector yields an ellipse, it is called *elliptically polarized*. The origins of these types of polarization will be considered in Section 10.15. Attention will be given in this section to linearly polarized light.

The relative intensities of the two orthogonal vibrational components in a beam may be determined by a second linearly polarizing device used as an *analyzer*. It also resolves light into orthogonal vibrations and selectively eliminates one. Accordingly, if linearly polarized light is incident, the intensity transmitted by the analyzer may be

1. 100%, if the direction of vibration of incident radiation is parallel to the characteristic (vibrational) direction of the analyzer;
2. Between 100% and zero if resolved into a favored and a rejected component;
3. Zero, if the direction of vibration of incident light is perpendicular to the favored direction of the analyzer. In this case the incident radiation generates *no* component in the vibrational direction passed.

Naturally, if unpolarized light falls on the analyzer, it should be transmitted at half intensity. Note that this is implied by Fig. 10.23b. These first and third orientations are pictured in Fig. 10.24. In general, a great deal about the state of polarization of

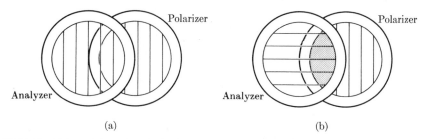

Fig. 10.24 Detection of linearly polarized radiation using Polaroid discs. (a) Analyzer oriented so that its vibrational direction is parallel to that of polarizer. (b) Analyzer aligned with vibrational direction perpendicular to that of polarizer (condition for *extinction*).

radiation can be learned by observing the intensity transmitted by an analyzer as it is slowly rotated through 360°. It is convenient to define the degree of polarization P or *polarizance* as

$$P = \frac{I' - I''}{I' + I''} \tag{10.21}$$

where I' and I'' are the maximum and minimum intensities observed through an analyzer rotated through 360°.

Example   To test the degree of polarization of a beam, it is allowed to fall perpendicularly on an analyzer. Regardless of the angular orientations of the analyzer, the beam is found to be transmitted with equal intensity. It can be concluded that the beam is unpolarized.

Selective absorption. Some crystalline materials exhibit *dichroism*, a preferential absorption of radiation vibrating in one direction. Incident radiation is resolved accordingly, and the component vibrating in the preferred direction is reduced in intensity. The extent of reduction depends on distance of travel and absorptivity. The component vibrating orthogonally to the preferred direction is passed unaffected. Thus, such materials are polarizers. The phenomenon is illustrated in Fig. 10.25. The thickness of slab required for complete polarization and the frequency range over which strong polarization can be expected are, of course, functions of the nature of the material.

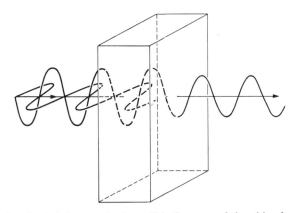

Fig. 10.25 Dichroic behavior. As a result of parallel alignment of absorbing functional groups, the horizontal vibration is completely absorbed and the vertical vibration is absorbed only to a slight degree.

Example   The several varieties of Polaroid sheets undoubtedly provide the best-known examples of dichroism. The widely used type H- and K-sheets are prepared from polyvinyl alcohol films. H-sheets are first stretched to align the molecules in the direction of extension and then impregnated with iodine. The I_2 molecules complex with the polymer and are thereby aligned. The component of incident light with vibrations parallel to the bond axis of I_2 molecules is absorbed; the component at right angles is transmitted. In type-K film selective absorption is achieved in a film of polyvinyl alcohol by catalytic dehydration followed by parallel alignment of double bonds by stretching.

Reflection. Rays either reflected or refracted by a substance are found to be partially polarized except for normal incidence. A schematic illustration of this phenomenon is given in Fig. 10.26. The plane of incidence is that of the page. The component vibrating perpendicular to this plane is the one that is more completely reflected; conversely, the component vibrating parallel to (or in) the plane of incidence is somewhat selectively refracted. As shown in the figure, for reflection from a dielectric there is a polarizing angle ϕ_B, for which the reflected beam is linearly polarized.

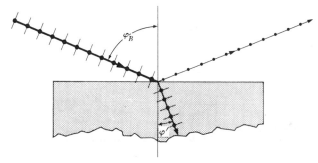

Fig. 10.26 Polarization by reflection from a dielectric. Radiation is incident at the polarizing angle φ_B, giving rise to a completely polarized reflected ray and a partially polarized refracted ray.

The reflectances of the two orthogonally polarized components are given by Fresnel's equations:

$$R_\perp = \frac{1}{2}\frac{\sin^2(\phi - \phi')}{\sin^2(\phi + \phi')} \tag{10.22}$$

$$R\| = \frac{1}{2}\frac{\tan^2(\phi - \phi')}{\tan^2(\phi + \phi')} \tag{10.23}$$

where ϕ is the angle of incidence (and reflection) and ϕ' that of refraction. Unpolarized light is assumed incident. Compare these expressions with Eq. (10.14).

As may be seen in Fig. 10.27, the reflectance of the two polarized components varies considerably with the angle of incidence. This dependence is shown for both external reflection and internal reflection. The overall external reflectance is also shown as a dashed curve.

Do Eqs. (10.22) and (10.23) predict one or more polarizing angles? Yes, since Eq. (10.23) goes to ∞ when $\phi + \phi' = 90°$. Whenever this condition is met, $R\|$ goes to zero. Two cases must be treated, $\phi' < \phi$ (incidence from the rarer medium) and $\phi' > \phi$ (incidence from the denser medium).

1. The polarizing angle for external reflection (into the medium of lower n) is termed *Brewster's angle* ϕ_B. It may be defined mathematically by substituting the

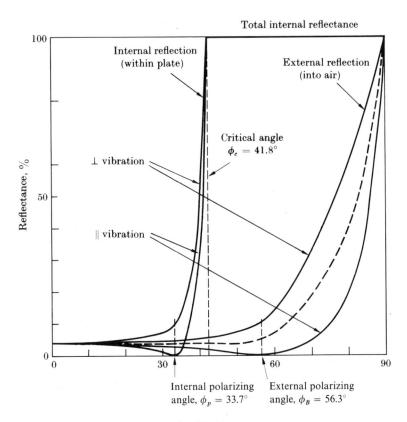

Total internal reflectance

Fig. 10.27 Reflectance as a function of angle of incidence and direction of polarization (perpendicular ⊥ and parallel ∥ to plane of incidence). The interface is between dielectrics of refractive index $n_1 = 1.00$ and $n_2 = 1.50$. External reflection (from interface into medium 1) is characterized by Brewster's (polarizing) angle ϕ_B, internal reflection (from interface into medium 2) by principal (polarizing) angle ϕ_p and critical angle ϕ_c.

condition $\phi + \phi' = 90°$ into Eq. (10.8) to give

$$\tan \phi_B = n_{21}. \tag{10.24}$$

2. For internal reflection, the polarizing angle is called the principal angle ϕ_p. Since $\phi + \phi' = 90°$ still holds, ϕ_p must be just the complement of ϕ_B, that is,

$$\tan \phi_p = n_{12}. \tag{10.25}$$

Since the index of refraction varies with wavelength, the two polarizing angles and the reflectances at those angles defined by Eqs. (10.22) and (10.23) will be wavelength-sensitive. The higher the value of n_{21}, the greater is the intensity (reflectance) of the polarized radiation. For example, the intensity of the externally reflected polarized beam is low (5–15% of the incident "unpolarized" intensity) for most dielectrics in the visible region ($n \leq 2$) but is about 40% of that of an unpolarized incident beam for germanium in the infrared ($n = 4$).

Reflection by metallic surfaces also produces partial polarization. As with dielectrics, the perpendicular vibrations have the higher reflectance. An important difference is the absence of a polarizing angle, as might be surmised from the form of Eq. (10.16). While the intensity of the parallel vibrational component goes through a minimum, it is nevertheless strongly reflected at all angles.

10.13 ANISOTROPIC MEDIA

In the absence of orienting force fields, homogeneous liquids and gases are optically isotropic. Radiation coming into contact with them is affected in the same way regardless of direction of vibration or direction of propagation. Most crystalline substances, on the other hand, exhibit *optical anisotropy*. Sodium chloride and other compounds that crystallize in the cubic system are exceptions. In anisotropic substances, one direction is not optically equivalent to another because of differences in the numbers of each kind of atom encountered or in the spacing of units in the lattice pattern. It should be recalled that so-called solids like glasses and polymers (under some conditions) are noncrystalline. These are in fact supercooled "liquids" whose order is only of the short-range variety. A listing of substances according to their refraction behavior appears in Table 10.2.

Table 10.2 Optical Classification of Substances

Type	Physical state	Refractive index
Isotropic	Gases, liquids, solutions in absence of orienting fields	Single value of n
	Isometric crystalline solids, glasses, noncrystalline polymers	Single value of n
Anisotropic	Uniaxial crystalline solids (tetragonal, hexagonal, etc.), nematic and smectic liquid crystalline phases	Two values, n_O and n_E*: (1) $n_E > n_O$, uniaxial positive, e.g., quartz; (2) $n_O > n_E$, uniaxial negative, e.g. calcite
	Biaxial crystalline solids (monoclinic, triclinic, etc.)	Three values of n
	Gases, liquids, solutions in strong dc electric field (Kerr effect)	Two or three values of n†
	Solutions of linear polymers flowing through narrow tube (flow birefringence)	Two or three values of n†

* Symbol n_O identifies the refractive index of the ordinary ray and n_E that of the extraordinary ray (see below).
† See Reference 5.

Depending on its direction of vibration and propagation, a polarized mono-chromatic wave train travels through anisotropic crystals with varying speeds. The only exception occurs in a particular *direction* known as the *optic axis*. By definition, this direction (it is not really an axis) is the one in which monochromatic light travels with the same velocity regardless of the orientation of its vibrations with respect to the crystal. While certain crystalline materials show two optic axes, i.e. are biaxial, this type of crystal will not be considered further. The optical character and constants of crystals reflect their degree of symmetry. Crystals belonging to the cubic system, such as NaCl, are optically isotropic. Those belonging to the tetragonal, hexagonal, or trigonal systems are uniaxial and the optic axis corresponds to the main or vertical axis of the crystals as they are usually represented. On the other hand, systems with lower symmetry such as monoclinic and triclinic are biaxial.

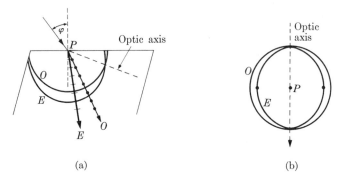

(a)   (b)

Fig. 10.28 Wavefronts in (a) calcite and (b) quartz. Note that the extraordinary wavefront travels more slowly than the ordinary one in quartz. In each drawing a monochromatic point source is considered to be placed at *P*.

A schematic representation of the difference between wave velocities in a uniaxial crystal (one with a single optic axis) is drawn in Fig. 10.28. Suppose the crystal resolves the incident radiation into two rays with mutually perpendicular planes of vibration. One vibration occurs in a principal plane, that is a plane formed by the optic axis and a perpendicular to one of the main faces of the crystal. The other vibration is in the plane perpendicular to the principal plane. As stated above, the velocity along the optic axis establishes the ordinary index of refraction n_O. Since it is found that the ray with vibrations perpendicular to the principal plane travels at the same velocity, it is termed the *ordinary ray*. The other component (the ray with vibrations *in* the principal plane) is the *extraordinary ray* and has an index of refraction n_E that varies with the direction of propagation.* When traveling in a direction perpendicular to the optic axis n will exhibit either a maximum or a minimum, depending on the type of crystal. [9]

Each of the refracted rays in an anisotropic substance may have a wavefront (Huygens construction) with a normal that makes an acute angle with respect to the

* In crystallographic literature, ω and ϵ are commonly used to represent n_O and n_E, respectively, for uniaxial crystals.

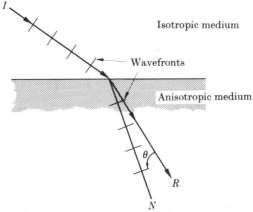

Fig. 10.29 Wavefronts of one of the refracted rays in an anisotropic substance at angle $\theta(\theta < 90°)$ relative to the direction of propagation. The wave normal direction N differs from the ray direction R.

ray direction as shown in Fig. 10.29. Two kinds of velocity may be defined: (a) the *velocity of the ray* V_r is the speed of propagation and (b) the *normal velocity*, the product of ray velocity V_r and $\cos \theta$. It is the latter velocity that defines the refractive index for the refracted ray, i.e., $n_{ray} = c/V_r \cos \theta$. These *normal* parameters allow the most straightforward optical description of the crystal. [13]

Double refraction. Now the actual results of anisotropy must be córrelated. Unless radiation traverses an anisotropic substance along the optic axis, double refraction or *birefringence* results. What enters as a single ray breaks into two. The crystal resolves the incident radiation into beams that are transmitted at different angles because of their different indices of refraction, as shown in Fig. 10.28. Since dispersion also occurs, two complete spectral sets of rays appear. Each set is linearly polarized, as may be established by an appropriate examination of the spectra with an analyzing device.

Double refraction occurs even for normal incidence of parallel light except when a crystal face has been cut parallel or perpendicular to the optic axis, as depicted in Fig. 10.30. Interference takes place in the case shown in Fig. 10.30a, as will be discussed in Section 10.15.

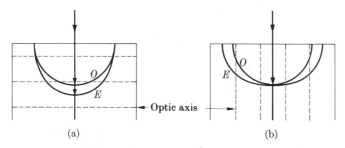

Fig. 10.30 Wavefronts in doubly refracting prisms of calcite ($CaCO_3$). (a) Optic axis (broken line) perpendicular to direction of beams. (b) Optic axis along direction of travel.

10.14 POLARIZERS

Any one of the effects that produce linearly polarized radiation can be used as the basis of a polarizing device. The effectiveness of a polarizer can be judged by three criteria:

1. Efficiency,
2. Spectral range of operation,
3. Angular aperture.

Reflection polarizers. These make use of the partial polarization that results when radiation passes through an interface. Ordinarily, several properly oriented slabs of transparent material are used as shown in Fig. 10.31 to secure substantial polarization. Even though designed mainly as transmission devices, it is convenient to use the term "reflection" to identify this class since a reflection process produces the polarization.*

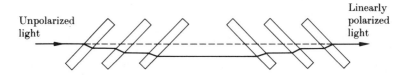

Fig. 10.31 A stack-of-plates reflection-type polarizer with plates mounted at the polarizing angle. The device makes use of selective transmission of light vibrating in the plane of incidence (the plane of the page).

The degree of polarization can be increased by adding more plates, since each new one will eliminate more of the vertical vibration component. This type of polarizer is seldom used in the visible, but finds wide application in the IR. There, a set of four to six silver chloride, selenium, or germanium plates is employed.

Note that in the representative "stack-of-plates" polarizer in Fig. 10.31, the use of two oppositely sloping stacks avoids any displacement of the beam. Further, the design permits commercial, relatively thick plates to be employed. High efficiencies (polarizances of 99) can be achieved over the IR range.

Dichroic polarizers. Such devices selectively absorb one of the orthogonal vibration components. Polaroid sheets (Section 10.12), frequently used in the visible and near IR, illustrate the type. A second example is films of pyrolytic graphite (oriented microcrystalline graphite prepared by deposition at temperatures in excess of 2500 °C), used for polarization in the IR from 2500 cm^{-1} to the microwave region.

Dichroic polarizers are still effective when incidence is off-vertical and polarize with nearly theoretical efficiency, i.e., their polarized output has nearly 50 % of the entering power. In addition they have the advantages of simplicity and, for those used in the visible, inexpensiveness.

---

* They are seldom used in the reflection mode, though a single reflection at Brewster's angle would yield linearly polarized light. Disadvantages of the method are that the angle varies with wavelength, reflectance at this angle is relatively small, and the incident beam is angularly displaced.

Double-refraction polarizers. These separate the two orthogonal vibrational components in space. Each is refracted in a different direction as will be discussed in the following section. Polarization is essentially complete. As a result, these polarizers are without peer in the UV, and are commonly used in precision instruments in the visible. In the IR they see little use because of limited transmission. Their chief disadvantages are low angular aperture, small size, and high cost.

Most doubly refracting polarizers are constructed from sections of calcite ($CaCO_3$) crystals. The strong double refraction (birefringence) of this uniaxial crystal is suggested by the large difference between its refractive indices: n_O, 1.66; n_E, 1.49* (*D*-line). Its useful spectral range is defined by its transparency: from about 220 nm to 1800 nm (2200 Å to 1.8 μm). Polarizers using uniaxial crystals of the dihydrogen phosphate type have proved useful in the UV to about 185 nm.

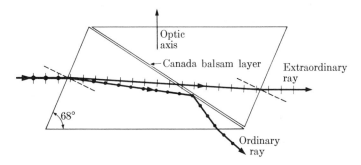

Fig. 10.32 Polarization by a nicol prism.

Nicol prisms. Nicol prisms or polarizers are prepared from calcite crystals with a minimum of alteration of natural crystal faces. The finished arrangement is pictured in simplified form in Fig. 10.32. An incident ray is resolved, as shown, into an ordinary ray vibrating perpendicular to the plane of the paper, which is a principal plane, and an extraordinary ray. By splitting the crystal at a suitable angle and cementing the halves with Canada balsam, an isotropic substance of $n_D = 1.55$, the ordinary ray can be made to suffer total reflection at the interface. For this ray there is a decrease of refractive index at the interface. The other necessary condition, that the angle of incidence exceed the critical angle, can be ensured by restricting the initial incidence angle on the external face. Only the extraordinary ray emerges in the original direction. It appears as a beam parallel to the entering beam, but displaced laterally from it.

Some disadvantages of the nicol device must be noted. The two most severe ones are (a) that the emergent beam moves in a circle about its axis if the nicol is rotated and (b) that complete "extinction" cannot be obtained on "crossing" (see below) if an intense source is used. Use is also restricted to the visible, since Canada balsam is opaque to UV. In addition, an incident beam can be neither highly convergent nor divergent, since the range of angular approach for total reflection of the ordinary ray

---

* The refractive index for the extraordinary ray ranges from this minimum value, applicable for a ray traveling perpendicular to the optic axis, to the value n_O.

is only a few degrees. The range can be increased with a slight sacrifice in intensity by substituting an air gap for the Canada balsam film. A final disadvantage is that some dispersion occurs if polychromatic radiation is used.

Glan or *Glan-Thompson prisms.* For these devices calcite is also used but crystals are trimmed so that the optic axis is perpendicular to front and rear faces. The Glan prism features an air gap; the parts of the Glan-Thompson prism are cemented either with Canada balsam or a resin of $n_O = 1.49$. In each of these polarizers the extraordinary ray emerges as the polarized beam and is achromatic, i.e., suffers no wavelength dispersion. While the Glan polarizer is transparent in much of the UV, its air gap is responsible for loss of some intensity and it has a very small angular field ($\pm 4°$ deviation from parallel). The Glan-Thompson polarizer suffers no appreciable intensity loss. If a resin cement is used, virtually all internal reflection of the extraordinary ray is eliminated, ensuring a lower intensity of stray, unpolarized light. The Glan-Thompson prism also has a slightly greater angular field. Both of these types and many other polarizers are occasionally referred to as nicols.

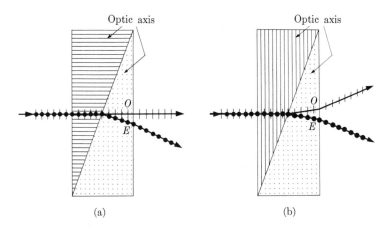

Fig. 10.33 Polarization by two types of compound quartz prism. Incident rays are monochromatic. (An optic axis perpendicular to the plane of the paper is indicated by dots.) (a) Rochon prism. (b) Wollaston prism.

Other polarizing prisms usable in the UV as well as the visible are the Wollaston and Rochon devices (Fig. 10.33). They are made from calcite or quartz pieces, which are cut and then cemented together with glycerine or castor oil (transparent down to 230 nm). As shown in Fig. 10.33b, parallel radiation enters the Wollaston prism perpendicular to the optic axis and leaves as two divergent, linearly polarized beams. The emergent beams are chromatic, i.e., their component wavelengths are dispersed, if polychromatic radiation is used. Even when polarized radiation is not primarily sought, the Wollaston device is a useful means of obtaining two optical images side by side for comparison purposes. The Rochon prism is similar, but the transmitted beams do not emerge symmetrically; its advantage is that the undeviated beam is always achromatic.

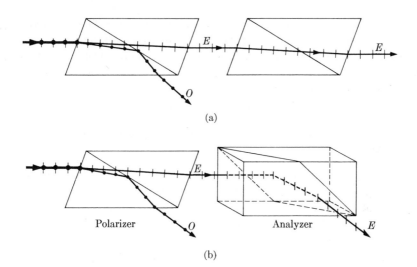

Fig. 10.34 Polarizer-analyzer pair. (a) Uncrossed pair. (b) Crossed pair; no light is transmitted by the analyzer.

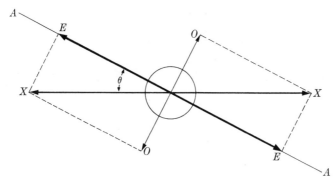

Fig. 10.35 Resolution of linearly polarized radiation by an analyzer in which the vibrational direction passed is AA. When radiation whose vibration is along XX is incident, it is resolved in the analyzer into components EE and OO, of which only EE is passed.

Polarizer-analyzer pairs. Pairs of polarizers are employed in most experimental arrangements (see Chapter 22). One serves as a polarizer, the other as an analyzer. The paths of radiation in what are called the *uncrossed* and *crossed* positions are shown in Fig. 10.34. The amplitude of the light leaving the analyzer will be a function of its orientation relative to the plane of vibration of the incident radiation. From the vector diagram in Fig. 10.35 this amplitude EE is

$$EE = XX \cos \theta, \qquad (10.26)$$

or, in terms of intensities,

$$\frac{I}{I_0} = \cos^2 \theta, \qquad (10.27)$$

where I_0 is the incident and I the transmitted intensity. If $\theta = 90°$, corresponding to placing the polarizer and analyzer in the crossed position, no radiation will emerge from the analyzer. This angle is said to be one of extinction. The orientation of the vibrational plane of linearly polarized light can be most easily ascertained by setting an analyzer to extinction. The vibrational plane is then at right angles to its angular setting.

10.15 INTERFERENCE EFFECTS AND CIRCULAR POLARIZATION

In anisotropic media, the interference of EM rays can lead to the production of elliptically and circularly polarized radiation, as well as the linearly polarized type. These polarizations are closely related, as will be seen.

In Fig. 10.23b it was suggested that a beam of natural light can be resolved hypothetically into two vibrations at right angles to each other. If the incident light is incoherent, i.e., the phase relationships among the waves comprising it are completely random, the emerging pair of orthogonal vibrational components will also be incoherent. As a result, no possibility exists for interference between them.

Consider now a simpler case in which the same representation applies. Let an unpolarized but coherent beam be perpendicularly incident on a uniaxial (anisotropic) crystal whose optic axis is parallel to its front face. This situation is pictured in Fig. 10.36. It is also assumed that $n_E > n_O$, as it is true for quartz. Accordingly, when the incident ray is resolved into two orthogonal components, the vibration along the direction of the optic axis (extraordinary ray) will travel more slowly because of the higher index for this vibration. Similarly, the vibration perpendicular to the axis (ordinary ray) will move faster. The greater the distance of travel, the more the phase of the extraordinary component will "lag" the ordinary component.

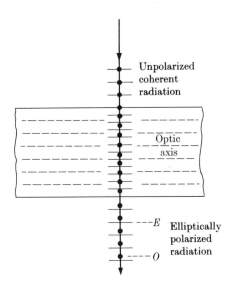

Fig. 10.36 Retardation of one set of polarized rays within a quartz crystal. The front and rear faces are cut parallel to the optic axis. After traversing the crystal, the ordinary wavefront is well ahead.

While these rays are out of phase at any point in their path through the slab, this fact cannot be detected conveniently until they emerge. At that point interference between the two components will be evident. It should be possible to calculate the phase difference δ since it will reflect the difference in the number of wavelengths of each ray required to traverse the the crystal. For the ordinary component $\lambda_O = \lambda_{vac}/n_O$, and the number of wavelengths across a slab is bn_O/λ_{vac}, where b is the thickness of slab. This expression is also termed the *optical path length* for the component. Taking the difference between this number and a similar value for the extraordinary ray and multiplying by 2π gives the phase difference in radians:

$$\delta = \frac{2\pi b}{\lambda}(n_E - n_O). \tag{10.28}$$

For example, the extraordinary ray may be $\pi/2$ radians (or 90°) behind. In this case, it is said to suffer a *quarter-wave retardation*.

Example The thickness of quartz necessary to retard the extraordinary ray one quarter-wavelength for the D-line can be calculated as follows from Eq. (10.28):

$$\delta = \frac{\pi}{2} = \frac{2\pi b}{589.3 \text{ nm}}(1.5553 - 1.5442).$$

Values of n_E and n_O for quartz have been substituted. Solving,

$$b = 13.3 \ \mu m.$$

Such a plate would be very fragile as well as difficult to cut. If δ were 450°, 810°, etc., the effect would still be that of one quarter-wave retardation and would allow more reasonable thicknesses to be used. For 810° ($9\pi/2$), b will be 119 μm or 0.119 mm. It is obvious that still greater thicknesses may be used if desired.

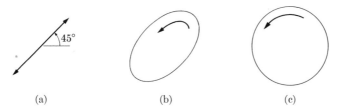

(a)   (b)   (c)

Fig. 10.37 Effect of phase difference δ on polarization. (a) Linearly polarized radiation, $\delta = 0°$. (b) Elliptically polarized radiation, $\delta = 40°$. (c) Circularly polarized radiation, $\delta = 90°$.

What is the effect of such interference on the character of the emergent light? If the vibrations of the two rays are in phase, they can be resolved into a single wave that is linearly polarized. Its vibrational plane will be at an angle of 45° to the vibrational planes of the rays, as indicated by the sketch in Fig. 10.37a. If the vibrations are out of phase by an angle between 0° and 90°, as in Fig. 10.37b, the resultant is a vector that does not lie in a plane but traces out an ellipse as the waves advance. A phase difference of 90° resolves into a circle as in Fig. 10.37c. It is common to describe the last two polarization phenomena by the figure traced by the resultant. Thus, they are *elliptically* and *circularly polarized radiation.* At greater phase differences the figures repeat. For example, a variation of 180° will again give linearly polarized radiation, but its vibrational plane will be perpendicular to that of Fig. 10.37a. Circular polarization will again appear at 270°, etc. Note that at all but a few phase differences the output will be elliptically polarized light.

In practice, it is not necessary to use coherent light. Instead, any source of linearly polarized radiation can be employed. When its beam is resolved into two orthogonal components, each will be self-coherent and undergo interference when directed toward a birefringent crystal.

At least two kinds of applications of circularly polarized light deserve mention. One is the measurement of the circular dichroism of complex substances, a phenomenon which will be discussed in the next section and in Chapter 22. The other is the study of the optical properties of crystals. [9] For either, a combination of a (linear) polarizer and a quarter-wave retardation device is employed to generate circularly polarized light.

One form of quarter-wave retardation device is the so-called quarter-wave plate, which is usually a specially cut quartz or mica slab. Because refractive index varies with wavelength, the selected wavelength for quarter-wave retardation is specified. Further, arrows are engraved on the holder to show the direction of vibration of fast and slow rays. A more versatile device is the quartz wedge, which has a continuously varying thickness so that retardations of varying amounts (or at different wavelengths) may be produced. The same effect can be secured by varying the anisotropy of an appropriate crystal by applying an adjustable voltage across it (see Section 22.5). This arrangement is termed a Pockels cell. Circular polarizers of Polaroid combine a linear polarizing dichroic layer with a quarter-wave retarding layer and are effective over different spectral ranges.

10.16 OPTICAL ROTATION

Substances whose molecules or crystals lack a plane or center of symmetry, that is, are asymmetric, have the ability to rotate the vibration plane of linearly polarized EM radiation. These are described by chemists as optically active or as showing optical rotatory power. Examples range all the way from the familiar case of sucrose to intricate complex salts of metals. If structural asymmetry occurs in molecules, the optical rotatory power is evident in all physical states and in solution. There are some instances, however, in which it is a property of the crystal lattice and is shown only by the solid form.

Optical rotation can best be treated as a case of *circular double refraction.* Consider that incident linearly polarized rays are resolved into two circularly polarized rays (Section 10.15), one whose vector turns clockwise as the beam advances, the other, counterclockwise. In a material with optical rotatory power, these rays travel at different velocities. The material therefore has two unequal refractive indices, one for the left-handed circularly polarized rays n_l, the other for the right-handed rays n_r. So long as there is no absorption of either ray and they follow the same path, they have a resultant which is a linearly polarized ray, but whose vibration is in a plane that has been rotated with respect to that of the incident ray. This result is shown

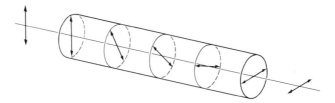

Fig. 10.38 Rotation of the plane of polarization in a medium with optical rotatory power.

diagrammatically in Fig. 10.38. The plane of polarization of the resultant, of course, moves through a steadily increasing angle as the beam progresses through the medium. In an optically *inactive* compound the formation of circularly polarized rays could also be pictured. Here they would proceed at the same velocity, and the resultant would have vibration in the original plane.

The relationship between the angle of rotation α' (in radians per centimeter)* of the vibration plane produced by a sample and the difference in refractive indices is given by

$$\alpha' = \frac{\pi}{\lambda}(n_l - n_r),\qquad\qquad(10.29)$$

where λ is the vacuum wavelength and n_l and n_r the refractive indices for the circularly polarized rays. The form of the expression is identical with Eq. (10.28) for ordinary circular polarization. How small the difference in refractive indices need be for a rotatory effect to appear is illustrated by solving Eq. (10.29) for the case where α is $10°$ per cm of travel and λ equals 500 nm (green light). In this case $\Delta n = 3 \times 10^{-6}$. Since the indices are dependent on the wavelength, different wavelengths are rotated by different amounts, a phenomenon known as *optical rotatory dispersion* or ORD.

In regions of transparency, the Drude equation reliably expresses the dependence of optical rotation of a substance on the wavelength. Drude's expression is

$$\alpha = \frac{k_1}{\lambda^2 - \lambda_1^2} + \frac{k_2}{\lambda^2 - \lambda_2^2} + \cdots = \sum_i \frac{k_i}{\lambda^2 - \lambda_i^2},\qquad\qquad(10.30)$$

where k_i is a constant evaluated from experimental rotations and λ and λ_i are the vacuum wavelengths of the incident radiation and of a characteristic active absorption, respectively. The k's may be either plus or minus. For many substances one term of Eq. (10.30) is sufficient; the behavior of almost all others is well described by two.

In an anisotropic medium like quartz, ordinary double refraction is superimposed on optical rotation and is the predominant effect. Clearly, if the differently circularly polarized rays were to diverge, there would be little opportunity to measure their differences relative to one another. Unambiguous information about rotation may be obtained best in anisotropic materials for the case of propagation of a beam along the optic axis of a crystal (Section 10.13).

Although differences in the polarizability of a substance in different directions are known to be involved, no completely satisfactory theoretical explanation of optical

---

* The phase difference between the two circular components is just twice the angle of rotation.

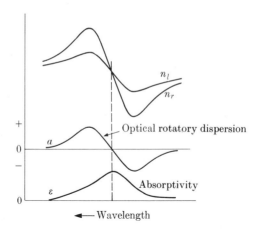

Fig. 10.39 Optical rotatory dispersion (ORD) of a substance. The top set of curves refers to the refractive indices for the circularly polarized rays, the middle curve to the optical rotation of the substance, and the lowest curve to its absorption.

rotation has been advanced. The fact that it undergoes a dispersion similar to that shown by ordinary refraction suggests a common dependence upon molecular absorption processes. Experimental evidence indicates that one or at most two or three electronic transitions in the UV exert the principal influence. In Fig. 10.39 the behavior of n_r and n_l is shown in an absorption region that is optically active. Note that the optical rotation decreases as the wavelength decreases in the region. The similarity of behavior to that of the ordinary refractive index causes this effect to be known as *anomalous dispersion* of the optical rotation. At wavelengths within an optically active absorption region, the two circularly polarized rays do not give a plane-polarized resultant but one that is eliptically polarized. Finally, the molar absorptivity in this region is also shown.

Circular dichroism. If an optically active electronic absorption is investigated by use of circularly polarized light, different molar absorptivities are obtained for left- and right-handed radiation. This phenomenon, termed circular dichroism, and the accompanying optical rotatory dispersion are often described as the *Cotton effect.*

In general, the wavelength of maximum circular dichroism corresponds to that of maximum absorption. This kind of differential absorption determination provides a measure of the asymmetry of an electronic transition and reflects a lack of symmetry in the molecular region in which the transition is localized. These points are expanded in Chapter 22.

10.17 IMAGE FORMATION

Lenses, curved mirrors, and aperture devices are indispensable in optical systems. Their role is the control of the flow of EM energy from one spot to another; more familiarly, they focus, collimate (render rays parallel), or diverge beams of radiation.

Focusing. Lenses and mirrors are characterized by two distinct sets of properties. One may be termed primary properties and includes refractive index, reflectance, absorbance, and curvature. The other is the set for which these optical elements are designed, definitely a derivative set. This group includes qualities such as focal length and focal point. Since these derive from the primary properties first cited, they will be as variable as are the primary properties.

As ordinarily used, the focal length and related qualities are considered constants. In this sense they are idealized concepts intended as standard. In general, they do define the behavior of optical elements precisely for rays that are *paraxial* and in a narrow spectral region. The term paraxial designates rays (a) making very small angles with the transverse axis of the mirror or lens or (b) lying quite close to the axis. A good approximation to these conditions is possible in an optical system if highly convergent or divergent rays are blocked from access to lenses or mirrors. This can be done simply by the use of a variable aperture (a stop) or diaphragm on the axis immediately in front of a lens or mirror. An arrangement of this kind is pictured in Fig. 10.40. As expected, the smaller the opening, the more closely any lens approximates ideal focusing behavior.

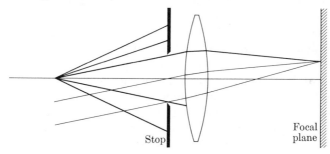

Fig. 10.40 A variable aperture or stop with a lens. Only paraxial rays are permitted to reach the lens.

The role of lenses and mirrors is the formation of optical images. A converging lens or mirror will form an image of an object placed beyond its focal point. Such optical elements are used to re-form an image of an object after some operation has been performed on the rays from the object. For example, a focusing lens is used in the spectroscope to produce images of the entrance slit after the radiation has been dispersed into the component wavelengths. As many images are produced as there are wavelengths present if these are not too close to each other.

When mirrors are used, it is desirable to eliminate the effects of having the object in the light path of the mirror. For example, Fig. 10.41 shows a conventional source-

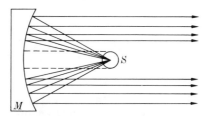

Fig. 10.41 Conventional placement of source S with respect to collimating mirror M. The reflecting surface directly behind the source is masked or vignetted by it.

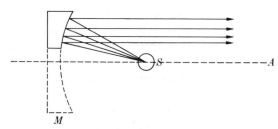

Fig. 10.42 Use of an off-axis mirror M, which is seen to be a portion of a full mirror of axis SA. By using it, masking of the reflecting surface is avoided.

mirror arrangement used to obtain a collimated beam. Though effective, a portion of the aperture of the mirror is masked or vignetted by the source and is thus unused. Further, if an object with a sharp edge replaces the source, diffraction effects may result. These undesirable effects are eliminated if an *off-axis mirror* is substituted. As illustrated in Fig. 10.42, in this arrangement the source is no longer in the optical path of the mirror. The greater expense of manufacture of off-axis optics is often offset by their improved performance. For example, they are frequently employed in IR spectrophotometers where full use of beam energy is desirable.

In Fig. 10.43 the way in which rays from one point of an object define a point of an image is drawn for a simple convex lens. All the rays that travel from the object's point to the lens must be converged at spot T' to give the image point. As they converge they interfere. The result will be a spot of high or low intensity, depending on the brightness of the object spot. Since interference forms an image point, the point must have a size related to the wavelength of the radiation. As a matter of fact, it can be shown that the point is a series of circular fringes with most of the intensity concentrated in the central spot. The greater the angle at which the rays from the lens cross and the shorter the wavelength, the more nearly does the image point duplicate the original one.

It is possible to set up several criteria that must be met for an image to be acceptable optically. Some of the more important of these are the following.

1. All wavelengths of a ray should come to a focus at the same point.

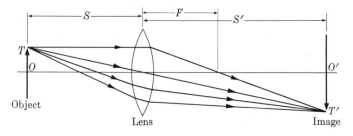

Fig. 10.43 Formation of an image point. The focal length F is defined as the distance from the center of the lens to the point at which incident rays parallel to the transverse axis of the lens are brought to a focus. The focal length, image distance S', and object distance S are related for a thin lens by the equation $1/S + 1/S' = 1/F$.

2. Each symmetrical pair of rays issuing from the image should focus in the same spot regardless of whether they are paraxial or whether they pass through a lens at an appreciable distance from its center.

3. Object points at a distance from the axis should be focused as points in the same plane as the paraxial points.

If an appreciable portion of a lens or mirror is used, these criteria are not met in practice. Sources of the difficulty may be cataloged in terms of aberrations shown by the optical elements. In other words, the aberrations are types of departure from ideality. One way to compensate for them would be to sacrifice image intensity and restrict rays to the paraxial case. Fortunately, this is not necessary, since there are feasible means of minimizing one or more aberrations at the same time. Very seldom, however, is it possible to eliminate all aberrations in a given case.

Numerical aperture. The solid angle over which light is "accepted" by a microscope, fiber optic, or other device is given in terms of its numerical aperture. Only light falling within this cone is transmitted. The numerical aperture (N.A.) is simply the sine of the semi-angle θ of the cone. Thus, a N.A. of unity implies acceptance over a solid angle of 180°.

Example What is the N.A. of a magnifier that accepts light making an angle no greater than 30° with the normal? Since N.A. = $\sin \theta$, N.A. = $\sin 30° = 0.50$.

$f/$ *number.* The geometrical light-gathering power of a lens is usually indicated by its $f/$ number. By definition, $f/$ (the / is part of the symbol) is the ratio of lens focal length f to lens clear aperture d. Light-gathering power increases as the inverse square of the $f/$ number. For example, an $f/2$ lens passes four times more light than an $f/4$ lens when they are equally illuminated. If several lenses are involved in an optical system, the one of largest $f/$ value will determine the light-gathering power. Thus, if both an $f/2.8$ and an $f/16$ lens are used in a beam, the latter effectively sets the light-gathering power.

An alternative index used in precise work is the T-number. It is an $f/$ number corrected for transmission of the lens and is defined by the equation T-number $= f/$ number $\div$ (transmittance)$^{1/2}$. Note that T-number will always exceed the $f/$ number for the same lens.

10.18 OPTICAL ABERRATIONS

At least five aberrations have been described for monochromatic light, spherical aberration, coma, astigmatism, curvature, and distortion. An additional one enters with the use of polychromatic radiation, chromatic aberration. Three of these will be described in detail, and a few common methods of correction will be suggested.

Spherical aberration. This aberration is perhaps the least complicated departure from ideality. As illustrated in Fig. 10.44, it results in a blurred image at a point on the axis. Each symmetrical pair of rays from a given object point comes to a focus at a different distance from the center of the mirror. The reader may establish the validity

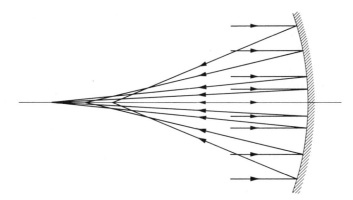

Fig. 10.44 Spherical aberration produced by a concave mirror.

of this result for the mirror shown by applying the usual laws of reflection to various incident rays; those farthest from the axis will be found to focus nearest the mirror. A simple spherical lens produces the same kind of distortion. In this case the interference of the convergent rays produces not a bright point but a circle if some average focal distance is selected. Appropriately, the result is known as the *circle of least confusion.* Any detecting element or additional optical device is ordinarily placed at this distance from the mirror or lens. For example in a spectrophotometer, uncorrected spherical aberration causes a monochromator slit to appear as an enlarged spot on the detector. The resolution of different images is thereby limited.

Some common methods of reducing spherical aberration are:

1. Decreasing the aperture diameter with concomitant loss of intensity,
2. Grinding the outer zone of the mirror or lens so that it is aspherical, or
3. Using a correcting device such as an additional element of special shape and refractive index.

Since a concave parabolic mirror is free of spherical aberration, as shown in Fig. 10.45, it can be substituted to avoid elaborate grinding procedure if a mirror is

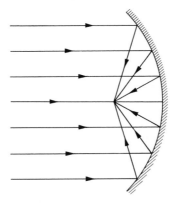

Fig. 10.45 Focusing for a parabolic concave mirror. It has no spherical aberration.

required. The third technique is frequently employed with lenses, so that compound lenses are the rule rather than the exception.

Off-axial rays give rise to *coma* and *astigmatism*. The first is closely related to spherical aberration and, like it, causes object points to become image areas. When object points are still farther from the axis, the distortion is termed astigmatism. In this case the blurring results from an object point being resolved only into two mutually perpendicular lines, though these exist in separate planes. It is best to intercept the focused beam at a distance intermediate between these planes. There the image is approximately disk-shaped and may again be said to be a circle of least confusion. A common measure taken to minimize astigmatism is the superposition of some cylindrical curvature on the basic spherical surface. Stopping down is obviously also effective.

Chromatic aberration. Different wavelengths of light focus at different distances from a single lens because of the variation of the refractive index with wavelength. By the same reasoning, it is apparent that all wavelengths cannot be collimated by a simple lens. For example, an inexpensive spectroscope with a single-element lens ordinarily renders parallel only green light, which falls about in the middle of the visual spectrum. Instead of collimating it converges shorter wavelengths slightly and diverges longer wavelengths. In better instruments a two- or three-element lens is used to eliminate the chromatic error at *two or three chosen wavelengths.* Each part of the lens is a material of different refractive index and curvature. Compare the chromatic aberration of the simple lens of Fig. 10.46 with that of the two-element lens depicted in Fig. 10.47. At wavelengths intermediate to those for which the corrections have been made, there is some residual chromatic aberration.

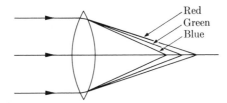

Fig. 10.46 Chromatic aberration produced by a simple lens.

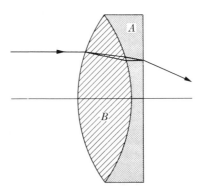

Fig. 10.47 A two-element collimating lens. A is quartz ($n_D = 1.54$). B is fluorite ($n_D = 1.43$).

The use of any correction scheme other than stopping down proves a compromise. In other words, not all optical aberrations may be corrected simultaneously. When one understands the requirements of any particular optical system, one can decide among the many varieties of lenses and mirrors.

REFERENCES

A general introduction to many branches of optics is provided by:

1. J. K. Robertson, *Introduction to Optics, Geometrical and Physical.* 4th ed. New York: Van Nostrand, 1954
2. James P. C. Southall, *Mirrors, Prisms, and Lenses.* New York: Dover, 1964

A clear, detailed discussion of physical optics on an intermediate level is provided by:

3. F. A. Jenkins and H. E. White, *Fundamentals of Optics.* 3d ed. New York: McGraw-Hill, 1957

An advanced and quantitative coverage of physical optics is given by:

4. R. W. Ditchburn, *Light.* New York: Wiley, 1964
5. Max Garbuny, *Optical Physics.* New York: Academic, 1965
6. J. R. Partington, *An Advanced Treatise on Physical Chemistry.* Vol. 4, *Physico-Chemical Optics.* New York: Longmans, Green, 1953
7. John Strong, *Concepts of Classical Optics.* San Francisco: Freeman, 1958

Particular aspects of optics are treated comprehensively in:

8. N. Bloembergen, *Nonlinear Optics.* New York: W. A. Benjamin, 1965
9. T. R. P. Gibb, *Optical Methods of Chemical Analysis.* New York: McGraw-Hill, 1942
10. N. J. Harrick, *Internal Reflection Spectroscopy.* New York: Interscience, 1967
11. Gustav Kortüm, *Reflectance Spectroscopy; Principles, Methods, Applications.* New York: Springer-Verlag, 1969
12. R. G. Newton, *Scattering Theory of Waves and Particles.* New York: McGraw-Hill, 1966
13. W. A. Shurcliff, *Polarized Light, Production and Use.* Cambridge, Mass.: Harvard University Press, 1962
14. W. H. Steel, *Interferometry.* New York: Cambridge University Press, 1967
15. H. C. Van der Hulst, *Light Scattering by Small Particles.* New York: Wiley, 1967

EXERCISES

A handbook listing physical constants will be needed in solving these exercises.

10.1 What are the velocity and wavelength (a) in water, (b) in benzene of the sodium emission line whose wavelength in air at 25 °C is 589 nm?

$$[Ans.: \text{a}) \ 2.25 \times 10^8 \text{ m s}^{-1} \text{ and } 442 \text{ nm}; \text{ b}) \ 2.00 \times 10^8 \text{ m s}^{-1} \text{ and } 393 \text{ nm.}]$$

10.2 Account for the fact that the dielectric constant of chloroform ($CHCl_3$) determined at 100 kHz is larger than the square of n_D for the substance.

10.3 Sellmeir proposed the equation $n^2 = 1 + A\lambda^2/(\lambda^2 - \lambda_0^2)$ to represent optical dispersion in optically transparent regions. How closely is this related to Eq. (10.11)? [*Hint*: Start by substituting λ for v in Eq. (10.11).]

10.4 In optical dispersion, does the rate of change of n with frequency or wavelength vary with wavelength? Where is it greatest?

10.5 Draw, without making any calculations, the dispersion curve in the visible and UV for a substance with characteristic electronic absorptions at 500 nm and 300 nm. Assume that $n_{600} = 1.50$ and that the 300 nm absorption is the stronger.

10.6a) What is the percentage of 589.3 nm light reflected from a diamond ($n_D = 2.417$) at perpendicular incidence?

b) If multiple reflections are ignored, what percentage of a perpendicularly incident beam of this wavelength will emerge from a thin slab of diamond? Assume air surrounds the diamond.

[Ans.: a) 17.5%; b) 68.1%.]

10.7 At 589 nm what is the reflectance in air of a polished plate of (a) silver, (b) aluminum? Pertinent constants are: for silver, $n = 0.1$, $k = 4$; for aluminum, $n = 1.0$, $k = 6$.

[Ans.: a) 0.98; b) 0.90.]

10.8 Will light incident at 35° on a glass-air boundary be totally reflected if the glass is extra-dense flint of index about 1.72?

10.9 The surfaces of a glass prism of refractive index 1.65 are coated with a CaF_2 layer of $n = 1.35$ to reduce reflection.

a) How thick must the layer be for maximum effectiveness with light whose vacuum wavelength is 5000 Å (500 nm)?

b) In this layer what is the phase difference for light of 4000 Å (400 nm) wavelength reflected from the upper and lower surfaces? Assume the refractive indices are constant over this range.

[Ans.: a) 925 Å; b) 228°.]

10.10 It is decided to construct a narrow-band IR reflection filter by making use of the change in refractive index across an absorption band. Mylar, which has an absorption band at 1740 cm^{-1} (5.75 μm), is selected and a layer of Mylar (average $n = 1.64$) is affixed to one of NaCl (average $n = 1.51$). Assume IR radiation is incident from the NaCl side. Discuss briefly how the device operates as a selective reflection filter in the region of the absorption band.

10.11 Determine an approximate reflectance versus wavelength curve for the following system over the range 550 to 450 nm: light is incident at a constant angle greater than the critical angle from a glass whose average n is 1.65 onto a liquid whose n is about 1.65 at 550 nm and 450 nm. The liquid has an absorption band at 500 nm whose half-width is 10 nm.

10.12 A beam of Na D-light traveling in Plexiglas ($n_D = 1.50$) is found to be plane-polarized when reflected from a rare-earth glass at an angle of 50°. What is the refractive index of the glass?

[Ans.: 1.79.]

10.13 Derive Eqs. (10.24) and (10.25), the expressions for Brewster's angle and the principal angle of a substance, from Snell's law, Eq. (10.8).

10.14 What is the polarizing angle for silver chloride in the near IR? Assume $n = 2.10$.

[Ans.: 64° 33′.]

10.15 What are the advantages of using silver chloride plates over quartz plates in constructing a transmission polarizer for the IR region? Consult a handbook for properties.

10.16 Unpolarized light is to be perpendicularly incident on a slab of strontium chloride hexahydrate whose sides are cut parallel to the optic axis. The piece is ground to a final thickness of 0.545 μm. $SrCl_2 \cdot 6H_2O$ is uniaxial and has D-line indices of $\omega = 1.536$, $\varepsilon = 1.487$. Will sodium light emerge elliptically polarized?

10.17 It has been shown that the degree of polarization produced by passing a radiation beam through a stack of dielectric plates oriented at the polarizing angle is given by

$$\frac{m}{m + \left(\dfrac{2n}{n^2 - 1}\right)^2},$$

where m is the number of plates and n the refractive index [p. 491 of 3]. (Multiple reflections have been considered.) A stack of six silver chloride plates is used as an IR polarizer. Assume $n = 2.10$. What fraction of the radiation emerging is polarized?

[*Ans.*: 0.79.]

10.18 Calculate the maximum angle at which light can be incident on a nicol prism if the ordinary ray is to be totally reflected by the Canada balsam layer. (See p. 267 for diagram and refractive indices. Note that the balsam layer is perpendicular to the front and back faces.)

[*Ans.*: 36°.]

10.19 How does the intensity transmitted by a polarizer-analyzer pair when their vibrations are at an angle of 45° relative to each other compare with that when they are at 70°?

[*Ans.*: at 45°, 50%; at 70°, 11.7%.]

10.20 Circularly polarized light is passed through a quarter-wave plate. What is the polarization of the emergent light?

10.21 The optical rotation of a 1 mm piece of quartz is 41.54° at 435.8 nm. What must be the difference in the refractive index for left- and right-handed circularly polarized light?

[*Ans.*: 5.03 × 10⁻⁵.]

10.22 What effect will a half-wave plate have on the transmission of a beam of linearly polarized light? Will its action be dependent on wavelength?

Chapter 11

SOME PHOTOMETRIC MODULES

11.1 INTRODUCTION

In this chapter and the next the groundwork for optical instrumentation is completed. The essentially optical modules, source, wavelength isolation device, and detector are discussed. We may surmise their central role from the line block diagrams of some optical instruments in Fig. 11.1. Later, in chapters that deal with specific optical techniques, the combination of modules into different kinds of instruments will be considered.

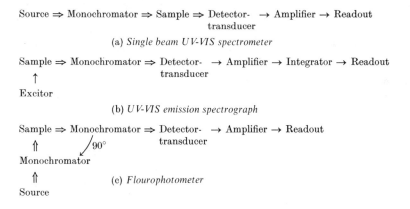

Source $\Rightarrow$ Monochromator $\Rightarrow$ Sample $\Rightarrow$ Detector- $\rightarrow$ Amplifier $\rightarrow$ Readout
transducer

(a) *Single beam UV-VIS spectrometer*

Sample $\Rightarrow$ Monochromator $\Rightarrow$ Detector- $\rightarrow$ Amplifier $\rightarrow$ Integrator $\rightarrow$ Readout
↑ transducer
Excitor

(b) *UV-VIS emission spectrograph*

Sample $\Rightarrow$ Monochromator $\Rightarrow$ Detector- $\rightarrow$ Amplifier $\rightarrow$ Readout
⇑ /90° transducer
Monochromator

⇑ (c) *Flourophotometer*
Source

Fig. 11.1 Line block diagrams of some optical instruments.

The intent of Chapters 11 and 12 is to present the main aspects of theory, operation, and properties of each major kind of basic optical module. Table 11.1 differentiates these major types of source, wavelength isolation device, and detector by spectral range. Many of the principles that govern optical behavior were discussed in Chapter 10 and the reader is expected to draw on this background. It will be necessary to do so, for example, in connection with input and output characteristics of modules, since these are usually not cited when they can be deduced by a knowledge of the principles of Chapter 10.

11.2 CONTINUOUS SOURCES

Continuous optical sources are those whose emission extends without break over a broad spectral region. They are indispensable as monochromator sources. Ideally, such a source ought to provide an intense output that is (1) uniform with wavelength and (2) constant with time. How closely can ideal performance be approached?

The first characteristic, equal output at all wavelengths, cannot actually be attained by use of an emitter alone. The reason is to be found in the characteristics of continuous emitters. The behavior of one important type, the heated solid, will be discussed below in terms of its ideal model, the blackbody. Later in the chapter, discharge lamps that give a region of continuous emission will be considered.

What of the second desired characteristic, constancy with time? It can at least be closely approached. Some obstacles are that the output of all sources is subject to drift and fluctuations. Drift is a consequence of aging processes. Hot electrodes lose material by sublimation and envelopes become fogged, causing a reduction in intensity long before the filament fails. One method of slowing aging is suggested below. Heating and cooling cycles also produce irreversible changes in output, effects best avoided by leaving a source on continuously whenever practicable.

Fluctuations in intensity occur during warmup as a source heats to its operating temperature, when the ambient temperature changes, or when the power energizing a source fluctuates. Continuous operation or allowance of an adequate time for warmup takes care of the first. The effect of ambient temperature changes can be minimized by insulation, e.g., by use of a thicker envelope. Power fluctuations can be minimized by use of a regulated power supply (Sections 4.5 and 4.13).

Feedback control of output intensity is probably the best guarantee of constancy. It is only necessary to monitor the output by means of an appropriate detector, compare its signal with that of a reference such as a Zener diode (Section 4.5), and use the different signal to actuate a device that will provide extra power in an amount proportional to the voltage difference.*

Blackbody radiation. An ideal standard, the *blackbody*, is a convenient model of a source like a heated solid, e.g., a Globar or lamp filament. The category includes most IR and VIS sources. A nearly perfect blackbody can be built by developing a spherical furnace with a very narrow opening through which radiation is emitted and absorbed. Ordinary emitters can be related to a blackbody by their emissivity ϵ, the proportionality constant ($\epsilon < 1$) by which blackbody emission must be multiplied to give the emission of an actual source. The constant depends on both temperature and wavelength.

By definition, a blackbody absorbs all radiation falling on it, and is also a "perfect" emitter. Conversely, a good reflector is a poor radiator of energy. The emission spectrum of a blackbody is described by the following laws:

1. The Wien displacement law, which states that the wavelength of maximum emission λ_m of a blackbody varies inversely with absolute temperature, i.e., the product $\lambda_m T$ remains constant. If λ_m is expressed in micrometers (microns) the law becomes

$$\lambda_m T = b = 2898, \tag{11.1}$$

---

* For example, see H. L. Pardue and P. A. Rodriguez, *Anal. Chem.* **39**, 901 (1967).

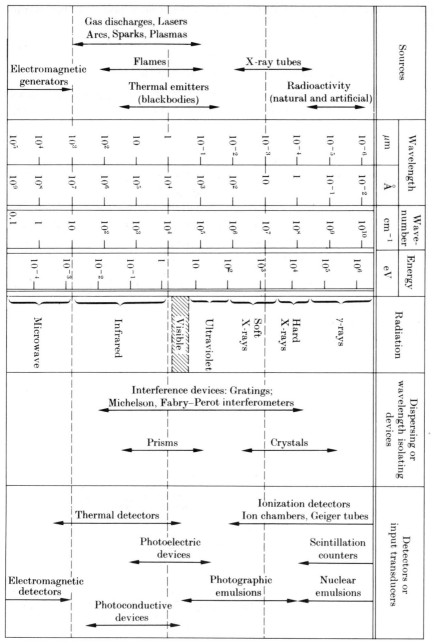

Table 11.1 Types and Range of Some Electromagnetic Sources, Wavelength Isolating Devices, and Detectors

or approximately $\lambda_m = 3000/T$. In terms of σ_m, the wavenumber of maximum emission, Eq. (11.1) becomes $\sigma_m = 3.48T$. Another useful version is $h\nu_m = 5kT$.

2. Stefan's law, which states that the total energy J radiated by a blackbody per

unit time and area (power per unit area) varies as the fourth power of the absolute temperature:

$$J = aT^4, \tag{11.2}$$

where a is a constant whose value is $5.67 \times 10^{-8} \text{ W m}^{-2} {}^{\circ}\text{K}^{-4}$.

3.   The Planck radiation law, which shows that the monochromatic emissive power J_{λ} of a blackbody is proportional to the reciprocal of the fifth power of the wavelength:

$$J_{\lambda} = E_{\lambda} d\lambda = \frac{2\pi hc^2}{\lambda^5} \left[\frac{d\lambda}{e^{hc/kT\lambda} - 1} \right]. \tag{11.3}$$

Here J_{λ} is the power per unit area for radiation whose wavelength is between λ and $\lambda + d\lambda$, and the other symbols have already been defined.

The source of radiation from hot bodies is the multitude of atomic and molecular "oscillators" that are thermally excited in any solid. Since their thermal energies vary widely, the distribution of emitted energies is broad. Curves showing the distribution for a blackbody at several temperatures are given in Fig. 11.2. The shift in the wavelength of maximum emission λ_m should be noted. The curve for 2100 °K is about what would be obtained for the tungsten filament in a light bulb. Actually all the solid curves are plots of Eq. (11.3).

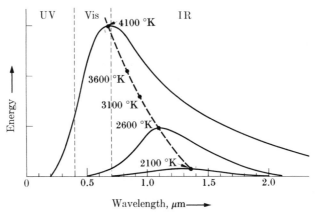

Fig. 11.2 Distribution of blackbody radiation at three temperatures. The broken line shows the dependence of the wavelength of maximum emission with temperature.

To find the total energy emitted at a given temperature, we must determine the area under the curve for that temperature. We can easily do this by integrating the expression in Eq. (11.3) from $\lambda = 0$ to $\lambda = \infty$. The result is Eq. (11.2).

Infrared sources. In the IR a heated inert solid ordinarily serves as a continuous source. Peak emission and the distribution of energy with wavelength can be determined approximately by use of Eqs. (11.1) and (11.2) for a blackbody. Emissivities are about 0.4 to 0.8.

How should a source operating temperature be decided? For example, is a good source for the middle IR one whose emission peaks at 1000 cm^{-1} (10 μm)? According to Eq. (11.1), such a source would be cooler than room temperature (290°K) and all parts of the instrument would radiate more energy than the source. A further problem is that the total energy it would produce—and thus also the energy it would emit at a given wavelength—would be quite modest. Contrast it with a source heated to 1000°K, which would radiate about 130 times as much energy. As hot a source as possible appears the best choice, since it furnishes better intensity over the whole range.

Practical IR sources operate at temperatures of about 1200–1800°K. Three factors preclude use of still higher temperatures.

1. Source operating life would be shortened.

2. More heat would be dissipated.

3. Higher-intensity visible and UV light would be radiated, creating severe stray light problems in any IR photometric system (Section 16.4).

Table 11.2 Some Continuous Radiation Sources

Type	Radiating "element"	Window or envelope	Useful wavelength range, μm
Globar	6 mm dia. SiC rod at 1300–1500°K	None	1 to 40
Nernst glower	1–3 mm dia., ZrO_2,Y_2O_3 filament at 1200–2000°K	None	0.4 to 20
Tungsten lamp	W filament at 2300–3300°K	Glass	0.35 to 2.5
Tungsten-iodine lamp	W filament at 3500°K, halogen scavenger	Quartz	0.2 to 0.8
H_2 or D_2 lamp	Arc discharge in H_2 or D_2	Quartz	0.18 to 0.38
Xe lamp	Arc discharge in Xe	Quartz, sapphire	0.23 to 2.1
Xe lamp*	Condensed discharge in low-pressure rare gas	LiF	0.15 to 0.20
Ar lamp*		LiF	0.10 to 0.15
He lamp*		None or Al foil	0.06 to 0.11
Hg lamp	Arc discharge in Hg vapor	Quartz	0.20 to 0.70

* Tanaka, Y., *J. Opt. Soc. Am.* **45**, 710 (1955); R. E. Huffman, J. C. Larrabee, D. Chambers, *Appl. Opt.* **4**, 1145 (1965).

Table 11.2 lists two commonly used IR sources, and gives the nature of the radiating element, its operating temperature, the window material, and the useful wavelength range. These sources are maintained at operating temperature by passage of an electrical current. Since the Nernst glower is a semiconductor, it must (a) be pre-heated to bring it to a conducting state and (b) be used with a series resistance or ballast to prevent burnout because of its negative resistance characteristics (Section

13.6). The Globar has the advantage of greater ruggedness and better emissivity at shorter wavelengths.

In the far IR there is at present no fully suitable source. The best one available is a mercury lamp with a fused-quartz envelope. At frequencies below 150 cm^{-1} this source is considerably more efficient than a Globar. Below 35 cm^{-1} the mercury arc contributes most of the radiation, and above that wavenumber the hot envelope itself is the main emitter. Often this lamp is used for work up to 500 cm^{-1}.

Near IR, VIS, UV sources. In the near IR and visible a conventional glass-enclosed tungsten filament operated at from 2600 to 3000 °K is a widely used source. The transmission of the envelope limits the useful range to about 350 to 2000 nm.

The tungsten-halogen lamp is more efficient. It is designed with an internal chemical cycle that returns to the filament most tungsten that sublimes.* The lamp has a life more than twice that of a regular lamp and an extended spectral range.

In most filament lamps, useful life can be "traded off" for higher intensity by use of higher voltage. For example, an operating voltage 10% above the normal will elevate the luminous output of a filament lamp about 35% and reduce its average life to about 30% of the normal value. [11]

The extent of the uniformly luminous area in a source greatly affects its optical applications. Lamps with vertical ribbon filaments are generally useful because they provide a large bright area. They are oriented so that the plane of the filament is also that of the slit to be illuminated. If very even illumination is required, the filaments should be considerably larger than the slit. In this connection arc lamps that provide an intensely illuminated circular spot are particularly valuable, especially the Pointo-lite lamps and the zirconium arc. By projection of their light a very uniform larger field can be secured.

Narrow-band semiconductor point optical sources are also available for the near IR and the longer-wavelength part of the visible region. For example, these diodes can be prepared from gallium arsenide or gallium phosphide–gallium sulfide combinations.

In the visible and UV, two high-intensity sources stand out: the high-pressure mercury lamp[†] and the high-intensity xenon lamp. In both the gas is excited by a dc arc. Naturally discrete lines of the filling element also appear in the spectrum. The positions of such lines relative to regions of continuous output are shown for mercury in Fig. 11.3. As may be noted, both visible and UV are well represented in its discharge spectrum.

By contrast, the output of the xenon lamp is small from 230 nm up to 320 nm, substantial from 330 nm to 1 μm, and modest at still longer wavelengths up to

---

* A halogen, e.g., iodine, is added, and the envelope is fabricated of quartz to tolerate the higher operating temperatures involved. Near the hot (500 to 1000 °K) quartz wall, gaseous iodine reacts with gaseous tungsten to form WI_2, a volatile iodide. When the diffusing gaseous iodide strikes the hot filament, it decomposes and tungsten is redeposited.

[†] A quartz-jacket, additive-type mercury arc light is also available. Its vapor is a mixture of mercury and iodine gas, the latter species originating from decomposition of an additive such as sodium iodide. (The gas is at about 6000 °K.) It has an efficiency twice that of the regular mercury arc, but about half its life.

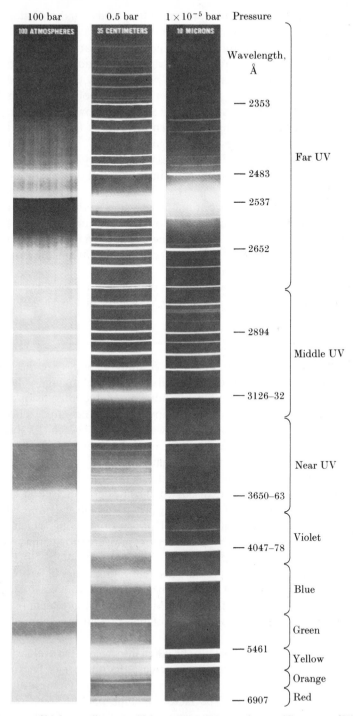

Fig. 11.3 Spectra of high-, medium-, and low-pressure mercury lamps. (Courtesy of Westinghouse Electric Corporation.)

2.5 μm. Several very intense emission lines are superposed on its continuous spectrum between 830 and 1120 nm. The xenon lamp ordinarily has a ceramic-metal envelope, a built-in and prefocused reflector that produces a very narrow uniform beam, and either a quartz or sapphire window, the latter giving superior UV transmission.

In discharge lamps run from a regulated power supply there are several sources of instability. One is arc wander, i.e., random movement of the arc over the anode surface. Operation at a power above the specified average power level reduces wander.

Another cause of drift is change in the temperature of the arc wall. Emission is affected because the internal pressure changes. Fortunately, such fluctuations are greatly reduced by the use of double-wall tubes or thicker windows. The output intensity of a lamp also diminishes gradually with time as a result of deposition of electrode metal on the lamp window.

For work only in the UV the continuous-emission spectrum of a high-pressure hydrogen or deuterium lamp is adequate down to 185 nm (1850 Å), the limit of transmission of a quartz envelope. A higher-energy emission is attained with a deuterium filling. The lamp's upper limit of usefulness is about 370 nm, for at longer wavelengths neither spectrum is continuous.

Finally, lamps utilizing short-wavelength continua of the rare gases allow work in the vacuum UV down to about 50 nm (500 Å), as indicated in Table 11.2.

11.3 DISCRETE SOURCES

Transitions between excited states and a lower state of species are the origin of the line spectra emitted by discrete or line sources. The preliminary volatilization (if necessary) and excitation are secured by inducing energetic collisions, usually by means of an electrical discharge. Since many higher states are excited, emission ordinarily comprises a number of definite wavelengths. The chief value of such a source is that any of these wavelengths may be isolated by use of a filter or monochromator to furnish essentially monochromatic light.

A truly monochromatic line is not even ideally possible. Since the various factors that cause lines to be broadened are discussed in some detail in Section 13.3, they will only be listed here. Some causes of broadening are: natural broadening, which reflects the finite lifetime of species in excited states; Doppler broadening, which results from the motion of excited species relative to a detector; pressure broadening, which occurs because of collisions; and field broadening, which is attributable to the action of electric or magnetic fields. In low-pressure discrete sources lines have breadth mainly as a result of the Doppler effect. As a consequence lines have an essentially Gaussian shape and widths of the order of 0.02 nm. Since pressure broadening can be very substantial indeed (see Fig. 11.3), the emission of high-pressure gas sources is essentially continuous, as already noted.

The purity of spectral lines must also be taken into account in evaluating a discrete source. Factors such as nuclear spin can increase the number of lines relating to a "particular" electronic transition by removing degeneracy. The resulting pattern is described as *hyperfine structure*. The factors include nuclear spin, isotopic effects (variation in mass, spin, or other properties of a nucleus), the Stark effect (external electric field), and the Zeeman effect (external magnetic field). For example, the

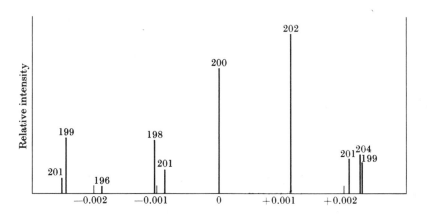

Wavelength difference from 253.7 nm in nanometers

Fig. 11.4 Hyperfine structure of the 253.7 nm emission line of a sample of mercury with normal isotopic abundance. The lines of each isotope are identified by mass number. In practice each line has a fine breadth. Note that there are several peaks for odd mass isotopes.

hyperfine structure of the mercury 253.7 nm line arising from isotope effects is shown in Fig. 11.4.

Vapor discharge lamps. Low-pressure (a few torr) gaseous discharge lamps are widely used as line sources. The charge carriers necessary to electrical conduction may be generated within the gas by ionization. Several modes are available. In practice, two or more are often effective simultaneously. Some are:

1. Exposure to cosmic ray showers and natural radioactivity: operative in all instances except where heavy shielding is employed (about 10 ions cm^{-3} s^{-1} are formed in a gas from these sources);

2. Illumination by energetic radiation: operative only if short-wavelength UV is used;

3. Exposure to electron emission from a hot electrode;

4. Heating to high local temperatures.

With any of the above, conduction starts when electrodes are inserted into the gas and a potential difference is applied. As will be noted below, electrodes are unnecessary if an rf or microwave field is imposed.

In any method of ionization the necessary condition to produce charge carriers in a gas is that the energy U available be equal to or greater than the energy E_i of ionization of the gas molecules, that is, $U \geqslant E_i$. Values of E_i range from about 9 to 13 eV; those for the inert gases, nitrogen, and a few others are higher; those for olefins and less stable molecules are lower. The energy criterion is not a sufficient condition, however, since the method of energy transfer must also make ionization probable. Often energy is transferred mainly as translational energy, as is the case when molecules, or an ion and a molecule, of roughly equal mass collide, and little energy is available for ionization. By contrast, collisions between electrons and molecules are comparatively efficient in inducing ionization.

In general, molecular ions are *positively* charged since negative ions of this type are unstable relative to free electrons. Thus the ion pairs formed on ionization commonly comprise an electron and a positive molecular ion.

Most discharge sources have cold electrodes* and rely on external agencies to ionize a few molecules and initiate conduction. To sustain it they use a voltage across the tube higher than the "breakdown value" of the system so that a self-sustaining discharge develops. It is made possible mainly by the bombardment of the cathode. Positive ions accelerated across the potential difference of the tube have sufficient energy as they strike the cathode to induce emission of secondary electrons. In turn, these electrons through collision with gas molecules maintain the level of ionization of the gas. Conventionally, a discharge of low current density is termed a *glow discharge* and one of large density an *arc*.

Actually, a tube with a self-sustaining discharge operates in an unstable current–voltage region. Unless an external resistance or inductance termed a ballast is placed in series, or other control is used, current will increase very rapidly (in milliseconds) until the tube "burns out," usually by cathode failure. The system is described as having a *negative resistance* characteristic since a current increase causes the voltage to fall. The reason is that increased current leads to still greater ionization and easier conduction. In Fig. 11.5 this type of current–voltage behavior is illustrated. A tube with a ballast will maintain a nearly constant voltage drop across it in spite of current changes, as indicated in the figure by the combined characteristic curve.

Perhaps the two best-known vapor discharge lamps are those based on sodium and mercury. Initial heating is required to bring the lamp to operating temperature. At low internal pressure most of the output of the sodium lamp is concentrated in

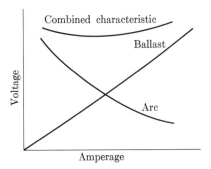

Fig. 11.5 Voltage–current curve for an electric arc. A series combination of arc and ballast has the characteristics given by the upper curve.

---

* An auxiliary heater may, however, be employed to volatilize an element, as in a sodium lamp. In this case, a low pressure of argon or neon is added to allow the discharge to be initiated easily. When the steady-state pressure of the element of interest has been built up (after 10 to 30 minutes) the emission of the starter gas is no more than 1 % of the total.

the *D*-lines at 589.0 and 589.6 nm; a few weak sodium doublets and neon lines are also present. The spectral richness of the low-pressure mercury lamp was shown in Fig. 11.3. Though the mercury emission is concentrated in resonance lines at 253.7 and 184.9 nm, the latter line is blocked by the fused quartz envelope used.* The power supplies for these and other discharge lamps usually include the necessary ballast.

Raising the pressure of gas in a discharge lamp radically alters the emission. The changes are well illustrated in Fig. 11.3. All lines are broadened (Section 13.3) and resonance line(s) in particular suffer self-reversal (see below). Note that each effect increases with pressure. When the pressure is high enough, an essentially continuous spectrum is secured. High-pressure sodium, mercury, and xenon discharge lamps are presently available commercially.

The phenomenon of *self-reversal* of a line, i.e., loss of its center, deserves comment. Resonance lines, which are mainly affected, involve an electronic transition to the ground state. Atoms in the ground state absorb such radiation in proportion to their population (Section 13.3) and an increase in gas pressure soon leads to virtually complete absorption of the characteristic (central) frequency. The "wings" of a line tend to remain.

RF and microwave discharge lamps. An electrodeless gas discharge in which there is also no appreciable rise in pressure during operation (heating is localized) can be obtained by subjecting a gas to a radiofrequency or microwave electrical field. These "cold plasma" sources can achieve very high intensities and narrow line widths. A wide variety of commercial lamps is available, those for zinc, copper, thallium, mercury, and cadmium being of especially high intensity. The discharge occurs in a small capillary perhaps 1 × 4 mm diameter.

Hollow-cathode lamps. The commercial development of the hollow-cathode lamp made possible construction of discharge sources even for elements that were difficult to volatilize. Figure 11.6 shows representative designs. The key feature of this type of lamp is a cathode in the form of a hollow cup that is either made of, or more often lined with, the element or an alloy of the element to be excited to emission. A few torr of a noble gas are added. In operation, voltage is applied across the electrodes, and the positive noble-gas ions produced in the discharge strike the interior of the cathode and sputter out, i.e., volatilize the desired element. It is then ionized by collision with positive ions or secondary electrons (from the cathode) as in any vapor discharge lamp. After the lamp has warmed for 10 to 30 minutes, a stable output is attained. The lines emitted emerge through a window at the far end (see Fig. 11.6).

What operating current should be chosen for a hollow-cathode lamp? A high current excites more atoms per second and gives a steadier, more intense output. Unfortunately, a large current also leads to undesirable effects. First it causes a large population of gaseous atoms in the ground state. Thus there is appreciable self-absorption of the desired resonance line (Section 13.3). Second, lamp lifetime is shortened. Third, there is more emission from excited *ions*. The optimum current is thus a value that ensures adequate intensity but minimizes undesirable effects. In general, recommended currents fall between 10 and 100 mA and potential drops

---

* Substitution of a fused silica envelope makes this line available.

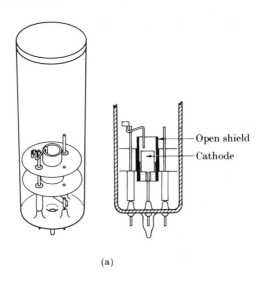

(a)

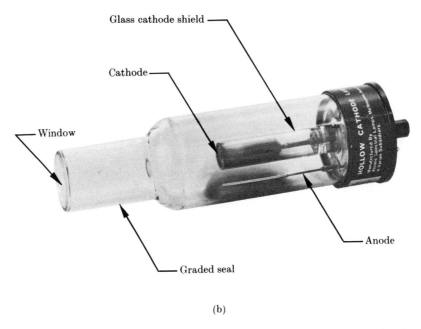

(b)

Fig. 11.6 Hollow-cathode lamps of shielded cathode design. (Courtesy of (a) Perkin-Elmer and (b) Varian Techtron.)

between 100 and 200 V. Ordinarily a maximum safe value is also quoted; exceeding it subjects the cathode surface to destructive bombardment by cations.

Much thought has been given to ways to raise the fraction of atoms excited without increasing the emission of ions. The use of insulating sleeves (as in the design of Fig. 11.6) and of other shielding causes the ion current in the tube to be directed more

efficiently *into* the cathode. Further improvements in design are to be expected.*
Commonly a bank of single-element lamps is mounted in a turret that provides easy
interchange.

Lasers. From the first experimental demonstration of laser action in a ruby crystal
(aluminum oxide doped with chromium oxide) lasers have developed as one of the
most important discrete sources. Unlike the other discrete sources discussed, lasers
can be constructed to concentrate nearly all their energy at a single wavelength whose
width is no more than 0.1 cm^{-1} at half height. Extremely high intensities and nearly
ideal monochromaticity are thus possible.

The mode of operation of a laser is suggested by the phrase for which it is an
acronym: *light amplification by stimulated emission of radiation.* Basically, a laser
is a column *resonator* in which light of the proper wavelength produces a standing
wave pattern. The source of radiation is a characteristic emission of a species that is
distributed homogeneously through the resonator. For example, in the ruby laser the
emitting species is Cr^{3+} ions, in the helium-neon laser it is excited neon atoms.
Resonance is achieved by use of a Fabry–Perot interferometer (see Section 11.6), i.e.,
a pair of parallel, plane mirrors. The actual laser column or rod is placed between
them.[†] The arrangement is shown schematically in Fig. 11.7. Exact parallelism of the
mirrors minimizes losses.

It is also common to form the resonator by spacing two spherical reflectors of
equal curvature a distance apart that is equal to the sum of their radii of curvature. In
Fig. 11.8 half this arrangement is shown in a represesentative type of noble-gas ion
laser. A spherical and a plane mirror (on the back of the Littrow prism) form the
cavity. Adjustment of this laser is relatively easy: no mirror parallelism is required.

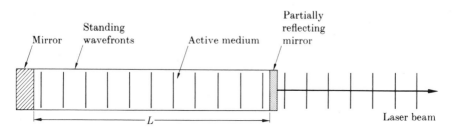

Fig. 11.7 Schematic diagram of a simple laser.

---

* Hollow-cathode lamps incorporating several elements are also available. In this type of lamp
an alloy, an intermetallic compound, or a sintered mixture of powders is used to coat the interior
of the cathode. Such a lamp provides characteristic wavelengths of all elements present. This gain
is offset in some instances by increased spectral interference. In addition, when multi-element
lamps are used, better monochromators are often required to achieve desired separations.
[†] The resonance modes in which a laser operates are termed transverse electric and magnetic
modes TEM_{mnq}, where m and n are transverse mode numbers ($m = n = 0$ for the desired coherent
output) and q is the axial mode number. It can be shown that the low-loss axial modes of the
resonant cavity are separated in frequency by $c/2L$, where c is the speed of light and L is the
mirror separation. Ordinarily, several axial modes are in simultaneous oscillation but frequently
it is unnecessary to distinguish them.

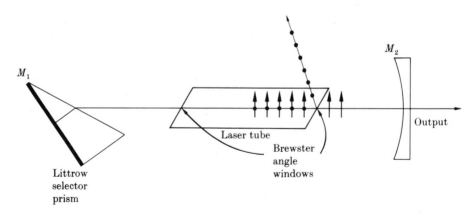

Fig. 11.8 Noble gas-ion laser. The resonator mirrors are M_1 and M_2. By design, M_2 is not quite totally reflecting. The particular wavelength whose emission is stimulated is that which the Littrow prism returns parallel to the axis of the laser cavity. Pumping is achieved by an electrical discharge *across* the tube (electrodes not shown). Note that the Brewster angle windows of the laser tube selectively pass radiation linearly polarized in the plane of this page, thus minimizing its reflection losses.

Losses are also smaller than for parallel-plate resonators. Since this type of laser can resonate at several wavelengths, a prism within the cavity selects the desired wavelength. On the other hand, for the helium-neon laser a pair of spherical mirrors is commonly employed since lasing occurs at a single wavelength in the visible, 632.8 nm. As would be expected, in any type of gas laser normal spontaneous emission accounts for the production of other, low-intensity lines characteristic of nonlasing transitions. These wavelengths are commonly removed by filtering, though the prism serves this role in Fig. 11.8.

The laser species that is to emit is first excited either by electrical discharge or optical excitation applied at right angles to the axis of the column. The exciting process is often termed "pumping." Before "lasing" can begin a nonequilibrium situation must be generated. The population of an excited state must be built up until greater than the population in the lower state to be reached by emission. This condition is described as a *population inversion*. Usually pumping leads to a state higher than the one sought. Then collisional mechanisms bring about a radiationless deactivation to the long-lived (metastable) state from which stimulated emission will occur. In Fig. 11.9 energy relationships are shown for the helium-neon gas laser.

For continuous emission it is essential there be adequate rates of pumping and of removal of atoms from the lower state. Once a population inversion has been secured, laser action can occur. A light wave of the characteristic frequency beginning anywhere in the column can grow in intensity by *stimulating* other excited species to contribute their excitation energy to it. It is important to draw a distinction between spontaneous and stimulated emission. The former occurs equally in all directions and is random in time. By contrast, stimulated emission is found to take place only in the direction of the incident radiation and in phase with it.

The direction of the triggering wave in the laser is critical. Only a wave traveling essentially along the axis can be reflected from the end mirror and build up amplitude;

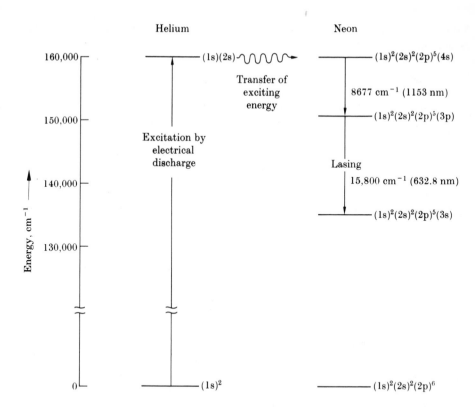

Fig. 11.9 Energetics of the helium-neon gas laser. An electrical discharge excites helium atoms to the metastable triplet level, which is only 313 cm^{-1} above one excited state of neon. As a result, a radiationless excitation of neon can occur on collision of excited helium and ground state neon atoms. As shown, lasing can occur either at 1153 nm or 632.8 nm. The latter is usually selected since it is in the visible range. The degeneracy of levels is not shown.

waves moving at more than a slight angle are lost through the sides. The ultimate intensity of a wave is determined by the supply of excited atoms. The output of the laser, of course, appears through the end mirror that is partially transparent.

The four important properties of a laser source may be identified with properties of stimulated emission and the behavior of the column resonator:

1. An intense output results since a very great many excited species contribute their emission to the beam that emerges;

2. A directional output is secured since nonaxial waves are lost;

3. A monochromatic beam is produced since the characteristic frequency resonates in the column;

4. A coherent beam is secured since excited species contribute in phase to the standing wave that exists between the mirrors.

A few laser systems are listed in Table 11.3. As is evident, lasers are presently known that give wavelengths from the UV into the IR. Only a small number of laser

Table 11.3 Intense Wavelengths of a Few Discrete Sources* (Vacuum Wavelengths in Nanometers)

Hydrogen discharge lamp (quartz)	Mercury discharge lamp (quartz)	Sodium discharge lamp (glass)	Lasers
	253.6		235.8 (Ne, gas, pulsed)
	313.0		325.0 (He-Cd, continuous)
			441.6 (He-Cd, continuous)
365.7†	366.3		488.0 (Ar II, gas, continuous)
	404.7		514.5 (Ar II, gas, continuous)
(G') 434.0	435.8		568.2 (Kr II, gas, continuous)
(F) 486.1			
	546.1		
	577.0	(D) 589.0	551.2 $(CaF_2 : 1\% \ Ho^{3+}$, solid)
		589.6	
(C) 656.3	690.8		632.8 (He-Ne, gas, continuous)
	772.9		694.3 $(Al_2O_3 : 0.05\% \ Cr^{3+}$, solid, continuous)
		818.3	850 to 900 [GaAs, p-n junction, solid,
		819.5	continuous]
	1,014.0		
	1,128.7	1,138.2	
		1,140.4	
			2,613.0 $(CaF_2 : U^{3+}$, solid, continuous)
	3,942.5		
			10,600.0 $(CO_2$-N_2-He, gas, continuous)
			27,900.0 $(H_2O$, gas, pulsed)

* Letters in parentheses designate Fraunhoffer lines identified originally in spectrum of sun.
† Short-wavelength limit of Balmer series.

systems are available commercially, though others are sure to be marketed as exploration and development continues. In addition there are continuing efforts to develop tunable, continuous lasers whose output frequency may be varied at will over at least a short range. Dye lasers and optical parametric oscillators appear the most promising possibilities.

Gas lasers are very widely used, even though many are inefficient in terms of power conversion. Their advantages are related to the fact that gases are peculiarly sources of atomic or molecular line spectra whose wavelengths of transition are both precisely known and essentially independent of environment. A further advantage is ease of pumping by means of an electrical discharge.

Where especially intense laser *pulses* are needed a process termed *Q-switching* is used. Here *Q* refers to the quality factor of the resonator. As in a resonant electrical circuit the term defines the ratio of energy stored to that dissipated. The technique calls for temporarily "spoiling" the resonator by blocking access to one mirror. As long as access is spoiled pumping continues and very high populations of excited atoms are attained. When the second mirror is suddenly made available, laser action generates a giant pulse lasting perhaps 10 ns with peak power of from 10 to 100 MW. A power increase of about three orders of magnitude can be secured by Q-switching.

Spoiling requires use of some type of interrupting device: a rotating shutter, electro-optical cell (Kerr cell), rotating reflector, or bleachable dye between the laser column and one of the end mirrors.

Q-switching by use of a bleachable dye is the simplest of the techniques. Weak light of laser wavelength is originally absorbed by the dye, allowing pumping to continue. Finally, the population of excited species is so large that spontaneous emission bleaches the dye and clears the light path. Then stimulated emission occurs and a giant pulse is emitted. If a fast-recovery dye that returns to its absorbing state within one nanosecond after completion of the pulse is used, high rates of repetition are possible.

11.4 OPTICAL MATERIALS

The range of transparency of substances suitable for absorption cells, lenses, prisms, and windows is, of course, a critical factor in photometric instruments. In general, use of a substance is precluded whenever its absorbance is greater than 0.2.

It is interesting to note that the materials in widespread use, the silicate glasses, transmit satisfactorily only from about 350 nm to 3 μm (3300 cm^{-1}). They are restricted to visible and near-IR photometry.

In the middle and far IR some relaxation of "mechanical" requirements is often made in the interest of adequate transmission. Many materials transparent in this region like Group IA and IIA metal salts are relatively soft and susceptible to attack by water or lower alcohols. Careful handling, moderate humidity, and avoidance of samples that have more than a few tenths percent of water or alcohol, will minimize surface erosion. Surfaces should be repolished at need.

The list of substances transparent in the IR also includes many insoluble, relatively hard materials. Both germanium and silicon, which are transparent from about 10,000 to 630 cm^{-1} (1–16 μm), make excellent single-element lenses because of their high refractive indices, 4.1 and 3.5, respectively. Since they reflect about 50% of incident radiation, they are often antireflection-coated for higher transmission in a particular range. Arsenic trisulfide is also often employed. Several water-insoluble, high-refractive-index, polycrystalline materials trademarked "Irtran" are also valuable in the near and middle IR. For example, Irtran-6 has a transmittance of about 60% from 10,000 to 350 cm^{-1} (1–28 μm).

In the far IR polyethylene and crystalline quartz are useful as window materials.

Fiber optics. Bundles of flexible, transparent fibers of about 0.06 mm diameter make useful light "pipes." Transmission depends on total internal reflection at the walls. To maintain reflection, fibers are kept apart by cladding them with a coating of lower refractive index such as polyvinyl chloride. Numerical apertures of 0.50 are common for fiber optics.*

With glass fibers, transmissions in the visible range of 60% are easily possible in 0.3 m lengths or 30% in 2 m lengths. Use of arsenic trisulfide or other substances extends the capability of filter optics into the IR, and use of quartz into the UV.

Not only are intensities transmitted but images can also be carried through a filter optics bundle. In this case bundles must be coherent, i.e. the relative position of each fiber in a bundle must be identical at the two ends and the fibers must be fused at each end to eliminate dead space.

Representative applications of fiber optics are remote illumination, lighting without heat (by transmission of only visible light from a source), even, constant illumination of a large area such as a punched card (by splitting a bundle of fibers exposed to a small source into many sub-bundles), and remote viewing of images. Design considerations are often crucial. [5]

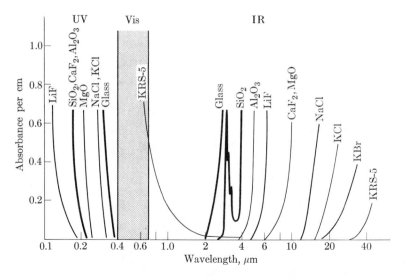

Fig. 11.10 Absorption curves for several optical materials. (Taken in part from Ref. 6, Chap. 17. Courtesy of Pergamon Press.)

Transparency. Partial absorption curves for several of the most widely used optical substances are graphed in Fig. 11.10. Note that all are transparent in the visible except *KRS*-5. In estimating transmission, one must also take into account reflection losses, which increase with increasing refractive index and vary with the angle of incidence (Section 10.8). An average loss at normal incidence in the absence of low-reflectance coatings is 10–20%.

---

* The numerical aperture (N.A.) is the sine of the maximum angle of incidence θ that permits transmission (thus also that permits total internal reflection). In this application it is defined as N.A. $= n_3 \sin \theta_{\max} = (n_1^2 - n_2^2)^{1/2}$ where n_1, n_2, n_3 are the refractive indices for the fiber, coating, and external medium (usually air), respectively.

The transparency of air must also be considered. Although it is nonabsorbing in the visible, two common components of air, CO_2 and H_2O, absorb in parts of the IR and all the gases absorb strongly at wavelengths shorter than 180 nm. In an IR instrument the reduction in beam intensity may be sufficient to warrant purging the interior of an instrument with dry nitrogen or evacuating it. For work in the far UV, evacuation is mandatory.

Refractive index. This also plays a decisive role in the selection of materials for lenses, dispersing devices, and windows. For example, reflection losses increase rapidly with increasing refractive index. It may also be anticipated that the rate of change of refractive index with wavelength will determine the usefulness of a substance as a prism material (Section 12.4). Refractive index data are given for several materials in Fig. 12.6.

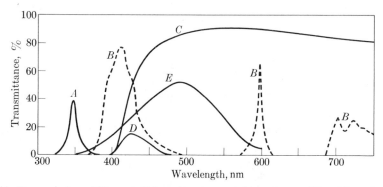

Fig. 11.11 Transmission of filters. *A*, Fabry–Perot or metal interference filter. (The primary band at 700 nm has been blocked.) *B*, Multilayer interference filter with "primary" band at 595 nm. *C*, Corning 3389 sharp-cutoff filter. *D*, Corning narrow band-pass filter made by combining filters 3389 and 5113. *E*, Corning 4060 glass filter.

11.5 FILTERS

A filter is a device that absorbs, reflects, or deviates all frequencies from an optical path except for one band or region. How well five representative types perform may be seen from transmission plots in Fig. 11.11. A band-pass filter like *A*, *B*, or *D* is valuable in separating an emission line or in isolating a narrow spectral band from the output of any continuous source, while a cutoff filter like *C* is useful in blocking a portion of a spectrum. To compare different band-pass filters, widths at half maximum transmittance, i.e., spectral bandwidths (or band-pass), are conventionally stated. For interference filters, which will be discussed in the next section, bandwidths are about 10 nm (e.g., *A* or *B*) as compared with 40 nm for glass filter *D*.

Glass filters of the band-pass type transmit only a selected optical region. Other wavelengths are absorbed or scattered. The "absorbing" type is suspended in a glass plate or dissolved in a layer of gelatin between clear plates. Band-pass filters can also be made by cementing two filters that pass only a narrow range in common.

Christiansen filter. This acts by deflecting all but a narrow band of wavelengths from the optical path. It consists of a suspension of tiny irregularly shaped particles of a transparent solid of a given dispersion $dn/d\lambda$ in a liquid of different dispersion. It is necessary that at one wavelength both have the same index of refraction. If a collimated beam is incident, only the wavelength at which particles and liquid have identical refractive indexes is transmitted freely; others are deflected. By choosing an appropriate binary mixture of liquids, composition can be varied to shift the wavelength of the band passed by the filter.

11.6 INTERFERENCE FILTERS

Optical filters based on interference between multiply reflected rays can be made for the region that extends from about 2000 cm^{-1} (5 μm) through the near UV. Two types of filter, based on different methods of producing interference have been developed, the metal or Fabry–Perot filter and the multilayer dielectric type.

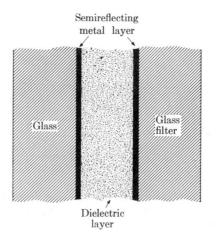

Fig. 11.12 Cross section of a Fabry–Perot type of interference filter. Thicknesses are exaggerated for clarity. The cover glass (outer layer) may be from 2 to 3 mm thick, the dielectric layer 0.4 μm, and the metallic films even thinner. Representative materials for the dielectric layer are calcium or magnesium fluoride and the metal is ordinarily silver. As shown, a filter may be used as a cover glass to pass a band of desired order.

Fabry–Perot filter. This consists of an extremely thin layer of dielectric sandwiched between semireflecting metallic films, usually of silver. The construction is shown schematically in Fig. 11.12 and is achieved by precise vacuum deposition. Suppose parallel light rays are perpendicularly incident on the left side. They suffer substantial reflection at each metal layer. Most of the radiation traversing the dielectric layer is reflected back. The interference that ensues as reflected rays superpose on incident rays, a phenomenon termed *Fabry–Perot interference*, causes the obliteration of all but several narrow bands of wavelengths. The transmission of such a filter is shown in Fig. 11.13.

In Fig. 11.14 an "exploded" picture is given as an aid in visualizing the interference. To separate the rays for the purpose of illustration, angular incidence is shown; actually normal incidence is required if rays are to interfere. The condition

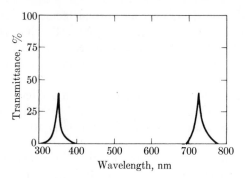

Fig. 11.13 Transmission curve of a Fabry–Perot interference filter.

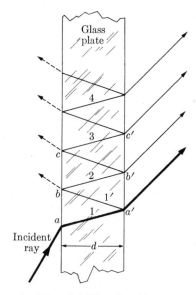

Fig. 11.14 An "exploded" sketch of the multiply reflected rays in an interference filter. Normal incidence is always used, although an obliquely incident ray is drawn here to allow the reflected rays to be shown.

for transmission is the condition for constructive interference: Path differences between superposed rays must be one wavelength or some multiple thereof. The expression for wavelengths at which full reinforcement will occur is

$$2d = m\lambda/n, \tag{11.4}$$

where d is the thickness of dielectric layer and n its refractive index at wavelength λ (vacuum), and m is the *order* ($m = 1, 2, 3, \ldots$), a factor that allows for path lengths that are a multiple of the wavelength. For example, rays 1 and 2 *completely* reinforce each other when $aa' + a'b$ is exactly one wavelength in the medium (λ/n), or a multiple. The same conclusion is reached for all unprimed ray pairs, e.g., 2 and 3, 1 and 3.

What if the radiation deviates from normal incidence? In this case, the band transmitted shifts toward shorter wavelengths. While the shift is only about 2.5 nm for a 10° deviation from normal incidence, it increases rapidly. Clearly, the aperture angle of light to be filtered should be kept small if bandpass is to stay within specifications for a filter.

The variation in transmission wavelength when a filter is tipped does suggest a method of continuous tuning or scanning over a short wavelength range. By tilting, the band passed can be shifted smoothly as much as 10 to 30 nm toward shorter wavelengths.*

Since partial reinforcement occurs for other path distances, the Fabry–Perot filter actually transmits a band. Equation (11.4) defines only the central wavelength. Intensity of transmission diminishes once path differences differ very much from any multiple of the wavelength. The maximum transmission in the center is dependent on the extent to which the metal mirrors absorb. For about 5% mirror absorption, peak transmission is usually 40%, half-bandwidths 12.5 nm, 1/100 bandwidths 77 nm. By sacrificing intensity, still narrower bands can be achieved.

When is the *order* of interference of importance? It is convenient to rewrite Eq. (11.4) in the form

$$\lambda/n = 2d/m \qquad (11.5)$$

to emphasize the influence of the order. Wavelengths that are one-half $2d$, one-third $2d$, etc. will also constructively interfere and be transmitted. The origin of the bands shown in Fig. 11.13 is now evident. The right band at about 720 nm must be first-order, and the left one at about 360 nm must be second-order.

Example How thick a dielectric layer is required in a Fabry–Perot filter to secure a first-order band at 500 nm? Assume a calcium fluoride dielectric of $n = 1.35$ is used.

Solving Eq. (11.5) for d and substituting values gives

$$d = \frac{\lambda m}{2n} = \frac{500 \times 1}{2 \times 1.35} = 185 \text{ nm}.$$

Ignoring the small change of n with λ, we find that this filter also passes a second-order band centered at 250 nm, a third-order band at 167 nm, etc.

Second- and third-order bands are narrower, and most interference filters are arranged to transmit one of these. If a third-order 500 nm band is desired, it must be isolated from bordering transmission bands at about 750 nm and 375 nm. These "side" bands may be blocked by an additional filter. It may be substituted for one of the cover plates usually present. An ingenious choice of filter is a Fabry–Perot system whose first-order matches the desired band.

Wedge filter. A continuously variable transmission filter is also obtainable. A wedge-shaped slab of dielectric is deposited between semireflecting metallic layers. In this case a different wavelength is transmitted at each point along the length of the filter.

---

* S. A. Pollack, *Appl. Opt.* **5**, 1749 (1966).

Different frequencies may then be isolated by passing a slit assembly along the filter. Such a filter can be used in place of a prism or grating as the dispersing element in a monochromator.

Multilayer filter. This kind of interference filter consists of alternating layers of high- and low-refractive-index dielectric materials of suitable thickness vacuum-depositited on a transparent slab. Layer thickness ranges between one-fourth and one wavelength, with 5 to 25 layers usually required for a filter. Although a detailed treatment is beyond the scope of this text, it should be noted that narrower half-peak widths (as small as 4 to 8 nm at present) and greater transmittances (40 to 70%) can be secured with multilayer dielectric filters. Very importantly, sharp cutoff filters are also possible. The disadvantages are greater cost and higher transmittance in unwanted parts of the spectrum. Generally, Fabry–Perot filters are more extensively used.

11.7 DETECTORS, RECEIVERS

The actual measurement involved in any photometric method might be said to begin with the detector or receiver, the device that produces a signal in response to radiation. The general name input transducer is also used. Radiation may be detected if it can be "absorbed." Broadly, this covers the possibility of absorption photoelectrically (either external ejection or internal energy promotion), thermally, or atomically. The last refers to the possibility of exciting an atomic or molecular system to a higher level. There are, of course, many methods of implementing each possibility. In evaluating them the following criteria must be kept in mind:

1. Sensitivity (change in output for a given change in input),

2. Linearity of response,

3. Noise level,

4. Response time,

5. Frequency dependence of response,

6. Stability.

Photoelectric (ejection) methods respond only to energetic photons and thus are best in the UV, visible, and near IR. In the IR, the procedures of choice are thermal methods (widely used) and photoconductive methods (less commonly used). Atomic methods are highly specific, and are infrequently used. Classes of detectors or input transducers were listed in Table 11.1 by spectral range. In Table 11.4 major examples of each type of optical detector are given, together with certain of their characteristics.

With a detector a threshold of sensitivity is established by the ratio of signal to noise (Section 8.2). For example, a thermocouple can be used with weak radiation, but it will be ineffective when the radiant power incident is so small that the signal generated is of the magnitude of the noise in the device.

To improve the signal-to-noise ratio in a system and facilitate automatic operation the beam of radiation is often chopped or electrically modulated. When this is done, the detector output is amplified by an ac amplifier tuned to the frequency of chopping,

Table 11.4 Characteristics of Some Radiation Detectors

Type	Sensitive "element"	Detection limit (D*)† and response time	Best frequency range, μm	Output: type; impedance; kind of noise
A. Photon detectors				
Photomultiplier tube	Group I and V metal oxide on cathode	5×10^{14} (1000 Hz); $< 1\,\mu s$	0.16 to 0.7	Current; high; shot noise
Phototube	Alkali metal oxide	$<1\,\mu s$	0.2 to 1	Current; high; shot noise
Photovoltaic cell	Semiconductor on metal	$<1\,\mu s$	0.4 to 0.8	Current or emf; low; shot noise
Photographic film or plate	AgX grains in emulsion§	Variable	0.2 to 1.2	
Photoconductive cell‡	I. PbS, PbSe, InSb	5×10^8 (90 Hz); 2 to 1000 μs	0.7 to 4.5	Resistance change; high; thermal noise
	II. Ge: Cu, Au, or Zn activated (op. at $\sim 5°$K)	10^{10} (900 Hz); 0.1 to 1 μs	2–15 to 2–100	Resistance change; high; thermal noise
B. Thermal detectors				
Thermocouple (thermopile)	Junction of dissimilar metals with blackened strip as absorber	2×10^9 (5 Hz); 50 to 100 ms	0.8 to 40	Emf; low; thermal noise
Bolometer (bridge detector)	Resistance wire or thermistor chip with blackened strip	2×10^8 (10 Hz); 10 ms to 5 μs**	0.8 to 40	Resistance change; low to high; thermal and $1/f$ noise
Pneumatic cell (Golay cell)	Blackened membrane of gas chamber	2×10^9 (10 Hz); 3 to 30 ms	0.8 to 1000	Current; thermal noise
Pyroelectric	Ferroelectric crystal under permanent electric polarization	3×10^8; 20 μs	0.8 to 1000	Emf; thermal noise

† Dimensions of dee-star (D^*) are cm $Hz^{1/2}\ W^{-1}$. Values hold for a source temperature of 500°K, the cited chopping frequency (in parentheses) and for a 1 Hz bandwidth. After James and Sternberg. [2, Chap. 12]

§ Chemical development and densitometer scanning are, of course, required.

‡ Two types are shown. Data for type I are for room-temperature operation. Type I devices are also operated at low temperature to enhance their response. For example, greater sensitivity (up to 100-fold) and wider frequency response (up to 7 μm) results on operation at −196°C.

** Shorter times are for a superconducting bolometer.

and the magnified signal demodulated. Phase-lock procedures (Section 8.7) or photon counting procedures (Section 8.8) are used at poor S/N ratios. Because of the interplay of signal and noise, detectors are rated by rather complex criteria, especially for work in the IR where intensities sometimes fall near the noise level. The criteria commonly used are defined as follows:

1.   *Responsivity R* is the rms signal voltage per unit rms power incident on a detector. The active area of the detector and the intensity–wavelength pattern of the source must be specified. The system bandwidth need not be specified, as responsivity is independent of noise. Responsivity is seen to be essentially the sensivity of the module.

2.   *Noise-equivalent power* (NEP) or P_n is the rms radiation power in watts that must impinge on a detector to produce an rms signal voltage equal to the rms noise voltage for a given radiation source, bandwidth, and chopping frequency. The smaller P_n is, the better the detector.

3.   *Detectivity D* is the reciprocal of P_n.

4. D^* is a figure of merit for a detector. It is defined by the expression $D^* = DA_d^{1/2}(\Delta f)^{1/2}$ where A_d is the detector area and Δf the bandwidth. The units of D^* are cm $Hz^{1/2}$ W^{-1}. "Dee-star" is just the S/N ratio at a given source temperature and chopping frequency with an amplifier bandwidth of 1 Hz when a detector of 1 cm^2 aperture is irradiated by a one watt flux. It is independent of detector area.

If the power in a beam varies rapidly, as it will during fast scanning when a source is modulated, the detector must have a short response time. The reasons for finite response times are varied, but some idea of what is involved may be gained from the discussion of the response of an IR thermocouple on p. 315.

Detection in the UV and visible. With the advent of stable amplifiers, photoelectric detection has tended to become predominant in the UV and visible. The term photoelectric is used somewhat loosely as including the energizing of bound electrons into conduction zones in semiconductors (Section 4.2) in the photovoltaic cell, as well as the actual photoejection of electrons in phototubes. The response of such devices is strongly frequency-dependent.

The photovoltaic, or self-generative, cell is used mainly in the visible region at fairly high levels of illumination like those available in a filter photometer. Another name for such a device is barrier-layer cell. It consists of a thin layer of a semiconductor like selenium deposited on a metal such as iron to form a rectifying junction. The semiconductor layer is coated with a transparent metal film. Electrical contact is made to this film and the base. When light passes through the film, electrons flow from semiconductor to metal, generating an output measurable as either current or emf.

This receiver is seldom chosen for the detection of very weak radiation since it is inferior to the multiplier phototube discussed below in the range where either can be used. A serious difficulty as these cells are conventionally used is the phenomenon of "fatigue:" immediately after exposure to bright light the output of a photocell is very high, but the output decreases exponentially with time as the illumination continues. Fatigue can be minimized, however, by selecting the best level of illumination and the proper circuit resistances.

The output of photovoltaic cells is linear with illumination only if used with a very small load resistance. As a result, this type of cell is commonly used where its output is sufficient to be registered directly on a microammeter or a sturdy galvanometer. Up to moderate illumination levels, output is practically linear with intensity. A typical application is shown in Fig. 15.4. The type of current balance circuit shown is widely used.

Phototubes, either single-stage or multiplier type, are very widely used. The simple phototube will be described first. In a typical vacuum phototube the light-sensitive cathode is roughly a half-cylinder of metal coated on its inside surface with successive layers of silver, alkali metal, and alkali metal oxide. The anode is a wire located along the axis of the cylinder. On exposure to radiation, electrons are ejected from the cathode and move toward the positive wire anode, constituting a current. All the electrons are collected by maintaining the anode at about $+90$ V relative to the cathode, and stable operation is achieved. For an accuracy of 1% or better, a calibration is required to overcome the slight nonlinearity in dependence of photo current on illumination unless a suitable null method can be employed. Even phototube signals as small as 10^{-11} A (produced at the low levels of illumination in precision spectrophotometry) may be easily amplified. The addition of an inert gas at low pressure permits amplification through ionization, perhaps by as much as a factor

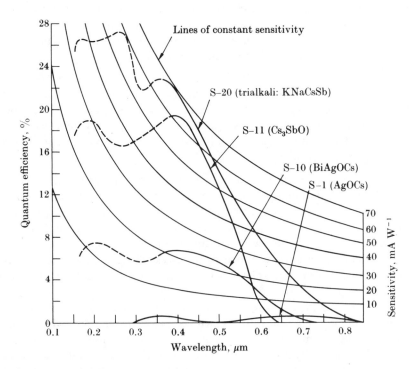

Fig. 11.15 Spectral response curves for several standard photocathode surfaces. Note the sensitivity scale at the right. Dashed portions of curves show response when UV-transmitting window is used in photomultiplier tube.

of 10 to 20 times. Such gas-filled tubes are not used so widely as the vacuum devices.

Vacuum and multiplier phototubes are presently manufactured with any of about two dozen different photosensitive surfaces. The characteristics of these surfaces are standardized and well defined. In Fig. 11.15 the spectral sensitivity of four is shown.

In the multiplier phototube, or *photomultiplier tube* as it is commonly called, several stages of amplification are incorporated within the tube envelope. This device comprises a photocathode, secondary emission stages or dynodes and an anode. Often the photocathode is only a semitransparent deposit on the inside of the tube window. Since electrons emitted when radiation strikes the photocathode are guided to dynodes by electrostatic fields, a suitable configuration is critical. Successive dynodes are maintained at higher voltages. The secondary emission at each produces a growing electron avalanche that finally impinges on the anode. One type of design is shown in Fig. 11.16. Alternatively, the secondary emission system may take the form of a venetian blind arrangement, or a box-and-grid structure. A potential difference of about 90 V between successive dynodes is very precisely controlled by a resistance voltage divider energized by a regulated power supply. The number of photoelectrons can be multiplied directly by a factor of as much as 10^8. The tube output may, of course, be further amplified.

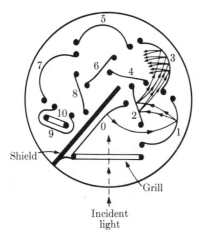

Fig. 11.16 A schematic diagram of the RCA 1P28 electron-multiplier phototube. 0, photocathode. 1–9, dynodes. 10, anode. Photoelectrons ejected from the cathode are focused into a beam by the electrostatic field set up by the electrodes and accelerated toward the first dynode. A great many secondary electrons result from the bombardment, and these are in turn beamed toward a second dynode, etc. The spectral response covers the range from 200 to 600 nm. (Courtesy of Radio Corporation of America.)

As a result of their large internal amplification, photomultiplier tubes can be used only at low power levels (about 10^{-14} to 10^{-4} lumens on a continuous basis). When power is on, exposure of a tube to even moderate levels of illumination can cause irreversible or at best slowly reversible changes in electrode surfaces. As a result these tubes are always mounted in lighttight housings with a shutter to control the entrance port.*

When a photomultiplier is operated in darkness, a current still flows in the anode lead, i.e., a *dark current* axis. Thermionic emission, emission caused by natural radioactivity such as that traceable to ^{40}K in the glass envelope, field emission, ohmic leakage, and other factors are responsible. The ohmic leakage component is basically dc but the other contributions to dark current are pulselike in character. They are electron bursts originating from emission at the cathode or any dynode. Thus, most "dark" pulses will be of lower amplitude than a photopulse, and it is possible in a pulse counting procedure to discriminate against them. Average amplitudes are suggested in Fig. 11.17.

Since the "dark" electrons also produce an amplified current at the anode, they set a lower limit to the light intensity that can be directly detected. For work at low intensity levels thermal dark current can be minimized by thermoelectric or other

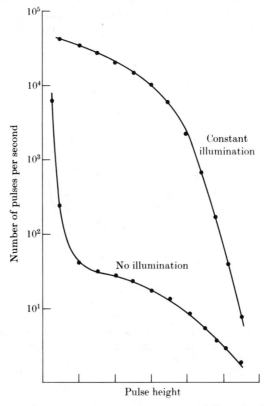

Fig. 11.17 Distribution of current pulses from a photomultiplier tube by amplitude. "Dark pulses" that originate when the tube is not illuminated are seen to be many fewer in number and much smaller in amplitude.

---

* Accidental exposure to daylight when the power is off will not cause damage but will energize the photocathode and lead to excessive dark current for 24–48 hours.

cooling of a photomultiplier tube to about $-40\,°C$ ($-185\,°C$ is required for a tube with an $S-1$ cathode). Other sources of dark current are less subject to control.

How is dark current related to noise? Noise appears as a statistical fluctuation in the emission of electrons and gives rise to unsteadiness in both signal and dark current. If a long time constant system is used for amplification, the noise will tend to average to zero. By contrast, the dark current represents a steady component that may be offset automatically by a potentiometer zeroing arrangement or manually subtracted.

Usually the gain of a photomultiplier is best enhanced by use of improved dynode surfaces, better geometry, or additional dynodes. An increase in operating voltage will enhance the gain, but is limited in practice by the possibility of tube damage by flashover or ionization of residual gas. Increasingly the output of photomultiplier tubes used for work at very low light intensities is determined by the technique called photon counting (Section 8.8).

In the vacuum UV, radiation can be successfully detected from 300 nm (3000 Å) to 30 nm (300 Å) by using a fluorescing plate as converter.* A coating of sodium salicylate on a Pyrex window serves the purpose. When vacuum UV radiation impinges, the compound fluoresces at about 400 nm. This light passes through the window to a photomultiplier tube. The response is reasonably linear across the range cited.

Magnetic electron multipliers. These are detectors that are similar to photomultiplier tubes in design but extend the detection of photons well into the X-ray region. Their range is 150 nm (1500 Å) to 0.2 nm (2 Å). Photons enter the detector through a thin metal film that is 90 % transparent to them and fall on a tungsten cathode. The photoelectrons ejected impinge on a dynode strip and cause a burst of secondary electrons. These electrons are constrained by geometry and crossed magnetic and electric fields and travel down the dynode strip in a series of cycloidal jumps. At each impact there is a multiplier effect as individual electrons release several other secondary electrons. The final avalanche of secondary electrons is collected by an anode. An overall accelerating potential of about 2000 V is used. Clearly, the strip must have sufficient resistance to sustain this voltage drop along its length without appreciable conduction. The dark current of the multiplier is very small (0.1 electron s^{-1}) and gains of the order of 10^8 are achieved.

Photographic detection. A photographic emulsion is also a sensitive detector. It actually serves as a composite detector-transducer-amplifier-recorder and provides a permanent record of the intensity and spatial pattern of the incident radiation. Such an emulsion consists of minute silver halide crystals dispersed in a transparent, water-expandable medium such as gelatin and is available on film or thin glass plates.

On exposure, the silver halide crystals receiving radiation build a latent image. Subsequent chemical development, which is analogous to amplification, produces a black deposit of silver at the site of the latent image. The spectral range and a few other properties of some widely used emulsions are given in Table 11.5. As may be

---

* Direct photoelectric efficiencies are generally low for these frequencies, precluding direct use of a phototube.

Table 11.5 Properties of Some Photographic Emulsions

Type	Useful wavelength range, nm	Speed	Contrast	Granularity*	Representative uses in analysis
Eastman					
SA No. 1	230–400	Low	Relatively high	0.2	Quant., trace
SA No. 3	230–500	Low	Relatively high	~ 0.2	Qual.
103–0	230–500	High	Low	~ 0.4	Qual., quant.
103–F	230–680	High	Low	~ 0.4	Qual., quant.
I–N	230–880	High	Low	~ 0.8	Qual., quant.
IV–N	230–680	Low	Relatively high	~ 0.2	Qual., quant.
Ilford					
Q-2	5–250				

* Granularity is a measure of the noise or background fluctuation of an emulsion. The smaller the granularity, the better the signal-to-noise ratio. For a faint line, a longer exposure with a low-granularity, high-contrast emulsion (which will be slow) is preferable to a short exposure with a fast film of higher granularity.

seen, the useful range is mainly the UV and VIS, and with special sensitizing, the near IR. Emulsions give high spatial resolution since their silver halide crystals are small. Different speeds (low, medium, high) and contrasts (medium, high, very high) are available. Speed is identified by an ASA rating, e.g., an ASA of 400 represents a very fast emulsion and one of ASA 0.004 a very slow one. Contrast is identified by a gamma-value (often 1 to 5).

Example Since the sensitive emission lines of most elements occur above 230 nm in the UV, SA No. 1 emulsion is very widely used in quantitative spectrographic analysis. It offers high contrast and freedom from graininess and thus gives sharp lines. Its cutoff at 440 nm ensures, even when no filter is used, that it can be used in a grating spectrometer at high orders with minimum overlapping of lines from the visible and IR.

The response of an emulsion is graphed in Fig. 11.18. Such a plot serves to calibrate the emulsion. As the figure shows, the density of deposit is related to the logarithm of *exposure*, the product of radiation intensity and time. The graph also makes clear the short dynamic range of an emulsion: a useful response is secured over about two decades of exposure.

How are contrast and speed related to the curve of Fig. 11.18? The contrast of an emulsion is seen to be proportional to the slope of the curve and speed to the range over which the curve is linear. For example, a fast, low-contrast emulsion will yield a curve of low slope whose linear range occurs at very low exposures. In general, speed and contrast cannot both be maximized.

The fairly short dynamic range of photographic emulsions makes a preliminary testing essential. Then an emulsion appropriate to the radiation level to be measured and to the longest feasible time of exposure can be selected. Two stratagems that are valuable in other cases are described in the following examples.

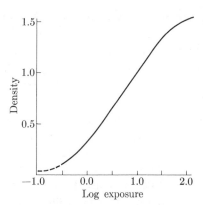

Fig. 11.18 Representative plot of image density versus the logarithm of exposure for a photographic emulsion.

Example 1 If a very low intensity is to be recorded and a long exposure is not feasible, an adequate response cannot be obtained even with a fast emulsion of adequate contrast. All possible exposures would give points at the left end of the plot of Fig. 11.18. The emulsion has no contrast in this range and thus no resolution. In this case *prefogging*, a practice commonly employed by astronomers, can be used. The film or plate is prefogged by flashing a lamp several times at some distance from the open film or plate. It is then used to record the desired signal. If prefogging is done correctly, even very faint radiation will bring the overall response into the linear range.

Example 2 Conversely, the intensity of incident radiation may be too great. In this case attenuation is logical. Neutral-density filters or a stepped rotating sector whose transmission varies along its radius can be placed in the optical path. The radiation is then attenuated by a precise, known amount.

For instance, in quantitative emission spectrometry a stepped rotating sector is useful to extend the dynamic range of photographic detection. The spectrograph slit is opened to the full height and a four-step rotating sector placed in front of it. As it rotates, it provides four widely different levels of illumination along the slit image. At least one level striking the photographic emulsion should fall in the range of proper exposure for every incident line, even though true intensities cover a range of 10^4 or more.

Fine descriptions of suitable methods for development, fixing, and washing of the plates or film are available in any standard volumes on spectroscopy [1, 3, and 5 of Chapter 13]. While it is difficult to control the chemical processes involved in development and fixing exactly, with a reciprocating, constant-temperature processing unit and nitrogen gas burst agitation* they are reproducible to $\pm 1\%$ or better.

The density of deposit is ordinarily determined by a photoelectric scanning procedure discussed in Section 13.14. The background density is subtracted before the ratio to the internal standard is taken.

Finally, even though it has not been included in Table 11.4, the human eye must

---

* Pamphlet E-57 (1965), Eastman Kodak Company.

be discussed briefly as a detector in the visible region. Perhaps the eye's most serious limitation is its inability to determine the radiant power level except by matching with a reference. Under favorable conditions the matching can be done visually to about $\pm 1\%$. This factor together with the eye's susceptibility to fatigue, slowness of response, tendency to color blindness, etc., restricts visual detection to semiquantitative or qualitative applications such as spot tests.

Detection in the near IR. *Photoconductive cells* based on PbS, PbSe, and InSb are by all odds the most sensitive detectors and are employed to the exclusion of other devices if use is to be limited to the region from 12,500 to 2500 cm^{-1} (0.8 to 4 μm).* If they can be operated at liquid nitrogen temperature, the range can be extended to about 1400 cm^{-1} (7 μm). Since their response drops off rapidly at still longer wavelengths, they cannot be used successfully if both the near and middle IR are to be scanned with a single detector, but must be replaced by one of the devices described below. Usually a photoconductive cell is made by depositing a thin film of semiconductor on glass either chemically or by a vacuum process. Protection against the atmosphere is provided by evacuation or by lacquering the layer. In operation, the larger the voltage across the cell, the stronger the output signal upon illumination. The voltage used is usually as high as is possible without producing appreciable heating (less than 0.01 W mm^{-2} can be tolerated). Like other IR detectors, the photoconductive cell does not show fatigue effects under continued illumination.

Detection in the IR. In the middle and far IR, radiation is ordinarily sensed by a thermal detector, a device that measures the temperature rise when radiation is absorbed. Most frequently used are the thermocouple or thermopile (a multiple junction thermocouple), bolometer (a resistance thermometer), and pneumatic or Golay detector (a gas thermometer). An important advantage of any thermal detector is that its response is independent of the wavelength of the radiation. Such a receiver responds to energy absorbed per unit area. The chief drawbacks of most thermal detectors are slow response, a moderate sensitivity, and a moderate "dee-star" (see Table 11.4).

The typical absorbing device is a tiny (2 × 2 mm) blackened metal strip. A condensing mirror is used to reduce the much larger IR beam to this size. A reduction of 6:1 is usually feasible by an arrangement such as is shown in Fig. 11.9. In general,

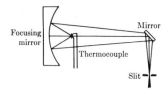

Fig. 11.19 A schematic diagram of the optical arrangement associated with the thermocouple receiver in the Perkin-Elmer Models 21 through 621 recording IR spectrophotometers. (Courtesy of Perkin-Elmer Corp.)

---

* Like other semiconductors, photoconductive materials respond to exciting energy by promoting electrons to a conduction level (Section 4.2). They are doped to reduce the energy gap.

the detector is shielded by an evacuated holder to minimize noise (fluctuations in background temperature), for the temperature rise caused by the beam is minute.

A thermocouple or bolometer that will give a large output per degree is attached intimately to the absorbing strip. With a bolometer, a reference resistor or thermistor that is not irradiated by the beam must also be provided for its bridge circuit.

What determines the magnitude of thermocouple response? Consider that incident radiation of power P is absorbed by the blackened strip affixed to the thermocouple junction. The rise in temperature is ΔT. Simultaneously, power is lost at the rate of L watts per degree rise, through radiation, conduction, convection, and the Peltier effect. The last may usually be neglected. The attainment of a final temperature is achieved exponentially, the response time t for 63% attainment being $t = C/L$, where C is the heat capacity of the blackened strip and thermocouple. For a short response time, C must be small and L large.

On the other hand, detector sensitivity is measured in terms of voltage E that is produced by the thermocouple per unit power P it receives. Let the thermoelectric power, i.e., the voltage produced per degree rise in temperature, be Q. The output voltage is simply

$$E = Q \,\Delta T = QP/L. \tag{11.6}$$

From Eq. (11.6), it appears that high sensitivity calls for a small L.

The conflicting requirements for L can be resolved by making the absorber tiny: Both the heat capacity and power loss will be small yet the loss rate L may be large relative to C.

Unlike the detectors just described, whose response depends on the energy absorbed per unit area, the *pneumatic* or *Golay detector* is essentially a differential gas thermometer that responds to total energy falling on it. Either the filling gas itself or a blackened membrane making up one wall of the gas cell serves as the absorber. As radiation impinges, the gas is heated and expands against a second flexible membrane. In some designs membrane movement deflects a light beam that is incident, in others the membrane is part of a capacitor whose capacitance alters as a result of expansion. Simpler optics may be used with a pneumatic detector since the absorber is larger.

If an absorbing gas is used, the Golay detector has high sensitivity at wavelengths at which the gas absorbs. A surprising degree of flexibility and specificity may be achieved by choice of a gas. As a result, this approach is widely used in nondispersing photometers (Section 17.10). If a blackened membrane is used, the device is termed a *Golay detector* and is equally sensitive at all wavelengths.

If a gas chamber absorber is used, it may be large enough for the incident beam not to need focusing. Even the membrane type may be about 3 mm in diameter, allowing somewhat simpler optics.

Low-temperature photoconductive devices (Type II in Table 11.4) are very sensitive and fast, broad-range IR detectors. The detector, usually a doped germanium crystal, is mounted in the bottom of a liquid helium dewar to permit operation at $4 °K$. Time constants are less than 1 μs. Ranges in wavenumber for different dopings are, Au, 5000–1400; Hg, 5000–650; Cu, 5000–330; In, 5000–100. By use of an indium antimonide detector a range from 300 μm to 8 mm (33–1.2 cm^{-1}) can be realized. An appropriate bias (5–40 V) is maintained across a detector of this type.

Image intensifiers.   The recording of optical information is often frustrated by low intensity. The use of an image intensifier tube can in effect increase light gathering power substantially. It can, e.g., speed the recording of a spectrum in astronomy. These devices, especially the cascade type, feature an *S*-20 trialkali surface (Fig. 11.15) on a semitransparent photocathode. Incident light ejects photoelectrons from its far side. These are accelerated linearly toward a transparent multilayer membrane coated on its far side with a phosphor layer that emits about 200–900 photons for each electron received. These fall on its farthest layer, a cathode surface from which about 50 photoelectrons are emitted into an evacuated space. Magnetic focusing ensures that the photoelectrons travel to the anode phosphor screen without loss of definition. An overall light intensity gain of 2500 is achieved but the light at the final screen diverges widely. An actual signal gain of about an order of magnitude over an unaided photographic plate is achieved.

REFERENCES

Design applications of physical and geometrical optics are treated in:

1. R. Kingslake, ed., *Applied Optics and Optical Engineering*. Vol. I–V. New York: Academic, 1965–69.
2. R. D. Hudson, Jr., *Infrared System Engineering*. New York: Wiley–Interscience, 1969
3. L. Levi, *Applied Optics: A Guide to Optical Design*. Vol. 1. New York: Wiley, 1968
4. Warren J. Smith, *Modern Optical Engineering, the Design of Optical Systems*. New York: McGraw-Hill, 1966

Particular optical modules or types of components are treated on a general or introductory level in:

5. Corning, *Glass Flexible Fiber Optics, Design Considerations*. Bulletin 2. Corning, N.Y.: Corning Glass Works
6. Lewis R. Koller, *Ultraviolet Radiation*. New York: Wiley, 1965
7. T. P. Melia, *An Introduction to Masers and Lasers, Their Theory and Applications*. New York: Barnes and Noble, 1967
7a. J. K. Nakamura and S. E. Schwartz, ". . . Sensitive Photomultiplier Detection Systems," *Appl. Opt.* **7**, 1073 (1968)
8. RCA, *Phototubes and Photocells*, RCA Technical Manual PT-60. Lancaster, Pa.: RCA, 1963
8a. RCA, *Photomultiplier Manual*, RCA Technical Manual PT-61. Harrison, N. J.: RCA, 1970
9. J. A. R. Samson, *Techniques of Vacuum Ultraviolet Spectroscopy*. New York: Wiley, 1967
9a. I. Simon, *Infrared Radiation*. Princeton, N.J.: Van Nostrand, 1966
10. Norman Slagg, "Chemistry and Light Generation," *J. Chem. Educ.* **45**, 103 (1968)
11. C. E. Weitz, *Lamp Bulletin*. Bulletin LD-1. General Electric, Large Lamp Dept, 1956

and on an advanced level in:

12. George Birnbaum, *Optical Masers, Advances in Electronics and Electron Physics*. Supplement 2. New York: Academic, 1964.
13. A. L. Bloom, "Gas Lasers" and following articles, *Proc. IEEE*. **54**, 1262 ff (1966)
14. N. S. Kapany, *Fiber Optics, Principles and Applications*. New York: Academic, 1967
15. P. W. Kruse, L. D. McGlauchlin, and R. B. McQuistan, *Elements of Infrared Technology*. New York: Wiley, 1962

16. A. E. Martin, *Infrared Instrumentation and Techniques*. New York: American Elsevier, 1966
17. D. H. Martin, ed., *Spectroscopic Techniques for Far Infrared, Submillimetre, and Millimetre Waves*. New York: Wiley, 1967
18. W. Slavin, "Photometric Standard for Ultraviolet Visible Spectrophotometers," *J. Opt. Soc. Am.* **52**, 1399 (1962)
19. R. A. Smith, F. E. Jones, and R. P. Chasmar, *The Detection and Measurement of Infrared Radiation*. Oxford: Oxford University Press, 1957
20. J. W. T. Walsh, *Photometry*. New York: Dover, 1969
21. W. A. Hiltner, ed., *Astronomical Techniques*. Chicago: University of Chicago, 1962

EXERCISES

11.1 To the degree that a carbon arc can be considered a blackbody emitter, what is the wavelength of maximum emission when its temperature is 5000°K?

[*Ans.*: 580 nm.]

11.2 Show by means of three sketches of intensity versus wavelength the appearance of the sodium *D*-lines of sodium vapor lamps of (a) low pressure, (b) medium pressure, and (c) high pressure. Identify in words the significant effects.

11.3 A layer of CaF_2 of 330 nm thickness is used as the spacer between semi-reflecting layers in an interference filter. At what wavelength is the second-order transmission region of the filter? Where do the first- and third-order bands lie?

[*Ans.*: 445 nm; 890 nm; 297 nm.]

11.4 What order interference will give a transmission band with a maximum at about 550 nm for an interference filter with a CaF_2 layer 0.61 μm thick? How close on the short wavelength side is the next transmitted band?

[*Ans.*: Third; 413 nm.]

11.5 A Fabry–Perot interference filter that passes only a second-order band centered at 600 nm is on hand. To eliminate the other bands an auxiliary Fabry–Perot filter is to be deposited on one side and the whole enclosed between glass plates. To secure optimum blocking of bands passed by the basic filter, what wavelength should be selected for the first-order band of the auxiliary filter?

[*Ans.*: 1800 nm.]

11.6 A bundle of 0.06 mm dia. glass fibers, packed coherently, is to be used for image transmission. What maximum resolution may be achieved? Consider that resolution involves seeing adjacent lines as separate objects.

[*Ans.*: About 0.18 mm.]

11.7a) In each fiber of a fiber optic bundle total internal reflection must occur at the boundary with its coating layer. On this basis suggest a minimum useful diameter for a single coated fiber optic that is to be used in the visible range. (Hint: consider the thickness of coating required.)

   b) What is the maximum resolution that might be attained in a coherent bundle?

   c) Would the transmission of a bundle be affected as the size of fibers that make it up is varied?
[*Ans.*: a) The thickness of coating must be at least half a wavelength; thus in cross section a coating will contribute 2 × 1/2 × λ or 600 nm thickness for 600 nm light. If the glass fiber is same thickness, a min. dia. of 1.2 mm is required.]

11.8 If a multiplier phototube with ten dynodes has a gain of 10^7, what must the average ratio of numbers of secondary to incident electrons be at each dynode?

[*Ans.*: 5.]

11.9 In Raman spectroscopy it is necessary to detect weak, inelastically scattered radiation of many frequencies in the presence of intense monochromatic, elastically scattered light. To simplify instrumentation, a filter that *passes* all wavelengths but the elastically scattered one would be very useful. It has been proposed* that two Fabry–Perot interference filters that *transmit* the elastically scattered light with 70% efficiency can be used for the purpose. Note that light they do not transmit is reflected. Thus, their reflectance is about 97% except at the transmitted wavelength band, where it is only 30%.

a) Sketch a multiple reflection arrangement using a parallel pair of such filters. It should pass only the desired scattered frequencies from a Raman sample to the slit of a monochromator.

b) If four reflections from the filter occur, what intensity of Raman frequencies is passed? of elastically scattered light?

[*Ans.*: b) 0.8%; 89%.]

---

* M. Tobin, *J. Opt. Soc. Am.* **49**, 850 (1959).

Chapter 12

MONOCHROMATORS

12.1 INTRODUCTION

Much versatile optical instrumentation is designed around a monochromator, a module whose output is a narrow wavelength band over a wide optical frequency range. For example, a combination of continuous optical source and monochromator provides monochromatic light to most dispersive spectrophotometers. The optical system of a monochromator consists in general of

1. An *entrance slit* that provides a narrow optical image,
2. A *collimator* that renders the rays spreading from the slit parallel,
3. A component for *dispersing* this radiation,
4. A *focusing element* to reform images of the slit, and
5. An *exit slit* to isolate the desired spectral band.

To illustrate the arrangement, a source and a simple prism monochromator are shown in Fig. 12.1 in schematic form.

Basic requirements imposed on a monochromator such as resolution, dispersion, spectral range, bandwidth, and simplicity figure prominently in evaluation of different designs. Each of these quantities will be discussed in considerable detail in the following sections but some brief definitions are provided in Table 12.1. It must be recognized that specifications for a monochromator can scarcely be considered apart from a choice of other components such as a source and a detector, which were treated in the last chapter. These interrelationships will be taken up in later chapters as particular optical methods are treated.

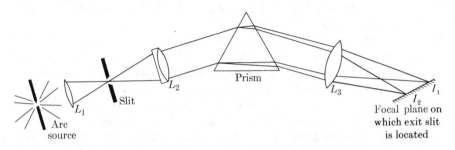

Fig. 12.1 Schematic diagram of a simple prism monochromator. Lens L_1 concentrates radiation on entrance slit, L_2 collimates light, and L_3 focuses the dispersed light. Note images of entrance slit I_1 and I_2 along the focal plane of L_3. The exit slit is not shown.

Table 12.1 Some Monochromator Specifications

Term	Definition	Symbol and dimensions
Resolution or resolving power	Ability to distinguish as separate nearly identical frequencies; measured in terms of closest frequencies Δv in a spectrum that are distinguishable	$R = v/\Delta v$ dimensionless
Dispersion	Spread of wavelengths in space	
Angular dispersion	Angular range $d\theta$ over which waveband $d\lambda$ is spread	$d\theta/d\lambda$ rad $(nm)^{-1}$
Linear dispersion	Distance dx over which a waveband $d\lambda$ is spread in the focal plane of a monochromator	$dx/d\lambda$ mm $(nm)^{-1}$
Linear reciprocal dispersion	Range of wavelengths spread over a unit distance in the focal plane of a monochromator	$d\lambda/dx$ nm $(mm)^{-1}$
Spectral slit width or bandwidth or band pass	Range of wavelengths included in a beam of radiation measured at half maximum intensity	

12.2 THE SLITS AND RESOLUTION

The entrance or aperture of a monochromator is a narrow slit whose width, at least, is generally adjustable. When illuminated by radiation, the slit is therefore a bright rectangle* that can easily be reproduced by appropriate optics. But what is the role of the slit? Before tackling the question, the manner of operation of a monochromator must be described.

Inside the monochromator rays spread from the entrance slit as illustrated in Fig. 12.1 and illuminate the collimator, which renders them parallel. In effect, the parallel set of rays is a broadened version of the slit. This rectangle of light must be large enough to illuminate the full width of the dispersing device, a grating or prism. In turn, this device separates the incident polychromatic pattern into an array of monochromatic blocks, each of which leaves the dispersing element at a slightly different angle. The blocks overlap badly. Focusing is used to reduce each block to an image of the entrance slit. These final images fall in a plane termed the *focal plane* in which a stationary exit slit is located.

Ordinarily the exit slit is adjusted to the dimensions of the entrance slit so that it is just illuminated by an image of that slit. Different wavelength images can be brought to the slit by pivoting the dispersing element. No image is a single wavelength to be sure, a matter that will be considered further below.

In order to separate wavelengths with any efficiency, the slits of a monochromator must be closed as much as is feasible. There will actually be an optimum "narrowness" for a slit; closing it further will not produce an additional increase in resolution but will reduce intensity. The limit on resolution arises because of diffraction of the

---

* Long slits may have curved sides. See p. 327.

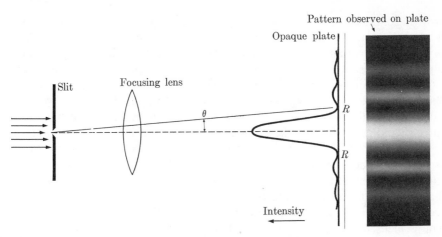

Fig. 12.2 Fraunhofer diffraction pattern of a single narrow slit. Illumination by monochromatic light.

Fraunhofer type illustrated in Fig. 12.2.* The drawing shows a horizontal cross-section through a long, narrow slit. As pictured, a narrow slit gives not a single sharp image but several closely spaced ones.

The origin of Fraunhofer diffraction by a very narrow slit can be explained classically by use of the Huygens principle. The various points across the slit become sources of secondary wavelets and rays can be drawn in all directions from them. Consider first the rays arising along the slit and travelling parallel to the entering rays. The central member of this set is shown in Fig. 12.2 as a dashed line. All rays in this set will travel an identical distance as they are brought to a focus and will arrive at line RR in phase. There is reinforcement as shown.

   Rays that leave the slit at angle θ, however, are shown to interfere destructively when focused. The one leaving the center of the slit is shown in oversimplified form as a solid line that terminates at R. Consider a ray parallel to it that originates from the "top" edge of the slit. For it to interfere destructively at R with the dashed ray, it must travel farther than the dashed ray by a distance equal to $\lambda/2$. The relation between slit width a and angle θ can now be deduced by constructing a right triangle whose apices lie at the top of the slit, the center of the slit, and the intersection of a perpendicular dropped from the top of the slit to the solid line. Applying trigonometry yields the equation $\sin \theta = \lambda/2 \div a/2$, that is, $\sin \theta = \lambda/a$. According to this relation, once diffraction becomes a factor, further narrowing of slit width a causes θ to increase and resolution cannot be improved further.

   For experimental work it is fortunate that most of the energy passing through a narrow slit is concentrated in the central band. Ideally, the ratio of the intensity of this band to the one just to the right or left proves to be about 22. The optimum

---

* In Fraunhofer diffraction an aperture is illuminated by essentially parallel rays and the aperture is observed on the far side from a relatively distant point. The second condition is secured within a short distance in Fig. 12.2 by inserting a converging lens that brings sets of parallel rays from the slit to a focus at points along line RR. When these conditions are not met, the diffraction is of the Fresnel type.

narrowing of the entrance slit (for maximum resolution) is attained in a monochromator when the central band fills the aperture of the collimating lens or mirror. Because
it is impossible to attain this condition for all wavelengths simultaneously, adjustments
should be made so that the condition will prevail in the center of the range of interest.

Energy throughput is an important consideration in photometric devices also.
While some aspects of throughput relating to the interior of the monochromator will
be discussed in the next section, it should be stressed here that as much light from a
source should enter through the slit as possible. Either mirrors or lenses are used to
"collect" light radiating from a source like an arc and direct it to monochromator
entrance slit. The intensity of such a condensed beam may approach that of the
source, but not exceed it. An especially effective collecting arrangement based on an
off-axis ellipsoidal mirror is illustrated in Fig. 12.3. When the source is placed at
focus B of the mirror, and the entrance slit at focus A, light gathered from a large solid
angle is focused on the slit. An example of a lens condensing system is shown in
Fig. 13.11.

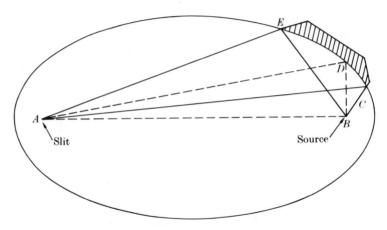

Fig. 12.3 Ellipsoidal mirror for gathering light from a source (not shown) at B, the near focus of
the ellipse. Light is collected over a large solid angle (represented by plane angle CBE) and focused
into a small solid angle (plane angle BAE) on a monochromator entrance slit (not shown) that is
located at the distant focus of the ellipse at A.

For quantitative work it is essential that the slit be uniformly illuminated also.
To achieve this end the slit may be narrowed or moved away from the focus of the
collecting lens, or an additional mirror or lens may be used (see Fig. 13.12). In addition,
the entrance slit and the (interior) collimating element that collects light from it should
be positioned so that the collimating element is illuminated over its entire useful
breadth. Otherwise, resolution will be poor.

Within a monochromator the necessary collimating and focusing is usually
performed by front-surface mirrors. By eliminating lenses, chromatic aberrations as
well as other errors are minimized. A more important reason for preferring mirrors
is that reflection is often more constant with wavelength than is transmission. Reflecting surfaces of mirrors and gratings are commonly of aluminum. It reflects well even
in the vacuum UV (down to 110 nm) if covered with a thin layer of a dielectric like

MgF_2 (see p. 335). Other metallic films, e.g., gold, are sometimes used in the IR to enhance reflectance.

Resolution.   The ability of a monochromator to separate nearly identical frequencies is described as its resolution or resolving power. In practice two operational definitions of resolution are used. One statement is that resolution is the narrowest line width (at half-height) actually achievable by a wavelength isolation device. By this criterion a monochromator is said to have a resolution of 0.05 nm (0.5 Å) if not only a 0.05 nm line but all narrower spectral lines emerge with a width of 0.05 nm. The more widely used definition and the one that will be employed in this text is based on finding the closest-lying frequency lines or bands that are separated by the device. This definition leads to a quantitative expression for resolution R:

$$R = \frac{v}{\Delta v} = \frac{\lambda}{\Delta \lambda} = \frac{\sigma}{\Delta \sigma}, \qquad (12.1)$$

where v and $v + \Delta v$ are the closest frequencies that can be regarded as having been separated. Note that R is also defined on a wavelength scale and in terms of wave numbers σ. Differences Δv, $\Delta \lambda$, $\Delta \sigma$ are measured between centers of lines or peaks.

How much drop in intensity must there be between adjacent spectral peaks for them to be considered resolved? In practice any of several answers may be given: The most liberal statement is that peaks are resolved when the intensity falls at least 10% between them. A much deeper valley is ordinarily insisted on, especially if intensities are to be read off.

Example   Estimate the resolution R of a device that can produce a spectral band at 300 nm that is no wider (at half height) than 0.05 nm. Two symmetrical or Gaussian profile peaks centered at 300.00 nm and 300.10 nm should emerge from the device with essentially a 100% intensity drop between them.

Then, from Fig. 12.1, $R = 300/0.10 = 3000$. This value suggests that the device is of low resolution.

The width of entrance slit plays a crucial role in determining resolution. How it does so may best be seen by first discussing the behavior of a monochromator on illumination with monochromatic light.

Consider a representative monochromator whose entrance and exit slits are 1 mm wide and whose optics permit the exit slit to be "filled" by the image of the entrance slit. Assume that monochromatic radiation of wavelength λ_0 is incident and the linear reciprocal dispersion D^{-1} (Table 12.1) of the instrument is 20 nm mm^{-1}. If the dispersing element is pivoted as in wavelength scanning, the image of the entrance slit will move along the focal plane and cross the exit slit opening at some time.

The dependence of intensity at the exit slit on wavelength setting may be seen from the successive images shown in Fig. 12.4a. The "front" of the image will appear at the edge of the exit slit when the dispersing element setting is $\lambda_0 - 20$ nm. In view of the dispersion given, this position should seem reasonable. At this setting the intensity of light emerging must be essentially zero. If the setting is advanced to $\lambda_0 - 10$ nm, half the 1 mm broad image should overlap the exit slit and 50% of its intensity be

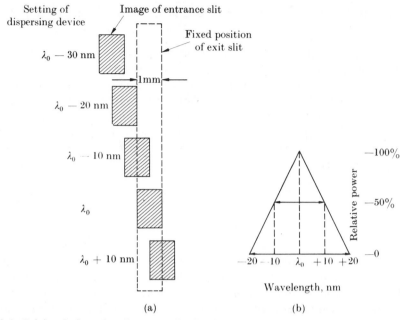

Fig. 12.4 Origin of triangular slit energy distribution. (a) Position of entrance slit image relative to exit slit during a wavelength scan. Monochromatic light of wavelength λ_0 is assumed incident. When the wavelength setting is λ_0, the exit slit is filled with light. (b) Intensity pattern at exit slit versus monochromator setting when monochromatic light is incident. This triangular pattern is also the intensity distribution at the exit slit as a function of wavelength when polychromatic light is present and the wavelength setting is λ_0.

transmitted. At the setting λ_0, the exit slit aperture should be filled. The transmitted intensity is 100% of that available.

When the dispersing element setting is increased to $\lambda_0 + 10$ nm, the image will have half departed and should again half fill the aperture, giving a relative intensity of 50%. The trailing edge will just disappear when the setting is changed to $\lambda_0 + 20$ nm. As graphed in Fig. 12.4b, a triangular plot of intensity versus wavelength setting is observed for monochromatic light on scanning.

Consider that the monochromator is next illuminated by a continuous source and that slits are still 1 mm wide. Now for *each frequency present* there should be a triangular distribution pattern like that of Fig. 12.4b. How wide a wavelength is passed at a given wavelength setting, for example λ_0? In accord with the earlier analysis, the exit slit should be fully illuminated only by the λ_0 wavelength image of the entrance slit. The images of wavelengths $\lambda_0 - 10$ nm and $\lambda_0 + 10$ nm should half illuminate it, and light from the $\lambda_0 - 20$ nm and $\lambda_0 + 20$ nm images should fall just short of emerging through the exit aperture. For continuous radiation a monochromator also gives a triangular intensity pattern like that in Fig. 12.4b but the abscissa now represents the range of wavelengths passed at the setting λ_0.

To define the width of wavelength band produced will require agreement on measurement at a particular intensity level. It is conventional to do so at half maximum intensity or half-height. This bandwidth is termed the *spectral slit width* or *band pass*.

For example, a spectral slit width of 20 nm is found from the pattern of Fig. 12.4b. Spectral slit width S can be defined formally in terms of the physical width of the slits W and reciprocal linear dispersion D^{-1} of the device:

$$S = W \times D^{-1}. \tag{12.2}$$

The application of Eq. (12.2) to the monochromator just discussed gives a spectral slit width of 1 mm $\times$ 20 nm mm^{-1} = 20 nm, in agreement with the number read from Fig. 12.4. If only the angular dispersion $d\theta/d\lambda$ (rad nm^{-1}) is known, Eq. (12.2) can be rewritten as $S = W[f\,d\theta/(d\lambda)]^{-1}$, where f is the focal length of the collimator.

Equation (12.2) has two limitations worth noting. First, it is valid only under conditions such that slit width alone limits resolution. For example, diffraction effects, mismatch of slit curvature (see next section), and optical aberrations may also lead to widening of the spectral slit width S. For narrow slits, poor optics, or a monochromator of inherently low resolution, all effects may be the same order of magnitude, i.e., no one will be limiting. Then the spectral slit width can be estimated by appropriate summing of the contributions or may be determined empirically. It is helpful to know that, for a grating monochromator, slit width is limiting if the instrument has a focal length of 0.5 m or greater.

Second, for narrow slits, the energy emerging from the slit of a monochromator is often best represented as a Gaussian curve.* The triangular pattern of Fig. 12.4b is a good approximation but it truncates the tails of the distribution. Only occasionally does the triangular approximation lead to serious error, as, for example, in measurement of an absorption that has a sharp edge, e.g., one in a semiconductor.

12.3 THE SLIT AND ENERGY THROUGHPUT

In discussing the intimate connection of slits and resolution in the last section, the effect of slit width on beam energy was largely neglected. What account should be taken of this aspect in treating monochromators? As a general rule, energy considerations become of interest when a source of limited energy, e.g., a weak spectral line, is involved, or when energy is unavoidably reduced in the process of securing high resolution. The reason is that the beam energy available at the detector will establish the signal-to-noise ratio in an instrument and thus determine precision achievable in measurement. Thus, in any instance where the signal-to-noise ratio is marginal (Chapter 8) the role of the slit in controlling the amount of energy that enters and leaves a monochromator must be considered.

This energy is described as the *energy throughput*† of the device. Nearly always the energy throughput of a monochromator is determined by a particular stop or slit and not by other optical elements. In the present case the exit slit will be assumed the limiting element. Two different definitions of throughput are necessary, one for a monochromatic source, the other for a continuous source.

---

* A. Lempicki, H. Samuelson, and A. Brown, "Slit-width Error in the Measurement of Absorption Constants," *J. Opt. Soc. Am.* **51**, 35 (1961).

† Collecting power, *entendue*, and luminosity are synonyms. The "speed" of a monochromator is proportional to this quantity.

When a monochromator is passing light from a monochromatic source, its energy throughput is measured by the product $Wl\rho$, where W and l are the width and height of the slit and ρ is the solid angle subtended at the slit by a preceding focusing element.*

When a continuous source is used, throughput still varies linearly with slit height and solid angle subtended, but now depends on the square of slit width. The reason is that both the energy flux and the spectral band passed by a monochromator increase as a slit is widened. As a result, the appropriate equation is now

$$\text{throughput} = W^2l\rho.$$

It is worth noting that the solid angle subtended will vary inversely with focal length. A short focal length will increase energy throughput. As will be noted, it will also diminish resolution and both cannot be maximized simultaneously.

Efficiency. The product *throughput* $\times$ *resolution* is termed the efficiency of an optical system. In many ways the efficiency is a useful criterion for comparison of different systems. The larger the product, the greater the power of the instrument in limiting cases when either resolution or energy throughput must be traded off to secure a desired level of the other. For the main types of sophisticated wavelength sorting devices, efficiency increases in the following order:

prism monochromator $<$ grating monochromator $<$ interferometric sorter.

It may be noted that cost also increases in this order while simplicity and reliability fall. The first two types of wavelength sorter are discussed in successive sections of this chapter; the last type is taken up in Section 17.12.

Slit adjustments. To achieve fine performance by a monochromator, slits must be constructed with knife-edge jaws so that the aperture has smooth edges, can be closed to very narrow widths, and eliminates reflection from its edges. Variable slits (width and height) are provided in a versatile monochromator. For example, heights may range continuously (or be adjustable in steps) from 2 to 25 mm and widths be continuously adjustable from 5 to 2000 μm. As noted earlier, a narrow slit will optimize resolution, while a wide one will optimize energy. In practice one must be "traded off" for the other.

For constant resolution, a spectrum should be scanned at constant spectral slit width regardless of the energy throughput. For example, such a constant-resolution scan with a prism monochromator would call for slit widths to be much narrower in the visible range than in the UV region to compensate for the variable dispersion of the prism (Section 12.4).

On the other hand, when the available energy is limited, as in the IR region, securing an adequate signal-to-noise ratio at the detector calls for monochromator slits to be progressively opened in scanning toward longer wavelengths. The sources

---

*A more general definition applicable to any optical system is that energy throughput is the smallest product of the following type encountered in the system: (area of a field stop or opening) $\times$ (solid angle subtended by the system at the field stop). Lenses, mirrors, prisms, or gratings used will, of course, affect throughput by their degree of transmission and reflection, but they are not ordinarily limiting.

available simply do not yield enough intensity at long wavelengths. Some resolution is, of course, sacrificed in the process.

An alternative way to increase energy throughput is to increase the height of the slits. On first examination this choice seems preferable because it appears that resolution would not decrease; however, an unfortunate complication frustrates the possibility. The optical system of a monochromator produces an inherent curvature in slit image that becomes evident when slit heights exceed about 3 mm. In the Czerny–Turner or Ebert mounting (see Figs. 12.17 and 12.18), for example, the radius of curvature of the entrance slit image formed at the exit slit is half the straight line distance between entrance and exit slits (usually no more than 10–15 cm). As a result of curvature of images at a given monochromator setting, one wavelength image passes through the middle of the exit slit and a different wavelength image passes through its lower and upper extremities. In precision instruments the loss of resolution on lengthening slits is sometimes diminished by giving the entrance slit a curvature that will oppose *the one produced* optically and thus lead to formation of a rectangular image at the exit slit.* In any case, a short slit height (3 mm or less) is preferred except at very low energy. Where slit curvature must be allowed for, an additive correction to the spectral slit width can be estimated by running a calibration.

Adjustments in slit height are essential to accommodate weak sources. For example, full height, if not full width, might be indicated, if spectra of a faint source such as the aurora borealis were being determined.

12.4 DISPERSION BY A PRISM

Dispersion of radiation in space involves angularly separating the different frequencies present in a wavefront. Either refraction by a prism or diffraction by a grating is the process ordinarily used.

A representative prism arrangement is depicted in Fig. 12.5. The two wavelengths present in the incident beam are refracted through different angles and are separated by $\theta_2 - \theta_1$, on leaving the prism. As we would expect, the normal increase in refractive index n as frequency or wavenumber increases causes wavelengths in the blue range to be refracted most. The angular dispersion of the prism is defined as $d\theta/d\lambda$ where

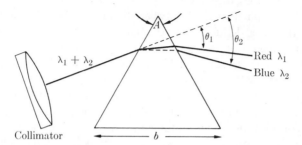

Fig. 12.5 Dispersion of light by a prism of apical angle A and base of length b. Blue wavelengths undergo a greater angular dispersion.

---

* Curvature is also somewhat dependent on wavelength and, even with compensating curvature, image superposition is completely possible at only one wavelength.

$d\theta$ is the angular separation of wavelengths differing by $d\lambda$ in magnitude. Actually, it is useful to resolve $d\theta/d\lambda$ into two factors as follows:

$$\frac{d\theta}{d\lambda} = \frac{d\theta}{dn} \cdot \frac{dn}{d\lambda},\tag{12.3}$$

where $d\theta/dn$ is a geometric factor that includes the influence of prism shape and the angle of incidence and $dn/d\lambda$ is a specific factor characteristic of the prism material.

Geometric factor. While dispersion will vary greatly with the angle of incidence, most symmetrical prisms are used at the *angle of minimum deviation D*. Under these conditions a ray passing through the prism traverses it parallel to its base and the angular deviation of the emerging ray is a minimum. For example, this condition holds for the blue ray in Fig. 12.5. For a symmetrical prism, the angle D is defined by the expression (obtainable by use of Snell's law)

$$n = \frac{\sin (D + A)/2}{\sin A/2},\tag{12.4}$$

where A is the apical prism angle and n is the refractive index of the prism material.*

Using a prism at minimum deviation secures two important advantages. Optimum resolution is obtained because astigmatism is eliminated. In addition, internal reflection (at the far prism face) is minimized, leading to good transmitted intensity and minimum stray light generation by internal reflection.

What apical angle should be selected for a symmetrical prism? This angle influences dispersion and resolution. For minimum deviation it can be shown that the geometrical factor in dispersion is given by

$$\frac{d\theta}{dn} = \frac{2 \sin (A/2)}{[1 - n^2 \sin^2 (A/2)]^{1/2}}.$$

Substitution of this expression in Eq. (12.3) indicates that resolution increases as angle A increases. It may be appreciated intuitively that resolution will also improve linearly with the length of prism base b.

Specific factor. How does dispersion depend on $dn/d\lambda$ for a prism? In Fig. 12.6 refractive index is graphed against wavelength in the VIS-UV range for several prism materials. It may be deduced from the shape of the curves (see Section 10.7) that they extend from a region of absorption in the IR to another one in the visible or UV. On inspection of these curves it is apparent that the dispersion of any prism must vary dramatically with frequency since it depends on the slope $dn/d\lambda$. Near the center of a range of transparency $dn/d\lambda \simeq 0$, but at either end of a range the slope has a large value. This type of variation in dispersion with wavelength is contrasted with the nearly constant dispersion obtained from a diffraction grating in Fig. 12.7.

In specifying dispersion, linear measures are also used as indicated in Table 12.1.

---

* The angle of minimum deviation at a given wavelength can easily be found. Observe the emergence of the beam from a prism when a collimated monochromatic beam of light is incident. Rotate the prism slowly until a slight further rotation no longer produces a change in the angle of emergence. The beam now traverses the prism with minimum deviation.

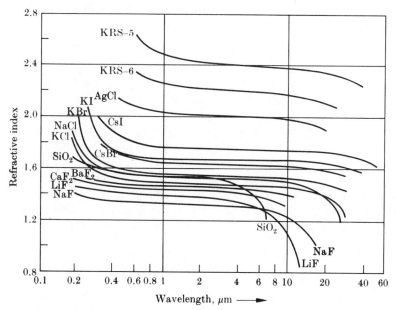

Fig. 12.6 Refractive index as a function of wavelength for many common optical substances. (Courtesy of Harshaw Chemical Company.)

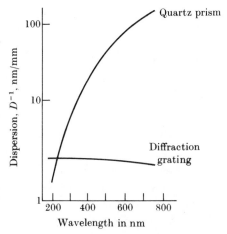

Fig. 12.7 A comparison of (linear reciprocal) dispersion provided by a quartz prism and a representative grating over the visible and UV range.

To relate linear dispersion D to the angular quantity $d\theta/d\lambda$, the following expression may generally be used:

$$D = f d\theta/d\lambda, \tag{12.5}$$

where f is the focal length of the optical system. The inverse of Eq. (12.5), the reciprocal linear dispersion D^{-1}, was introduced in the last section and is also in common use.

For example, a spectrograph with a linear dispersion of 0.0075 mm nm^{-1} at 4000 Å has a linear reciprocal dispersion of 133 nm mm^{-1}.

12.5 SOME PRISM DESIGNS

One of the most widely used prism monochromator designs is the *Littrow mounting* shown in Fig. 12.8. The characteristic feature is that the angles of incidence and emergence from the prism are nearly equal. It should be noted that mirror *M* need not be integral to the prism as shown but may be separate. The particular advantages of the Littrow mount are: (a) a high degree of dispersion in a compact arrangement (each ray traverses the prism twice), (b) a single lens or mirror serves as both collimator and focusing device, (c) avoidance of double refraction if an anisotropic material like quartz is used (light rays traverse nearly the same path in both directions). With this monochromator, selection of wavelength is accomplished by turning the prism (or mirror *M* alone, if separate) through an appropriate angle.

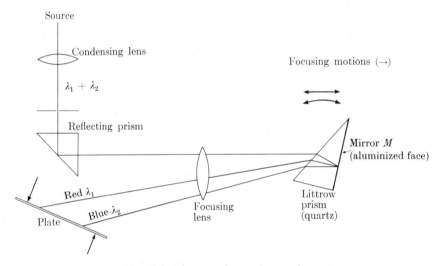

Fig. 12.8 Littrow prism and mounting.

In most other mounts there is only a single pass through the prism. As a result, to avoid birefringence either prisms must be made from an optically isotropic medium like fused silica or special pains must be taken in design.

A *constant-deviation* prism makes possible a monochromator with the advantage that the wavelength isolated by the exit slit can be easily identified from the setting of the prism table. For example, for the Pellin–Broca prism, shown in Fig. 12.9, a 90° deviation occurs between entrance and exit beams. When it is used in a monochromator, the wavelength centered at the exit slit is the one that has been deviated exactly through 90°.

A *Cornu* prism is a symmetrical prism whose apical angle is 60°. It might be used in either a Littrow mounting with separate mirror or in the Wadsworth mounting to be considered below. If crystalline quartz is used, two 30° prisms, one of right-

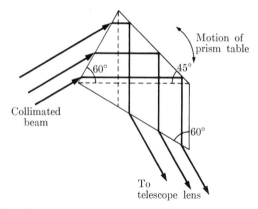

Fig. 12.9 Constant-deviation glass prism and mounting. This one-piece Pellin–Broca prism is equivalent to two 30° prisms cemented to a 45° totally reflecting prism. When a polychromatic beam enters at the angle of minimum deviation, only one of its wavelengths is incident on the back face at 45°. That wavelength emerges deflected through just 90°. By turning the prism table, successive wavelengths are brought into 90° deviation.

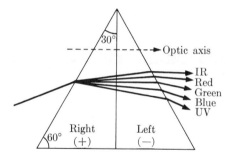

Fig. 12.10 Cornu prism of quartz. The circular double refraction (not shown) produced by the first half is just offset by the equal and opposite effect in the second half. Two overlapping spectra would result if the prism were all of one kind of crystalline quartz.

handed and the other of left-handed quartz, are cemented as shown in Fig. 12.10. The two pieces compensate each other and avoid the birefringence that would otherwise cause two images of the slit to appear for each frequency.*

Wadsworth mounting. This mounting, illustrated in Fig. 12.11, operates at the angle of minimum deviation regardless of wavelength. A further advantage is that the ray leaves mirror LB (as ray HI) parallel to the entering ray EF. The deviation D is canceled by a reflection from the plane mirror at angle α, where $D = 2\alpha$. Further, by use of Eq. (12.5), the angle of reflection α for wavelength λ can be shown to be $\sin^{-1}$ $[(n_\lambda/2) - 30]$ where a cornu prism is used. Wavelengths are scanned by pivoting the entire mounting rigidly about H.

---

* Since rays traversing the prism at or near minimum deviation make at most small angles to the optic axis, there is no appreciable birefringence as a result of the anisotropy (Section 10.13) of quartz. It is the optical rotatory power (Section 10.16) that would lead to birefringence in this case if there were no compensation.

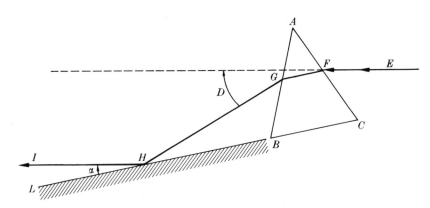

Fig. 12.11 Wadsworth prism mount. Entrance ray *EF* and exit ray *HI* are parallel for the wavelength that traverses the prism at minimum deviation. *ABC* is a symmetrical prism. Front-surface mirror *LB* is aligned with the prism so that *LBC* is a straight line.

12.6 DISPERSION BY A DIFFRACTION GRATING

Where the ultimate in a dispersing device is needed, a diffraction grating is employed. Two outstanding advantages may be cited:

1. Resolution and dispersion are very high for a long, fine grating, and

2. With proper arrangement of optics, a dispersion is obtained that is almost constant with wavelength.

The latter is, of course, very desirable for ease of establishing the wavelength of radiation appearing at the exit slit of a monochromator. In addition, it makes possible a simpler method of wavelength adjustment.

Since it is now possible to obtain fine replica gratings at a cost comparable to that of prisms, gratings are usually preferred as dispersing devices in monochromators. Actually, their principal disadvantages relative to prisms are that they are less rugged and generate slightly more scattered light, particularly at shorter wavelengths.

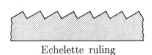

Echelette ruling

Fig. 12.12 Enlarged cross section of typical reflection grating surface.

Gratings. A grating like that sketched in Fig. 12.12 may be designed either to reflect or to transmit light. Dispersion results from a complex process of diffraction and subsequent interference. So far as radiation is concerned, the rulings provide a series of slits (for transmission) or narrow mirrors (for reflection) uniformly placed along a smooth surface.

The grating equation. For an understanding of the fundamentals of grating behavior, consider first the simplest case, that of illumination of a *transmission grating* by parallel monochromatic radiation perpendicularly incident on the grating. This

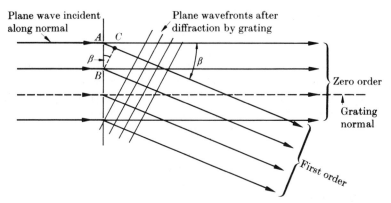

Fig. 12.13 Diffraction of monochromatic radiation by a transmission grating. A plane wavefront is incident from the left along the grating normal. Zero-order transmission results when transmitted light forms a new wavefront along the grating normal. A first-order plane wave appears at angle β to the normal. At this angle light from "slit" A has traveled one wavelength farther than that from "slit" B. A second-order plane wave appears (not shown) at a larger angle and still higher orders at still greater angles. Negative orders also exist on the opposite side of the normal.

situation is shown in Fig. 12.13. After transmission, interference among the wavelets from the slits gives rise to a series of very sharp wavefronts, each at a different angle relative to the grating.* Some radiation passes straight through to give a parallel beam along the grating normal. If several wavelengths had been incident, this *zero-order* beam would still contain all of them; there has been no dispersion. A second parallel beam (plane wavefront) appears at angle of diffraction β. It is formed as a result of constructive interference between wavelets originating at adjacent "slits." For example, those from slit A travel just one wavelength further than those from slit B. This wavefront is the result of *first-order* diffraction. Similarly, a third wavefront will exist (at an angle to the normal larger than β) in which light from slit A has traveled precisely two wavelengths farther than that from slit B. The process of finding other wavefronts can be continued though intensities usually fall rapidly with increasing order.

According to the geometrical representation of Fig. 12.13, the extra distance light from slit A travels for first-order diffraction is just AC. Since angle ABC is also β, $AC/AB = \sin \beta$. But AB is the grating constant d so that $AC = \lambda = d \sin \beta$. This expression can be generalized. First, since the extra distance from slit A to any of the successive wavefronts that appear at even larger angles is just $m\lambda$ where $m = 1, 2, 3, \ldots$, a more general expression is

$$m\lambda = d \sin \beta. \tag{12.6}$$

The integer m may be positive or negative and is designated the *order*. Second, allowance must also be made for instances of oblique illumination of a grating. If

---

* This pattern contrasts with the pattern from a single slit illustrated in Fig. 12.2. In that case, some transmitted radiation appeared in secondary or side images of the slit. With the many slits of a diffraction grating, the secondary maxima are weakened so greatly by multiple interference that they are seldom detected.

light is incident at angle α, Eq. (12.6) becomes

$$m\lambda = d\,(\sin\alpha \pm \sin\beta). \tag{12.7}$$

This expression is termed the *grating law* and holds for both a transmission grating and a reflection grating. Note the possibility of a negative sign. It arises since light that is incident may be diffracted on either side of the normal. By convention, if angles α and β are on opposite sides of the normal, the negative sign applies in the equation; if both are on the same side, the positive sign is used.

Example 1   To illustrate the use of Eq. (12.7), the wavelength of radiation diffracted in the first order ($m = 1$) may be calculated for a grating with 1000 lines or grooves per mm. Consider that $\alpha = 30°$ (on one side of the grating normal) and $\beta = 5°$ (on the other side of the normal). The grating constant is $d = 1\ \text{mm}/1000 = 10^{-3}$ mm. Substituting in Eq. (12.8) one has

$$\begin{aligned}
\lambda &= 10^{-3}\ \text{mm} \cdot (\sin 30° - \sin 5°) \\
&= 10^{-3}(0.500 - 0.087) = 4130 \times 10^{-8}\ \text{cm} \\
&= 4130\ \text{Å} \qquad \text{or} \qquad 413\ \text{nm}.
\end{aligned}$$

Example 2   If the sum $\alpha + \beta$ is fixed and both angles are on the same side of the normal, as in many plane grating mountings, what first-order wavelength will appear for $\alpha = 40°$, $\beta = 5°$? Assume $d = 10^{-3}$ mm as before. Equation (12.7) gives $\lambda = 10^{-3}(0.643 + 0.087) = 7300\ \text{Å}$ or 730 nm.

If parallel rays of polychromatic light are incident on a grating, there will, of course, be a different value of β for each wavelength. Actually, there will also be submultiples of this wavelength, each corresponding to an order higher than the first.

For example, at a given β there will be superposed a first-order 800 nm ray, a third-order 267 nm ray, etc. The overlapping orders are illustrated in Fig. 12.14.

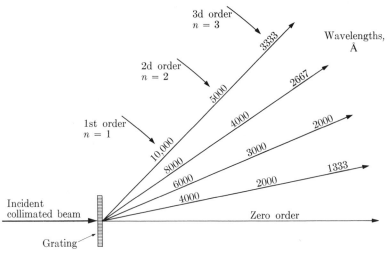

Fig. 12.14 Overlapping orders of spectra from transmission grating. A similar set of orders is formed at equal angles below the normal.

Although the overlap of orders is potentially troublesome, it can be avoided in straightforward fashion. Commonly, cutoff filters are used to exclude unwanted spectral ranges. Sometimes light is first dispersed by a fore-prism so that no more than a narrow spectral region falls on a grating. The movement of the prism is synchronized with the rotation of the grating so that both are responding in the same range. Natural factors operate to eliminate spectral regions or to "sort orders" as well. For example, a detector insensitive to UV and still shorter wavelengths may be used if only the first-order visible region is of interest (see Fig. 12.14). In all cases, the energy distributed into higher orders is smaller than that going into the first.

Example A grating monochromator is to be used in the first-order for examination in spectra in the range 400 to 800 nm (4000 to 8000 Å). It can be preceded by a cutoff filter to block the second-order, 2000 to 4000 Å, wavelengths that would otherwise be superposed. Third and higher orders, if present with any intensity, would also be eliminated.

If it is later desired to scan the second-order UV spectrum, the first-order spectrum can be blocked by interposing a sharp cutoff filter that transmits only UV. How serious a problem will the accompanying third-order 133.3 to 266.6 nm spectrum be? It can be mostly neglected since the shorter wavelengths will be blocked by air and all third-order lines will be comparatively low in intensity.

Reflection gratings. Today virtually all gratings are of the reflection type. Rulings number from 20 grooves mm^{-1} for the far IR to as many as 3600 or more grooves mm^{-1} for the VIS and UV ranges. Master gratings are cut by a properly shaped diamond tool directly into an aluminum film that has been deposited on glass or another polished surface. Interferometric controls and elaborate apparatus have been devised to ensure the necessary evenness of spacing of grooves over the required ruling distances of from 10 to 25 cm.

Replica gratings are commonly used in monochromators. The process of replicating a master grating involves (a) applying a film of "parting agent" to the master, (b) vacuum depositing a layer of aluminum, and (c) attaching a glass or quartz base to the aluminum layer with epoxy cement. After an appropriate time interval the replica is separated.

If a grating is to be used in the vacuum or far UV it is customary to add a layer of MgF_2 of appropriate thickness (about $\lambda/4$ where $\lambda = 1200$ Å) to boost the reflectance in this region to around 70%.*

Figure 12.15 shows the geometry of a reflection grating of the *echellette* type. This kind of grating has a blaze, i.e. each groove has a broad face at angle θ_0 relative to the grating normal (and a narrow face that is seldom used). The grating is highly efficient in diffraction of wavelengths close to those for which specular reflection occurs. In Fig. 12.15 this case is illustrated for the incident and diffracted rays. If ϕ is the angle of incidence and reflection, $\phi = \alpha - \theta_0 = \beta + \theta_0$. Rearranging gives $2\theta = \alpha - \beta$, or since β may be on either side of the normal,

$$\theta = (\alpha \pm \beta)/2.$$

---

* The refractive index of aluminum falls to unity and below in this region, giving rise to low reflectance. Magnesium fluoride has a higher index.

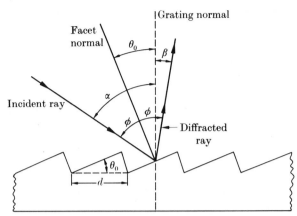

Fig. 12.15 Cross section of a blazed reflection grating. Here α is the angle of incidence, β that of diffraction, and ϕ that of reflection. The blaze angle is θ_0, and the grating constant d.

Again the plus sign applies only when β is on the same side of the grating normal as α. The wavelength for which specular reflection and first-order diffraction coincide is called the *blaze wavelength* λ_B. With an echellette grating nearly all the diffracted light appears on one side of the grating normal. A particular advantage is that most light is concentrated in the first few orders and centered about λ_B in the first order, $\lambda_B/2$ in the second, and λ_B/m in the mth order. Note that the wavelengths most favored in orders beyond the first follow from the grating law.

The *efficiency* of a reflection grating is one of its most important characteristics. It is defined as the percentage of monochromatic light diffracted in a given order relative to the percentage specularly reflected by a flat aluminized mirror. Clearly, a particular wavelength can be *efficiently* diffracted in only one order. For example, if 60% of the radiation of wavelength λ_B is diffracted in the first order, only 40% is left to be diffracted in other orders. The higher the efficiency, the more useful is the grating, since it can ensure a greater energy throughput and less scattered light in a monochromator. In the first order the efficiency of an echellette grating at the blaze wavelength may be 60 to 70% but in the second order it is seldom more than 55% (at $\lambda_B/2$). A rule-of-thumb guide is that efficiency in the first order falls to half the value at λ_B when the wavelength becomes as short as $\frac{2}{3}\lambda_B$ and as long as $2\lambda_B$. For example, a grating blazed at 300 nm operates at greater than 30% efficiency in the first order from 200 to perhaps 600 nm. A similar rule relates to the blaze wavelength in other orders.

Most gratings used in the infrared operate at somewhat smaller efficiency. Coarse rulings are used since wavelengths in the micron range can be obtained at reasonable angles of diffraction only with gratings that have relatively few grooves mm^{-1} (see Eq. 12.7). Thus, in the IR each ruling must have a much wider face. Efficiency falls both because it is difficult to rule large flat facets and to ensure there is no unruled surface between such wide grooves.

The stated or nominal blaze wavelength applies strictly to the Littrow configuration (Section 12.7) for which $\alpha = \beta$ and diffracted radiation returns along the path of incident radiation. The actual blaze wavelength is nearly the nominal value with most other mountings. The major exception arises when a grating is used at grazing incidence, as for spectral studies in the very far UV. In any case, the actual blaze value λ_A is related to the nominal value λ_B by the equation $\lambda_A = \lambda_B \cos \delta/2$, where δ is the difference between absolute values of angles α and β.

Gratings that offer good efficiency in high orders also became available in the 1960s as precision of grating fabrication improved. These are *echelle* gratings in which the "step" between groove faces is made much greater (10 to 200 wavelengths high). The location of a step is indicated in Fig. 12.16. By contrast, the step in echellette gratings averages only 0.5 to 5 wavelengths high. A coarse ruling is required to form such large steps (typically 8 to 200 grooves mm^{-1}). Echelles are blazed at about 63° and are always employed in the Littrow mode at an angle of incidence and diffraction of about 63°. As the schematic representation in Fig. 12.16 shows, the steep facets of the ruling are used and incident and diffracted radiation enters and leaves nearly parallel to the wider facets.

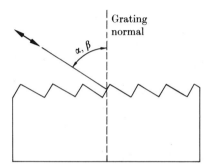

Fig. 12.16 An echelle, which is essentially a coarse grating ($d_{echellette} \ll d_{echelle}$). It is used in the Littrow mode as indicated. By offering good spectral efficiency in high orders, the echelle makes very high resolution possible.

It is characteristic of ruling of this type that it is effectively blazed for all wavelengths. The reason is that its spectral efficiency peaks in order at the center of its free spectral range. [8] Since these gratings provide the possibility of large dispersion in a small monochromator, they seem certain to be increasingly used. Orders are separated vertically by making use of a device such as a fore-prism as an *order-sorter* (Section 13.8).

Concave gratings. It is also possible to rule the surface of a concave mirror. Indeed, this type of grating was one of the earliest developed, and until the 1950s was in common use. By virtue of the curvature of a concave grating it can be used in a monochromator without auxiliary collimating and focusing elements. The grating law, Eq. (12.7), describes its diffraction behavior. A careful mathematical analysis is required, however, to determine optimum angles and distances at which to place slits in order to image the entrance slit at the exit slits with minimum aberration. [3] The chief advantage of a concave grating is the high energy throughput secured by eliminating two monochromator mirrors. It is this gain that has led to the wide use of concave grating instruments in the far UV region.

The general use of concave gratings in spectrometric work proves a mixed blessing, however. It introduces both *astigmatism* and *coma*, aberrations characteristic of spherical mirrors. Since the first produces images that are elongated and reduced in intensity, it is of greater concern. For example, in quantitative spectrographic studies this aberration distorts the relation between element concentration and line intensity. A further disadvantage of concave gratings is that no successful process of making replicas exists, and each concave grating must be a costly master.

Grating characteristics. The theoretical *resolution R* of a grating may be shown to be defined by the relation

$$R = mN, \tag{12.8}$$

where m is the order and N is the *total number* of rulings illuminated. If we substitute for m from Eq. (12.7) this expression becomes

$$R = W(\sin \alpha \pm \sin \beta)/\lambda, \tag{12.9}$$

where W is the length of ruled area $(W = Nd)$* and λ is the vacuum wavelength of incident light.

Equations (12.8) and (12.9) are based on the *Rayleigh criterion* for resolution by a multi-"slit" system like a diffraction grating. It defines resolution at the diffraction limit, which represents the ideal upper bound to resolution. By the Rayleigh criterion two spectral lines are said to be resolved when the maximum of the interference pattern of the first line is incident on the first minimum, e.g., R in Fig. 12.2, of the interference pattern of the other line. There is about a 20% valley between peaks of lines so resolved.

These equations present key ideas. Equation (12.9) reveals surprisingly that, given the angles of incidence and diffraction, the resolution at a particular wavelength depends ideally on only the total ruled length of a grating. The order of spectrum does not appear in the expressions. Clearly, long gratings are much to be desired in precision work. The other main idea is the statement of the dependence of R on the angular configuration in which a grating is used and wavelength. Large angles of α and β are advantageous if they can be accommodated in a monochromator. For example, the ability to use angles as great as 63° is one attraction of the echelle grating discussed earlier.

Example 1   What is the maximum resolution of a grating for a particular wavelength? From Eq. (12.9), R will be a maximum when $\sin \alpha + \sin \beta = 2$. Thus, the maximum resolution possible is $R_{max} = 2W/\lambda$.

Example 2   How should a grating be designed for work in the IR? Assume it is to be blazed at 2500 cm^{-1} (4 μm), have a first-order resolution of 20,000 and a ruled length of 10 cm.

The number of rulings N required can be obtained from Eq. (12.8), $R = mN$. Since $R = 20,000$, $N = 20,000/1 = 20,000$. To calculate the blaze angle θ_0 required, assume operation in the Littrow mode where $\alpha = \beta = \theta_0$. The grating constant $d = 10$ cm/20,000 rulings $= 5\ \mu$m. Substitution in the grating law gives $1 \times 4 = 2 \times 5 \sin \beta$ and $\sin \beta = 0.4$. Thus, $\beta = 23.5°$. This is the blaze angle.

---

* The width of a ruled area is equal to the length of a groove.

The *free spectral range F* of a grating describes the wavelength band in a given order that is present only in that order. In this range there is no overlap of wavelength from adjacent orders. Its breadth can easily be established mathematically. Let the free spectral range in the mth order be from λ_1 to λ_2, where $\lambda_2 > \lambda_1$. The shorter wavelength λ_1 must be just the wavelength that appears in the $(m + 1)$th order at the same angle as λ_2 in the mth order. From Eq. (12.7), $(m + 1)\lambda_1 = m(\lambda_1 + \Delta\lambda)$, where $\lambda_2 - \lambda_1 = \Delta\lambda$. Thus $F = \Delta\lambda = \lambda_1/m$.

Example   Light of wavelengths 800 to 200 nm is incident on a diffraction grating. What is its free spectral range in the first and second orders?

In a given order it is the shorter wavelengths that will also occur in the next higher orders. When the grating is set at an angle at which 800 nm light is diffracted in order 1, it will also diffract 400 nm light in order 2, 267 nm light in order 3, etc. The free spectral range must be 800 to 400 nm in order 1, 400 to 267 nm in order 2, and 267 to 200 nm in order 3. The equation given above confirms the length of the range as $400/1 = 400$ nm in order 1, $267/2 = 133$ nm in order 2, and $200/3 = 67$ nm in order 3. Such a range will exist in each order.

The *dispersion* of a grating may be found by differentiating the grating law. Consider the Czerny–Turner mounting shown in Fig. 12.17. Let the sum $\alpha + \beta$, which is fixed, equal 2ϕ. Grating angle θ is variable. In terms of angles θ and ϕ, the grating law, Eq. (12.7) becomes

$$m\lambda = 2d \sin \theta \cos \phi. \tag{12.10}$$

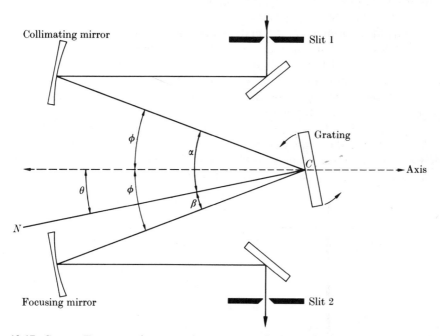

Fig. 12.17   Czerny–Turner grating monochromator. CN is the grating normal. Angle ϕ is fixed. To scan, the grating is pivoted about point C, increasing angle α from $\alpha = \phi$ to $\alpha = 2\phi$.

The angular dispersion can be found by differentiating both sides and rearranging to give

$$\frac{d\theta}{d\lambda} = \frac{m}{2d \cos \theta \cos \phi}. \tag{12.11}$$

Since the cosine function is nearly constant at low angles, $\cos \theta$ will change little during a wavelength scan. For example, an increase in θ from 15° to 30° causes $\cos \theta$ to decrease from 0.95 to 0.85, about a 10% change. According to Eq. (12.11), grating dispersion is nearly constant with wavelength. Grating and prismatic dispersion were contrasted in Fig. 12.7. The equation also indicates that grating dispersion increases linearly with order and with the number of rulings per millimeter.

Polarization. In general, it is only near the wavelength for which a grating is blazed that it diffracts radiation without changing its polarization. At low grating angles parallel light is most efficiently diffracted, at high angles, perpendicularly vibrating light (Section 10.12). Polarization appears to be independent of groove spacing. At wavelengths greater than λ_B, the ratio of intensities of the two vibrational components, $I_\perp/I_{||}$, is relatively flat. Corrections can be applied in this range with ease. [p. 604 of 7, Chap. 10] If polarized or partially polarized radiation is to be sent through a mono-chromator, it is often useful to pass it through a polarization scrambler to depolarize it prior to its entrance. Intensity effects are minimal for unpolarized light.

12.7 SOME GRATING SYSTEMS

Most early gratings were used in spectrographs and, as noted above, were of the concave variety. Unfortunately, appropriate mountings for concave gratings are bulky and require intricate movements of slits and grating to maintain imaging as the wavelength is changed (Section 13.8). For that reason they are presently used mainly in the far UV region (see below). In their place plane gratings are now employed. Several types of grating monochromators will be described briefly in this section.

The *Littrow plane-grating mount*, like its prism counterpart, requires a single element for focusing and collimating. As a result, angles of incidence and diffraction are on the same side of the grating normal and are nearly equal. In terms of Fig. 12.15, $\alpha = \beta = \theta_0$. The grating equation becomes $m\lambda = 2d \sin \beta$. This mounting has been widely used in IR monochromators. It ensures high grating efficiency, good spectral purity, small aberrations, compactness, and economy.

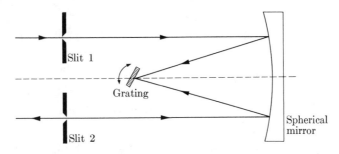

Fig. 12.18 The Ebert mounting.

Ebert mounting. This mounting was historically the first compact, simple arrangement for a plane grating system substantially free of aberrations. The optical features of the design are shown schematically in Fig. 12.18. Entrance and exit slits are on either side of the grating and a single concave spherical mirror is used as a collimating and focusing element. Rays entering from slit 1, which is in the focal plane of the mirror, strike the upper half of the mirror, and are collimated as they are reflected to the grating. The diffracted radiation goes to the bottom half of the mirror and is focused on slit 2. The slit image suffers no aberrations since two reflections occur off-axis. Since the entering and diffracted beams use different portions of the mirror, no scattering into the optical path results from the mirror. A further advantage is that a wavelength is selected by simple pivoting of the grating about the monochromator axis (shown as a dashed line).

Czerny–Turner mounting. This similar arrangement, whose design was discussed implicitly in the last section (see Fig. 12.17), is still more frequently used. It differs from the Ebert mounting in that two smaller concave mirrors are used in place of a single large one. Parabolic mirrors may be used as well, though they introduce some astigmatism. All advantages of the Ebert mounting hold for this one also.

Mountings for the far UV. Monochromators for the vacuum and far UV, 180 to 50 nm (1800 to 500 Å) are nearly always based on diffraction gratings though prisms of lithium fluoride can be used down to about 120 nm. In this spectral region the chief design problems are adequate reflectance and compactness. Even with a MgF_2 over-coat, aluminum mirrors have only 70% reflectance at 120 nm and no more than about 15% reflectance at 50 nm. Thus, if three reflections are required (from two mirrors and a grating) the beam intensity level falls to about 1 to 30% of the original figure. Compactness is important because of the need for evacuation of a monochromator to avoid absorption of radiation by air. While the Czerny–Turner mounting is often employed in the UV, its useful short wavelength limit is about 105 nm.

Both the above problems are surmounted by use of concave gratings. The *Seya–Namioka* and *Robin* mounts, usable to about 50 nm, and a *grazing incidence* mount,* for still shorter wavelengths, are available. Only the last is based on the Rowland circle (Section 13.8) and has a comparatively elaborate scanning-focusing mechanism. The other monochromators rely on particular angles and/or a special mechanism to maintain acceptable focusing. In the Seya–Namioka mounting [p. 460 of 3] a constant angle of about 70° is maintained between fixed entrance and exit slits and scanning is accomplished by rotating the grating about its vertical axis. This simple arrangement offers lower resolution than plane grating mounts but features mechanical and economical advantages. By contrast, in the Robin monochromator, [4] a constant, *small* angle (5 to 15°) is maintained between beams from the fixed entrance and exit slits. For scanning, an ingeniously simple assembly (Fig. 12.19) rotates the grating and simultaneously moves it toward the slits as longer wavelengths are approached to maintain nearly a perfect focus. Each of these monochromators

---

* For work below 50 nm (500 Å) only grazing incidence at present offers the possibility of sufficient reflectance, there being no suitable optical materials that do so. As will be recalled, nearly all materials show substantial reflectance at large angles of incidence (80 to 85°).

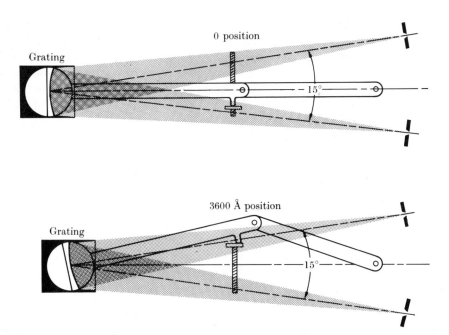

Fig. 12.19 Functional drawing of the Robin concave grating mounting. The constant angle between entrance and exit beams from the fixed slits may also be as small as 5°. Note the simple mechanical device that alters the grating-distance as a scan is made. (Courtesy of Jarrell-Ash.)

operates in the first order with a useful range of from about 50 to 300 nm at optimum resolution.

With fixed slits, the volume to be evacuated can be kept small and source and detector can also be located in fixed positions. A further advantage is that monochromatic radiation always emerges from the monochromator at the same angle.

A Rowland circle arrangement can be employed for low-angle or grazing-incidence diffraction with both grating and exit slit being moved along the circle mechanically.

12.8 STRAY RADIATION

Radiation of frequencies entirely different from that for which a monochromator is set will also be present in its output, though at low intensity. Assuming the monochromator compartment is lighttight, this unwanted or stray radiation will be light that originates from the source but that has been lost from the beam directed through the device by being:

1. Diffracted from a grating at unwanted angles;
2. Diffracted from edges of slits;
3. Reflected from interior surfaces of any filters, lenses, or prisms present;
4. Scattered by imperfections, dirt, or scratches in optical components.

If such radiation eventually reaches the exit slit, it contains unwanted wavelengths since the proper operations have not been performed on it.

Let it suffice here to list several ways to reduce stray light: (a) paint the interior of the monochromator a flat black; (b) insert baffles to obstruct radiation from all except a key direction; (c) use high-quality optical elements and slits that have knife-sharp edges; and (d) use windows in front of the slits to exclude dust and fumes.

In spite of these measures, the intensity of stray radiation may reach several percent of that of the optical beam. The problem is especially severe at monochromator settings far from those of maximum emission of a source. Unfortunately, wide slit settings are required at such wavelengths to compensate for inherently low intensities, and more total radiation is admitted.

Under these conditions a filter is often effective. For example, a Beckman DU monochromator employs a blue filter through the range 400 to 350 nm. It effectively excludes all the frequencies (green, yellow, red, and near IR) at which the tungsten lamp source emits intensely and to which the detector is sensitive.

A second example relates to monochromators used in the middle and far IR. They are plagued by stray light of 1–5 μm. Usually two or three of the following types of filter are used:

1. A *transmission* filter, e.g., polyethylene (with graphite dispersed in it) or crystalline quartz. Both transmit only in the far IR.

2. A *reflectance* filter, one that will reflect efficiently only over a narrow wavelength band. For example, an alkali halide crystal can be so used in its particular 10–15 μm-wide reststrahlen region* in the far IR where it has a reflectance of 0.8 or higher.

3. Scatter plates made by aluminizing a ground glass surface are also useful; they have a high reflectance only in middle and far IR.

The level of stray radiation at the exit slit may be measured in at least two simple ways. Basically the determination is a measurement of the apparent transmission of a substance that is opaque. The sample is inserted between source and monochromator.

Example The stray light level at 13 to 14 μm can be found with a polystyrene film at least 0.07 mm thick. It passes no light at 765 cm^{-1} (13.1 μm) and 705 cm^{-1} (14.1 μm).

Care must be taken, however, that the film is not heated by the incident radiation so that it becomes a black-body source! A 20–40 °K temperature rise is sufficient for it to radiate in this range.

The apparent transmittance of a slab with a sharp cutoff can also be found as a measure of stray light. Plates of quartz (opaque below 2300 cm^{-1}) and calcium fluoride (opaque below 900 cm^{-1}) can be so used.

A discussion of the magnitude of error that stray radiation may introduce into spectrophotometry will be given in Section 16.4.

---

* Most ionic crystals exhibit high reflectance in the middle or far IR over a characteristic 10–25 μm region in which their absorption coefficient is very large. The reflection is the result of resonance between incident radiation and a natural lattice vibrational frequency. For example, NaCl crystals have a high reflectance region centred at 52 μm.

12.9 DOUBLE MONOCHROMATOR

A more elegant and very satisfactory approach to reduce stray radiation (and increase resolution) is the introduction of a second dispersing element in series with the first, giving what is termed a double monochromator. For example, with this arrangement stray radiation can be cut to less than 0.0001 % of the intensity of the optical beam in the visible and UV and to about 0.1 % or less in the IR at about 650 cm^{-1} (15 μm). Ideally, both dispersion and resolution are doubled, since dispersion by the second element is in the same direction as that by the first.

Alternatively, the greater resolution of the double monochromator can be "traded off" for a gain in energy throughput. A resolution comparable to that of a single monochromator can be secured by opening the slits to twice the width needed if half the monochromator were used. As a result, a quadrupling of energy at the exit slit is secured in the double unit, offset only slightly by reflectance losses in the second monochromator.

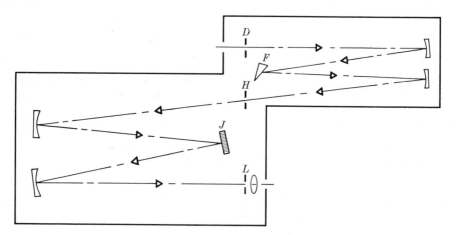

Fig. 12.20 A schematic drawing of the double monochromator portion of the Cary Models 14 and 17 spectrophotometers. Its spectral range is from 0.18 to 2.6 μm. In the UV and visible, radiation enters through slit D. It is dispersed in turn by prism F and grating J. H is a variable-width intermediate slit. Radiation leaves through exit slit L. In the near IR, radiation enters through slit L and leaves through D. (Courtesy of Cary Instruments.)

An example of a double monochromator is shown in Fig. 12.20. The first dispersing element is an especially clear quartz prism, which acts as an order-sorter. The second element is an echelette diffraction grating. The instrument combines the high resolution of a long grating with the low scattered light characteristic of a prism.

Somewhat the same effect as that of using two dispersing elements may be secured by simply arranging for a second pass through a single dispersing unit. Not all such arrangements reduce stray radiation or are compatible with double-beam design, however. [6]

12.10 SCANNING

Monochromator modules are used in one of several ways: for several measurements

at a particular wavelength perhaps followed by more measurements at other wavelengths, as in an atomic absorption spectrophotometer; for measurement simultaneously at all wavelengths over a range as in a spectrograph (the exit slit is removed);
or for observation at successive wavelengths, i.e. in a scanning mode, as in a spectrophotometer recording an absorption spectrum. For the last case new questions arise.
Perhaps the most basic is a choice of scale. A speed must also be selected but this
matter is best settled in terms of photometric considerations (Section 17.7). Here
attention will be given different ways to scan.

Should a scan linear in wavelength or wave number (equivalent to a linear
frequency scan) be selected? The former is advantageous for a prism monochromator
where dispersion is a constantly changing function of wavelength. If this mode of
scanning is selected, a program to turn the prism table through an appropriate angle
can be produced by cutting a cam to drive the prism mount. Linear wavelength
recording results if a single motor turns the cam and drives the strip chart recorder.
A second cam can also be used to vary slit width to maintain constant energy throughput.

As interest in spectral transitions has increased, the desire for a linear wave
number readout has grown, and modern grating instruments have increasingly been
provided with such a scan. (It may be noted that a linear wave number readout for a
prism spectrometer poses unusual difficulties, especially if it is to be linear in time.
For example, over the 5000 to 650 cm^{-1} (2 to 15 μm) range, the rate of change of
angle with time would have to vary by a factor of 225!)

Linear wavelength drive. The Czerny–Turner and Ebert mountings for gratings are
ideally adapted to linear wavelength and linear wave number drives. The first is
illustrated schematically in Fig. 12.21. A metal bar BC, termed a *sine bar* because of

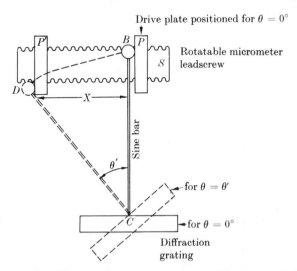

Fig. 12.21 Sine bar grating drive for a linear wavelength scan. The sine bar is rigidly affixed to the
grating holder. As the micrometer leadscrew turns, it drives threaded plate P. The plate pushes
the sine bar, whose spherical end is held against it. When plate P has advanced distance X along
the leadscrew, the sine bar and grating have shifted through angle θ'.

its use, is rigidly affixed (at its lower end) to the grating holder. Its farther end is spherical and is held in contact with a drive plate P. This plate moves as the micrometer lead screw turns. The position of the sine bar when the grating angle θ is $0°$ is shown as a solid line. According to Fig. 12.17, only zero wavelength could appear at this position. As the lead screw turns, it moves plate P to the left through a distance X that corresponds to rotating the sine bar through angle θ. The grating has been pivoted about its axis by this angle. Note that θ is just angle BCD and that $\sin \theta = X/CD$. Since $CD = BC = \text{constant}$, $X \propto \sin \theta$. Plate P advances a distance proportional to $\sin \theta$. With reference to Eq. (12.10), if the lead screw turns linearly with time, the sine bar drive will produce a linear wavelength scan.

Linear wave number drive. In Fig. 12.21 a similar drive that affords a linear wave number scan is shown. In this instance the sine bar BC is moved through angle θ by a circular plate P of radius r. Note that BC is affixed to the pivot point of the grating C but is no longer perpendicular to the grating. While plate P is driven by the lead screw, it can only move forward along channel A, which is fixed in position. Thus θ increases in a clockwise direction. Because it is a radius, r is perpendicular to BC. Since $\sin BCP = r/CP$, where r is constant, distance $CP \propto 1/\sin \theta \propto 1/\lambda = \sigma$. By reference to Eq. (12.10), it is evident that in the system of Fig. 12.22 the distance the lead screw advances is proportional to the frequency or wave number σ. A linear wave number scan is thus arranged. One exercise at the end of the chapter deals with a simple device for converting a linear wavelength to linear frequency scan.

Rapid scanning monochromators. These are of interest for the study of chemical reactions. Two design possibilities to achieve rapid scanning with a Littrow prism mount are suggested in Fig. 12.23. In the normal scan a Littrow mirror is turned slowly through an angle of a few degrees by a cam shaped to give a linear wavelength

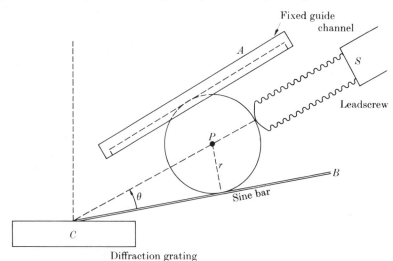

Fig. 12.22 Linear wavenumber drive. The sine bar is rigidly attached to the grating holder. The leadscrew drives forward circular plate P whose center moves along the axis passing through the grating center and the center of plate P. The plate is constrained to move along a channel cut in bar A, which is fixed in position.

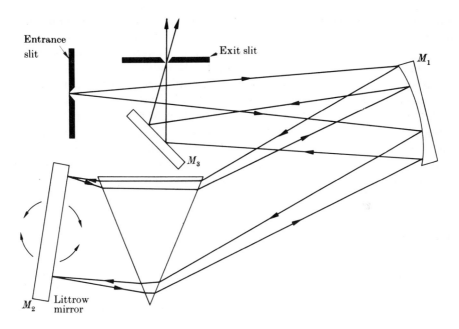

Fig. 12.23 Schematic optical diagram of a rapid-scan prism spectrophotometer. Rapid oscillations of Littrow mirror M_2 cause repeated sweeping of a narrow spectral region. Scanning could also be arranged by oscillation of mirror M_3.

or wave number drive. For fast scanning the mirror is driven by a rotating cam of appropriate shape. A chopper may be synchronized with the cam to insure that only the wavelength range of interest reaches the detector. Other spectral regions would be blocked by the chopper.

In the second approach, rapid scanning is achieved by rotating the Littrow mirror at a uniform frequency. This arrangement is mechanically simpler and permits faster scan rates. A further advantage arises from the possibility of positive synchronization. The rotation of the shaft can be monitored by reflecting light from a mirror mounted on it. In turn, this pulse of light provides a trigger to synchronize scanning of a spectrum with detection.

Other arrangements are discussed in detail in Section 17.9.

12.11 WAVELENGTH CALIBRATION

Precisely known atomic emission lines or molecular absorption peaks are nearly always used to calibrate the wavelength scale of a monochromator. If the device is incorporated in a spectrophotometer, the calibration is applied to the preprinted charts used for recording spectra. Paper with good dimensional stability ensures that once a chart is lined up with a fiduciary mark on the chart bed the calibration is preserved. In other, more versatile, instruments the wavelength setting may be indicated by the register of a counter or printed out digitally.

In the visible and UV the best reference lines are in general those furnished by low-pressure elemental discharge lamps such as a mercury lamp (Section 11.3). Lines used must be of good spectral purity and adequate intensity. For example, gaseous discharge lamps or hollow-cathode lamps giving spectra for mercury, cadmium, zinc, helium, neon, and rubidium allow wavelength calibration over the range 0.194 μm to 2.33 μm. Over essentially the same range the absorption peaks of rare-earth glasses are useful. Thus, a holmium filter in a UV transmitting glass such as Corning CS3-138 provides eight sharp absorption peaks over the UV–visible range.

In the IR, mercury emission lines are useful up to 4350 cm^{-1} (2.3 μm) but gas absorption lines of common molecular substances, such as water, carbon dioxide, and ammonia are used up to 250 cm^{-1} (40 μm). In addition, polystyrene films offer many sharp absorptions that are useful for calibration in the near and middle IR. A good discussion of calibration techniques is available. [7]

REFERENCES

See also references at ends of Chapters 10 and 11.
Lucid, brief accounts of diffraction grating behavior and specifications are given on an introductory to intermediate level in:

1. Bausch and Lomb Staff, *Diffraction Grating Handbook*. Rochester, N.Y.: Bausch and Lomb, 1970

1a. S. P. Davis, *Diffraction Grating Spectrographs*. New York: Holt, Rinehart, and Winston, 1970

Monochromator design is treated on an advanced level in:

2. J. F. James and R. S. Sternberg, *The Design of Optical Spectrometers*. New York: Barnes and Nobel, 1969

Other references of interest are:

3. T. Namioka, "Theory of the Concave Grating," *J. Opt. Soc. Am.* **49**, 446, 460, 951 (1959)
4. S. Robin, "Method of Focusing of a Far UV Monochromator with Fixed and Distant Slits," *J. Phys. Radium.* **14**, 551 (1953) [French text]
5. Walter Slavin, "Stray Light in Ultraviolet, Visible, and Near-Infrared Spectrophotometry," *Anal. Chem.* **35**, 561 (1963)
6. A. Walsh, "Multiple Monochromators. I. Design of Multiple Monochromators," *J. Opt. Soc. Am.* **42**, 94 (1952)
7. K. N. Rao, C. J. Humphreys, and D. H. Rank, *Wavelength Standards in the Infrared*. New York: Academic, 1966
8. G. R. Harrison, "The Production of Diffraction Gratings. II. The Design of Echelle Gratings and Spectrographs," *J. Opt. Soc. Am.* **39**, 522 (1949)

EXERCISES

12.1 On the basis of transparency and the variation of n with λ given in Fig. 12.6, (a) select two substances that should be good prism materials in the UV and two good in the visible; (b) indicate the optical range(s) where the following materials are most valuable for prisms: quartz, germanium, lithium fluoride.

12.2 A 453.8 nm ray is incident on a glass Cornu prism for which $A = 60°$ and $n_{453.8} = 1.63$.

a) What is the angle of incidence for minimum deviation?

b) What is the angle of minimum deviation D?
c) What is the mathematical relation for this prism between the angle of incidence and the angle of minimum deviation?

[*Ans.*: a) 54.6° ; b) 49.2° ; c) $\sin \frac{1}{2}(D + A) = \sin i$.]

12.3 What is the angle of minimum deviation for the 546.1 nm Hg line for a Cornu quartz prism ($n_{546.1} = 1.5442$)? The refractive index for the ordinary ray is given (see Fig. 12.10).

[*Ans.*: 41° 16′.]

12.4 For 60° incidence, what will be the total angular deviation of the 404.7 nm Hg line by a 60° fused quartz prism ($n_{404.7} = 1.4697$)?

[*Ans.*: 36° 35′.]

12.5 A direct-vision spectroscope can be based on an Amici compensator. As shown in Fig. 21.3a, it is made by cementing three prisms whose n_D's are nearly identical but whose dispersions are different. Where should the entrance slit be located? Consider the paths shown in the figure for red (650 nm), D-line, and blue (450 nm) wavelengths and assign very rough refractive indices to subprisms A, B, and C. Should any portion of a ray be redrawn?

12.6 Symmetrical prisms are usually employed at the angle of minimum deviation. Show that internal reflection (back into the prism) increases steadily when an angle of incidence smaller than the angle of minimum deviation is used.

12.7 Why are most mirrors used in monochromators front-surfaced?

12.8 It has been stated that a monochromator reimages its entrance slit at every wavelength along the focal curve. Yet when a spectrograph, which essentially contains a monochromator, is used with a fixed width of entrance slit to record emission spectra on a photographic plate, some lines are wider than others. Explain.

12.9 How does dispersion in a grating monochromator vary with angles of incidence and diffraction? Substitute for m/d in Eq. (12.11) using Eq. (12.10). When θ is varied from 15° to 65°, what change in dispersion can be expected at fixed wavelength?

12.10 For light of wavelength 1 to 5 μm (10,000 to 2000 cm^{-1}) calculate the angle of diffraction for normal incidence on a reflection grating of grating constant $d = 10 \ \mu$m.

a) Tabulate λ, $\sin \beta$, β, and $\Delta\beta$ for $\lambda = 1, 2, 3, 4$, and 5 μm.
b) What variation is there in $\Delta\beta/\Delta\lambda$ over this wavelength range?

[*Ans.*: b) $\Delta\beta/\Delta\lambda$ is nearly constant at 6° μm^{-1}.]

12.11 a) At what angle must a grating be blazed for it to have a peak efficiency in the first order at 1000 cm^{-1}?
b) If a grating operates with 50% or more of its peak efficiency from 2/3 λ_B to 2 λ_B, over what frequency range will it achieve such efficiency?
c) Using the diagram of Fig. 12.17 and assuming ϕ is constant, over what range of grating angles θ will a grating operate with 50% or greater efficiency?

12.12 How can one tell that a grating is blazed in the visible range by visual inspection of the diffraction pattern?

12.13 It can be shown that the actual blaze wavelength λ_B' for a diffraction grating is related to the nominal value λ_B by the equation $\lambda_B' = \lambda_B \cos(\alpha - \beta)/2$ where α and β are angles of incidence and diffraction. What nominal value of blaze should be selected for a grating to be used at grazing incidence ($\alpha = 85°$, $\beta = 85°$) in a monochromator intended for work centered around 80 nm in the first order?

12.14 Show from Eq. (12.9) that when a grating is used in the Littrow mode, its theoretical resolution is given by the equation $R = 2W \sin \beta/\lambda$ where β is the angle of incidence and diffraction and W is the ruled width of the grating blank ($W = dN$).

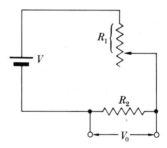

12.15 A simple version of a device proposed by Baker and Barnes for conversion of a linear wave-length scan to one linear in wavenumber is shown in Fig. 12.24.* Show that $V_o \propto 1/\lambda \propto \sigma$. Resistances are selected so that $R_2 \ll R_1$, where R_1 is the portion of the potentiometer resistance in the circuit. Output voltage V_o drives the chart for linear wavenumber recording.

* E. W. Baker, and W. C. Barnes, Pittsburgh Analytical Conference, March 1968.

SOME SPECTROMETRIC METHODS

Chapter 13

EMISSION SPECTROMETRY

Spectroscopic regions differ principally in wavelength of electromagnetic radiation and in the energy of quanta associated with each region. A comprehensive listing was given in Table 11.1. Both characteristics define the possibility of interaction, the first because of appropriate dimensional matching, and the second because of matching of quanta to the energy of transition.

In general, radiation of frequency v will be absorbed or emitted during a change ΔE in the energy of a system. The expression $\Delta E = hv$ establishes the close interrelation of energy transitions in matter and electromagnetic waves. The product hv also defines the energy of a photon. A representative process of excitation of a system by electron bombardment and varied modes of loss of energy during its return to the ground state is indicated schematically in Fig. 13.1.

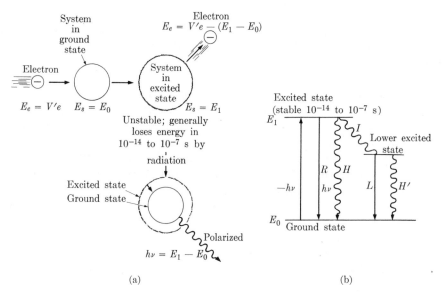

(a)   (b)

Fig. 13.1 Generalized energy changes in an elementary system. (a) Excitation by impact and subsequent radiation. (b) Absorption of radiation and subsequent energy loss by one of the following processes: reradiation R, redistribution of energy in system and loss as heat H, internal conversion to lower excited state (triplet) and partial loss of energy as heat I, followed by reradiation L or by redistribution and loss as heat H'.

353

In certain cases energy states are so closely spaced that they are essentially non-resolvable, i.e., can be considered continuous. The more important of these cases are:

1. Translational motions of molecules, ions, etc., in free space, and

2. Internal motions in molecules, ions, etc., in condensed phases where a given system is subjected to strong and constantly varying perturbing forces.

These cases present only apparent exceptions to the general principle of quantization of energy states.

While the frequency of radiation is the basic variable related to quantum changes, it is not always the quantity most precisely determinable. In the electrical part of the EM spectrum it is very precisely measurable by comparison with the frequency of a standard oscillator. In the optical part (frequencies beyond the microwave region), however, wavelengths can be more precisely observed.* Partly for this reason, in the optical range the radiation accompanying a transition is usually cited in terms of the reciprocal of the vacuum wavelength.† This quantity, proportional to the frequency, is called the *wave number* (units: cm^{-1}). A wave number can be seen to describe the number of wave crests per centimeter distance.

Sources of emission spectra.   Any substance may be forced into an unstable yet allowed energy state, i.e. one above the ground level, by means of thermal or electrical excitation or by exposure to radiation of appropriate frequencies. In the first two methods collision with energetic molecules or electrons is the basis for excitation. Not only are higher states of individual atoms produced, but excited states of ions and radicals can also be formed.

The excited species so formed are always unstable, as Fig. 13.1 shows. They may lose energy by collision, by entering into a chemical reaction, by dissociation, or by radiation. It is the last process that is of interest here. For a host of atoms of an element excited to different states there will be many radiative transitions possible. As each atom returns to the ground or to a lower state its emission frequency is observed; the set of all such frequencies is just the *emission spectrum* of the species. The normal spectrum obtained from excited atoms is distinguished from that for excited ions. Thus, a spectrum is described as of the first, second, or higher order, depending on whether the atom emitting is unionized, singly ionized, or multiply ionized, respectively. Roman numerals designate the condition. For example, Fe I indicates a spectrum associated with unionized iron atoms, and Fe III a third-order spectrum arising from doubly charged iron ions. As might be expected from the close relation between electronic structure and the periodic table, the spectra of all species of ions and atoms in an isoelectronic sequence resemble one other. For example, the spectrum of Sc III resembles that of Ca II and K I.

Only separate atoms or monatomic ions emit sharply defined wavelengths, i.e., a *line spectrum*. Excited condensed systems such as solids emit continuous spectra

---

* Frequencies might then be precisely calculated by means of the expression $\lambda v = c$, but the velocity of light c is not known with comparable accuracy.

† Recall that λ_0, the vacuum wavelength, is defined by $\lambda_0 = c/v$ and that the wavelength in air, λ, is shorter, i.e., $\lambda = \lambda_0/n$, where n is the refractive index of air. The difference is of the order of 3 parts in 10^4.

instead. These are "blackbody" radiations that depend principally on thermal vibrations and thus on temperature rather than chemical nature (Section 11.2). Thus, "atomic" spectroscopy necessarily calls for volatilization and dissociation of a sample into atoms as well as for its excitation.

In contrast, separate molecules give rise to *band spectra* when excited. "Molecule" is used as including transitory species such as OH and C_2 that exist at high temperature or in very dilute gases. For these species there cannot be only electronic transitions; almost invariably each electronic change will be inseparable from a rotational and vibrational transition that occurs simultaneously. There are a large number of different ways the other changes can occur. Thus, for each electronic change there will be many closely spaced lines that will appear as a band except when dispersed by a spectrograph of high resolution. Band spectra are not to be confused with lines broadened by pressure, a phenomenon resulting from the distortion of regular emission patterns. Nearly all emission spectra excited in air or other gases contain bands as well as lines.

13.2 ATOMIC SPECTRA

Emission and absorption spectra of hydrogen-like atoms can be successfully accounted for by the use of the Bohr model. Summing the potential and kinetic energy of the single electron possessed by such atoms gives the following expression for the nth electronic energy level:

$$E_n = \frac{2\pi^2 m_e e^4 Z^2}{h^2} \cdot \frac{1}{n^2}, \tag{13.1}$$

where m_e is the mass of the electron, e is the electronic charge, Z is the atomic number, h is Planck's constant, and n is the principal quantum number for the level.* For spectroscopic purposes (and historically) Eq. (13.1) is often rewritten in terms of the wave number σ_n of the nth level. When this is done, the constant quantities are grouped together in the *Rydberg* constant for hydrogen, R_H. One has

$$\sigma_n = -\frac{E_n}{hc} = -\frac{2\pi^2 m_e e^4}{h^3 c} \cdot \frac{1}{n^2} = \frac{R_H}{n^2}. \tag{13.2}$$

It will be seen below that R_H/n^2 is called the term value for the nth state.

According to the lower state to which transitions are made, a line spectrum for a given atom can be analyzed into different series. This procedure is clearly illustrated for hydrogen in Fig. 13.2. Note, for example, that the Balmer series for hydrogen represents transitions to the second electronic level ($n = 2$).

For any set, the *series limit* represents the greatest energy (shortest-wavelength line) possible for the series. Such a line would be associated with a downward transition from the ionized state. For example, the limit for the Balmer series of hydrogen

---

* Actually, the reduced mass μ of the system should be used in lieu of the electronic mass. This quantity is defined as $\mu = m_e M/(m_e + M)$ where M is the mass of the nucleus. For hydrogen μ is 0.07 % less than m_e; for heavier atoms the difference is still smaller and becomes insignificant as M increases.

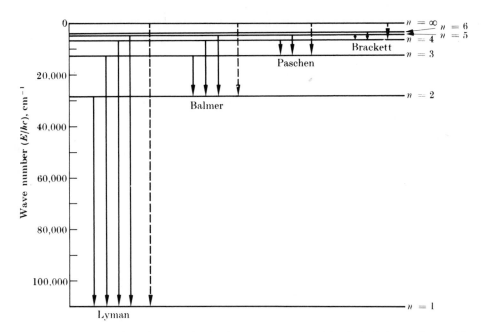

Fig. 13.2 Spectroscopic emission series for the hydrogen atom. The dashed electronic transition in each case indicates the series limit. The wave number of each emission line is the difference between the values at each end of its arrow. Principal quantum numbers n are given at the right.

would be observed when a separated electron ($n = \infty$) of zero kinetic energy was captured in an $n = 2$ hydrogen level. These limits are indicated in Fig. 13.2.

Three other properties of series may be noted. First, there is an increasingly close spacing of levels as the principal quantum number increases, thus a convergence of emission lines toward a *series limit*. Second, different series of lines overlap in an actual spectrum, which causes most emission spectra to be complex. Third, since most separated electrons have finite translational kinetic energies, their capture will give rise to a continuous spectrum that extends from the series limit toward shorter wavelengths.

For multielectron atoms both electrostatic repulsion between electrons and the effect of electron spin also enter into the determination of energy levels. As a result energies differ for different patterns of electron motion. In describing the emission spectra of these elements it is conventional to assign a term or *term symbol* T to each different atomic state. Electronic transactions are then described by a difference such as $T_q - T_p$, where T_q is the term symbol of a particular upper state and T_p that of a particular lower state. Each term is also associated with a wavenumber value marking its position relative to a common reference energy. Thus, a downward transition gives rise to an emission line (in cm^{-1}) given by $\sigma = T_q - T_p$. The formal statement of this relationship between levels is called the *Ritz combination principle*.

A term diagram, sometimes called a Grotrian diagram, after its initiator, represents graphically the simpler electronic transitions for a given atomic species. It should be understood that not all differences between terms correspond to actual spectral lines and that whether transitions are "allowed" must be deduced from quantum-mechanical principles.

In Fig. 13.3 is shown the term diagram for sodium. Note that values of the (orbital) angular-momentum quantum number l are given across the top and values

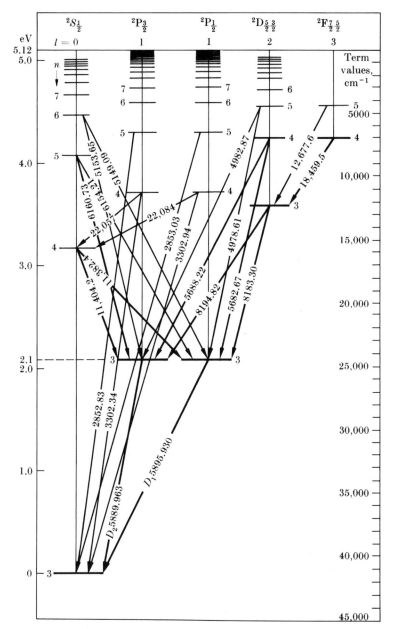

Fig. 13.3 Term diagram for the sodium atom. Emission transitions are shown by arrows with wavelengths in Angstroms. These values may be converted to manometers by dividing by ten. (After Grotrian. Courtesy of Springer-Verlag, Heidelberg.)

of n downward. Allowed transitions are shown as diagonals that include the wavelength of the emission line.

To unravel the complexity of this diagram, consider the formal scheme used to construct it. Both angular momentum and electron spin can be represented as vector quantities. The summing of such motions becomes vector addition. When a species has a single valence electron, as sodium does, coupling can be represented by $l + s$ when the vectors are parallel and by $l - s$ when they are oppositely directed. The coupling is described by the so-called inner quantum number j. When the valence electron of sodium is in an s-level, $(l = 0)$, $l + s$ and $l - s$ gives a single value, $1/2$; when it is in a p-level $(l = 1)$ the coupling produces j values of $1/2$ and $3/2$. Now the term for an atom is symbolized by the capital letter describing the angular momentum of its highest-energy electron. Thus S is the symbol for the ground state of sodium in an s-state. The value of j is given as a right subscript of the term, e.g., $S_{1/2}$ or $P_{1/2}$ or $P_{3/2}$. Finally, a left superscript is used to indicate multiplicity, which is just $2s + 1$, where s is the resultant electron spin quantum number. Since sodium has a single valence electron, its multiplicity is $2(\frac{1}{2}) + 1 = 2$ for all states. In Table 13.1, the term and the values of the inner quantum number are given for sodium for each value of l. The complete term symbols in Fig. 13.3 have now been identified. A more detailed treatment is beyond the scope of this text.

Table 13.1 Values of j Possible for Sodium

Term	l	Value of j
S	0	1/2
P	1	1/2, 3/2
D	2	3/2, 5/2
F	3	5/2, 7/2

In Fig. 13.4 the so-called principal series spectrum for each of the alkali metals is shown. Each series marks transitions from a higher electronic level to the ground state for that atom. In all cases the ground state is the same, $^2S_{1/2}$. Thus, the lines are described by a term combination $T_q - {}^2S_{1/2}$. For example, the doublet comprising the sodium D-lines is the pair $^2P_{3/2} - {}^2S_{1/2}$ and $^2P_{1/2} - {}^2S_{1/2}$ at about $17{,}000 \text{ cm}^{-1}$ (589 nm). It is instructive to identify the origin of many of the lines.

In the emission spectrum of an element it is found that its strongest lines are those for transitions terminating in the ground state. The most intense of these originates from the first excited state that can "combine" with the ground state to give an allowed transition. This line is termed the *resonance line*. For example, in the case of sodium the brightest "line" is actually the D-doublet, and the 589.0 and 589.6 nm pair are resonance lines.

While the fine structure of atomic spectra can be accounted for quantitatively by term diagrams, so-called *hyperfine structure* cannot. These very slight (hundreds of wave numbers) splittings of many lines have two nonexclusive origins. There is a definite isotope effect for any element that is traceable to isotopic variations in nuclear

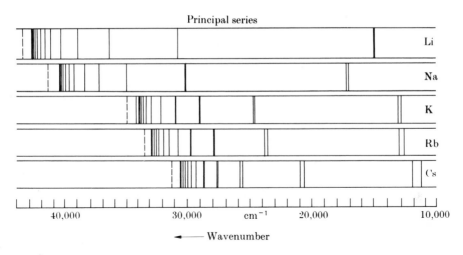

Fig. 13.4 The so-called principal emission series for the common alkali metals, i.e., the set of transitions to the ground electronic state (1s for Li, 2s for Na, etc.). Since only transitions for which $\Delta l = \pm 1$ are allowed by selection rules, all these transitions are from upper "p"-states ($l = 1$) to the ground "s"-state ($l = 0$). Each transition gives rise to a doublet since the spin ($s = \frac{1}{2}$) may couple either $l + s = \frac{3}{2}$ or $l - s = \frac{1}{2}$ in the "p"-state. The separation of lines in the doublets of sodium and potassium has been exaggerated.

volumes. The energy of very penetrating electrons such as those in s-orbitals is affected. The other source of hyperfine structure is nuclear spin. It couples with orbital motion in vector fashion to give sums and differences for all isotopes except those of zero spin.

13.3 INTENSITIES AND SHAPES OF SPECTRAL LINES

Whether for absorption or for emission, whether for atomic or molecular transitions, line intensities are proportional to the population of the initial level, and to the *Einstein probability coefficient* for the transition. Approximate values can in many instances be calculated. The possibility of absolute spectroscopic measurements clearly depends on knowledge of such values.

For transitions between two nondegenerate states p and q of a system that have energy E_p and E_q, three probability coefficients can be considered.

1. A_{qp}, the probability coefficient for *spontaneous emission*. The number of atoms (or molecules) dN spontaneously undergoing a transition from higher state q to lower state p during an interval of time dt is just:

$$dN = N_q A_{qp}\, dt, \tag{13.3}$$

where N_q is the population of state q. Representative values of the probability coefficient A_{qp} for allowed transitions are of the order of 10^8 s^{-1}.

2. B_{qp}, the probability coefficient for *stimulated emission*, i.e. emission brought about by irradiation of the excited species by (a uniform field of) the frequency of the radiation. The number of species dN undergoing emission from excited state q to state p

in time interval dt is

$$dN = N_q B_{qp} \rho(v)\, dt, \tag{13.4}$$

where $\rho(v)$ is the spectral volume density of the incident radiation.

3. B_{pq}, the probability for (stimulated) *absorption*. The number of atoms (or molecules) dN absorbing radiation from a uniform radiation field of frequency v in the interval dt is

$$dN = N_p B_{pq} \rho(v)\, dt. \tag{13.5}$$

In defining these coefficients, Einstein showed that $B_{qp} = B_{pq} = 8\pi^2|R|^2/3h^2$ and $A_{qp} = 8\pi h \sigma^3 B_{qp}$ where R is a *transition dipole moment** and σ the wave number in cm^{-1}. Unfortunately, since it is difficult to formulate wave equations for the states involved, few transition probabilities have been calculated reliably. Ordinarily probabilities are measured.

A distinctive difference between spontaneous and stimulated transitions must be noted. The probability of an induced transition, B_{qp} or B_{pq}, is independent of frequency (or wave number), but the probability of a *spontaneous* transition varies as the third power of the frequency or wave number. For this reason, emission lines from electronic transitions, which are of high frequency, are very much more intense than absorption peaks in the IR that correspond to vibrational changes.

Most transitions that occur in the optical range depend upon an electric dipole moment. Such a moment exists if there is a nonsymmetrical charge distribution about the center of mass. Since this condition is met only for transitions between certain states of an atomic system, probable or *allowed* transitions can easily be specified. The specifications are called *selection rules*.† Further, higher-order effects may also give rise to such transitions. One is a magnetic dipole transition, which is roughly only 10^{-5} times as likely as an electric dipole transition. Another is an electric quadrupole transition, which is only 10^{-8} times as probable as an electric dipole transition.

When there is an unsymmetrical charge distribution in a single direction, as along a bond axis, the transition is well adapted to investigation by use of linearly polarized radiation. For example, a stretching vibration of a heteronuclear bond might be so studied in a crystal.

In still other instances charge distributions that are symmetrical around a bond axis may not be symmetrical in space. These cases give rise to an electric *quadrupole moment*, defined by the expression

$$Q = \sum_i q_i x_i^2.$$

Here q_i is a particular charge and x_i is its distance from the center of mass. There is a distinct difference between dipole and quadrupole transitions. Usually the latter are

---

* Thus, $|R|^2$ is the square of the absolute value of the moment between the states p and q. In general R is resolved into components along a set of axes so that
$$|R|^2 = |R_x|^2 + |R_y|^2 + |R_z|^2.$$
† When a molecule is perturbed by a collision or interaction with near neighbors, transitions that are improbable or forbidden may occur though they will be much lower in intensity.

of very low intensity. Such transitions are among those observed in Raman spectroscopy.

Example The basis for selection rules in atomic transitions may be appreciated qualitatively by considering the case of the hydrogen atom in its ground state. On the average its electronic charge is distributed symmetrically around the proton, i.e., the electron is in a 1s state. A transition to a 2s configuration, which is also spherically symmetrical, would fail to yield a transition dipole and would be "forbidden." However, if the incident radiation were of proper energy the atom could undergo a transition to a $2p_x$, $2p_y$, or $2p_z$ configuration. If linearly polarized light of this energy with its electric vector in the y-direction impinges on a hydrogen atom, the only change that can occur is that from the 1s to the $2p_y$ configuration. Only this change can yield a transition dipole. The field intensities of the $2p_x$ and $2p_z$ configurations along the y-axis are zero; while they would yield a transition dipole, they have no projection along the direction of the incident radiation.

The intensity I_{qp} of an emission line is defined as the energy radiated per second. It is the product of the number of atoms of a species spontaneously undergoing a given transition in a second, and the energy of the photons released. The former is given by Eq. (13.3), the latter by $h\nu_0$. The resulting expression for I_{qp} is

$$I_{qp} = h\nu_0 A_{qp} N_q. \tag{13.6}$$

How shall N_q be found? If thermal equilibrium has been attained, it can be defined in terms of the Boltzmann distribution. In this case population N_q can be related to the total population of the species in all states N by the expression

$$\frac{N_q}{N} = \frac{g_q}{Z(T)} e^{-E_q/kT} \tag{13.7}$$

where g_q is the *statistical weight* of state q, and $Z(T)$ is the quantum mechanical partition function for the species. In a representative system where few atoms are in an excited state, $Z(T) = g_0$, the statistical weight of the ground state.*

It may be quoted that statistical weights are found from multiplicities and express the degeneracy or weighting of a level in the absence of electric or magnetic fields. Finally, a general expression for line intensity is obtained by substituting Eq. (13.7) in (13.6):

$$I_{qp} = h\nu_0 A_{qp} N_q \frac{g_q}{Z(T)} e^{-E_q/hT}. \tag{13.8}$$

Radiative lifetime. Spontaneous emission is by nature a first-order kinetic process, i.e., one whose rate is dependent only on the concentration of excited species at a given time. If there is an initial population N_q in an excited state, and additions to the population are not made, an exponential decay rate will be noted:

$$N_q(t) = N_q(0)e^{-t/\tau}, \tag{13.9}$$

where τ is a constant termed the radiative lifetime of the excited state. Its value will be principally determined by the Einstein coefficient A_{qp}; by comparison of Eq. (13.3)

---

*In the more general case $Z(T) = \Sigma_j g_j e^{-E_j/kT}$, where the sum is taken over all states.

and (13.9) it is seen that this coefficient and τ are reciprocally related. Since most values of A_{qp} are of the order of 10^8 s^{-1}, lifetimes tend to be in the range of 10^{-8} s.

It is clear that spontaneous emission may also be viewed as a relaxation process. The usual exponential type of decay of the excited state is observed.

Example Once excitation is stopped in a system undergoing resonance emission, the fraction of the original number of excited atoms remaining after a time in seconds equal to $1/A_{qp}$ can be found from Eq. (13.9). It is just $N_q(t)/N_q(0) = e^{-1} = 0.37$.

Shape of spectral lines. All emission and absorption lines have a finite width. There are several causes. A so-called *natural width* is defined by the mean lifetimes of initial and final states involved in a transition, i.e. the average length of time a species remains in each state before undergoing a transition. According to the Heisenberg principle, the uncertainty in energy of each state is complementary to this lifetime and is given by $\tau_i \Delta E_i \simeq h/2\pi \simeq \tau_i \cdot h\Delta v_i$, where h is the Planck constant. If atoms could remain an essentially infinite time in excited and ground states, the uncertainty in the energy of the states would become vanishingly small. Then a transition from excited state E_q to lower state E_p would yield a single transition frequency v_o of magnitude $(E_q - E_p)/h$. But only ground state lifetimes are "infinite," and actual transitions lead to the emission of a band of frequencies that has a breadth Δv_N at half maximum intensity. It can be shown that if τ_q and τ_p are lifetimes in the two states, the natural line width of the emission (or absorption) is given by

$$\Delta v_N = \frac{1}{2\pi}\left(\frac{1}{\tau_q} + \frac{1}{\tau_p}\right).$$

In general, natural line widths are minute. The narrowest lines are resonance lines, those for which state p is the ground state. For example, the mercury resonance line at 253.7 nm has a natural width of 3×10^{-5} nm.

Example What is the natural width of a representative resonance line of wavelength 250 nm? Assume $\tau_q \simeq 10^{-8}$ s. For a resonance line, the equation defining Δv_N reduces to $\Delta v_N = 1/2\pi\tau_q$ since $\tau_p = \infty$. Substituting in the equation gives

$$\Delta v_N = \frac{1}{6.78 \times 10^{-8}} \approx 10^7 \text{ s}^{-1}.$$

This breadth may be converted into a wavelength by use of the wave relationship $c = \lambda v$. Since $\Delta\lambda$ is desired, this expression must be differentiated. One obtains

$$d\left(\frac{c}{\lambda}\right) = dv = -\left(\frac{c}{\lambda^2}\right) d\lambda = dv \quad \text{or} \quad \Delta\lambda_N = \lambda^2\frac{\Delta v_N}{c},$$

when increments are substituted for differentials. At 250 nm,

$$\Delta\lambda_N = (250)^2 \times 10^{-18}\,\text{m}^2 \times 10^7\,\text{s}^{-1} \div 3 \times 10^8\,\text{m s}^{-1} = 2 \times 10^{-6}\,\text{nm}.$$

Other influences also act to broaden lines. In Table 13.2 the effects are summarized. *Doppler broadening* results from the fact that wavelengths increase if an emitting (or absorbing species) is moving away from a detector, and *vice versa*. The effect is sufficiently large for Doppler broadening usually to define the lower limit of widths that can be observed. Collisions of species undergoing transitions also increase line widths. The phenomenon is termed *pressure broadening*. This factor is also known as Lorentz and/or Holtsmark broadening.

Table 13.2 Influences on the Width of a Spectral Line

Influence	Finite lifetime of states	Motion of emitting or absorbing species relative to detector	Collision of emitting or absorbing species with other molecules
"Mechanism" by which influence is exerted	Heisenberg uncertainty principle	Doppler effect	Intermolecular forces causing "shift to red," or nonradiative transitions
Designation of effect	Natural broadening	Doppler broadening	Pressure broadening
Variables influencing effect	Nature of species initial and final states	$(\text{Temperature})^{1/2}$ $(\text{Mass})^{-1/2}$	Nature of surrounding gas, gas density, temperature
Contribution to width of 253.7 nm mercury emission line	3×10^{-5} nm	~ 0.02 nm	Very variable

At low pressures the Doppler effect is the main cause of broadening and lines have an essentially Gaussian shape. At flame temperatures, values of line half-breadths are of the order of 5 to 50×10^{-4} nm. Pressure broadening can be very substantial indeed. A detailed treatment will be found in Ref. 3, Chapter 14.

This chapter has dealt with general aspects of absorption and emission. Yet a consideration of molecular transitions has been deferred. These will be treated briefly in Section 16.3.

An accurate rendering of a narrow line will be impossible with a spectrograph of low resolution (Section 12.2). All such lines will have an apparent intensity that is too small and an apparent breadth that is too great. In most such cases the *integrated intensity* $I(v)$ expresses intensity as a function of frequency. The integrated intensity is given by

$$I = \int_{v_1}^{v_2} I(v)\, dv, \tag{13.10}$$

where v_1 and v_2 are the limits of the line. Clearly, with a narrow line the integrated intensity best expresses true intensity. In general, Einstein transition probabilities are determined from such measurements.

13.4 SCOPE OF EMISSION SPECTROMETRY

In terms of its principal analytical applications, emission spectroscopy could usefully be labeled atomic spectroscopy. It is valuable chiefly as a technique for identification and quantitative determination of elements. It can be used with all the metals and with certain nonmetals such as boron and phosphorus. The technique is useful for any element that can be volatilized and excited under the conditions available.

Actually, emission spectroscopy offers extreme specificity and sensitivity in identifying and measuring concentrations of elements. All ranges of concentrations can be handled in qualitative work, down to about 1 part per billion in many cases. Analyses may be performed on samples as small as 1 μg. Another advantage, a result of the specificity of the method, is the possibility of making a nearly complete elemental analysis on a single sample of a complex material.

Many other instrumental or chemical methods are more precise for concentrations greater than 2%. Below that level, however, spectroscopy often has the advantage in precision and accuracy and is widely used; knowing the concentration of a trace element from 2 to 5% is frequently quite adequate. When speed is important and high accuracy is not required, as in many metallurgical analyses, even if dilution with inert material cannot be arranged, spectroscopy is employed for the determination of major constituents as well. Applications are more fully discussed in later sections.

In research, spectrographic analysis is also employed in the study of energy levels. Atoms, ions, simple molecules like C_2N_2, and radicals such as C_2, NH, or $\cdot$OH are so investigated. It is widely used in the identification and study of species in flames, rocket exhausts, plasmas, and stars. Much of the information about bonds in excited species is derived from emission spectroscopy. There is, of course, no opportunity to examine molecules of any complexity at the high temperatures ordinarily used for excitation, since chemical bonds are too easily broken. Instead, such molecules are usually studies by absorption (Chapter 16) or fluorescence techniques (Chapter 15).

In addition, spectroscopy offers a means of determining temperature (and even field strengths) in hot systems. Since line intensities are exponentially dependent on the temperature, it is only necessary to determine the relative intensity of a particular line to measure the temperature of the emitting species. Further, by analyzing the radiation from a system, i.e., measuring both line widths and intensities for many species, a spectroscopist can ascertain the electric and magnetic field strength (from splitting of lines), pressure, degree of ionization, and temperature (up to values as high as $1 \times 10^9 \, °K$). [4]

13.5 SOME DESIGN CRITERIA

An emission spectrometer or spectrograph must provide for volatilization and intense excitation of a sample as well as for observation of its emission as a function of wavelength. The choice of modules and their arrangement must reflect these needs.

In addition, the fact that nearly all spectroscopic samples are mixtures and most are solids imposes a further requirement. The volatilization of a solid is inherently selective: it usually involves a different energy for each constituent. Thus, many solid samples should be completely volatized or all elements present will not be fully represented in the emission.* Accordingly, the detector output should be integrated over the entire interval of volatilization. Integration is also desirable as a means of averaging out some of the instability attributable to fluctuation in rates of volatilization and excitation of the sample.

Volatilization
and excitation
device   Readout

$\downarrow$ $\uparrow$

Emitting $\Rightarrow$ Wavelength $\Rightarrow$ Detector- $\rightarrow$ Amplifier $\rightarrow$ Integrator
vapor   isolator   transducer

Fig. 13.5   Line block diagram of a generalized-emission spectrometer.

On the basis of the functions to be performed a generalized emission spectrometer can be blocked out as shown in Fig. 13.5. How important is the contribution of each module? To answer the question, consider the dependence of the detector signal from unionized atoms on pertinent variables. It can be shown [13] that the signal developed by the detector is related to the concentration of an analytical species by the expression:

$$\text{Signal} = \left[\frac{(1 - \alpha)MC}{\psi} \right] \left(A_q h v_q \frac{g_q}{Z(T)} e^{-E_q/kT} \right) f(\theta, \lambda) g(\lambda). \qquad (13.11)$$

The terms are identified from left to right as follows. First, the bracketed quantity contains: α, the fraction of analytical species that is ionized; M, the weight of sample atomized (volatilized as atoms) per second; C, the concentration of analytical species in the sample; and ψ, the velocity of transport of sample through the excitation zone. Thus, the bracketed quantity represents the concentration of volatilized atoms in the region of excitation. Second, the parenthetical quantity is seen to be the product of the fraction of species excited (Eq. 13.7) and all factors but concentration necessary to convert this value to an emission intensity. Third, $f(\theta, \lambda)$ represents the geometrical factor that defines the solid angle of the emission observed by the monochromator and its transmission efficiency with wavelength. Fourth, $g(\lambda)$ represents the efficiency of the detector as a function of wavelength. Since the signal is integrated over a period of time, $\int_0^t Q \, dt$ should be substituted for MC, where Q is the rate of volatilization and dt is the interval.

It becomes evident on inspecting Eq. (13.11) that the effectiveness of atomization or volatization and of excitation is of paramount importance. Ideally the procedure used should maximize the rate of volatilization M, provide as slow a rate of transport ψ (through the excitation zone) as possible, and maximize the temperature T without unduly increasing the degree of ionization α. As some of the modules are individually examined in the next section, these criteria should be kept in mind. Since standard procedure discussed in the preceding chapters can ensure an efficient performance by the monochromator, detector-transducer, amplifier, integrator, and readout, these optical modules will receive little attention here. The reader should consult earlier chapters for information.

---

* Alternatively, a solid sample could be dissolved and the solution introduced into the excitation device. Often this option is less attractive because of time and/or solubility considerations.

In concluding this overview, it may be noted that any variable such as volatilization that is not easily controlled through instrument design must be allowed for by variations in measurement procedures. For example, where volatilization of a sample is not selective, as in arcing a solution or certain metal electrodes, a steady-state method suffices. A sample is excited only long enough to allow averaging of most random error to sero. On the other hand, if volatilization is known to be selective a sample is usually completely volatilized.

13.6 EXCITATION METHODS

Many different excitation techniques are in use in spectrochemical analysis. They should be compared with several criteria in mind:

1. Intensity and "sensitivity,"

2. Reproducibility, and

3. Ease of use.

An excitation source must be "intense" enough to volatilize and excite all the elements in a mixture like an alloy, or a substance like a silicate, yet must be "sensitive" to every element and introduce its frequencies at an intensity reflecting its concentration. Both the constancy of excitation and the transfer of reproducible amounts of energy from the source to the sample are of concern. The latter is especially important in quantitative work where intensities of spectral lines must be measured to calculate concentrations.

Flame excitation.   This is useful for easily activated substances. The low-temperature gas-air flame (1100 °C) of a Bunsen or Tirrill burner induces several of the characteristic electronic transitions of alkali metal atoms; other gas combinations used in efficient burner–aspirators provide temperatures high enough to volatilize and excite sensitively to emission about 40 additional elements. This type of source has found its widest use in the quantitative emission and absorption flame methods that will be discussed in Chapter 14 and will not be considered further here.

Electrical discharges.   These are very effective in volatilizing and exciting samples. Depending on the manner in which discharges are generated and their specific properties, they are classified as *arcs*, *sparks*, or *glow discharges*. The first two categories are generally restricted to systems with high current densities and the last to a discharge at low current density in a closed tube. What constitutes an arc or spark is loosely defined, and some procedures may be classified by either term. Conventionally, arcs are recognized as discharges that (a) must be initiated by an auxiliary spark or momentary mechanical connection across a gap and (b) produce minimal ionization. Sparks, on the other hand, will (a) jump their gaps unassisted and (b) give spectra richer in frequencies corresponding to higher-energy transitions.

The stability of an electrical discharge generally increases in the sequence arc < spark < glow discharge. Yet until recently the requisite sensitivity and intensity of emission was most easily obtained from arcs and sparks. Accordingly, they will be discussed first.

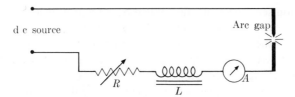

Fig. 13.6 Circuit for a direct-current arc.

Electric arc. The dc arc is one of the most versatile excitation devices in use. Its high sensitivity makes it valuable for qualitative analyses, and if its current is well stabilized it is also satisfactory for some quantitative determinations. Figure 13.6 shows a standard dc arc circuit. The dc source is usually a regulated power supply that furnishes 110 to 220 V at 3 to 30 A. Ammeter A and variable resistor R allow the current to be adjusted after the arc has been started between the electrode pair. Some stabilization against arc fluctuations is imperative. In this circuit it is provided by introduction of a series combination of iron core inductor L and resistor R that has a long time constant (L/R). The initial resistance of the air gap is too high to permit conduction; as a result the arc is "started" by closing its gap momentarily while 110 to 220 V dc are applied. Either the electrodes are brought together for an instant or both are contacted simultaneously by a noncontaminating conductor like a graphite rod.

An arc is an example of a sustained discharge in a gas (Section 11.3). Like all plasmas, it is a complex phenomenon. Three aspects deserve emphasis.

1. The energy available for excitation varies along the length of the arc. Near the cathode the plasma energy is highest—the temperature is about 5000 °C—as a result of a concentration of high-velocity ions, electrons, and atoms. For this reason samples to be examined are placed on the cathode where they are quickly vaporized into the high temperature region. There they are excited by bombardment.

2. It has a negative resistance characteristic, i.e. its resistance falls rapidly as its current increases. Thus, an external resistance like R in Fig. 13.6 must be added to limit the current. The means by which it serves as a ballast may be seen in Fig. 11.5.

3. The arc is actually a discharge between the anode and a small spot on the cathode; during operation it tends to wander over the cathode surface. Current fluctuations result from the changing arc length and temperature. While they are opposed by the RL circuit, they cannot be completely suppressed. Such arc "wander" causes emission intensities to fluctuate from moment to moment.*

As suggested, samples are nearly always introduced at or in the cathode. Procedures will be discussed in Section 13.12. Since volatilization is selective, not all lines can appear immediately in the spectrum. Higher-boiling substances enter the vapor last. Proper timing of the length of excitation and recording of spectra allow all components to contribute.

---

* The intensity of a reference line from the sample can be monitored and a feedback arrangement used to control the current supplied to the arc. Such an approach is not completely successful and in any event is more attractive for a steady-state analysis in which only a portion of a sample is volatilized.

The excitation sensitivity of a dc arc can be enhanced by a *Stallwood jet*, a device that surrounds the arc with a concentric curtain of gas such as an Ar-O$_2$ mixture. It serves both to cool the electrodes and the outer layer of the arc plasma and to exclude atmospheric gases. By cooling the plasma it slows sample volatilization and keeps a sample in the arc a longer time. Thus, it permits more efficient excitation. Further, by reducing pressure it narrows line widths. By excluding the atmosphere, the jet eliminates the formation of cyanogen (C$_2$N$_2$), whose intense emission bands often obscure or provide a heavy background for emission lines of interest.

High-voltage *ac arcs* are also used. These differ little from conventional low-voltage dc arcs except in the alternation of electrode polarity, a property that appreciably improves reproducibility.

Electric spark. Spark discharges have found their best application in quantitative work. They furnish high precision rather than great sensitivity. Basically, their circuitry is simple and much like that for an ac arc, although elaborate units have been devised to provide constancy and intensity of excitation as well as reasonable flexibility. Sources differ principally in the arrangement used to initiate breakdown in the spark gap.

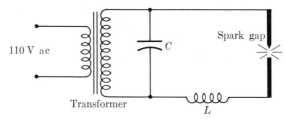

Fig. 13.7 Circuit for a spark excitation unit.

Figure 13.7 schematically illustrates a circuit for a condensed spark. The output of the transformer, which operates on a 115 or 230 V ac line, may range from 10,000 to 100,000 V, depending on the application. Capacitor C and inductor L bring about a series of sparks at the gap, each of which is in fact an oscillating electrical discharge. Oscillations are of a damped type and cause the polarity of the gap electrodes to reverse rapidly during the short (10^{-4} to 10^{-5} s) pulses, which may occur 1000 to 2000 times per second. Figure 13.8 suggests the current pattern of a single spark. The frequency of oscillation, duration of a spark and the amount of current will depend on the magnitudes of L and C and on electrode separation. Sparks will be produced whenever the transformer builds the voltage up to the breakdown potential of the gap. Yet conditions for starting the discharge are not strictly reproducible, and some timing provision is ordinarily made. A practical means is to use a second gap located between a rotating and a fixed electrode with control of the rate of rotation, so that discharges can occur only once per half-cycle, i.e., at the time of maximum charging of the capacitor.

Sparking may also be used for excitation of solutions. One such arrangement calls for the sparking electrode to be immersed to a depth of 1 or 2 mm and the other to be considerably deeper. Cooling must be provided to dissipate the heat produced by the electrolysis and sparking.

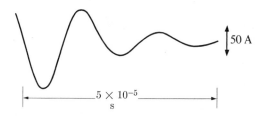

50 A

5 × 10⁻⁵
s

Fig. 13.8 Current oscillations during a discharge in a condensed spark circuit.

Multipurpose sources. Several compact commercial spectrograph excitation sources are available. They usually provide for a dc arc, ac arc, and a mechanically interrupted, high-voltage damped spark. The variety of discharges is sufficient to accommodate most types of qualitative and quantative analyses.

Plasma jet. All the foregoing devices have generated a plasma; i.e., a nearly neutral mixture of electrons* and positive ions. A higher-energy plasma should provide still more efficient excitation, if a means can be found to introduce a sample without extinguishing the discharge. The plasma jet or torch provides the condition needed by "pushing" a high-energy plasma from a dc arc by use of a flowing stream of gas. The plasma is propelled through a metallic ring, thereby constricting it and forcing its electron temperature into the range 8000 to 20,000 °K.† Excitation of a dissolved sample can be very efficiently accomplished in this atmosphere.

A plasma can also be formed within an induction coil if an external ignitor like a Tesla coil is available to start the discharge. Stability in this form of torch depends on matching the impedance of the induction heater coil to that of the plasma.

Glow discharge. Recently a way was described to secure a glow discharge sufficiently sensitive and intense to be generally useful in emission spectrometry. [14] The design of the excitation device is shown in cross section in Fig. 13.9. Precision-machined blocks for anode and cathode are penetrated by numerous ports (for evacuation, introduction of inert gas, and cooling) and form the sides of the cylindrical discharge chamber. A quartz window closes one end of the cylinder. The sample, which becomes part of the cathode, closes the other. Note that "O" rings are used to secure a seal. Anode and cathode are insulated from each other by a Teflon gasket.

In operation the sample is held tightly in place, the discharge chamber quickly evacuated and then filled with argon or other inert gas to 1 to 20 Torr. A potential difference (700 to 2500 V) is applied to start and sustain a glow discharge. Bombardment leads to volatilization and excitation of the surface layer of the sample.

The excited atoms collect in a slender (thickness about one mean-free-path length), flat emission layer as shown in the figure. The process is much like that in the hollow-cathode lamp (Section 11.3). The small distance between cathode and anode causes

---

* In a gas negative molecular ions are unstable relative to free electrons.

† Equilibrium is far from being attained and gas molecules are only at a temperature of about 3000 °K!

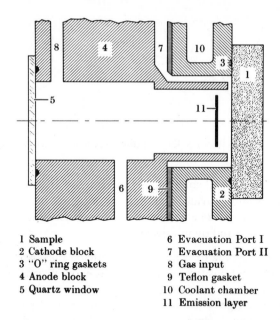

1 Sample	6 Evacuation Port I
2 Cathode block	7 Evacuation Port II
3 "O" ring gaskets	8 Gas input
4 Anode block	9 Teflon gasket
5 Quartz window	10 Coolant chamber
	11 Emission layer

Fig. 13.9 Glow discharge source for emission spectroscopy. Ion bombardment of the sample releases atoms that are excited to emission in the thin layer shown. (Courtesy of Carl Zeiss, Inc.)

the cathodic sputtering to occur over a narrow volume and also defines the thin emission layer. There is little ionic emission and emission lines are sharp.*

Advantages of the source are many. Samples are volatilized and excited at a sufficiently uniform rate (reproducibility $\pm 1\%$) that a very stable intensity is achieved. Integration of emission over a short interval (after the surface layer of oxide is removed in the first 1 to 60 s) ensures a relative error less than $\pm 1\%$ in determination of a concentration. Matrix effects essentially disappear. Since emission occurs in a thin layer, self-absorption is minimized and a linear relationship between intensity and concentration is *observed up to* 100%. While emission lines are identical to those obtained in an arc, their intensity is of the order of a condensed spark discharge.

In general, samples must be metallic. Plates, wire, and foil samples are easily analyzed. In the case of small samples, an inert holder of graphite can be used. Depth analyses are possible also because of the uniform sputtering rate.

Microprobe. Microsampling of the surface of any specimen is possible by use of a focused laser beam (a microscope is used) or a microspark. In this way an analysis can be performed on an area whose dimensions are of the order of 10 μm. A laser microprobe accomplishes the vaporization of the spot and sometimes also its excitation. If necessary, an arc between auxiliary electrodes placed just above the target spot can excite the vapor. A spark microprobe makes use of an electrode whose tip is polished to a 1 μm point. After it is positioned about 25 μm from the sample (which must either conduct electricity or be deposited as a thin film on a conductor), an ac

---

* Though not shown, a "hollow-cathode" mode can also be achieved by use of a different cathode assembly.

spark is used to volatilize and excite to emission an area just below. Such microprobes allow effective sampling of small areas of any material such as individual cells in biological samples or inclusion areas in alloys.

13.7 THE SPECTROSCOPIC OPTICAL SYSTEM

Emission spectra may be examined by means of any optical arrangement that will identify component frequencies and their intensities. Generally instruments for this purpose are classified as *spectroscopes* if they are visual devices, *spectrographs* if they record many wavelengths simultaneously (either by photographic or photoelectric means), *and spectrometers* if they scan a spectrum. Actually, in nearly all types except the first intensities are also determined. These distinctions lose their usefulness in a modular approach where a great many kinds of modules can be considered. Accordingly, the terms spectrograph and spectrometer will be used nearly interchangeably. In the discussion that follows only dispersing instruments will be taken up; interferometric spectrometers will be treated in Section 17.12.

The optical system of a spectrometer is basically a monochromator, though many spectrometers lack an exit slit. For that reason the detailed examination of monochromators in the previous chapter will be assumed to provide the essential treatment of theory and main aspects of design of spectrometers. In this section the general optical operations to be performed will be summarized and a few aspects of design especially pertinent to emission spectrometry will be reviewed briefly.

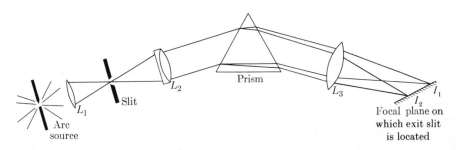

Fig. 13.10 Schematic diagram of a simple prism spectroscope. The focal plane is usually curved.

The general functions to be accomplished by a spectrometer may be deduced from an examination of the simple device illustrated in Fig. 13.10. In sequence:

1. The system must collect a maximum amount of radiation from the excitation source and illuminate the (entrance) slit, a narrow, adjustable rectangular aperture. (In Fig. 13.10 lens L_1 gathers light from the source and focuses it on the slit. The illuminated slit is a sharp, bright rectangle that can be imaged easily by the optics of the instrument. Its images are the familiar "lines" of a *line spectrum*.)

2. The rays from the far side of the slit must ordinarily be collimated (made parallel) to achieve optimum performance by the dispersing element. (Lens L_2 collimates.)

3. The system must disperse or separate closely lying frequencies. (The prism shape, orientation, dimensions, and optical properties will determine the dispersion.)

4. The dispersed light must be focused to an image of the entrance slit. (Lens L_3 focuses.)

5. A detector must respond to the intensity of the signal at each position along the focal curve. (A detector is not shown in Fig. 13.10; in general, a photomultiplier tube or a photographic plate or film serves this purpose.)

The quality of a spectrum will vary greatly with the slit design (Section 12.3) and conditions of illumination. To secure reasonable line intensities, light from the excitation source must be collected over as large a solid angle as feasible and focused efficiently on the slit. An arrangement of a condensing lens L_1 which fills the collimating lens L_2 with light and provides maximum spectral line intensity and resolution is illustrated in Fig. 13.11. Note that only a small fraction of the light from the source is utilized. The slit may not be uniformly illuminated by this arrangement, and for quantitative work a longer focal length condensing lens is sometimes substituted as in Fig. 13.12. In all cases the collimating lens and slit should be positioned so that light from the slit covers the entire height of the collimator, and the prism or grating in turn is illuminated over its useful breadth. Otherwise, resolution will be poor.

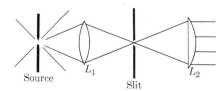

Fig. 13.11 Illumination of a slit by an arrangement providing maximum intensity at the slit.

While resolution is a measure of the quality of horizontal definition of a line, *astigmatism* is a measure of the lack of quality in vertical definition. Most spectrographs show little astigmatism, especially in their useful ranges. The more stigmatic, or free of astigmatism, a spectrograph is, the less spectral lines are spread out vertically and reduced in intensity per unit height. In photographic recording only "horizontal" differences in density of lines are measured as a spectrum is scanned; thus astigmatism can introduce serious errors in quantitative work. The error is less serious if photoelectric detection is used, for in this case a whole line image is detected.

13.8 SPECTROGRAPH DESIGNS

A variety of spectrographs has been designed because of varied needs for dispersion, resolution, wavelength range, speed, and other characteristics in actual applications. It should be kept in mind that certain characteristics may be mutually exclusive. For example, resolution is nearly always achieved by sacrificing "speed." Dispersion and wavelength range are another such pair: A high-dispersion instrument inherently has a short spectral range. For convenience, definitions of resolution and dispersion for prism and grating systems discussed in Chapter 12 are summarized in Table 13.3.

Both prism and grating spectrographs will be discussed below. In general, prism instruments offer advantages of (a) lower cost, (b) lower scattered light, (c) greater

Table 13.3 Some Spectrographic Performance Parameters

Parameter	Defining equations for	
Resolution	**Prism spectrometer**	**Grating spectrometer**
Resolution or resolving power R is a measure of ability to achieve a separation of nearly identical wavelengths λ and $\lambda + \Delta\lambda$. $R = \lambda/\Delta\lambda$ (Dimensionless)	For a single pass through a symmetrical prism at minimum deviation, $$R_{max} = t\left(\frac{dn}{d\lambda}\right),$$ where t is prism thickness at base and $dn/d\lambda$ is the change in its refractive index with wavelength.	$R_{max} = mN$, where N is the total number of rulings and m the order of the spectrum observed.
Dispersion		
1. *Angular* dispersion $d\theta/d\lambda$ is the angular separation $d\theta$ achieved for a wavelength interval $d\lambda$. (Unit: rad nm^{-1})	For a single pass through symmetrical prism at minimum deviation: $$d\theta/d\lambda = \frac{d\theta}{dn}\cdot\frac{dn}{d\lambda}$$ $$= \frac{1}{(1 - n^2/4)^{1/2}}\frac{C}{(\lambda - \lambda_0)^2},$$ where λ_0 and C are constants to be evaluated for a given prism.	For a fixed angle of incidence: $$\frac{d\theta}{d\lambda} = \frac{m}{d\cos\beta},$$ where d is the grating constant and β the angle of diffraction.
2. *Linear* dispersion $dl/d\lambda$, is a measure of the spread dl of wavelength interval $d\lambda$ along the focal curve of an instrument. (Unit: mm nm^{-1})	$dl/d\lambda = f\,d\theta/d\lambda$, where f is the effective focal length of the optical system.	$$\frac{dl}{d\lambda} = \frac{mr}{d\cos\beta},$$ where r is the focal length if a lens is used, or the distance from grating to focal curve, if a mirror is used.
3. *Reciprocal linear* dispersion $d\lambda/dl$ is the inverse of the linear dispersion. (Unit: nm mm^{-1})	$$d\lambda/dl = \frac{1}{f}\frac{d\lambda}{d\theta}$$	$$\frac{d\lambda}{dl} = \frac{d\cos\beta}{mr}$$

compactness, (d) sturdiness, and (e) simpler maintenance. In turn grating spectrographs will possess advantages in terms of (a) greater dispersion, (b) a dispersion nearly linear with wavelength, and (c) higher resolution.

Prism spectrographs. The simplest prism instrument is the Cornu type that was illustrated in Fig. 13.10. It is often used as a spectroscope. The Amici prism shown in Fig. 21.3 sees frequent use as a *direct-vision spectroscope*. If so used, a slit defines the entering ray.

Constant-deviation prism spectrographs.   In these a fixed angle is maintained between the entrant ray and the central exit ray, i.e. one directed to the center of the focal plane; the instruments are based on mountings such as the Pellin–Broca or Wadsworth arrangements (Section 12.5). Since the central wavelength in the exit beam is identified by the prism setting, which facilitates scanning, this type of mounting lends itself to use in a spectrometer. Large prisms are ordinarily employed to secure high resolution.

One of the most widely used arrangements is the *Littrow mounting* shown in Fig. 12.8. Since every light ray traverses the prism twice, the design features a considerably greater dispersion in a quite compact arrangement. And because the two passes of the beam in opposite directions cancel birefringence and optical rotation, even anisotropic and optically active substances can be used for the prism. Note that a single lens serves the dual function of collimator and camera lens. Clearly, a mirror might serve in lieu of the lens.

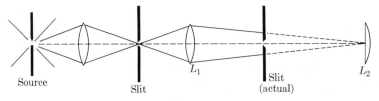

Fig. 13.12 An arrangement providing uniform illumination of a slit at moderate intensity.

Large commercial Littrow spectrographs usually have quartz prisms and cover a wavelength range of from 200 to 800 nm (2000 to 8000 Å). The dispersion is sufficiently great so that three 25 cm photographic plates are required to record a complete spectrum. Thus, about a third of the range impinges on the plate holder at a time. To shift from one part of the spectral region to another, adjustments of the prism table, focusing lens, and plate holder are required. These operations are well defined and easily accomplished. If studies are confined to the visible range, a glass prism is often substituted to secure greater dispersion.

Concave grating spectrographs.   Early grating spectrographs were nearly all designed around a concave reflection grating. High dispersion and resolution were achieved by use of a long, closely ruled grating. Since the concave surface made a collimator and focusing device unnecessary and eliminated the energy loss associated with them, energy throughput was also enhanced. There were several accompanying disadvantages. Mechanical problems were created since for a focus to be maintained on changing spectral regions, both slit and detector had to be moved in complex fashion relative to one another and the grating. The grating cost was high since each spectograph required an original grating. A further problem is that a concave grating introduces two aberrations, *astigmatism* and *coma*.

A variety of commercial concave grating instruments is presently available. Actually, the differences are not marked and most types are based on the Rowland circle described below. Since gratings of long focal length are ordinarily used to secure high dispersion and resolution, such spectrographs are inherently bulky. Also, they must be designed for very fine adjustment to realize the high-quality spectra they are capable of.

The earliest arrangement, the *Rowland mounting*, is historically interesting but infrequently used because of its bulk and the difficulty of making the necessary precise adjustments of the heavy moving parts. In this mounting, regardless of the portion of the spectrum being observed, the angle enclosed by lines drawn from grating center to the slit and from the slit to the center of the photographic plate is always 90°. Slit, grating, and plate are so arranged as to lie on the circumference of the *Rowland circle*, which is just the focal curve of the concave grating. Thus, the circle has a diameter equal to the radius of curvature of the grating. Unfortunately, this mounting produces considerable astigmatism.

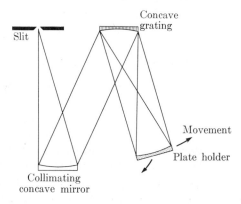

Fig. 13.13 The Wadsworth mounting for a concave grating.

Adding the concave mirror as in the *Wadsworth mounting*, Fig. 13.13, can virtually completely eliminate astigmatism. The extra mirror collimates light from the entrance slit before it impinges on the grating. The speed and light-gathering power of this design are greater than for many others, since the grating is used at about half the image distance. But bulk is again a disadvantage, and the focal curve is not quite circular. The mounting is often used. It is one of the very few that utilize a concave grating yet are not based on the Rowland circle.

A more compact instrument based on the Rowland circle is obtained by use of the Eagle arrangement. In this design, shown in Fig. 13.14, all components are on one side of the Rowland circle, giving a layout that resembles the Littrow prism arrangement. Since rays from the grating return over a path nearly the same as that taken in incidence, astigmatism is slight. Note that by use of a totally reflecting prism the slit may be located within the Rowland circle.

Other useful designs for concave-grating spectrographs based on the Rowland circle are the Paschen–Runge mounting, which has often been preferred for large gratings, the Abney mounting, and the off-axis Eagle mounting. Most have been used for research instruments.

As discussed in Section 12.7, concave-grating instruments are now chiefly constructed for work in the far UV, where their smaller reflectance losses offer a decided advantage. For other spectral regions grating spectrographs are usually designed around planar gratings in mountings that require concave mirrors for collimating and focusing.

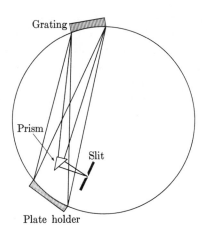

Fig. 13.14 The Eagle mounting for a grating spectrograph.

Plane-grating instruments. Spectrographs based on planar diffraction gratings owe their attractiveness relative to concave-grating instruments to the development (a) of processes for precision replication of gratings and (b) of designs and components permitting more compact spectrometric systems substantially free of optical aberrations. The optical features of a representative plane-grating spectrograph are shown schematically in Fig. 13.15. The mounting is of the Ebert type. In contrast to the side-by-side positioning of slit and detector in the Ebert monochromator in Fig. 12.18,

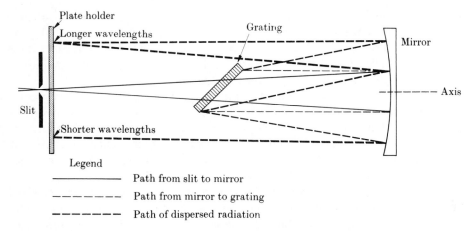

Fig. 13.15 Top view of an Ebert spectrograph. This modification features an over-under arrangement in which the slit and plate holder are centered on the mirror axis *below* and *above* the grating, respectively. The entrance slit is directly below the plate (though it is here shown farther from the mirror for clarity). It is necessary to tilt the slit slightly to overcome a slight tilting of lines on the plate. The focusing action of the mirror is shown (by the heavy lines) for a single relatively long wavelength. No provision is shown for separating orders; a fore-prism or filter might be so used. (Courtesy of Jarrell-Ash Co.)

this mounting is an over-under arrangement.* The Czerny–Turner design (Section 12.7) offers nearly identical possibilities.

Example An Ebert spectrograph with a 3.4 m focal length mirror and a 900 line/mm grating blazed at 330.0 nm gives a useful range of 210.0 to 470.0 nm in the first order when set at an angle of incidence of 5.8°. The linear reciprocal dispersion is 0.5 nm mm^{-1} (5.0 Å mm^{-1}). The second-order UV spectrum (105.0 to 235.0 nm) will overlap unless blocked.

A plane-grating instrument offers several advantages over one with a concave grating. With a flat grating greater spectral brightness, or grating efficiency, can be achieved since the grating can be blazed for peak efficiency in the spectral region of interest (Section 12.6). An optical design can be realized that permits a mechanically simple arrangement for wavelength adjustment, the possibility of regular, aberration-free use of large angles of incidence, and features a virtually flat focal curve. As a result, a planar instrument has the potential of:

1. A considerably greater wavelength range; since large angles of incidence can be used without difficulty, such instruments have access to the long-wavelength region ($\lambda > 700$ nm) found in the first-order spectrum at these angles.

2. A high dispersion and resolution in a moderately compact instrument: High-order (large m) visible and UV spectra can be efficiently observed with an appropriate planar grating and a large angle of incidence.

Example A 2950 line/mm grating blazed at 4 μm is used in an Ebert spectrograph with a 37.6° angle of incidence. At this angle the 18th order (219.0–241.0 nm) band is centered at the detector. A high dispersion, 0.044 nm mm^{-1} (0.44 Å mm^{-1}), and a theoretical resolution of 725,000 are secured. All the lower-order, longer-wavelength bands that also appear can be separated by an order-sorter arrangement (see next paragraph).

Order-sorters. How can different orders of spectra be effectively prevented from superposing? One attractive solution is use of a preliminary prism spectroscope. Since it can be positioned in such a way that only a narrow band of wavelengths enters the companion grating instrument at each prism setting, it may be termed an order-sorter (Section 12.6). In this case it is advantageous to employ a spectroscope of relatively low dispersion so that a fairly broad wavelength band (perhaps 30 nm) can be directed to the entrance slit of the grating section.

There are two useful orientations of the order-sorter relative to the grating disperser. If it is desired to photograph only a narrow portion of a spectrum at a time, the prism disperser can be arranged to give horizontal dispersion, i.e., dispersion in

---

* In the side-by-side Ebert mountaing aberrations are missing at the exit slit, making the design attractive for a scanning spectrometer. Astigmatism and coma occur on either side of the slit position, however, and are appreciable a few centimeters from it. The over-under arrangement of Fig. 13.15 achieves relative freedom from these aberrations even at the ends of a 75 cm plate centered as shown.

the same direction as the grating unit. For example, this orientation is used in a double monochromator.

What is the consequence of turning the axis of the order-sorter through 90°? This shift yields the other useful orientation. The spectrum produced by the prism stage will now appear along the height of the entrance slit of the grating unit. In the grating spectrum different orders will appear at different heights. [15] Since successive orders will appear one above another, wavelengths in each can be identified by the usual techniques (Section 13.13). A photographic plate will be a suitable detector for this kind of complex spectrum or "sorted ordergram."

Example A fore-prism is used as an order-sorter for an echelle grating or an echellette grating blazed at a large angle (see Section 12.6) and the resultant spectrum is recorded on a photographic plate. Consider that the fore-prism causes "red" or longer wavelengths to appear at the top of the slit and "blue" or shorter·wavelengths to appear at the bottom. Recall that a grating must display longer wavelengths in lower orders. As a result, in this case the lowest-order grating spectrum produced will appear at the top of the photographic plate. Successively higher orders will be arrayed parallel to the first at lower and lower positions on the plate. Note that a given wavelength will appear at a particular height along the entrance slit. Thus, for an incident wavelength to be imaged simultaneously, in say the tenth and eleventh orders, it must be at the same vertical position on the plate in each order. This can be true only if the orders run uphill across the plate. (See Exercise 13.1.)

It can be shown that the height of lines in each order is fixed by the slit width of the fore-prism stage. For that reason a slit width of at least 2 mm is desirable so that lines can be observed.

The physical separation of orders on the plate is determined by the dispersion of the prism instrument. If its dispersion is small, there will be little separation, but a wide range of wavelengths can be registered on the spectrograph plate. Conversely, a large dispersion will lead to well-separated orders, each of which registers a short wavelength range. Both vertical separation and range are important and a compromise must be struck.

Polychromators. Direct readout of several wavelengths simultaneously can be arranged also. It is only necessary to locate several slits and detectors at appropriate positions along the focal curve of a spectrometer. Since 10 to 25 wavelengths can be monitored simultaneously, this type of spectrometer is a versatile device that is attractive for routine precision elemental analysis. The detection and computational aspects of this type of spectrometer will be discussed in Section 13.11.

Alignment. It should be emphasized that a very stable mounting and constant room conditions are required to maintain wavelength calibration in a spectrometer for any length of time. Changes in temperature will affect the grating constant d, the refractive index of air, the refractive index of a prism (an effect smaller than the variation of n_{air}), and in more subtle ways the alignment of spectrograph parts. In a direct-reading instrument servo-control to maintain exact alignment is therefore well worthwhile.

It is generally sufficient to monitor the position of a single reference line to preserve alignment. One alignment from an auxiliary source such as a mercury lamp is directed through the spectrograph toward a very closely spaced pair of *exit* slits arranged so that one passes the right side of the reference line and the other the left side. When alignment is correct, uniform illumination is received by the phototube detectors behind each slit. Should there be a shift in alignment, the unbalance signal can be used to drive a servomotor to effect realignment. A straightforward way is to rotate a quartz slab behind the entrance slit. Such an adjustment displaces all wavelengths and is continued until the reference line returns to correct registration. Note that a similar arrangement is used to null beam displacements in some recording refractometers (Section 21.6).

13.9 INTEGRATION OF RESPONSE

Regardless of kind of sample and method of excitation, instantaneous line intensities in an emission spectrum vary randomly and rapidly. Two reasons may be cited. (a) There is at present no way to control with high precision the many variables involved in volatilizing and exciting atoms, and (b) since only a minute fraction of the atoms are in excited states at one time, the emission of a sample is sensitive even to small changes in conditions. When these fluctuations are superposed on the selective volatilization that occurs with many samples, it is clear that quantitative analysis cannot be based on the instantaneous signal. A way to solve this problem is to integrate the detector output over many seconds or minutes.* If the total response is obtained for an interval that is long compared with the period of the unsteadiness, the random fluctuations should tend to average out. Of course, only if an internal standard, that is a reference, is simultaneously monitored, will any drift be allowed for.

Two different approaches to detection and integration have been used, the photographic and photoelectric. They differ mainly in the nature of their response. A photographic emulsion acts as detector-transducer *and* integrator, but a phototube is only a detector-transducer. Accordingly, it must be followed by a suitable electrical integrator. Each approach is important in its own right and will be considered in some detail in the sections to follow.

There is sufficient remaining variability and drift in excitation conditions during a "burn" to make an *internal standard* method a necessity for quantitative work (Section 13.14). Even in qualitative analyses it is desirable since approximate concentration levels are of interest. Since a reference element is brought to emission and measured under the same conditions as the "analytical" elements, the method provides a "second channel." The ratio of the integrated intensities of a sample–reference pair of lines may be interpreted with the knowledge that the effect of large fluctuations and drift has been at least greatly reduced.

13.10 PHOTOGRAPHIC DETECTION

A photographic emulsion is a simple, versatile, composite detector-transducer-recorder that is widely used in emission spectrometry. It offers simultaneous detection of lines over a broad wavelength range (though a later line-by-line determination of density must be made for quantitative work), sensitivity, and high resolution. Section

---

* An optical or electrical null procedure can stabilize an arc but not entirely eliminate arc wander or suppress variation in excitation conditions across an arc. Similarly, while reproducible sparking can be achieved, fluctuations in excitation across the spark gap cannot be removed. The glow discharge method of excitation reduces variability still further.

11.7 should be consulted for details of this type of detector. Use of emulsions in quantitative work is discussed in Section 13.14.

13.11 PHOTOELECTRIC DETECTION

For spectral work in the 190–850 nm range, i.e., in all the regular UV and visible, a multiplier phototube detector offers the advantage of extreme sensitivity (at least 100 times that of the most sensitive emulsions), speed of response, and ease of use. Where many samples are to be analyzed or analysis at trace levels is frequent, this means of measuring intensities offers great advantages.

Two physical arrangements for photoelectric detection are in common use. One is provided in the scanning spectrometer. This device is basically a scanning mono-chromator (Section 12.10) in which a phototube is placed behind the exit slit. For details of multiplier operation of this type of detector at regular low light levels the reader should consult Section 11.7. For measurements at very low light levels phase-sensitive detection or photon counting techniques are used (Section 8.8).

The other arrangement is exemplified by the *direct*-reading spectrograph. In this device multiplier phototubes are located behind movable slits placed along the focal curve of a spectrograph, one wavelength being detected per tube. It can be set to receive no more than 25 to 65 lines at one time, as a result of spacing and other restric-tions. While such an instrument is too expensive and limited for general use, it is ideally suited to the analysis of a great many similar samples. For example, the steel, aluminum, and metallurgical industries make use of many instruments of this type.

In operation, the intensities of lines are compared by determining the ratios of the total outputs of the properly positioned detectors during an interval of from perhaps 25 to 40 seconds. At the output of each detector is a suitable capacitor-resistor circuit, which receives and integrates the output signal. Since the voltage across the capacitor at the end of the exposure is a function of the accrued charge (detector current × time), the capacitor voltage is proportional to the time integral of the line intensity. Inten-sities can be compared by forming voltage ratios electrically. Finally, reference must be made to the calibration data in some other fashion to calculate the composition of the sample. Often this step is also done automatically. Since all the variables in this detector-integrator arrangement are under effective control, quantitative results of $\pm 1\%$ precision can be secured under optimum conditions. As the concentration of an element falls below 2%, the uncertainty rises gradually.

13.12 PREPARATION OF MATERIALS

Metal samples are often arced or sparked directly, i.e. they are formed into self-electrodes by casting or machining. If they are cast, rapid cooling is important so that a solid of uniform composition is obtained. This method is particularly suitable for the quantitative analysis of alloys melting above 500 °C.

For quantitative studies on other materials it is more convenient to prepare powdered samples and, sometimes, solutions. After powdering, the sample is mixed thoroughly with a suitable base material to minimize the matrix effect (see below) and introduced into a hollow that has been machined in the cathode or lower electrode. Ultra-pure graphite is ideal for preparation of cathodes of this type; it machines well, introduces very little background in the emission spectrum, and is very high-melting. A variety of cup shapes are available commercially in graphite rods of about 7 mm diameter. Sometimes flat copper electrodes are used also.

Interferences with volatilization, dissociation, and excitation processes are common in emission spectrometry. For a given element the rate and extent of these processes are dependent on the chemical compound and the state in which the element occurs in a sample. Accordingly, the interferences are termed a *matrix effect*. How can the effect be minimized? The best way proves to be powdering a sample and mixing it thoroughly with a *buffer* such as powdered graphite. When the buffer is in excess, it determines the rate of volatilization and the temperature and plasma composition of the arc. As a result, matrix effects are "leveled" or held constant in a series of samples. For maintenance of constant conditions in the arc, the buffer should have a low ionization energy, as graphite does. In some instances lithium carbonate or zinc oxide are added to provide an internal standard and a smoother "burn." Interference from unduly strong lines of major constituents is also avoided by such dilution.

Alternatively, a sample such as a slag or an ore may be fused with lithium borate (or with a lithium carbonate–boric oxide mixture) to form a glass, cooled, powdered, mixed with graphite, and pelletized.

Solutions or liquid samples may be introduced into an arc or spark by a variety of procedures. Often a drop or two is placed on the upper surface of a carbon or copper rod, evaporated, and the residue volatilized and excited to emission. Alternatively, the solution is brought into the arc by a rotating electrode, the lower edge of which dips into the solution, or may be handled by some other means prior to excitation. Graphite electrodes are versatile and very widely used, but copper electrodes are often preferred for dilute solutions. Since copper is not porous like graphite, all the solution residue is left on the electrode tip after evaporation of the solvent, and high sensitivity is secured.

The sensitivity of detection of many elements is improved by the use of an atmosphere other than air. For example, CN bands can be eliminated and volatilization enhanced by use of an $Ar-O_2$ mixture with a Stallwood jet (Section 13.6).

13.13 QUALITATIVE ANALYSIS

Elements can be precisely determined by emission spectrometry. Wavelengths and especially the pattern of wavelengths comprising a spectrum are unique for each element. Thus, determining a single line with great exactness, or three or more with ordinary precision, is sufficient to confirm an element's presence. A disconcerting feature may be the exceptional sensitivity of spectrographic analysis: It is common to find ten elements in a sample suspected to contain three. To lessen confusion, a qualitative report should always include the approximate concentrations of the elements detected.

The technique of qualitative spectral analysis devolves into a search for the most persistent or sensitive lines of elements. Except for some of the Group IA and IIA metals, the most persistent lines are found in the ultraviolet. In general they result from a transition between the p- and s-levels in the atom.

As useful lines are located, their intensities should be noted in a consistent way.

Table 13.4 Most Sensitive Lines of a Few Elements

Element	Lines, nm	Detection limit, ppm
Al	309.27, 308.22	5
Ba	455.40, 614.17	2
Cr	425.43, 427.48	1
Fe	374.56, 241.05	1
Mn	259.38, 257.61	1
V	309.31, 290.88	5

The designations "very strong," "strong," etc., are frequently used. But before these labels can be converted into an estimate of concentration, allowance must be made for the relative ease of excitation of the lines, which is reflected in the sensitivity of detection of elements. From Table 13.4 it may be seen that a faint barium line will represent a higher concentration than will a faint chromium line.

Sensitivity. The primary consideration in obtaining sensitivity is to use the highest dispersion possible. Whether a faint spectral line can be measured depends on the ratio of its intensity to that of the background. In other words, sensitivity depends on the signal-to-noise ratio. The background is simply stray light that has been scattered and reflected by the optics instead of being transmitted. Since the amount of this radiation will be governed by the slit width, the greater the dispersion of an instrument the lower is the background intensity at any wavelength. The stray light must be spread over a greater area in an instrument of high dispersion. The width and intensity of spectral lines, however, is essentially constant. Changing from one spectrograph to another should not alter line intensities so long as equal slit apertures are used. The instrument of highest dispersion thus gives the largest signal-to-noise ratio and the best sensitivity. By the same token a grating spectrograph should be used at its highest useful order for maximum sensitivity.

Identification of wavelengths. Generally, wavelengths are established by a direct comparison with one or more known spectra. These are best photographed side by side with the unknown spectrum. The spectral range being recorded should be noted. If a grating instrument is being used, linear dispersion can be expected but one must watch for overlapping orders. Less frequently, a comparison spectrum is prepared separately. For example, this method is used with some grating instruments, which are supplied with composite master spectra containing three or four of the most persistent lines of each element. Though convenient, there is the problem of accurate alignment of the spectra in this case.

Relatively simple spectra, like those emitted by many brasses, are best compared with a constituent metal like copper. More complex spectra are bracketed by the iron spectrum, which is rich in lines and a valuable wavelength standard. Once an unknown wavelength is established, the element corresponding to it may be identified by use of tables. [17, 18] Figure 13.16 shows portions of a copper and an iron spectrum photographed on the same plate. When the analyst is inexperienced, it is also advisable to photograph additional spectra on plates to aid in the initial identification of the lines

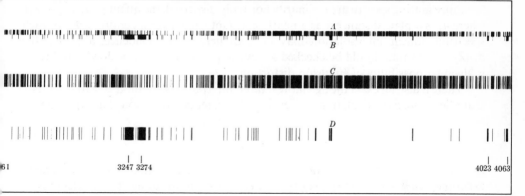

Fig. 13.16 Portions of a copper and an iron spectrum produced by a high-dispersion spectrograph. Spectra A and B of iron and copper, respectively, are repeated at a much greater slit height in curves C and D. This first-order grating spectrum was obtained with a linear reciprocal dispersion of 5.4 Å mm^{-1} on glass plates. Conditions: 10 μm slit width, 3 A dc arc, 10 s exposure for iron, 35 s for copper. (Courtesy of Jarrell-Ash Co.)

of the standard. Spectra quite poor in lines, such as those of sodium or mercury (vapor lamp sources), serve well for this purpose. As he gains experience a spectroscopist increasingly recognizes lines by identifying patterns. For example, the intense iron triplet at 310 nm (3100 Å) is one familiar cluster.

Some sort of magnification is necessary in the comparison to realize the resolution inherent in a spectrographic plate or film. Commonly, enlarged images of the several spectra are projected onto a flat screen. An imposed scale or a ruler can then be used for distance measurements. Alternatively, high precision can be secured by employing a traveling microscope mounted so that it can move horizontally along a micrometer screw and scan neighboring spectra simultaneously.

In the comparison, a line falling between two known lines can be assigned a wavelength by interpolation. If the dispersion is prismatic (Section 12.4), the interpolation may be done linearly only over very short ranges and in a region where the dispersion is fairly high. In the case illustrated in Fig. 13.17, interpolation between known λ_1 and λ_2 will locate λ_x. It may be assumed that

$$\frac{d_1}{d_2} = \frac{\lambda_x - \lambda_1}{\lambda_2 - \lambda_1} \quad \text{or} \quad \lambda_x = (\lambda_2 - \lambda_1)\frac{d_1}{d_2} + \lambda_1 \qquad (13.12)$$

to a first approximation.

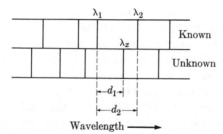

Wavelength ⟶

Fig. 13.17 Determination of a wavelength by interpolation.

Since grating spectra are ordinarily normally dispersed, the quantity $d_1/(\lambda_2 - \lambda_1)$, where d_1 is a plate distance, has a nearly constant value over an entire order of each spectrum. Linear interpolation may be used here with confidence, although the $d_1/(\lambda_2 - \lambda_1)$ value should be checked at several points. It will vary slowly, and there is always a possibility of emulsion distortion.

There is also an exact though more tedious interpolation method, due to Hartman, that allows precise calculation of λ even with prismatic dispersion. The equation

$$\lambda_x = \lambda_0 + \frac{c}{d_x - d_0} \tag{13.13}$$

is used. Note that there are three constants, λ_0, c, and d_0, that must be evaluated experimentally. The process may be carried out by substituting the wavelengths λ_x and distances d_x of three known lines from an arbitrary point and solving the three equations simultaneously.

13.14 QUANTITATIVE ANALYSIS

Spectroscopy is deservedly popular as a means of rapid quantitative elemental analysis. The highest present development in this direction is that of the photo-electric recording instrument, which gives almost instantaneous results of good precision ($\pm 1\%$). An internal standard is nearly always required with arc and spark excitation.

When photographic detection is used, spectrographic accuracy is sometimes lower than is desirable. Yet the convenience and versatility of this approach, as well as the advantage of a compact permanent record, has led to its very wide use. With spark excitation an accuracy of 2 to 5% is ordinarily achieved. Photographic spectrography with arc or spark excitation is further limited by a loss of sensitivity as concentrations increase. Even where considerable accuracy can be sacrificed, 10 to 20% of an element is the practical upper limit in an ordinary quantitative analysis. On the other hand, with glow discharge excitation, which is especially suitable for metallic samples, good accuracy extends to high concentrations.

In trace element analysis, an accuracy of about 5% becomes much more attractive. Furthermore, the sensitivity of the technique is high at concentrations below 0.1%. In this concentration range emission spectroscopy is superior to many other quantitative methods.

Almost all quantitative studies in spectroscopy are based on the measurement of the intensity of the line of an unknown relative to the intensity of a suitable line of an *internal standard* or reference element. The pair of lines should be close in wavelength, about equal in excitation energy, and influenced alike by variations in procedure or conditions. Because of these requirements they are sometimes called a homologous pair. Although suitable pairs may be selected by experiment, extensive data are available in literature and ought to be consulted. Wherever possible, the element serving as standard should be one present originally in high concentration, although it may also be one that can be added without too much difficulty. For example, if a routine steel analysis is being run, one or more iron lines would be appropriate internal standards. Figure 13.18 illustrates an intensity ratio–composition curve for

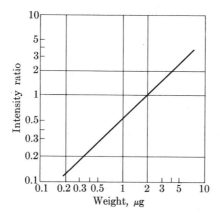

Fig. 13.18 Plot of spectrographic intensity ratio for Ni 2632.9/Mo 2775.4 as a function of the concentration of nickel. (By permission, from N. H. Nachtrieb, *Principles and Practice of Spectrochemical Analysis.* New York: McGraw-Hill, 1950.)

a good pair obtained by sparking a solution between copper electrodes. Note the wide concentration range over which the nickel is varied.

Photographic procedures. In most spectrography, photographic detection is used for reasons of convenience and flexibility. Section 11.7 provides information about photographic emulsions. First, the type of emulsion used must be calibrated in the wavelength region of interest. A curve relating the density of a line (as read by a microphotometer or densitometer) to its intensity must be developed. The details of a very reliable two-line procedure for calibration of emulsions have been given by Churchill.* In general, this method seems preferable to the step sector and other calibration procedures. With the emulsion calibration curve, densities of lines can be translated into intensities and a working curve like Fig. 13.18 can be prepared for each unknown element. This curve must be obtained under constant conditions of excitation, photographic recording and processing, and examination of the plate. To prepare the curve a series of standard samples covering the expected range of the sought component should be used. The standards should hold the internal reference element concentrations constant. An alternative to obtaining a "working" curve is bracketing the unknown spectrum with knowns believed to have concentrations of the element being analyzed just above and below the value in the unknown, and then interpolating. In this case as well, all spectra must be produced under identical conditions.

When only moderate precision (5 to 20%) is needed, a *semiquantitative analysis* will suffice. This type of analysis can be carried out more quickly. One method is the dilution technique described in the following example.

Example In the dilution method of semiquantitative analysis the following set of mixtures is made up from graphite and the analytical sample: (1) 100 mg of sample (2) 10 mg sample and

---

* J. R. Churchill, *Ind. Eng. Chem., Anal. Ed.* **16**, 653 (1944).

90 mg graphite; (3) 1 mg sample, 99 mg graphite; (4) 0.1 mg sample and 100 mg graphite. Each mixture is a tenfold further dilution of the original sample. This set and a 100 mg standard that contains known concentrations of elements thought to be present (in a graphite base) is completely "burned."

Relative line intensities are then observed and approximate concentrations of elements are determined by simple comparison. For example, if the intensity of a sensitive copper line in mixture (3) approximately matches that in the standard, the copper concentration in the original sample must be about 100 times that in the standard. Similarly, an intensity match between a lead line in the standard and the lead line from mixture (2) indicates the lead is present at 10 times its concentration in the standard.

Microphotometry. The comparison of line intensities on a photographic film or plate requires the use of an instrument that will measure the relative transmittance of the line images. Figure 13.19 shows a schematic diagram of such a device, a simple microphotometer. As the instrument scans a spectrum, the amount of light impinging on the detector will change, and different currents will result. These may be registered by a galvanometer or balanced out in a bridge circuit and then presented as a pen record on a chart.

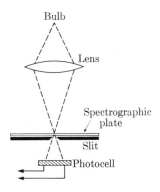

Fig. 13.19 Schematic diagram of a simple microphotometer.

Two important requirements for the reliable operation of microphotometers are stability and a suitable slit width for scanning. Reliable components will ensure the first. The other will be decided by the graininess of the emulsion and will require setting the scanning slit so that errors caused by nonuniformity of a line will be avoided. Usually the slit width should be less than half the line width.

Since microphotometers operate at low intensity levels, it is very important that *scattered light be excluded.* Any light reaching the sensing device other than that which originates through the lines will make line densities low.

Many commercial microphotometers operate somewhat differently, using a projection technique that allows simultaneous density determinations and comparison of enlarged images on a groundglass plate. They are often called *comparator-microphotometers.* The general term densitometer is also used.

REFERENCES

Some general references on emission spectrometry are as follows:

1. Wallace R. Brode, *Chemical Spectroscopy*. 2d ed. New York: Wiley, 1943
2. George R. Harrison, Richard C. Lord, and John R. Loofbourow, *Practical Spectroscopy*. New York: Prentice-Hall, 1948
3. N. H. Nachtrieb, *Principles and Practice of Spectrochemical Analysis*. New York: McGraw-Hill, 1950
4. B. F. Scribner and Marvin Margoshes, "Emission Spectroscopy," in *Treatise on Analytical Chemistry*. Part I, Vol. 6, Chapter 64. I. M. Kolthoff and P. J. Elving, eds. New York: Wiley, 1965

Detailed practical information on emission spectrometric analysis is given by:

5. L. H. Ahrens and S. R. Taylor, *Spectrochemical Analysis*. 2d ed. Reading, Mass.: Addison-Wesley, 1961
6. American Society for Testing Materials, *Methods for Emission Spectrochemical Analysis*. Philadelphia: ASTM, 1964

Processes occurring in the dc arc are extensively treated in:

7. P. W. J. M. Boumans, *Theory of Spectrochemical Excitation*. New York: Plenum, 1966

Atomic spectra are discussed on an introductory level in:

8. S. Walker and H. Straw, *Spectroscopy*. Vol. 1, Atomic, Microwave, and Radio-frequency; Vol. 2, Ultra-violet, Visible, Infra-red, and Raman. New York: MacMillan, 1962

An advanced treatment of atomic spectra may be found in:

9. G. Herzberg, *Atomic Spectra and Atomic Structure*. New York: Prentice-Hall, 1937; also Dover, 1944
10. G. H. Kuhn, *Atomic Spectra*. New York: Academic, 1962

Instrumentation is emphasized in:

11. R. A. Sawyer, *Experimental Spectroscopy*. 3d ed. New York: Prentice-Hall, 1951; also Dover 1963

Other publications of interest are:

12. P. W. J. M. Boumans and F. J. M. J. Maessen, "Evaluation of Determination Limits in Emission Spectroscopy." *Z. Anal. Chem.* **220**, 241 (1966); **225**, 98 (1967)
13. L. De Galen, "The Possibility of a Truly Absolute Method of Spectrographic Analysis," *Analyt. Chim. Acta* **34**, 2 (1966)
14. W. Grimm, "A New Glow Discharge Lamp for Optical Emission Spectral Analysis," *Spectrochim. Acta* **23B**, 443 (1968)
15. R. F. Jarrell, *Stigmatic Plane Grating Spectrograph with Order Sorter*, *J. Opt. Soc. Am.* **45**, 259, 1955
16. *The Spex Speaker*, a company quarterly that treats methods and developments of interest to emission spectroscopists, published by Spex Industries, Metuchen, N.J., Vol. 1 (1956)

Compilations of spectral lines of elements are available in standard handbooks as well as in [1] above and in:

17. G. R. Harrison, *Wave Length Tables*. 2d ed. Cambridge, Mass.: MIT Press, 1969
18. W. F. Meggers, C. H. Corliss, and B. F. Scribner, *Tables of Spectral Line Intensities*, Parts I and II, National Bureau of Standards, Monograph 32. Washington: Govt Printing Office, 1961

EXERCISES

13.1   Consider that an order-sorter prism unit produces a spectrum along the length of the entrance slit of a grating spectrograph that it accompanies, with 260 nm appearing at the bottom of the entrance slit and 500 nm at the top. Other wavelengths present fail to enter the slit. Assume the grating angle is such that spectra of fifth and higher orders appear on the photographic plate of the spectrograph.

 a) How many orders will be seen on the photographic plate? Note that the largest pertinent value of the product $m\lambda$ is $5 \cdot 500 = 2500$.
 b) Sketch in rough fashion the several sets of spectra as they would appear vertically. [See R. F. Jarrell, *J. Opt. Soc. Am.* **45**, 259 (1955).]

13.2   A grating spectrograph has a linear reciprocal dispersion of 5 Å mm^{-1} in the first order. The iron triplet at 3099.9, 3100.3, and 3100.7 Å is photographed in two orders. What is the separation of the extreme lines in the first order? in the second order?

[*Ans.*: 0.16 mm and 0.32 mm.]

13.3   A concave reflection grating with 300 grooves mm^{-1} and a focal length of 1.5 m is available. A collimated beam containing wavelengths 550.0 and 540.0 nm is normally incident. In the curved focal plane at a distance of 1.5 m, what is the separation (in millimeters) of these wavelengths in (a) the first-order spectrum, (b) the fourth-order spectrum?

[*Ans.*: approximately (a) 6.6; (b) 21.7.]

13.4   Is a spectrometer of resolution 10,000 capable of resolving the 5538.57 and 5539.28 Å (553.857 and 553.928 nm) iron lines?

13.5   What is the theoretically attainable resolution of a grating with 600 grooves mm^{-1} whose ruled area extends 10 cm?

[*Ans.*: 60,000.]

13.6   Self-electrodes of brass are arced by a spectroscopist interested in determining their lead content. He finds that a spectrum photographed when a dc arc is first struck shows good contrast throughout. One recorded after the arc has operated two minutes shows appreciable continuous background, especially in the red portion of the spectrum. Offer a possible explanation for the change.

13.7   To establish the approximate concentration level of aluminum, silicon, and copper in an unknown, the technique of successive dilutions of unknown S is to be used. Let S-1 and S-2 identify the unknown after 10-fold and 100-fold dilution with pure graphite. Let G, G-1, and G-2 designate standards containing 0.1%, 0.01%, and 0.001% concentrations of each of 40–50

Table E13.7 Relative Intensity*

Sample	Al (3092 Å)	Si (2881 Å)	Cu (3247 Å)
S	7	1	2
S-1	6	0	1
S-2	4	0	0
G	4	4	4
G-1	3	3	3
G-2	2	2	2

* Range: 7 indicates a maximum response and 0 means undetected.

elements. From the data in Table E13.7 determine approximate concentrations for each element sought.

$$[\textit{Ans.}: \text{Al} \simeq 10\%; \text{Si} < 10^{-3}\%; \text{Cu} \simeq 10^{-3}\%.]$$

13.8 What type of spectrograph should be used for precision quantitative analyses of steel samples? List reasons for the choice and cite data where possible.

13.9 Suggest suitable excitation methods for the following quantitative spectrographic determinations: (a) lead in chamber-process sulfuric acid, (b) calcium in blood, (c) zinc in a brass casting, (d) traces of silicon in germanium powder, (e) potassium in porcelain chips. Consult references if necessary.

Chapter 14

FLAME SPECTROMETRY

14.1 INTRODUCTION

A flame has a marked tendency to atomize a sample, i.e., literally to furnish atoms of most elements present. Its ability to do so without simultaneously producing appreciable quantities of ions is mainly responsible for the development of flame spectrometry. Clearly, the choice of a flame for the atomization process relates to its reproducibility, efficiency, and relative inexpensiveness coupled with the low luminosity of properly burning gases. In the case of emission techniques, of course, the flame also serves to excite after atomization.

Two flame techniques, flame emission spectrometry* and atomic absorption spectrometry, have been highly developed. A third, atomic fluorescence spectrometry, has enjoyed a considerable exploration of its potentialities but has not been developed commercially as yet. It is convenient to group these techniques together because of their essential similarity, their common dependence upon flames and, generally, upon solution samples.

Flame emission spectrometry, also called flame photometry or atomic emission spectrometry, does not differ basically from the emission methods discussed in Chapter 13. A sample introduced into a flame is atomized, a fraction of the atoms is excited, and the intensity of an emission line of each element of interest is determined. Since most metals have low-lying electronic levels into which their atoms may be excited by flames, the technique is widely applicable. The technique is chiefly attractive as a quantitative method. Several problems preclude easy use in qualitative analysis: the frequency of overlap of spectral lines, various interelement interferences and background emission by flame constituents and oxides.

In atomic absorption spectrometry (or spectrophotometry) it is the absorption of characteristic wavelengths by atoms in a flame that is monitored. As long as intense radiation of a characteristic wavelength is available, e.g., from a hollow-cathode lamp, an element can be determined in a flame as it absorbs the radiation. Because the process does not involve emission, some of the interelement interferences are absent or less marked than in emission. Atomic absorption spectrometry is also used chiefly as a quantitative method widely applicable to metals.

In atomic fluorescence spectrometry, the fluorescence of atoms excited in a flame is the basis for determination. A flame containing a sample is irradiated with intense radiation of a characteristic wavelength as in the absorption method. The fluorescence

---

* Until the general development of atomic absorption analysis (post-1960) flame emission work was treated as a branch of emission spectrometry.

incident radiation. With a very intense source, the technique is a highly sensitive quantitative method.

While a detailed consideration of relative advantages of these flame procedures will be given later in the chapter, three points should be noted here. First, such atomic methods are specific for a particular element, given instrumentation of sufficient precision to separate a characteristic wavelength for one element from nearby wavelengths of others. Second, all three methods are useful in trace analysis of metals and certain other elements. They are effective at the microgram, nanogram, or sometimes even at the picogram level. Finally, with easily excited elements emission methods are often best and with elements that are more difficult to excite absorption methods are preferable; fluorescence methods may be the most sensitive of all given a sufficiently intense source.

14.2 BURNER-NEBULIZER

There are many ways both to atomize* substances, i.e., dissociate them into free atoms, and to achieve electronic excitation. Yet only the flame is presently of analytical importance in both emission and absorption atomic techniques. Other procedures such as use of electrical arcs or plasma jets often prove less convenient and offer no greater stability in operation. They can, however, provide temperatures generally higher than those in a flame. In atomic absorption and fluorescence techniques atomization is sometimes also accomplished simply by heating a sample in an appropriate vessel.

Since solutions are commonly used, the introduction of a sample involves nebulization and entrainment of the resulting droplets in the gas going to the burner. *Pneumatic nebulizers* are the simplest and most widely used type. In these devices, one of the gases to be burned is used to aspirate the liquid stream into a spray. Unfortunately, no more than 5 to 15% of the sample generally appears in the flame. As will be seen below, special steps can be taken to improve the efficiency of the process. Alternatives to pneumatic nebulization are, of course, continuing to be investigated.

The aerosol produced by a pneumatic nebulizer is stable but has an undesirably wide distribution of drop sizes. During its passage through a flame there is seldom sufficient time for larger droplets to evaporate; accordingly, they are often removed by letting the aerosol pass through a small chamber with baffles in which larger droplets coalesce and are drained away. Such an arrangement is evident in Fig. 14.1. A further problem is that all the solvent in drops must be evaporated. Anything hastening this process automatically ensures that a larger fraction of a sample will interact with a flame. For example, the aerosol drift chamber can be heated to accomplish this.

A considerable variety of burners has been developed. In order to discern relative advantages of different types it is helpful to develop a set of ideal criteria for a burner-nebulizer combination. It should

1. Produce a stable flame that has minimal luminosity, absorption, and flicker and a well-defined structure and shape;

---

* As noted earlier, the term is used in its literal sense. The process of creating a spray of droplets from a liquid will be called nebulization.

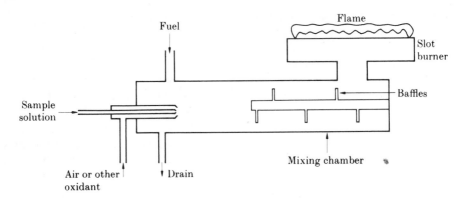

Fig. 14.1 A general slot-type premix burner-nebulizer arrangement. The baffles are introduced in the mixing chamber to remove larger drops. The burner usually has a flat face with a single slot down its center or as many as three parallel slots.

2. Prevent flashback* into the burner;

3. Nebulize as large a fraction of a sample solution as possible;

4. Eliminate large droplets of solution and preferably evaporate much of the solvent before the droplets reach the flame;

5. Be mechanically well designed so that cleaning and adjustment are easy, solution viscosity effects are small, and minimal encrustation or residue is left by a sample, or carbon deposit by a fuel-rich flame;

6. Ensure rapid response to new samples; and

7. Produce a flame that provides large populations of atoms and/or electronically excited atoms from species introduced.

The separate aspects of burner-nebulizer design may now be considered.

Gas regulation. Except where air is used as an oxidant, both fuel and oxidant gases are supplied from high-pressure steel cylinders. Ordinarily a steady flow of gases is secured by use of a two-stage regulator for each.

How are appropriate gas pressures decided? Once a burner has been selected, a process discussed below, two properties of flames can be used to narrow the range. First, the concentration of fuel gas in the mixture must fall between the upper and lower *limits of flammability* to sustain combustion. For example, the volume percent of fuel in an oxy-hydrogen mixture must fall between approximately 10 and 90%. It can be assumed that nearly stoichiometric mixtures of combining gases are used unless otherwise stated.

Second, each gas mixture is characterized by a *burning velocity*. The term defines the speed of propagation of a flame front in the gas mixture. To be sure, it also depends somewhat on burner design and conditions such as pressure. Burning velocities are

---

* Flashback occurs when flame propagates within the burner.

usually of the order of 1 m s^{-1} to 10 m s^{-1} at atmospheric pressure.* [3] It is found that a flame can be maintained at a burner head only if the fuel gas or combustible mixture moves at a speed three to ten times the burning velocity. Thus gas pressures must be appropriate to the size of the burner channel. Higher gas velocities cause a flame front to blow away, lower ones can lead to flashback. Precautions must be taken to avoid flashback, especially during changes of conditions, e.g., during ignition, alteration of pressures, or extinguishing a flame. Unfortunately, flashback can lead to explosion. With C_2H_2–N_2O flames flashback can virtually always be avoided if on starting, the C_2H_2 is ignited first and then the N_2O turned on; and on shutting down the N_2O is first turned off and then the C_2H_2 flame is extinguished.

Burners. It is possible to obtain flames of at least two distinctly different types by varying the manner of mixing gases. In the widely used *premix burners*, gases are blended prior to emergence from the burner head. For example, this type of burner was shown in Fig. 14.1. The burner yields a laminar, i.e. layered, flame. It has a stable internal structure, low luminosity, and little flicker (noise). Most theoretical studies have been made on such flames since thermodynamic equilibrium is attained in their outer zone (Section 14.3).

Other advantages of the premix burner are that solution viscosity is no particular problem since the solution enters through a large tube, and big droplets can be eliminated before they enter the burner slot. Because of the mixing chamber there is only modest dependence of signal on sample flow rate. The device is also mechanically simple and can provide a long flame path.

A premix burner head has one or more flame slots that may be as long as 10 cm. The design gives emission and absorption intensities proportional to flame length. In the Boling type of burner three closely adjacent, parallel slots are used in a flat

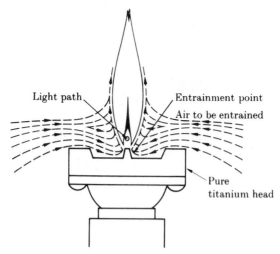

Fig. 14.2 A single-slot burner design featuring air entrainment at base of flame. (Courtesy of Varian Techtron.)

---

* Detonation velocities, realizable when reaction is initiated by a shock wave, are usually about 100 times greater.

surface; this has the advantage that a large central portion of the flame is protected against the unsettling diffusion of air, the outer slots providing a type of peripheral flame curtain. Use of a single slot with wide (6 mm) grooves on either side is another effective design, illustrated in Fig. 14.2. Air is again entrained in controlled fashion and carbon build-up is avoided when fuel-rich flames are used. In addition, the grooved burner gives results only slightly dependent on fuel flow.

There are two possible disadvantages of a premix burner. When a solvent mixture such as alcohol-water (Section 14.7) is used, selective evaporation may cause sample to remain in the unevaporated portion of the drops. This potential difficulty is avoided if almost all solvent is evaporated from the drops prior to their entering the flame. There is also a minor possibility of flashback explosion. For this reason gas mixtures containing oxygen are generally not used with premix burners. Air, or nitrous oxide (with acetylene), is employed instead. Good design can minimize the volume occupied by the mixed gases and lessen the danger. Automatic optical monitoring of the flame and use of a mixing chamber with a blow-out diaphragm that ruptures at a low excess pressure are worthwhile additional safeguards.

Alternatively, in the *total-consumption burner*, reacting gases mix by diffusion in the combustion zone. In this type the sample is aspirated directly into the flame, as shown in Fig. 14.3, and a small flame of circular cross-section results. The flame itself is often termed a diffusion flame. Although all sample appears in the flame, only the smallest droplets have time to evaporate and the efficiency of introducing a sample is no greater than for the usual premix arrangement. Such burners are mainly used in emission work.

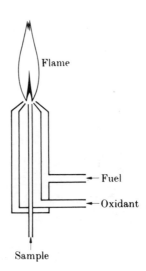

Fig. 14.3 Total consumption or diffusion burner.

Advantages of this type of burner are that it responds rapidly to new samples, is better adapted to microsampling, is compact, mechanically very simple, offers no explosion hazards, and ensures that a representative sample reaches the flame.

The disadvantages are several. It provides a smaller flame that has greater flicker and that is more luminous, turbulent, and (acoustically) noisy. Its internal structure is uncertain and variable. The long capillary also makes it awkward to use with concentrated (10,000 ppm) solutions because of increased viscosity.* Finally, the temperature of the flame may drop drastically (often as much as 100 to 400 °C) as sample droplets appear in it. Slot-type premix burners are steadily displacing total-consumption burners.

14.3 FLAME DISSOCIATION AND EXCITATION

The dissociation of a substance into atoms in a flame is seldom complete. To the extent that equilibrium is attained, the usual thermodynamic criteria can be applied to the process. For a dissociation represented by

$$MX_{(s)} \rightleftarrows M_{(g)} + X_{(g)}$$

the degree of dissociation will increase as the concentration of gaseous species decreases.

Example The flame spectrometric determination of sodium in a NaCl solution is affected at high concentration levels by any other chlorides present. Such chlorides depress dissociation, apparently by increasing the concentration of chlorine atoms. Thus they lower the apparent concentration of sodium. Other mechanisms may also affect the analytical response.

Three other factors influence dissociation. The lower the bond energy of MX, and the higher the temperature, the greater the extent of dissociation. Yet because concentrations of radicals such as O and OH exist in a flame many elements tend to exist as monoxides and not as free atoms.

Against this background, it is important to ask how closely chemical species in a flame and their abundances are related to flame properties. The question can best be answered for a premix flame since it has a stable structure. In turn, a knowledge of areas where particular reactions occur allows an appraisal of different regions for their atomizing and exciting efficiency. In the premix flame the flame front appears as a blue cone of 0.1 to 0.3 mm thickness close to the burner tip. This inner cone is termed the *primary reaction zone*. Its color and luminosity result from both band and continuous emission of molecular fragments such as C_2, CH, and CHO that are produced in this region during partial combusion. When a sample is introduced, it is strongly excited in the primary zone, apparently because of vigorous collisions with highly energetic molecular fragments. This region is little used in flame spectroscopy, however, though it offers analytical possibilities if the problem of sensitive detection of emission against a heavy flame background can be overcome. [3]

Outside the blue cone is a narrow *interconal region* and a few millimeters beyond it is the hottest portion of the flame. The entire outer cone extending upward several centimeters is termed the *secondary reaction zone*. Some continuous background

---

* To some degree the capillary feed problem can be overcome by use of an additional (fourth) channel in the center of the burner. High pressure oxygen is forced through this passage to push the sample solution into the flame.

emission and band spectra persist in this region, but their intensity is much smaller. It is here that an optimum blend of long path length, maximum concentrations of sample atoms (or excited atoms), and steady-state conditions is ordinarily attained. As a result, the middle part of the secondary reaction zone is commonly used for flame spectroscopic determinations. A serious drawback is that the concentration of O and OH radicals in the lower temperature stoichiometric flames is sufficient to cause many elements to appear mainly as oxides. The hotter the flame used, the smaller the concentration of such oxides, however, and the nitrous oxide–acetylene flame greatly reduces this problem.

Two ways to lengthen the interconal zone and make it analytically useful have been investigated, especially for flame emission measurements. One is to use a fuel-rich premix flame. In this case molecular fragments such as C_2 persist into it and lend it a reducing character. As a result, the concentration of oxides of elements present in a sample is lower in this region and populations of both atoms and excited atoms are higher. A second, more extensively explored approach is the formation of a *separated flame*. The interconal region is extended by a tactic such as fitting a tubular silica sleeve of 2 to 4 cm length to the top of the burner or by using a surrounding sheath of flowing gas (nitrogen or argon). The flame temperature drops somewhat in a separated flame but background emission from burning gases is reduced one or two orders of magnitude and oxide and hydroxide formation lowered by forestalling the diffusion of atmospheric oxygen into this region. Recall that the Boling burner also yielded improved results for this reason. In flame emission methods where molecular band emission interferes, a separated flame can lead to a significant improvement in specificity and sensitivity.

Excitation. During dissociation of a species in a flame or immediately afterward, excitation to higher energy levels can occur. Unfortunately the transitory passage of a species through a flame largely frustrates attainment of equilibrium. The exception appears to be the center of the secondary reaction zone of a premix flame, where the Boltzmann equation can be taken as defining the concentration N_2 of a species in an excited state, relative to its concentration in the ground state, N_1:

$$N_2 = \frac{N_1 g_1}{g_2} e^{-E/kT}. \tag{14.1}$$

Here E is the difference in energy of the states and g_1 and g_2 are the statistical weights of the states. The ratio g_1/g_2 is thus the *a priori* probability of the ratio of atoms in these states.

Most excitation in flames has been found to occur by one or two mechanisms. Often a straightforward conversion of energy between a vibrationally excited molecule and an atom can occur on collision. Since molecular vibrational levels are closely spaced and collisions frequent, the probability that a molecular level will match an electronic level of the other species and lead to a transfer of energy on collision is good. Second, a chemical reaction may occur in which one "product" is the desired species of atom in an excited state. Actually, the atom must be involved in a complex collision with other atoms that form a molecule on impact. For example, a potassium atom might be so excited not far above the inner flame cone by participation in a collision involving the union of hydrogen atoms. Shortly thereafter a photon would be emitted. The entire process is an example of a *chemiluminescent* reaction.

Emission. As discussed in Section 13.3, spontaneous emission occurs very shortly after excitation. The intensity of an emitted wavelength can be shown to be just $N_2 E_{21}/\tau$, where N_2 is the number of excited atoms, E_{21} the energy of transition, and τ the lifetime in the excited state. Thus the intensity of an emission line depends linearly on the transition energy and frequency (since $E = h\nu$). According to Eq. (14.1) the intensity also depends exponentially on temperature.

Example In order to appreciate the exponential dependence of excitation on transition energy and temperature consider the following illustration. The fraction of atoms excited to a state 2.1 eV above the ground state is about 5×10^{-4} at 3000 °K and 1×10^{-3} at 3500 °K. If the upper level is 4.2 eV higher, the fraction excited is 2×10^{-7} at 3000 °K and 2×10^{-6} at 3500 °K.

Assuming equal lifetimes in the states, emission from the 2.1 eV state at 3000 °K will be much brighter (intensity $5 \times 10^{-4} \times 2.0$) than that from the 4.2 eV level (intensity $2 \times 10^{-7} \times 4.2$). Because of the exponential dependence on temperature, however, a 500 °K increase will enhance emission from the 4.2 eV state substantially more.

In Table 14.1 are shown some experimentally determined maximum flame temperatures. For information on flame temperature determinations and temperature profiles the reader is referred to Ref. 3. Such measurements are usually made on premixed flames, though there is no limitation in principle.

Table 14.1 Some Analytically Useful Flames and Their Temperatures*

Mixture	T_{max}, °C
H_2-air	2000
H_2-O_2	2600
CH_4-O_2	2700
C_2H_2-air	2300
C_2H_2-O_2	3100
C_2H_2-N_2O	2900
C_2N_2-N_2O	(3200)

* Maximum experimental temperature determined in outer cone of premixed flame formed from stoichiometric mixtures at 25°C and 1 bar total pressure.

14.4 FLAME SPECTROMETRIC SYSTEMS

The instrumentation of any flame spectroscopic system is, of course, nearly identical to that for an ordinary spectroscopic system (Section 13.7). The essential similarity is stressed in Fig. 14.4. As shown, flame methods differ from each other mainly in modules used in the optical path prior to the flame. Only for flame emission (FE) methods does the optical path begin with the flame; in atomic absorption (AA) and

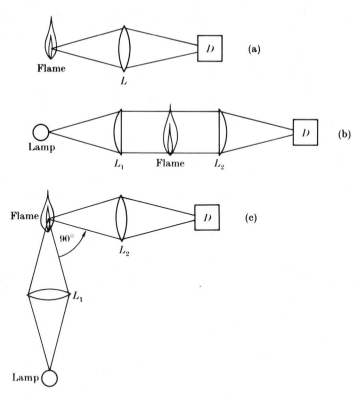

Fig. 14.4 Comparison of instrumentation for flame spectroscopic techniques: (a) flame emission; (b) (flame) atomic absorption; (c) (flame) atomic fluorescence. Symbols used in all parts: L for lens; D for combined spectral isolation device, detector, amplifier, and readout device. The lamp is generally a hollow-cathode lamp modulated to give a fluctuating signal. Sample is introduced into flame in all techniques.

atomic fluorescence (AF) techniques, a prior source is required. In these methods the flame serves both as sample cell and "atomizer," and is often labeled a *flame cell*. For a discussion of basic types of spectrometric instrumentation see Chapters 12 and 13. Attention will be given here to (a) general aspects of FE spectrometric systems, (b) modifications introduced for AA work, and (c) designs for multipurpose instrumentation.

Flame emission spectrometers. In block diagram form an FE spectrometer can be represented as shown in Fig. 14.5. What is the influence of modules prior to the detector on the signal developed? This question directs attention to the heart of an FE spectrometer. It can be shown (p. 1939 of Ref. 15) that the following expression

Flame ⇒   Filter or
  ↑   monochromator ⇒ Detector → Amplifier → Readout
Burner-
nebulizer

Fig. 14.5 Line block diagram of a flame emission spectrometer.

describes their influence if assumptions cited in the next paragraph are valid:

$$\text{Signal} = \frac{f(\theta, \lambda)\Phi\epsilon\beta}{e_f Q} Lhv_0 A_{21} c \left[\frac{g_2}{g_1} e^{-E_{21}/kT} \right]. \tag{14.2}$$

Each term except the expression in brackets requires brief definition. First, the bracketed portion is seen to be just the fraction of excited atoms as given by Eq. (14.1); their product with A_{21}, the Einstein coefficient for spontaneous emission, c, the solution concentration, and hv_0, the size of quantum emitted, gives a quantity proportional to the intensity of emission. Second, $f(\theta, \lambda)$ is a function including "monochromator" response in terms of the solid angle of the flame that enters the filter or monochromator and the efficiency of the "monochromator" (see Chapter 12). Third, Φ is the rate at which sample is aspirated. Fourth, ϵ is the efficiency of introduction of sample into the flame, a combination of nebulization and evaporation efficiencies. Fifth, β is the efficiency of atomization. Thus, the product of factors three through five, and factor one gives the intensity of emission. Sixth, L is the length of path through the flame. Seventh, the product $e_f Q$ in the denominator expresses the flow rate Q of unburned gases, and the expansion factor e_f takes care of the increase in volume on combustion and expansion in the flame.

Three assumptions have been made: First, that thermal and chemical equilibrium obtain, a condition that holds reasonably in the central region of the outer cone of a premix flame; second, that the flame is optically thin, i.e. does not self-absorb or fluoresce (clearly, the latter assumption is valid only at low concentrations); third, intensity from sources other than the species of interest has been neglected.

Basically, Eq. (14.2) predicts a linear dependence of response on concentration and flame path length at a given flame temperature and at low solute concentration. What can be learned from Eq. (14.2) about procedure or instrumentation decisions? It is found that for a given element, ϵ and β vary with chemical environment, i.e. specific "chemical effects" alter response, as might be expected. Such factors affect procedures and will be treated in Section 14.5. Second, the exponential dependence on temperature suggests that the choice of flame will be a crucial "instrumental" decision. Third, background intensity will have to be corrected for whenever it is appreciable. Finally, the central role of burner and nebulizer is emphasized. A discussion of instruments is deferred until later in the section.

Atomic absorption spectrometers. In similar fashion inquiry can be made as to the influence of modules prior to the detector in an AA spectrophotometer. Figure 14.5 can represent the instrument preliminarily if a spectral source and lenses are added to the left of the flame, as in Fig. 14.4. Further modifications will be taken up below.

Since absorption is being observed, Beer's law (Section 16.2) will describe the process as long as a steady state exists and monochromatic light is incident on the flame cell: $I_t = I_0 e^{-abc}$. Here I_t and I_0 are the transmitted and incident intensities (or powers, as discussed later), a is the absorptivity, b the path length, and c the molar concentration. It will be assumed that a hollow-cathode lamp (Section 11.3) or other narrow-line resonance source supplies the incident I_0. Further, it is presumed that I_t is corrected for flame background radiation of the wavelength of the absorption line.

To adapt Beer's law to the instrument a and c must be defined for a gaseous system and the effect of the monochromator on I_t symbolized. It can be shown (p. 1947 of Ref. 15) that the signal incident on the detector is

$$\text{Signal} = f(\theta, \lambda) I_0 \exp\left[-\left(0.037\, \lambda_0^2\, \frac{g_2}{g_1}\, A_{21}\, \frac{\delta}{\Delta v_D} \right) b \left(c\, \frac{\Phi \epsilon \beta}{e_f Q} \right) \right]. \qquad (14.3)$$

The exponential term, which now appears in brackets, has been grouped by parentheses into factors that represent the original Beer's law variables. These terms will be discussed below. A preexponential term $f(\theta, \lambda)$ defines the "monochromator" response in terms of the solid angle of the incident beam entering the monochromator and the energy throughput of the monochromator (see Section 12.3).

The first parenthetical factor in the exponent represents the "atomic absorptivity," the appropriate value of a. Several special points must be made. First, a is defined for the *center* of the absorption line that corresponds to the resonance transition 1 to 2. Clearly, it could also be defined for any other appropriate transition. Second, the width of the source line (spectral slit width of incident light) is assumed negligible. Third, the absorptivity has been defined in terms of spontaneous emission from state 2 to 1. The new term λ_0 is the wavelength at line center. The lone numerical coefficient includes a variety of factors. Finally, two variables relating to the width of the absorption line are included. The first is Δv_D, the Doppler half-width (in s^{-1}) of the absorption line, i.e. the broadening due to movement of atoms relative to a fixed point. This term appears in the denominator since the wider this line the smaller is the degree of absorption of the incident radiation. The second factor, δ, which is always a fraction, represents a broadening due to other causes such as increased partial pressure.

In the rest of the exponential expression there appear b, which has been left unchanged, and a second parenthetical factor, $(\Phi \epsilon \beta / e_f Q)$. This set of terms defines the concentration of atoms of the analytical species in the flame and also appeared in Equation (14.2).

In absorption measurements it is customary to observe either the ratio I/I_0, the transmittance, or $\log I_0/I$, the absorbance A. A full discussion will be given in Section 16.2. The conversion of Eq. (14.3) to either form is straightforward. For example, since $A = abc$, the absorbance equals the exponent in Eq. (14.3).

According to the equation, flame absorbances should vary linearly with solution concentration. Actually, linearity is usually obtained only over one order of magnitude. At increasing partial pressure of atomic vapor, the absorption line broadens, resulting in a smaller δ and reduced absorption at the center of the line. While temperature does not appear explicitly in the equation, the probability coefficient A_{21} varies as $T^{-1/2}$, and there is a small dependence. As in flame emission measurements, a great source of variability is the set of factors ϵ and β, which depend on chemical interactions to a considerable degree. Such interferences will be considered in the following section.

Criteria for "monochromator." Before considering overall design and special problems the device isolating the analytical wavelength deserves attention. What requirements must be imposed on the "monochromator" module?

1. For specificity, the device should pass the selected analytical line but block neighboring lines or bands and as much flame background radiation as possible: For general and versatile use a slit adjustable to give a spectral slit width as narrow as 0.05 nm is required.

2. For photometric precision and accuracy the device should have as great a light throughput as possible: Slit widths should be as wide as is tolerable.

3. For completeness of coverage and versatility a wavelength range from about 195 to 850 nm (1950 to 8500 Å) should be accessible.

4. Wavelength accuracy need be no better than about 1 nm, since an instrument can be tuned to the characteristic wavelength.

The first two requirements imply an instrument of variable spectral slit width. Indeed, the versatility of a flame spectroscopic system will be determined in considerable measure by this bandwidth. The use of filters, as in the filter photometer described below, will give a rugged, sensitive instrument of low to moderate versatility while a monochromator capable of a bandpass as narrow as 0.05 nm can be used to build a highly flexible, precision instrument for either flame emission or absorption use. An example is the spectrophotometer discussed later in this section.

In general, as great a throughput of light as possible is desirable to maintain a high signal-to-noise ratio. Slit widths can usually be set to give band passes from 1 to 4 nm for most elements, though a band pass of only 0.2 nm can be tolerated if ferrous alloys are being analyzed. When background is not strong, the wider the slit, the more light admitted, and the greater the photometric precision possible.

Special design considerations. A special instrumental challenge arises in flame spectrometric measurements. How can background radiation be successfully dealt with? Over the wavelength band being observed background radiation may arise from several sources: luminosity of the flame, emission by excited species, and stray light. Such radiation will appear as stray radiation and may contribute substantial error. The challenge is especially great in atomic absorption spectrometry because of the emission of the analytical species itself. In this technique, emission by some atoms of the analytical species, already excited by the flame or the incident radiation, will be at exactly the wavelength which the atoms that are still in the ground state will absorb.

The most widely used solution to this dilemma in atomic absorption spectrometry is to modulate or chop the output of the hollow-cathode source. If the source radiation is modulated but flame-emitted light is steady, selective amplification of the detector output can be used to ensure that the spectrometer responds only to transmitted light from the source. In general, a beam chopper is not needed; the power to the source can be modulated instead. (See Exercise 14.2 for discussion of a chopper version, however.)

As an illustration of this approach, examine the block diagram of a single-beam AA spectrometer shown in Fig. 14.6. The dc flame emission is detected but not amplified. The modulated source radiation that has passed through the flame is detected, amplified, and finally demodulated by a phase-sensitive detector (Section

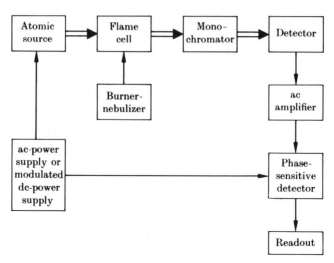

Fig. 14.6 Block diagram of a single-beam atomic absorption spectroscopic system. The flame "cell" is just the flame produced by the burner-nebulizer system.

8.7). The resulting dc is reported by the readout device. As in any system based on application of Beer's law, a blank solution is used to obtain a 100% setting (Section 16.2).

Independence of changes in source intensity can be achieved if in addition to modulation of the source a (partial) double-beam arrangement is employed. Some type of beam-splitter must be used to divert a fraction of the output of the source around the flame to a second detector. The ratio of outputs of the two detectors gives a signal independent of source variations such as occur during "warm up" or because of current fluctuations.

It should be evident that no provision has yet been made to minimize the effect of drift or fluctuation in the flame itself or in nebulization of a sample. All flame techniques will be subject to this effect. Ideally, a true second channel, a reference channel, might be set up in the flame by use of an *internal standard*. The internal standard or reference is an element introduced at fixed concentration in all samples. Its emission (or absorption) is then separately monitored. The essential aspects of instrumentation for this approach can be deduced from the internal standard flame emission device pictured schematically in Fig. 14.7.

An internal standard is effective to the degree it responds to changing conditions in the way the analytical species does. Ideally, such a reference should be an element that (a) is absent from the original sample and (b) undergoes a transition at a frequency well away from the resonance line(s) of the constituents of the sample. Lithium is often used as an internal standard in flame emission procedures. Fewer instances of use of an internal reference have been reported in atomic absorption methods; strontium has ordinarily been selected.

The additional advantages of the internal-standard method are compensation for drift in burner gas pressures, reduction of nebulization variability arising from solution viscosity and surface tension differences, and reduction of errors attributable

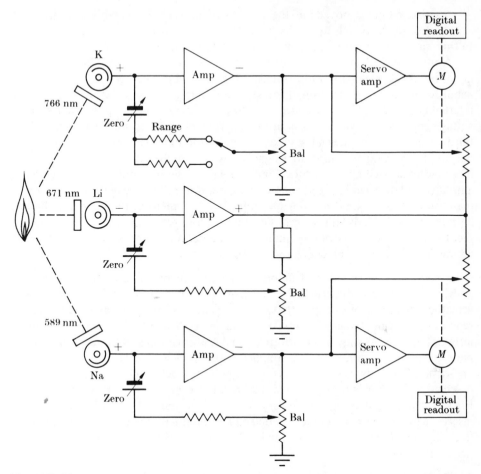

Fig. 14.7 Three-channel filter photometer for flame emission spectroscopy of selected elements. The central channel is used for a lithium internal standard. A zero adjustment taken with only the internal standard present allows automatic subtraction of the flame emission background and dark current of each photometer. Readouts are made relative to the internal standard. (Courtesy of Instrumentation Laboratory, Inc.)

to some interferences. Disadvantages of the method are that it is sometimes slightly more time-consuming, and in cases in which the internal standard line and the analytical line are affected differently by interferences it may give poor results.

Emission filter photometers. Where no more than two to four elements with simple spectral patterns, such as sodium and potassium, are to be determined routinely by FE photometry, a filter is often adequate to isolate the appropriate wavelength of each for analysis. Sometimes a dye filter is suitable, but more often a narrow band pass interference filter is desirable. Its narrower band pass also blocks possible interference lines and excludes more flame background and stray light. Yet its light throughput is much larger than that of a monochromator and a modest amplifier provides adequate sensitivity. A readout device completes the photometer.

A separate filter is moved into the optical path for each element. It is advantageous simultaneously to switch in a separate calibration control into the readout circuit. In this way a change from element to element can be made quickly.

A multichannel filter (FE) photometer that allows precise simultaneous determination of two elements is illustrated in Fig. 14.7. Here the light from the burner-nebulizer flame is incident on three separate channels. Each has an appropriate interference filter, photomultiplier detector, an operational amplifier (current-to-voltage converter). Two channels of this instrument are used for measurement, the third to monitor an internal standard such as lithium. The system compares the output of each sample channel to a signal derived from the internal standard channel in an electrical nulling procedure. First, the sum of sample and reference signals is amplified and directed in proper phase to a servomotor. Because of the phase control, the motor turns in the direction that adjusts the input from the reference channel until the sum of signals falls to zero. The final readout is the ratio, $V_{analyt}/V_{int\,std}$ where the V's are the outputs of the analytical channel and internal standard channel corrected for the dark current (zero signal).

AA spectrophotometer. Once a monochromator is incorporated in a spectroscopic system, the device is often called a spectrophotometer. It is possible to develop a versatile instrument of this type that can serve either as an FE or as an AA spectroscopic device. A single-beam version of such an instrument was given in block diagram form in Fig. 14.3. As shown, it is set up for an AA absorption spectrometer or spectrophotometer. Since atomic spectra supplied by hollow-cathode lamps are usually not line-rich, a fairly low-resolution, low-dispersion monochromator is often adequate. A sensitive detector is nearly always required, however. To convert the device to an FE spectrometer, it is only necessary to inactivate the hollow-cathode lamp and insert a chopper between flame and detector to modulate the emission signal at the frequency to which the amplifier is tuned. An alternative approach is to modulate the detector output.

Multichannel devices. At least three instrumental possibilities exist for the rapid flame determination of two or more elements. One is the type of multichannel FE filter photometer just described. Another is the multiple-wavelength AA photometer with a set of hollow-cathode lamps, filters, detectors, and readout. A third is essentially a direct-reading spectrometer (Section 13.11).

A *direct-reading flame* spectrometer may be used in either an absorption (AA) or emission (FE) mode. As described in Section 13.11, in this type of instrument one exit slit and detector are positioned along the monochromator focal curve for each wavelength (element) of interest. With multiple channels it becomes easy to use an internal standard to enhance precision. If used in an emission mode, radiation from the flame is directed to the monochromator entrance slit. Note that the output of each detector can be integrated over a time interval to improve the signal-to-noise ratio.

If the device is used in an absorption mode, the output of several hollow-cathode lamp beams can be optically merged prior to passage through the flame. Multielement hollow-cathode sources can be used to increase the number of elements detectable. The basic limit to the number of "channels" in an absorption mode would seem to depend on the number of hollow-cathode lamps whose outputs could be merged in a single beam.

Resonance monochromator.   In atomic absorption units intended to determine a single element, an ingenious counterpart to the emission filter photometer is available. For each element it employs a resonance monochromator, or resonance detector, as the spectral isolation device. An AA photometer based on its use is shown in block diagram form in Fig. 14.8.

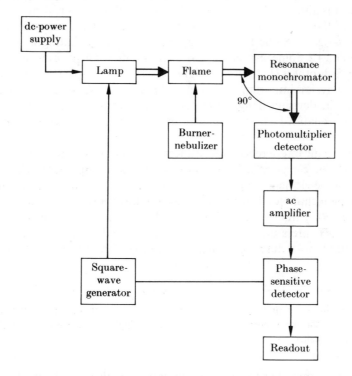

Fig. 14.8 Block diagram of an atomic absorption photometer utilizing a resonance monochromator or "detector" to isolate a characteristic wavelength.

A resonance monochromator contains a cloud of atoms of the element of interest, usually produced by cathodic sputtering (as in a hollow-cathode lamp) or by direct heating. Its atoms absorb only the characteristic resonance wavelength of the element. They subsequently emit the wavelength with an intensity proportional to the incident radiation. The emission is best monitored at right angles to the input beam by a multiplier phototube or other detector.

If more than one element is to be detected, a dual-element resonance monochromator may be possible. Since the atomic cloud contains both elements, two filter-photomultiplier tube combinations will be needed at right angles to the incident light, one for each element. A second or additional resonance monochromator may be put in series with the first.

At the present there is a loss of sensitivity over use of a regular monochromator (by a factor of from two to ten), especially if an element has a complex resonance spectrum. The saving in cost, and gain in reliability and sturdiness, are substantial, however, if only a few elements are to be determined.

14.5 INTERFERENCES: DETECTION LIMITS

The effectiveness of flame spectroscopic procedures for a particular element depends only in part on external variables such as the fuel gas pressure and the width of the burner slot. It is also determined by variables internal to the chemical system such as the nature of the solvent and kinds of atoms present. These variables are usually termed *interferences*. Some types and general ways of combating interferences are listed in Table 14.2. Some (especially 3, 4, 5) are specific for a given element; others are nonspecific. Still others (1, 2) affect a blank as well as a sample solution itself.

Accordingly, it is important to recognize kinds of interferences that must be taken into account in devising flame spectroscopic procedures that are to be sensitive, accurate, and reliable. Detailed information for particular elements can be found in a number of references. [2, 7, 9, 10]

Among specific interferences, those affecting dissociation into atoms are the most troublesome. The category includes so-called cation or anion interferences and the tendency of some elements to form stable monoxides in a flame. These interferences affect all flame techniques. For example, calcium interferes with the determination of aluminum since $CaAlO_2$, which is difficult to dissociate, forms in the flame. Similarly, phosphate ions depress the atomization of calcium and other alkaline earth metals. Several methods to reduce or eliminate this type of interference are suggested in Table 14.2.

Example Aluminum sulfate is observed to suppress the production of magnesium atoms in an air-acetylene and other lower temperature flames. In the higher temperature $N_2O-C_2H_2$ flame the interference vanishes.

Interferences that alter the atomic population by affecting the fraction of atoms that ionize in the flame are another important specific inter-element effect.

Example Cesium enhances the number of atoms of sodium or potassium that appear in a flame. If sodium and potassium are present alone, a certain fraction of each determined by relative ionization energies appears as ions and is unavailable for flame spectroscopy. If cesium is added, it adds to the population of electrons and depresses the ionization of the other two. Thus, the atomic absorption or flame emission of these elements is enhanced, though to different degrees. Similarly, potassium has this effect on sodium, and vice versa.

As the table suggests, addition of a large amount of an easily ionized element that does not interfere spectrally provides a "radiation buffer" or "ionization suppressant" to stabilize the percent ionization. Its presence at about 100 to 1000 $\mu g\ ml^{-1}$ concentration becomes especially important in the hotter flames such as $N_2O-C_2H_2$.

Table 14.2 Interferences in Flame Spectroscopy. It is assumed (a) that the spectral slit width of an instrument has been fixed, (b) the instrument wavelength has been set at a resonance line, and (c) that operating variables such as gas pressures are being maintained constant.

Type of interference	Nature of interference; technique affected	Method of reducing interference
1. Spectral or radiation	a) Unwanted background emission at wavelength of analysis such as band or continuous emission by flame; FE (much less important for AA and AF) b) Absorption or scattering by molecular species in flame, AA, AF c) Emission or absorption of another atomic species or its oxide within waveband passed, FE, (AA),* (AF)*	If possible, use another resonance line in a spectral region free of such interference; change flames; modulate source emission in case of AA and AF; for (b), use second channel energized by continuous source and take ratio of beam intensities
2. Nonspecific	Change in rate of solution transport, of nebulization, or evaporation of solvent. Results mainly from effect of viscosity or surface tension, FE, AA, AF	Exercise care that blank approximates sample closely; reduce concentration
3. Dissociation: "cation or anion effects"	Formation of stable bonds that are broken with difficulty in flame, FE, AA, AF	Use hotter flame or fuel-rich flame; avoid certain anions; use solvent extraction or ion-exchange to effect prior separation of offending ion; chelate analytical species to reduce effect of anions
4. Ionization	Reduction in atomic population in flame by ionization; FE, AA, AF	Add large amount of extraneous easily ionized element to sample and standards; lower flame temperature
5. Excitation	Alteration of flame temperature; FE	Ensure constant solvent composition if solvent mixture used

* The extreme narrowness of hollow cathode emission lines greatly lessens the probability of such overlap. Thus, in AA and AF spectrometry the effect is usually unimportant.

Solvent enhancement of sensitivity.   Sensitivities of flame techniques can be surprising-ly enhanced by use of a partly nonaqueous solvent. To retain good solubility an alcohol or ketone is ordinarily chosen. Because the rate of aspiration and of evaporation of spray is increased, the population of atoms in the flame is substantially increased. Care should be taken to ensure that there is not an accompanying increase in interferences. [14]

Detection limits.   Whether a flame spectroscopic method is usable for trace determina-tions depends finally on detection limits observed. Values for a dozen common ele-ments as found by flame and spark emission spectroscopy and atomic absorption spectroscopy are given in Table 14.3. The definition of detection limit was based on background fluctuations. The emission data were taken under optimum conditions, i.e. alcohol-water solutions were used and emission was observed in the interconal region of a fuel-rich, premixed oxyacetylene flame [11] or N_2O–C_2H_2 flame. [14]

Table 14.3 Some Detection Limits*

			Detection limits‡		
	Wavelength,	Excitation† potential,	Flame	Atomic	Spark
Element	nm	eV	emission	absorption	emission
Aluminum	309.2	3.1	0.005§‖	0.1	0.3§
Antimony	259.8	5.8	20	0.1§‖	2
Calcium	422.7	2.9	0.0001‖	0.002‖	0.01§
Chromium	357.9	3.4	0.005§‖	0.005	
Copper	324.8	3.8	0.01§‖	0.005	0.05§
Iron	248.3	3.3	0.05§‖	0.005‖	0.2§
Magnesium	285.2	4.3	0.005‖	0.0003‖	0.003§
Silicon	251.6	5.0	5	0.2	1
Sodium	589.0	2.1	0.0005	0.002‖	
Tin	224.6	4.3	0.5§‖	0.06‖	2§
Titanium	364.2	3.1	0.2§‖	0.1	0.1§
Zinc	213.8	5.8	50	0.002	

* After Fassel and Golightly [11] and Pickett and Koirtyohann. [14]
† Excitation potential of most sensitive flame emission line.
‡ Concentration of element in $\mu g\ ml^{-1}$ which, upon nebulization into flame, gives a line intensity twice the standard deviation of the background fluctuation.
§ Limit at a different wavelength than that listed. [11]
‖ See Ref. 14.

When sensitivity is the main criterion, the value of the excitation potential of the most sensitive emission line of an element provides a rough criterion for choice between FE and AA techniques. In general, FE is more sensitive or comparable in sensitivity to AA if the excitation potential is 3.4 eV or smaller. Elements from groups I_A, II_A, III_A, III_B, and a number of other transition metals fall in this category. When the excitation potential is greater than 3.4 eV, AA is the more sensitive method.

Thus, most of the less active metals such as those in Groups IB and IIB are more sensitively determined by AA photometry. For an individual element, one or the other technique may be much superior.

14.6 EMISSION FLAME PHOTOMETRY

Flame emission spectrometry is basically a quantitative technique. The term photometry suggests this emphasis. With modern burners, flame photometry is sensitively applicable to about 40 elements at the level of 1 ppm (1 μg ml^{-1}) or below, as shown below in Table 14.4. Many additional elements can be determined quantitatively at somewhat higher concentration levels. The technique is in general somewhat less versatile than arc spectrographic techniques because of flame background and other interferences and hence is little used in qualitative analysis.

For a series of measurements, in which standards are run before and after each set of samples, the reliability of quantitative emission results is usually about $\pm 2\%$. If each sample is preceded and followed by a standard of closely similar composition, the reliability can be improved to $\pm 0.5\%$ to $\pm 1\%$.

Correction for spectral background is also desirable in precision work. Ordinarily, the background intensity can be found (while the sample is being nebulized) by a

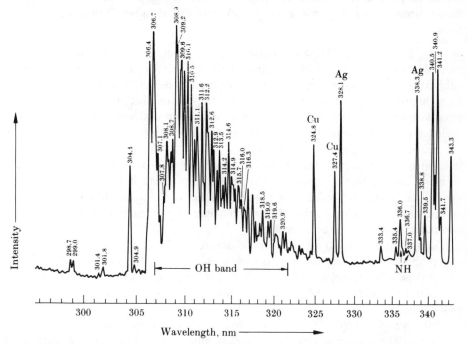

Fig. 14.9 Flame background in one region of the spectrum. The emission of a cobalt sample aspirated into an oxy-cyanogen flame was examined with a Beckman DU spectrophotometer whose slit was set at 0.02 mm. All lines are due to cobalt emission unless otherwise identified. A continuous OH band extending from 322 to 306 nm is superimposed on the emission lines of cobalt and elevates the background substantially. Note the impurity lines of copper and silver and two NH band emissions. Because of this interference cobalt is ordinarily determined at 345 or 241 nm. (Courtesy of Interscience Publ. Co.)

measurement on either side of the analytical line. If possible, the determination should be made at a distance (in nanometers) from the center of the line that is about twice the spectral slit width and should be the average of a scan over a nanometer interval. The background reading should be subtracted from the signal. Both values should, of course, be measured relative to the instrument baseline, which is observed on nebulization of pure solvent. Frequent checks of baseline are desirable.

In the instrumentation, high gain and low noise are essential to sensitive measurement near the limit of detection. Sensitivity is raised by increasing the amplifier gain. As a result either the noise in the measuring circuit or the level of continuous background emission may be limiting.

Selection of analytical wavelength. One of the most sensitive emission lines (*raies ultimes*) is ordinarily selected for determining an element. There are extensive published data on lines. [1, 2, 3] Clearly, the one chosen for a particular sample should be free of spectral interference from other elements, from molecular fragments, or from the flame (see Table 14.2). The nature of interference from radicals and fragments is illustrated by Fig. 14.9, where the OH band spectrum produced in an oxy-cyanogen flame is shown superimposed on a portion of the emission spectrum of cobalt. It would be preferable to avoid the region of these bands and others in which the flame radiates, since they give a heavy background against which to detect emission lines.

Working curves. Since flame techniques depend on many instrumental and matrix variables not accessible to direct control, analysis is usually carried out by developing calibration or working curves. These are prepared by use of standard solutions made from high-purity reagents. Their general composition, including solvent, should closely match analytical samples because of the complexity of interferences. Even their temperature should be as nearly identical as possible.

If some of the interfering components vary in concentration from sample to sample, it is often impractical to match concentrations in standards and samples. In this situation an effective approach to the "matrix" problem is often a *swamping out* procedure. A fixed but sufficiently large amount of each interferent is added both to sample and to standard so that the final concentration of each interferent is large in comparison with that usually present.

Representative working curves for sodium are shown in Fig. 14.10. The nonlinearity observable at high concentrations is caused mainly by self-absorption, as discussed earlier. Viscosity and vapor pressure effects tend to depress nebulization at very high concentrations (above 10,000 ppm), giving still further loss of intensity and downward curvature.

Interestingly, at low concentrations working curves may have upward (concave) curvature. The reason is usually ionization interference. For example, curves for potassium often slope upward. When an easily ionized element is present at very low concentration, much of it may be present in the flame as ions. As its concentration increases, a greater fraction appears as atoms and the relative intensity of emission is greater. Actually, since atomic concentrations vary a great deal along the height of the flame (Section 14.2), the degree of curvature also depends on the section of the flame observed.

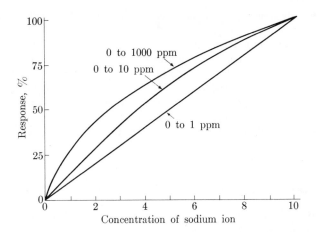

Fig. 14.10 Flame photometer calibration curves for sodium. Three concentration ranges are represented.

Operating conditions. Once sensitive wavelengths and possible interferences are known, the choice of an appropriate instrument, spectral line for each element, and a slit width that ensures adequate resolution optimizes a procedure. Yet the selection of operating conditions is equally important.

1. *Gas mixture*: If a variety of burner heads is available it will be important to have a hot flame (oxy-hydrogen, oxy-acetylene, or nitrous oxide-acetylene) for trace work and a cool flame (air-acetylene) if only alkali metals are to be determined.*

2. *Fuel-to-oxidant ratio*: Manufacturers ordinarily recommend suitable gas pressures. For metals that form difficulty dissociable oxides, use of a fuel-rich mixture with some adjustment of the flame areas viewed may enhance intensities.

3. *Addition of nonaqueous solvent*: Using a solvent mixture that is 75 volume % ethanol or a ketone should enhance sensitivity.

4. *Addition of ionization suppressant*: Adding about 200 μg ml^{-1} of potassium (if it is not being determined) enhances intensities of alkali metals, Ca, Sr, Ba, Al, Ga, Su, Pb, Sc, Ti, V, Cr, Mn, Y, Zr, Mo, Ta, Nb, and lanthanides.

Example The determination of sodium is especially easily accomplished using its resonance line at 589 nm (5890–5896 Å doublet). Self-absorption causes departure from the linearity in the working curve above concentrations of 2 ppm, especially in hot flames. Clearly, if a sample does fall in a curved region of a working curve, dilution may improve precision by allowing operation in a more linear portion.

Since for sodium there is little spectral interference from other elements, it seems preferable to minimize the possibility of such interference still more by use of a cool flame. Thus, a filter

---

* For minimum flame background the oxy-hydrogen flame is preferable to the oxy-acetylene and air-acetylene flames. To lessen possibilities of explosion, oxygen is usually excluded from premix burners, however.

photometer is entirely satisfactory for the determination; indeed, its wide band-pass will also ensure sensitivity.

If calcium is also present in the sample, its orange-red band ("head" of band at 603 nm) may cause spectral interference. Since it is more difficult to excite than sodium, a cool flame is desirable. The intensity of its emission will also be proportional to the concentration. As long as the calcium concentration is modest (below 100–200 ppm), its emission will be slight and a filter photometer will achieve satisfactory separation. At higher calcium levels a spectrophotometer must be used, however. In general, the cooler the flame the higher the calcium concentration that can be tolerated with a filter photometer without loss of precision in a sodium determination.

14.7 ATOMIC ABSORPTION PHOTOMETRY

Atomic absorption photometry is a widely applicable and generally sensitive technique for the quantative determination of elements.

A list of more than 40 elements often determined by atomic absorption photometry is given in Table 14.4.* As is evident from the sensitivity levels, the technique is excellent for the determination of a variety of elements at the trace level. Note also that many other elements are equally or more sensitively determined by flame emission.

As a general technique, atomic absorption photometry is capable of a precision of $\pm 2\%$. The precision is better when several measurements are taken, and is better than $\pm 1\%$ when a double-beam or dual-channel procedure is employed. Since atomic absorption depends upon the measurement of a small difference between two substantial signals, stability of all instrument modules is of crucial importance.

Some of the limitations of the technique can be traced to the use of a "flame cell." Flame gases such as oxygen absorb strongly below 190 nm, blocking the direct determination of elements whose sensitive lines are at shorter wavelengths, i.e., in the vacuum UV. Nonmetals such as sulfur, phosphorus, and the halogens are in this category.† The tendency of certain elements such as zirconium and tantalum to form in a flame that are difficult to dissociate severely limits sensitivity for such elements. The instability, i.e., flicker, of the flame itself is a more fundamental restriction on sensitivity since it fixes a minimum value for the noise. Burners of improved design, especially of the multiple-slot or grooved type, have lessened this influence.

Selection of wavelength. The choice of wavelength for a determination is straightforward in most cases. Hollow-cathode lamps (Section 11.3), generally the most intense "monochromatic" sources available for atomic absorption photometry, are manufactured for all elements listed in Table 14.4. Many multiple-element lamps are also available. In general, the resonance line of an element is the best choice since it offers the highest intensity. Excessive flame background, close-lying lines of other elements that cannot be excluded by the wavelength isolation device, or other factors may suggest that another sensitive line produced by the lamp be selected. True

---

* As many as 67 elements can be determined.

† Sometimes absorption by molecules containing the element offers an indirect method.

Table 14.4 Elements Determinable by Flame Methods*

Sensitivity: high (1 μg ml^{-1} or below)								Sensitivity: moderate	
More sensitive by atomic absorption		About equally sensitive by absorption and emission		More sensitive by flame emission				More sensitive by atomic absorption	
Ag	Ni	Cr	Pd	Al	In	Sr		Ce	Re
As	Pb	Cu	Rh	B	K	Tb		Hf	Sm
Au	Pt	Dy	Sc	Ba	La	Tl		Ir	Ta
Be	Sb	Er	Ta	Ca	Li	Tm		Nd	Th
Bi	Se	Gd	Ti	Cs	Lu	W		Os	U
Cd	Si	Ge	V	Eu	Na	Yb		Pr	Zr
Co	Sn	Mn	Y	Ga	Rb				
Fe	Te	Mo	Zr	Ho	Ru				
Hg	Zn	Nb							
Mg									
19 elements		17 elements		22 elements				12 elements	

* Adapted from Koirtyohann [12] and Pickett and Koirtyohann. [14]

spectral interferences are rare since lines emitted by a hollow cathode lamp are extremely narrow (about 0.002 nm).*

Working conditions. As is true of most photometric measurement systems (see Section 16.4) precision is best when absorbance falls in the range 0.15 to 1.0 (about 70 to 10% transmittance). Concentrations should be adjusted accordingly. If an internal standard is used in a dual-channel instrument, the absorbance range can, of course, be extended with good precision.

If the concentration range of an element in a sample exceeds values that give optimum absorbance, several options are open. One is rotation of a burner of the slot type about an axis perpendicular to its head. The optical path length through the flame may be varied in this way, allowing absorbance to be varied by as much as a factor of ten. A second possibility is use of a less sensitive line of the element. Indeed, this option might yield a linear calibration curve at higher concentrations. A third possibility is dilution of the sample, though this process is commonly less desirable because it may introduce contamination. Finally, where somewhat reduced precision is no problem, the concentration range can be extended even though a nonlinear calibration curve is obtained.

In general, AA measurements are subject to all forms of interference that affect nebulization or flame dissociation (see Table 14.2). There is, of course, a basic

---

* Should a continuous source such as xenon lamp be used, there is, of course, a greater chance of interference. In this case, the limiting factor is the spectral slit width of the source monochromator. Usually it is in the range 0.05 to 0.15 nm.

independence of flame excitation factors. Neither the flame temperature nor the absorption frequency is of great concern.

Sensitivity can be enhanced by introducing a sample directly into a flame to avoid nebulization losses. The sample is placed in a 1 ml tantalum *sampling boat* and dried if in liquid form. The boat is positioned in the flame, and absorption is monitored for as much as 30 seconds.

For quantitative procedures a choice is usually made between the use of working curves and a standard addition method. Working curves are obtained from standard solutions prepared from ultrapure reagents. Unless it is done automatically by the instrument, background absorbance must naturally be subtracted from the absorbance for each solution before the curve is plotted. The average of several corrected values for each sample should be taken to plot the curve.

In general, a standard addition method is more attractive only if samples of relatively low concentration are to be assayed. The method calls for measurements on three solutions: sample solution, sample solution after addition of a known amount of a standard solution, and a blank (solution) to which the same addition is made. A reliable estimate of background absorption is especially important in this technique Often background may be neglected, but its nature should be known in any event. Necessary corrections for background are usually determined by measurements at a wavelength close to the absorption line used.

Example For the determination of zinc in a brass sample the optimum concentration level is 0.5 to 5.0 $\mu g\ ml^{-1}$ if the zinc resonance line (213.9 nm) is used, and 2000 to 20 000 $\mu g\ ml^{-1}$ for another possible line (307.6 nm). An air-hydrogen flame (2000 °C) provides maximum sensitivity and is to be preferred to the hotter air-acetylene flame.

A band-pass of 5 nm can be tolerated if a zinc lamp is used, but it must be reduced to 1 nm for a brass hollow cathode lamp, which also produces 216.5 and 217.9 nm copper lines. The latter lamp, of course, would provide for determination of both zinc and copper.

While interferences are slight even with a 200-fold excess of other elements, zinc is usually complexed with ammonium pyrrolidine dithiocarbamate when determined at the trace level and then extracted into a solvent such as methyl isobutylketone. Constant flame conditions are important if zinc is determined at 213.8 nm because of appreciable absorption by flame gases. The extent of absorption should be ascertained.

14.8 ATOMIC FLUORESCENCE SPECTROMETRY

Atomic fluorescence photometry is also basically a sensitive quantitative method for determining elements. As noted in the introduction, the technique calls for measurement of the fluorescence emission of atoms excited by incident radiation of appropriate wavelength. Not all the (electronically) excited atoms return to the ground state in fluorescing; those that do are said to undergo *resonance fluorescence*. The dependence of the measurement on a variety of parameters will be considered in detail in Section 15.2 when molecular fluorescence, a similar phenomenon, is taken up.

It is the direct dependence of fluorescence on the intensity of the external source that suggests the potential of the technique. In principle it is capable of greater sensitivity than the other flame techniques, given strong sources. Indeed, published results suggest that this is true. In range, atomic fluorescence is limited only by the present use of a "flame cell." Absorption by flame gases precludes work in the vacuum ultraviolet (below 190 nm). Thus, the technique is applicable over essentially the wavelength range accessible to AA spectroscopy.

The technique has two other advantages. First, the nature of fluorescence allows usable calibration curves to be obtained over a concentration range of 10^3 to 10^5. A similar result was obtained in flame emission methods. Second, as in atomic absorption studies, spectral interferences are uncommon if a hollow-cathode lamp or other narrow line source is used. Thus, interferences that relate to nebulization and to dissociation are the most important types.

Instrumentation is basically like that for flame emission except a source is used and fluorescent emission is detected at an angle of 90° to the path of exciting radiation. Thus an FE spectrometer can be modified for fluorescence work. Electrodeless discharge tubes operated at radio or microwave frequencies and some hollow-cathode lamps are valuable as intense sources. To improve the signal-to-noise ratio, many systems call for chopping the exciting radiation and using ac amplification and a phase-sensitive amplifier.

Perhaps the chief disadvantage of atomic fluorescence photometry is practical: Only for about a dozen elements are sufficiently intense sources available to justify the trouble in setting up the necessary instrumentation. However, it seems likely that the technique will be developed further for trace analysis.

REFERENCES

Some basic general references are:

1. John A. Dean and Theodore C. Rains, eds. *Flame Emission and Atomic Absorption Spectrometry*. Vol. 1. New York: Dekker, 1969
2. Roland Herrmann and C. T. J. Alkemade, *Chemical Analysis by Flame Photometry*. 2d ed. New York: Interscience, 1963
3. R. Mavrodineanu and H. Boiteux, *Flame Spectroscopy*. New York: Wiley, 1965

General references dealing with atomic flame, or molecular spectroscopy on an intermediate level are:

4. A. G. Gaydon, *The Spectroscopy of Flames*. New York: Wiley, 1957
5. R. W. B. Pearse and A. G. Gaydon, *The Identification of Molecular Spectra*. 3d ed. New York: Wiley, 1963
6. S. Walker and H. Straw, *Spectroscopy*. Vol. 1, Atomic, Microwave, and Radio-frequency. New York: Macmillan, 1962

Particular techniques and their instrumentation are well covered in:

7. W. T. Elwell and J. A. F. Gidley, *Atomic-Absorption Spectrophotometry*. 2d ed. New York: Pergamon, 1966
8. J. Ramirez-Munoz, *Spectroscopy and Analysis by Atomic Absorption Flame Photometry*. New York: Elsevier, 1968
9. James W. Robinson, *Atomic Absorption Spectroscopy*. New York: Dekker, 1966
10. Walter Slavin, *Atomic Absorption Spectroscopy*. New York: Wiley, 1968

Also of interest are:

11. V. A. Fassel and D. W. Golightly, "Detection Limits of Elements in the Spectra of Pre-mixed, Oxy-Acetylene Flames," *Anal. Chem.* **39**, 466 (1967)
12. S. R. Koirtyohann, "Recent Developments in Atomic Absorption and Flame Emission Spectroscopy," *Atomic Abs. Newsl.* **6**, 77 (1967)
13. M. L. Parsons, W. J. McCarthy, and J. D. Winefordner, "The Selection of Optimum Conditions for Spectrochemical Methods, Part III, Sensitivity of Atomic Fluorescence, Absorption, and Emission Flame Spectrometry," *J. Chem. Educ.* **44**, 214, (1967)
14. E. E. Pickett and S. R. Koirtyohann, "Emission Flame Photometry—A New Look at an Old Method," *Anal. Chem.* **41** (14), 28A (1969)
15 J. D. Winefordner and T. J. Vickers, "Calculation of the Limit of Detectability in Atomic Emission Flame Spectrometry," *Anal. Chem.* **36**, 1939, 1947 (1964)

EXERCISES

14.1 A sodium vapor discharge lamp relies on neon as a starter gas. When the lamp is first started, a strong neon spectrum is obtained, but when all the sodium is vaporized the neon spectrum is very weak. Explain briefly the cause of its suppression.

14.2 In Fig. 14.11 a schematic layout of the optical part of a double-beam atomic absorption spectrophotometer is given.

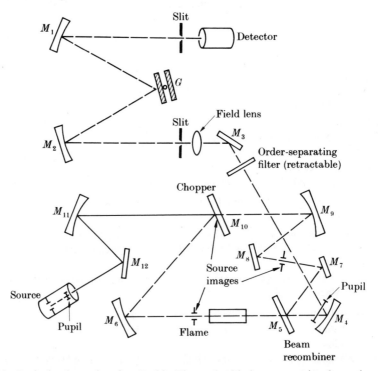

Fig. 14.11 Optical schematic of a Perkin-Elmer double-beam atomic absorption spectrophotometer. M_{10} is a rotating sector mirror. M_5 is a semitransparent beam recombiner. Note the Czerny-Turner monochromator at the top. (Courtesy of Perkin-Elmer Corp.)

a) Draw a block diagram of this part of the instrument. Indicate components associated with each block in the dragram.

b) What type of monochromator is used? Explain the pair of gratings G.

c) Is the omission of some provision to remove unwanted orders of spectra a serious one? Comment briefly.

d) If the chopper were deleted and the current of the hollow-cathode lamp were modulated, what changes would need to be made in the instrument?

14.3 Sketch the layout of the optical components of an atomic absorption spectrometer based on use of two dual-atom resonance detectors. Four elements are to be determined simultaneously. Show the optical path. In principle, what loss in sensitivity will occur for each element? [See *Appl. Opt.* **7**, 1271 (1968).]

14.4 Aluminum can be sensitively determined by flame emission photometry by complexing it with thenoyltrifluoracetone and extracting the chelate into methyl isobutyl ketone; this solution is aspirated into a flame and observed at 484 nm. An experimenter prepared a calibration curve for the system from the following data (in each case the first figure is the concentration of the standard solution in ppm, the second the meter deflection): 20, 12; 45, 26; 90, 51; 120, 70; 150, 87. He found that a similar aliquot of an unknown gave a meter reading of 57. What was the aluminum concentration of the aliquot?

14.5 The spectrum of a titanium hollow-cathode lamp was observed at several operating currents. Up to a current of 50 mA all the lines gave sharp peaks. At higher currents the most intense line at 364.3 nm developed a cup-like crater in its peak. Explain.

14.6 Why cannot reliable determinations usually be made by flame emission spectrometry on concentrated solutions of alkali metal salts without dilution? A modification of the usual monochromator based on the use of a pair of exit slits, one on either side of the characteristic wavelength, has been suggested as a means of overcoming this difficulty. Explain how the dual-slit arrangement avoids the usual problem. [See J. C. Burridge and R. O. Scott, *Spectr. Letter* **1**, 379 (1968).]

14.7 Should it be possible to perform *molecular* absorption flame photometry? For example, molecular sulfur has absorption bands at 320–261 nm, 230–180 nm, and 158–152 nm. The second listed is the most intense. For a determination of sulfur, suggest a source, type of wavelength isolation device, flame arrangement, and detector. [See K. Fuwa and B. L. Vallee, *Anal. Chem.* **41**, 188 (1969).]

14.8 Why is it important in the atomic absorption spectrometric determination of a metal that the type of compound, e.g. nitrate, used in establishing the standard curve be the same as analyzed?

14.9 There is considerable noise in most flame signals. How may a useful readout be secured (a) if a meter is used? (b) if a potentiometric recorder is used? Note some advantages and disadvantages of the methods suggested.

14.10 In the atomic absorption spectrometric determination of zinc in 10% NaCl solutions it is found that light scattering occurs in the flame.

a) How will light scattering affect the readout, which is in absorbance? What is the probable origin of the scattering?

b) To correct for light scattering, measurements are made at the zinc wavelength (213.9 nm) using both a zinc hollow-cathode lamp and a hydrogen or deuterium (continuum) lamp. The standard addition method is used and the following measurements are recorded:

Zn concentration (μg ml^{-1})	0.00	0.1	0.2
Readout with			
zinc hollow cathode lamp	0.10	0.27	0.44
hydrogen lamp	0.10	0.10	0.10

What concentration of Zn will be reported with and without the use of the hydrogen lamp?

[*Ans.*: b) 0.06 μg Zn ml^{-1}; 0.0 μg Zn ml^{-1}.]

14.11 The simple atomic absorption spectrometer shown in Fig. 14.12 proved more sensitive for mercury determinations than a regular flame cell instrument. Mercury present in samples is reduced to the metallic form in aqueous solution, usually by pretreatment with tin(II) in 1–3M H_2SO_4. With proper choice of conditions good accuracy is obtained. A quantity as small as 10 ng can be determined when the 253.7 nm (2537 Å) mercury wavelength is used.

a) Show how this instrument differs from a flame cell device and justify the difference. Why might a flame cell lead to lower sensitivity?

b) State any assumptions that must be made in using the instrument of Fig. 14.12.

c) Draw a schematic diagram of an operational amplifier system that could serve as the amplifier. How can its gain be varied? [See L. P. Morganthaler, *MPI Application Notes* **5**, 25 (1970).]

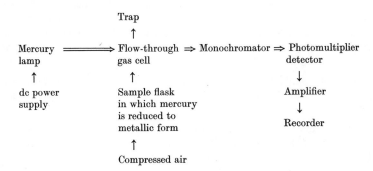

Figure 14.12

Chapter 15

FLUOROMETRY

15.1 INTRODUCTION

A number of processes may result from the electronic excitation of a molecule or a group of molecules by non-ionizing radiation. The number includes processes such as molecular dissociation, photochemical reaction, fluorescence, and phosphorescence. Chemical processes like the first two are important in biology and chemistry but need only be mentioned here. Phosphorescence will be considered below. In this chapter molecular fluorescence, the type of fast emission occurring in about 10^{-8} sec after excitation, will be treated and techniques for its measurement examined. Such fluorometric methods prove a sensitive means of determining the concentration of many molecules, of establishing some idea of molecular environment, and of furnishing information about the concentration and behavior of excited state species.

Molecular fluorescence is a much more complex phenomenon than atomic fluorescence, which was discussed briefly in the last chapter. Two obvious factors are responsible. First, in molecules vibrational and rotational energy levels are associated with electronic levels. As a result, possible transitions are numerous. Here attention will be given only to relaxation processes by which molecules return to the ground electronic state from excited electronic states. Refer to Section 16.3 for a general discussion of absorption processes. The second reason for the complexity of molecular fluorescence phenomena is that studies are ordinarily carried out in condensed phases where the proximity of other molecules to one that is electronically excited presents a great many opportunities for the exchange of energy and other relaxational processes.

How does fluorescence differ from other ways in which an excited molecule can lose energy? The diagram shown in Fig. 15.1 describes the main types of relaxation process that are postulated to account for observed transitions. The notation used is as follows

S_0 ground singlet state S_1 first excited singlet state
    (spins paired ↑↓)   (spins paired ↑↓)

T_1 first excited triplet state   wavy line: nonradiative transition
    (two unpaired spins ↑↑)   solid line: radiative transition

Several comments are in order. Note that only two singlet electronic states are shown, the ground state S_0 and the first excited state S_1. Ordinarily no others are important in relation to fluorescence.* It should also be noted that singlet to triplet

---

* Though not shown in Fig. 15.1, the possibility exists that the initial absorption of a photon may lead to a still higher excited singlet state such as S_2 or S_3. In the majority of instances, non-radiative relaxation occurs very quickly from such states to S_1, a process called internal conversion. There are only a few instances known in which fluorescence occurs from an electronic state above S_1.

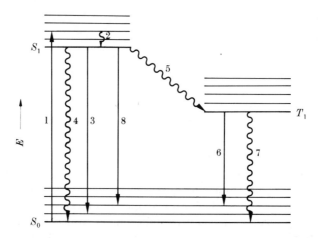

Fig. 15.1 Diagram showing energy relationships among some molecular absorption and relaxation processes. Shown are several vibrational levels in three electronic states, singlet states S_0 (ground) and S_1 (excited) and triplet state T_1. Processes shown are: 1, absorption; 2, vibrational relaxation (nonradiative); 3, fluorescence; 4 and 7, quenching (nonradiative conversion of electronic energy to heat); 5, intersystem crossing (nonradiative; change of spin); 6, phosphorescence; 8, delayed fluorescence.

transitions like $S_0 \rightarrow T_1$ require a change of spin and are of low probability. [1]

As discussed in Section 16.3 the vibrational change accompanying electronic excitation nearly always leaves the excited molecule with one or more of its normal vibrations in a high vibrational level. This result is suggested in Fig. 15.1 by terminating upward transition 1 in the third vibrational level associated with S_1. Further, in most molecules the extra vibrational energy will be dissipated quickly by nonradiative or "dark" processes. Collisions with surrounding molecules during the roughly 10^{-8} s between excitation and fluorescence will tend to bring the electronically excited molecule to its lowest vibrational state. Fluorescence will nearly always occur from that level.

Though an excited molecule may possess sufficient total vibrational energy to dissociate, it will seldom do so. Thus, in fluorometry the fraction of molecules that dissociates is minute. Two factors mitigate against molecular breakdown: (a) a relatively small flux of energy is actually incident on a sample; much is blocked by the monochromator or filter and (b) vibrational energy must ordinarily remain large over an interval sufficiently long for it to be redistributed into a vibrational mode that favors dissociation. Since collisions of an excited molecule with its neighbors occur rapidly, it is more probable that vibrational energy will be lost than that dissociation will take place. It should also be stressed that the shorter the wavelength of the irradiating light, the more likely molecular dissociation or other photochemical reaction will be. In fluorometry very short wavelengths (e.g., below 200 nm) are avoided for this reason.

Fluorescence is the radiative return from excited state S_1 to one of the vibrational levels of the ground electronic state S_0. It is "spin-allowed" and is the most probable radiative relaxation process.* The duration of fluorescence (after excitation is stopped) is 1 to 10^3 ns.

A representative excitation spectrum and fluorescence spectrum for a molecule is pictured in Fig. 15.2. Note the rough "mirror-image" relationship of the two spectra. This phenomenon arises because the excitation process requires an amount of energy equal to the basic electronic energy change *plus* a vibrational energy increase; conversely, each de-excitation yields the basic electronic excitation energy *minus* a vibrational energy increase. Often there is as much detail in the fluorescence spectrum as in the absorption spectrum. The fluorescence spectrum appears at longer wavelengths because of the nonradiative losses in the excited electronic state.

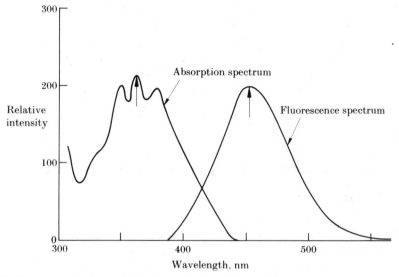

Fig. 15.2 Representative interrelation between absorption and fluorescence spectra. The absorption or excitation spectrum was obtained by observing fluorescence at 450 nm (see arrow), and the fluorescence or emission spectrum by excitation at 362 nm (see arrow). Curves are for an anthracene carbamide conjugate of glutamic acid dehydrogenase (see R. F. Chen in Ref. 2). (Courtesy of Marcel Dekker.)

Naturally, nonradiative mechanisms that allow the electronic energy to be degraded to heat also operate. Collectively, these are called fluorescence *quenching* (Section 15.3 below).

In Fig. 15.1 the possibility of a nonradiative intersystem crossing from singlet state S_1 to triplet state T_1 is also shown. This process occurs with moderate probability in many molecules. Once a molecule is in a triplet state either *phosphorescence*, the radiative transition $T_1 \rightarrow S_0$, or the nonradiative intersystem crossing between the same pair of states, can occur. Phosphorescence is spin-forbidden since an electron spin must change and is thus longer lived (10^{-3} to 10 s) than fluorescence. It is most likely to be observed if the triplet state molecule is in a rigid solution or glass where

---

* Fluorescence can be defined as a radiative transition between states of the same multiplicity (see Section 16.3).

the rate of the competing nonradiative transition is very slow. [13] It is beyond the scope of the book to treat phosphorescence further. Fortunately, fluorescence measurement procedures are easily modified for measurement of phosphorescence.

Structural factors.   What kinds of molecules fluoresce? How sensitive are fluorescing species to alterations in structure caused by absorption on a substrate, complexing with a metal ion, or dissociation of a proton? Answers to queries such as these will largely determine the scope of fluorometry.

Two related classes of substance that fluoresce are aromatic compounds and those that possess long conjugated bond systems (alternating single and double bonds). Both have delocalized π-electrons that can be placed in low-lying excited states. For example, benzene fluoresces. It has an absorption peak at 254 nm and shows a fluorescence maximum at 291 nm. Substituents strongly affect fluorescence. Thus, aniline fluoresces but nitrobenzene does not. Undoubtedly, fluorescence can also occur with aliphatic or saturated cyclic compounds, but both the high energy required for electronic excitation and the fact that a bonding electron must be excited cause excitation to lead ordinarily to photodissociation. These types of molecules are not observed to fluoresce under ordinary conditions.

A third class of molecules that would seem to meet the criterion are those with a nonbonding pair of valence electrons, e.g., an amine with a lone electron pair on its nitrogen atom. Such electrons can be "promoted" without disruption of bonding. In general a delocalized π-system must also be part of this type of a molecule to ensure easy fluorescence.

Most species that fluoresce intensely have rigid, planar structures. The possibility of competing nonradiative transitions is lessened by molecular rigidity. [1] For example, the rigid molecule fluorescein displays fluorescence, but the similar nonrigid molecule phenolphthalein does not.

The detailed relationship of structure and fluorescence is quite complex. Changes in environment, especially changes in temperature, affect energies of fluorescence and its intensity. In instances in which nonrigid molecules undergo fluorescence, the matter of molecular conformation is strongly involved. For example, the fluorescence of such a molecule changes if it is absorbed onto a protein. Indeed this type of procedure is sometimes employed to estimate protein conformation.

Analytical applications of fluorometry extend far beyond analysis of fluorescing substances. As is true with absorption photometric procedures, a great many non-fluorescing species such as metal ions can also be determined by complexing with a fluorescing ligand. The technique thus has considerable breadth as well as sensitivity.

15.2 INSTRUMENTATION

An instrument to measure fluorescence, a fluorometer, must provide an intense excitation source, a holder for the sample, and a system for observing fluorescence. In addition to regular optical and photometric considerations two special factors influence design.

First, fluorescence must be detected while a sample is simultaneously illuminated with high-intensity radiation. A linear alignment of source-sample-detector would thus offer severe discrimination problems. The usual design takes advantage of the fact that emission occurs at all angles. When the detector is placed at right angles to the path of irradiating light, discrimination is limited to distinguishing fluorescence emission from low-intensity scattered light.

Second, for greater sensitivity it is necessary to select particular wavelengths for excitation and for detection. Either filters or monochromators can be used. A line block diagram of a generalized fluorometer is shown in Fig. 15.3.

```
              Filter or
  Source ⇒ monochromator ⇒ Sample
                  90° \ ⇓
                      Filter or          → Detector → Amplifier
                      monochromator                      ↓
                                                      Readout
```

Fig. 15.3 Line block diagram of a generalized fluorometer.

In order to assess the contribution of each module to a measurement, consider the dependence of the signal on several variables. It can be shown [9] that the signal developed by the detector is related to the concentration of analytical species by the following expression:

$$\text{Signal} = f(\theta)\, g(\lambda)\, \phi_f\, P_0\, (1 - e^{-\epsilon bc}). \tag{15.1}$$

Each of the terms requires brief definition. First, the term $P_0(1 - e^{-\epsilon bc})$ defines the fraction of incident radiation of power P_0 absorbed by the sample (see discussion of Beer's law in Section 16.2), where ϵ is the molar absorptivity ($1\ \text{mol}^{-1}\ \text{cm}^{-1}$) at a particular wavelength of excitation λ, b is the path length (cm) in the sample cell, and c is the molar concentration of solute. Second, ϕ_f represents the fraction of excited species that fluoresces rather than undergoes intersystem crossing. Quenching, which would result in an entirely nonradiative relaxation to the ground state S_0, is assumed absent. Third, $f(\theta)$ represents the geometrical factor and is determined by the solid angle of the fluorescing radiation observed by the detector. Fourth, $g(\lambda)$ is a factor defining the efficiency of the detector as a function of the fluorescing wavelength incident on it.

Source. Of particular interest in Eq. (15.1) is the linear dependence on the power of exciting radiation P_0: It is advantageous to use a source as powerful as possible. A high-pressure mercury arc is often used but a xenon arc lamp is generally preferred (see Section 11.2). A continuous source like the xenon lamp has the advantage that at any wavelength in its range there is sufficient intensity; the advantage of a discontinuous source like the mercury arc is that very high intensities are available in bands centered about its emission wavelengths. If a sample absorbs in one of these bands, the mercury arc would be preferred.

Clearly, a laser would also be an acceptable source, provided monochromatic light were needed for excitation. Since a band is often adequate, arc lamps can usually furnish a greater total intensity. Lasers have been used, however, for excitation of vibrational-rotational transitions in the infrared and attendant observation of "fluorescence."

Since only radiation impinging on a sample can lead to excitation, light-collecting arrangements are necessary to take full advantage of most sources. Either mirrors or lenses are used, the former being more common. For example, an off-axis ellipsoidal mirror is an effective collector when the source is placed at its near focus and a monochromator entrance slit at its far focus.

With an intense source a substantial amount of light is scattered at right angles to its beam. Accordingly, it is desirable to use only the wavelength band most efficient in excitation. Since fluorescence occurs at longer wavelengths, it is not difficult to separate scattered and fluorescent radiation. Either a filter or a monochromator can be used to isolate the desired excitation and "detector" bands. Fluorometers based on both types of device are common.

Filter fluorometer. For routine quantitative analyses a pair of appropriate filters (Section 11.5) is in general preferred for wavelength isolation. Since filters pass a broader band of radiation and permit use of wider apertures, a filter fluorometer is usually capable of greater sensitivity than a monochromator-equipped device.

Instruments employing glass filters can, of course, operate only in the visible and near UV. The use of interference filters extends the range further into the UV. A representative filter fluorometer is shown in Fig. 15.4. Both filters may be sharp-cutoff types. As shown, these instruments almost always use a partial double-beam arrangement to lessen effects of fluctuations and drift in source intensity and detector response. A variety of ingenious ways for obtaining the monitoring channel have been devised. It should be noted that a filter fluorometer can be quickly adapted for absorption photometric work in the visible by installing a detector in line with the sample and source.

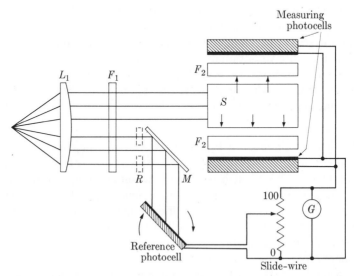

Fig. 15.4 A simplified schematic diagram of a partial double-beam filter fluorometer, the Lume-tron Model 402-EF. L_1, collimating lens. F_1, primary filter passing only exciting UV. F_2, secondary filter passing only fluorescent light. R, reduction plate. M, front-surface mirror. G, galvanometer. An electrical balance is obtained between the response of reference and measuring photocells by use of a current bridge. (Courtesy of Photovolt Corp.; B. A. Brice, *Rev. Sci. Instr.* **8**, 279 (1937).)

Example The Beckman ratio fluorometer is designed around a special dual-anode mercury lamp that operates on ac. The anodes are located on opposite sides, each attracting the mercury arc discharge on alternate halves of the ac cycle. The inside of the envelope is coated with a phosphor to convert the intense 184 and 253 nm mercury lines to a UV-VIS continuum peaking at 254, 310, 360, and 450 nm. The lamp is dark for a brief interval between each period of emission.

The UV alternately emerging from one side of the lamp and then from the other is directed through filters that pass only the excitation wavelengths. One beam goes through the sample and the other through a reference solution that may be the most concentrated sample likely to be of interest. The fluorescent light emerging from the sample at about 75° to the incident beam is collected by a lens system that directs it through a filter to a photomultiplier detector. The filter excludes any of the exciting UV that has been scattered. A similar lens arrangement collects fluorescent light from the reference and directs it through the same filter and to the detector. Since reference and sample beams reach the detector alternately, an operation of full double-beam type is secured.

The reference beam fluorescence is held constant by varying the dynode voltage on the photomultiplier tube and is used to establish the maximum readout setting. The photomultiplier output for the sample then indicates the fluorescence intensity of sample relative to that of the reference.

"Reflectance" fluorometers, i.e., instruments that rely on detection of fluorescence emitted at 180° to the incident beam, are widely used also. For example, paper and thin-layer chromatograms of fluorescing species can be monitored in this way. Various fluorescent solids, e.g. uranium ores, are also routinely assayed by such devices. (See Exercise 15.3.)

Fluorescence spectrometers. The modules needed for a spectrophotometric version of a fluorometer are just those used in absorption spectrophotometry. Two monochromators are employed, of course, one in the excitation and the other in the fluorescence path. Czerny–Turner grating monochromators (Chapter 12) are commonly used. Gratings ensure a higher throughput of light than prisms. Since absorption and fluorescence peaks are broad in most instances, the resolution and spectral slit width of the monochromator need not be as fine as for atomic or gas-phase spectrometric studies. A representative device is shown in Fig. 15.5.

Where energetics are of interest, it is necessary to record spectral intensities accurately. In order to obtain such *absolute* or energy-corrected fluorescence spectra the variation with wavelength for both P_0 and $g(\lambda)$, the detector response function, must be taken into account. If an excitation spectrum is sought, a slit program that maintains P_0 at a fixed value is generally used since high resolution is not crucial.[*] Alternatively, if constant resolution is needed, the entrance slit may be held at fixed width, and the difference signal from the detector furnished to a computing stage to reduce the measured fluorescence to a constant excitation energy basis.

How should a correction be made for change in detector response with wavelength?

---

[*] The entrance slit of the excitation monochromator may be controlled by directing part of the output of the monochromator to a monitoring detector that is wavelength-insensitive. A thermopile or other thermal detector (Section 11.7) is ideal. The monitor output is compared with a constant voltage, and the amplified difference signal directed to a servomotor controlling the width of the entrance slit.

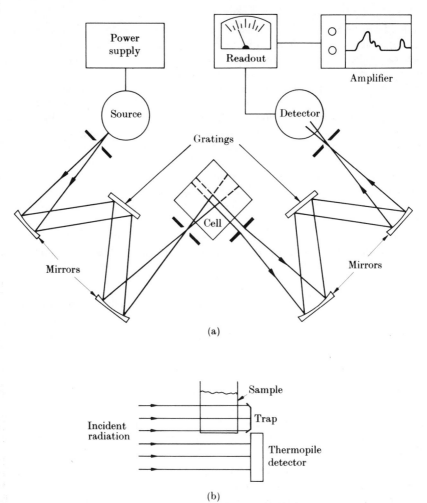

Fig. 15.5 A fluorescence spectrometer, the Aminco-Bowman SPF. Note that two Czerny–Turner monochromators are used. (a) Optical schematic with block diagram of other modules. (b) Detail of arrangement to monitor incident intensity. The output of the thermopile detector is used to obtain energy-corrected spectra. (Courtesy of American Instrument Company.)

Usually a cam is cut to represent this function. Then, if the entrance slit of the excitation monochromator has been controlled, the cam can be used to operate the exit slit of the fluorescence monochromator in such a way that any difference in detector response is offset. Alternatively, if a computer stage has been added, the cam may be used to drive a potentiometer that will correct the detector output electrically. By either scheme, energy-corrected or true fluorescence spectra are obtained.

15.3 ANALYTICAL PROCEDURES

Attention will be focussed on quantitative analytical methods since fluorometry does not lend itself to qualitative analyses. In part this is attributable to the small number of species that fluoresce, in part to the great sensitivity of fluorescence to solution conditions, and in part to the lack of detail in fluorescence spectra. It is also beyond the scope of the text to treat the host of important spectrometric studies made by studying fluorescence. These types of investigation are well covered in references (see, e.g., Refs. 1, 1a).

Over what concentrations is fluorometry valuable for quantitative determinations? What degree of control of solution conditions is necessary to secure valid measurements? These important questions will be considered in sequence.

The relation between fluorescence and concentration involves the response of both the molecular system and the instrument system. The first is usually described in terms of the *fluorescence quantum efficiency*, the ratio of fluorescence photons to absorbed photons. Here it must suffice to state that for most fluorescing substances efficiency is constant only at low concentrations (below 10^{-4}M). This restriction fixes the upper limit of usable sample concentrations. Concentrations can be calculated only if efficiency is independent of concentration.

The relation between the response of the instrument system and concentration may be examined by returning to Eq. (15.1). Note that concentration appears in the exponential factor ϵbc. As a result, instrument response will be linear in concentration only when the exponential term reduces to a term linear in c. It can be shown that when $\epsilon bc \leq 0.05$, the replacement is possible and Eq. (15.1) can be rewritten in the form*

$$\text{Signal} = f(\theta)\, g(\lambda)\, \phi_f P_0 \epsilon bc. \tag{15.2}$$

Since typical values of ϵ are of the order 10^3 to 10^4, if $b = 1$ cm, the condition $\epsilon bc \leq 0.05$ requires that c be no greater than 10^{-5} to 10^{-6}M!

The restriction on concentration proves unduly severe. In practice, working curves (instrument readout *vs* c) can be extended upward in concentration until the fluorescence efficiency begins to fall. The loss of sensitivity and precision occasioned by departure from linearity is not substantial.[†]

Equation (15.1) also reminds one that the sensitivity and limit of detection (Section 8.2) in fluorometry is directly related to P_0. While the choice of instrument source will mainly determine P_0, conditions in the sample cell will affect it also. First, any foreign substance that absorbs at the same wavelengths as the sample will reduce P_0. If its concentration varies from sample to sample, measurement precision will be low. Second, absorption by the analytical species itself will cause P_0 to fall across the width b of the sample cell. How will a measurement of fluorescence be affected? If, as is usual, only a portion of the sample cell is "viewed" by the detector, the fluorescence–

---

* A series expansion is made. It gives

$$1 - e^{-\epsilon bc} = \epsilon bc - \frac{(\epsilon bc)^2}{2!} + \frac{(\epsilon bc)^3}{3!} - \cdots$$

Only the first term need be retained if $\epsilon bc \leq 0.05$.
† Should the concentration increase to the level where absorption is essentially complete, however, Eq. (15.1) indicates that the fluorescence intensity will be independent of concentration, since the exponential term $e^{-\epsilon bc}$ will go to zero!

concentration curve will actually peak and then decrease. [9] If determinations are to be made at relatively high concentrations, this effect should be avoided by increasing the solid angle $f(\theta)$ subtended by the detector.

Quenching. There are a number of processes that compete with normal molecular fluorescence and that must be minimized if fluorescence is to be used for quantitative determinations. They are collected under the heading quenching, which signifies loss of fluorescence. One is internal quenching, the intersystem crossing S_1 to T_1 (see Fig. 15.1), which usually leads to a subsequent nonradiative relaxation from the triplet state. In Eq. (15.1) it was allowed for by including factor ϕ_f. In addition there are several types of potent bimolecular quenching processes.

Collisional impurity quenching leads to loss of fluorescence because of the formation of an exciplex or excited complex between the excited analytical species and a ground-state impurity molecule and subsequent nonradiative energy losses. Dissolved oxygen is the most common impurity quencher. It is a very effective quencher but can be removed easily by bubbling pure N_2 through a solution or by alternate freezing and pumping of a solution. *Energy transfer quenching* is a second type of impurity quenching that occurs when an impurity is present whose first excited singlet state is at an energy below that of the excited singlet state of the analytical species. A nonradiative energy transfer can occur (even though there is no collision), followed by a further radiationless loss by the impurity. Aromatic substances are prime offenders in this category. In any event, pure solvents are essential for careful work. Attention needs also to be given to the possibility that a solute of interest may contain impurities that will quench part or all its fluorescence.* A preliminary separation is indicated if such quenching occurs. In a few instances dilution may also be effective in reducing such quenching if fluorescence intensity is not lowered too greatly in the process.

The third main type is *concentration quenching*. It is this kind of self-quenching with increasing concentration that is responsible for the loss of fluorescence quantum efficiency described above. In this case quenching occurs because of formation of an excimer, i.e., a collisional complex between one molecule of the analytical species that has been excited to the singlet state and a second identical unexcited molecule. Subsequent radiationless processes degrade the extra energy to heat.

Quantitative procedures. The scope of fluorometry is broad. Among the types of substances that fluoresce are crystalline salts, dye-metal complexes, and aromatic and other unsaturated organic compounds. Thiamine and riboflavin belong to the last category and can be estimated directly. Most analyses, however, are based on the formation of a fluorescing species from the substance sought. For example, traces of uranium can be determined by fusing a sample with a KF–$NaKCO_3$ mixture to form a fluorescent salt complex. In other instances the "formation reaction" and the analysis are carried out in solution; for example, aluminum may be analyzed as the fluorescent chelate formed with the dye Pontachrome blue-black.

To determine appropriate wavelengths for a new determination, one must learn

---

* The presence of longer wavelengths than normal in the solute fluorescence spectrum is indicative of the presence of energy transfer type quenching impurities.

the fluorescence spectrum of the species of interest. If not available in references, the spectrum may be determined with a spectrofluorophotometer. With the sample in place, an arbitrary broad UV waveband is selected for excitation and a fluorescence spectrum observed by scanning with the fluorescence monochromator. The optimum fluorescence wavelength for a determination will be that of peak fluorescence. With the fluorescence monochromator set at this optimum value, the excitation wavelength range should now be scanned until the fluorescence reaches a new peak. The excitation wavelength together with the optimum fluorescence wavelength will give greatest sensitivity and precision of quantitative determination.

In carrying out an analysis care must be taken to keep concentrations below levels at which concentration quenching begins to affect precision, as discussed earlier. Oxygen should be removed, especially for work in organic solvents, and other impurities that can lead to impurity quenching must be avoided.

In addition, pH and temperature should be regulated in most cases. These variables influence fluorescence intensity in many systems by their effect on the point of equilibrium. For many molecules, as simple a structural change as the addition or deletion of a proton is enough to shift wavelengths of fluorescence or to destroy fluorescence. The optimum pH and temperature for a flurorescent species in a given solvent must generally be found experimentally.

All the regular analytical procedures for determining concentration such as the use of a working curve or the standard addition method are usable in fluorometry. (See the latter part of Section 25.10 for general details about these methods.)

Qualitative analysis. Since a fluorescence spectrum has much less structure than an absorption spectrum, fluorometric methods tend to be used mainly as spot tests. For example, they are frequently used in this way in locating and preliminarily identifying species on a paper chromatogram.

Comparison with absorption photometry. It is also of interest to compare fluorometry and absorption photometry, which will be discussed in the next chapter, as analytically valuable techniques. Absorption spectrophotometry is a very valuable qualitative technique that is broadly applicable. Yet it has poor selectivity since absorption spectra of different species tend to overlap. By contrast, fluorometry has a much smaller range of application, since the number of fluorescing molecules is limited. But it has excellent selectivity, precisely because so few substances fluoresce. Fluorometry has a further advantage in terms of detection limit: It offers the possibility of determining some species at the level of parts per trillion. The detection limit in absorption photometry is the order of parts per billion.

REFERENCES

Some lucid general references on an intermediate to advanced level are:

1. J. B. Birks, *Photophysics of Aromatic Molecules.* New York: Wiley-Interscience, 1970
1a. E. J. Bowen, ed., *Luminescence in Chemistry.* Princeton: Van Nostrand, 1968
2. G. G. Guilbault, ed., *Fluorescence, Theory, Instrumentation, and Practice.* New York: Dekker, 1967

3. D. M. Hercules, ed., *Fluorescence and Phosphorescence Analysis: Principles and Applications.* New York: Interscience, 1966

A thorough, advanced treatment with special coverage of instrumentation will be found in:

4. C. A. Parker, *Photoluminescence of Solutions with Applications to Photochemistry and Analytical Chemistry.* New York: American Elsevier, 1968

Two representative analytical applications of fluorometry are:

5. M. Pesez and J. Bartos, "Elements of the Fluorometry of Organic Functional Groups," *Talanta* **14**, 1097 (1967) [in French]
6. C. E. White, H. C. E. McFarlane, J. Fogt, and R. Fuchs, "New Fluorometric Reagent for Aluminum *N*-salicylidene-2-amino-3-hydroxyfluorene," *Anal. Chem.* **38**, 367 (1967)

Also of interest are:

7. R. J. Argauer and C. E. White, "Fluorescent Compounds for Calibration of Excitation and Emission Units of Spectrofluorometer," *Anal. Chem.* **36**, 368 (1964)
8. R. F. Chen, "Fluorescence of Dansyl Amino Acids in Organic Solvents and Protein Solutions," *Arch. Biochem. Biophys.* **120**, 609 (1967)
9. D. M. Hercules, "Some Aspects of Fluorescence and Phosphorescence Analysis," *Anal. Chem.* **38** (12), 29A (1966)
10. H. H. Jaffe and A. L. Miller, "The Fates of Electronic Excitation Energy," *J. Chem. Educ.* **43**, 469 (1966)
11. Peter F. Lott, "Instrumentation for Fluorometry," *J. Chem. Educ.* **41**, A327, A421 (1964)
12. W. J. McCarthy and J. D. Winefordner, "The Selection of Optimum Conditions for Spectrochemical Methods, Part II, Quantum Efficiency and Decay Time of Luminescent Molecules," *J. Chem. Educ.* **44**, 136 (1967)
13. M. Zander, *Phosphorimetry.* New York: Academic, 1968

EXERCISES

15.1 Show that the term $I_0(1 - e^{-\epsilon bc})$ appearing in Eq. (15.1) expresses the intensity of incident radiation absorbed by a sample. [See Eq. (16.3).]

15.2 Assume a linear fluorometer using an intense source is to be designed. Indicate modules or types of components necessary if very-low-intensity fluorescence is to be quantitatively detected.

15.3 Uranium can be determined in solids at trace levels by fluorometry. Samples are ground, mixed with a flux-like sodium carbonate or sodium fluoride–lithium fluoride and melted. Assume it is desired to construct a very compact instrument to determine uranium in such samples. Suggest (a) a suitable shape into which the melt can be cast for measurement of fluorescence and (b) a compact design of instrument in which two exciting lamps (source) and detector are located on the same side of the sample. Indicate where baffles are used. The Jarrell-Ash Division of Fisher Scientific Co. markets such an instrument.

15.4 An excitation spectrum is observed for a fluorescent species using a grating spectrophotofluorometer with a xenon lamp source. Several slit settings are employed in the excitation monochromator. As slits are narrowed, increasing fine structure appears in the observed spectrum. Is the source of this "detail" likely to be the instrument or the species being excited? Suggest a procedure to check your answer.

15.5 a) Draw a schematic optical diagram of the ratio fluorometer described on p. 425.
   b) Draw a block diagram of the rest of this instrument beginning with the detector.

Chapter 16

ABSORPTION SPECTROMETRY

16.1 INTRODUCTION

As long as color has been recognized as characteristic of particular materials under given conditions, it has been used as a means of identification. Qualitative analysis schemes, for example, have traditionally been committed to color tests such as observing the orange hue of lead chromate to confirm the presence of lead or chromium ions. Yet tests of this type are inherently limited in precision and range, for they rely on the human eye as a detector of radiant energy. Where it fails, they fail. It is a tribute to the ingenuity of the analytical chemist that so large a number of reliable qualitative and quantitative visual tests have been devised.

The perfection of other detectors of radiation together with the general advance in instrumentation has produced a vast extension of absorption techniques. In range, these now cover the electromagnetic (EM) spectrum (Table 16.2) from the far infrared (IR) through the ultraviolet (UV). Since such techniques are concerned with the measurement of the intensity or power of radiation as a function of wavelength, the term *photometric* or *spectrophotometric* may be used to identify them. In some cases their sensitivity is so great that concentrations as small as 0.01 to 0.001 parts per million can be detected. The instrumentation of absorption photometry will be considered in detail in Chapter 17.

Photometric techniques are based on the ability of substances to interact with characteristic frequencies of radiation. Since each isolated species of ion, atom, or molecule will exhibit an individual set of definite energy levels, it will absorb only the frequencies that correspond to excitation from one level to another. These matters will be considered in detail in Section 16.3. The absorption spectrum of an unknown substance may be measured in qualitative analyses to establish its identity. Quantitative procedures can be devised by relating the intensity of absorption to the number of the species of interest in the optical path. This chapter will be concerned with all of these topics.

Classic colorimetric methods, on the other hand, are distinguished by their dependence on the subjective perception of color originating in the human brain. By definition, color is restricted to the visible frequencies. It is always related to (a) some source of radiant energy, a fluorescent lamp, perhaps, (b) the chemical constitution of the material to which the color is ascribed, and (c) the eye of the individual who observes the color. As any of these varies, the "quality" of color will change. A distinction may also be drawn between the quality of color perceived by transmitted and reflected light. Generally, classic methods prove less reliable than instrumental

methods as a result of fatigue, poor ability to establish intensities, and other characteristics of the average eye.

16.2 BEER'S LAW

Whenever a beam of broadly polychromatic radiation passes through a medium,
e.g., a liquid or gas, some loss of intensity occurs. First, reflection takes place at the
phase boundaries as a result of refractive index differences between the medium and
its surroundings (Section 10.8). Second, scattering caused by inhomogeneities (in
mixtures) or by thermal fluctuations in the bulk of the medium produces an additional
small loss of power from the main beam (Section 10.10). Neither of these is as significant in accounting for the intensity diminution,* however, as the fact that the medium
itself is not perfectly transparent but will absorb the radiant frequencies that promote
energy changes within its molecules and ions. A schematic representation of the effect
of reflection and scattering is given in Fig. 16.1.

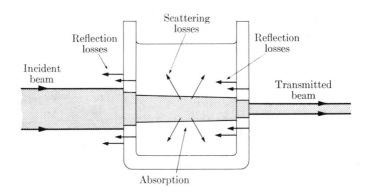

Fig. 16.1 The effect of a cell and sample on the intensity of a transmitted beam. Intensity is represented by the breadth of the beam. The cell walls are not shown as absorbing but may absorb in
other cases.

A distinction should be made between the process by which the power level of
the radiation is changed (e.g., absorption) and the quantitative measure of the effect.
For easy identification let the suffix -*ion* refer to the process, and -*ance* to the measured
value. For example, *transmission, reflection,* and *absorption* are occurring in Fig. 16.1
and lead to a measurable *transmittance, reflectance,* and *absorbance.* These terms are
still to be defined. Since the absorption will not be directly measurable, it must be
derived from a determinable quantity, the *radiant power P* of the beam. *P* is simply
the energy of the radiation reaching a given area per second.[†]

---

* It should be noted that scattering becomes significant for large ions or molecules such as poly-
electrolytes or polymers. In these the intensity of the scattered light serves as a measure of molecular weight and shape (see Section 20.4).
[†] It is closely related to, but not identical with, the intensity *I* of radiation, which is the power
per unit solid angle.

The absorbance depends on (a) the nature of the medium, i.e., its composition, and (b) the length of optical path in the medium. This dependence is expressed by Beer's law.* The assumptions that are made in obtaining the law are important. They are:

1. The incident radiation is monochromatic,
2. The absorbing centers (molecules and ions) act independently of one another regardless of number and kind, and
3. The absorption is limited to a volume of uniform cross-section.

We will consider later the effect of these assumptions for practical work. Beer's law may be expressed as: *the absorption of a medium is directly proportional to the number of absorption centers.* In other words, each centimeter thickness of a solution obeying Beer's law will absorb an equal fraction of the power incident upon it.

From the differential equation [28] expressing Beer's law, there is obtained

$$\ln \frac{P}{P_0} = -kn, \tag{16.1}$$

where P_0 is the power incident on *the sample*, P is the power leaving *the sample* (see Fig. 16.1), ln indicates a natural logarithm, k is a constant, and n is the number of absorbing centers of *one kind* in a volume of unit cross section. This equation predicts that the power of the emergent beam will drop off logarithmically (exponentially) as the number of centers in the beam increases.

Equation (16.1) is not operationally useful as it stands. The number of absorbing sites in the beam must be expressed in terms of a path length for the beam and of the concentration of the absorbent. Assuming for the moment a rectangular cell, the total number N of absorbers in the beam will be the product

$$N = c \times 6.02 \times 10^{23} \times b \times S,$$

where c is the concentration of absorbent substance in mol ml^{-1}, 6.02×10^{23} is the number of molecules in a mole, b is the thickness of the vessel in cm, and S is the cross-sectional area perpendicular to the radiation in cm^2. The number n of absorbers in a unit cross-sectional area of the path will be N/S or cb. Finally, as a matter of convenience, the logarithmic term of Eq. (16.1) may be shifted from the natural to the Naperian base, 10 (designated by "log"), the concentration changed to units of molarity, and the constant k modified accordingly. Let the new constant be ϵ. With these substitutions, and the additional relation $T = P/P_0$, Eq. (16.1) may now be written

$$\log \frac{P}{P_0} = -\epsilon bc = \log T. \tag{16.2}$$

---

* Several scientists, Beer, Bouger, Lambert, Bunsen, and Roscoe, have contributed by their investigations and theorizing to the development of this relation. Often it is called the Beer–Lambert or the Bouger–Beer law. However, it has been shown by Liebhafsky and Pfeiffer [28] that Beer's original conception was sufficiently broad to include both concentration and length dependence. For that reason and for simplicity, the formal statement will be termed Beer's law.

Here ϵ is the molar absorptivity and T is the transmittance, the fraction of the incident power transmitted. Taking the reciprocal of the ratio P/P_0 removes the negative sign and gives

$$\log \frac{P_0}{P} = A = \epsilon bc. \qquad (16.3)$$

This expression defines the absorbance A and is the simplest mathematical statement of Beer's law.*

In absorption photometry, both the transmittance and the absorbance figure prominently. The latter is the more useful, however, because of its linear dependence on concentration and path length. The difference in behavior of T and A may be seen clearly in Fig. 16.2. For purposes of compound identification, the logarithm of A may be preferable to either T or A. (See Fig. 16.15 and accompanying discussion in the text.)

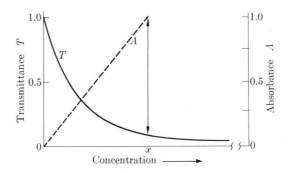

Fig. 16.2 The absorbance and transmittance of a solution at a given wavelength as a function of concentration. For example, at concentration x an arrow links the transmittance (0.10) and the absorbance (1.00). The path length b and other variables are constant.

The important definitions and concepts of absorption photometry are summarized in Table 16.1. Other names and symbols that have been given these variables are noted in parentheses. Two typical calculations will provide illustrations of the interrelationship of these variables by use of Eqs. (16.2) and (16.3).

Example 1   The absorbance of a solution of a colored inorganic material at a particular frequency is found to be 0.90, using a 1.00 cm cell and a concentration of 0.0020 M. For a more accurate measurement, an absorbance of 0.43 is desired. What concentration must be made up?

Solution. Knowing that $A = 0.90$, find ϵ:

$$A = \epsilon bc = 0.90 = \epsilon \cdot 1 \cdot 0.002; \quad \epsilon = 450.$$

The new conditions call for $A = 0.43 = 450 \times 1 \times c_2$, and the desired concentration is

$$c_2 = 9.5 \times 10^{-4} \text{ M}.$$

---

* Often other concentration units are used in Eq. (16.3). The concentration may be given in $g\,l^{-1}$, for example. If that is done, ϵ is replaced by a, the (specific) absorptivity.

Example 2 The incident power of a beam of a particular frequency is reduced 20% in passing through 1.00 cm of a colored solution. What will be the reduction after going through 5.00 cm of the same solution?

Solution. The transmittance at a distance of 1 cm is $0.80/1.00 = 0.80$. The product ϵc of Eq. (16.2) is constant and must be evaluated.

$$\epsilon c = \frac{1}{1} \log \frac{1.00}{0.80} = 0.096.$$

When $b = 5$ cm,

$$\log \frac{P_0}{P} = 0.096 \times 5 = 0.48$$

and

$$\frac{P_0}{P} = \text{antilog } 0.48 = 3.02,$$

so that

$$P = \frac{P_0}{3.02} = 0.331 P_0.$$

The power is reduced to 33% of its original value.

Table 16.1 Concepts and Symbolism of Absorption Photometry

Term	*Symbol and Definition*
Absorbance (optical density, extinction)	$A(D, E) = \log \dfrac{P_0}{P}$ *
Transmittance (transmission)	$T = \dfrac{P}{P_0}$
Path length	$b(l, d)$
Absorptivity (extinction coefficient, absorbancy index)	$a(k) = \dfrac{A}{bc}$ $(c, \text{in g l}^{-1})$
Molar absorptivity (molecular or molar extinction coefficient, molar absorbing index)	$\epsilon = \dfrac{A}{bc}$ $(c, \text{in mol l}^{-1})$

* Absorbance can also be stated in terms of the intensity ratio I_0/I.

Note that for substances following Beer's law the molar absorptivity ϵ for a substance is independent of concentration and optical path length. It is truly a characteristic constant determined by the nature of the absorbing substance, the solvent, and by the wavelength of the incident radiation. Its occasional apparent dependence on temperature and other variables will be taken up in Section 16.4. Beer's law also extends to mixtures of absorbers of different types. So long as they act independently, the law holds. Each species has a different molar or specific absorptivity, and the absorbances may be added. Equation (16.3) in the form applicable to homogeneous mixtures is

$$\log \frac{P_0}{P} = A_t = \epsilon_1 bc_1 + \epsilon_2 bc_2 + \cdots = b \sum_i \epsilon_i c_i, \qquad (16.4)$$

where solvent, path length b, and wavelength are presumed constant.

Concentration limit on validity. The restriction that absorption centers do not interact with themselves or other species causes Beer's law to be a limiting law applicable mainly in dilute solutions (concentrations $< 10^{-2}$ M). The interference alters the charge distribution either in the absorbing or excited species or both and thus changes the energy needed for excitation. As a result, the position, shape, and height of the absorption region may be altered. Not all interactions are between neighboring molecules; through electrostatic forces, influences may be exerted at a relatively great distance. Many complex organic molecules, such as eosin and methylene blue, are particularly susceptible to interference and may follow Beer's law only below 10^{-5} M if certain simple salts are present.

A second limit on the validity of the law is that the index of refraction of the solution alters as the concentration changes. It may be shown that it is $\epsilon \cdot n/(n^2 + 2)^2$ rather than ϵ itself that is constant with concentration. [26] Whenever the variation of $n/(n^2 + 2)^2$ exceeds the experimental error over a concentration region of interest, again Beer's law does not hold. In this instance a correction can be used at high concentrations; however, deviations larger than 0.01 % from this source occur only at concentrations above 10^{-2} M.

16.3 ABSORPTION PROCESSES AND INTENSITIES

Beer's law relates absorption to concentration, but provides no clue as to the dependence of absorption on molecular structure. The connection is established through quantum-mechanical study of the characteristic "motions" that permit a molecule to interact with radiation. Since the energy of such motions, especially vibrations, is characteristic of particular molecules, absorption spectra are a sensitive structural tool. The manifold processes related to the absorption (and emission) of EM radiation are classified in Table 16.2. This section deals with the simpler aspects of molecular absorption; transition probabilities and intensities, line widths, and lifetimes of excited states were treated earlier in Section 13.3.

The energy of a molecule is usually characterizable as being distributed among motions of sufficiently different energy that each can be treated separately,* that is,

$$E_{\text{molecule}} = E_{\text{translation}} + E_{\text{rotation}} + E_{\text{vibration}} + E_{\text{electronic}} + E_{\text{nuclear orientation}}.$$

The absorption of a quantum of incident light may, depending upon its size and the particular molecule, simultaneously promote transitions in one or several categories of motion. Quantum-mechanical *selection rules* describe the combinations allowed.

---

* At high levels of excitation, interactions among such "motions" are no longer negligible and correction terms must be added.

Table 16.2 Processes of Absorption and Emission of Radiation

Wavelength, μm	$\to 1000$	100	10	1	0.1	0.01	0.001
$\leftarrow$ Wave number, cm^{-1}	10	100	1000	10 000	10^5	10^6	
Spectral regions:	*Microwave*	*Far*	*Middle* *Infrared*	*Near*	*Near* *Visible*	*Far* *Ultraviolet*	*X-Ray*
Characteristic molecular process excited in region:	Rotation of molecules in gases	Rotations of molecules in gases and intermolecular vibrations in crystals, liquids		Vibrations in molecules	Electronic transitions of outer shell electrons in atoms and n, π electrons in molecules		Electronic transitions of inner shell electrons in atoms
Characteristic transition:	Pure rotation	Rotation-vibration			Electronic band spectra (rotation-vibration-electronic)		
Energy of transition: (kJ mol^{-1})	0.1196	—	11.96	—	1196	—	119,600
(eV mol^{-1})	1.24×10^{-3}	—	0.124	—	12.4	—	1240

Neither translational nor nuclear orientation changes are treated in this chapter;*
the latter are reserved for Chapter 19.

Rotational transitions.   For gaseous, i.e., isolated molecules, energy changes associated
with pure rotational shifts are observable, but only in the microwave and far IR range.
In the easily accessible 4000 to 650 cm^{-1} IR range, only those rotational changes
that accompany vibrational transitions are observed. Molecular rotational levels are
spaced on the order of 10^{-2} J mol^{-1}, corresponding to radiation of a frequency of
about 10 cm^{-1}.

It can be shown that the rotational energy of a molecule is generally expressible
as a sum of terms, each proportional to the reciprocal of one of the molecular moments
of inertia. These moments are taken around a set of internal, mutually orthogonal
axes. For example, rotation of a rigid linear molecule lying along the z-axis can occur
around both x- and y-axes. Its two moments of inertia are equal, and the rotational
energy is given by the equation,

$$E_{rotation} = J(J + 1)(h^2/8\pi^2 I)$$
(16.5)

where J is the rotational quantum number ($J = 0, 1, 2, 3, \dots$), h is Planck's constant,
and I is the single moment of inertia. Exactly $2J + 1$ different orientations of a particular rotational axis in space are allowed. In the absence of an external field, these are
of equal energy, giving each rotational energy level a $(2J + 1)$-fold degeneracy. The
quantum-mechanical selection rule that applies to pure rotational transitions is
$\Delta J = \pm 1$.

Example   The microwave rotational spectrum of $^{12}C^{16}O$ consists of evenly spaced lines at
3.84 cm^{-1} ($J = 0$ to $J = 1$), 7.68 cm^{-1} ($J = 1$ to $J = 2$), 11.52 cm^{-1} ($J = 3$ to $J = 4$), 15.36 cm^{-1}
($J = 4$ to $J = 5$), etc. The wavenumber spacing is $2B/hc$ where $B = h^2/8\pi^2 I$.

A further source of complexity in treating rotation may be noted. A molecule in
a high rotational state is stretched, causing each moment of inertia to be larger. If a
molecule is in a high vibrational state, anharmonicity (see below) and an average
lengthening of bonds lead to greater moments of inertia.

In liquids and solids rotational motions need not be treated as quantized. The
reason is that molecular collisions or cooperative vibrations are frequent. Any
rotation that occurs is satisfactorily treated by classical models. Actually, in crystalline
solids free rotation is usually not possible.

Vibrational transitions.   In contrast to rotational changes, vibrational transitions
persist through all the states of matter. Since chemical bonds are stretched or bent in
molecular vibrations, much larger energies are involved. These are of the order of
10 kJ mol^{-1}, corresponding to frequencies of the order of 2000 cm^{-1}. Thus quanta in
the middle IR range are sufficiently large to promote vibrational changes.

Each vibrational degree of freedom of a molecule or *normal mode* can be treated
in first approximation as a separate harmonic oscillator. Its potential energy curve

---

* An essentially continuous range of translational energies is available. Collisions are more
important in bringing about such changes than interaction with radiation.

is parabolic, and during vibration atoms move equal distances on either side of equilibrium positions. The vibrational energy in each mode is given by the expression

$$E_{\text{vibrational}} = (V + \tfrac{1}{2})h\nu_0 \tag{16.6}$$

where V is the vibrational quantum number ($V = 0, 1, 2, 3 \cdots$) and ν_0 the frequency of vibration. There are no degeneracies, except as symmetry causes two or more modes to be identical in energy. At room temperature, most molecules are in the ground state ($V = 0$) and possess the so-called *zero point energy* $\tfrac{1}{2}h\nu_0$ predicted by Eq. (16.6). Thus, the vibrational transition commonly observed in molecular absorption spectra is of the $V = 0$ to $V = 1$ type.

Actually, molecular vibrations are slightly anharmonic, the degree of anharmonicity increasing with vibrational amplitude. The potential function is a distorted parabola. Although Eq. (16.6) predicts an even spacing of vibrational levels, the separation between them actually diminishes as V increases. Because of anharmonicity no selection rule really holds; any transition is allowed to a degree. For example, overtones of *diminished* intensity such as a $V = 0$ to $V = 2$ transition are observed and appear at a frequency somewhat less than twice the fundamental ($V = 0$ to $V = 1$). Correction terms can be added to Eq. (16.6) to compensate for anharmonicity.

In the quantum-mechanical treatment of molecular vibrations the formula for the frequency ν_0 is identical to that derived from a classical Hooke's law treatment. If we treat a molecule as a simple harmonic oscillator we obtain

$$\nu_0 = \frac{1}{2\pi}\sqrt{\frac{k}{\mu}} \tag{16.7}$$

where k is the bond force constant and μ the reduced mass. Of course the amplitudes of vibration are quantized as required by Eq. (16.6).

Example Equation (16.7) can be used to find the force constant of the bond in a diatomic molecule like CO. For the $V = 0$ to $V = 1$ transition of CO, absorption occurs at 2140 cm^{-1}. Its reduced mass, $[\mu = m_1 m_2/(m_1 + m_2)]$, is just

$$\mu = \left(\frac{12.0 \times 16.0}{12.0 + 16.0}\right) \text{g mol}^{-1} \times \frac{10^{-3} \text{ kg g}^{-1}}{6.02 \times 10^{23} \text{ atom mol}^{-1}} = 1.14 \times 10^{-26} \text{ kg.}$$

Since $\nu_0 = c\sigma$, where σ is the wave number of the absorption,

$$\nu_0 = 2140 \text{ cm}^{-1} \times 3.0 \times 10^{10} \text{ cm s}^{-1}.$$

Substitution in Eq. (16.7) gives

$$\nu_0 = 6.42 \times 10^{13} \text{ s}^{-1} = \frac{1}{6.28}\sqrt{\frac{k}{1.14 \times 10^{-26} \text{ kg}}}$$

and

$$k = 18.4 \times 10^2 \text{ N m}^{-1}.$$

The selection rule that defines allowed transitions in the gas phase states that only vibrational transitions for which $\Delta V = \pm 1$ are allowed. Nearly always rotational changes accompany vibrational transitions for a gas molecule, and the selection rule $\Delta J = \pm 1$ simultaneously applies. Accordingly, each vibrational absorption gives rise to a collection of lines or a band. Figure 16.3 shows an example under both high and low resolution.

The so-called "P-branch" of such a spectrum includes all vibrational transitions for which the accompanying rotational shifts are $\Delta J = -1$ and is the "wing" at lowest frequencies. An absorption peak for which $\Delta J = 0$, the "Q-branch," appears for most molecules.* Note its presence as the strong absorption in the middle of the pattern in Fig. 16.3. Finally, transitions for which $\Delta J = +1$ comprise the highest frequency set, the "R-branch."

Infrared spectra become more complex the greater the number of atoms N in a molecule. Each of the $3N - 6$ degrees of vibrational freedom ($3N - 5$ for a linear molecule) gives rise to a fundamental frequency and an absorption pattern like that in Fig. 16.3. We approach the situation mathematically by establishing a set of internal coordinates that reduce complex vibrations to so-called *normal modes* of vibration that are mathematically more straightforward. While it is difficult to relate such modes to IR absorption peaks, assignments have been made for most simple molecules.

Exact motions of atoms during a vibration are hard to describe. All atoms participate but fortunately there is often a great deal of localization in one chemical bond or a set of bonds. For example, if a molecule has an "unassociated" N—H bond, a vibration that stretches the bond almost always absorbs IR in the 3550 to 3340 cm^{-1} range. The motion of other atoms in the molecule exercises a small perturbing force so that a wave number range rather than a specific value has to be given. Thus, vibrational spectra provide a very important basis for identification of chemical bonds in molecules (see Section 16.10).

Electronic transitions. No other characteristic molecular "motion" has as great a charge displacement as an electronic transition. The resulting large dipole moment leads to high intensities for such transitions; even forbidden electronic transitions are commonly observed. For this reason and also because there is no general expression covering these transitions in terms of properties that are readily observable, electronic selection rules are seldom useful in the study of absorption electronic transitions. Characteristically, quanta of order of magnitude 20 000 cm^{-1} are absorbed, and most electronic transitions occur in the visible and UV from about 750 to 110 nm (15,400 to 91,000 cm^{-1}).

Typically an electronic transition in a molecule is accompanied by a change in vibrational and, in the gaseous state, rotational motion as well. In Fig. 16.4 a possible transition is shown for a diatomic molecule. The chart also provides a comparison with other characteristic transitions.

What vibrational change occurs during an electronic transition? We may partly resolve the question by applying the Franck–Condon principle, which states that nuclei in a molecule do not move during the short interval required for such excitation. The vibrational change also depends on (a) the relative positions of ground and

---

* For diatomic molecules, as predicted by quantum mechanics, the Q-branch is absent. It is also worth recalling that for homonuclear diatomics like N_2 and O_2 even the basic vibrational transitions cannot be brought about by IR radiation since there is no transition dipole moment.

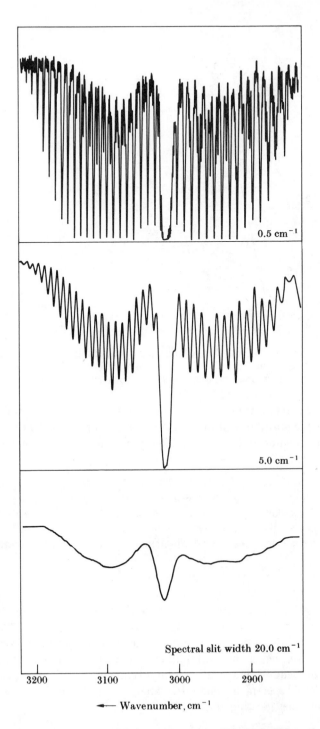

Fig. 16.3 The C-H stretch band of methane as observed with widely different resolutions. The instrument spectral slit width is noted underneath each trace. (Courtesy of Beckman Instruments.)

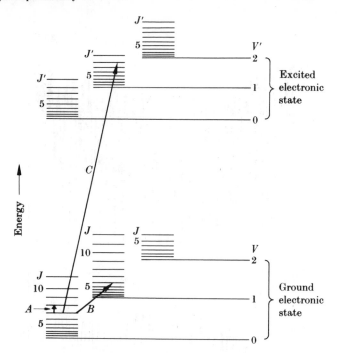

Fig. 16.4 Schematic illustration of energy levels in a diatomic molecule. Representative types of transitions and the region in which they are observed are as follows: A, pure rotational (far IR), B, vibrational-rotational (middle and near IR), C, electronic (VIS and UV).

excited state potential energy curves (or surfaces for a polyatomic molecule) and (b) the most probable position of atoms in the initial and final states. In the ground state the equilibrium separation of atoms is likely; in higher vibrational states either the minimum or the maximum separation of atoms is more probable.

Example To predict a probable vibrational transition accompanying an electronic excitation, potential energy curves for the ground and excited states are sketched first. With the information at hand, vibrational states are added next. A line is then drawn vertically (Franck–Condon principle) from the center of the ground vibrational state, a position that corresponds to the equilibrium separation of atoms, upward with the first vibrational level in the excited electronic state until it intersects. That transition is the most probable one.

The localization of one or more electronic levels is common. For instance, aldehydes and ketones are typified by a UV absorption band between 280 and 320 nm (2800 to 3200 Å). This has been ascribed to a transition from an (nonbonding) orbital on the carbonyl oxygen to an antibonding π^* orbital associated with the carbonyl bond. The phenomenon of localization is important analytically; it provides a foundation for use of UV spectra in qualitative analysis and for rather precise structural analyses of molecules (Section 16.10).

Classification of electronic states. Molecular electronic states are classified mainly according to total electron spin or symmetry. The total spin or intrinsic angular momentum of a molecule is well described by the vector sum of the spins of its electrons provided there is only weak coupling between spin and orbital angular momentum of electrons. In general this condition holds for simple molecules with light atoms. Given that the spin per electron is $+1/2$ or $-1/2$, for a molecule the possible value of total spin S for two electrons is 0 or ± 1. For a total of three electrons, $S = \pm 1/2$ or $\pm 3/2$; for four, $S = 0$, ± 1, or ± 2.

Since many states of the same energy have the same total spin, the multiplicity, $2|S| + 1$, is frequently cited instead of the total spin. For example, any state in which all electrons are paired has $S = 0$ and a multiplicity of unity. Such a state is a *singlet*. If there is one unpaired electron the multiplicity is two, and the state is a doublet. Similarly, with two unpaired electrons with parallel spins, the state is a *triplet* since $S = \pm 1$ and $2|S| + 1 = 3$.

Though the electronic states of linear molecules can be further detailed in terms of angular momentum, for most polyatomic molecules states are classified principally in terms of symmetry. This is possible because the potential field in which electrons move has the same symmetry as the molecule.

Integrated intensities. An absorption band may be characterized by its intensity and band half-width as well as its frequency. For quantitative work it is usually sufficient to know ϵ_{max}, the molar absorptivity at the absorption peak. For molecular studies, however, the integrated intensity is usually of greater interest. In particular it is closely related to the polar properties of molecules.

The absolute intensity of an absorption is defined by abs. intensity $= \int_{\nu 1}^{\nu 2} \alpha_\nu \, d\nu$, where α_ν, the absorption coefficient, is integrated over the entire band. In most spectrophotometric work an *integrated* intensity is defined by

$$\int_{\nu_1}^{\nu_2} \epsilon_\nu \, d\nu = \frac{1}{cb} \int_{\nu_1}^{\nu_2} A_\nu \, d\nu, \tag{16.8}$$

where the molar absorptivity (or the absorbance) is integrated. The reliability of the integration depends greatly on whether the spectral slit width (Section 12.2) is appropriately narrow for the absorption peak. It should be noted that an integrated intensity can often be approximated as $\epsilon_{max} \cdot \Delta \nu_{1/2}$ where $\Delta \nu_{1/2}$ is the bandwidth at half-intensity. Representative integrated intensities in the IR are of the order of 0.1 l mol^{-1} cm^{-2} with the largest values appearing for OH and C=O vibrations.

In certain cases the integrated intensities of IR vibrational bands can be related more effectively to molecular properties than can molar absorptivities. [32] In any event better functional group identification can be made if both intensity and frequency data are used.

The absolute intensity of an electronic transition is often described in terms of its "f" number or *oscillator strength*. This term arises from the classical treatment of dispersion and is just the "f" given in Eq. (10.11). It can be regarded as the effective number of electrons set into oscillation in a given absorption. Further, f can be related to both the quantum-mechanical dipole strength D of an oscillator and the Einstein transition probability of absorption B_{mn} (Section 13.3). It can be shown that

$$f = \left(\frac{8\pi^2 m_e c g_n}{3he^2}\right) 2\pi v D$$

where m_e is the mass of an electron, g_n is the degeneracy of the excited state, and v is the frequency of absorption. The second expression is

$$f = \left(\frac{m_e hc^2 \, 2\pi v}{\pi e^2}\right) B_{mn}.$$

Finally, one has

$$f = \frac{2303 m_e c^2}{\pi N_0 e^2} F \int_{v_1}^{v_2} \epsilon \, dv$$

where F is a factor near unity that corrects for the refractive index of the solution medium. This expression relates f to the usual integrated intensity of a band. Typical values of f for electronic transitions are 10^{-4} to 10^{-3}.

16.4 SOURCES OF ERROR

The uncertainty in photometric measurements can conveniently be treated as arising both from "static" errors, i.e., errors inherent in determinations at set wavelengths, and "dynamic" errors that arise only in spectral scanning. In this section the first type is examined; they are characteristic of all chemical photometric work. Since those photometric errors peculiar to scanning relate particularly to instrument parameters such as scanning speed, they are discussed below in Section 17.7.

In *quantitative* photometric work, probably the most generally useful indicator of error is Beer's law. True failures of the law in homogeneous systems, e.g., solutions, are unknown, [2] so long as there is no interference between absorbing centers and no refractive index correction. Both factors as sources of true failure of the law were discussed in Section 16.2. The upper limit of concentration for validity of the law ranges from 10^{-5} to 10^{-2} M. It follows then, in dilute solution, that in most cases of apparent failure one or more determinant errors must have occurred. The evidence for failure will be the production of a nonlinear curve when a series of absorbances at a given wavelength is plotted against concentration. Whether the error should then be traced to its source will depend on the circumstances. New analytical procedures, new reagents, and new instruments should always be scrutinized for error. If, after investigation, the source of deviation proves to be something that cannot easily be controlled, subsequent photometry can probably still be performed reliably on a relative basis, i.e., by the comparison of unknown absorbances with those obtained under the same conditions with standards. Actually, most quantitative photometric analyses are performed in this way to minimize the influence of undetected errors. The calibration curves are usually obtained as A vs. c or $\% \, T$ vs. c plots and can conveniently be called *working curves*.

In *qualitative* photometric studies, error is detected by the use of line spectra or the spectra of known compounds.

Chemical.   Several chemical sources of error can be listed: uncontrolled pH, temperature variations, the presence of impurities, and the changing of solvents. They may give rise either to positive or to negative Beer's law deviations. These variables influence absorption mainly through their effect on equilibria involving the dissolved species. Particular conditions for a given analysis should be understood and followed.

Example 1 Beer's law will not hold for sodium chromate in water unless a small amount of strong base is added, for the chromate tends to condense somewhat depending on concentration, and the dichromate formed absorbs at different wavelengths. The equilibrium involved is

$$2CrO_4^{2-} + 2H_3O^+ \rightleftarrows Cr_2O_7^{2-} + 3H_2O.$$

Added base will ensure that condensation is suppressed.

Example 2 If a particular solvent and solute interact, the absorption spectrum of the solute may be markedly altered when another solvent is used. Thus, acetic acid gives an absorption characteristic of the molecule in hexane, but in water the spectrum has many features attributable to the ionic species that result from dissociation.

$$CH_3COOH + H_2O \rightleftarrows CH_3COO^- + H_3O^+.$$

Example 3 When the analytical species has been formed by complexing, a suitable excess of complexing agent must be present. The stability of the complex will determine the concentration needed. For example, copper (II) can be determined in aqueous solution by adding ethylenediamine (EDA):

$$Cu(H_2O)_4^{2+} + 2EDA \rightarrow Cu(EDA)_2^{2+} + 4H_2O.$$

An insufficient excess of EDA will mean the presence of a little of the aquo complex.

Instrumental. Instrumental and procedural errors are less easily traced. The finite spectral width of radiation beams, the presence of stray radiation, photocell fatigue, source fluctuations, the loss of wavelength calibration, and many other factors are properly classified as instrumental errors. The paper of Goldring *et al.* is an interesting study of such errors. [22] Initial checks and routine calibrations, such as the two procedures described below, are highly desirable to keep such errors under control. In addition, the most favorable general conditions for measurement can often be deduced theoretically, as will be discussed.

Wavelength calibration. The wavelength control of a monochromator can be standardized by using known absorption or emission spectra. For example, in the visible, one can employ the transmission of a piece of Corning 5120 didymium glass. The didymium spectrum is shown in Fig. 16.5. In the visible and UV the emission spectrum of mercury, as produced by a mercury vapor lamp, or of various lasers are often used. Tables of reference wavelengths are readily available. [38, 40]

Photometer calibration. In similar fashion solutions of known absorbance may be used to standardize the photometric response. [1, 2, 27A]

Bandwidth. The proper choice of spectral bandwidth is of major importance in photometric investigations. In the accurate analysis of a substance that has relatively

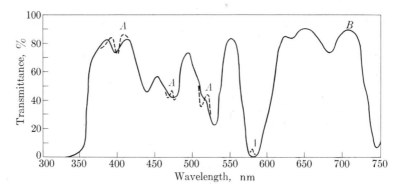

Fig. 16.5 The absorption spectrum of Corning 5120 didymium glass. Spectral slit width for *A*, 0.3 nm; for *B*, 30 nm.

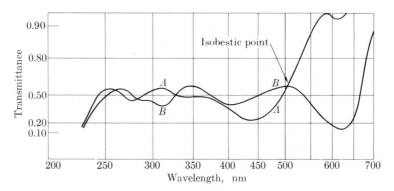

Fig. 16.6 Absorption spectrum of bromthymol blue in water. Curve *A*, pH 5.45. Curve *B*, pH 7.50. An isobestic point is evident at about 500 nm.

sharply defined regions of absorption, such as gaseous methane (Fig. 16.3), a beam with a very narrow spread of wavelengths is needed. By contrast, bromthymol blue can be determined with accuracy even when the radiation beam is perhaps 30 nm wide judging by Fig. 16.6. The degree of resolution at two different bandwidths is illustrated by Figs. 16.3 and 16.5. Clearly the wide-band absorption study produces a somewhat inaccurate absorption curve for didymium glass.

Many negative deviations from Beer's law may be traced to the use of instruments with band passes that are too wide. The reason may be explained in terms of Fig. 16.7. Suppose the bandwidth isolated by the monochromator or filter is *ab*. At each concentration the instrument will report an effective absorbance that is between the extreme values at wavelengths *a* and *b*, but it will not be the mean.

This is because the detector response varies directly with the transmitted power. Since the absorbance varies logarithmically (and inversely) with the power, the absorbance calculated from the average of power received across the band will be different from the absorbance *d* or *d'* at the mean *λ*. For the case illustrated by curve *B* in Fig. 16.7, the high level of power at wavelengths near *a* will contribute more to the

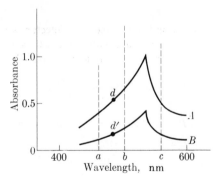

Fig. 16.7 Absorbance of a substance obeying Beer's law. Curve A, 3 concentration units; curve B, 1 concentration unit.

instrument response than will the much lower levels at wavelengths near b. The absorbance determined using radiation of bandwidth ab will thus be *smaller than the absorbance at the mean wavelength.* At the higher concentration (curve A) the difference in the values of the transmitted power at a and at b is greater than for curve B, and the difference between the measured and "mean" absorbances is larger. In general, the higher the concentration, the greater the variation. Since the absorbances at the mean wavelength are not obtained, an apparent negative deviation from Beer's law is observed. A similar deviation will occur for wavelength band bc even though it is centered on a maximum, since the curve is asymmetrical. Clearly, the extent of the deviation will be determined by the exact dependence on wavelength of the power in the beam, the transmitted power, and the sensitivity of the detector.

Since a working curve may be readily prepared, are such negative deviations from Beer's law of any consequence? Since the working curve has a lessened slope at high concentration, it should be evident that they are. Any error or uncertainty in absorbance will yield a greater uncertainty in concentration than if the law held. If the bandwidth error is large, it is desirable to work at low concentrations. In quantitative IR analyses, where bandwidths are often comparable to the half-width of an absorption band, this approach is often used.

Pressure broadening in gases. In the spectrophotometric analysis of gaseous mixtures some special sources of error enter. It is found, for example, that gaseous absorption curves vary not only as a function of concentration but also with the total pressure. At a fixed concentration of a constituent, increasing pressure usually produces broadening of its absorption bands (Section 13.3). An effectively larger absorbance will thus be detected instrumentally. At higher pressures the absorption is fortunately much less sensitive to further changes. If the total pressure can be maintained in that range and a narrow band of radiation used, Beer's law may be expected to hold.

Stray radiation. In all photometric apparatus some stray radiation adds to the regularly transmitted beam registered by the detector (Section 12.8). The magnitude of the error so introduced will depend both on the power level of stray radiation *detected* and on the absorbance of the sample under study. At high absorbances the error will be greatest, and vice versa. In this situation also, Beer's law will appear to fail negatively.

Example Assume the stray radiation S, registered by a detector, is 1.5% of the power level P_0 transmitted by the reference cell. Consider a given sample with a transmittance of 0.1. If there were no stray radiation, the true absorbance A^0 would be measured as

$$A^0 = \log_{10} \frac{P_0}{P} = \log_{10} \frac{1.00}{0.1} = 1.$$

With stray light S also detected, P_0 and P increase. The measured absorbance is

$$A = \log_{10} \frac{P_0 + S}{P + S} = \log_{10} \frac{100 + 1.5}{10 + 1.5} = \log_{10} 8.83 = 0.95.$$

An error of 5% in the absorbance is incurred.

Fluorescence. If the mixture under photometric examination fluoresces under the incident illumination, the fluorescent radiation will produce an error exactly like that induced by stray radiation. It must be blocked somehow.

Since the fluorescence will be of longer wavelength than the incident radiation (Section 15.1), it can often be absorbed by a suitable filter placed just before the detector. The filter must, of course, pass the primary beam.

Optimum concentration or cell thickness.   It is possible to determine a range of optimum transmittance values for each type of photometric device and procedure. This information in turn will allow the most favorable concentration or cell thickness for an analysis to be calculated.

Most photometers produce a response directly proportional to the power falling on the detector. In addition, the conventional operational procedure calls for adjusting slits or other beam intensity controls so that the transmittance of the reference is 1.00. In this situation Eq. (16.2) applies.

The methods of Section 1.7 may be used to calculate the error in the concentration resulting from error in the photometric response. The range of transmittance values in which the propagation of error is smallest may be ascertained in a second operation.

The relative error in the concentration c is dc/c, where dc represents a very small error in c. Rearranging Eq (16.2) results in

$$c = -\frac{1}{\epsilon b} \log T. \tag{16.9}$$

For a given absorbing species and path length, ϵ and b are constant and all the error in the determined concentration can be attributed to the uncertainty dT in the measured transmittance T. By taking the total differential of Eq. (16.9) and dividing through both sides by c one obtains

$$\frac{dc}{c} = -\frac{1}{c\epsilon b} \frac{\log_{10} e}{T} dT. \tag{16.10}$$

To find the transmittance at which the propagation of error is smallest, dc/c must be minimized. This may be done by differentiating Eq. (16.10) and setting the derivative equal to zero. First, a simplification may be made. By using Eq. (16.2),

$$\frac{1}{c\epsilon b}\frac{\log_{10} e}{T} = \frac{\log_{10} e}{T \log T} = \frac{\log_{10} e}{A}\log^{-1} A. \qquad (16.11)$$

Differentiating Eq. (16.11) and equating it to zero yields

$$\frac{d\{[\log_{10} e/(T \log T)]\,dT\}}{dT} = -\,dT(\log T + \log_{10} e) = 0. \qquad (16.12)$$

This yields the nontrivial solution $\log T = -0.4343$ or $T_{\text{optimum}} = 0.368$ and $A_{\text{optimum}} = 0.4343$. The relative error dc/c as expressed by Eq. (16.10) is graphed in Fig. 16.8 as a function of absorbance.

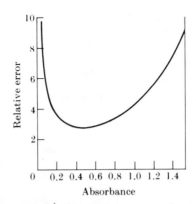

Fig. 16.8 Relative error, $[\log_{10} e \cdot \log^{-1} A]/A$, in the concentration traceable to the instrumental uncertainty in the transmittance. (dT is assumed constant.)

From Fig. 16.8 it is seen that the best analytical results will be secured in an ordinary photometric procedure if the absorbance is maintained in the range from 0.2 to 0.9. The concentration of the sample or the thickness of the cell should be adjusted accordingly. As would be expected, the range for optimum transmittance holds whether the data are obtained under single- or double-beam operation.

If a differential spectrophotometric procedure is used instead, better precision can be secured as will be considered in Section 16.7.

16.5 SAMPLE PREPARATION

In spectrophotometric work substances are ordinarily examined in a suspension such as a KBr pellet, in dilute solution, or in the gaseous state. By this means two important gains are secured. First, any *matrix effect*, i.e., dependence of the absorption spectrum of a species on the medium in which it occurs, is minimized.* Second, ions or molecules of a species are dispersed sufficiently to be essentially independent and for Beer's law to be applicable. For work in the visible and UV most species are soluble in a solvent

---

* Absorption frequencies of a substance change somewhat, of course, when it is transferred from the gaseous to liquid state or from solvent to solvent. When only differences in van der Waals forces are responsible, changes are small. If specific substance-solvent interactions like solvation or hydrogen-bonding are altered, either in the ground or excited state, frequency shifts are somewhat larger.

that is transparent, and examination in dilute solution is common. In IR work, suspensions are used more often: Both the dissolving ability and transparency of available solvents are limited.

Solvents. Table 16.3 shows ranges of transparency for several spectrophotometric solvents. These "windows" are shown in black, and the wavelength at which the absorbance of a 1 cm layer of the solvent reaches unity in the UV is noted at the left.

Table 16.3

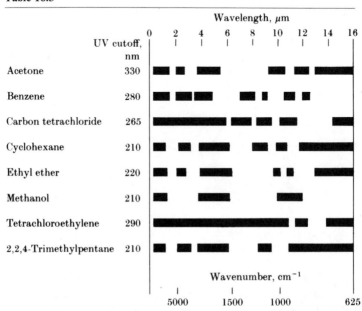

From the standpoint of transmission, all common solvents are suitable in the visible, many fewer are usable down to 210 nm (2100 Å), and very few transmit enough radiation below this wavelength. The useful solvents include water, most alcohols, ethers, and saturated hydrocarbons.

For the IR, few liquids have long regions of transparency, as Table 16.3 demonstrates. Carbon tetrachloride, tetrachloroethylene, and carbon disulfide are three of the best. Solvents useful in the IR range beyond the table (625 to 400 cm^{-1}) include carbon tetrachloride, *n*-heptane, and several others. Often, with polymers or other difficultly soluble materials, solvents must be employed that have limited windows such as methylethylketone, dimethylformamide, or tetrahydrofuran. The volatility of solvents and the small quantities required make it desirable to prepare solutions for IR work by weighing and to transfer them to cells with care to avoid evaporation losses.

The amount of solvent absorption that can be tolerated in analytical procedures will depend ultimately on how seriously it limits the energy of the light beam. The greater the sensitivity of the detector and the more stable the electronics, the greater the tolerable absorption from this source. Cells as thin as 0.025 mm can be used to reduce such absorption.

Mulls and pellets. Particularly in IR analysis it is desirable to examine solids as such. Both poor solubility in useful solvents and saving of time in sample handling are responsible. A few milligrams of solid sample suffices, since the final concentration in the suspension should be 0.01 to 0.5%. A widely used procedure is the preparation of a "mull" or suspension in a medium with few absorption bands and high refractive index, such as a viscous liquid like mineral oil (Nujol) or a solid like potassium bromide. The solid is first intimately ground into the suspending medium. In the case of liquid mulls, grinding must reduce the particle size to no more than one-fifth to one-tenth the wavelength of interest to lessen light scattering losses. The requirement does not apply to solid suspensions, providing that sintering occurs during the pressing of the mixture into a disc. Liquid mulls are usually examined in a demountable liquid cell, KBr discs in a simple frame.

Alkali halide suspensions are compressed by a laboratory hydraulic press into thin pellets under pressure of $7 \times 10^7 \, \text{N m}^{-2}$ to $14 \times 10^7 \, \text{N m}^{-2}$ (10,000 to 20,000 lb in^{-2}). The halide should be as dry as possible. A vacuum is often applied during the pressing to improve the clarity of the discs. The disc method offers the advantage of freedom from most extraneous absorption bands (sometimes weak O-H bands appear from water picked up during preparation) and is usable to the limit of transparency (KBr, about 250 cm^{-1}; CsI, about 200 cm^{-1}). Mineral oil mulls are especially satisfactory in the far IR, being virtually transparent throughout.

For quantitative work pellets and mulls must be prepared by careful weighing. Their thickness must also be known; alternatively an internal standard such as KSCN may be used. Since mulls have an uncertain cell thickness, an internal standard is nearly always necessary with them.

Pyrolysis. Substances that are difficult to grind or dissolve in a suitable solvent, e.g., carbon-filled rubber, are sometimes pyrolyzed before examination. The process involves partial decomposition by heating. A sample is usually placed on an internal reflectance plate (Section 16.8) and subjected to a controlled high temperature (up to 1300 °C) for a selected period in an evacuated chamber. After pyrolysis its spectrum is interpretable in terms of molecular fragments present.

Complexing. Samples containing metals are usually dissolved. The resulting metal ions are then converted to a highly absorbing form by complexing with a chromogenic reagent such as an organic dye.

Extraction. This is a valuable approach to concentration of a trace constituent or to removal of a constituent from interfering absorbers. A liquid-liquid extraction is used. Often a reagent that will complex interfering species is added. By this means, the interferents are either prevented from reacting with the chromogenic agent used or kept from being extracted.

16.6 QUANTITATIVE PROCEDURES

This field represents the largest application of absorption photometry. Because of the high intensity of electronic transitions ($\epsilon \sim 10^3$ to 10^5) compared with vibrational transitions ($\epsilon \sim 10$ to 100), sensitivity is greatest for determinations that can be made in the visible or UV. At moderate to high concentrations all optical regions can yield

Table 16.4 Relative Advantages of Absorption Measurements in Different Spectral Regions*

Region	Range of applicability		Accuracy and precision by concentration range				Frequency of interferences
	Qualitative analysis	Quantitative analysis	Trace	Moderate	High		
IR	Excellent	Very Good	Poor	Good to excellent	Good		Common
Near IR	Limited	Limited	Poor	Good	Fair to good		Common
VIS	Limited†	Moderate†	Excellent if applicable†	Good	Fair to good		Infrequent
UV	Limited†	Moderate†	Excellent if applicable†	Fair to good			Infrequent

* After S. Siggia, *Survey of Analytical Chemistry*, New York: McGraw-Hill, 1968.
† While the range of applicability is limited, species that absorb (either intrinsically or after reaction with a chromogenic reagent) can be very sensitively determined.

accurate and precise quantitative results. The different optical regions are compared for their usefulness in Table 16.4.

From the table it is evident that in terms of *decreasing* convenience and ease of quantitative measurement, the regions may be ranked (a) visible, (b) near ultraviolet, and (c) infrared. Measurements in the visible and near UV tend to be preferred. Fortunately, many substances that do not absorb in the visible or near UV can be reacted with a chromogenic reagent to develop a characteristic and useful absorption in this region. Metal ions, nonmetals, and some classes of organic substances are included. Occasional interferences that arise can usually be minimized (see below). In favorable cases substances at the level of 0.1 ppm can be determined approximately. At the ppm level a precision of $\pm 1\%$ is common.

A very wide range of substances can be analyzed quantitatively in the infrared. Virtually any substance with covalent bonds, whether molecular or ionic (e.g., a salt one of whose ions is polyatomic), can be determined. While the IR region is not suited to trace analysis, determination carried out at the moderate concentration level (1% to 10%) or above can be quite reliable. Interferences are common and are dealt with by usual techniques (see below). Solids are nearly always analyzed by reflectance techniques (Section 16.8).

Accuracies of quantitative spectrophotometric analyses are usually good. With a single-beam instrument a relative accuracy of $\pm 0.5\%$ to $\pm 2\%$ is realizable, depending on the reliability of the instrument and the care taken in analysis. With a double-beam optical null instrument the accuracy may be as great as $\pm 1\%$ if the optical wedge has a transmission that varies linearly along its length or $\pm 0.5\%$ for a ratio-recording instrument. Calibration or potentiometric compensation techniques can significantly improve accuracy. Indeed, with the latter an accuracy of $\pm 0.3\%$ is realizable.

Cell thickness. For quantitative measurements in the UV, and up through the near IR, either pairs of matched cuvettes or sturdy sample cells of known thickness b are readily available. In the middle and far IR, however, cell thicknesses must ordinarily be measured.*

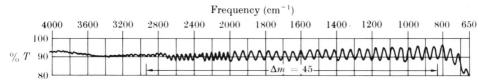

Fig. 16.9 Interference fringe pattern obtained for an empty 0.1 mm cell. (Courtesy Perkin-Elmer.)

The cell dimension b needed for a Beer's law calculation can easily be determined interferometrically. The cell of interest, filled with air, is placed in the sample beam of the IR spectrophotometer, the reference channel is left empty, and a regular spectral scan is made. The form of curve that results is shown in Fig. 16.9. A small sinusoidal wave appears superposed on the transmittance curve over a considerable

---

* The cells used either are of the demountable type whose thickness varies with sealing pressure or have windows of relatively soft optical materials that erode as they are used.

range. The wave maxima arise from constructive interference, the minima from destructive interference between the small fraction of radiation reflected twice (or four times) internally and the greater fraction directly transmitted. Since this case is analogous to that of the Fabry–Perot interference filter (Section 11.6), Eq. (11.4) is also applicable here if radiation is vertically incident. After rearranging the equation and substitution of cell thickness b, we have

$$b = m\lambda/2n = m/2n\sigma \qquad (16.13)$$

where m is an integer (interference order), λ the vacuum wavelength, σ the vacuum wave number, and n the refractive index of filling material (air). It is simplest to apply Eq. (16.13) to adjacent maxima since it can be shown that they represent orders m that differ by unity.

Example An air-filled demountable cell gives transmission maxima at 1000 cm^{-1}, 1050 cm^{-1}, 1100 cm^{-1},.... What is its thickness? Assume $n = 1$ and essentially vertical incidence. For the fringes at 1000 cm^{-1} and 1050 cm^{-1},

$$2b = m_1/1000 \cdot 1 \quad \text{or} \quad 2000b = m_1$$
$$2b = (m_1 + 1)/1050 \cdot 1 \quad \text{or} \quad 2100b = m_1 + 1.$$

Subtracting the first equation from the second,

$$100b = 1 \quad \text{and} \quad b = 0.01 \text{ cm}.$$

The value of m_1, surprisingly, is 200, a high order.

To increase the precision of the estimate the number of maxima is more commonly totaled over a long spectral region. Then Eq. (16.13) becomes

$$b = \Delta m/2n\,\Delta\sigma \qquad (16.14)$$

where Δm equals the number of maxima (and the increase in order) and $\Delta\sigma$ equals the wave number range over which maxima are tallied.

The equation also lends itself to determination of refractive indexes in the IR. To apply it several conditions must be met: A cell of known thickness must be available to hold the sample, the substance must have a transparent range in the IR at least 200–500 cm^{-1} long, $|n_{\text{sample}} - n_{\text{window}}| > 0.3$ to 0.5 (for adequate reflection). If a converging IR beam is used (true of most spectrophotometers) provision must be made for off-vertical incidence. [25]

Digital recording. In quantitative work digital recording, especially when tied to computer calculations, offers advantages. The frequency of an absorption maximum can be located and the absorbance value observed automatically. It is straightforward to apply photometric and frequency corrections and to obtain integrated band intensities. In general, mathematical smoothing methods can be used to reduce noise while introducing minimal distortion and overlapping curves can be resolved.

Single unknown. The simplest case is one in which the concentration of a single substance is sought. In devising a procedure, the absorption curves of all the constituents of the sample should be studied for two kinds of information, the wavelength and the concentration at which the analysis can best be done. A suitable concentration level will, of course, also depend on the instrument and cell.

Ideally the species of interest should absorb (a) in accordance with Beer's law or with little apparent deviation from it and (b) in a spectral region free of absorption by other constituents in the sample. Meeting the first condition requires preliminary trials to establish a suitable concentration range. If the second condition is not met, either a preliminary chemical operation must be performed or the sample must be treated as a mixture. Possible preliminary treatments of a species include (a) complexing to give an intensely absorbing species at a suitable wavelength, (b) separation from the sample by a method like precipitation or extraction, and (c) conversion to another oxidation state or other new form.

In inorganic analysis, complexing is probably the simplest and most effective means of minimizing absorption interference. Not only are the majority of inorganic ions colorless or weakly absorbing, but most organic agents are specific, i.e., complex with one or at most a very few species of ions. Substances that would otherwise interfere can therefore usually be left in solution without ill effects. The reader is referred to the voluminous literature on the analysis of inorganic substances for details for different species.

Example   Nickel in steel can be determined photometrically by dissolving the steel in hot HCl solution, oxidizing with bromine water, and complexing the nickel with dimethyl glyoxime. A soluble red complex of unestablished identity is formed, and the other metals (Fe, Cr, Mn, etc.) do not interfere.[21] The analysis may be carried out with a spectrophotometer at about 350 nm or with a filter photometer by using a blue-green filter that is opaque above 430 nm.

If complexing fails to eliminate troublesome interferences, whether to attempt a chemical separation or a conversion procedure will have to be decided in each case. Precision will decrease with each step added, and it may prove advantageous to seek an entirely different quantitative method requiring fewer operations.

In organic analysis the high frequency of IR interferences dictates a variety of strategies. Where interferences are not severe, a direct determination, by differential procedure if necessary, is desirable. A shift of region is a good strategy. Clearly, substances like ketones that absorb both in the UV and IR can in all probability be determined directly in the UV. For some types of substances complexing with a chromogenic reagent develops useful absorption bands in the visible. For most organic mixtures, however, a combination of techniques is more fruitful. In these cases IR, NMR, UV, and/or mass spectrometry are used to identify the constituent as its concentration is quantitatively determined by gas-liquid chromatography or another separation technique.

What wavelength and slit width should be selected for an accurate and sensitive analysis of a species? In general, the wavelength chosen should be that of the maximum in the strongest absorption band that is free of interferences. There are two reasons. First, that wavelength will be the one at which there is the greatest change in absorption with concentration. Second, taking data at wavelengths on the side of an absorption band where absorbance is changing rapidly should ordinarily be avoided, since a slight inaccuracy in setting the monochromator wavelength may produce an appreciable error. Further, the spectral slit width or bandwidth of the instrument selected,* except in unusual cases, should be no wider than the value needed to obtain absorbances obeying Beer's law. Both resolving the selected absorption peak from neighbouring absorptions and excluding regions of higher transmittance on either side of the peak are involved. In general, the broader the absorption peak of a species, the less stringent any of these requirements is.

Fortunately, many frequently performed photometric analyses are based on broad absorption regions and can be made with either a filter photometer or a spectrophotometer. If there is only a short spectral range free of interference, filter photometers are seldom suitable. In this case, the narrower band pass of a spectrophotometer beam is indispensable.

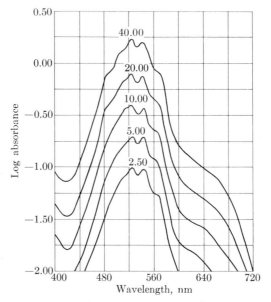

Fig. 16.10 Log absorbance vs. wavelength for aqueous solutions of potassium permanganate of different concentrations. Concentrations given in ppm; 1 cm cell path.

Example 1 An analysis for manganese based on its oxidation to the permanganate form could be performed with a blue-green filter passing a broad band of from 440 to 560 nm according to the plots of Fig. 16.10. Ordinarily a much narrower band pass filter would be used. A spectrophotometer would probably be set at about 520 nm for best precision. Unless interferences made it necessary to do so, it would not be set at 450 or 580 nm.

---

* Spectral slit widths are usually set by the slit program a manufacturer has prepared. In the case of filter photometers (Sections 17.3), the value is set by the filter bandpass. If the slit width of an instrument must be selected manually, data furnished about slit width vs. spectral slit width over the wavelength range of interest should be consulted to decide on an appropriate value.

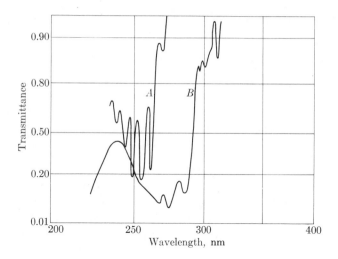

Fig. 16.11   Absorption spectrum of A, benzene and B, naphthalene.

Example 2   Naphthalene absorbs in about the same spectral region of UV as benzene does. The absorption curves are given in Fig. 16.11. If naphthalene in mixtures with benzene is to be determined by photometric analysis, a spectrophotometer is required. Only the naphthalene absorbs appreciably at 285 nm. The wavelength control can be set to that figure and the slit adjusted to give a spectral band width of from 1 to 2 nm.

If the wavelength selected is on the side of an absorption band, special attention must be given to the reproducibility of the settings of wavelength and slit width on the instrument used. Further, a precise setting is nearly always called for in systems that have an *isobestic* point. An example is shown in Fig. 16.6. Substances of biochemical interest and compounds useful as indicators exist in different forms at different pH's. If these forms are simply interrelated, there is a wavelength at which the molar absorptivity of a substance is the same in all its forms, a so-called isobestic point. Determinations at this wavelength greatly simplify procedures.

It should also be noted that a correction for small amounts of extraneous absorption may be feasible. The conditions are that the absorbances be additive and that not more than one or two interfering substances be involved. The approximate concentrations and absorptivities (at the analytical wavelength) must be known for the interferents. The contribution of each to the measured absorbance may then be estimated and subtracted (see the discussion of mixtures below).

Example   In a copper determination an absorbance of 0.65 is measured. It is known that there is about a 10^{-4} M concentration of an interferent with molar absorptivity of approximately 100. The cell has a 1 cm path length. The correction is:

$$\epsilon bc = 100 \times 10^{-4} \times 1 = 0.01;$$

the absorbance due to copper alone is

$$0.65 - 0.01 = 0.64.$$

An uncertainty of 10 % in the molar absorptivity or concentration of the interfering species will produce relatively little error in calculating the copper absorbance.

Finally, even if Beer's law appears to fail, photometric methods can still be used for a particular constituent. One then works entirely from a calibration curve.

Suspensions. Some absorption photometric procedures, like the analysis of nickel by complexing with dimethyl glyoxime, actually involve measurements on suspensions. To be useful in absorption photometry, the conditions of formation of these suspensions must be closely reproduced in each analysis and stable, very finely divided colloids produced (Section 20.3). Since the power transmitted by this kind of sample will be reduced by both absorption and scattering, use of calibration curves is necessary. Other examples of absorption photometric analyses involving colloids are the determination of acetylene by ammoniacal chloride and the determination of antimony as the sulfide.

Baseline method. When the concentration of a single species in a mixture is to be determined, allowance must be made for the absorption of the other substances present. In such instances the baseline method can be useful.

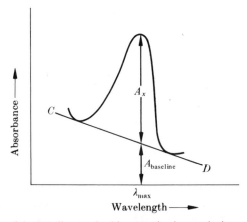

Fig. 16.12 Application of the baseline method in quantitative analysis to one species in a mixture. An absorption peak of the species of interest is shown. It is assumed that baseline CD is the sum of the absorption of all other components in this region. On this basis A_x, the absorbance of the analytical species at the maximum, equals $A_{total} - A_{baseline}$ at λ_{max}.

The procedure is illustrated in Fig. 16.12. A "baseline" CD is drawn tangent to the minima on either side of an analytical absorption peak. The peak absorbance is taken from the curve at λ_{max} and is just $A_{species} = A_{total} - A_{baseline}$. This method is valid if the spectra of the other substances change linearly with wavelength in the region of the absorption peak. Where the condition is not met, the usual Beer's law procedure for a multi-component mixture to be described below can be carried out.

Mixtures. Many mixtures can be analyzed quantitatively for several components if the absorption curves of all the constituents are available. For example, petroleum refineries often make use of infrared spectrophotometry for the direct determination of the composition of various hydrocarbon process streams. No preliminary separation is required provided there are not more than 8 or 10 constituents and the mixture is homogeneous. A primary requirement is that a spectrophotometer of high resolution and reliability be used.

The theoretical basis for a simultaneous photometric determination of several components is implicit in one of the assumptions of Beer's law, that each absorbing centre interacts with radiation independently. In other words, each ion or molecule is assumed to absorb an amount of radiant energy that is unaffected by the presence of neighbors. Some severe difficulties are foreseeable in the case of polar mixtures; suffice it to say that such cases ought to be investigated thoroughly before photometric analysis is attempted.

If Beer's law holds for each constituent (or for all but one constituent [2]) under the conditions of the mixture, Eq. (16.4) can be applied. This equation states that at any particular wavelength λ,

$$A_\lambda = \log_{10} 1/T_\lambda = b\sum_i \epsilon_{i\lambda} c_i, \tag{16.15}$$

where the subscripts i denote the several solutes. The manner in which the equation is used may be seen by noting that

1. All the solutes are in the same cell, and the cell thickness b is a known constant,
2. The molar absorptivities ϵ_i of the different solutes may be found by securing the individual absorption curves, and
3. The "unknowns" in the equation are the concentrations.

Since a single equation can be solved for only one unknown, a set of as many equations as there are absorbing constituents in the mixture is needed if the concentrations are to be found. For instance, analyzing for five constituents will necessitate measurements of A at five wavelengths. The optimum wavelengths will be those giving as widely different values of molar absorptivities as possible. The set of equations is then solvable for the concentrations by the usual methods applied to simultaneous equations.

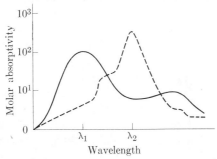

Fig. 16.13 Wavelengths for analysis of a two-component system whose molar absorptivities are given by the full and broken curves.

Example A two-component mixture is to be analyzed photometrically. The *molar absorptivities* of these substances are shown in Fig. 16.13. The measurements on the mixture are carried out at wavelengths λ_1 and λ_2, where the absorptivities differ most. The two equations

$$A_{\lambda_1} = (\epsilon_{11}c_1 + \epsilon_{21}c_2)\,b$$
$$A_{\lambda_2} = (\epsilon_{12}c_1 + \epsilon_{22}c_2)\,b$$

are obtained. On the right side the first subscript of terms refers to the substance, the second to the wavelength. The pair of simultaneous equations may be solved for c_1 and c_2.

Observations at different wavelengths must, of course, be made rapidly enough to avoid composition changes. It is essential that the spectral slit width be precisely that used in determining the absorption curves of each constituent. Otherwise, the accuracy of the determination will be low. If possible, the same spectrophotometer should be used for all measurements. As suggested earlier, measurements on the steep slopes of absorption regions should be avoided where feasible.

Computer programs are available to solve sets of sumultaneous equations. They are fed data consisting of the appropriate absorbances and molar absorptivities, and they yield composition reports almost immediately. They find a ready application in industry in the analysis of process streams.

For mixtures for which Beer's law seems not to hold, there is still a possibility of spectrophotometric analysis if there is no interaction among components. Some methods are described by Lothian. [1]

Trace analysis. Absorption spectrometry is widely used for trace analysis at the 1 to 0.1 ppm level and sometimes below. It is true that chemical and analytical steps requiring considerable skill and care are generally necessary prior to the actual spectrometric determination. Yet this disadvantage is offset by the fact that spectrophotometric measurements are simple, fast, specific, and suitable for automation.

In many trace determinations a preliminary separation by extraction (often after chelation), distillation, or a chromatographic procedure is necessary to isolate a trace constituent from one or more interferents present at much higher concentrations. Here efficiency is a key requirement. Further, a preconcentration step, e.g., by use of an ion-exchange resin column, is often essential in order to ensure either stoichiometric reaction with the chromogenic agent or to secure adequate absorption by the substance itself. During all these steps inadvertent introduction of interfering contaminants must be kept to a minimum. The sensitivity of spectrophotometric trace methods can be increased by preconcentration, use of a longer cell, and especially by finding more highly absorbing chromogenic agents.

As a result of continuing research good trace methods are presently known for most metals and the number of satisfactory nonmetal procedures is steadily growing. Most organic substances that absorb in the UV or VIS can be analyzed directly at the trace level. Those that absorb only in the IR can ordinarily be handled by combining preliminary concentration by wick stick with use of a KBr pellet.

Dual-wavelength photometry. Small changes in the concentration of a species are difficult to determine with any precision when it is present in a highly absorbing or strongly scattering (turbid) solution. Basically, the problem is one of measuring absorbance reliably to 1 part in 10,000. In such experimental situations a considerable advantage is gained by using a dual-wavelength procedure. Spectrophotometers that have a duochromator, i.e., a device for isolating two wavelengths of interest when illuminated by a continuous source, are commercially available.

In dual-wavelength photometry, one wavelength is selected as that of an isobestic point, a wavelength at which the absorbance of a system will be constant though the concentration of at least one species is changing.* The second wavelength is selected as that of a distinctive absorption peak of the species of interest. The instrument is adjusted initially so that there is a balance between the signals produced at the two wavelengths. Departures from the balance may be very sensitively determined by a null procedure. If a time-base recorder is used to monitor the output, information about the kinetics of a reaction may be followed. Studies in biological systems are especially facilitated by such measurements. In Exercise 16.27 the application of Beer's law to the dual-wavelength method is examined.

16.7 DIFFERENTIAL SPECTROPHOTOMETRY

When either a highly absorbing ($T < 10\%$) or a weakly absorbing ($T \sim 100\%$) species must be determined, the regular photometric procedure gives less accurate results. Recall that the optimum range is 20 to 65% T with a readout linear in transmission. With such samples a differential photometric procedure can be used effectively.

From an instrumental perspective, usual photometric readout scale settings such as the 100% reading are made consistently but arbitrarily. What patterns of setting are useful? As is familiar, in regular absorption measurements when a shutter blocks light from the detector, the readout is set at 0% T; when light from a blank reaches it, at 100% T. An actual determination then requires, at minimum, two measurements: one of the transmittance of a standard, the other of the sample.

By contrast, in a differential procedure settings are such that a portion of the scale is basically expanded. Either the 0 or the 100% T setting, or both, is made with a solution of known concentration in the radiation path. The details are shown in Table 16.5.

It will be helpful to discuss one procedure in detail. As noted in the table, the high-absorbance method (also termed the transmittance ratio or *differential photometric* method) requires setting 100% T on the basis of the transmittance of a standard solution that is slightly less concentrated than the unknown. In other words this known [c_1] serves as blank (in a single-beam instrument) or reference (in a double-beam one). To accomplish this end, it is necessary to increase the intensity of the incident radiation over that required with a solvent blank. For example, the entrance slit of the monochromator or a light control wedge (in some single beam instruments) may be opened wider.† The 0% T setting is made as usual. In Fig. 16.14 the way

---

* In the usual more restricted sense, an isobestic point is characteristic of a system in equilibrium such as an acid-base indicator.
†An adjustment of slit width may affect the dark current in the detector. If so, it must be rezeroed. Sometimes successive adjustments of one, then the other are required.

Table 16.5 Differential Spectrophotometry

Name of Method	Basis for Setting Readout at		Type of Working Curve of A vs. c
	$0\% \, T \, (A = \infty)$	$100\% \, T \, (A = 0)$	
Regular	No light	Blank transmission	Linear: $A_x = \epsilon b c_x$
Differential methods			
Transmittance ratio	No light	Soln. (conc. c_1) transmission	Linear: $A'_x = \epsilon b (c_x - c_1)$
Trace analysis	Soln. (conc. c_2) transmission	Blank transmission	Nonlinear: Use std. solns.
Ultimate precision	Soln. (conc. c_2) transmission	Soln. (conc. c_1) transmission	Nonlinear: Use std. solns.

Definitions: c_x, sample concentration; c_i, std. soln. concentration where $c_1 < c_x, c_2 > c_x$; A', readings observed.

in which the method effects a scale expansion is illustrated. Once these settings are made, the absorbance A of the sample is the only reading required.

How do we interpret these apparent transmittance readings to calculate the concentration of a sample? Consider the case in Fig. 16.14. Regardless of the scale, if both solutions obey Beer's law, $A'_1 = \epsilon b c_1$ and $A'_x = \epsilon b c_x$, where primed absorbances designate measurements made on the new scale. Subtracting the first expression from the second gives $A'_x - A'_1 = \epsilon b (c_x - c_1)$. Since $A'_1 = 0$ by virtue of the way the device has been set, $A'_x = \epsilon b (c_x - c_1)$. Because more of the scale is used now than before, the precision of measurement may increase by a factor as great as the scale expansion factor. For example, a tenfold increase (100/10) is theoretically possible in the case in Fig. 16.14. In practice, instrumental noise tends to make the gain in precision somewhat smaller.

Similar gains in precision can be realized by the *trace analysis* method also listed in Table 16.5. After the scale expansion, however, a calibration curve must ordinarily be obtained, since the relation between absorbance and concentration is in this method slightly nonlinear. The trace technique is usable providing there is a separate

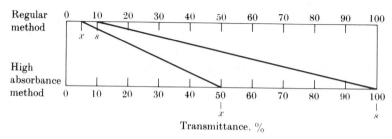

Fig. 16.14 The scale expansion achievable using the high-absorbance method. A sample x of $5\% \, T$ is compared with a standard solution s of $10\% \, T$ whose concentration is $[c_1]$. On the new scale the apparent transmittance of $[c_1]$ becomes 100% and that of the sample, 50%. The scale expansion factor is $100/10 = 10$.

dark-current control that can be adjusted to set the $0\%\ T$ with the dilute standard solution in the beam.

Finally, with a stable spectrophotometer, it is also possible to employ the *ultimate precision* method. In this case a central portion of the scale is expanded. A sample response is bracketed closely by responses of knowns that are used to establish the $0\%\ T$ and $100\%\ T$ settings. In this case also a calibration curve is needed.

16.8 REFLECTANCE SPECTROMETRY

While transmission methods are the most widely used procedures for obtaining absorption spectra, reflectance techniques are increasingly employed. If the sample is a film or a solid, a direct or specular reflection technique is occasionally used. The angle of incidence is noted and a surface of known reflectance is employed as a reference. A spectrum can be obtained by scanning a wavelength region.

If the sample is a powder or a suspension, a *diffuse reflectance* measurement can be readily made. Radiation reflected from the sample is collected by the walls of an integrating sphere, and a definite fraction reflected to an exit slit and detector. A calibrated reflection standard such as magnesium oxide is generally used as a reference.

More commonly, however, the technique of *internal reflectance spectrometry* is used. The method is based on the phenomenon of total internal reflection (Section 10.9). Other common designations for the technique are attenuated total reflectance or multiple internal reflectance spectrometry. A standard spectrometer can be used; only the sample holder need be different (Section 17.8). In this technique the sample is held tightly against a transparent plate of higher refractive index. Radiation is incident on the sample through the plate. When its angle of incidence on the plate-sample interface is greater than the critical angle, the radiation reflected is a spectrum characteristic of the sample that is nearly identical to a transmission spectrum. [15]

As was discussed in Section 10.9, total internal reflection is accompanied by penetration of the radiation only a fraction of a wavelength into the sample (the rarer medium). Indeed, the short depth of penetration is one of the most attractive features of internal reflectance spectroscopy. Even highly absorbing samples such as leather may be examined. If a transmission method were used instead, an absorption spectrum could not be determined because it would be impossible to cut a thin enough layer. On the other hand, if a sample is only weakly absorbing, *multiple* internal reflections can sometimes be used to secure sufficient signal.

Example By means of internal reflectance spectrometry water and other agents on the surface of semiconductors have been detected (by IR measurement) at the level of 10^{-7} g. An internal reflectance plate is used at an angle of incidence that permits hundreds of reflections at the semiconductor surface before the beam enters the spectrometer.

Several further advantages of internal reflectance spectrometry are

1. Penetration of a sample is independent of its thickness;
2. Absorption in a sample is independent of direction; and
3. Interference and scattering phenomena do not occur in a sample.

As a result, two types of application are especially attractive: analysis of anisotropic substances; analysis of trace constituents in films whose small absorption might otherwise be obscure by interference fringes.

The chief decisions to be made in using the technique are the shape of the reflector plate and its composition (Section 17.8). It is essential that the plate have a refractive index greater than the highest index of the sample to avoid serious distortion of absorption bands.* It is also desirable for purposes of strengthening absorption to use an angle of incidence on the sample somewhat greater (three to five degrees) than the average critical angle over the wavelength of the region of interest.

If the conditions outlined are met, a high-contrast spectrum can be obtained whose absorption bands are nearly identical to those in a transmission spectrum. Actually, the depth of penetration of a sample does increase slightly with wavelength, causing absorption bands at longer wavelengths to be relatively stronger. Further, for broad bands there is a noticeable widening on the long-wavelength side.

The limitations of the method are several. It is not particularly useful with weakly absorbing species such as gases, or for the determination of end points of titrations where there is a weak color change. Wherever surface properties of a material are different from its bulk characteristics, the technique is quite limited. Since the index of refraction of the place and the angle of incidence must be chosen judiciously, it is certainly not a routine technique. Corrosive samples are difficult to use because they may attack the reflectance element. Perhaps the most serious limitation of the technique is that since contact problems may severely limit the reliability of intensities obtained it is difficult to use for quantitative measurements. If quantitative work is to be done, it is an advantage to work with polarized light. [15]

16.9 PHOTOMETRIC TITRATIONS

An absorption photometer may serve efficiently as a means of following a wide range of titrations. Its function is to monitor the change in absorbance of at least one substance involved in the titration, whether a reactant, titrant, or product. As long as the measured species follows Beer's law roughly, the change in absorbance will vary essentially linearly with concentration and yield two straight lines that intersect at the end point. Accuracies of 1 % or better are attainable. Two typical plots are given in Fig. 16.15. Note the similarity to conductance titration curves (see Fig. 28.8).

In a number of classes of titration, absorption photometry offers advantages over techniques like potentiometry and conductometry. Its superior features stem from the linear dependence of absorbance on concentration, the high degree of sensitivity often possible in measurement, and the fact that no electrodes or probes need contact the solution. In addition, there is ordinarily no difficulty in working in solutions of either high or low ionic strength.

As a result of its high sensitivity and linear dependence on concentration, photometry is especially useful in the accurate titration of dilute aqueous systems, those that contain weak electrolytes, and in the titration of many nonaqueous systems. The

---

* Recall that the refractive index of a sample can be expected to increase in regions of absorption (Section 10.7). If n_1 (plate) $< n_2$ (sample) in an absorption region, a transmittance curve resembling a first derivative of an absorption peak is obtained.

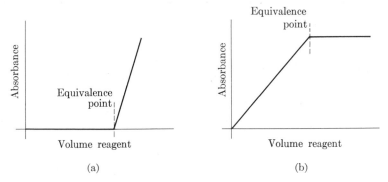

Fig. 16.15 Some types of absorption photometric titration curves. (a) Only the titrant absorbs. (b) Only the reaction product absorbs.

important fact is that the end point may be determined graphically by the intersection of straight lines (Section 28.7). The lines are extrapolated into the end-point region and depend little on points affected by hydrolysis, appreciable solubility, and similar influences. At least two graphical photometric titration procedures have been suggested [23, 27], one of which allows the extension of the titration to very weak acids and bases. Clearly, precipitation titrations yielding a salt of moderate solubility can also often be done photometrically with good precision.

Example The titration of a *p*-bromophenol sample in water with sodium hydroxide solution

$$Br\text{---}\bigcirc\text{---}OH + Na^+OH^- = Br\text{---}\bigcirc\text{---}O^-Na^+ + HOH$$

can be done photometrically. The end point is located by measuring the absorption of the *p*-bromophenolate ion at 325 nm, where there are no interferences. A titration plot of absorbance versus volume of reagent added is given in Fig. 16.16. The absorbance will increase linearly during the formation of bromophenolate ion, but will level off at the end point, when no more of that ion is formed. After the end point the absorbance will probably decrease very slightly because of the dilution caused by further titrant. The deviation of the data of Fig. 16.16 from linearity near the end point is probably caused by hydrolysis.

Procedure. Suitable titration equipment will be described in Section 17.11. If the titration produces a sharp break in absorbance, an automatic titrator may be used. Initially a suitable wavelength at which to monitor the titration must be decided by inspection of the absorption curves for the several species. Provision should then be made to select a concentration range for the absorbing species such that Beer's law is roughly obeyed and a (titration) cell length such that the absorbance falls in the optimum range. Usually dilute ($<10^{-2}$ M) solutions give best results. Finally, it should be appreciated that in an automatic photometric titration the titrant need not necessarily be added from a buret but may often be generated by electrolysis (Section 27.2).

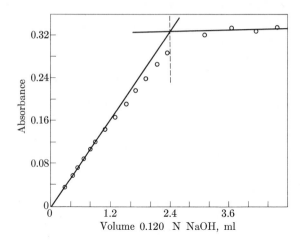

Fig. 16.16 Absorbance curve for photometric titration of 100 ml of 2.8×10^{-3} N p-bromophenol solution at 325 nm with 0.120 N NaOH under nitrogen with a Beckman Model B spectrophotometer. Theoretical end point = 2.32 ml. [Courtesy of *Analytical Chemistry*; R. F. Goddu and D. N. Hume, *Anal. Chem.* **26**, 1740 (1954).]

16.10 QUALITATIVE ANALYSIS

Spectrophotometry provides sufficient information for these kinds of qualitative analysis:
 1. Pure substances can be identified and characterized as to structure, and
 2. Characteristic groupings of atoms can be identified.
     Very few instrumental techniques provide as positive an identification of a pure substance as does absorption spectrophotometry. This is true because the *complete* absorption curve of a substance is unique, depending as it does on the kind, number, mass, and geometry of all the atoms in a molecule. Thus, not only does the absorption curve allow a substance to be distinguished from all others, but it also provides information about the kinds of atoms present and identifies the groupings in which they occur. IR and UV spectra are commonly cited as confirmatory evidence for postulated structural features. An illustration of the power of this method of analysis is provided by the comparison in Fig. 16.17 of the IR spectra of three similar substances. Even their small differences produce significant changes.
     Spectrophotometry is much less well adapted to the study of impurities and gross mixtures. The basic difficulty is that the substances in mixtures present so many overlapping regions of absorption that the maxima and other shape details on which one relies to establish the identity of a particular compound are obscured. Ordinarily, in a qualitative analysis, mixtures are rather completely resolved before spectrophotometric study. For further information on dealing with mixtures, references should be consulted.
     It should be emphasized that exploiting all the potentialities of a photometric analysis requires that the shape, height, and wavelength of absorption maxima be known precisely. In most instances this requirement can be met by the use of an instrument of high resolution, i.e. one with a good monochromator and a detector sufficiently sensitive so that very narrow wavelength bands can be used (Section 11.7).

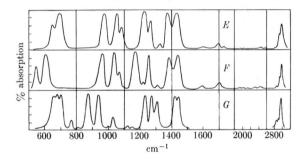

Fig. 16.17 IR absorption spectra of *E*, 1,1-dichloroethane; *F*, 1,1-dibromoethane; *G*, 1,2-dichloro-ethane. [Courtesy of the Faraday Division of the Chemical Society; H. W. Thompson and P. Tarkington, *Trans. Faraday Soc.* **42**, 432 (1946).]

Presentation of data. An absorption curve is so dependent on instrumental and chemical variables that it will not stand by itself; it must be accompanied by certain data before its validity and accuracy are established. A thorough report should give or clearly imply (a) the type of instrument, (b) wavelength calibration points or references, (c) spectral slit width or effective bandwidth, (d) the interval between points (manual instrument) or scanning speed (recording instrument), (e) the thickness of cells, and (f) all pertinent chemical information such as concentrations, pH, and temperature. In recognition of the necessity of reporting these data, appropriate blanks are placed on the charts for recording spectrophotometers.

Most qualitative studies require the examination of individual absorption curves as well as the intercomparison of different curves. Each of these processes is greatly facilitated by systematization in recording or plotting data. The routine devised should, of course, take into account both the available instrument(s) and the use to which the data will be put. Whether a spectrophotometer registers absorbance (optical density) or transmittance directly does not make much difference. Either variable gives a satisfactory representation of absorption when graphed as a function of wavelength or wave number (Fig. 16.17). Detailed specifications for taking IR spectra have been made to facilitate intercomparison. [36] For computer storage digital recording is desirable.

There are two graphical methods that are important because they lessen or remove completely any dependence on concentration. One involves plotting the logarithm of the absorbance, the other, the logarithm of the molar absorptivity. In Fig. 16.10 the character of the log *A* plot is demonstrated. Note that the *shape* of the absorption spectrum does not change with concentration though the curve "height" does. In other words, the slope of a log *A* curve depends only on the absorptivity of a substance. In the more conventional *A* vs. *λ* graphs the curves change both in slope and position as concentration is varied. The behavior of log *A* plots can be better understood by taking the logarithm of both sides of Eq. (16.3):

$$\log A = (\log \epsilon bc) = \log \epsilon + \log bc. \qquad (16.16)$$

In this form the absorptivity ϵ, the only factor dependent on wavelength and the nature of a substance, is separated from the concentration-dependent term. Thus, the outline of a family of log A curves is specific for each substance. The height of a curve above the abscissa, however, is directly proportional to log bc.

If a library file of curves is being prepared, or if absorption data are primarily of research interest, it is probably worth the additional effort to calculate log ϵ and graph it. Although ϵ itself could be plotted, its range is ordinarily so great (perhaps from 0.1 to 1000 or more) that the logarithmic representation is advantageous. A straightforward and systematic computation procedure based on Eq. (16.16) can be devised.

Procedure. The IR and UV, in that order, are the best regions for qualitative analysis. Actually, the best evidence to establish structural features, and thus the identity, of a substance will come from the very important vibrational transitions appearing in the IR that are known as *group frequencies*. While a whole molecule vibrates as a unit, certain stretching or bending vibrations depend primarily on the mass of a small number of bonded atoms and on the force constants of the bonds joining them. In these cases other atoms have only a slight effect on the frequency of vibration. For example, the stretching of bonds between hydrogen and other atoms such as C—H and O—H occurs at about 2900 to 3600 cm^{-1}. Many group frequencies are listed in Table 16.6.

In general the smaller a group frequency, the more sensitive it is to the structure of a molecule as a whole. For example, the exact frequency of a group whose vibration appears below 1300 cm^{-1} is often useful in identifying the position of the group if it is bonded to an aromatic ring or details of chain structure if in an aliphatic substance. Since the entire molecule as well as the group determines group frequencies in this range, the lower frequency IR is often termed the fingerprint region.

Absorption in the near UV (400 to 200 nm) is found only for species with electron clouds that are somewhat loosely bound such as compounds with π-bonds. Thus, conjugated double-bond systems with their delocalized orbitals show especially strong UV absorption. Since electron levels are more nearly molecular in character than group frequency vibrations, less information can generally be obtained from the UV than the IR. A further disadvantage of the UV is the relative scarcity of absorption peaks; most substances show only one or two in the usual condensed phase sample.

Assuming that one has isolated an unknown substance in a fairly pure state, the best analytical approach is to determine its IR absorption from 4000 to 650 cm^{-1} (2.5 to 15 μm). Alternatively, the UV or the near IR can be scanned.* It must be emphasized that an analysis cannot be based on an examination of only a small spectral region, e.g., a range of 100 nm, because similar compounds may have nearly identical spectra over short ranges.

If an extensive file of curves (plotted on the same coordinates) is available, identification of the unknown may be a matter of intelligent comparison. For this operation, translucent charts and an illumination box (a glass-topped box lighted from inside) are advisable. If a known with the same absorption features (wavelengths of maxima, principally) is found, the identification may be assumed virtually conclusive. Identical UV features will indicate strongly that the substances are identical. To speed identi-

---

* In the near IR (14,000 to 5000 cm^{-1}) spectral absorptions are characteristic of overtones (harmonics) or combinations of fundamental vibration frequencies. Thus, they are helpful in confirming molecular identity but not generally useful in elucidating molecular structure.

Table 16.6 Some Characteristic Group Frequencies*

Functional Group	Approximate Position of Absorption Band	
	μm	cm^{-1}
$-NH_2$ (primary amine)	2.85 to 3.15	3180 to 3505
$-OH$ (alcohols)	2.84 to 3.22	3100 to 3520
$>C-H$ (aliphatic)	3.3 to 3.6	2780 to 3050
$>C-H$ (aromatic)	3.2 to 3.35	2995 to 3140
$-CH_2-$ (methylene)	3.42 to 3.55	2810 to 2920
$-C\equiv N$ (nitrile)	4.16 to 4.55	2200 to 2405
$-C\equiv C-$	4.42 to 4.65	2150 to 2270
$>C=O$ (esters)	5.71 to 5.81	1722 to 1752
$>C=O$ (acids)	5.75 to 6.01	1660 to 1740
$>C=O$ (aldehydes and ketones)	5.76 to 6.05	1650 to 1740
$-NH_2$ (amine)	6.08 to 6.35	1575 to 1645
$-C=C-$	5.98 to 6.17	1620 to 1670
$>C-Cl$	13.1 to 15.2	660 to 765
$>C-Br$	15.6 to 18.9	530 to 640

* Though not listed, inorganic ions such as SO_4^{2-} and NH_4^+ also exhibit characteristic group frequencies. These vibrations are found in the 4000 to 400 cm^{-1} region also.

fication, the absorption maxima of all knowns can be compared by use of an appropriate computer program with the characteristic frequencies found for the unknown.

It is more likely that only a partial file or no file of curves will be available. In this case, the unknown curve must be translated into the type of "groups,"

$$>C-H, \quad >C-C<, \quad -CH_3, \quad >C=O, \quad \text{etc.,}$$

Table 16.7 Comparison of Several Methods of Qualitative Analysis*†

Technique	Usefulness in Characterizing Type of Substance	Range of Usefulness	Finger-Print Type Identification	Deductive Type Identification	Cost of Instrumentation
Absorption spectrometry UV, VIS	Limited	Narrow	Fair at best	Poor	Low to high
IR	Good	Very wide	Very good	Fair	Low to high
Raman spectrometry	Limited	Narrow to moderate	Fair	Fair	Moderate to high
NMR spectrometry	Limited	Very wide	Excellent	Excellent	Moderate to high
Optical rotary dispersion	Very limited	Narrow	Fair to poor	Fair to poor	Moderate to high
Mass spectrometry	Limited	Very wide	Excellent	Excellent	High
X-ray diffraction spectrometry single crystal	Limited	Narrow	Excellent	Excellent	High
powder	Limited	Narrow	Excellent	Poor	Moderate to high

* After S. Siggia, *Survey of Analytical Chemistry*, New York: McGraw-Hill, 1968, pp. 135–36.

† Qualitative analysis is used only in the sense of identification of a species or characterization of its structure. No methods are listed that lend themselves principally to elemental analysis such as emission spectroscopy and neutron activation analysis or to functional group determination such as electroanalytical procedures.

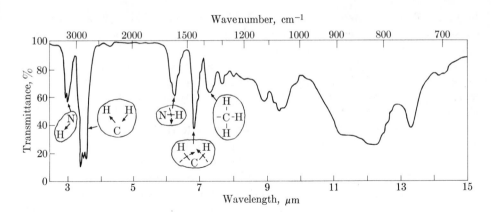

Fig. 16.18 Correlation of atomic groupings with absorption maxima in the 4000 to 650 cm⁻¹ region for 3,3'-diamino-N-methyldipropylamine,

$$CH_3-N\begin{matrix} \diagup CH_2-CH_2-CH_2-NH_2 \\ \diagdown CH_2-CH_2-CH_2-NH_2 \end{matrix} \qquad \text{(0.01-mm cell path).}$$

that are present beyond reasonable doubt in the substance, e.g., by use of a listing such as that in Table 16.7. Extensive compilations of this type of information in tabular form are available. [4] With a little experience, deciding which groupings of atoms are present can be accomplished quickly. An example of what is involved is illustrated in Fig. 16.18.

One should not be misled by some slight differences in curves in regions of high transmittance; these may result from impurities. Since their concentrations will be low, impurities will be unlikely to absorb enough radiation to show their presence except in regions where the substance being analyzed has a high transmittance. Impurities will ordinarily have little effect on the absorption peaks.

It is clear that functional group determinations in new compounds may also be made by spectrophotometric methods. Indeed the methods used are the same as those employed in identifying an unknown substance except that the search is limited to the wavelength regions that will reveal the groups of interest. Both the UV and IR are useful regions for this type of study.

Comparison of qualitative methods. Because of the increasing capabilities of modern analytical chemistry in identifying species, i.e. establishing their structure, an intercomparison of qualitative analytical techniques is useful. Each method has its areas of strength and its limitations. In Table 16.7 this type of comparison is made for the more important techniques of qualitative analysis. As noted, methods that furnish elemental analysis or serve mainly for functional group determinations are not included.

16.11 STRUCTURAL INVESTIGATIONS

One of the more important applications of spectrophotometry is obtaining information about characteristic energy levels and the structural parameters of molecules. The

IR and UV regions provide a rich yield of such data. Bond stiffnesses, i.e. force constants, are calculable from vibrational frequencies, moments of inertia and internuclear distances from rotational frequencies (Section 16.3). From higher-order rotational transitions some notion of the distortion produced in a molecule by rotations may be secured. The excited molecular electronic states can be located and used to refine present mathematical molecular models. Bond dissociation energies are also accurately estimated from UV spectra.

Spatial aspects of molecules are also susceptible to IR analysis. Where rotational isomers exist, as in a molecule in which bulky substituents are attached to both sides of a carbon-carbon single bond, they can be detected. Conformational studies can be made of molecules such as the cyclohexane derivatives. For example, an axial C—X bond vibration ordinarily is found at a lower frequency than an equatorial C—X vibration. As would be expected, tautomeric shifts such as keto-enol transformations can be followed. Structural isomerism, as in molecules that have *cis*- and *trans*- configurations, is also easy to examine.

Of equally great interest is the application of spectrophotometry to the investigation of intermolecular interactions. The degree of hydrogen bonding (either *inter*- or *intra*molecular), molecular association, and attraction of polar molecules to metal ions has been determined spectrophotometrically. These studies usually involve a measurement of the shift in (a) the frequency of a vibrational transition involving the O—H, N—H, or other bonds, as well as (b) intensities. Complexing studies, on the other hand, have typically made use of spectrophotometry as a quantitative tool both for determination of formulas and information about bond character.

Studies of crystals with polarized IR radiation have yielded increasing information about the orientation of groups and the nature of vibrations. Either the depolarization ratio or the dichroic ratio $A_\perp/A_{\parallel}$ is determined.

REFERENCES

Some general references are:

1. G. F. Lothian, *Absorption Spectrophotometry*. 2d ed. London: Hilger and Watts, 1958
2. Edward J. Meehan, "Optical Methods. Emission and Absorption of Radiant Energy," and "Fundamentals of Spectrophotometry," in *Treatise on Analytical Chemistry*. I. M. Kolthoff and P. J. Elving, eds. New York: Interscience, 1964

Molecular spectroscopy is treated on an intermediate level in:

3. Gordon M. Barrow, *Introduction to Molecular Spectroscopy*. New York: McGraw-Hill, 1962
4. N. B. Colthup, L. N. Daly, and S. E. Wiberley, *Introduction to Infrared and Raman Spectroscopy*. New York: Academic, 1964

Molecular spectroscopy is treated more theoretically in:

5. Gerald W. King, *Spectroscopy and Molecular Structure*. New York: Holt, Rinehart, and Winston, 1964

Absorption spectroscopy is presented on an introductory level with emphasis on methods and application in: (any restriction to one optical region indicated in the title)

6. G. H. Beaven, E. A. Johnson, H. A. Willis, and R. G. J. Miller, *Molecular Spectroscopy. Methods and Applications in Chemistry*. New York: Macmillan, 1962.

7. J. R. Edisbury, *Practical Hints on Absorption Spectrometry*. London: Hilger and Watts, 1966
8. C. E. Meloan, *Elementary Infrared Spectroscopy*. New York: Macmillan, 1963
9. R. G. J. Miller, ed., *Laboratory Methods in Infrared Spectroscopy*. London: Heyden, 1965

Absorption spectroscopy in the infrared is presented on an intermediate level with more emphasis on its practice in the IR in:

10. N. L. Alpert, W. E. Keiser, and H. A. Szymanski, *IR, Theory and Practice of Infrared Spectroscopy*. 2d ed. New York: Plenum, 1970
11. Mansel Davies, ed., *Infra-red Spectroscopy and Molecular Structure*. New York: Elsevier, 1963
12. W. J. Potts, Jr., *Chemical Infrared Spectroscopy*. Vol. 1, Techniques. New York: Wiley, 1963

and in the UV-VIS in:

13. R. P. Bauman, *Absorption Spectroscopy*. New York: Wiley, 1962
14. W. West, ed., *Chemical Applications of Spectroscopy*. 2d ed., Part 1. New York: Wiley, 1968

Internal reflection spectroscopy is treated lucidly in:

15. N. J. Harrick, *Internal Reflection Spectroscopy*. New York: Interscience, 1967
16. Gustav Kortum, *Reflectance Spectroscopy; Principles, Methods, Applications*. New York: Springer-Verlag, 1969
17. W. William Wendlandt and H. G. Hecht, *Reflectance Spectroscopy*. New York: Wiley, 1966

Detailed practical information on visual and absorption photometric methods of analysis for elementary ions and compounds is given by:

18. D. F. Boltz, ed., *Colorimetric Determination of Nonmetals*. New York: Interscience, 1958
19. Fritz Feigl, *Spot Tests in Organic Analysis*. 7th ed. New York: Elsevier, 1966
20. E. B. Sandell, *Colorimetric Determination of Traces of Metals*. 3d ed. New York: Interscience, 1959
21. Foster D. Snell, Cornelia Snell, and Chester A. Snell, *Colorimetric Methods of Analysis*. Vol. 2A. Princeton: Van Nostrand, 1959

Theoretical or experimental treatments of interest are presented in:

22. L. S. Goldring, R. C. Hawes, G. H. Hare, A. O. Beckman, and M. E. Stickney, "Anomalies in Extinction Coefficient Measurements," *Anal. Chem.* **25**, 869 (1953)
23. T. Higuchi, C. Rehm, and C. Barnstein, "Photometric Determination of Indicator End Points," *Anal. Chem.* **28**, 1506 (1956)
24. H. K. Hughes *et al.*, "Suggested Nomenclature in Applied Spectroscopy," *Anal. Chem.* **24**, 1349 (1952)
25. R. E. Kagarise and J. W. Mayfield, "Simple Interferometer for Dispersion Measurements of Liquids in the 2–22 μ Region," *J. Opt. Soc. Am.* **48**, 430 (1958)
26. G. Kortüm and M. Seiler, "The Critical Choice of Colorimetric, Spectrophotometric, and Spectrographic Methods of Absorption Measurement" (German text), *Angew. Chem.* **52**, 687 (1939)
27. G. F. Lothian, "Beer's Law and Its Use in Analysis," *Analyst* **88**, 678 (1963)
27a. W. W. Meinke, section on spectrophotometry in "Standard Reference Materials for Clinical Measurements," *Anal. Chem.* **43** (6), 28A (1971)
27b. J. A. Perry, "Quantitative Analysis by Infrared Spectrophotometry," *Appl. Spectr. Rev.* **3**, 229 (1970)
28. (a) H. G. Pfeiffer and H. A. Liebhafsky, "The Origins of Beer's Law," *J. Chem. Educ.* **28**, 133 (1951); (b) H. A. Liebhafsky and H. G. Pfeiffer, "Beer's Law in Analytical Chemistry," *J. Chem. Educ.* **30**, 450 (1953)

29. E. Rabinowitch and L. F. Epstein, "Polymerization of Dyestuffs in Solution. Thionine and Methylene Blue," *J. Am. Chem. Soc.* **63**, 69 (1941)
30. David Z. Robinson, "Quantitative Analysis with Infrared Spectrophotometers," *Anal. Chem.* **23**, 273 (1951); **24**, 619 (1952)
31. G. Svehla, "Differential Spectrophotometry," *Talanta* **12**, 641 (1966)
32. A. S. Wexler, "Integrated Intensities of Absorption Bands in Infrared Spectroscopy," *Appl. Spectr. Rev.* **1**, 29 (1967)

Compilations of absorption spectra, references to methodology for obtaining such spectra, are available in:

33. ASTM Committee E-13, *Manual on Recommended Practices in Spectrophotometry*. 3d ed. Philadelphia: ASTM, 1966
34. L. J. Bellamy, *Advances in Infrared Group Frequencies*. New York: Barnes and Noble, 1968
35. L. J. Bellamy, *The Infra-red Spectra of Complex Molecules*. 2d ed. New York: Wiley, 1958
36. Coblentz Society Board of Managers, "Specifications for Evaluation of Infrared Reference Spectra," *Anal. Chem.* **38** (9), 27A (1966)
37. Herbert M. Hershenson, *Ultraviolet and Visible Absorption Spectra. Index for* 1930–1954. New York: Academic, 1956
38. IUPAC, *Tables of Spectrophotometric Absorption Data of CPDS Used for the Colorimetric Determination of Elements*. London: Butterworth, 1963
39. M. J. Kamlet, ed. Vol. 1, and H. E. Ungnade, ed. Vol. 2, *Organic Electronic Spectral Data*. New York: Interscience, 1960
40. K. N. Rao, C. J. Humphreys, and D. H. Rank, *Wavelength Standards in the Infrared*. New York: Academic, 1966

The application of IR and UV (as well as NMR and, usually, mass spectrum) spectral results to the elucidation of structure of organic molecules is effectively introduced in:

41. J. C. D. Brand and G. Eglinton, *Applications of Spectroscopy to Organic Chemistry*. New York: Davey, 1965
42. J. R. Dyer, *Applications of Absorption Spectroscopy of Organic Compounds*. Englewood Cliffs, N.J.: Prentice-Hall, 1965
43. D. J. Pasto and Carl R. Johnson, *Organic Structure Determination*. Englewood Cliffs, N.J.: Prentice-Hall, 1969
44. R. M. Silverstein and G. C. Bassler, *Spectrometric Identification of Organic Compounds*. 2d ed. New York: Wiley, 1967
45. D. H. Williams and I. Fleming, *Spectroscopic Methods in Organic Chemistry*. New York: McGraw-Hill, 1966

EXERCISES

16.1 a) If a liquid absorbs strongly in the spectral region from 500 to 700 nm, what is its color?

b) If the absorption band of a solution is from 450 to 600 nm, what color does it have?

16.2 A solution of potassium permanganate in a 1 cm cell is found to have a transmittance of 60% at a particular wavelength. If the concentration is doubled, what will be

a) the percent transmittance?

b) the absorbance?

c) What concentration of the $KMnO_4$ must be used to give 60% transmittance in a cell 10 cm long?

[*Ans.*: a) 35.9%; b) 0.44; c) 0.1 original.]

16.3 The molar absorptivity ϵ of benzoic acid in methanol is about 1950 at 275 nm. What is the maximum concentration of benzoic acid in g ml^{-1} that can be used in a 1 cm cell if the absorbance is not to exceed 1.3?

[*Ans.*: 8.1×10^{-5} g ml^{-1}.]

16.4 A 2.0×10^{-5} M solution of a substance gives 50% transmittance in a 1.00 cm cell at 230 nm. What is its molar absorptivity?

16.5 In spectrophotometry the terms stray light and scattered light are both used. How do they differ in meaning? Define each term and indicate the module of an instrument to which it is principally related.

16.6 A source of difficulty in IR spectrometers is that a sample or any instrument part that is above room temperature is also a net IR emitter. Assume the IR absorption spectrum of a polystyrene film is to be measured in a double-beam spectrophotometer with air in the other path.

a) What effect will the gradual heating of the film by the radiation beam have on the wavelength of the absorption peaks? on absorbance at the peaks?

b) If the instrument is at 298 °K, the film is heated to 325 °K, and the real source is at 1500 °K and both "emitters" behave as blackbody sources, at what wavelength will film emission generate the larger error, at 2000 cm^{-1} or 700 cm^{-1}?

[*Ans.*: b) at 700 cm^{-1}.]

16.7 While Beer's law is theoretically valid only if monochromatic radiation is used, the strictness of this requirement depends on the degree to which the absorptivity (a or ϵ) of a sample is constant over the wavelength band corresponding to the spectral slit width. In a determination what is actually measured is not the power transmitted at one wavelength but an intensity $\int I_0(v)\,dv$ where the integration is carried out across the spectral slit width. Thus an apparent absorbance A' is determined for a sample where A' is given by

$$A' = \log \frac{\int I_0(v)\,dv}{\int I_0(v) \times 10^{-\epsilon(v)bc}\,dv}.$$

a) Show that this expression follows from Beer's law.

b) Show that if $\epsilon(v) =$ constant over the spectral band passed by the slit, Beer's law will hold. (See W. E. Wentworth, *J. Chem. Educ.* 43, 262 (1966).)

16.8 It is found by a study on solutions of known absorbance that a given spectrophotometer has 0.2% stray radiation at 450 nm.

a) For a concentrated solution, an apparent transmittance of 2.3% is observed. What is its apparent and true absorbance?

b) What relative error in concentration will result if this apparent absorbance is used in a calculation without correction?

[*Ans.*: a) apparent, 1.638; true, 1.668; b) 1.8%.]

16.9 The species HA has an absorption band centered at 500 nm in water. In this solvent the HA also dissociates somewhat according to the equation $HA \rightleftharpoons H^+ + A^-$. Neither H^+ nor A^- absorb in the visible.

a) Will a plot of the absorbance of HA solutions at 500 nm display a positive or negative deviation from Beer's law?

b) If a considerable excess of NaA, a soluble salt, is added and the measurements are repeated, will a deviation be observed?

c) Should the above results be reported as showing that the substance HA does not follow Beer's law? Explain.

16.10 Sketch the type of spectrophotometric titration curve that will be obtained if at the wavelength chosen for monitoring

a) both reactant and titrant absorb and the reactant absorbs more than the titrant,
b) reactant and product absorb and the reactant absorbs more than the product,
c) only the reactant absorbs.

16.11 It is decided to follow the titration of an acid photometrically using phenolphthalein (only its anionic form absorbs). The acid being titrated and its conjugate base do not absorb in the spectral range observed. Will a curve like Fig. 16.16 be obtained as base is added? Explain.

16.12 A sample is to be analyzed for a component R by a trace analysis procedure (Section 16.7). Consider that the transmittance of the sample is 98% at a wavelength at which R characteristically absorbs. Select an appropriate transmittance solution of R as a standard. Decide on a basis for photometer settings of 0% and 100% T and explain your choice. Draw a sketch like Fig. 16.14 for this case, and state the scale expansion factor achieved over a regular measurement of absorption.

16.13 A differential spectrophotometric procedure is used to determine a metal A in an alloy. After dilution and complexing with a chromogenic ligand, the transmittance at the absorption maximum for complexed A is found to be less than 10%. A 1 cm cell is used. A 1.35×10^{-3} M solution of A similarly complexed and diluted is accordingly used to set the 100% T reading while the 0% T setting is made with no light. Under these conditions, the sample transmittance is 55% T. The molar absorptivity of the complex is 3.87×10^{-3} l mol^{-1} cm^{-1}. What is the concentration of A in the solution?

[*Ans.*: 1.42×10^{-3} M.]

16.14 The thickness of a polystyrene film (refractive index 1.6 in the IR) is to be determined by use of an IR spectrophotometer. A regular spectrum is obtained with the film in the sample beam and air in the reference beam. Between 2000 and 2800 cm^{-1}, where polystyrene is transparent, the baseline shows 30 small interference maxima. How thick is the film?

[*Ans.*: 0.16 mm.]

16.15 For ethylene
a) identify molecular orbitals by conventional notation and state their electron occupancy in the ground state.
b) What electronic transitions are open to the most easily excited electron(s) $n \rightarrow \pi^*, \sigma \rightarrow \pi^*$, or $\pi \rightarrow \pi^*$?
c) Will the same type of transition be the easiest to excite in 3-octene? in cyclopentene?
d) The longest wavelength UV-VIS absorption of these olefins is at about 185 nm. Is this result consistent with the answers to (b) and (c)?

16.16 Develop an equation giving the energy change for a combined vibrational-rotational transition for a diatomic molecule.

16.17 a) Should the spacing between high rotational levels (say $J = 9$ to $J = 10$) of CO (see Example in Section 16.3) have the same value, $2B/hc$?
b) Will the spacing between levels of a lighter molecule like H_2 be smaller or larger?

16.18 Show that the wave number σ of an absorption corresponding to a prerotational transition for a diatomic molecule is given by $(J + 1)h^2/4\pi^2 hcI$ where J is the lower quantum number involved.

16.19 What is the wavelength and wave number of the absorption maximum for the fundamental vibrational band for HBr? Assume a force constant equal to 0.5×10^3 N m^{-1}.

[*Ans.*: 3.45 μm, 2900 cm^{-1}.]

16.20 Which bond will give more closely spaced vibrational levels, to a molecule, $\diagup C\!\!=\!\!C\diagdown$ or $\diagup C\!-\!C\diagup$? Explain.

16.21 At about what wave numbers in the IR should the molecule

$$H-\underset{\underset{\displaystyle O}{\displaystyle \|}}{C}-\!\!\!\bigcirc\!\!\!-OH$$

absorb? Indicate the characteristic vibration responsible for each absorption.

16.22 If a colorless species is to be determined by absorption photometry in the visible range, it must be complexed with an appropriate chromogenic reagent. Suggest several properties desirable in such a complex if it is to be used in quantitative analysis.

16.23 A cadmium-zinc alloy is known to contain about 5% iron. It is proposed to analyze for the iron by specific complexing with 5-sulfoanthranilic acid. As carried out, a 0.2 g sample is dissolved in dilute sulfuric acid, the pH adjusted, and complexing agent added. The final volume is 400 ml. At 455 nm this solution shows an absorbance of 0.637 in a 1 cm cell. Previously it was established that the molar absorptivity of the pure iron complex under the same conditions is 1306. A blank containing only complexing agent at the supposed excess concentration gave an absorbance of 0.015. Calculate the concentration of iron in the sample.

[Ans.: 5.33%.]

16.24 The manganese content of a steel sample is determined spectrophotometrically by oxidation to permanganate and measurement at 575 nm. The absorbance of the three standards and a blank is also determined at 575 nm. From the results tabulated below, calculate the percentage of manganese in the sample.

[Ans.: 0.72%.]

Solution	Concentration	Absorbance
Unknown	0.5000 g steel in 250 ml soln.	0.456
Blank	0.5000 g steel in 250 ml soln., but Mn unoxidized	0.020
Standard (1)	0.020 mg Mn ml^{-1}	0.600
Standard (2)	0.010 „ „	0.301
Standard (3)	0.0040 „ „	0.115

16.25 Describe a spectrophotometric procedure that can be used to determine the pK_a of an indicator such as phenolphthalein.

16.26 It is desired to analyze heavy water that is more than 99% D_2O for isotopic purity. Differential IR spectrometry is chosen as a method that is suitably accurate. Since small concentrations of ^1H appear almost entirely in HDO molecules, the analysis may be made at 1.67 μm (5980 cm^{-1}), a combination vibrational wavelength of HDO. Describe roughly how such an analysis might be arranged, mentioning choice of cell (window) and a basis for setting 100% T and 0% T.

16.27 The dual-wavelength photometric procedure described in Section 16.6 is to be applied to a kinetic study of an oxidation of cytochrome c. At wavelengths λ_1 and λ_2, let ϵ_{R1} and ϵ_{R2} be the molar absorptivities of reduced form, ϵ_{O1} and ϵ_{O2} be the molar absorptivities for the oxidized form, and A_1 and A_2 be the total absorbances. Let C_R and C_O be the concentration of reduced and oxidized forms at a given time. Assume λ_1 is an isobestic point and that $C_R + C_O = $ constant. Derive an expression that relates the change in concentration of the oxidized form, ΔC_O, to the other parameters.

$$[Ans.: \Delta C_O = \Delta A_2/(\epsilon_{o2} - \epsilon_{R2}).]$$

Chapter 17

INSTRUMENTATION FOR OPTICAL ABSORPTION SPECTROMETRY

17.1 INTRODUCTION

The basic absorption photometric system used in the kind of determinations treated in Chapter 16 is shown in Fig. 17.1. The diagram pictures a *single-beam* or single-channel device that requires separate observation of light transmitted by a blank, or reference, and a sample. This design and various modifications, the double-beam design, the Fourier transform spectrometer, the nondispersive photometer, and the reflectance spectrometer will be systematically considered in this chapter. Much background essential to the discussion was developed earlier. Important chapters were: 11 and 12, which treated basic optical modules; 10, which presented principles of physical optics; 1 and 8, which dealt with basic design and performance of instrument systems. Since amplifiers and electronic systems were considered at some length in Chapters 5–9, electronic aspects of photometers will be only mentioned here.

$$\text{Source} \Rightarrow \begin{array}{c} \text{Wavelength} \\ \text{isolation} \\ \text{device} \end{array} \Rightarrow \text{Sample} \rightarrow \text{Detector} \rightarrow \text{Amplifier} \rightarrow \text{Readout}$$

$$\updownarrow$$

$$\text{(Reference)}$$

Fig. 17.1 Line block diagram of a generalized absorption photometer. A signal-processing stage often appears between amplifier and readout. The wavelength isolation module and sample are sometimes interchanged.

Before we discuss different photometric instruments we must relate the performance of their modules to overall performance. Consider the static operation of the instrument shown in Fig. 17.1. The signal developed by the detector of an absorption photometer can be related to modular performance as follows:

$$\text{Signal} = [p(\theta, \lambda)m(\lambda)l(\theta, \lambda)]e^{-abc}[f(\theta)g(\lambda)]. \tag{17.1}$$

Each factor will be identified in turn. Discussion of the dynamic aspects of operation, e.g., those important in recording absorption curves, will be deferred to Sections 17.6 and 17.7. The factors within the first bracket are simply those collected in Beer's law as P_0, the power transmitted by a blank. Thus, $p(\theta, \lambda)$ is the power furnished by the source as a function of wavelength and solid angle θ subtended by the next module, $m(\lambda)$ is the efficiency of the wavelength isolator as a function of wavelength, and $l(\theta, \lambda)$ is the transmission of the blank. It is now desirable to rewrite Eq. (17.1) as

$$\text{Signal} = P_0 e^{-abc}[f(\theta)g(\lambda)]. \tag{17.2}$$

The exponential term that follows P_0 is the factor by which the sample reduces the power in the beam. Accordingly, $P_0\,e^{-abc}$ is just the power transmitted by a sample (Section 16.2). In the final bracket of Eq. (17.1), function $f(\theta)$ is a geometrical factor based on the solid angle of the transmitted radiation observed by the detector, and $g(\lambda)$ is a factor giving the efficiency of the detector as a function of the wavelength of radiation incident on it.

In order to use Eq. (17.1) or (17.2) in evaluating photometer performance recall that for a reliable measurement the signal should be as large as possible, or that in any event the signal-to-noise ratio should be large. Inspection of Eq. (17.2) indicates that P_0, the energy throughput of the optical system (Section 12.3), should be maximized.

Example Should a set of filters or a monochromator be used as a wavelength isolation device in a photometer that is to be used exclusively for quantitative determinations in the visible region? Since electronic transitions responsible for absorption in the visible in general give rise to broad absorption bands, a broad band pass wavelength isolator will be adequate. A set of filters would be adequate to ensure Beer's law performance, and would also provide maximum energy throughput. For reasons of versatility in measurement, however, a monochromator might be substituted and used with a wide entrance slit to secure comparable throughput.

Coupling optical modules. Once the modules for a photometric instrument are known they must be coupled in optimum fashion. Several questions arise. How can energy be transferred from one module to the next with minimum loss? What cross section beam is needed, and at what points must the power level be uniform across the beam? What considerations tend to decide whether the wavelength isolator X should precede the sample (in most instruments) or follow it (in IR instruments)? Arranging an efficient transfer of energy involves minimizing reflection, scattering, and absorption losses as well as excluding unwanted radiation (see Chapters 10 and 12).

It is important that a source have some area of essentially uniform high intensity. This area should be imaged on the entrance aperture of the wavelength isolator. Then, at later points in the system the uniformly illuminated entrance aperture can be imaged and reimaged by mirrors or lenses as frequently as a spot of uniform intensity is needed for good operation, providing optics have introduced no serious aberrations.* At points between images, however, the beam cross section will be nonuniform. Ordinarily intensity will be high at its center and will slowly drop to zero toward all sides.

Some common places where images of the entrance aperture are formed are at the site of any attenuator, e.g., a wedge in an optical null system, and at a detector. Further, a sample is usually located at an image point to take advantage of the small cross section a beam has at such a point. In this way small samples, and in some instances even microcells, can be accommodated with no further optics when desired.

It is the need to minimize stray radition that ordinarily governs whether sample or wavelength isolator is next to the source in a photometric system. When the most intense radiation from a source is at frequencies higher than those of interest, as in IR

---

* The use of front-surface off-axis mirrors for focusing can maximize energy transfer and keep aberrations low.

spectrometry, the order of modules is usually source–sample–monochromator. Higher frequencies are strongly scattered out of a beam (Section 10.10) and the intensity of unwanted radiation reaching the detector is reduced by this arrangement. On the other hand, in UV-VIS work, peak emission occurs at frequencies lower than those of interest and there is no reason not to place the monochromator first. Indeed, if a strongly scattering sample is to be examined, it may be advantageous to place the cell close to the detector so that light traversing the cell will not be lost. Insertion of a diffusing plate (opal glass) between cell and detector secures a uniform illumination of the detector.

17.2 VISUAL PHOTOMETERS (COLORIMETERS*)

Today the human eye finds very limited use as a photometric detector. The eye has too many disadvantages: limited spectral range, low accuracy in distinguishing intensities, high fatigue rate, and slow response. Undoubtedly, however, visual means will always be employed for spot tests for chemical species, some indicator end points, and rough color checks on concentrations.

Only one visual photometer type will be mentioned, the comparator manufactured by Helige, Inc., which utilizes several sets of standard glass filters. Each set is designed for a particular analysis and has several filters with the same absorption pattern but varying absorbance. A series of standard solutions was the precursor of this instrument. To determine the concentration of an unknown, the proper disc is inserted, and its filters are compared visually with the sample. Both must be illuminated by the same source. The filters are calibrated in terms of concentration for the path length of the sample cell supplied with the instrument, and when the best match with the unknown is found, the approximate concentration is immediately known. For example, the residual chlorine in city water supplies is often determined in this fashion. A sample of chlorinated water is inserted into the cell, mixed with a little o-tolidine to develop a characteristic green color, and compared with the appropriate set of filters. Most sets of glass filters match absorption curves only approximately, but an overall accuracy of perhaps $\pm 5\%$ is attainable.

17.3 FILTER PHOTOMETER

A useful nonscanning absorption photometer can be designed around a set of filters (Sections 11.5 and 11.6). Such instruments are simple and rugged. With a large energy throughput guaranteed by the filter, an amplifier is often unnecessary. A simple single-beam filter photometer is shown schematically in Fig. 17.2. Note that it includes a tungsten lamp energized by a constant voltage power supply as source, a guillotine wedge to control beam intensity, a filter (or a wheel of several filters), a slot to insert the sample cuvette, a moderately sensitive detector, and a rugged meter. Since it is direct-reading, under optimum conditions an accuracy of about $\pm 2\%$ in transmittance may be attained.

---

* The term *colorimeter*, sometimes broadly used to include all filter photometers, is here restricted to those devices in which the eye is used as a detector, since only the eye and brain can be said to detect color.

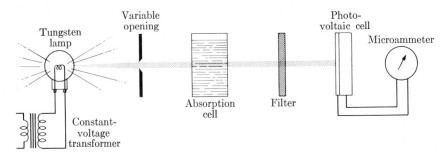

Fig. 17.2 Schematic of a simple photoelectric filter photometer.

Even this degree of reliability can be secured only if there are frequent resettings of the 100% T value by adjustment of the intensity control while the blank is in the beam. Drift in the performance of the components can be minimized in this fashion.

As implied in the example given in Section 17.1, since filters have an inherently large band pass, a filter photometer is ideal for quantitative analysis of a substance that has a broad absorption band in the visible or near UV (or gives one on complexation). It is likely to be much less effective in analyzing a substance that has only narrow absorption bands, particularly if there is interfering absorption. Naturally, the filter photometer cannot be used for qualitative analysis.

A double-beam arrangement (Section 17.5) and a null-balance output may be incorporated to minimize error from instability in source and other modules. Both beams will be affected similarly and effects should cancel. A schematic diagram of a filter photometer of this design is shown in Fig. 17.3. Note that a portion of the incident beam is deflected to a second photocell, and the currents produced by the two cells

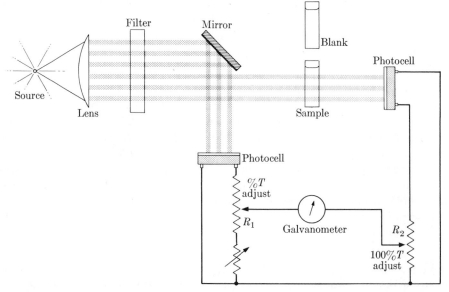

Fig. 17.3 Schematic diagram of a simple double-beam, null-balance filter photometer.

are brought into electrical balance. An initial balance is obtained with the blank in the measuring beam. Then it is replaced by the sample and the actual measurement made. The accuracy of observation with this design may be as good as $\pm 0.5\%$ T. As long as narrow band pass filters are used and a proper potentiometer or bridge output circuit is incorporated, slow fluctuations in source intensity are eliminated.

Automatic analyzers. Devices have been developed that automatically carry out many different photometric analyses on each of a large set of samples. Such instruments are invaluable in medical clinics where concentration levels of sodium, potassium, albumin, glucose, and other physiological constituents must be routinely determined on sample after sample. If a constituent cannot conveniently be determined by absorption photometry, provision is made to use another simple method. For example, concentrations of alkali and alkaline earth metals are usually found by flame emission photometry.

A straightforward way to develop such an instrument is to automate a filter photometer. Provision must be made for access to an individual optical filter for each photometric determination. A source, detector, amplifier (if necessary), and readout device are, however, sufficient. The arrangements must also include appropriate preparative features in which interfering species are separated or masked, dilutions are made, pH is adjusted, chromogenic reagents are added, etc. Indeed, the simple arrangement of the preparative aspects is a considerable challenge. Finally, an automatic analyzer should have access to information about standard solutions to permit a direct readout of concentrations. A good illustration of appropriate instrumentation is provided by the schematic diagram of a widely used automatic analyzer pictured in Fig. 17.4. Some of its main features are discussed below.

Example In the Technicon Autoanalyzer preparative steps, such as aliquoting, addition of reagents, dilution, mixing, and dialyzing (to remove protein), are carried out in a maze of tubing that resembles the track pattern of a railroad freight yard. Each main sample is subdivided into as many aliquots as there are components to be determined and these portions are kept separate by air bubbles. Amounts of chromogenic reagents or diluents added are regulated by proportional pumping. Finally, each channel incorporates a debubbler tee where the air bubble divider is removed. A sample then passes through a section of tubing of such a length that it fills the cell in its channel just as the cell slides into the (stationary) photometer. This type of multiple-cell, multiple-filter photometer is shown schematically in Fig. 17.4. To obtain a steady reading each cell remains in the light path about 20 s.

Of particular interest in Fig. 17.4 are the provisions for computation and readout. Two self-balancing potentiometers are used, one isolated from the other. Potentiometer 1 monitors the output of the sample photocell. Its servomotor balances the voltage developed across R_L^* against that produced in the main slidewire by the reference phototube. The null position is proportional to the transmittance. As the servomotor balances, it also drives a separate, logarithmically wound potentiometer that is energized to be opposite in polarity. Its output is thus proportional to $-\log T$, i.e., to absorbance.

In turn, the second self-balancing potentiometer receives this signal and balances it on a calibrated slidewire. Note the resistors labeled high and low standard adjust. One set appears in each measurement channel and is adjusted when standardizing solutions are introduced. In the instrument shown in the figure, the chart completes the "computation." It is preprinted so that a direct readout in concentration of each constituent is possible.

A widely used change in the arrangement of Fig. 17.4 is addition of a retransmitting slidewire to potentiometer 2 that sends the data to a digitizer and thence to a computer to make the calculations.

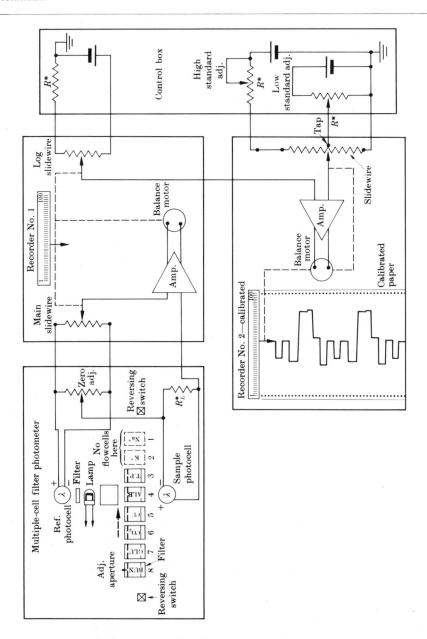

Fig. 17.4 Schematic diagram of an automatic multiple-cell, multiple filter photometer, the Technicon Autoanalyzer. Sample 4 is in position in the sample beam. Note the source (lamp), the individual filter that accompanies each sample cell, and the two photocell detectors. The reference beam is directed upward. (Courtesy of *Clinical Chemistry*.)

17.4 THE SPECTROPHOTOMETER

The incorporation of a monochromator (Chapter 12) as the wavelength isolation device distinguishes a spectrophotometer from simpler type photometers. The distinctive properties which result are operability at any wavelength over its spectral range and, usually, some flexibility in selecting the operating resolution and energy throughput. In general, the better the monochromator, the more versatile the spectrophotometer.

Other modules comprising a spectrophotometer should operate with comparable sensitivity and precision. In a single-beam instrument it is important that they be of high quality if precision is sought. The frequency with which the 100% setting will have to be checked for reliable operation will be strongly affected by stability of operation. A good discussion of single-beam designs will be found in Section 1.8.

Single-beam spectrophotometers are particularly well adapted to determining concentrations of substances alone or in simple mixtures. Yet since the majority are manually operated, they are not well suited to any type of qualitative analysis that requires observing an absorption spectrum over a wavelength range.

Direct-reading spectrophotometers are basically limited in reliability as a result of the lack of accuracy of their indicating meters (accuracies of $\pm 1\%$ of full-scale deflection are very good). As a result, they are usually constructed from components of moderate quality and seldom offer high sensitivity or resolution. By virtue of being direct-reading, however, they feature fast operation, and because of their simple design they are relatively inexpensive and require a minimum of maintenance. Where moderate accuracy (± 1 to $\pm 3\% T$) is acceptable, the direct-reading instruments are widely used.

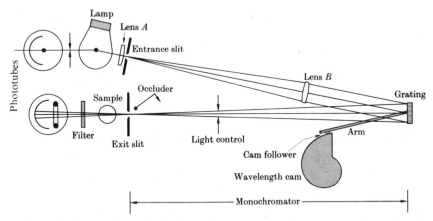

Fig. 17.5 Optical schematic of a single-channel grating spectrophotometer, the Bausch and Lomb Spectronic 20. The Regulated Model is shown. A constant voltage for the tungsten lamp (source) is ensured by a feedback system based on monitoring the lamp output by the upper phototube.

In the optical system the field lens focuses light from the entrance slit on the objective lens. This lens in turn provides a slit image at the exit slit. The filter in front of the measuring phototube (detector) passes only the visible range and blocks unwanted orders of spectra from the grating. To set the 100% transmittance reading the light control is adjusted with a blank in the beam in place of the sample. The 0% transmittance reading is established while the occluder blocks the beam by balancing a differential amplifier. (Courtesy of Bausch and Lomb, Inc.)

Example An optical schematic of the direct-reading manual Spectronic 20 spectrophotometer is given in Fig. 17.5. It has a fixed spectral slit width of 20 nm and is of moderate precision. Its range is limited to the visible (350 to 650 nm) but can be extended up to 900 nm in the near IR by the use of a red-sensitive phototube and a filter to reduce stray radiation. (See Section 5.6 for a discussion of its amplifier.)

To develop high precision in a single-beam spectrophotometer, a null readout must be incorporated (Section 1.8). In addition, stable components of high quality must be used. A *null circuit* is simply a potentiometer (Section 3.2) or a bridge circuit in which the dc signal from the amplifier is balanced against a known electrical signal. Accuracies as good as $\pm 0.2\%$ in transmittance can be obtained. Naturally, the cost of such an instrument is much greater, and measurements will usually require more time. Maintenance will be more difficult, but should be required infrequently. The versatility and reliability of the instrument will generally be high.

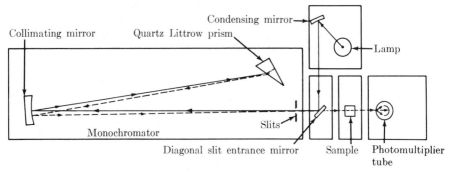

Fig. 17.6 Schematic optical diagram of the Beckman DU and DU-2 spectrophotometers. The desired wavelength is obtained by rotating the Littrow prism in the monochromator (cf. Fig. 12.8) on its mount. One slit is above the other in the monochromator and the exit beam passes over the top of the entrance mirror. (Courtesy of Beckman Instruments, Inc.)

Example A schematic optical diagram of the Beckman DU and DU-2 precision UV-VIS spectrophotometer is given in Fig. 17.6. Its Littrow monochromator uses a quartz prism. Its slits are adjustable and spectral slit widths as narrow as 0.5 nm can be obtained at 700 nm and 0.01 nm at 200 nm. A photomultiplier tube (UV and VIS) and a red-sensitive phototube (S–1 response for longer wavelengths in the visible and near IR) and two sources, a tungsten lamp and a hydrogen lamp, are required to cover the entire range from about 200 to 1000 nm. It features a null-balance output.

For photometric accuracies of the order of $\pm 0.2\%$ over a period of time, the light source and detector may require additional modification. The use of "optical feedback," i.e., monitoring the output of the source to obtain a signal that can be used to adjust the power it receives, is one method of securing effective long-term stability for a light source (Section 1.8). The nonlinearity of a detector with intensity must also be minimized. The best approach must be investigated for each type of detector.

17.5 DOUBLE-BEAM SPECTROPHOTOMETER

Whenever the transmission of a sample over a range of wavelengths or whenever automatic operation even at a fixed wavelength is of interest it is desirable to add a second channel to a spectrophotometer. Then one channel can permanently accommodate a reference or blank and the other the sample. By referring intermittently or continuously to the reference beam when making measurements of sample transmittance, errors that the blank is particularly designed to minimize are continuously compensated, as are errors that arise from slow fluctuations and drift in source intensity, detector response, and amplifier gain. The double-beam or double-channel spectrophotometer thus has distinctive areas of use that well justify its higher cost, greater complexity, and heavier maintenance requirements.

Immediate questions about design arise. Are two beams required throughout a double-beam spectrophotometer? What modes of comparing information in the beams give best results? In other words, how should the basic design of Fig. 17.1 be elaborated for double-beam operation? Since the need is ideally for a second *identical* channel, the most favorable arrangement is to:

1. Employ a single beam except in the sample-reference area;
2. Split the beam before it enters the sample-reference area and recombine beams at the detector;
3. Sample (measure) information in the two beams either alternately (a time-sharing procedure) or simultaneously (a space-sharing procedure).

Beam splitting.   The original beam can be split either in space or in time. If it is divided into two equal beams by letting it impinge on an appropriate arrangement of front surface mirrors, it is split in space. Since the energy in each of the resulting beams is half the original value, this approach is ordinarily infrequently used.

Alternatively, if beams are to be chopped, as is true in a time-sharing procedure, "splitting" is combined with modulation. One widely used means of accomplishing both tasks is through insertion of a rotating sector mirror. It alternately passes the beam (open sector) to one channel and reflects it (mirror sector) to the second. Each has pulses of light as bright as the original beam. A device with this arrangement is shown in Fig. 17.7. A second effective time-splitting approach is use of a vibrating mirror assembly.

Optical null readout.   To measure the absorption of a sample, intensities of sample and reference beams must be compared. Many spectrophotometers accomplish the task by an optical null procedure. This method is illustrated in Fig. 17.7. The two chopped beams fall alternately on the detector (note one method of recombining them in the figure) and are amplified. The response time of the detector must, of course, be shorter than the interval during which radiation from each beam falls on it. If intensities are identical, the amplifier has a dc output. Any difference in intensities will result in an ac signal of the frequency of chopping. This unbalance signal is further amplified and used to drive an optical wedge or attenuator into or out of the reference beam. A common design for an attenuator is a thin, flat metal comb with several precision shaped teeth whose width increases linearly with distance. The fraction of open space

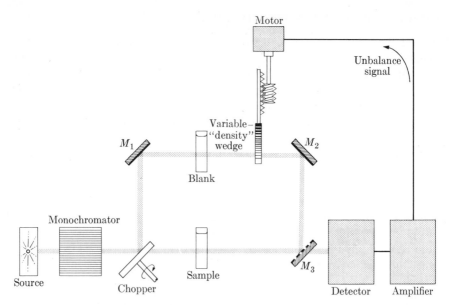

Fig. 17.7 Schematic diagram of an automatic, double-beam, optical null spectrophotometer. A servomotor is used to achieve automatic balancing. The readout is in effect the relative position of the variable density wedge.

a comb gives in a beam (% T) can be varied linearly by careful positioning. Note that the attenuator must be inserted at a point where the power level across the beam is uniform (Section 17.1).

The relation of beam intensities to the signal driving the wedge motor is shown in Fig. 17.8. Depending on the phase of the unbalance signal, the wedge is driven so as to increase or decrease the intensity of the reference beam until it equals that of the sample beam. Only when intensities in the beams are again identical is there no signal, and does the attenuator stop. Since the attenuator position is a measure of the relative absorption of the sample, by transmitting its position to a recording drum or a digital device the absorption is indicated.

Particular advantages of the optical null method are several. The detector is effectively utilized since it need determine only small differences in intensity. Further, a good signal-to-noise ratio is obtained; the possibility exists of using differential photometry; and the instrumentation required is relatively inexpensive. Some disadvantages are the moving parts, which wear with time, inertia in movement that frustrates a rapid response, and a relatively inaccurate response with low transmission samples since the energy throughput is severely reduced in both beams. A photometric accuracy of ± 1% is realizable with a calibrated wedge.

Ratio-recording readout. For photometric work of greater precision, especially at higher absorbances ($A \geq 1$), a ratio-recording procedure has the advantage over an optical null method. Two factors are involved. First, ratio recording allows use of electrical nulling with the inherent gain in accuracy that a long slidewire offers over positioning an attenuator in a small beam. Second, a good level of energy in the

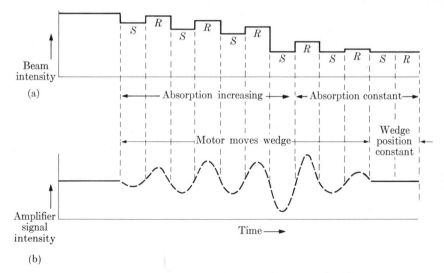

Fig. 17.8 Signals in double-beam, optical null spectrophotometer of preceding figure. (a) Intensity of beam at detector. S, sample beam. R, reference beam. (b) Unbalance signal from amplifier to servomotor driving the optical wedge. The ac signal (shown as a broken line) drives the motor at a speed determined by signal amplitude and in a direction determined by its phase.

reference beam can be maintained even when the sample transmittance is small. As a result, there is adequate energy to ensure efficient operation of the balancing motor.

In Fig. 17.9 a manually operated ratio-recording arrangement is shown schematically. Note that the output of the detector is sent alternately to the sample buffer circuit and the reference buffer circuit. Switching is synchronized with the rotation of the chopper sector mirror. The ratio of signals from these channels is nulled on the slidewire in the reference channel.

A final point in ratio recording is that the reference signal in electrical modules is frequently kept constant by a feedback loop that supplies a difference signal to control either monochromator slit width or the dynode voltage of the detector (if a photomultiplier detector is used).

Ratio recording is inherently easier in UV-VIS instruments than in IR spectrometers. In the UV and visible range there are fewer energy-limited situations, detectors are much faster, and narrow absorption bands are less common.

17.6 RECORDING SPECTROPHOTOMETERS

As long as a spectrophotometer has been set up as a double-beam instrument, it is scarcely worthwhile to stop without adding appropriate servomotors and developing a fully self-operative instrument. Only instruments that rely on dispersive monochromators will be considered here; interferometric spectrometers will be taken up in Section 17.12. A spectrophotometer that will automatically secure the transmission of a sample over a spectral range offers marked advantages for qualitative analytical studies. Quantitative studies, particularly of mixtures, are also facilitated by having the transmittance recorded at many wavelengths.

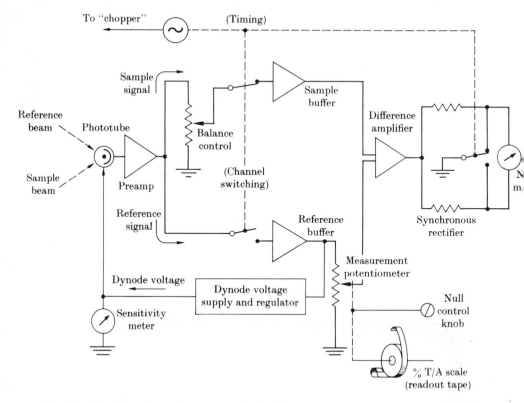

Fig. 17.9 Simplified schematic of a manual, double-beam, electrical null spectrophotometer, the Cary Model 16. In the optical portion of the device (not shown) the beam from the monochromator is alternately directed through sample and reference cells. Note the arrival of each beam at the detector. The amplified detector signal is directed by the synchronous vibrating channel switch, to the sample or reference measurement circuits. Note the buffer or isolating amplifiers. The current from the reference amplifier generates a voltage drop proportional to the reference signal in the measurement potentiometer slidewire. The signal in the sample circuit, which is ordinarily smaller because of absorption, is compared with this value. If there is an inequality between signals, a net ac signal appears at the difference amplifier, which accepts only ac of the chopper frequency. Its output is synchronously demodulated, filtered, and registered on the null meter. The operator moves the slidewire wiper until this meter registers zero; the wiper position then gives the sample transmission reading. (Courtesy of Cary Instruments.)

Almost all recording spectrophotometers are of double-beam design and all achieve automatic control by suitable use of servomotors. A very high degree of operational and calibrational stability must be designed into these devices for them to function with a minimum of operator control and also a minimum of maintenance. The components that must be made automatic in operation include: the wavelength drive, the slit control, the photometric balancing system, and the readout device. Usually, the motor that actuates the wavelength scan also drives either a digital indicator or the chart drive in the recorder. The "instructions" for the servomotor that controls the slit jaws are provided in most instances by a takeoff lever that rides a carefully shaped cam on the shaft of the wavelength drive. Further, the photometric balancing system supplies the signal to the pen of the recording potentiometer (Section 3.2) or to a digital output (Section 9.7). It is beyond the scope of the text to deal with servomotors and self-balancing systems [see Ref. 3 of Chap. 5]. A block diagram of a representative versatile optical null IR recording spectrophotometer is shown in Fig. 17.10.

Recording instruments are available for all ranges in the present analytical optical spectrum, which extends from the vacuum UV to the far IR (about 50 nm to 1000 μm). Most of these devices employ grating monochromators (Section 12.7), but a few employ a quartz prism monochromator. Nearly always a spectrophotometer is restricted to one spectral range such as the vacuum UV, UV-VIS, or IR.

17.7 OPTIMUM VALUES OF ADJUSTABLE PARAMETERS

In versatile, precision absorption spectrometers* one or more instrumental variables like slit width must be set by the operator. The list also includes: scanning speed, amplifier gain (sensitivity control), ordinate scale expansion, source intensity, and range of wavelengths to be scanned.† By what criteria can an operator decide on optimum values, i.e., settings that permit data of required precision to be obtained as quickly as possible? While the answer must finally be a particular one for each system, general principles can be sketched.

Slit width. Slit width appears to be the variable to consider first since slit width, resolution, and energy throughput are inseparably linked (Sections 12.2 and 12.3). Basically, the entrance (and exit) slits must be sufficiently narrow to ensure that resolution is adequate:

1. To separate closely adjacent absorption peaks;

2. To represent accurately the natural bandwidth (width at half maximum height) of each peak;

3. To render peak heights accurately.

The choice of a suitable slit width will, of course, depend on the character of the absorption curve sought. To generalize the treatment, assume first that an isolated absorption peak of Gaussian shape is to be scanned under conditions of good signal-to-noise ratio and scanning rate, a matter that will be described below. Consider further that the monochromator has a triangular slit function (see Fig. 12.4). It can be shown that under these conditions if the ratio of the spectral slit width to the bandwidth of the peak (at half height) $B_{1/2}$, is about 0.1, the spectrometer will report the peak height (and breadth) with no more than 0.5% error. The reliability of a measurement will decrease rapidly if the slit is widened; if $S/B_{1/2} = 0.5$, the apparent peak height will be about 90% of the true value; if the ratio is 1.0, the apparent peak height will be about 70% of the true value. The error in the molar absorptivity that

---

* Hereafter spectrometer will be used as synonymous with spectrophotometer.
† The choice of wavelength range need not be further examined. It will be dictated by the nature of the spectrum of each species of interest and possible interferences.

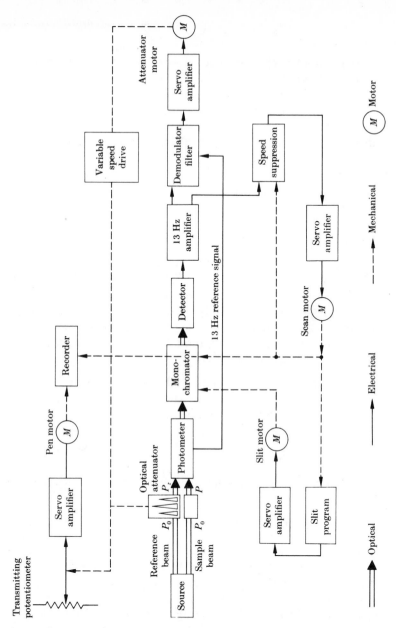

Fig. 17.10 Block diagram of Perkin-Elmer Models 421 through 621 double-beam, optical null IR spectrophotometers. A 13 Hz rotating sector mirror in the photometer module combines the beams after their traversal of sample and reference and directs them to the monochromator entrance slit. The detector is a thermocouple. When sample and reference beam intensities are equal a dc signal is presented to the 13 Hz amplifier. When intensities are unequal, a 13 Hz signal appears, is amplified, and is converted (arrangement not shown) by the demodulator-filter module to a 60 Hz signal. It powers the attenuator motor that drives an optical wedge in or out of the reference beam until reference and sample powers P_z and P are again equal. The wedge position is relayed mechanically to the transmitting potentiometer. Its output is directed to the servo amplifier that powers the pen motor and is recorded as a transmittance or absorbance. Note also the slit and wavelength scan (grating drive) motors. A strong difference signal from the detector amplifier reduces the speed of the scan and recorder motors. (Courtesy of Perkin-Elmer Corp.)

results is of the same magnitude though that in the integrated peak intensity (Section 16.3) is only half as large.

Example   It is desired to obtain a precise measurement on a broad absorption peak in the UV whose natural bandwidth is 21 nm. What slit setting should be used with an instrument whose reciprocal linear dispersion is 30 nm mm^{-1}?

First, using the criterion for adequate resolution given above, the spectral slit width should be $0.1 \times 21 = 2.1$ nm. Second, since the spectral slit width S is related (Section 12.2) to the geometrical slit width W by the expression $S = W \times D^{-1}$ where D^{-1} is the linear reciprocal dispersion, W can be found easily. One has $W = S/D^{-1} = 2.1/30 = 0.07$ mm. A slit opening of 0.07 mm (or less) can be used. Unless the source energy is quite limited (unlikely in the UV) or the solvent is strongly absorbing, there should be no problem in obtaining the measurement at a good signal-to-noise ratio.

But what slit width will be appropriate where no information is available as to the character of a spectrum? In this case, it is best to scan at different slit widths. The optimum value will be the widest setting that yields maximum peak heights and as deep valleys between peaks as possible. Naturally, complex spectra or very fine spectral details, such as shoulders on peaks, may be beyond the capacity of the mono-chromator of a given instrument to resolve no matter how narrow its slits. In this case, a spectrometer of higher inherent resolution is needed. A curve resolver may also be helpful.

Energy and photometric accuracy. A decision on slit width may also have to take into account whether beam energy will be adequate. Recall that narrowing a slit to improve resolution rapidly decreases beam energy, reduces the instrument signal-to-noise ratio (S/N), and decreases photometric accuracy.

Example   What is the energy "cost" of doubling spectrometric resolution? Can the loss be overcome by increasing slit height?

In Section 12.3 the relationship of geometrical slit width W and spectral slit width to beam energy was shown to be energy $\propto W^2h \propto S^2h$, where h is the slit height. To double resolution, the spectral slit width must be cut in half: thus, beam energy must be reduced by a factor of four.

According to the expression given, increasing the slit height will improve the energy through-put in direct proportion. Recall that in Section 12.3 it was also discussed that resolution will decrease as height increases much beyond 5 mm unless the monochromator has curved entrance slits.

Fortunately, a decision between resolution and energy is required only when beam energy is limited, whatever the reason. In the UV and VIS the question will arise infrequently since bright sources and very sensitive fast detectors are available. In the IR, because all sources are of low energy, the question is ever present. The appropriate decision is clear in two limiting cases:

1. In a survey scan of a spectrum, resolution can be traded off for energy to permit a fast scan since only the presence or absence of peaks is of interest;

2. In quantitative work the decision must be made in favor of energy since a good value of S/N is essential. The value of S/N can sometimes be maintained at an adequate level without serious loss of resolution simply by reducing noise.

Example   In a quantitative determination of concentration by absorption photometry resolution can ordinarily be sacrificed for energy. A working curve (A vs. c) will nearly always be required under these circumstances since Beer's law may not hold.

Two factors may make it impossible to sacrifice resolution in quantitative work: spectral interference with a sample peak and fine detail in an absorption spectrum that is being precisely determined. In these cases since the signal energy has been reduced, the best strategy is to lower noise by a larger factor by going to a longer response time (see below) and slower scan.

If the process of obtaining adequate resolution has reduced photometric accuracy below a tolerable level, at least three instrumental means to improve S/N are available even at a fixed wavelength. First, it may be worthwhile to increase source intensity. Either a brighter source can be used, if available, or current in the original source can be made greater. The latter will of course lead to a seriously shortened lifetime.*

Second, it may be feasible to substitute a monochromator of comparable theoretical resolution but higher efficiency, i.e., greater energy throughput. An alternative is substitution of a double monochromator with its higher dispersion. For example, if the dispersion is doubled, a slit twice as wide will give the same resolution but yield a beam with four times the energy.†

Third, time constants of the associated electronics can be increased. Even with an inadequate value of S/N the effect of observing the beam for a longer interval will be to diminish noise as it averages to zero. Thus, $S/N \propto \tau^{1/2}$, where τ is the longest time constant of the system. Alternatively, an auxiliary signal-averaging stage or other signal "extracting" device can be added (Section 8.5).

Compensation for the often drastic energy decreases produced by solvent absorption or cell window absorption may also be incorporated. In this case, the reference signal is monitored and automatically used to signal a slit servo system to open the slit sufficiently to maintain a constant dc reference signal. In a ratio-recording readout (discussed in the last section) it is likely that this adjustment will be made automatically. An alternative arrangement is to increase the amplification of the reference signal. For example, if a photomultiplier detector is used, greater amplification can be secured by increasing dynode voltage. Since the noise level is also raised by an increase in gain the maintenance of a proper S/N depends upon selecting a suitable slit width at the beginning.

Scanning speed.   An appropriate choice of scanning speed must also be made or the precision already secured by a good decision about slit width may be lost unneces-

---

* The trade-off of intensity for life is likely to be more attractive for VIS-UV sources. It is less effective for IR sources since brightness at wavelengths far from the intensity maximum increases only linearly with absolute temperature.

† Interferometric spectrometry with its higher beam energy (Section 17.12) tends to be especially attractive under these conditions. This type of spectrometer is presently available for the IR.

sarily. Automatically recorded spectra can be accurate only if both the "static" sources of error already considered and the "dynamic" sources of error that arise from the finite response time of an instrument system are minimized.

Usually the fastest scanning speed is sought that will permit a desired spectral resolution and accuracy to be secured. Slit width and monochromator design will establish the maximum resolution attainable. During scanning, however, there will be an interplay of dynamic factors such as the time constant of the electronics (e.g., the amplifier, the time constant of the optical wedge or ratio-recording wiper, the recorder pen or digital readout, and the wavelength scanning speed). As a result, resolution is often limited by rates of instrument response during scanning and not by optics.

Some definitions are in order. Any electronic system requires a certain time interval to respond fully to a signal. To the degree that its response follows an exponential path, the rate of response may be stated in terms of its *time constant* τ, which is the interval required for a 63% or $1 - 1/e$ response when a sudden signal (step function) is received at the detector. Modular response may also be stated in terms of a response time, which is an interval equal to four time constants. Within a time equal to 4τ, a 98% response will be achieved. Accordingly, the maximum scanning speed that will allow the inherent instrumental resolution to be realized can be defined as

$$\text{Speed} = S/4\tau,$$

where S is the spectral slit width.

Example An IR spectrometer whose band pass or spectral slit width is 1 cm^{-1} and whose time constant is 0.1 s is available. What is the maximum scanning speed that will allow the inherent resolution to be realized?

According to the above equation the speed is

$$1 \text{ cm}^{-1}/4 \times 0.1 \text{ s} = 2.5 \text{ cm}^{-1} \text{ s}^{-1}.$$

If one is to scan a spectrum from 4000 to 2000 cm^{-1} (2.5 to 5 μm), the time required will be $2000/2.5 = 800$ s, or about 13 min.

A straightforward check to ensure that dynamic error has been minimized is to compare a spectrum run at the desired speed with one run at one-fourth that speed. If peak heights differ by less than 0.02 absorbance units, the desired speed is satisfactory.

Example A versatile optical-null IR pen recording spectrometer that has been used for spectral surveys (fast scan) is to be reprogrammed for quantitative analysis. In the survey mode it is known to have a value of S/N of about 300, a scan time of 15 min for the range 4000 to 200 cm^{-1}, and an attenuator response time of 3 s. What adjustments should be made to shift to conditions of high quantitative accuracy?

First, resolution may be traded off for energy. Doubling its S/N and beam energy will be desirable. The slit width should be increased $(600/300)^{1/2} \simeq 1.4$ times. Now the amplifier gain

---

* In general either the time constant of the readout or that of the amplifier will be limiting. This figure can then be cited as the overall response time.

can be reduced by about a factor of two; if this change is not made, the recorder response will be too strong.

Second, the desired increase in recording accuracy can be assured by decreasing scan speed by a factor of about two. Note that recording accuracy could also have been increased by decreasing the response time by a factor of two. To have used this adjustment, however, would also have increased the photometric noise and offset the gain of opening the slits wider.

Third, since slits have been opened somewhat, it will be important to select as broad a band for the analysis as possible. The $\Delta\sigma_n/\Delta\sigma_s$ should be five to ten or greater if possible, where $\Delta\sigma_n$ is the bandwidth of the analytical peak and $\Delta\sigma_s$ the spectral slit width.

Most spectrometers provide several scanning speeds. Surveys can be made at fast speeds and careful studies at slow ones. Some instruments feature a time-saving arrangement that does not sacrifice resolution or photometric accuracy known as a *speed suppression* system. It allows fast scanning in spectral regions where there is little absorption but greatly slows the scan whenever absorption begins to occur. Such an arrangement is advantageous: it gives quality spectra, conserves time, and yet does not greatly increase mechanical complexity.

Scale expansion. In either regular or differential analysis it is often necessary to examine bands that are too faint for use with the regular photometric scale. For this reason ordinate expansions of up to 10 or more times the regular scale are provided. Since increasing the pen deflection for a particular change in absorption multiplies both signal and noise by the same factor, scale expansion is ordinarily accomplished by adjustments to increase the recorded S/N as described above.

Example An ordinate scale expansion of 5× is desired for a scan over the 1400–1200 cm^{-1} range. The expansion is selected by switch. It is then necessary to reduce the noise and scanning speed by about this factor to secure accuracy under expanded conditions comparable to that under regular conditions.

Under conditions of scale expansion, it is transmittance changes between the start of the region of expanded scan and a point of interest that are observed. To find the true transmittance with a 5× expansion, these changes must be divided by five. Then they can be added to (or subtracted from) the actual transmittance at the start of the scan to secure the true figure at the point of interest.

17.8 MULTIPLE INTERNAL REFLECTION ASSEMBLY

In most instances internal reflection spectrometry is carried out with a standard spectrophotometer by substituting an appropriate multiple reflection assembly for the regular sample cell. A representative arrangement is shown in Fig. 17.11. A dual mirror system reduces the size of the already converging beam sufficiently rapidly for it to enter easily the aperture of the reflection plate. The sample whose absorption is sought is pressed tightly against the side(s) of the plate. During each internal reflection at the plate-sample boundary, the beam penetrates a minute distance into the sample (Section 10.9). As a result, radiation is absorbed at wavelengths characteristic of the sample. After the beam emerges from the plate a second dual-mirror system directs

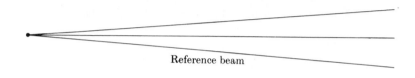

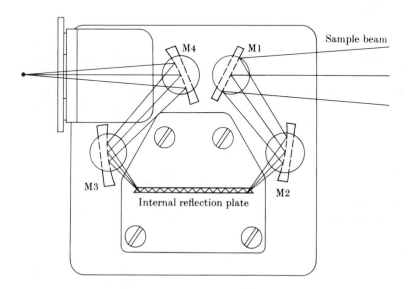

Fig. 17.11 Optical schematic of Wilkes Scientific Model 9 multiple internal reflection attachment. Many total reflections at the plate-sample interface lead to production of an absorption spectrum characteristic of the sample. (Courtesy of Wilkes Scientific Co.)

it to the next module. Precision optics must be used to redirect the beam in this manner without defocusing, altering angular spread, or displacing it.

More versatile arrangements are also available that permit use of double sampling plates, plates of varying length, and a wide range of angles of incidence. In general, such devices also permit specular reflection measurements, e.g., on selected faces of single crystals, or determination of the thickness of epitaxial films.

Internal reflection plate. A choice of a suitable transparent material for an internal reflection plate depends on the spectral range in which it will be used, relative physical properties desired (e.g., hardness, solubility), and the sample(s) to be studied. The material must, of course, have a higher refractive index than the sample over the spectral range. It should be of high purity, since the typical path length in a reflection plate is of the order of 70 mm (as opposed to 2 to 5 mm through a conventional window). Some commonly used substances are listed in Table 17.1. Other factors such as the orientation of a crystal and its type must also be considered in preparation of a plate.

Table 17.1 Properties of Some Materials Useful for Internal Reflection Plates

Substance	Refractive Index (mean)	Range of Transparency, μm	Hardness	Resistance to Chemicals
KRS-5	2.5	0.6–40	Soft	Poor
Germanium	4.0	2–12	Brittle	Excellent
Silver bromide	2.2	0.45–30	Soft	Good
Aluminum oxide	1.7	0.22–4.5	Hard	Inert
Magnesium oxide	1.7	0.35–7.0	Hard	Inert

One of the most desirable substances for work in the IR is KRS-5 (thallium bromide-iodide). It transmits beyond 25 μm, has a mean refractive index of 2.5, and takes an excellent polish. Unfortunately, it has poor chemical resistance and is soft. Perhaps the next best IR material is germanium, which has an index of 4, but is brittle and absorbs at wave numbers smaller than 870 cm^{-1} (11.5 μm). For UV, VIS, or near IR spectrometric work both aluminium and magnesium oxides are ideal.

Two requirements limit the range of useful shapes for internal reflection elements:

1. Reflecting faces should be planar to give predictable angles of internal reflection, and

2. Entrance and exit surfaces should be beveled to permit normal incidence and emergence and thus eliminate refraction.

It is important that the reflecting surfaces be precisely parallel (since after multiple reflections the exit beam is easily deflected from the desired direction) and highly polished (for scattering losses can dissipate energy quickly).

Figure 17.12 suggests several shapes for internal reflection elements. The proper ratio of length to thickness insures that the central ray will enter and leave via the middle of the entrance and exit apertures and avoids the problem of split beams. Actually, the ratio is not critical, since the angle of incidence can be altered if necessary. Common lengths are about 5 cm, and common thicknesses from 1 to 2 mm.

The quality of an internal reflection plate is customarily assessed by measuring its transmittance as a function of wavelength with air on either side. Under these conditions the chief loss should arise from reflection on entrance and emergence. For example, a KRS-5 plate in good condition should show a constant transmission of about 40% over the range of its transparency. The presence of internal or external impurities or of surface roughness in a plate is indicated by transmittance changes. Thus, a useful rule of thumb is that surfaces need repolishing when there are 10–20% changes in transmittance as a function of wavelength.

17.9 RAPID-SCANNING SPECTROMETER

By incorporating a mirror that can be oscillated, or rotated, quickly and reproducibly through a certain arc (or distance in an interferometer) it is possible to scan limited wavelength ranges many times per second.*

A rotating refractor plate can be used in lieu of a moving mirror. In general

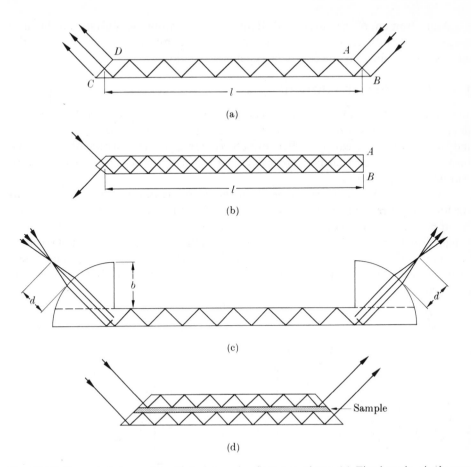

Fig. 17.12 Several designs of multiple internal reflectance plates. (a) Fixed-angle, single-pass plate. AB is the entrance aperture, CD the exit aperture. The entire plate is filled by light. (b) A double-pass plate (note total internal reflection at AB). This plate is more easily aligned than plate (a) because of the common focal point for entrance and exit beams. It may be dipped in liquids or inserted into special environments. (c) Variable-angle plate employing a quarter round entrance and exit aperture. Best results are secured with entrance beam focused at distance d as shown. The distance is defined by $d = r/(n - 1)$ where r is the radius of the quarter round and n its refractive index. (d) Capillary internal reflection cell for samples as small as $10\,\mu l$.

repetitive scanning over a range of about 200 cm^{-1} can be carried out in times as short as $200\,\mu s$ per scan.

    Clearly, the other modules needed to complete a rapid scanning spectrometer are those specified in Fig. 17.1. In particular, the detector should be sensitive and have a very short response time and the source should be intense and stable. To achieve the fast readout demanded by the apparatus, an oscilloscope can be employed. The optics of such an instrument are shown schematically in Fig. 17.18.

---

* Since a fixed slit width is dictated in fast-scanning dispersive instruments, most such devices rely on a grating as the dispersing element in order to secure an essentially constant spectral slit width.

An instrument of this sort is well adapted to the continuous analysis of a chemical system for one or perhaps several components. For example, it offers some particular advantages in following the course of a chemical reaction.

17.10 NONDISPERSIVE PHOTOMETERS

In routine analyses for one particular component, it is possible to omit the dispersing device and still obtain precise, *quantitative* data. For example, the IR absorption of industrial process streams is often monitored for a single constituent by a non-dispersing photometer. Such an apparatus is rather inexpensive and rugged compared with laboratory devices.

In one type of nondispersion photometer, a double-beam arrangement permits the total power transmitted by the sample cell to be compared with that of an identical beam passing through both sample cell and a reference cell filled with the substance sought. The transmitted radiation in each beam is then absorbed by a pair of receivers forming arms of a Wheatstone bridge (Section 3.3). The point of balance is indicative of the concentration of the sought constituent in the sample. A sketch of this kind of instrument is given in Fig. 17.13.

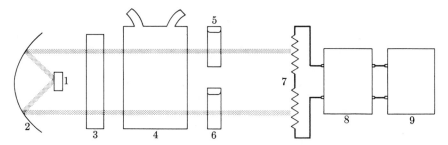

Fig. 17.13 A representative negative nondispersive infrared analyzer. 1, source. 2, spherical focusing mirror. 3, interference cell. 4, sample cell. 5, reference cell (filter cell). 6, compensator cell. 8, bridge incorporating bolometers (7) as arms. 9, recorder.

Interferences are a special problem, and the two additional cells 3 and 6, shown in Fig. 17.13, are intended to suppress them. When substances are present whose absorption patterns overlap that of the substance sought, a variation in their concentrations is likely to be detected as an alteration in the concentration of the substance being analyzed for. By putting a suitable concentration of the interferents in cell 3, the energy that these are capable of absorbing is removed ahead of time in reproducible fashion. In severe cases, an appropriate concentration of the interfering substance can also be placed in the compensator cell; the result is a greatly reduced differential sensitivity to the part of the spectrum where interference occurs.

17.11 PHOTOMETRIC TITRATION EQUIPMENT

Relatively few changes are necessary to adapt an absorption photometer to the monitoring of titrations. Whether a filter photometer or a spectrophotometer is used depends on the system being titrated, i.e. whether a narrow waveband is required for sensitive end-point detection. (See p. 665 for an analogous type of titrator.)

17.12 FOURIER TRANSFORM SPECTROMETERS

In the Fourier transform or interferometric type of spectrometer a two-beam, variable-path-length interferometer is used in lieu of a monochromator.* The name Fourier transform spectrometry describes the use of such a device since its output is not regular spectral data but the Fourier transform of the data. Such instruments are becoming increasingly important, especially in IR spectrometry. The key advantage of this type of spectrometer over a conventional dispersive instrument is that in many energy-limited situations it offers a superior signal-to-noise ratio. The gain results from the fact that in an interferometric unit

1. Energy throughput is inherently greater (no entrance slit is required) and
2. All wavelengths present reach the detector during the entire time required to observe a spectrum.

The behavior just described may be contrasted with that of an ordinary dispersive spectrometer. In a dispersive device an entrance slit greatly reduces energy throughput (Section 12.3) and a particular wavelength is observed only during the brief interval in which it is incident on the exit slit and detector. If much of a spectral scan is given over to observation of frequencies at which there is no net absorption (or emission), the process is inefficient. Taken singly or together, the two factors cited allow the Fourier transform spectrometer to realize an appreciable improvement in performance in energy-limited situations. Three such cases are readily identifiable: measurements with weak sources, e.g., studies of IR absorption or emission processes; determination of high-resolution spectra where band pass must be severely narrowed; and very rapid scanning of spectra. The extent of exhancement possible is examined in more detail at the end of this section.

Design. A Fourier transform spectrometer is nearly always constructed around an interferometer whose path length can be varied in known and systematic fashion. The interferometer is coupled to a detector and a computer that reduces the data to an ordinary spectral curve. The composite instrument can be represented by the line block diagram of Fig. 17.14. Since the interferometer is basically the only new module it is the only instrumentation module that is further considered.

In Fig. 17.15 a schematic diagram of a Michelson interferometer is shown. Radiation from source S falls on beam-splitter plate O where it is either reflected (at the back surface) toward mirror M_1 or transmitted to mirror M_2. After reflection

Mirror drive   Amplifier → Computer → Readout

↓   ↑

Source ⇒ Interferometer ⇒ Sample ⇒ Detector

Fig. 17.14 Line block diagram of a Fourier transform spectrometer.

---

* Interferometric spectrometers of the Fabry–Perot type (Section 11.6) are made but are relatively uncommon.

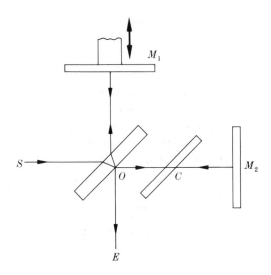

Fig. 17.15 Optical schematic of a Michelson interferometer. The beam incident from source S is divided into two rays by beam-splitter plate O. The rays are reflected by mirror M_1 and M_2 and recombined at O, where they interfere. In spectrometric scanning, mirror M_1 is moved up and down slowly.

from the separate mirrors the beams recombine at O and emerge as a single beam E. In general, since there will be a difference in optical paths OM_1O and OM_2O interference will result on recombination. If plate O is optically "thick" a compensator plate C is inserted to equalize optical path lengths (see Section 10.15).

Consider that a detector is placed at E and source S is monochromatic. As the two beams interfere at O, darkness or light will result and be sensed by the detector. Destructive interference occurs whenever the path difference is exactly $\lambda/2$. If mirror M_1 is slowly moved, a series of bright and dark bands termed *interference fringes* will sweep across the detector. With a continuous source very many wavelengths will be present simultaneously, and a complex pattern will be obtained. In any case, the record of the detector signal as a function of the path difference is called an *interferogram*. If several frequencies are present simultaneously, the spectral output at the detector will be complex and is said to be *multiplexed*. A typical interferogram is illustrated in Fig. 17.17e.

For spectrophotometric use it is only necessary to mount mirror M_1 on a carriage driven by a precision lead screw and couple an electric motor to the drive by a gear transmission. To interpret the detector signal the position of M_1 at all times must be known. As Michelson showed, the interference pattern, when the path difference between beams is varied, is simply the *Fourier transform* of the incident spectrum.

At least two other forms of interferometer have also been employed. One is the Fabry–Perot design. It is based on the repeated reflections a diverging beam undergoes between a pair of parallel, highly reflecting plates called an etalon. It is closely related to the Fabry–Perot interference filter (Section 11.6). In the pattern created on the far side of the device any fringe can be directly scanned to extract a spectrum. The system's simplicity is a marked advantage, but its extremely exacting optical and mechanical requirements appear to make it impossible to realize more than a fraction of its theoretical potential.

The *lamellar grating interferometer* developed by John D. Strong is a two-beam device that may be used in an Ebert mounting [page 432 of 7, Chapter 10]. One set of parallel strip mirrors is slid in and out with respect to a stationary set. Interference occurs between rays reflected from the two different sets of mirrors. Again an interferogram is obtained that on Fourier transform yields a regular spectrum.

Fourier transform spectroscopy. In Fig. 17.16 a block diagram is given for a Michelson type of interference spectrometer. Note that the optical system is now represented by a single module termed the optical head. Basically, the interferometer of Fig. 17.15 is enclosed in a central chamber that is evacuated to eliminate atmospheric absorption. If the instrument is intended for use in the far IR, beam-splitter plate B is likely to be Mylar or polyethylene, either of which transmits well in this range. More conventional materials will be needed for work at wavelengths shorter than 25 μm. Compensator plate C equalizes losses (by reflection and transmission) between the two beams. After beam recombination, radiation is modulated and focused by mirrors onto the sample and then transmitted to a detector.

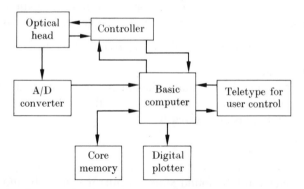

Fig. 17.16 Modular diagram of a Block Engineering Model FTS-14 Fourier transform infrared spectrometer. The interferometric system is located in the optical head module. Its output signal is amplified and digitized by the wide dynamic range analog-to-digital (A/D) converter. The basic computer (central module) carries out the Fourier transformation necessary to yield a regular spectrum. Prior to computation, while data are accumulating, it also controls the operation of the spectrometer.

If mirror M_1 moves about 10^{-4} m s^{-1}, the detector output will be in the audiofrequency range when IR radiation is incident. In other words, the interferometer modulates light of about 10^{14} Hz in such a way that an audiofrequency output is obtained.

Commonly the mirror is driven once through its fixed displacement, an arrangement termed *aperiodic* scanning, since there is no repetition. In this method the spectrum is ordinarily scanned slowly enough to average noise (from source fluctuations and other factors) to an acceptable minimum. The resulting interferogram is finite and ends abruptly. Exacting mechanical specifications must be met to ensure that a smooth, steady movement of the mirror is achieved. In some instruments multiple "scans" are achieved by use of a saw-tooth frequency to drive the mirror through its displacement repeatedly, a type of scanning termed *periodic*.

It is essential the mirror position be known at all times in order to correlate path difference with the interferogram. Since mechanical drives seldom produce a constant velocity, an ingenious way to learn where the mirror is calls for addition of an essentially monochromatic line, e.g. from a laser, to the interferometer beam. The fringe pattern (see Fig. 17.17a) superposed on the interferogram can be monitored to determine position.

In order to reduce the data obtained from the interference spectrometer to an actual spectrum, complex calculations are required that are best handled by computer. What must be accomplished is a translation of the interferogram, a curve in which intensity is expressed as a function of distance, into an optical spectrum, a curve in which intensity is displayed as a function of frequency. This type of conversion is often described as a transformation from the time domain to the frequency domain. There are several steps in the process. First, an exact mathematical analysis leads to the following equations. One is for the difference function $F(x)$, which is defined in terms of $I(x)$, the radiant intensity incident on the detector for path difference x, and $I(0)$, the intensity incident when $x = 0$. It can be shown that $F(x)$ is given by

$$F(x) = I(x) - \tfrac{1}{2}I(0) = \int_{-\infty}^{+\infty} I(v) \cos 2\pi x v \, dv, \tag{17.3}$$

where v is the frequency.

Since $I(v)$ is a function that generates the optical spectrum sought, Eq. (17.3) must be solved for $I(v)$. What makes the step possible is that $I(v)$ is the Fourier transform of $F(x)$. Their interrelationship is given by

$$I(v) = \int_{-\infty}^{+\infty} F(x) \cos 2\pi v x \, dx. \tag{17.4}$$

It should now be apparent that some way to simplify the mechanical operation of the interferometer must be found since its mirror cannot be moved an infinite distance as required by Eq. (17.4). Nor can an infinite frequency range be observed by the detector as implied by Eq. (17.3). Actually, any simplifications will also make the computation required by Eq. (17.4) more feasible. The computation may be further simplified by substituting a summation for the prescribed integration and summing only over a finite distance interval.

Second, specifications for the mechanical operation of the Fourier transform spectrometer and for the computation process can be obtained by applying information theory. The result is a set of criteria to be met. They are

1. The moving mirror in the interferometer must be driven precisely to generate a sufficiently long path difference x. The resolution or band pass $\Delta\sigma$ (in cm^{-1}) that can be realized is defined by $\Delta\sigma = 1/x$.

2. In computation an appropriate function, called an *apodizing function*, should be applied to control the rate of truncation of the interferogram and improve resolution further. Line shape and spurious fine structure at the base of a line are affected.

3. To carry out the necessary summation, the interferogram must be sampled at appropriately small, uniform distance intervals. If the spectral range of interest is 1 cm^{-1} to σ_{max}, the sampling interval Δx must be just $\Delta x = (2\sigma_{max})^{-1}$.

4. To avoid generation of an ambiguous spectrum that partially folds over on itself the maximum wave number in the instrument must be limited to σ_{max}.*

In Fig. 17.17 the effect of applying criteria (1) and (2) is illustrated for the case of a monochromatic source. While this example is the simplest possible one, the results show clearly the effect of distance of mirror movement on resolution and of the application of two types of apodizing functions. Other such functions are used also. [See Chapter 8 in Ref. 2 of Chapter 12.]

Example It is desired to obtain an IR spectrum from 1 to 250 cm^{-1} with a resolution of 0.2 cm^{-1} by use of a Fourier transform spectrometer. What settings should be used on the spectrometer? First, the desired resolution defines the maximum path difference x that must be generated. Since $\Delta\sigma = 0.2 \text{ cm}^{-1}$, where $\Delta\sigma = 1/x$,

$$1/x = 0.2 \text{ cm}^{-1} \quad \text{and} \quad x = 5 \text{ cm}.$$

The mirror must be driven half this distance or 2.5 cm.

Second, while the mirror is moving, the intensity incident on the detector must be sampled at precisely equal intervals Δx given by

$$\Delta x = 1 \div 2 \times 250 \text{ cm}^{-1} = 2 \times 10^{-3} \text{ cm}.$$

Finally, it may be anticipated that the number of sampling points will be given by $x/\Delta x = 2\sigma_{max}/\Delta\sigma$. In this example the number of points is simply

$$500 \text{ cm}^{-1}/0.2 \text{ cm}^{-1} = 2500.$$

Improvement in signal-to-noise ratio.   The energy throughput increase cited earlier results of course in an improvement in signal-to-noise ratio (S/N). When a source illuminates the entire instrument aperture, energy at the detector is often increased about 100 times. Noise also increases, however, and the gain is S/N must be determined in each case.

What further enhancement in S/N is realized by a Fourier spectrometer from the *multiplex advantage*, i.e., the fact that all frequencies are viewed simultaneously? In a dispersive instrument only one spectral slit width $\Delta\lambda$ is passed at a given λ setting. Each such slit width is observed for an interval of t seconds during a linear wavelength or a linear wave number scan. The signal from the detector is therefore proportional to the time t. If resistor noise dominates the noise output of the detector, as with a thermal detector, and is white or random in character, the noise output of the detector will be proportional to $t^{1/2}$. Thus, in a dispersive spectrometer S/N is proportional to $t/t^{1/2}$, that is to $t^{1/2}$.

---

* The term *aliasing* is often applied to the overlap. Each possible spectrum is called an alias of the principal one. The effect arises from the periodic sampling, which causes false signals of wave number $n(2\sigma_{max}) - \sigma$ to be generated, where n is a small integer and σ is the true wave number observed in the Fourier transform.

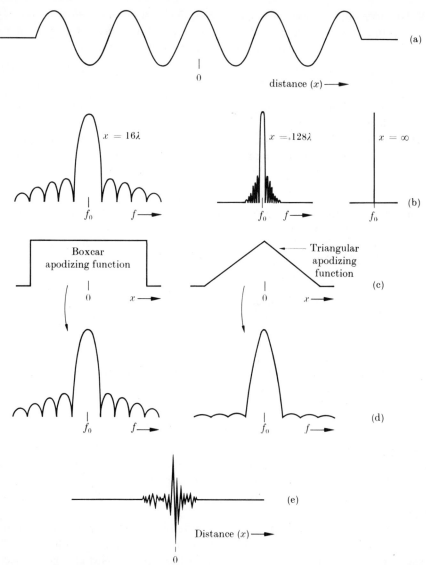

Fig. 17.17 Interferograms, apodizing functions, and Fourier transforms of interferograms. (a) Interferogram for a monochromatic source of frequency f_0. The interferogram is defined by a cosine wave and corresponds to the fringe pattern usually seen in an interferometer. Only a short section of the actual infinite wave that is obtained by moving the interferometer mirror from path difference $-x$ to path difference $+x$ is shown. (b) Fourier transforms of the interferogram in (a). At the left the transform obtained when the mirror is moved a distance corresponding to a path difference of 16 wavelengths is shown. Next is the interferogram obtained for movement through 128 wavelengths. At the right is given the transform that would be obtained from an infinite interferogram. (c) Graphical representation of two common truncating or apodizing functions that are applied to interferograms. (d) Fourier transforms of the $x = 16$ wavelength interferogram above using different apodizing functions. (e) An interferogram of a multifrequency spectrum. The large central maximum contains most of the information about the background intensity and the "wings" define spectral peaks.

In an interferometric spectrometer, all wavelengths fall on the detector simultaneously. If the interval cited for a spectral slit width, t seconds, is required to obtain an interferogram, the situation for a particular frequency is unimproved over that of the dispersive device. But a dispersive instrument that scans a spectral region X spectral slit widths broad will require Xt seconds. When this interval is also used for the interferometric instrument, effectively X times longer measurements of each wavelength are made than in the comparable dispersive scan. If the earlier assumptions about the detector hold, the interferometer realizes from this multiplex advantage an enhancement in S/N of $X^{1/2}$.* This gain is also termed Fellget's advantage.

Spectral range. While interference spectrometers are at present more often used in the IR, it should be clear that they may be employed in any portion of the EM spectrum. Whether such a spectrometer should be developed or used in other regions usually depends on how badly its greater energy throughput is needed. Its other main asset, the multiplex advantage, may well be lost, as will be seen below. Both advantages are realized by the interferometric spectrometer in the far IR, in IR emission studies, and in IR studies of the atmosphere of other planets. To realize the energy throughput advantage a source must give an image sufficiently large to fill the aperture of the instrument. For example, to gain the advantage in viewing a star, a large telescope is required.

In the visible and UV source intensity is usually adequate, but energy reaching the detector may be limited by the speed of scan required or for a dispersive instrument, by the requirement of a very narrow band pass to obtain high resolution. For such applications, the Fourier transform instrument offers an advantage whenever a determination cannot conveniently be repeated many times or it is desired to shorten the time of measurement.

REFERENCES

The titles listed at the ends of Chapters 11, 12, and 16 should be consulted as well as the sources below.

Discussions mainly restricted to optimization of system performance and sources of error are:

1. Lee Cahn, "Some Observations Regarding Photometric Reproducibility between Ultraviolet Spectrophotometers," *J. Opt. Soc. Am.* **45**, 953 (1955)
2. A. B. Calder, *Evaluation and Presentation of Spectro-Analytical Results.* New York: Macmillan, 1960
3. Cary Instruments, *Optimum Spectrophotometer Parameters.* Application Report AR 14-2. Monrovia, Calif.: Cary Instruments, 1964
4. A. E. Martin, "The Accuracy of Infrared Intensity Measurements," *Trans. Faraday Soc.* **47**, 1182 (1951)

---

* If a detector whose noise increases proportionately with an increase in signal level is used, the multiplex advantage is lost. For example, the noise (shot noise) of a photomultiplier tube increases in this fashion.

Discussions mainly restricted to instrumentation and components are available in:

5. H. H. Cary and A. O. Beckman, "A Quartz Photoelectric Spectrophotometer," *J. Opt. Soc. Am.* **31**, 682 (1941)
6. Wilbur Kaye, "Near-Infrared Spectroscopy. II. Instrumentation and Technique," *Spectrochim. Acta* **7**, 181 (1955)
7. S. Z. Lewin, "Photometers and Colorimeters (and Spectrophotometers)," *J. Chem. Educ.* **37**, A197, A271, A341, A401, A455, A507, A637, A781 (1960); **38**, A5, A71 (1961)
8 Peter F. Lott, "Recent Instrumentation for UV-VIS Spectrophotometry," *J. Chem. Educ.* **45**, A89, A169, A273 (1968)
9. H. V. Malmstadt, R. M. Barnes, and P. A. Rodriguez, "A Multipurpose High Precision Recording Photometer," *J. Chem. Educ.* **41**, 263 (1964)
10. H. V. Malmstadt and C. B. Roberts, "Automatic Derivative Spectrophotometric Titrations," *Anal. Chem.* **28**, 1408 (1956)
11. W. Niesel, D. W. Lübbers, D. SchneeWolf, J. Richter, and W. Botticher, "Double Beam Spectrometer with 10-msec Recording Time," *Rev. Sci. Instr.* **35**, 578 (1964)
12. H. L. Pardue and P. A. Rodriguez, "High Stability Photometer Using Optical Feedback," *Anal. Chem.* **39**, 901 (1967)
13. L. W. Price, *Electronic Laboratory Techniques.* London: Churchill, 1969
14. L. T. Skeggs, Jr., and H. Hochstrasser, "Multiple Automatic Sequential Analysis," *Clin. Chem.* **10**, 918 (1964)
15. David C. Walker, "Sensitive Absorption Spectrophotometry for Electrochemical Studies by a Continuous Specular Reflection Technique," *Anal. Chem.* **39**, 896 (1967)
16. W. W. Wendlandt, "Reflectometers, Colorimeters, and Reflectance Attachments," *J. Chem. Educ.* **45**, A861, A947 (1968)
17. J. V. White and M. O. Liston, "Construction of a Double Beam Recording IR Spectrophotometer," *J. Opt. Soc. Am.* **40**, 29 (1950)

Fourier transform or interferometric spectrometry is discussed in:

18. G. Horlick, "Introduction to Fourier Transform Spectroscopy," *Appl. Spectroscopy* **22**, 617 (1968)
19. W. J. Hurley, "Interferometric Spectroscopy in the Far Infrared," *J. Chem. Educ.* **43**, 236 (1966)
20. M. J. D. Low, "Multiple Scan Infrared Interference Spectroscopy," *J. Chem. Educ.* **43**, 637 (1966)
21. M. J. D. Low, "Fourier Transform Spectrometers," *J. Chem. Educ.* **47**, A163 and A255 (1970)

The principles of Fourier transform spectroscopy are discussed in detail on an advanced level in:

22. G. A. Vanasse and H. Sakai, "Fourier Spectroscopy" in *Progress in Optics*, Vol. VI. E. Wolf, ed. New York: Wiley, 1967

EXERCISES

17.1 Sketch absorption curves for a filter and an analytical species for a case in which the filter is well suited to a sensitive determination of the substance.

17.2 Would amplification be desirable or appropriate in a filter photometer? Support your answer with several reasons.

17.3 Why does a filter photometer with broad band pass filters give results of low accuracy when used to determine the concentration of a species with a narrow absorption band?

17.4 Would you expect the stray radiation in an IR single-prism spectrophotometer to increase or decrease with increasing wavelength in the range from 5 to 15 μm? Assume that the instrument is operated so as to provide constant power at the detector. What steps may be taken to minimize the stray radiation?

17.5 A "double-pass" Littrow prism monochromator is to be fabricated to achieve enhanced resolution. In this design, the beam leaving the Littrow prism is reflected back for a second pass through it before being directed to the exit slit. Where should the beam chopper be placed for maximum effectiveness in reducing the effect of stray radiation? Consider that it could be located before the first or third pass or after the fourth and that the detector output will be selectively amplified at the modulation frequency.

17.6 Assume a laser whose emission can be tuned to cover the visible range is available.

  a) Consider briefly how an absorption spectrophotometer might be designed to use its distinctive properties.
  b) Would it have any advantages with microsamples? [See M. J. Houle and K. Grossaint, *Anal. Chem.* **38**, 768 (1966).]

17.7 A rapid-scanning spectrometer is shown in Fig. 17.18.

  a) What type of monochromator does it employ? Identify all the components of the monochromator.
  b) In what sense is it actually a duochromator, i.e., a device producing two "pure" wavelengths? What determines
  c) the wavelength range of the monochromator?
  d) the wavelength range scanned?
  e) the scanning speed?
  f) the resolution obtained? [See also H. J. Babrov and R. H. Tourin *Appl. Optics* **7**, 2171 (1968).]

17.8 It is possible to use a helium glow discharge to excite dissolved metals in samples as small as 10 nanoliters. A drop of solution is delivered by micropipet to a heated iridium filament and vaporized into a helium atmosphere. An rf glow discharge is started simultaneously to excite the metallic components of the vapor to emission.

  a) By means of a block diagram indicate the types of optical modules that must be added to the excitation module if one is to carry out a quantitative determination of metals like Na.
  b) Suggest by diagram or in words the essentials of the associated electronics. In this connection decide on the relative merit of an instantaneous versus an integrative type of observation. [See also G. V. Vurek, *Anal. Chem.* **39**, 1599 (1967).]

17.9 A simple absorption photometer for detecting mercury vapor can be built around a low-pressure mercury discharge lamp that furnishes principally resonance radiation of 253.7 nm wavelength. No wavelength isolator is needed.

  a) Draw a block diagram for the device and classify it as to type of photometer.
  b) Explain its operation.
  c) Will any atomic or molecular interferences be likely? Will sensitivity be as great for any interfering species as for mercury?

17.10 A program for the slit of an IR spectrophotometer is to be developed to compensate for the decrease in source energy at longer wavelengths. Assume the instrument incorporates a Globar source that behaves as a blackbody emitter at 1500 °K, a grating monochromator, a wavelength-independent thermal detector. Further, assume that a geometrical slit width of 0.2 mm gives adequate energy at 4000 cm^{-1} and that the instrument is to scan from 4000 to 400 cm^{-1} (2.5 to 25 μm).

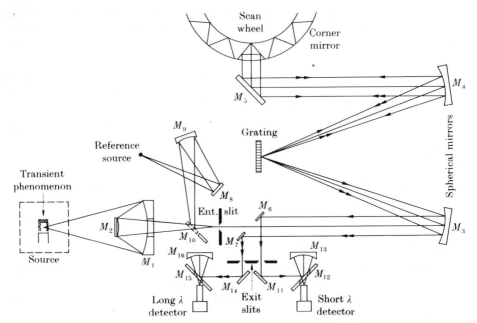

Fig. 17.18 Optical system of the Warner and Swasey Model 501 Rapid Scanning Spectrometer. A Czerny–Turner monochromator is used. Provision is made for two sources: (a) an emission or absorption source, whose output is collected by a Cassegranian optical system (M_1 and M_2) that directs radiation to the monochromator entrance slit and (b) a "reference" source for intensity calibration that is available by flipping mirror M_{10}. A "scan wheel" with sets of corner (right-angle) mirrors around its periphery is positioned at the focus of monochromator mirror M_4 instead of an exit slit. As the wheel is turned each corner mirror in sequence laterally displaces rays that are incident and returns them to the diffraction grating along a different path for a second dispersion. The two dispersions add but the reflection reverses the spectrum. Scanning of a spectrum occurs as the mirror wheel rotates. By use of two exit slits, two portions of a spectrum can be traversed simultaneously; thereby scanning speed is increased and detectors appropriate to each range can be used. Wavelengths appearing at the exit slits are indexed relative to the position of each corner mirror by a sensing device that triggers the readout during each scan. (Courtesy of Warner and Swasey.)

a) If the source energy is taken as unity at 4000 cm^{-1}, what is its relative value at 3000, 1500, and 500 cm^{-1}?

b) What should be the slit widths at these three frequencies to give a constant detector output?

c) What are the relative spectral slit widths that result at 1500 and 500 cm^{-1}?

17.11 If a sample being examined in an IR spectrometer is heated by the beam, its blackbody radiation will add to the beam intensity.

a) Will chopping the beam after passage through the sample minimize this spurious effect?

b) Will chopping the beam before passage through the sample reduce its effect?

c) Suggest a procedure or instrument design for IR spectrometry of molten salts that will minimize this problem.

17.12 In internal reflectance spectroscopy, why is it desirable to avoid refraction as a beam enters or exits from an internal reflection plate?

17.13 Consider that the nondispersive IR analyzer shown in Fig. 17.13 is to be used for analysis of CO_2 in air over the concentration range 0–10%.

a) Indicate the gas or gas mixture that should be placed in the various cells.

b) Explain the operation of the device in this analysis.

17.14 A nondispersive IR analyzer can be used as a leak detector for systems pressurized with nitrous oxide gas.

a) Draw a block diagram of such an instrument, indicating content of all cells.

b) Will the presence of other gases be likely to cause spurious readings?

17.15 Draw transmission curves to show how a nondispersive spectrometer is sensitized to CO in CO-CO_2 mixtures by filling the interference cell with CO_2. CO_2 has an absorption band at 2300 cm^{-1}, CO one at 2600 cm^{-1}. Draw a rough transmission wavelength curve for the reference path and for the sample path.

17.16 Several types of malfunction possible with a dispersive spectrophotometer are listed below. Some can be corrected by calibration, some are compensated by the differential character of double-beam operation, and others require an appropriate instrument adjustment. For each malfunction listed suggest

a) how it would be discovered from an inspection of absorption curves and whether

b) compensation will usually take care of it or calibration or adjustment of some type is necessary.

    i) Speed of scan is too high;

    ii) Gain of amplifier is set too high;

    iii) Mechanical beam attenuator (in optical null instruments) is nonlinear or not functioning properly;

    iv) Good optical alignment is lost;

    v) Stray light levels are high over some regions of wavelength;

    vi) Nulling system is not balancing correctly for zero signal;

    vii) Monochromator mirror is fogged.

17.17 Consider that an emission spectrum is to be recorded first by a dispersive spectrometer and then by a Fourier transform spectrometer.

a) Is the incident radiation in the time domain or the frequency domain? How can it be represented mathematically?

b) Can it be said that a dispersive spectrometer takes the Fourier transform of the incident radiation? Discuss briefly.

c) Does the optical system plus detector of the Fourier transform spectrometer take the Fourier transform of the incident radiation? At a given interferometer path difference, what does the detector output represent? What is the role of the computer in processing the data?

Chapter 18

RAMAN SPECTROMETRY

18.1 INTRODUCTION

In addition to molecular processes in which a photon of light is either absorbed or emitted, quantized changes can also be brought about during scattering of radiation. As a result, scattered light is found to contain not only wavelengths that were incident, an effect termed Rayleigh scattering, but also new wavelengths at extremely low intensity which reflect the interaction that has occurred, an effect called *Raman scattering*.

The Raman effect may be explained in terms of the classical model of interaction of EM radiation and matter (Section 10.7), by the fact that incident radiation of any arbitrary frequency induces an oscillating dipole in a molecule. Virtually all of the energy is immediately reradiated as a secondary wave of the same frequency. But the induced dipole interacts mildly with the nuclear motions characteristic of the molecule. The interaction may also be described by stating that the scattered light has been weakly modulated by some of the vibrational frequencies of the molecule.* The modulation gives rise to difference and sum frequencies $v_i - v_m$ and $v_i + v_m$ where v_i is the incident frequency and v_m corresponds to the frequency of a molecular vibration. The existence of frequencies $v_i \pm v_m$ is the basis for Raman spectroscopy. Because the intensity of these frequencies is quite small, only when an intense monochromatic source like a laser is available, does Raman spectroscopy become routinely feasible.

In Fig. 18.1 the origin of Raman spectra is indicated schematically. Here the energetic relationships are presented though the nature of the interaction is not. The upper levels shown as dashed lines are not, of course, actual excited states. Indeed, an important difference between Raman emission and fluorescence emission is that in fluorescence a photon must first be absorbed and the molecule promoted to a definite upper electronic level. Because of the finite lifetime in the excited state, there is a time delay of the order of 10^{-8} s before fluorescence re-emission. In Raman spectroscopy there is no delay.

At room temperature Raman transitions tend to occur from the lowest vibrational level associated with the ground electronic state since most molecules are in this vibrational level. These transitions will account for the so-called *Stokes lines* ($v_i - v_m$)

---

* Most Raman frequencies represent vibrational transitions; accompanying rotational fine structure is observed mainly for Raman spectral studies on gaseous samples. In the usual liquid or solid sample rotation is seldom possible. In specialized cases, it is also possible to observe electronic Raman spectra in solids.

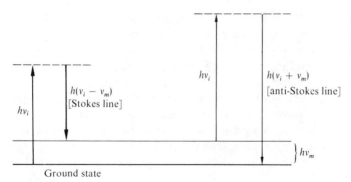

Fig. 18.1 Schematic representation of the quantum-mechanical origin of a Stokes and anti-Stokes pair of Raman lines. Monochromatic light of frequency v_i is incident on a molecule. In the light scattered by the molecule three frequencies appear: v_i and Raman lines $v_i - v_m$ and $v_i + v_m$.

that appear in a Raman spectrum, which represent a subtraction of energy from the incident light. As shown in Fig. 18.1, the incident light may also induce downward vibrational changes which will give rise to *anti-Stokes lines*. They will be of quite low intensity.* A Raman spectrum comprises the set of lines on either side (but mainly on the lower frequency side) of the exciting line. Raman lines are identified by their difference in frequency from the exciting line and are ordinarily given in wave numbers.

Example What is the wave number of a Raman line that appears at 680 nm when the incident light is the 632.8 nm wavelength of a helium-neon laser? The line will have a wave number of

$$(1/632.8 \times 10^{-7} - 1/680.0 \times 10^{-7}) = (15\,802 - 14\,706) \text{ cm}^{-1} = 1096 \text{ cm}^{-1}.$$

For Raman vibrational spectra to be observed, two general energy conditions are necessary.† First, an incident photon must be large compared with the quantum required to excite a vibration. Second, the incident photon must be much smaller than the quantum needed to produce electronic excitation. Both conditions are ordinarily met by a frequency in the visible region.

When a *second-order* or scattering interaction is the basis for a transition as in Raman spectroscopy, polarizability α of the molecule must alter during a particular motion.‡ If the magnitude of the incident field is not too large, the induced oscillating dipole created by the interaction is defined by the expression

$$\mu = \alpha E = \alpha E_0 \cos 2\pi c \sigma t, \tag{18.1}$$

---

* It is worth noting that the intensity of anti-Stokes lines is temperature dependent. Populations of higher vibrational levels increase as the temperature increases.
† The treatment to be given is generally applicable to other types of Raman spectra with appropriate modifications.
‡ Recall that interaction which leads to *absorption* of energy is possible only if a dipole is created during the interaction. Thus IR, VIS, and UV absorption spectrometry are possible when molecular vibrations, rotations, or electronic changes yield an asymmetric charge distribution. Such interactions are sometimes called first-order interactions.

where E_0 is an amplitude factor, σ its wave number, c the velocity of light, and t the time. For a molecule that is spherically symmetrical, or for an isotropic medium, α is a constant, i.e., it does not vary with direction. More commonly, however, molecules are asymmetrical and their polarizability must be represented by a tensor.* In this case, an oscillating polarization is responsible for reradiation.

How does molecular motion alter polarizability? During characteristic vibrations of vibrational wave number σ_v, the alteration in α can be expressed as $\alpha = \alpha_0 + \alpha_v \cos 2\pi c\sigma_v t$ where α_0 represents the polarizability of a molecule in the ground vibrational state and α_v is the polarizability change that occurs during a vibration whose wave number is σ_v. Substituting this expression into Eq. (18.1) gives for the polarization

$$P = \alpha_0 E_0 \cos 2\pi c\sigma t + \alpha_v E_0 \cos 2\pi c\sigma t \cos 2\pi c\sigma_v t. \qquad (18.2)$$

It suffices for present purposes to indicate that the last term can be resolved into terms in $\cos 2\pi c (\sigma + \sigma_v)t$ and $\cos 2\pi c (\sigma - \sigma_v)t$. Thus, there will be oscillating polarization of wave numbers σ, $\sigma + \sigma_v$, and $\sigma - \sigma_v$. It is the latter two that give the weak Raman lines. The selection rule for a vibrational Raman change is $\Delta v = \pm 1$.

With the intense radiation a laser provides, nonlinear terms in the polarizability, even though having a very small coefficient, also give rise to transitions. These very weak overtone transitions in general appear at $\sigma \pm 2\sigma_v$ or at slightly lower wave numbers. In this case the selection rule is $\Delta v = \pm 2$.

How should rotation affect α? It will vary during this motion also. Twice per rotation α will have the same value, and Eq. (18.2) will apply if $2\sigma_R$ is substituted for σ_v. The selection rule for rotational Raman charges are $\Delta J = 0, \pm 2$.

It is of interest to note that *stimulated Raman scattering* is also possible. A Raman-active medium placed within the optical cavity of a pulsed laser leads to lasing at the one or two most intense Stokes and anti-Stokes frequencies as well as the characteristic laser frequency.

Comparison of Raman and IR spectrometry. Since Raman and IR spectra arise from the same molecular transitions a comparison is of interest. For the most part, frequencies found in a Raman spectrum are those also observed in an IR spectrum. Yet Raman spectroscopy complements IR spectroscopy. One way it does is to provide information about vibrational transitions missing in IR spectra. Two examples will illustrate this point.

Example 1 What frequencies should appear in the Raman spectrum of a molecular species? If it has no symmetry elements, each normal vibration will alter its polarizability and give a Raman line. If the molecule is symmetrical not all vibrations may alter polarizability. Any vibration that does not, fails to appear in a Raman spectrum and is termed Raman-inactive.

In either type of molecule any normal vibration that does not develop an electric dipole but is accompanied by a change in polarizability will cause a line only in the Raman spectrum. Thus, to secure full information about molecular vibrations in most instances requires examination of a Raman spectrum as well.

---

* The magnitudes of the nine tensor coefficients are usually expressed as a polarizability ellipsoid.

Example 2   Carbon dioxide $O=C=O$ is a familiar symmetrical linear molecule with no permanent dipole moment. Its symmetrical stretching vibration during which oxygen atoms move away from the carbon in phase, a "breathing" mode, is not excited in the IR. No transition dipole moment exists. This mode is Raman-active, however, since the polarizability changes.

    A second vibrational mode, in which the oxygen atoms move away from the carbon asymmetrically, is both IR-active, since a dipole moment is created, and Raman-active, since the polarizability changes.

    Actually, Raman spectra often yield more information than IR spectra. Since absorption and fluorescence spectra arise from a dipole, they allow at most a calculation of three dipole components that may give information about a molecule. By contrast, Raman spectra ideally yield at most the nine components of the molecular polarizability tensor and thus offer the possibility of greater molecular characterization.

    A second example of their complementarity relates potentially to analytical applications. For organic substances Raman spectra tend to characterize the skeletal or hydrocarbon portion. By contrast, IR absorption provides most information about the polar, functional groups in a molecule. Both kinds of information are essential in most analyses (Section 18.3).

    Finally, it is useful to list relative advantages of Raman spectroscopy when used with an intense source that gives nearly monochromatic radiation (0.05 cm^{-1} line width) such as a He-Ne laser.

1. Spectral measurements relating to most of the characteristic rotational and vibrational motions of a molecule can be made *within the visible range*. (Thus, glass cells and aqueous solutions offer no problems and mulling procedures are not required for solids. It is also unnecessary to change instrumental arrangements several times to obtain the whole spectrum.)
2. The intensity of a Raman line is linearly related to the concentration of the species excited.
3. Depolarization studies (measurement of the intensity ratio $I_{||}/I_{\perp}$) are especially easily made. (A laser gives 99.9% linearly polarized incident radiation.)
4. It is easy to fix Raman wavelengths precisely. (There are many excellent emission standards in the visible and UV.)

On the other hand, there are certain relative disadvantages.

1. Samples of solids or liquids must be free of particles. Their Tyndall scattering might mask weak Raman lines.
2. Precision instrumentation is required to isolate Raman lines, which are much weaker than the incident radiation. There are severe signal-to-noise ratio problems.

18.2   INSTRUMENTATION

The measurement of Raman spectra is basically a problem in precision spectrophotometry under conditions of low signal-to-noise ratio, and much of the discussion

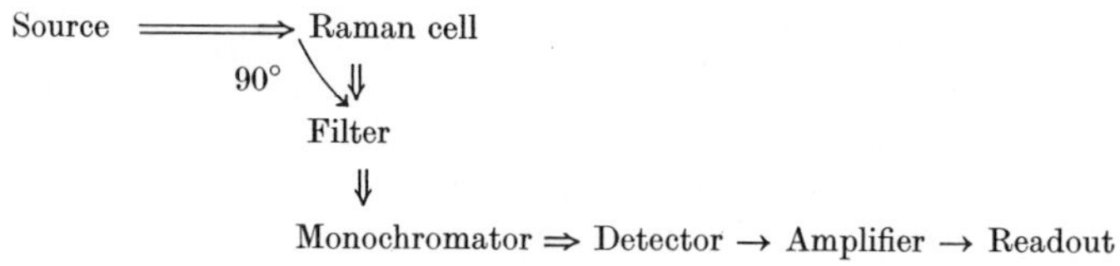

Source $\Longrightarrow$ Raman cell

$90°$ $\searrow\Downarrow$

Filter

$\Downarrow$

Monochromator $\Rightarrow$ Detector $\rightarrow$ Amplifier $\rightarrow$ Readout

Fig. 18.2 Line block diagram of a Raman spectrometer. Raman scattering is observed at 90° to the direction of irradiation to lessen stray light problems. A band-pass filter is introduced to exclude frequencies such as the nonlasing lines of a laser and pass a band including the incident frequency and Raman lines.

of Chapters 8, 16, and 17 is pertinent. The spectrum must be dispersed, its frequencies established, and intensities measured. As shown in Fig. 18.2, the general design of the instrumentation is familiar.

Some special problems arise in Raman measurements that are only occasionally encountered in absorption or emission photometry.

1. At best, Raman lines are about 0.01% the intensity of the incident radiation. Thus, a bright source, sensitive detection, and careful separation of signal from noise are called for.

2. Because Raman lines appear close to an exciting frequency, a source should provide monochromatic radiation of very narrow width.

3. Heroic means must be taken to minimize stray radiation, for Raman lines appear against the background of intense scattered radiation of the exciting frequency.

Source and cell. To overcome the first two problems, a bright monochromatic source is needed. A continuous laser (Section 11.3) is ordinarily selected, though occasionally

Table 18.1 Comparison of Some Light Sources for Raman Spectroscopy*

	Helium-neon laser	Argon-ion laser†	Mercury arc
Total power used, kW	0.100	8	20
Exciting line wavelength, nm	632.8	(1) 488.0 (2) 514.5	435.8
half-width, cm^{-1}	0.05	0.15	0.20–0.25
Power inside laser or arc in exciting line, W‡	1–2	5	2
Relative intensity of scattering by v^4 law	0.225	(1) 0.636 (2) 0.515	1
Degree of linear polarization	99.9%	99.9%	0

* Adapted from Ref. 5. A filter must be used with any of the three sources to exclude undesired spontaneous emission lines.

† More than one lasing line is available. By use of Xe or Kr still other lasing lines are available.

‡ Exterior to the laser the power is from 80 to 100 times smaller.

a mercury arc-filter combination is employed.* Table 18.1 characterizes three sources.

How should an excitation frequency be selected? Clearly, it should not be one that is absorbed or that gives rise to fluorescence. In either case energy would be lost and, in the latter, fluorescence would probably obscure Raman lines. In general, a frequency just below that at which photodecomposition begins to occur is desirable. Since Raman spectra originate from a scattering mechanism, intensity will increase with the fourth power of the exciting frequency.

Two methods of illumination of cells with a laser source are shown in Fig. 18.3. In one case intensity of illumination is enhanced by use of a reflector mirror behind the Raman cell, and in the other by installation of the cell (with Brewster angle windows) within the laser cavity. Multiple-pass cells and microcells are common. A method of illuminating the latter is also shown in Fig. 18.3.

Monochromator. To minimize the problem of stray light, a carefully designed monochromator or, better, a double monochromator (Chapter 12) is indicated. Further, the intense incident radiation is eliminated by arranging to observe the Raman radiation at right angles to the exciting beam. With a double monochromator, the exclusion of stray radiation is sufficiently good to permit even weak Raman lines near the exciting frequency to be detected. In addition, it is usually unnecessary to filter a sample with great care to eliminate particles. The greater dispersion of a double monochromator allows the scattered radiation to be separated very effectively.

Actually, monochromators introduce a degree of polarization that varies with the orientation of the dispersing device. In many instances correction curves are needed if polarization effects are studied. The correction is less if a beam is depolarized prior to entrance into the monochromator. A crystal quartz polarizing scrambler wedge can be used for this purpose.

Detector. Photoelectric detection and, to a lesser extent, photographic recording are employed. The latter is usable, but is less sensitive and suffers from failure of the density of the silver deposit to be related exactly to intensity in a given exposure time. A layout similar to that in Fig. 18.2 is used for photographic Raman work. Exposures of one or more hours are necessary for the recording of weak lines.

Photoelectric detection using a multiplier phototube is superior, especially at limits of dectability (Section 11.7), and is incorporated in most new apparatus. At low light levels it is best used in the mode termed photon counting (Section 8.8).

18.3 ANALYTICAL PROCEDURES

A range of 40–100 nm centered about the exciting wavelength is sufficient to cover the span of energies associated with most Raman-induced transitions. Figure 18.4 shows the Raman spectrum of *p*-dioxane, obtained with an instrument of high resolution. Strictly analytical applications of Raman spectroscopy have been limited by two factors, (a) compression of a spectrum that is spread over many micrometers in the

---

* If a mercury arc is used, intensity is boosted by nestling the sample cell in a cluster of tubular mercury arcs or along the axis of a single-helix Toronto arc. To minimize sample heating and provide optical filtering, some sort of jacketing of the cell is common. Conventionally a solution useful as a filter [2] is circulated for temperature control.

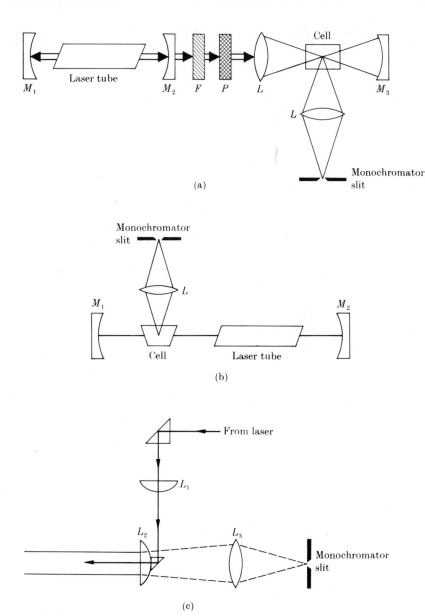

Fig. 18.3 Methods of irradiating a Raman cell by use of a laser. In (a) the cell is external to the laser cavity, which extends from resonating mirror M_1 to M_2, which is partially transmitting. F is a filter to exclude nonlasing frequencies, P is a half-wave plate to rotate the plane of polarization, if desired. In (b) the Raman cell is within the laser resonant cavity to take advantage of the much higher intensity level inside. Some of the scattered light, which contains the Raman frequencies, is collected at 90° to the incident light by lens L and focused on the slit of a monochromator (not shown). Components F and P may also be used in (b). In (c) a tubular microcell (about 0.7 mm i.d.) is shown. Scattered light collected by hemispherical lens L_2 is directed toward the monochromator slit. Thus, it is viewed at an angle 180° to the irradiating beam.

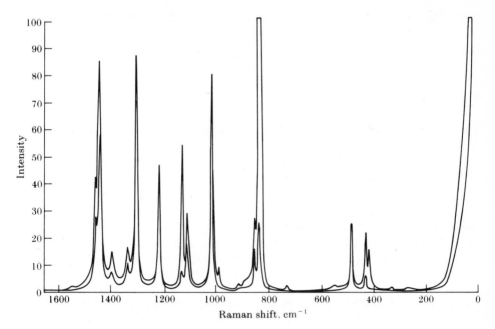

Fig. 18.4 A portion of the Raman spectrum of *p*-dioxane obtained with a Cary Model 82 Raman Spectrophotometer. The sample was run neat in a multipass cell with excitation at 514.5 nm, a $3\,\text{cm}^{-1}$ spectral slit width, and a scan rate of 3 $\text{cm}^{-1}\,\text{s}^{-1}$. The upper curve represents the intensity of the Raman emission component whose electric vector is vibrating parallel to the cell axis and the lower curve that whose electric vector is vibrating perpendicular to it. The depolarization ratio of a Raman line is then $I_{\parallel}/I_{\perp}$. (Courtesy of Cory Instruments.)

IR into a small range of the visible spectrum and (b) the low intensity of Raman frequencies.

For the reason just cited, Raman spectroscopy is used only occasionally in qualitative analysis. In addition, only a relatively small body of known spectra has been accumulated on pure compounds, though this situation has been improving rapidly since the advent of the laser.

There are many quantitative analytical applications of the method, particularly in analysis of liquid hydrocarbon mixtures. [1] The technique offers an advantage when working on such mixtures, since the absorption bands are narrow and do not overlap as badly as do those in the IR, where rotational fine structure is superimposed on the vibrational transitions. Heights of Raman absorption lines may be reproduced to about $\pm 0.2\%$ accuracy with a good instrument under optimum conditions.

18.4 RESEARCH APPLICATIONS

Raman spectrometry has benefitted a wide variety of investigations, especially since the advent of the laser. The area receiving most attention is that of molecular structure. Investigations of bond angles, molecular shapes, and bond stiffnesses all require data from Raman studies to be at all complete.

In addition, Raman spectrometry is a powerful tool for study of other types of inelastic scattering such as Brillouin scattering, in which incoming light is scattered by acoustical waves in a solid or liquid, and scattering from spin waves in ferromagnetic substances. [4, vol. XIII, No. 2]

REFERENCES

The references on molecular spectroscopy at the end of Chapter 16 should also be consulted. Additional references are:

1. T. R. Gilson and P. J. Hendra, *Laser Raman Spectroscopy*. New York: Wiley-Interscience, 1970
2. H. A. Szymanski, ed., *Raman Spectroscopy: Theory and Practice*, 2 vols. New York: Plenum, 1967, 1970

Raman instrumentation and procedures are discussed in:

3. B. J. Bulkin, "Raman Spectroscopy, Part I," *J. Chem. Educ.* **46**, A781, A859 (1969)
4. The *Spex Speaker*, a company quarterly published by Spex Industries, Metuchen, N.J. Issues of interest are XI (1) and (4), (1966); XII (2), (1967); XIII (2) and (4), (1968); XIV (2) and (4), (1969); XVI (1), (1971)
5. A. Weber *et al.*, "High Resolution Raman Spectroscopy of Gases with CW-Laser Excitation, *J. Opt. Soc. Am.* **57**, 19 (1967)

EXERCISES

18.1 Should the nitrogen molecule absorb in the IR? Should it be Raman-active? Why?

[*Ans.*: No; yes.]

18.2 In the Raman spectrum of a compound obtained with He-Ne laser excitation (see Table 18.1) lines are observed at 650.0, 661.5, and 670.3 nm. Calculate the wave-number shift ($\Delta \sigma$) of each line.

18.3 Should a helium-neon laser or an argon-ion laser be used to obtain a Raman spectrum of a substance that absorbs strongly in the blue-green region of the spectrum?

18.4 Draw a block diagram of a laser Raman spectrometer designed to operate with phase-sensitive detection. Draw a second block diagram for one with photon counting detection.

18.5 The helium-cadmium laser that emits at 441.6 nm is also a useful source in Raman spectroscopy. What is the ratio of its scattering power to that of the helium-neon laser characterized in Table 18.1?

[*Ans.*: 4.2.]

18.6 Consider that an argon-ion laser source, double-grating monochromator, and photomultiplier detector are to be employed as elements of a Raman spectrometer. Would it be preferable to use gratings blazed at 500 nm (first-order) or at 400 nm? Consider the response of monochromator and detector as well as any other relevant factors.

18.7 It is desired to calibrate the wavelength scale of a laser Raman spectrometer. Suggest at least two basically different ways to do so.

Chapter 19

NUCLEAR MAGNETIC RESONANCE SPECTROMETRY

19.1 RADIOFREQUENCY SPECTROMETRY

Spectroscopic techniques such as nuclear magnetic resonance that are based on radio-frequency measurement (from about 10^6 to 10^{11} Hz, i.e., up to the far infrared) are becoming increasingly important. This development largely parallels design improvements in radiofrequency (rf) spectrometers. In this chapter a single rf technique will be discussed at length, but it is desirable to recognize and to some degree characterize the other methods in order that similarities in instrumentation may be appreciated.

From the standpoint of instrumentation the rf methods require a very stable source of rf (or microwave) radiation, an appropriate detector, and amplifier. From an energy standpoint these techniques measure transitions between close-lying levels such as those shown by many nuclei when an external magnetic field is applied. A useful comparison of transitions observed in rf spectral studies with those studied at optical frequencies is made in Table 19.1. Note that the "frequencies" (given in cm^{-1}) and energies are meant to suggest only a rough order of magnitude; transitions for particular substances may be smaller or larger by more than a factor of ten.

Another characteristic feature of these rf spectroscopies is that absorption intensities are limited. As the table shows, there is only a very small difference between the population in the ground state and the population in the excited state. Absorptions are weak because with an extensive excited population stimulated emission becomes nearly as likely on exposure to EM radiation as does absorption and little net absorption can be observed.

The rf spectroscopies are:

1. Microwave, which responds to pure rotational transitions,
2. Nuclear magnetic resonance (NMR), which observes transitions between the energy levels of magnetic nuclei in an external magnetic field,
3. Electron paramagnetic resonance (EPR or ESR) which records transitions between spin levels of molecular unpaired electrons in a magnetic field, and
4. Nuclear quadrupole resonance, which responds to transitions between states of nuclei that have electrical dissymmetry.

This chapter will be given over to a discussion of NMR spectrometry. For discussion of the instrumentation and applications of other rf spectroscopies, appropriate monographs should be consulted.

Table 19.1 Energy Separations and Relative Populations

Transition represented	Energy of transition* wave number, cm^{-1}	eV	$kJ\ mol^{-1}$	Ratio of populations ($N_{excited}/N_{ground}$)
Electronic	20,000	2.6	240	10^{-41}
Vibrational	1,000	0.12	12	10^{-2}
Rotational	10	1.2×10^{-3}	0.12	0.95
Electron spin† (unpaired)	0.1	1.2×10^{-5}	1.2×10^{-3}	0.9995
Nuclear spin†	1×10^{-3}	1.2×10^{-7}	1.2×10^{-5}	0.999995
kT (at 298 °K, as index)	200	2.6×10^{-2}	2.4	—

* These values are meant to suggest an order of magnitude.
† Different spatial distributions of the moments exist at all times, but their energies are the same (degenerate). Energies differ with orientation only when an external field is applied. The separations given are for a field of about 10^4 gauss.

19.2 INTRODUCTION TO NMR SPECTROMETRY

Basically, NMR spectrometry involves the measurement of frequencies at which energy is absorbed by a magnetic nucleus such as ^{19}F when subjected to an external magnetic field. Each absorption corresponds to a transition between a pair of magnetic states or energy levels of the nucleus. Some 150 different isotopes of elements have magnetic nuclei and are potentially observable. Their relative usefulness in elucidating the structure of molecules depends on:

1. The strength of the magnetic moment,

2. The natural isotopic abundance,

3. The degree to which electric charge is distributed evenly over the nucleus,

4. The commonness of the element in compounds.

Example   More than 90% of NMR spectroscopy is based on ordinary hydrogen (^1H). All four factors are satisfied. It has a strong magnetic moment (2.79 nuclear magnetons) and thus can be more sensitively detected (see Table 19.3) than most other magnetic nuclei, which have smaller moments. For example, two other commonly used nuclei, ^{19}F and ^{31}P, have moments of 2.67 and 1.13 magnetons, respectively. Further, the natural abundance of the ^1H isotope is 99.98%, a factor that also contributes strongly to sensitivity of detection. Its nucleus also has a spherical charge distribution, as do the two other isotopes mentioned. Finally, hydrogen is to be found in most organic compounds.

Does the frequency of absorption of energy by a given magnetic nucleus depend only on the external field as the Zeeman splitting of atomic spectral lines does? The analogy to Zeeman, i.e. magnetic-field, splitting is valid as will be seen below. Yet, unlike atomic spectroscopy which characterizes separate atoms, NMR transitions characterize atoms within molecules. In fact, each nucleus is shielded somewhat from the external magnetic field by surrounding electrons. The degree of shielding depends, as would be expected, on the number of electrons and the orbitals they occupy. In general, each environment gives rise to a nuclear magnetic transition at a different frequency. The set of such transitions for one kind of magnetic nucleus in a sample is simply an NMR spectrum. (The independent variable is frequency if the applied magnetic field is held constant, or the independent variable is magnetic field strength if frequency is fixed.) NMR spectrometry is thus widely used for identifying molecules and detailing their structures. In fact, it is much more sensitive in this regard than IR spectrometry, as will be shown.

Table 19.2   Relationship of Spin Number I to Atomic and Mass Numbers

Atomic No.	Mass No.	Spin I	Examples
Odd	Even	1, 2, or 3	^2_1H, $^{14}_7N$ $(I = 1)$; $^{10}_5B$ $(I = 3)$
Even	Even	0	$^{12}_6C$, $^{16}_8O$ $(I = 0)$
Odd or even	Odd	1/2, 3/2, 5/2, ...	$^{13}_6C$, $^{31}_{15}P$ $(I = 1/2)$; $^{11}_5B$ $(I = 3/2)$

Nuclear magnetism. Nuclear studies have shown that protons and neutrons comprising a nucleus have characteristic motions and spins much as do electrons in an atom. As a result, most nuclei possess an angular momentum $\hbar I^*$ where $\hbar = h/2\pi$ (h is Planck's constant) and I is the spin quantum number. For example, $I = 1/2$ for ^{1}H. In addition, since it is charged, a spinning nucleus has a magnetic moment (or magnetic dipole) μ. Both quantities are vectors, directed *along* the axis of rotation. The spin I is related to the numbers of neutrons and protons in a nucleus, as shown in Table 19.2.

The simplest model that suggests the origin of nuclear magnetism was developed for the proton; it treats the proton as spherical with its mass and charge spread uniformly over the surface and spinning about a fixed axis with constant angular velocity. The relationship between magnetic moment and angular momentum in this simple model is given by the equation

$$\mu = \frac{e}{2Mc}\hbar I, \tag{19.1}$$

where c is the velocity of light and M is the mass of the proton.

When allowance is made for the actual complexity of internal nuclear motions in any nucleus, Eq. (19.1) may still be used if a proportionality constant g is introduced. This quantity, termed the nuclear g-factor, is dimensionless and of the order of unity. The equation may now be rewritten as either

$$\mu = g\left(\frac{e}{2Mc}\right)\hbar I$$

or more often as

$$\mu = \gamma\hbar I, \tag{19.2}$$

where γ is fixed for a particular nucleus and is identified as the magnetogyric ratio (or gyromagnetic ratio, especially in the older literature). Since $\gamma = \mu/\hbar I$, it is really the ratio of magnetic moment to angular momentum for a particular nucleus.

Before we leave Eq. (19.2), note that magnetic moments are often reported in terms of their value in *nuclear magnetons* μ_0. This quantity is defined as $\mu_0 = e\hbar/2Mc$. This quantity multiplied by I is seen to be the moment defined by Eq. (19.1), the moment a proton would have if exactly represented by the simple model described above. The value of μ_0 is 5.05×10^{-31} J gauss^{-1}. The actual μ for a proton is 2.79 times larger than the value based on the magneton. Thus, its value in nuclear magnetons is 2.79.

It is of interest to compare the nuclear magneton with the value obtained for an

---

* This value results on application of Bohr's condition that angular momentum be quantized in units of $\hbar$. It is used here in the treatment that leads to Eqs. (19.1) and (19.2). A more accurate but only slightly different value, $[I(I + 1)]^{1/2}\hbar$, is obtained on application of the Schroedinger equation. It may be substituted for $\hbar I$, if desired. The energy levels [in Eq. (19.4)] are *correct* as given. The reason is that the quantum-mechanical restriction on energies generates values of cos θ and m (see below) that are given by cos $\theta = m/[I(I + 1)]^{1/2}$. Thus, allowed energies are identical in the two treatments.

unpaired electron using a similar model. The electron analog, the *Bohr magneton*, is 9.27×10^{-28} J gauss^{-1}, 1836 times larger since the *mass of the electron is now used.**

Nuclear quadrupole moment. All nuclei whose I's are greater than 1/2, such as the common $^{14}_{7}N(I = 1)$, behave as though their electric charge is nonspherically distributed. As a result they are also assigned an *electric* quadrupole moment. Such a nucleus experiences a molecularly generated electric field gradient except in cases of high symmetry, e.g. for Cl in the ClO_4^- ion. The quadrupole moment, and thus the nucleus itself, has a preferred alignment relative to the molecule. Thus, nuclear spin states differ in energy even in the absence of an external magnetic field. It is transitions between such states that form the basis for nuclear quadrupole resonance specrometry.

Nuclear magnetic energy levels. In the absence of any magnetic field other than that arising from a magnetic nucleus itself, the energy attributable to the magnetic moment of a nucleus is essentially constant, i.e. it does not alter with changes in its orientation. But once an external magnetic field H_0 is imposed, the nucleus is subjected to a torque, which tends to align the moment parallel with the field. It is not the torque but the resulting potential energy that is of interest here. By means of a classical treatment it can be shown that the energy of interaction is just

$$E = -\mu \cdot H_0 = -\mu H_0 \cos \theta = -\mu_z H_0, \qquad (19.3)$$

where the field is taken to be along the positive z-direction and to make angle θ with the nuclear magnetic moment and μ_z is the component of μ in the z-direction.†

Quantum-mechanical restrictions, of course, limit the possible range of energies to a few discrete values. These prove to be easily expressed as allowed values of μ_z. For a given I there are just $2I + 1$ such values, the set $I, I - 1, I - 2, \ldots - I$. These are commonly called the *magnetic quantum numbers m*. If these numbers are substituted for I in Eq. (19.2), the allowed values of μ_z are obtained. In turn these can be inserted in Eq. (19.3) to obtain the nuclear magnetic energy states:

$$\gamma\hbar I H_0, \ \gamma\hbar(I - 1)H_0, \ \ldots - \gamma\hbar I H_0. \qquad (19.4)$$

Such a "splitting" of the original (unobserved) energy level by a magnetic field is called *nuclear Zeeman splitting*, in analogy to the Zeeman splitting of electronic levels of an atom by an external magnetic field. On the basis of a classical model, the levels correspond to different orientations of the nuclear magnetic moment with the field. Nearly complete alignment (a positive value of m) corresponds to a low energy, and increasingly antiparallel alignment (increasingly negative values of m) to successively higher energy levels.

---

* The difference in basic magnitudes of the magnetic moments is decisive in determining the size quanta required for transitions between magnetic energy levels. Thus it also determines the difference in the region of the EM spectrum where NMR and EPR spectra are ordinarily observed (see Tables 19.1 and 19.3). The latter must appear, for a given magnetic field, at frequencies about 2000 times greater.

† An alternative convention is to take H_0 along the negative z direction, i.e. down the z-axis. Under this convention, signs of quantum levels are the opposites of those in this chapter. For example, the two nuclear magnetic states for a spin 1/2 nucleus are $m = -1/2$ (lower energy) and $m = +1/2$ (higher energy).

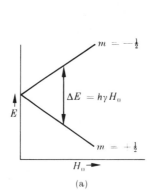

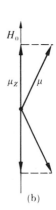

(a)   (b)

Fig. 19.1 (a) Energy level diagram for an isolated magnetic nucleus of spin quantum number $I = \frac{1}{2}$ as a function of the strength H_0 of applied magnetic field. The energy of transition ΔE is proportional to the field strength. (b) The orientations of the magnetic moment of a nucleus of spin $I = \frac{1}{2}$ in a magnetic field H_0. The two quantum mechanically allowed orientations correspond to essential alignment with, and opposition to, the field.

Example 1 For a proton with $I = \frac{1}{2}$, the nuclear magnetic quantum numbers m are $\frac{1}{2}$ and $-\frac{1}{2}$. Equation (19.4) gives two levels:

$$\tfrac{1}{2}\gamma\hbar H_0 \qquad \text{and} \qquad -\tfrac{1}{2}\gamma\hbar H_0.$$

A transition from the lower level ($m = \frac{1}{2}$) to the higher ($m = -\frac{1}{2}$) calls for an observable energy of transition of $\Delta E = \gamma\hbar H_0$. The two states are illustrated in Fig. 19.1.

Example 2 For the $^{14}_7N$ nucleus $I = 1$. Applying a magnetic field splits the unobservable original energy level into the three levels identified by magnetic quantum numbers $+1$, 0, and -1. The corresponding potential energies possible for the nucleus are $-\gamma\hbar H_0$, 0, and $+\gamma\hbar H_0$, respectively. For $m = +1$, there is substantial alignment with the field, for $m = 0$, 90° opposition, and for $m = -1$ substantial antiparallel alignment.

For NMR spectrometry it is the transitions between states that will be of interest. What transitions are allowed? For a given external magnetic field, at what frequency will a given magnetic nucleus absorb? The answer to these interrelated questions is straightforward. Since the selection rule for transitions among nuclear magnetic states proves to be just $\Delta m = \pm 1$, the energy of a transition is always

$$\Delta E = \gamma\hbar H_0. \tag{19.5}$$

If an upward transition results from radiating the nucleus with EM energy, absorption will occur at frequency v_0, for which the quantum $h v_0 = \Delta E$. It is convenient to rewrite this in terms of the angular frequency $\omega(= 2\pi v)$,

$$\Delta E = \frac{h}{2\pi}(2\pi v_0) = \hbar\omega_0.$$

Now Eq. (19.5) becomes $\Delta E = \gamma\hbar H_0 = \hbar\omega_0$, which reduces to the Larmor equation:

$$\omega_0 = \gamma H_0. \tag{19.6}$$

It is Eq. (19.6) that is in a real sense the basis for NMR spectrometry. Note that it prescribes that transitions occur for a particular nucleus at a frequency directly proportional to:

1. The magnetic field it experiences, and
2. Its magnetogyric ratio.

Thus, the transition energy for a given nucleus is characteristic of its overall magnetic environment.

While the energy of transition has been defined, there remain some important questions relating to the probability of transitions and their mechanisms. What are the equilibrium populations in the different states? What are the mechanisms by which transitions occur? Meaningful measurements will require answers to both. The second will be dealt with in the next section.

A transition from an upper magnetic level to a lower one will of course cause the emission of energy; one from a lower state to an upper, an absorption. As discussed in Section 13.3, either transition can be set in motion or "stimulated" by incident radiation of the characteristic frequency. Because the probability coefficients for the stimulated upward and downward transitions are equal, the likelihood of a particular transition will depend only on the population in the initial state. Thus, it will be the relative populations of the states at thermal equilibrium that will determine whether the *net* change that occurs is likely to be absorption or emission.

At equilibrium the population of the various nuclear magnetic states is predictable by use of a Boltzmann distribution. For a magnetic nucleus of spin 1/2 the distribution predicts a population ratio of

$$n_-/n_+ = e^{-\gamma\hbar H_0/kT}, \tag{19.7}$$

where n_+ identifies the number of nuclei per cm^3 in the lower state and n_- the number per cm^3 in the upper state. Table 19.1 gives a representative room-temperature value for the ratio as 0.999995. It is clear that only a small net absorption of energy is possible in NMR spectrometry.

19.3 MAGNETIC RESONANCE

Since a collection of magnetic nuclei reaches an equilibrium distribution in a magnetic field with a slight surplus in the lower energy states, there is a net microscopic magnetization in the z-direction. What means exist to promote some of these nucleii to higher energy levels and thus make NMR spectrometry possible? The means widely used recognizes that the alignment of the nuclear moments must be changed. This shift can be accomplished by applying an rf magnetic field H_1 of appropriate frequency at right angles to the direction of the strong steady field H_0. For example, H_1 may be directed along the y-axis. The mechanism by which the magnetic moments of the nuclei interact with the exciting rf field may now be explored.

Classical treatment.   The classical equation of motion for a nucleus of magnetic moment μ can be written vectorially as

$$d\mu/dt = \gamma(\mu \times H_0), \qquad (19.8)$$

where the cross-product of the magnetic moment and the magnetic field H_0 is taken. This equation proves identical with the mathematical expression obtained by rotating the nuclear magnetic moment about the direction of H_0 at angular velocity ω_0. As a result of this identity, it is possible to describe the behavior of each nuclear magnet by stating that it behaves as if it were *precessing* around the direction of the applied magnetic field at angular velocity ω_0, as sketched in Fig. 19.2.

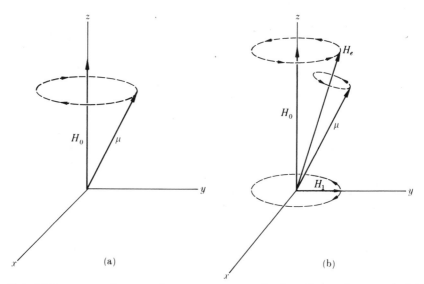

Fig. 19.2 (a) Precession of a magnetic moment μ on application of a steady magnetic field H_0 along the z-axis. (b) Precession of μ on application of both a steady magnetic field H_0 (along the z-axis) and an rf magnetic field H_1 (along the y-axis). The fields add to give effective field H_e. The rf field H_1 is shown as the resultant of two superposed circularly varying fields of equal amplitude, one rotating clockwise, one counterclockwise. Only the component rotating in the same sense as the precessing nuclear magnetic moment can interact with it. When the angular velocity of H_1 ($2\pi\nu$) equals the Larmor frequency ω_0, resonance occurs. The resonance is pictured as a simultaneous precession of μ about H_e and of H_e about H_0. The resonance may also be described as a vigorous wobbling of the precessing moment about its equilibrium position.

Consider that an rf magnetic field H_1 is now applied along the y-axis. It is represented as an oscillation along the x-axis in Fig. 19.2b. More usefully, however, it can be resolved into two counter-circulating components that add vectorially to give H_1. Their angular velocity must be the same as that of H_1. The component moving in the same sense as the magnetic moment's precession will be able to interact with this moment, whereas the one rotating in the opposite direction will not and may be disregarded. Consider that the rf frequency is small initially. As the rf frequency approaches that of a nuclear Larmor frequency, there is increasing interaction of H_1 and the precessing magnetic moment. When the frequencies are identical, resonance absorption will be observed. If the frequency of the rf field is swept through the region of the Larmor frequency, peak absorption of energy from the oscillating field will be observed at the resonance frequency. Many of the aspects of the interaction as deduced from such a model have been treated quantitatively in the elegant Block formulation of NMR spectroscopy. [4]

Table 19.3 Magnetic Resonance Properties for Some Common Nuclei

Nucleus	I in units of $h/2\pi$	Frequency MHz/kG	Relative sensitivity at constant H_0*	Relative sensitivity at constant v_0*	% Isotopic abundance
^{1}H	1/2	4.258	100	100	99.98
^{3}H	1/2	4.54	120	107	—
^{13}C	1/2	1.070	1.59	25.1	1.1
^{15}N	1/2	0.432	0.10	10.1	0.4
^{19}F	1/2	4.006	83.4	94	100
^{31}P	1/2	1.724	6.64	40	100
^{2}H	1	0.654	0.96	40.9	0.02
^{14}N	1	0.308	0.10	19.3	99.6
^{7}Li	3/2	1.655	29.4	194	92.6
^{11}B	3/2	1.366	16.5	160	81.2
^{35}Cl	3/2	0.417	0.47	49	75.4
^{27}Al	5/2	1.109	20.7	304	100
^{17}O	5/2	0.577	2.9	158	0.04
^{10}B	3	0.458	2.0	172	18.8
Electron	1/2	2799			

* Sensitivity relative to the proton, assuming equal numbers of nuclei and the same relaxation time ratio T_2/T_1.

Resonance frequencies. According to Eq. (19.6), characteristic frequencies of magnetic resonance absorption are predictable for isolated nuclei from magnetogyric ratios and the value of the applied magnetic field. Table 19.3 lists frequencies in megahertz for a number of nuclei of chemical interest for an applied field of 1 kG. Direct proportionality will yield the frequency at other fields, or the field at other frequencies.

Example What magnetic field is required for proton resonance at 220 MHz? From the data of Table 19.3 the field will be just $220/4.258 = 51.6$ kG.

In addition, Table 19.3 lists the relative sensitivity with which resonance for a magnetic species can be detected when a measurement involves sweeping the frequency at constant magnetic field H_0 and vice versa. For this purpose the proton sensitivity is taken as 100.

19.4 THE LOCAL MAGNETIC FIELD

In any system except a collection of isolated atoms the magnetic field actually experienced by a nucleus is altered by the local environment. As a result, for a given sample and a fixed applied field, a species like ^1H will shown an NMR resonance at as many different frequencies as there are kinds of nuclear environment. In principle, the different environments in which each kind of magnetic nucleus is situated in a molecule or crystal should thus be determinable from an NMR spectrum. A necessary condition would of course be that the variables contributing to the local magnetic field be quantitatively established.

The steady magnetic field at a particular nucleus can be considered to be the sum of several terms:

$$H_{local} = H_0 + h_1 + h_2 + h_3 + h_4 \tag{19.9}$$

where small fields h attributable to the sample add to or subtract from the strong external field H_0.

Bulk magnetization. Field h_1 is that from the bulk magnetization of the system by H_0. How does this field affect a molecule or ion containing a magnetic nucleus? It is customary to use a Lorentz ion cavity model to estimate whether any *bulk magnetic susceptibility correction* is necessary. The model assumes that the molecule of interest resides in a spherical cavity and that the medium outside the cavity is continuous. There is in general no correction for the effect when the sample itself is spherical.

Experimentally, however, it is more convenient to place samples in cylindrical tubes. Even for this case, a bulk susceptibility correction can be eliminated by observing magnetic resonances relative to an internal standard, which is usually an added reference compound soluble in the same solvent. If an external standard, i.e. a reference compound sealed in a capillary tube, is positioned in the center of the sample tube, then bulk susceptibility differences between sample and reference must be calculated for exact determination of resonance frequencies. This matter of referencing is discussed in more detail in Section 19.11.

Direct coupling. Field h_2 results from direct influence of magnetic nuclei in neighboring molecules or ions. It is a dipole-dipole interaction that alters the local field. Its magnitude is appreciable in solids or liquid crystals where relative orientations between molecules are maintained but is ordinarily negligible in liquids and gases where they are not. For example, a proton 10^{-8} cm from a second proton and *fixed* in position relative to both it and H_0 gives rise to an additional magnetic field at either nucleus that may be as large as 25 G.

The fixed orientations of magnetic nuclei in solids are responsible for the broad resonance peaks usually observed in their NMR spectra. The width of their "lines" becomes an index to molecular geometry, and the term *wide-line NMR* is used to describe such measurements.

In liquids and gases, by contrast, molecules are constantly subjected to thermal agitation—causing tumbling and rotation—and direct dipole-dipole interactions of magnetic nuclei are usually effectively averaged to zero. This fortunate result allows attention to be focused on smaller magnetic differences due to molecular structure.

Most samples examined by NMR spectroscopy are therefore liquids or liquid solutions and the term *high-resolution NMR* is used to characterize this type of measurement.

Field h_3 results from the remaining interaction between molecules, allowing explicitly for that between solvent and the sample molecule. Solvent effects may be elucidated by work at two or more concentrations and corrected, for example, by extrapolation to infinite dilution. In general, solvent effects are complex to interpret theoretically.

Intramolecular effects. Field h_4 combines all influences arising within the sample molecule. There are two: the screening of a magnetic nucleus by electrons, described in terms of a *chemical shift*, and indirect coupling between magnetic nuclei, termed *spin-spin coupling*. Both are illustrated in the NMR spectrum of ethanol in Fig. 19.3. Together, these intramolecular effects provide the basis for NMR spectrometry. They are dealt with at some length in Sections 19.11 and 19.12.

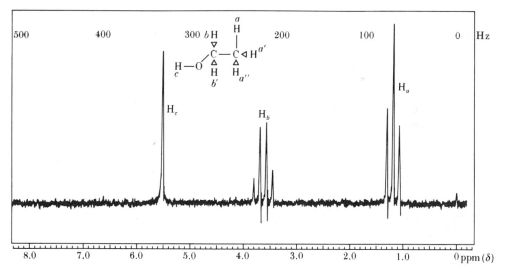

Fig. 19.3 NMR spectrum of ethanol in $CDCl_3$ at 60 MHz. There are three basically different kinds of local magnetic fields for protons as a result of variations in electron screening: the field in which the three equivalent methyl protons (a, a', and a'') exist, that in which the two equivalent methylene protons (b and b') exist, and that in which the hydroxyl proton (c) exists. The chemical shifts from the tetramethylsilane reference resonance are H_a, 1.2 ppm; H_b, 3.6 ppm; and H_c, 5.5 ppm. In addition, the methylene protons and methyl protons interact indirectly (spin-spin couple) to split resonance H_a into a triplet and of H_b into a quartet. Rapid exchange (see below) cancels this effect for the hydroxyl proton.

In summary, it is possible by judicious choice of experimental conditions for NMR spectrometry to simplify Eq. (19.9) greatly. It becomes

$$H_{local} = H_0(1 - \sigma), \tag{19.10}$$

where σ, the *screening constant*, is a dimensionless number dependent upon the chemical environment, but not on H_0. As implied, the local field is ordinarily smaller than the external field. For example, σ averages about 10^{-5} for a proton and about 10^{-2} for an atom that has many electrons. The relative magnitudes of the screening constants imply that proton magnetic resonance spectrometry will cover only a small spectral range compared with that required by heavier magnetic nuclei. Clearly, σ will be closely related to the chemical shift.

Example Because the screening constants of protons are all about 1×10^{-5}, at fixed magnetic field H_0 only a small frequency range need be scanned to obtain a proton NMR spectrum. At 60 MHz a range of 0 to 600 or 0 to 1000 Hz is usually sufficient. These ranges correspond to σ-values as high as $600/60 \times 10^6 = 1 \times 10^{-5}$ and $1000/60 \times 10^6 = 1.7 \times 10^{-5}$.

Finally, if NMR spectroscopy is to yield valid measurements representative of magnetically unperturbed systems, the extent to which intense magnetic fields will influence the positions of any chemical equilibria or rates of chemical reaction must be known. It can be shown that a magnetic field H_0 supplies an energy per mole of sample of $\frac{1}{2}\chi_v M_0^2$, where χ_v is the volume magnetic susceptibility of the system. Since χ_v is, in general, about 10^{-4}, a field of 10 kilogauss produces an energy of interaction of 5×10^{-4} J mol^{-1}. By contrast, at room temperature thermal energy kT is 2.5×10^3 J mol^{-1}. Accordingly, the influence of a magnetic field on chemical changes should be negligible.

19.5 RELAXATION PROCESSES AND SATURATION

Since the difference in populations among the various magnetic states is small, the magnitude of any net nuclear resonance absorption is strongly influenced by relaxation processes. These are simply mechanisms by which energy can be exchanged between a nucleus and its environment and thus represent paths by which a system that has absorbed energy can return to thermal equilibrium. For example, the nuclear property that corresponds to precession is one important means of transferring energy.

Only if relaxation can occur at least as rapidly as absorption will the intensity of nuclear absorption at a given frequency remain constant. If relaxation does not keep pace with absorption, the net amount of absorption falls rapidly. This phenomenon is called saturation, as noted earlier. Since saturation is so easy to bring about experimentally, insight into relaxation processes is important.

It is of value to separate out two types of relaxation, though the same local fluctuations may contribute to each. One, *spin-lattice relaxation*, relates to decay of the excess population in excited state(s). The other, transverse relaxation, relates to the phase of the precessing nuclei but not to their state. After the excitation of nuclei under the influence of an rf field the excited nuclei and others will be likely to precess in phase. This will produce a net magnetization in the x- and y-directions as well as in the basic z-direction. Upon removal of the rf field, varying local magnetic fields will cause the coherence of the precession to decay and the net magnetization in x- and y-directions will tend toward zero (transverse relaxation). Perhaps at the same rate, perhaps not, the energy distribution will tend toward equilibrium and a restoration of the original value of net magnetization in the z-direction (longitudinal relaxation). Each type of relaxation can now be dealt with individually.

Spin-lattice relaxation. A sample examined by NMR spectroscopy can be regarded as a lattice of nuclear spins. The rate at which a lattice either assumes a steady state distribution of spin states upon application of a magnetic field H_1 or relaxes is often very slow. Relaxation may be pictured as occurring, in part at least, from thermal motions of other magnetic nuclei. Their movement gives rise to magnetic fields that occasionally have a fluctuation whose frequency is equal to the precession frequency of the nucleus to be "relaxed", thus permitting interaction and conversion of magnetic to thermal energy.

Basically, the process is first-order and has a rate constant that depends upon temperature, viscosity, and the concentration of magnetic nuclei. Thus it has a rate that decreases exponentially. As with other processes, it is useful to define a time constant. In this case it is called the spin-lattice relaxation time, T_1, and defined by the expression $(n - n_{eq}) = (n - n_{eq})_0 e^{-t/T_1}$ where n is the initial excess population $(n_+ - n_-)$ in the ground state and n_{eq} its equilibrium value. The quantities in parentheses are the difference in these values at time t and at time 0. When a time equal to T_1 has elapsed, the difference between the excess population and the equilibrium values has been reduced to 37 % $(1/e)$ of its original value. Since at thermal equilibrium there remains, of course, a net magnetization along the z- or magnetic field direction, time T_1 is also termed a "longitudinal" relaxation time.

Spin-lattice relaxation times of the order of 10^{-2} to 100 s are usually observed in liquids. They are seldom shorter unless paramagnetic ions like Cu^{2+} are present. Such species hasten relaxation, giving rise to values of T_1 as short as 10^{-4} s. Very long values of T_1 are common in solids.

Direct dipole-dipole interactions between magnetic nuclei also aid relaxation. Movement of magnetic dipoles in a nearby molecule can also produce frequencies with components equal to the precession value, in spite of the fact that thermal agitation averages out their influence on local magnetic fields. In addition, relaxation can be enhanced by interactions between a magnetic nucleus and the electric field gradients produced by nuclei with quadrupole moments.

Example It is difficult to observe resonance absorption in proton NMR spectrometry of protons bonded to nitrogen. The quadrupole moment of the common ^{14}N nucleus causes such rapid relaxation of the proton magnetic spin that the proton absorption line is broadened nearly to the point of vanishing. The relation of line width to relaxation time will be further treated in the next section.

Transverse relaxation. A second time constant T_2 is assigned to so-called spin-spin or transverse relaxation processes. These processes lead to destruction of the net magnetization in the x- and y-directions brought about initially when the rf field is applied. Such magnetization can continue only as long as the moments precess in phase about the z-axis. As a result of differing local fields the spins soon tend to fall out of phase and the net magnetization in x- or y-direction falls toward zero. If δH is the range of varying local magnetic fields, nuclei will tend to precess at frequencies that cover a range $\gamma \cdot \delta H$. It is convenient to use this idea to define T_2. Thus, T_2 may be defined as $T_2 = 1/\gamma\delta H$ and is a measure of the time required for different nuclei to get out of phase.*

Actually, in liquids and gases where molecular diffusion and rotation are rapid processes, the local field usually changes sufficiently rapidly so that the mechanisms responsible for longitudinal and transverse relaxations are essentially identical and $T_1 = T_2$.†

19.6 LINE SHAPE AND BREADTH

Very sharp resonance or absorption lines are generally obtained in NMR spectrometry. In a properly executed frequency (or magnetic field) scan in which saturation is avoided the width of an absorption peak at half its maximum height is just $2/T_2$, which may be as small as 0.1 $\sec^{-1}$. Since the range of frequencies scanned is some 600 to 1000 Hz, even in proton NMR, line widths are about 1 part in 10^4 of the total spectrum.

With the usual NMR instrumentation the question arises of how best to present resonance signals. When a rf field H_1 interacts with a magnetic nucleus both a signal component that is in phase with H_1 and one 90° out of phase with it can be extracted. Their significance can be understood in terms of a treatment of ac magnetization. In contrast to magnetization of a sample by a static magnetic field, an ac field produces a changing magnetization that is in phase with the field from dc up through lower frequencies. If the frequency is increased until it corresponds to a transition between nuclear magnetic energy levels, the magnetization lags the field and its amplitude decreases. Thus, it undergoes *dispersion* in a manner analogous to the dispersion of refractive index (Section 10.7). The NMR signal in phase with H_1 is thus the magnetization signal and its display through the resonance region is termed the *dispersion mode* signal.

Simultaneously, a signal 90° out of phase with H_1 becomes significant in regions of nuclear magnetic transition. It is the absorption signal corresponding to energy withdrawn from the field to promote the quantum transition. Indeed, it is the lag in magnetization that signals the beginning of absorption. These two aspects of magnetization are treated theoretically by regarding the bulk magnetic susceptibility χ as comprising both a real (in phase) component χ' and an imaginary (90° out of phase) component χ'', that is, $\chi = \chi' + i\chi''$. A display of the out-of-phase component is termed an *absorption mode* signal.

Both aspects of an NMR resonance signal are plotted in Fig. 19.4. They may be usefully compared with their analogs for refraction in Figs. 10.11 and 10.39. It may

---

* Alternately, T_2 can be defined in terms of a line shape function $g(v)$. This quantity is introduced in the quantum-mechanical treatment of NMR to allow for line broadness. This definition gives the expression $T_2 = 1/2g(v)_{max}$ and emphasizes the role of transverse relaxation processes in broadening NMR resonance lines. The longer T_2 is, the narrower is the line.

† Any difference between T_2 and T_1 is treated theoretically by introducing a *correlation time* τ_c, which is a measure of the time of rotation or of the time of diffusion of a molecule. When thermal motions are sufficiently rapid that $\omega_0\tau_c \ll 1$, $T_1 = T_2$. In liquids $\tau_c \simeq 10^{-10}$ s at room temperature. For 60 MHz proton NMR $\omega_0 = 6.28 \times 6 \times 10^8$ rad s^{-1} and $\omega_0\tau_c \simeq 37 \times 10^{-2} \simeq 0.4$. The relation holds.

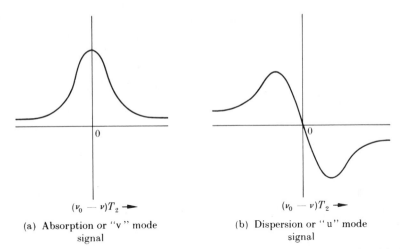

(a) Absorption or "v" mode
signal

(b) Dispersion or "u" mode
signal

Fig. 19.4 NMR resonance peak or line shapes. The absorption form of curve in (a) is the out-of-phase component of the rf signal that is represented by magnetic susceptibility component χ''. The dispersion mode form of resonance peak shown in (b) is the in-phase component denoted by magnetic susceptibility component χ'.

also be noted that both curves have a Lorentzian shape, a pattern characteristic of spectroscopic transitions in which random processes such as molecular collisions are the principal perturbing influence. If inspected closely, a Lorentzian type of curve is distinguishable in that its amplitude does not fall off as rapidly in the "wings" as does the amplitude of a Gaussian curve. These curves were obtained under so-called steady-state or slow-scan conditions, a matter extensively discussed below.

It can be shown that the absorption mode NMR signal arises from the average magnetization in the xy-plane as well as from the χ'' component of the magnetic susceptibility. If saturation is avoided, the absorption mode signal produced when frequency is scanned is given in terms of the total equilibrium magnetization M_0 by

$$\frac{M_0 \gamma H_1 T_2}{1 + T_2^2(\omega_0 - \omega)^2 + \gamma^2 H_1^2 T_1 T_2}, \qquad (19.11a)$$

or if a spectrum is being obtained by varying the magnetic field H_0 by

$$\frac{M_0 \gamma H_1 T_2}{1 + T_2^2 \gamma^2 (H_0 - H)^2 + \gamma^2 H_1^2 T_1 T_2}. \qquad (19.11b)$$

It is important to observe that these equations are symmetrical about ω_0 or H_0, attaining a maximum at that value, and that the term $\gamma^2 H_1^2 T_1 T_2$ in the denominator of each equation leads to a decrease in the average xy-magnetization if the rf field H_1 is strong. This dependence may now be examined as a tendency of the nuclear spin system to saturate.

Saturation. As noted earlier, the net energy absorbed at a resonant frequency depends mainly on the difference in populations in the excited and ground states. Once irradiation by the rf field is started, the excess population in the lower state diminishes and *saturation*, i.e., lessened absorption, begins to be observed. How prone a particular nuclear magnetic transition is to saturation depends on whether thermal relaxation can occur as rapidly as magnetic absorption. As a spectrum is scanned, however, the degree of saturation can be minimized if the amplitude of the rf field is kept low or the frequency (or H_0) range of interest is scanned rapidly. Unfortunately, resolution is lost in a rapid scan. Both possibilities are discussed further below.

A more quantative statement about saturation can be obtained from inspection of either form of Eq. (19.11). As the rf field H_1 is increased, the net xy-magnetization, and thus absorption, will first increase, since H_1 appears as a coefficient in the numerator and in an additive term in the denominator. As H_1 is further increased, eventually the term $\gamma^2 H_1^2 T_1 T_2$ will overtake the linear term in the numerator and magnetization will decrease. This trend is shown in Fig. 19.5 where the absorption mode magnetization at resonance is plotted as a function of H_1. From the graph it is evident that the optimum value of H_1 is that for which $\gamma^2 H_1^2 T_1 T_2 = 1$, an expression that might also have been obtained analytically. The effect of H_1 on the dispersion mode signal has

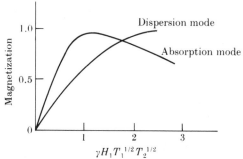

Fig. 19.5 The different behavior of magnetization of the two resonance "modes" as the rf field H_1 is increased at a resonance frequency. The maximum value of the absorption signal is $2H_1\chi''$ and is attained at $\gamma H_1 T_1^{1/2} T_2^{1/2} = 1$, while the maximum value of the dispersion mode signal, $2H_1\chi'$, is attained when the abscissa quantity reaches infinity.

also been shown in the illustration. Note that in this case the optimum practical value of H_1 is several times larger than for the absorption mode.

It is convenient to "extract" the term $1/[1 + \gamma^2 H_1^2 T_1 T_2]$ from the forms of Eq. (19.11) and define it as the *saturation factor*, since it is just the factor by which absorption is diminished at high values of H_1.* At the optimum value of H_1 for a conventional absorption mode readout, the saturation factor is just one-half. Substitution of some values of T_1 and T_2 representative of NMR samples in the saturation factor expression gives the following values for H_1:

Value of T_1 and T_2, s	Optimum value of H_1, G
0.1	10^{-3}
1.0	10^{-4}
10.0	10^{-5}

---

* A system suffering from saturation can be said to be "hotter" than its surroundings. A *spin temperature* T_s, given by the expression $T_s = T(1 + \gamma^2 H_1^2 T_1 T_2)$, may be defined to account quantitatively for the effect, where T is the bulk sample temperature.

The correlation suggests that an NMR spectrum of a system with a relaxation time of 10 s or longer might be more reliable if obtained by a dispersion mode readout (see Fig. 19.5).

In NMR spectroscopy, saturation is avoided for several reasons. Not only are resonance absorptions reduced—leading to less sensitivity of measurement—but resonance lines are broadened—leading to poorer resolution. In addition, resonance peaks are not always equally subject to saturation—leading to a distorted spectrum. Finally, under conditions of saturation, multiple-quantum transitions are possible—leading to new absorption lines. For example, two quanta of different magnitude may be absorbed simultaneously, promoting two nuclei in the same or different environments to a higher level.[*] As a result an NMR spectrum is ordinarily obtained by scanning rapidly at a comparatively large rf field or by scanning slowly at low power. *Fast passage* and *slow passage* are alternate terms applied to these rates.

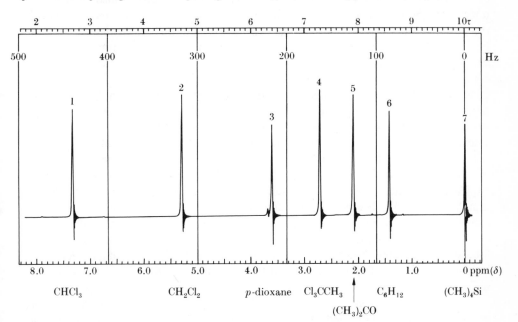

Fig. 19.6 An NMR spectrum of a mixture that could be used for calibration. Each absorption shows "ringing."

If a resonance peak is scanned rapidly, a condition termed *ringing* is observed. It is found that under conditions of fast passage a resonance typically has too little time to relax before the frequency (or field) is changed, and so-called wiggles are observed on the far side of the resonance peak. Ringing is well illustrated in the calibration spectrum of Fig. 19.6. It may be explained simply in terms of the classical model. During a fast scan nuclear moments persist in their in-phase precession at ω_0 after the frequency has increased. As a result they interact with the increasingly higher frequency rf field to produce an audiofrequency beat signal as there is alternate

---

[*] Kaplan, J. I., and Meiboom, S., *Phys. Rev.* **106**, 499 (1957).

destructive interference and reinforcement. The ringing is a typical damped oscillation with an envelope decaying at the same rate as the resonance absorption. Its appearance is also a useful index that the magnetic field H_0 is homogeneous.

Line width. Since the usefulness of an NMR line in analysis often varies inversely with its breadth, questions of line width are of central importance. The so-called natural width of an absorption line, based on a quantum-mechanical consideration of lifetime in the excited state, is of negligible importance in NMR spectrometry, since mechanisms for spontaneous radiation from a magnetic spin state are unavailable. Instead, the breadth of a line is nearly always determined by the rapidity of (external) relaxation processes. While magnetic field inhomogeneities broaden lines, it will be assumed that such instrumental problems have been minimized.

From Eq. (19.11a) the width of an absorption mode signal at half maximum may be shown to be $\Delta\omega = (1 + \gamma^2 H_1^2 T_1 T_2)^{1/2} \cdot 2/T_2$. This expression also defines the interval $\Delta\omega$ between the maximum and minimum of the dispersion mode signal. If the power in field H_1 is very small, as can be seen, the line width reduces to $2/T_2$. However, if the optimum value of H_1 is used, the parenthetical expression has the value $\sqrt{2}$ and the line width is 1.41 times broader. It is evident that in practice a compromise must be struck between sensitivity and resolution.

Line width can also be estimated by use of the uncertainty principle. The uncertainty in the energy of the excited state ΔE and the average lifetime of an excited nuclear spin Δt are related by the uncertainty expression $\Delta E \cdot \Delta t \approx h/2\pi$. Since Δt is essentially τ, the overall relaxation time, and since $\Delta E = h\Delta v$, one has $\tau\Delta v \approx 1/2\pi$. The uncertainty in frequency Δv is just the line width. These expressions predict a line width of about $1/2\pi T_2$. Since $T_1 \approx T_2$ in most instances, T_1 might also be used in the expression. In the event that longitudinal and transverse relaxation times are not equal, T_2 is usually shorter and thus determinative.

In solids, liquid crystals, and highly viscous liquids, direct interaction of magnetic dipoles becomes possible, since nuclei stay in a fixed position relative to each other for a substantial time. As a result, relaxation times are greatly reduced and resonance lines are very broad. Relative line breadths in different NMR systems are compared in Table 19.4.

When a nucleus of spin greater than 1/2 is present in a molecule, relaxation times are usually greatly shortened. As discussed in Section 19.2, such a nucleus will in most cases have a preferred orientation *within the molecule* because of the *nuclear electric quadrupole moment*. On application of a fixed-direction external magnetic field, the nucleus will also experience its pull toward alignment. The two influences

Table 19.4 Representative Line Widths of Proton NMR Signals

Type of substance or physical state	Line width Hz
Liquids, solutions	0.1–10
Crystals	10^4–10^5
Polymers	10–10^4

will generally be in different directions, especially if the molecule is tumbling. The result will be that the quadrupole interaction will act to relax the excitation produced by the applied field. Line broadening from this cause is often substantial. For example, broad lines are characteristic of ^{14}N and ^{11}B NMR spectra. An accompanying advantage is that saturation is no longer a problem! In the limit of very fast relaxation processes, such as are obtained for Cl, Br, and I nuclei, the breadth of lines is so great that their resonances cannot be detected directly.

19.7 THE BASIC NMR SPECTROMETER

A basic version of a high-resolution NMR spectrometer is shown in Fig. 19.7 in block diagram form. Since the actual magnitude of any magnetic resonance absorption is minute and must be located precisely according to the ratio to be meaningful, a high-resolution instrument requires at least the following components:

1. A magnet producing a very steady, strong, homogeneous field, H_0, to produce intense nuclear Zeeman splitting;

2. A highly stable rf oscillator (or transmitter) to produce a low-power rf magnetic field H_1 from which energy can be absorbed for magnetic transitions;

3. A sensitive rf amplifier-detector (or receiver) to detect the resonance signal of the sample and separate it from the rf oscillator signal;

4. A linear sweep circuit to vary the steady magnetic field or the rf frequency through a range of values that includes all resonances of interest in order to obtain a spectrum;

5. A readout device to display the NMR spectrum.

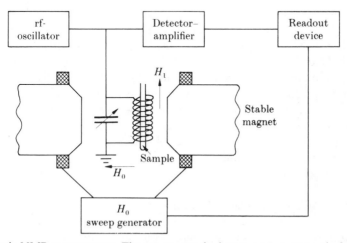

Fig. 19.7 Basic NMR spectrometer. The strong, steady, homogeneous magnetic field H_0 basic to the instrument is established by the magnet. A weak rf magnetic field H_1 is applied at 90° to the basic field. Field H_1 results from directing the output of the rf oscillator through the coil around the sample tube. An NMR spectrum is obtained by sweeping either the basic magnetic field (as here) or the rf frequency over the range of interest.

The instrument pictured in Fig. 19.7 is a single-channel, unmodulated spectrometer. Yet the types of modules shown are common to nearly all NMR spectrometers and it will be helpful here to consider the important aspects of each in detail. In the next section those additional features necessary to obtain the field-frequency "lock" characteristic of a double-channel spectrometer are discussed. Further, the assembling of modules into a Fourier transform spectrometer is considered in Section 19.10.

Magnets. Either permanent magnets, electromagnets, or superconducting solenoids can be used to supply the field H_0. Precision spectral uses require that the field be as intense as possible to maximize the sensitivity of the method. A very high degree of homogeneity and time-stability are also necessary. Given these requirements, practical limits on field strength for permanent magnets appear to be about 14 kilogauss (kG), electromagnets 23.5 kG, and superconducting solenoids 100 kG or greater. Corresponding proton resonance frequencies are approximately 60, 100, and 400 MHz. Feedback-stabilized dc power supplies provide the current for electromagnets and superconducting solenoids. With any of the three types of magnet, spectral resolution equivalent to a homogeneity of magnetic field of a few parts in 10^9 has been realized. The distinctive advantages of permanent magnets are simplicity and freedom from most maintenance problems; the advantage of electromagnets, greater field strength without excessive complexity; the advantage of superconducting magnets, unsurpassed field strength.

All types of magnets require *shimming* to reduce local inhomogeneities. Permanent magnets and electromagnets are based on a core of appropriate metal that is formed into a "U" in which a gap of as much as two to three inches is left to create the poles. Then, on either side of the gap, the magnet is capped with a pole piece of metal of desired magnetic properties that is designed and carefully polished to reduce fringing at the edges and maximize field homogeneity at the center of the gap. With both permanent magnets and electromagnets, close shimming also involves the use of *homogenizing coils.* Several coils are placed on the pole faces to impose a small magnetic field of adjustable gradient on the small residual gradients remaining in the basic magnet field. By adjusting the current in these shim coils one can cancel the gradients in the main field. A feedback-stabilized dc voltage supply is a prerequisite for an electromagnet to minimize fluctuations and drift. Often "automatic shimming," an additional control of field homogeneity, is provided by feedback from monitoring resonance signals. The last process is especially important in maintaining homogeneity over long intervals such as are needed in time averaging (Section 19.9).

In a superconducting solenoid type of magnet, homogeneity of the field depends entirely on the pattern of the coil winding. Shim coils are also used to minimize gradients.

In addition, all types of magnets require temperature control. With a permanent magnet the temperature coefficient of field strength is somewhat larger than that with an electromagnet. Room-temperature thermostating provides the necessary temperature control for the magnet. Superconducting solenoids are maintained in a liquid helium cryostat at 4 °K to ensure superconductivity of their wire or ribbon (usually a copper-coated niobium alloy).

To reduce the effects of hysteresis in the metal core of an electromagnet, the current in an electromagnet is "cycled" above normal values for a few minutes when a magnet is first turned on. This process removes previous magnetic history and produces a more uniform field. When a superconducting solenoid is turned on, applications of successively larger currents are required before the desired level of field intensity is attainable while maintaining superconduction.

RF oscillator.   The rf oscillator is ordinarily crystal-controlled to ensure stability and precision in fixing its frequency. For example, a crystal cut to oscillate at exactly 15 MHz (to one part in 10^7) might be used with two frequency-doubling amplifier circuits (which use harmonics of the crystal frequency and thus retain the original precision of specification) to obtain an output of 60 MHz. Close thermostating of the crystal and proper circuit design allows achievement of a frequency constant to 1 ppm. Only a low-power output signal is needed.

A frequency sweep to scan a spectrum can be provided by adding a variable small frequency to the basic frequency. For routine proton NMR spectroscopy of organic substances a scan over a range of about 10 ppm (600 Hz at 60 MHz) suffices, while for nuclei like ^{19}F and ^{11}B sweeps of as much as 300 ppm (16 kHz at 56.6 MHz) are usually required. On mixing the sweep and basic rf frequencies both sum and difference frequencies are obtained. For the purpose, a single sideband modulator can be used to select the sum $\omega_0 + \omega_m$ and reject the difference frequency. Techniques of tuning and modulation are briefly discussed in Section 19.8.

A second oscillator is used to generate the sweep frequency. In general, it is a variable-frequency audiofrequency oscillator tuned to about the frequency at which it operates most efficiently. For example, a 2 kHz oscillator might be tuned from 1 to 3 kHz to obtain a sweep of 2 kHz.

Though the magnet and rf oscillator are independently stabilized, their outputs may drift relative to each other, lessening the accuracy of measurements. A means of maintaining an exact field-frequency ratio by control of the rf oscillator frequency is discussed in the next section.

Field or frequency sweep.   In Fig. 19.7 the scan necessary to obtain a spectrum is shown as accomplished by sweeping field H_0 while a constant rf frequency is imposed on the sample. In this case it is customary to generate a dc-sweep signal, which is applied to a sweep coil on the pole faces of the magnet. In simplest form the generator is a potentiometer whose wiper is driven over a voltage range and at a rate selected by the operator. For example, in proton NMR spectrometry H_0 need be swept only through about 10 milligauss for a 60 MHz instrument.

The approach first discussed, sweeping the rf oscillator through a small range of frequencies at constant H_0, has become more widely used as it has become possible to vary the frequency of stable rf oscillators in reproducible fashion. Each approach has advantages.

Sample probe and sample tube.   As sketched in Fig. 19.7 the output of the rf oscillator energizes a very small coil that surrounds the sample tube. Usually the coil and related components are incorporated in a probe that is designed to utilize the narrow space between the magnet pole pieces efficiently. The rf coil is perhaps one mm long and consists of a very few turns of wire. The sample is placed along the axis of the coil. Provision is also often made for thermostating the portion of the probe containing the sample, in order that the temperature dependence of resonance amplitudes may be studied as well as changes in exchange rate (Section 19.11).

Customarily, a small capacitor is wired in parallel with the rf coil to form an LC circuit that can be tuned to resonance at the rf frequency. This arrangement increases the Q of the circuit (Section 2.8) and thus:

1. Facilitates the transfer of energy from the rf oscillator since the LC circuit and sample appear as a pure resistance and

2. Improves the sensitivity of detection of resonance absorption if the coil also serves as the detector, as it often does.

The sample shape should be an ellipsoid of revolution to minimize distortion of the magnetic flux. Since most NMR samples are liquid solutions, a cylindrical shape is usually chosen. A precision bore tube is filled until the length/diameter ratio of the sample roughly approximates that of an infinite cylinder (a ratio of five is adequate in practice). If an external standard is needed, it is ordinarily placed in a concentric capillary tube. For minute samples a tube with a capillary bore that widens to a spherical cavity at the position of the rf coil seems the best arrangement.

In any event, the size of the coil, and thus of the sample, is a compromise between securing greater sensitivity by having more magnetic nuclei within the field of the exciting coil and securing better resolution by confining the coil to a region small enough for the magnetic field H_0 to be nearly homogeneous.

Spinning. Inevitably, in spite of automatic shimming and use of a small sample, there are residual field inhomogeneities within the sample volume. If the axis of coil and sample tube is taken as the y-direction, inhomogeneities in the x- and z-directions may be substantially reduced by the simple expedient of spinning the sample tube at from 20 to 40 Hz. The rate of spinning should be proportional to the remaining field gradient ΔH_0 across the sample and to the rate of spectral scanning, so that a magnetic nucleus behaves as if exposed to the time-averaged—thus uniform—field. For a slow scan, the spinning rate suggested averages out gradients of about 10^{-3} G. An air-driven rotor placed in the top of the sample tube is sufficient to produce the desired spinning. A reduction valve serves to keep the air pressure constant and stroboscopic effects based on the 60 Hz flicker of fluorescent lights can be used to ascertain an approximate spinner speed.

Where a superconducting solenoid is used to develop H_0, a cylindrical probe coaxial with the solenoid is employed. The features described above are carried over to it in general. A single exception is the rf coil, which must be arranged perpendicular to the sample tube, which in this unit is *along the z-direction*. The probe is kept at room temperature, though the solenoid is maintained near $4\,°K$.

Since the spinning modulates H_1 at the rate of spin v_{spin}, it may also give rise to low-intensity *spin bands* or spinning sidebands in the spectrum, "ghost" lines located at $v_0 \pm nv_{spin}$, where $n = 1, 2, \ldots$ on either side of a strong magnetic resonance absorption at v_0. These bands may be identified by their movement as the rate of spinning is changed and thus can also be shifted to avoid superposition on a spectral line.

Detector-amplifier. In the single-channel NMR spectrometer, a single coil usually serves to impose the rf magnetic field and to detect resonance absorptions. Somehow these signals must be separated from the larger "carrier wave." This may be done by use of an rf bridge in which the exciting signal is balanced against an equal amplitude reference with the modulation appearing as bridge unbalance and extractable in that form. Alternatively, the signal can be amplified for stability and then subjected to diode detection to extract the resonance spectrum. Where resonances are weak, as is often the case, this procedure is poor, since the noise level attendant on handling the basic rf output is so high as to provide a very poor signal-to-noise ratio.

The detection of resonances against the background of the strong exciting rf field may also be simplified by use of separate coils for excitation and detection. This *crossed-coil arrangement* is not as common as the single-coil procedure. If the H_0 field is directed along the z-axis, and the rf coil and sample tube are along the y-axis, a detection coil can be placed along the x-axis. Since magnetic resonance produces a net magnetization in the xy-plane, this design permits selective pickup of the resonance while virtually excluding the rf field. [24] The coupling between coil and sample is not as efficient as with a single coil, since a split coil is necessary, with part of it located on either side of the sample holder. In a crossed-coil system an audiofrequency amplifier replaces the rf unit of Fig. 19.7.

Calibration. Both relative separations of resonance lines and their intensities, in terms of areas under the peaks, must be known for an NMR spectrum to be interpreted with assurance. Since many variables affect such measurements, it is customary to determine position relative to a standard resonance peak. The most widely used proton NMR standard is tetramethylsilane, $(CH_3)_4Si$, which can be dissolved in many solutions as an internal reference and whose 12 magnetically equivalent protons give a single absorption line of unusual strength. Choosing a reference, deciding between an internal and an external reference, and determining when bulk diamagnetic susceptibility corrections are necessary will be discussed in Section 19.11.

Actually, observing resonance spectra relative to a standard solves only a part of the problem of locating lines accurately. Some further means of measurement to calibrate the spectral scale, usually in hertz, must be employed. The field/frequency stabilization process discussed in the next section in fact provides such a calibration for the double-channel instrument. The maintenance of the "lock" ensures that the ratio ω_0/H_0 is at a standard value. A set of substances with known single resonances such as that shown in Fig. 19.6 can also be used.

With a single-channel spectrometer, however, the most convenient calibration method is the *sideband* technique. A stable audiofrequency (af) oscillator is used to superpose a known frequency ω_m on the radiofrequency signal or on the magnetic field H_0. If the amplitude of the audiofrequency is small, each of the original resonance lines will appear at $\omega_0 - \omega_m$, ω_0, and $\omega_0 + \omega_m$. The lines on either side of the central resonance (at ω_0) are the sidebands, separated from it by the exact frequency of the oscillator in the manner that spinning sidebands were. The frequency separation of two lines can be established by varying the frequency of the af oscillator until a sideband of the first line exactly coincides with the second. Usually line separations can be determined to ± 0.5 Hz.*

If spectral lines are closely spaced, signal distortion often makes it difficult to use the sideband of an internal reference. An external reference is then useful. Its sidebands can be superposed in the same way. Other methods are available as well. [4]

Peak areas are, in general, proportional to the number of equivalent nuclei involved in a resonance as long as saturation is minimized. (Unfortunately, peak heights are seldom usable to fix the number of nuclei per molecular constituent responsible for a particular resonance. They can be so used if line widths are equal, i.e., if T_2's for the resonances are equal.)

Actually, peak areas also depend on the rf field strength and the longitudinal and transverse relaxation times. If a slow scan rate and low rf field strength are used, and only a $\pm 5\%$ reliability is required, these factors can usually be neglected. There is sufficient dependence, however, to make it difficult to compare exactly areas associated with resonances that have unequal relaxation times because of different magnetic environments or different solvent influences. Unfortunately, slow passage can also lead to saturation and is thus not always practicable if high resolution is required. In summary, if a quantative analysis is to be performed on a multicomponent system, it is essential that a calibration curve be run using known quantities of material (Section 19.14).

19.8 DOUBLE-CHANNEL SPECTROMETER

With a dual-channel NMR spectrometer the calibration of the instrument can be maintained over a period of time. To accomplish this goal the design must provide that

1. The ratio ω_0/H_0 be held constant, i.e., the stability of the resonance condition must be ensured.
2. Either H_0 or ω_0 also be fixed, and
3. The level of oscillator output, detection, and amplification be kept constant, i.e. "baseline stabilization" must be maintained.

Accordingly, instrumental means must be provided to limit both fast fluctuations and long-term drift to a few parts in 10^9.

The double-channel design, when coupled with af modulation of H_0, is well suited to meet these needs. One channel is locked on the sharp single resonance of a reference substance, such as water or tetramethylsilane, while the other is used to scan the spectrum of a sample. Both channels use the same crystal-controlled rf oscillator and magnet. In general, their rf coils, sample holders, amplifier-detectors, and other stages are separate, with the control channel providing a feedback correction signal to the rf oscillator and/or magnet to maintain the ω_0/H_0 ratio.

---

* Sideband modulation at *high* sideband amplitudes introduces errors, since the sidebands do not appear at exactly $\omega_0 \pm \omega_m$ but rather at $\omega_0 \pm (\omega_m + \omega')$ where ω' increases with increasing relative sideband amplitude.

AF modulation. An audiofrequency modulating field of frequency ω_m is also applied to the sample and reference compound in double-channel NMR spectroscopy. Since the effect of modulation is to produce sidebands on each line, in regular high-resolution NMR spectrometry ω_m is chosen to be greater than the width of the typical spectral range for the nucleus under study. For example, in 60 MHz proton NMR, any modulation frequency greater than 1 kHz should be suitable. A modulating frequency of 4 or 5 kHz is usually selected. In most cases the modulation is applied to H_0. The af signal is applied to a separate coil on the magnet face, and its amplitude is regulated to give a fluctuating H_m of about 0.1 mG.

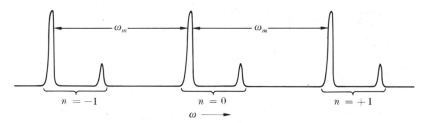

Fig. 19.8 Effect of modulating H_0 at frequency ω_m for the proton NMR spectrum of toluene. Sidebands are formed at $\omega_0 \pm n\omega_m$ for each resonance line. In a double-channel NMR spectrometer all replicate spectra are rejected except those for which $n = +1$. In this example, $\omega_0 = 60$ MHz and $\omega_m \approx 1$ kHz.

When af modulation is used in high-resolution spectrometry, three or more replicate sets of spectra appear. The result for toluene is illustrated in Fig. 19.8. A given resonance peak is separated from its counterparts by integral multiples of ω_m. That is, resonances are found at $\gamma H_0 = (\omega_o \pm n\omega_m) = $ constant, where $n = 1, 2, 3, \ldots$. It is customary to isolate the first sideband resonance on the high-frequency side ($n = +1$) of the centerband in the detection process in both channels.

It can be shown [11] that if the absorption-mode component is detected the resonance at the upper sideband is like a regular signal except that its amplitude is reduced by a factor depending on the modulation index ($\gamma H_m/\omega_m$) of the af signal. Thus maximum amplitude (and sensitivity) in NMR spectral measurements depends on keeping the modulation index small (it is about 0.1 in some instruments) and letting the saturation parameter be at its optimum value. Then the effective rf field is $H_{eff} = H_1(\gamma H_m/2\omega_m)$.

Sideband oscillator NMR spectrometer. One type of double-channel proton NMR spectrometer featuring 5 kHz modulation of H_0 is shown in block diagram form in Fig. 19.9. It incorporates a so-called nuclear sideband oscillator loop in the control channel. Its operation is as follows. Field H_0 is fixed at 14.092 kG and the rf oscillator frequency is set at 60.000 MHz. Water is used as a reference compound in the rf coil that is part of the control channel. Any instantaneous instability that causes the water proton to undergo magnetic resonance gives rise to a 14.005 MHz signal in the reference channel.

As a result of the positive feedback provided by the nuclear sideband oscillator loop, this resonance frequency can be sustained. The water signal at 60.005 MHz is

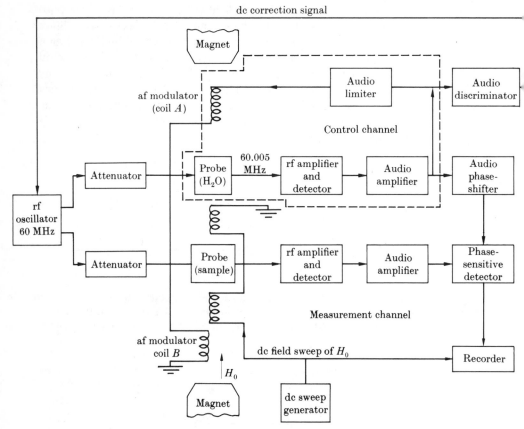

Fig. 19.9 Block diagram of the Varian A-60 series double-channel proton NMR spectrometer. It features (a) a magnetic field sweep or scan, (b) a field-frequency lock (based on the resonance of the water reference in the upper probe coil and operation of the control channel), and (c) noise-reduction (based especially on audiofrequency modulation of the sample in the lower probe coil and phase-sensitive detection of the resonance signal). Both reference and sample are subject to a fixed-frequency 60 MHz magnetic field H_1, and a roughly 5 kHz modulation of the static magnetic field H_0. This modulation is in effect a modulation of H_1 also. The probe modules include the coils that generate field H_1. Different dc magnetic fields prevail, however. The reference is exposed only to H_0 but the sample is exposed both to H_0 and $H_{sweep-coil}$. As a result, the sample is swept through a range of H_0 values sufficient to generate its proton NMR spectrum. (Courtesy of Varian Analytical Instrument Division.)

amplified and mixed with the 60.000 MHz signal from the rf oscillator after a 90° phase shift. After mixing, the signal is diode-detected. Only the 5 kHz difference signal corresponding to the resonance absorption survives. This 5 kHz signal is also amplified, then limited appropriately in amplitude and used to modulate H_0. Without the limiter stage the amplitude of the 5 kHz signal increases sufficiently for it to begin to saturate the water resonance. If this happens, frequency stabilization is lost. Since precise phasing is also essential to stability, the af amplifier is designed to offer minimum phase change with frequency. Such change as does occur is usually offset by the phase slope of the water-resonance line.

How is the frequency-field ratio maintained constant? The output of the audio amplifier is partly sent to an af discriminator circuit to generate a dc control signal. This signal is fed back to the crystal oscillator to maintain its frequency exactly and to the magnet to control its field. If the value of ω_0/H_0 alters, the water-resonance position shifts. As a result, the audiofrequency changes and a different dc voltage appears at the discriminator output. This voltage is applied to a variable capacitor used to tune the output of the rf oscillator through a small range. In this case the capacitor is a specially designed semiconductor diode whose capacitance is a linear function of the voltage across it (Section 4.4). When there is a proper choice of variables, the basic oscillator is automatically and essentially instantaneously returned to the proper frequency. The magnetic field control will be established somewhat similarly. The arrangement is known as a frequency-field "lock."

In a double-channel instrument the sample probe is more complex, since it contains both channels. A second rf coil is required for the sample tube. It is located sufficiently close to the rf coil about the reference compound so that they are subject to static H_0's that are as nearly the same as possible. Since the 5 kHz output of the sideband oscillator modulates H_0, the sample is also in the modulated field. In the sample channel after the resonance signal is separated from the rf signal (detected) and amplified, it enters a phase-sensitive detector (Section 8.7). Only the component in phase with the modulating 5 kHz signal from the measurement channel emerges. This absorption-mode readout is nearly the same signal as would have been obtained without af modulation. It may also be noted that the measurement channel provides for automatic gain control such that dependence of signal amplitude on H_1 is largely removed.

Frequency synthesizer spectrometer. A related spectrometer design using a crystal-based frequency synthesizer is shown in Fig. 19.10. A 14 kG permanent magnet is used. The different frequencies needed for NMR spectroscopy of ^{19}F, ^{31}P, ^{11}B, and ^{13}C, as well as ^{1}H, are synthesized. For each frequency a suitable harmonic—up to the twelfth harmonic of an approximately 5 MHz crystal oscillator—is selected and mixed with the output of the most appropriate of several stable low-frequency incremental oscillators.

The control channel "locks" on the proton resonance of a water sample at 60.005 MHz. Its frequency synthesizer uses the twelfth harmonic of the base oscillator at 59.9 MHz and mixes this frequency in a single-sideband modulator with the 0.1 MHz frequency output of one of the incremental oscillators to give 60.0 MHz. The final increment of 5 kHz is supplied by a stable 5 kHz af oscillator that also modulates the H_0 field of the permanent magnet. The rest of the control circuit is similar to that shown in Fig. 19.9. In this case the control signal adjusts only the frequency of the basic crystal oscillator.

If the measurement channel is used for proton NMR, its components are nearly identical to those in the control channel. An rf bridge-amplifier arrangement is used to balance the signal from the rf oscillator against that from the sample coil. The output is a 5 kHz signal only when a resonance signal is received; otherwise, it is a steady dc signal that provides baseline stability. Af amplification and phase-sensitive detection using the output of the 5 kHz oscillator completes the channel.

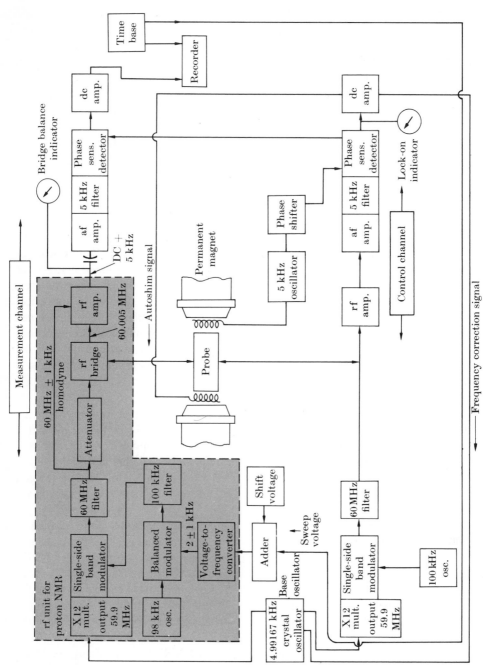

Fig. 19.10 Block diagram of Hitachi-Perkin-Elmer R-20 Double Channel NMR Spectrometer. (Courtesy of Perkin-Elmer Corporation.)

For other nuclei, plug-in units provide a different multiplier (circuit for selecting the desired harmonic), incremental oscillator, sweep oscillator, and rf bridge-amplifier arrangement. For example, for NMR spectrometry with ^{11}B, a $4\times$ multiplier (yielding an output of 20 MHz), a 0.7 MHz incremental oscillator, and a single sideband modulator that mixes the two outputs and selects the lower sideband ($20 - 0.7 = 19.3$ MHz) are used. This is just the value of the ^{11}B resonance frequency when $H_0 = 14.09$ kG. Spectra are obtained by using a 20 kHz sweep oscillator whose frequency is variable from 10 to 30 kHz.

Since any correction for drift of fluctuation in the ω_0/H_0 ratio is applied to the base crystal oscillator, it is of interest to examine the instability contributed by the incremental and sweep oscillators with the instrument locked on water protons. It can be assumed that very little instability is contributed by an incremental oscillator stable to 1 part in 10^6 per hour, if it provides only 0.1 MHz to the crystal oscillator.

A general treatment is desirable. Let F_H and F' be the proton resonance frequency and particular incremental oscillator frequency, respectively, and let K be the fraction of the proton frequency used for some nucleus F_i whose magnetogyric ratio is γ_i. Then the resonance condition will be $H_0\gamma_i = 2\pi(KF_H + F')$. Any variability in F' can be treated as an apparent instability in γ_i. Substituting for H_0 from the resonance condition for the proton, $H_0\gamma_H = 2\pi F_H$, one obtains

$$\gamma_i = (KF_H + F')\gamma_H/F_H.$$

Taking the differential of γ_i allows the sources of variability to be assessed:

$$d\gamma_i = \frac{dF'\gamma_H}{F_H} - \left(\frac{F'\gamma_H}{F_H^2}\right)dF_H.$$

With feedback control it can be assumed that dF_H is kept to a minimum, and the second term is negligible. Then the relative variation in γ_i, $d\gamma_i/\gamma_i$ is

$$\frac{d\gamma_i}{\gamma_i} = \frac{dF'\gamma_H}{\gamma_i F_H} = \frac{dF'}{(KF_H + F')} = \frac{dF'}{F_i}. \tag{19.12}$$

Eq. (19.12) can be used for an estimation of the instability. For proton NMR, the relative uncertainty in the measurement channel is about $dF'/F_i = 0.1$ Hz/60 $\times$ 10^6 Hz $= 1.66 \times 10^{-9}$, an absolute uncertainty of about 0.1 Hz. The sweep oscillator, which may be treated as a second incremental oscillator, is stable to 1 part in 10^4 and contributes an uncertainty of less than 0.2 Hz. The overall stability proves sufficiently great to make it possible to locate a proton resonance precisely to within less than 0.4 Hz. For other nuclei, which give much broader resonances than protons, the uncertainty in resonance positions is from 2 to 5 Hz.

A frequency synthesizer spectrometer can be extended with equal precision to nuclei such as ^{14}N and ^{17}O which undergo resonance at comparatively low frequencies (4.3 and 8.1 MHz when $H_0 = 14.1$ kG) by use of a lower-frequency crystal oscillator (perhaps 0.25 MHz) and appropriate changes in the incremental oscillators. [12]

For versatile NMR spectroscopy, four additional types of modules prove especially valuable: filter, integrator, double resonance oscillator, and time-averaging computer. Each will now be described briefly.

Filter. An RC low-pass filter (Section 3.5) is nearly always used to reduce random noise, especially of the $1/f$ variety, and enhance the signal-to-noise ratio. Actually, this simple network is a good approximation to the optimum filter for a spectral line, usually termed a matched filter. A double-section RC filter (one low-pass filter followed by an amplifier and a second low-pass filter) gives nearly the maximum possible enhancement. In filtering, a compromise must be struck between the gain in sensitivity and the accompanying increase in signal distortion. In this case, for a double-section filter the peak height is reduced about 40–50 %, and the width doubled. The *optimum time constant* for a filter can be shown to be $2.2\omega_2/\alpha$ for a single-section unit and ω_2/α for a double-section unit, where ω_2 is the half-width of the resonance peak at half-height and α is the sweep rate.

Example   For a resonance signal with a half-width at half-height of 0.2 Hz scanned at a sweep rate of 2 Hz s^{-1}, an optimum filter can be prescribed. If it is a double-section filter its time constant ($\tau = RC$) should be $RC = \omega_2/\alpha = 0.2/2 = 0.1$ s. If a single-section filter were used, its time constant should be 0.22 s.

Integrator.   Any standard type of electronic integrator (Section 7.6) can be used to obtain areas under resonance peaks for quantative applications. It is coupled to the spectrometer output. A time-averaging computer also can function as an integrator.

Double resonance oscillator.   This module is a stable, variable-frequency oscillator that establishes a second rf magnetic field H_2 perpendicular to the dc field H_0. It is convenient to label the first rf field, H_1, the observing field and the second, H_2, the perturbing field. The output of the double resonance oscillator is "added" to that of the first rf generator. The effect of the perturbing field is identified by measuring the signal from the sample when the frequency of the observing field is varied. An oscilloscopic display of the NMR spectrum aids greatly in the final tuning of the double resonance oscillator. Its frequency is varied until a characteristic change occurs in the lines of a particular resonance multiplet (Section 19.12). For example, in the simplest double resonance procedure, spin decoupling, a multiplet collapses into a singlet or simpler multiplet when the *proper perturbing frequency* is reached.*

Homonuclear double resonance involves simultaneous excitation of nuclei of the same kind in different magnetic environments and requires that the frequency of H_2 be very close (about 10–100 Hz for protons) to that of H_1. In this case field H_2 can be generated by use of an audiofrequency oscillator. An rf oscillator is required for *heteronuclear* double resonance such as is taken up in the example below. The second oscillator must be stable yet variable both in frequency and amplitude. In still other applications a "white noise" audiofrequency double resonance oscillator is useful since it can accomplish blanket excitation of all resonances of a particular nuclear species of interest and accomplish massive spin decoupling. Double resonance techniques will be further treated in Section 19.13.

---

* In double resonance procedures a sweep of H_0, the static magnetic field, cannot be used to generate the spectrum. If H_0 were varied, the effect would be the same as varying the frequency of both H_1 and H_2 simultaneously.

Time-averaging computer. By coupling a highly stable NMR spectrometer to a digital computer it is possible to scan a spectrum repeatedly and sum the results. In this instance the NMR resonance signals will add linearly with the number of times n the spectrum is scanned. The background will add only as $n^{1/2}$ if it consists principally of random thermal noise. For other types of noise, this dependence is essentially valid also. As a result of such time-averaging an improvement in the quality of a spectrum proportional to $n^{1/2}$ is achieved (Section 8.5). For example, averaging 100 scans or traces of a resonance improves the quality tenfold. It is clearly advantageous to add as many scans as possible within the time available.

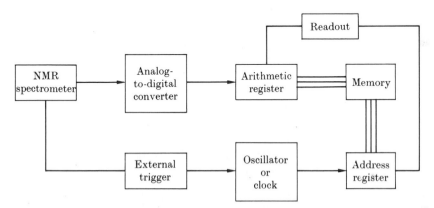

Fig. 19.11 Time-averaging computer connected to receive the output of an NMR spectrometer. All modules to the right of the NMR spectrometer are part of the computer. The oscillator or clock provides a sequence of equally-spaced, equal-duration pulses that determine the intervals at which the spectrum amplitude is sampled and registered. Thus a clock rate is used that matches the scan rate of the spectrometer.

A block diagram of a time-averaging computer is shown in Fig. 19.11. It provides that each NMR spectrum be converted to a digital output, i.e. translated into data points, and stored in a memory. The amplitude of the NMR signal is simply recorded at as many regularly spaced frequencies as the computer has memory channels— often 1024. The address register ensures that each memory channel receives the proper data points. Sampling is begun when an external trigger pulse, usually obtained from the resonance of TMS or other reference, starts the clock.*

Since an entire spectrum is seldom of interest, scanning is usually limited to the range containing resonance peaks of interest. Given a sufficiently small portion of a spectrum of interest, one can achieve as much as a hundredfold improvement of sensitivity by scanning it 10,000 times. The real advantage of the method is that more dilute solutions and smaller samples can be studied by NMR spectrometry.

19.9 OPTIMIZING SENSITIVITY

Since nuclear magnetization effects are inherently small and must be detected in the presence of a great deal of thermal noise (see Table 19.1), methods to enhance sensi-

---

* This process also provides compensation for drift in the NMR spectrometer.

tivity of measurement assume great importance. Indeed, conventional NMR methods are limited to reasonably concentrated samples (10 parts per thousand or higher) even for magnetic isotopes giving strong signals. Often applications of NMR methods fail because of lack of sensitivity, e.g., in instances where the transitions observed are of isotopes of weak magnetic moment or low abundance, such as ^{13}C, ^{17}O, and ^{33}S. In this section most of the known procedures for enhancing the signal-to-noise ratio are brought together even though many are also treated elsewhere in the chapter. In the following section a different type of NMR spectrometry, Fourier transform spectrometry, will be discussed as another significant way to enhance sensitivity.

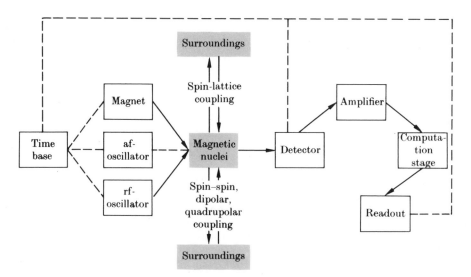

Fig. 19.12 Schematic diagram of the complex of influences that affect an NMR response.

In considering sensitivity it is helpful to discern the complex interrelationships that affect an NMR system. These are suggested schematically in Fig. 19.12. The magnetic nuclei in a sample are shown to be (a) coupled by various means to nearby atoms and molecules and (b) subjected to the fields applied by the magnet and the rf and af oscillators. The resonance NMR signals from the sample, which include noise (and a portion of the rf exciting energy if a single-coil arrangement is used), are coupled electrically to a detector and all the "information-processing components" of an NMR spectrometer. As a result of the inherent intricacy of the system, there is no single procedure for optimizing sensitivity, but a variety of methods each achieving particular limited objectives.

Enhancing the signal. Methods that produce an enhancement of signal amplitude will be taken up first. When a steady-state or equilibrium method—as opposed to a pulse method—is used, an external rf voltage $V = V_0 \cos \omega t$ is applied to the tuned circuit of the probe, and an absorption signal V_s is produced. It can be shown that V_s is given in terms of the frequency by the expression

$$V_s = Q^{1/2}v_c^{1/2}\zeta Nh^2\gamma I(I + 1)(T_2/T_1)^{1/2}v_0^{3/2}(6kT)^{-1}. \qquad (19.13)$$

Here Q is the quality factor of the LC circuit of which the coil is a part, v_c is the effective volume of the sample coil, ζ is a filling factor that defines the fraction of the effective rf-coil area occupied by the sample, N is the number of nuclei per cm^3, and other symbols are as defined earlier.

Inspection of Eq. (19.13) allows one to assess any of several ways in which variables may be adjusted to secure maximum signal. First, assume a particular nuclear species and molecular sample, fixing γ, I, and N. Then, the largest value of V_s can be obtained by arranging for as many of the following conditions to hold as possible.

1. The sample irradiation circuit consisting of rf coil and capacitors should be designed to have a high Q-value (Section 2.8). Basically, the coil should be small.

2. The sample (volume v_c) within the coil should be as large as possible. It is necessary to compromise between placing more nuclei within the coil and having a less homogeneous magnetic field. The longer the sample volume, the greater the field inhomogeneity experienced. The decision is usually made on the basis of the resolution sought, i.e., calls for maximum homogeneity.

3. The rf coil volume should be as fully occupied by sample as possible and the number of turns in a given volume should be large to increase ζ. All space needed in order to accomplish spinning and thermostating tends to reduce coupling with the rf coil. The compromise noted above affects the filling factor similarly.

4. It is advantageous to cool the sample. Again, a compromise must be struck. Lowering the temperature may also bring about an undesirable phase change such as freezing, or may lengthen the relaxation time T_1 to such an extent as to cause the factor $(T_2/T_1)^{1/2}$ in Eq. (19.13) to decrease. Further, an increase in T_1 may also make very slow scanning necessary to avoid saturation.

5. Actually, in terms of the ratio $(T_2/T_1)^{1/2}$, T_1 should be shortened if possible. For a species of spin $\frac{1}{2}$, T_1 can in many instances be decreased by introduction of paramagnetic ions. As stated earlier, such ions provide a faster relaxation mechanism through direct dipolar coupling. This procedure is well adapted to shortening proton relaxation times, but relatively ineffective for a nucleus like ^{13}C.

On the other hand, if T_2 is short and lines are broad, two other procedures effect an apparent shortening of T_1. First, it is sometimes possible to use a flow arrangement that permits a sample to be irradiated by rf field H_1 too short a time for saturation, but sufficiently long to permit an accurate measurement of a spectral trace. The flow rate must also be such that the time the magnetic nucleus spends in the rf field is at least as long as T_2 in order that further line broadening may be avoided. Alternatively, a fast sweep of the spectrum can shorten exposure of nuclei in particular molecular environments and avoid saturation. It is important that the sweep be slow enough to avoid line broadening, any shift in apparent frequency of the resonance line, and excessive relaxation "wiggles."

6. Indirect or spin-spin couplings between magnetic nuclei within a molecule (Section 19.12) can be eliminated. In most instances spin-spin coupling converts a given resonance from a strong single peak to a many-branched multiplet of the same total area under it. Spin-decoupling procedures allow the intensity distributed over

several lines to appear in a single resonance. The use of such procedures in quantitative analysis must be made with some caution, for area ratios may be affected.

7.   A higher frequency (and magnetic field) provides greater sensitivity. In spite of the theoretical $\frac{3}{2}$-power dependence indicated, practical considerations of achieving sufficiently stable fields are limiting. Thus the sensitivity at 100 MHz for protons is greater than at 60 MHz, but perhaps only 100/60 better.

Reducing noise. Sensitivity can be enhanced not only by increasing the amplitude of the signal, but by reducing the noise level. Indeed, in NMR measurements in which the amplitude of the noise is high, reduction of noise is of primary concern. As shown earlier (Section 8.3), the rms thermal noise is given by the expression $V_n = (4R_0kT\Delta f)^{1/2}$, where R_0 is the series resistance of the sample coil and Δf is the effective bandwidth of the circuit passing the narrowest band.

For improvement in sensitivity, as many of the following noise reduction procedures should be implemented as are appropriate in a given measurement.

1.   The noise arising within the electronic components should be reduced by using a low-noise detector, perhaps at low temperature, to diminish thermal noise.

2.   The instrumentation should feature a preamplifier and an amplifier first stage that have noise figures (Section 8.4) as close to unity as possible.

3.   The basic magnetic field or, uncommonly, the rf field, may be modulated by an appropriate audiofrequency to separate a great deal of noise from the signal. The essentials of this important method have already been presented in connection with fixing or "locking" the ω_0/H_0 ratio (Section 19.8).

Where an NMR spectrum covers a modest range, e.g., 600 Hz in the case of most proton NMR, it is desirable to modulate with a sine-wave frequency at least four or five times this figure.[*] If broad-line or broad-range spectra are involved, as in the NMR of solids, ESR, or quadrupole resonance spectroscopy, a low frequency that will give sidebands within the basic line width is appropriate. After rf amplification and electronic detection, a band pass filter can be used to eliminate $1/f$ noise (Section 8.7). Demodulation of the signal in a phase-sensitive detector follows.

4.   Methods using time-averaging are also very valuable (Section 19.9). Since noise is random, adding successive tracings of a spectrum tends to average it out. As an alternative, why isn't a single very slow scan preferable to analyzing many rapid scans obtained during the same time interval? Aside from instrumental instability, an important factor is that low-frequency $(1/f)$ noise can often obscure a portion of a spectrum regardless of scanning speed. Thus time-averaging of multiple scans is preferable.

An intermediate procedure of utility in the absence of a time-averaging computer is to sample a spectrum in discrete field steps.[†] The output at each point during a set

---

[*] Alternatively, square-wave modulation can be used and a gated "transmitter-detector system" provided. The oscillator output and rf detection system work alternately. It is necessary that the alternation be fast enough for the magnetic spin system not to be affected. RF oscillator noise is completely eliminated and difficulties in increasing the power to maintain a favorable modulation index are avoided.

[†] M. M. Crutchfield, *Abstracts of 4th Oceans Conf.*, Pittsburgh, 1963, Session C-3, Paper 7.

interval, e.g., 30 s, is applied to an integrating amplifier. Its output is recorded and the field advanced to the next point. The result takes the form of a series of adjacent parallel lines whose envelope is the desired spectrum.

5.   Following demodulation, a low-pass RC filter can be used to reduce the amplitude of frequencies of little or no interest. In practice a choice of a particular filter represents a compromise between reduction of noise and distortion of the basic signal.

6.   Data smoothing procedures using a computer are also valuable. They involve implementing the assumption that spectral data form a continuous, reasonably smooth curve. Corrections are applied in terms of a convolution function. [9]

19.10 FOURIER TRANSFORM NMR SPECTROMETRY

Two essentially equivalent procedures for obtaining an NMR spectrum have been discussed up to this point: (1) a frequency sweep method, in which the frequency v of rf magnetic field H_1 is varied while the dc field H_0 is held constant, and (2) a field sweep procedure, in which the intensity of field H_0 is varied while v is fixed. Since these methods employ a constant amplitude rf field, they are often called *continuous wave* (cw) *procedures*.

This section deals with an alternative way to obtain a spectrum, the Fourier transform method. The procedure consists of holding H_0 constant and applying the rf field, H_1, to the sample as a series of short (1 to 10^3 μs), comparatively strong (0.2 to 200 G) pulses. The pulse amplitude is made sufficient to saturate all the magnetic spin transitions of the nuclear species of interest. Between pulses a magnetic signal called the free induction decay is observed as the excited spin system relaxes. This signal is directed to a computer, which performs a Fourier transformation and converts the data to a regular NMR spectrum. Because all transition frequencies are observed simultaneously, the method can yield substantially greater sensitivity than cw NMR spectrometry. As a result, it is attractive for nuclei such as ^{13}C that inherently give weak NMR signals (Section 19.2) and for samples with concentrations less than 1%. We shall consider its sensitivity further below.

How are appropriate values for pulse amplitude H_1 and pulse length τ found? The nuclear species of interest and the spectral range of its resonances at a given rf frequency are determinative. It can be shown that excitation of the nuclear species occurs over the expected frequency range F (in hertz) when H_1 is sufficiently large that

$$\gamma H_1 > 2\pi F,$$

where γ is the magnetogyric ratio of the species. Usually the value of H_1 is fixed on this basis. On the other hand, the strength of free induction decay signals is significantly affected by both H_1 and the length of pulses. When an rf pulse of length τ is applied, the collection of nuclear spins is tipped through an angle α, where $\alpha = \gamma H_1 \tau$. After the pulse, relaxation effects cause the spins to move back toward the Z-axis. It can be shown that maximum signal is secured when the tipping is just balanced by relaxation effects and a "steady state" is achieved. It proves convenient to fix H_1 (see above) and adjust α by varying the value of τ empirically.

It is the free-induction decay signal that contains the desired spectral information about the nuclear species of interest.* All spin transition frequencies of the sample are present, each changing in intensity with time according to its characteristic relaxation time. The free induction signal is thus an interference pattern that changes with time and is often termed an *interferogram*. This pattern, unfortunately, does not lend itself to straightforward interpretation in terms of constituent frequencies, line widths, and amplitudes.† The Fourier transformation of the interferogram to yield the desired spectrum can be performed quickly (in a few seconds) by a digital computer using the Cooley-Tukey algorithm.

How long should the decay signal be observed? The answer will determine the spacing of pulses and the total time required to obtain a desired sensitivity of measurement. Resolution, i.e., peak width (at half height) will also be determined in the process. Since a resonance line width is fixed by the magnitude of relaxation time T_2, for high resolution the observation time T should satisfy the inequality

$$T \gg T_2.$$

A further factor of interest is that the interferogram is the true Fourier transform of a regular NMR spectrum only if the induction signal is observed for an infinite time. When the signal is observed for only T seconds, it can be shown that spectral lines are broadened to a width nearly equal to $1/T$. For example, if $T = 1$ sec the line width will be about 1 Hz. Other effects, such as slight line shifts also occur, but can generally be neglected. Again it is clear that a longer observation will enhance resolution.

Unfortunately, the noise content of the induction signal rises with increasing time. This inherent tendency can be offset in part by applying an exponentially decreasing weighting function‡ to the induction signal. Nevertheless, if maximum sensitivity is needed, T should be short and additional pulses should be applied as rapidly as possible. For each system therefore a decision must be made between resolution and sensitivity.

To take the Fourier transform of the induction decay signal its amplitude must be sampled at regular time intervals. It can be shown from information theory that to cover an nmr spectrum F Hz long, the sampling interval t must be just $t = 1/2F$. After each interval the signal is sampled and its amplitude is digitized (Section 9.7) and stored in a computer channel. Clearly, the number of channels must equal $2F$. The nature of the sampling process causes a "folding back" or aliasing (Section 17.12) of the spectral features. Normally this undesirable behavior is avoided by use of a cut-off filter that blocks frequencies greater than the highest frequency known to be of interest, F.

---

* The inhomogeneity of the magnetic field H_0 also contributes to the decay signal because it leads to a loss of coherence in phase of the precessing nuclei.
† The interferogram can be described as the nmr spectrum in the "time domain." By contrast, the usual spectrum is the same display in the "frequency domain," i.e., each point along the abscissa corresponds to a different frequency.
‡ Cf. discussion of apodizing function in Section 17.12.

Example How long must the free induction decay of ^{13}C be observed and how often must it be sampled if a 25 MHz spectrometer is used and a resolution of 1 Hz is sought? Assume the desired spectrum covers 200 ppm.

Recall that when the observation time is T seconds, resolution is defined by the equation $T = 1/R$, where R is the resolution sought. Applying the expression to this case gives $T = 1/1$ Hz $= 1$ s for the observation time. The sampling interval must be

$$t = 1/2F = 1/(2 \times 200 \times 10^{-6} \text{ Hz}) = 1 \times 10^{-4} \text{ s}.$$

During an observation interval 10,000 data points will be taken.

The demand on the associated computer is high: it must have 10,000 data channels. Many computers have no more than 4096 channels. Use of such a computer for the present work means either that resolution must be reduced or a smaller spectral range must be examined.

Sensitivity. The enhanced sensitivity of Fourier transform NMR spectrometry stems from the fact that all resonance frequencies are sampled during the entire period of measurement. Contrast this program with that of the usual frequency or field scan where a spectrometer spends most of its time registering the baseline between peaks. The gain in S/N of Fourier method over the slow passage cw procedure is given approximately by

$$(\text{spectral range/resolution})^{1/2}.$$

This expression assumes the same total time given to the Fourier and cw methods.

Alternatively, if a comparable S/N is sought in the two types of spectrometric technique, the Fourier method results in considerable time saving. The factor of gain in time is roughly given by spectral range/resolution.

Example What sensitivity enhancement is realized in applying pulse NMR spectrometry to ^{13}C spectroscopy? What time advantage can be realized? Assume 1 Hz resolution is required with a 25 MHz instrument and a spectral range of 200 ppm is to be observed.

The gain in sensitivity when equal times are spent can be as much as

$$(200 \times 10^{-6} \times 25 \times 10^{6}/1)^{1/2} = (5000)^{1/2} = 70.$$

To calculate the time advantage under conditions of equal S/N, assume that the cw spectrum is scanned at 1 Hz s^{-1}. Observing the ^{13}C spectrum will require 5000 s. By contrast, only 1 s is required by Fourier spectrometry.

Instrumentation. Pulse NMR spectrometers are basically similar to cw instruments. In the Fourier device an rf gate and clock (Section 9.4) must be added to generate pulses of precise length. The detector of the free induction signal must have circuitry suitable to allow it to recover quickly from each pulse. Because all frequencies are present simultaneously the detector-amplifier system must have good linearity. Field/frequency control is secured by use of an internal reference (whose frequency is isolated by a phase-sensitive detector). The differences in the spectrometers and the addition of digitizing and computing equipment make a Fourier transform NMR spectrometer presently more expensive and complex than a cw instrument. Continuing instrument development and the steady increase in use should lead to reduced costs. Fortunately, the cost of the associated small computers is also falling rapidly.

Finally, it should be emphasized that in addition to the growing use of the Fourier transform method for sensitivity enhancement, the method lends itself also to the determination of spin-lattice or longitudinal relaxation times of all transitions in a system.

19.11 THE CHEMICAL SHIFT

Proton NMR spectrometry is used routinely as a qualitative analytical technique, especially in identifying pure organic compounds. The dominance of proton spectroscopy may be traced to the widespread occurrence of hydrogen in compounds and the favorable sensitivity of the proton magnetic resonance signal. In this section attention will be given to one important basis for interpreting NMR spectral patterns.

Spectra are nearly always reported in terms of the *chemical shift*. This term is a measure of the difference in the degree of shielding experienced by a magnetic nucleus at a particular site in a molecule and in a reference compound. As noted earlier, a chemical shift is in general the result of diamagnetic shielding that arises because the lines of force of the applied external field H_0 are turned outward by the electrons around a nucleus. The smaller the amount of diamagnetic shielding, the weaker the external field required for resonance. There is also the possibility of a paramagnetic effect from surrounding electrons (lines of force turned in), but such an effect is of second order. According to Eq. (19.10), chemical shifts are directly proportional to the strength of the applied field H_0.

Three interrelated measures of chemical shift are in common use. Values are frequently cited in hertz whether a frequency scan has been used or not. This presentation lends itself to calculation of energies of transition and of coupling and also identifies spectral positions. Its disadvantage is that it depends linearly on the rf frequency used. For example, a 200 Hz shift at 60 MHz becomes at 100 MHz a $200 \times 100/60 = 333$ Hz shift. For this reason relative shifts δ and τ are used widely in spectral studies. For a proton spectrum obtained by *sweeping the magnetic field H_0* (while the rf is fixed) δ and τ are defined by the expressions

$$\delta = \frac{H_{ref} - H_{peak}}{H_{ref}} \times 10^6 = \frac{v_{ref} - v_{peak}}{v_{ref}} \times 10^6, \qquad (19.14)$$

$$\tau = 10 - \delta,$$

where H_{ref} and H_{peak} are the values of the magnetic field H_0 at which reference and sample protons resonate and v_{ref} and v_{peak} are the *equivalent* frequencies calculated from Eq. (19.6). When a *frequency sweep* or scan is used at fixed field H_0, the defining expression for δ changes to

$$\delta = \frac{v_{peak} - v_{ref}}{v_{ref}} \times 10^6. \qquad (19.15)$$

[The apparent discrepancy between Eqs. (19.14) and (19.15) may be resolved by considering the expression $v_0 = \gamma H_0(1 - \sigma)/2\pi$, which is obtained by combining

Eqs. (19.6) and (19.10).] On the δ scale *increasing values represent decreasing shielding* of the resonating nucleus relative to the reference. This scale will be used in this book.* Note that the τ scale is simply an alternate mode of representation in which increasing values correspond to increasing shielding. The dimensionless units of Eqs. (19.14) and (19.15) are preferable for reporting chemical shifts since these values are independent of instrumentation. Since the protons in tetramethylsilane (TMS), the most widely used reference in proton magnetic resonance spectrometry, are very well shielded virtually all chemical shifts are downfield from their resonance peak and give rise to positive values of δ. For nuclei other than H, δ is usually defined to be positive for upfield shifts. Representative ranges for some proton shifts are given in Table 19.5.

Table 19.5 Some Proton Chemical Shifts (Me_4Si internal reference)

Type of proton		Chemical shift, ppm
$Si-(CH_3)_4$		0.0
$R-CH_3$	(Methyl)	0.9–1.6
$RRCH_2$	(Methylene)	1.3
R_3CH	(Methyne)	2.5–3.2
⬡—H	(Aromatic)	6.4–8.0
⬡—OH	(Phenolic)	7.4–7.9
$R-OH$	(Hydroxylic)	1–5.5
$RCOOH$	(Carboxylic)	10.5–12
$RCHO$	(Aldehydic)	9–10
$H_3C-COOH$	(Methyl)	2–2.6
$RCOOCH_3$		3.7–4.9
$ROCH_3$		3.5–4

R = alkyl group.

Example All the ring protons in benzene are identical in terms of their local shielding from an external magnetic field. As a result they give rise to one resonance line 97 milligauss downfield from the TMS resonance when $H_0 = 14.092$ kG. The value of δ is then calculated to be (97 × 10^{-3} gauss/14,092 gauss) × $10^6 = 6.9$ ppm. If frequency scanning is used, the downfield shift of the benzene line for a basic rf frequency of 60 MHz proves to be 414 Hz. Again, δ is calculable as (414 Hz/60 × 10^6) × $10^6 = 6.9$ ppm.

---

* Alternatively, Eq. (19.14) can be written as

$$\delta' = (H_{peak} - H_{ref}) \times 10^6/H_{ref} = (\nu_{peak} - \nu_{ref}) \times 10^6/\nu_{ref}.$$

Note that $\delta' = -\delta$. Unfortunately, when δ' values are cited, the sign of δ', which is nearly always negative for proton chemical shifts relative to tetramethylsilane, is usually ignored.

It is useful to note two qualitative correlations between the chemical shift of a given nuclear magnetic species and its bonding. First, bonding to another atom of greater electronegativity should deshield the magnetic nucleus and shift its resonance downfield, i.e. to a lower value of H_0.

Example 1   As may be seen in Table 19.5, a proton resonance associated with a methyl group is shifted from $\delta = 0$ for a methyl group bonded to silicon (electronegativity, 1.8) to about $\delta = 1$ when the methyl group is bonded to carbon (electronegativity, 2.5) in a alkyl group.

Example 2   The substitution of successive chlorine atoms (electronegativity, 3.0) for hydrogen in methane gives rise to the following set of increasing chemical shifts: the proton resonance in CH_3Cl is at $\delta = 3.4$, in CH_2Cl_2 at $\delta = 5.4$ and in $CHCl_3$ at $\delta = 7.3$.

Example 3   In the compound

$$\underset{\text{(a)}\ \ \text{(b)}}{CH_3CH_2}-O-\underset{\text{(c)}}{CH_2}\overset{\displaystyle \overset{O}{\|}}{\underset{\text{(d)}}{C}}-OH$$

the four proton resonances marked occur at (downfield δ values in ppm) (a) 1.27, (b) 3.66, (c) 4.13, (d) 10.95. It is especially interesting to compare the resonance positions associated with the two sets of methylene protons. That between an ether oxygen and a carboxyl group has the greater downfield shift.

Second, increasing the acid character of an atom should deplete its electron density and shift its resonance downfield. For example, in Table 19.5 there is a striking downfield shift of the hydroxyl proton in going from ROH to RCOOH.

The identification of an absorption peak is aided by finding its integrated intensity or area. Such data are commonly traced by an electronic integrator on the same chart as the spectrum. Often they allow an unambiguous assignment to a particular set of atoms.

For example, an integrator would show the relative areas of the peaks in the ethanol spectrum of Fig. 19.3 as 1:2:3 in the upfield direction—the exact ratio of the number of protons in hydroxylic, methylene, and methyl sites.

Whether groups are placed symmetrically on a molecule can often be deduced by use of the chemical shift. If identical groups are located symmetrically, they will have the same chemical shift; if they are located in different structural positions, they will not. Thus, isomers of differing symmetry can sometimes be distinguished simply by counting the number of sets of peaks. For example, t-butyl alcohol has two resonances, n-butyl alcohol, four.

Variables affecting the chemical shift.   To what extent is the chemical shift of a given nucleus in a molecule dependent on solvent or other factors?

At least two kinds of solvent effects can be identified:

1. Those caused by a difference between the bulk diamagnetic susceptibility of the solute and solvent, and

2. Those originating in interactions between solute molecules or between solute and solvent molecules.

It is precisely to minimize the first that most NMR spectroscopic studies employ an *internal* standard. In this way the reference compound and sample are in a medium of the same bulk susceptibility, i.e. the solution. With an internal standard bulk magnetic susceptibility corrections need seldom be made. On the other hand, if there are substantial differences in homogeneity from point to point in a solution, as might be true if a solute is a macromolecule or if micelles form, bulk magnetic susceptibility corrections are desirable. Estimation of the correction for such cases is beyond the scope of this text.

In instances where an external reference must be used, a susceptibility correction is commonly called for. In terms of the Lorentz model introduced earlier (Section 19.4) in which a continuous medium of volume magnetic susceptibility χ_v lies outside the spherical cavity containing the molecule of interest, the effective field at the molecule is

$$H_{\text{eff}} = H_0[1 + (4\pi/3 - \alpha)\,\chi_v],$$

where α is a shape factor. For a sphere $\alpha = 4\pi/3$, for a cylinder of high length-to-width ratio $\alpha = 2\pi$. The equation may now be applied to the common case. Assume that a sample solution of susceptibility $\chi_{v,\text{sample}}$ and external reference of susceptibility $\chi_{v,\text{ref}}$ are in cylindrical coaxial tubes in the same external field H_0. After appropriate substitutions the equation above can be compared with Eq. (19.10). It is then evident that the screening constants σ_i of nuclei in each have been increased by the factors $(2\pi/3)\chi_{v,i}$. It is the difference $(2\pi/3)(\chi_{v,\text{ref}} - \chi_{v,\text{sample}})$ that is crucial, since, in effect, the sample solution must be corrected to the conditions of the external reference. Finally, since chemical shifts are directly related to screening constants, the corrected chemical shifts for the sample solution are just

$$\delta_{\text{corr}} = \delta_{\text{obs}} + (2\pi/3)(\chi_{v,\text{ref}} - \chi_{v,\text{sample}}). \tag{19.16}$$

What allowance to make for the second type of solvent effect is best determined for each case. Corrections for solvent effects are important mainly for proton NMR. For example, hydrogen bonding between a hydroxylic solute and solvent will alter the chemical shift of at least the hydroxyl proton. Solute-solute interactions are also marked for highly polarizable molecules such as those incorporating iodine or bromine. In addition special effects arise for aromatic compounds.*

If possible, such interactions should be minimized by a change of solvent. In any event, it is desirable to obtain measurements at several concentrations and extrapolate the chemical shift to infinite dilution.

Chemical exchange processes between different molecules also influence chemical shifts. An example is the exchange of hydroxyl protons between water and an alcohol in mutual solution, a process greatly accelerated by acid. Whether the separate chemi-

---

* The distinctive behavior of aromatic molecules is interpreted on the basis of a ring-current model. Mobile pi-electrons are assumed to produce a diamagnetism by circulation around the ring. As a result any solute molecule located directly above or below the plane of an aromatic molecule finds itself in a magnetic field smaller than the external field, causing its resonance to be displaced to a higher field. (The same model correctly predicts that aromatic protons or substituents will experience a local field larger than the external field, causing their resonances to appear downfield.) Clearly, aromatic substances are unattractive as NMR solvents.

cal environments of the exchanging atom can be sensed depends on the rate of exchange, thus also on temperature. If exchange is sufficiently fast, an average environment is sensed and the NMR resonances corresponding to the separate environments coalesce.

The influences of the rate of exchange on NMR spectra can be understood best in terms of the uncertainty principle. Recall that this principle also serves in the interpretation of the role of relaxation time T_1 and the effect of spinning a sample tube. In this application it is used to define τ, the shortest time interval in which the two environments occupied by the exchanging species can be distinguished. The uncertainty principle takes the form $\tau \Delta v \approx 1/2\pi$, where Δv is the difference between the values of the chemical shifts in the two environments.

Whenever the temperature is high enough for exchange to occur in less than the critical time τ, a single resonance is seen. If the temperature is lower, separate resonances are observed. All the other factors that affect rates, such as concentration and catalysts, are also operative here.

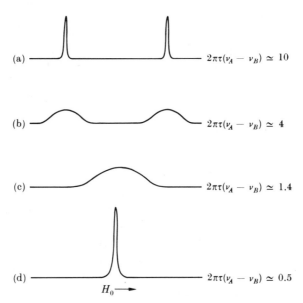

(a) $2\pi\tau(v_A - v_B) \simeq 10$

(b) $2\pi\tau(v_A - v_B) \simeq 4$

(c) $2\pi\tau(v_A - v_B) \simeq 1.4$

(d) $2\pi\tau(v_A - v_B) \simeq 0.5$

$H_0 \longrightarrow$

Fig. 19.13 The influence of rate of exchange of protons between two different environments in which the resonant frequencies are v_A and v_B. The rate of exchange increases from (a) to (d) as the time interval τ during which the exchanging proton is in each environment decreases.

The influence of exchange rate on the magnetic resonance of the exchanging species is illustrated in Fig. 19.13. If there are equal populations in the two states, if the lifetimes in the excited states are equal, and if the transverse relaxation time in the two environments is relatively large, then the spectra of Fig. 19.12 can be simply interpreted. Let v_A and v_B be the resonant frequencies in the two environments and let τ be half the lifetime in either. Then the relationship of rate of exchange ($\frac{1}{2}\tau$) to the chemical shift between environments is as given in the figure. For example, the rate in (a) is one-twentieth as fast as the rate in (d).

Usually exchange and thus temperature have little effect on an NMR spectrum. In a very few instances, however, temperature may alter a chemical shift because of its effect on amplitudes of internal vibrations.

Shifts for other nuclei. It is characteristic of other magnetic nuclei such as ^{13}C or ^{31}P that their chemical shifts are more substantial than proton shifts. Basically, their larger shifts reflect their greater number of shells of electrons. Changes in bonding can thus induce larger differences in shielding than are possible for a hydrogen atom. Some representative chemical shifts for ^{17}O are shown in Fig. 19.14. Since spin-spin coupling constants (see below) are also much larger, measurements need be reliable to only to 1–2 ppm for results comparable to those in quality proton NMR. The experimental procedures and rules of interpretation developed for proton NMR spectrometry are generally applicable to other magnetic nuclei.

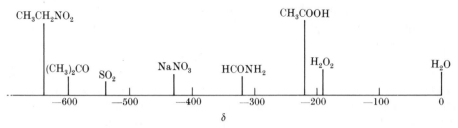

Fig. 19.14 Oxygen-17 chemical shift relative to water for several substances giving simple resonances. As in proton NMR spectrometry, δ is given in ppm.

19.12 SPIN-SPIN COUPLING

Magnetic nuclei in an identical electronic environment, such as the three hydrogen atoms in a methyl group, are said to be *equivalent*. They sense an external magnetic field equally, and since they cannot for quantum-mechanical reasons couple with each other, they give rise to a single strong peak.

Actually, this is true only if the group of which they are a part enjoys free rotation. Conditions that restrict free rotation (or inversion in the case of a nitrogen atom) or introduce asymmetry in general lead to nonequivalence. For example, the protons shown in the following substances are nonequivalent.

$$\begin{matrix} H \\ \diagdown \\ \diagup \\ H \end{matrix} C{=}C \begin{matrix} R \\ \diagup \\ \diagdown \\ R \end{matrix} \qquad CH_3{-}\underset{H'_A \quad\; H'_B}{\overset{H_A \quad H_B}{\bigcirc}}{-}NO_2$$

Other causes of nonequivalence, such as restricted rotation about a single bond produced by bulky substituents, or slow inversion at a nitrogen atom, can sometimes be removed by raising the temperature.

Equivalent protons give rise to a singlet resonance peak as in toluene, however, only if they are free of interaction with other magnetic nuclei in different environments. It is not direct dipolar interactions that are of concern: these effects tend to average to zero in liquids and gases as a consequence of normal thermal motions and may be neglected in most cases. Rather, it is the type of indirect coupling known as spin-spin coupling that must be explored. It takes place through bonding electrons and gives NMR spectrometry its sensitivity to the structural position of a magnetic nucleus and to the properties of chemical bonds.

Spin-spin coupling between nonequivalent magnetic nuclei causes resonance lines to split into *multiplets*. For example, evidence of such splitting was seen in the NMR spectrum of ethanol in Fig. 19.3. The coupling may be regarded as originating in the tendency of a magnetic nucleus such as a proton to align the spin of its electrons somewhat antiparallel to its nuclear spin on the average. When one of its electrons participates in a covalent bond, the influence toward alignment is weakly transmitted through the bond. As a result, the next nucleus, and to a diminishing extent more distant nuclei, sense a weak impetus toward alignment. For protons such coupling is seldom effective over more than three bonds. For example, in organic compounds only protons on adjacent carbon atoms tend to couple.

For nuclei of spin numbers I_i and I_j, the energy of the interaction takes the form $J_{ij} \cdot I_i \cdot I_j$, where J_{ij} is a constant called the *coupling constant*. Actually, constants such as J_{ij} are independent of the value of any external magnetic field and depend only on molecular structure. For this reason they are also nearly temperature-independent. Customarily coupling constants are stated in hertz. Observed values range from 0.1 to about 1000 Hz. The minuteness of the interaction is evident from the frequency. For example, 1000 Hz corresponds to transition energy of 10^{-7} cm^{-1}, or about 10^{-11} eV. Proton-proton coupling constants are usually smaller than 20 Hz. On the other hand, other types of coupling involve larger energies. For example, for B and H in B_2H_6, $J = 125$ Hz; for ^1H and ^{14}N in NH_3, $J = 46$ Hz; for ^{19}F and ^{31}P in PF_3, $J = 1400$ Hz; for F and F′ in ClF_3,* $J = 400$ Hz.

Example For protons, coupling constants depend strongly on structure. If they are:

1. *Para* to each other in a benzene ring, $J \simeq 1$ Hz,
2. On adjacent carbon atoms in an ethyl group, $J = 6$–8 Hz,
3. *Trans* to each other across an ethylenic linkage, $J = 17$–18 Hz.

Fortunately, in many systems spin-spin coupling leads to a simple or *first-order spectrum*. This result follows if couplings occur between nonequivalent nuclei i and j whose resonant frequencies v_i and v_j are widely spaced compared with the magnitude of splitting that results from spin-spin coupling. More precisely, if the coupling constant is J_{ij}, a necessary condition for the generation of a first-order spectrum for the system is that *all* its $\Delta v / J$ ratios be large.† A further minor condition is that if i and j each represent sets of equivalent nuclei, the nuclei within each set must be magnetically as well as chemically equivalent. When these conditions hold, the energetics of each resonance and coupling in the system may be considered separately and the spacings within each multiplet will equal J_{ij}. A further advantage of first-order spectra is that they are more easily interpreted to identify a species or elucidate its structure. A discussion of spectra more complex than first order is beyond the scope of this book.

---

* The fluorines are in two different environments.
† This is essentially equivalent to requiring that spin-spin couplings be relatively weak.

Why does splitting occur in resonances? In simple terms, when an external magnetic field H_0 is applied, the alignment of all the magnetic nuclei in a molecule is influenced. Some will be in an excited level, some in the ground state. What is important is that the alignment of adjacent magnetic nuclei slightly affects the separation of energy levels for a given magnetic nucleus.

Thus spin-spin coupling leads to splitting of a resonance into an integral number of lines, the original intensity being distributed among them. To discover the pattern involved in first-order spectra, consider that each member of a set of equivalent nuclei A is subject to the same coupling. How their transitions are affected is basically determined by energetically distinguishable arrangements of the magnetic nuclei with which coupling occurs. In the presence of an external magnetic field H_0, the number of arrangements of nuclei B in the second set will depend on their number n_B and the value of I_B. The discussion will be limited to the proton NMR spectrometry, that for which $I_A = I_B = \frac{1}{2}$. Thus the nuclei in the second set will have two definable spin states $+\frac{1}{2}$ and $-\frac{1}{2}$, which may be identified by α and β, respectively.

Consider the case in which there are three equivalent nuclei in set B. Table 19.6 shows the number of distinguishable combinations of the spin states and the number of ways they can be arrived at. The four spin arrangements resulting from these nuclei would lead the resonance of the A-nuclei to be split into a quartet. Note that relative probability of each combination is determined by the number of ways of attaining that spin arrangement. In turn, these probabilities are reflected in the relative intensities of the four components of the quartet, $1:3:3:1$. On coupling to a nucleus of spin $\frac{1}{2}$, the "original" resonance absorption splits into $n_B + 1$ components whose relative intensities fall into a symmetrical pattern determined by the binominal coefficients.* In each case the separation of the components of the multiplet is just J_{AB} Hz.

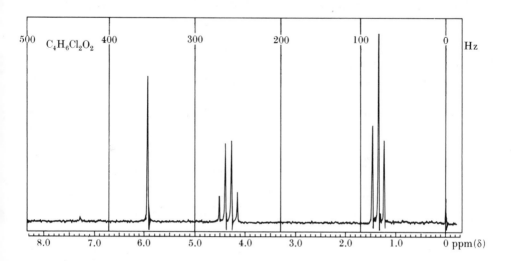

Fig. 19.15 A proton NMR spectrum taken at 60 MHz. The compound was dissolved in $CDCl_3$. A small amount of impurity, $CHCl_3$, was responsible for the peak at $\delta = -7.3$.

---

* The spin states α and β are taken n_B at a time, giving the sets of combinations defined by $(\alpha + \beta)^{n_B}$.

Table 19.6 Combinations of Spin States in a Set of Three Equivalent Nuclei of Spin $\frac{1}{2}$

Combinations of spins			ΣI	Relative probability of combination*
Nucleus and spin†				
1	2	3		
α	α	α	$+\frac{3}{2}$	1
α	α	β		
α	β	α	$+\frac{1}{2}$	3
β	α	α		
α	β	β		
β	α	β	$-\frac{1}{2}$	3
β	β	α		
β	β	β	$-\frac{3}{2}$	1

* Probabilities are proportional to the number of ways in which the combination can occur.
† The spin is designated α for the state $+\frac{1}{2}$, β for $-\frac{1}{2}$. Thus, ΣI totals $+\frac{3}{2}$ when all spins are α.

Example 1 The case of an ethyl group $-CH_2-CH_3$ presents an NMR pattern (see Fig. 19.3) of a triplet resonance for the CH_3 protons and a quartet for the CH_2 protons. If the ethyl group is attached to $-OH$ as in ethanol, the chemical shift between the CH_3 and CH_2 resonances is about 140 Hz at 60 MHz. The *methyl* protons spin-couple with three different spin combinations of the two methylene protons: $\alpha\alpha$, $\beta\alpha$, and $\alpha\beta$, (which are indistinguishable energetically), and $\beta\beta$. (Recall that ^{12}C and ^{16}O are nonmagnetic and will not interact.) Similarly, the two methylene protons give a quartet because of their coupling to three methyl protons. This case is treated in Table 19.6. The separation of the branches of both multiplets of the ethyl group in Fig. 19.3 is found to be 7 Hz. Since the two interactions are between the same sets of protons, this would be expected, since $J_{AB} = J_{BA}$ in general.

Finally, note that the criterion for a first-order spectrum is met by the ethyl group since $\Delta v_{AB}/J_{AB} = 140/7 = 20$.

Example 2 Consider the 60 MHz proton spectrum in Fig. 19.15. The spectrum is for a compound of molecular formula $C_4H_6Cl_2O_2$. What structural formula can one deduce from the patterns?

The combination of a quartet centered at $\delta = 4.3$ and a triplet at $\delta = 1.3$ should be suggestive. On the basis of this lead, can a structural formula be postulated that successfully accounts for the singlet at $\delta = 5.9$? Does it also account for the relative chemical shifts, e.g., the 180 Hz shift between the triplet and quartet? The answer is given on page 578.

A problem in correct identification of a multiplet arises when it has five or more lines. In such cases the outermost lines—those in the "wings"—may be of such low intensity as to be lost in the noise. For example, when $n_B = 5$ and a resonance is split into a sextet, the intensity ratios are $1:5:10:10:5:1$. Not only is the intensity of the outermost pair of lines only one-tenth of the central ones, but each contains only one-thirty-second of the intensity of the unsplit resonance.

In general, it is desirable to rescan at higher amplification any portion of a spectrum with a complex multiplet.

An interesting case of loss of coupling arises when one of the magnetic species undergoes rapid *chemical exchange*. In the ethanol spectrum just under discussion in the example, only a singlet was observed at $\delta = 5.5$ for the hydroxyl proton (see Fig. 19.3), even though it is separated by only three bonds from the methylene protons. Explanation is found in the rapid exchange of hydroxyl protons between ethanol molecules as a result of hydrogen bonding. As a result, spin orientations are averaged out. It ethanol is cooled to $-40\,°C$, the rate of exchange is slowed sufficiently for spins to couple. At low temperatures the hydroxyl resonance and adjacent protons have their expected multiplicity (see Exercise 19.2).

In general, a resonance is split into $2n_B I_B + 1$ components in a first-order spectrum with a nonequivalent set of magnetic species B containing n_B atoms of spin I_B. Note particularly that when $I_B > 1/2$, multiplets become much more complex. It should also be emphasized again that splittings are independent of the applied magnetic field. A splitting can always be distinguished from a new resonance by the fact that the absolute separation between branches is independent of the field strength.

Example In *HD*, the nuclei have spin numbers of $\frac{1}{2}$ and 1, respectively. The deuterium resonance is split into a doublet by spin-spin coupling to the single proton. In turn, the proton resonance appears as a triplet because of the spin states of the deuteron $+1, 0, -1$; thus, $2n_B I_B + 1 = 3$.

In systems that give higher-order spectra, interactions are more complex and it is necessary to sum over all the groups of nuclei that are coupled to determine energy levels and transitions. Many more transitions become possible. Actually, one need not look only to complex molecules for such spectra. Even simple species like ethanol under very high resolution show a few additional lines that arise from small departures from first-order conditions.

19.13 ELUCIDATION OF MOLECULAR STRUCTURE

In many instances molecular structure determinations are carried out or confirmed by proton NMR spectroscopy. If the substance under examination also contains magnetic nuclei such as ^2H, ^{31}P, or ^{19}F, it may also be of value to obtain the NMR spectrum of one or more of these nuclei. For any organic compound the possibility of examination of the ^{13}C NMR spectrum is also a live option.

Liquid samples may be examined as such, with an external reference. More often samples are dissolved in a suitable solvent that also permits use of a small amount of tetramethylsilane (TMS) as an internal reference standard. At least 0.1 to 0.4 mg of sample is needed in most cases, though a few micrograms *may* suffice for a glass microtube with a bubble cavity. In this case the bubble must be positioned to coincide with the center of the rf coil. For a capillary tube about 0.4 ml of liquid is required.

Solvents and references. As in other types of spectrometry, the best solvents for NMR are liquids that offer the broadest "windows." A solvent should also have minimum intermolecular interaction with a solute, even for qualitative analysis. Carbon tetrachloride is ideal from either standpoint, regardless of the nucleus being observed.

For proton NMR many other liquids, such as those in Fig. 19.6 that give no more than one intense singlet, have much better dissolving power and are often used for polar solutes. Though more expensive, several polar deuterated solvents like $CDCl_3$, D_2O, and $(CD_3)_2CO$ meet both window and "solvent" requirements and are frequently employed. In cases in which solution is difficult to effect, special consideration should also be given to pyridine, dimethylformamide, or acetonitrile as solvents.

Since an internal standard is preferable, a suitable reference is a compound that is adequately soluble and has a single strong resonance. In proton NMR when TMS cannot be used, any of the substances mentioned in Fig. 19.6 could be used.

Table 19.7 A Few Proton NMR Spectra (Shifts relative to Me_4Si)

Molecular formula (Each set of equivalent protons is identified by a small italic letter.)	*Characteristics of spectrum* (For each set of equivalent protons the multiplicity, downfield chemical shift, (in ppm) and relative integrated intensity in units $1H$, $2H$, etc. are given.)
Br—CH$_2$—CH$_3$ b a	a, triplet, 1.18; $3H$ b, quartet, 3.40; $2H$
Br—CH$_2$—CH$_2$—CH$_3$ c b a	a-triplet, 1.04; $3H$ b-sextet, 1.90; $2H$ c-triplet, 3.38; $2H$
⬡—CH$_3$ a b	a-singlet, 2.31; $3H$ b-singlet, 7.13; $5H$
⬡—CH$_2$OH b a c	a-singlet, 3.69; $1H$ b-singlet, 4.42; $2H$ c-singlet, 7.2; $5H$
e c a h f H CH$_2$—CH$_3$ g⬡—N—C h f H CH$_3$ d b	*a-triplet, 0.77; b-doublet, 0.92; c-complex multiplet, 1.27; d-sextet, 3.12; e-singlet, 3.37; f-doublet, 6.39; g-triplet, 6.58; h-triplet, 7.05

* Intensities are not given for these resonances but correlate with the number of protons of each set. The resonances arising from the aromatic protons could not be identified by their shift and multiplicity alone; coupling constants derived from the splitting of their multiplets were also required.

In NMR based on other nuclei, the same criteria apply in selecting a solvent or reference.

Identification. The following comments relate to proton NMR spectroscopy but also illustrate the general procedure for spectra based on other nuclei. Since one ordinarily has several types of spectral information, as well as an empirical formula at hand, it is possible to examine an NMR spectrum quite systematically. Indeed, the main question may be whether one substance or another has been formed, in which case the answer may sometimes be arrived at quite simply by looking for the presence or absence of a particular multiplet or measuring splittings. Table 19.7 gives spectra obtained for a few compounds whose proton NMR behavior is especially straight-forward, i.e., all are first-order and all resonances are resolved.

In the analysis of complex spectra a great deal depends on the recognition of spin-spin coupling patterns. Usually one can predict the outstanding features of a pattern associated with a given structure quite systematically. [3, 27] Computer programs have been written to solve the secular equations that describe the energies of the transitions for cases involving couplings of as many as seven or eight magnetic spins. Computer programs are also valuable for predicting splittings in systems that give higher-order spectra.

Additional techniques. Structural questions that remain unsolved following a detailed examination of a proton NMR spectrum often yield to other appropriate magnetic resonance approaches. Several possibilities will be reviewed briefly in the following paragraphs.

Often portions of proton NMR spectra of substances are inadequately resolved. Multiplets arising either from spin-spin coupling of protons in different magnetic environments or from spin coupling of protons with other magnetic nuclei tend to overlap, causing analysis to be an uncertain process. In this situation one or more of the following approaches may permit more definite identification.

A variety of *double magnetic resonance* techniques may be used to identify and study particular transitions. As described in Section 19.8, in these techniques two radiofrequency fields, an observing field H_1, and a perturbing field H_2, are applied simultaneously to a sample. The spectrometer output is a response to sweeping the observing rf frequency through the desired spectral range while the perturbing field is set at the frequency of a spin transition of interest. The amplitude of H_2 is adjusted according to the type of study intended.

If the amplitude of perturbing field H_2 is small, resonance peak intensity changes known as *Overhauser effects* are observed. The effects can be utilized to give information about relaxation processes. If a multispin system is under study and the strength of the perturbing field is increased, as in a *tickling experiment*, some transitions will be split. Lines can be identified and often it is possible to find the signs of coupling constants.

The only additional double resonance procedure that will be described is *spin decoupling*. In this case, a strong perturbing field is used and its frequency is set to that of one of the components of a double spin system. The multiplet structure of the observed resonance collapses and a singlet replaces it. Complex spectra can be system-atically simplified in this manner.

Spin decoupling is also important as a means of diminishing the extent of broadening of a proton resonance line by a magnetic nucleus with a quadrupole moment ($I > \frac{1}{2}$). Such nuclei shorten the relaxation time of other magnetic nuclei greatly. For example, the resonance of protons bonded to a ^{14}N atom is seldom observed because it is broadened so excessively that it has negligible amplitude. By irradiation at the resonant frequency of the quadrupolar nucleus, the coupling giving rise to the relaxation can be essentially eliminated, the additional proton resonance detected, and the spectrum analyzed.

Weak resonance signals can often be enhanced by *time averaging* (Section 19.9). This technique is especially valuable when a sample is poorly soluble in a solvent of choice. Again, it may be useful as a means of identifying fine structure of a resonance.

Where an alternate frequency spectrometer is available, a complex spectrum can often be interpreted by observing it at a frequency other than that originally available. Thus a 100 MHz instrument can sometimes resolve portions of spectra that overlap at 60 MHz, and great improvement is often obtained by study at still greater frequencies. Figure 19.16 illustrates a dramatic improvement of this type. The difference in shifts vs. splitting can also be distinguished from data taken at two frequencies.

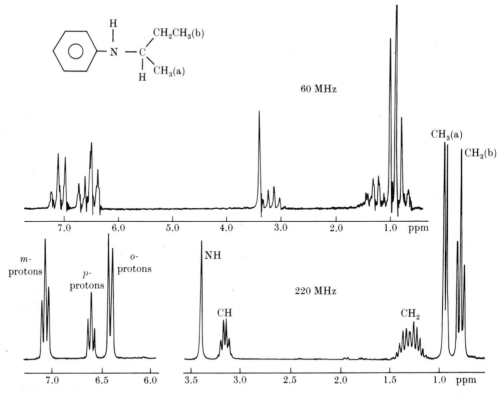

Fig. 19.16 The proton NMR spectrum of N-sec-butylaniline at 60 and 220 MHz. At the higher frequency all the resonances are resolved. Since spin-spin splittings are constant, branches of multiplets are more closely spaced at the higher frequency (note that a δ or ppm scale is used) while chemical shifts are unchanged. Proton assignments are shown beside resonance peaks. [17] (Courtesy of *Science*.)

Often the molecular structure of a substance can best be identified by obtaining an NMR spectrum of another magnetic nucleus to complement the proton spectrum. A species already present, like ^{31}P in a phosphorus compound, or ^{13}C (present to the extent of about 1% in all carbon positions in any organic compound), can be used to give a spectrum that provides a great deal of additional information.

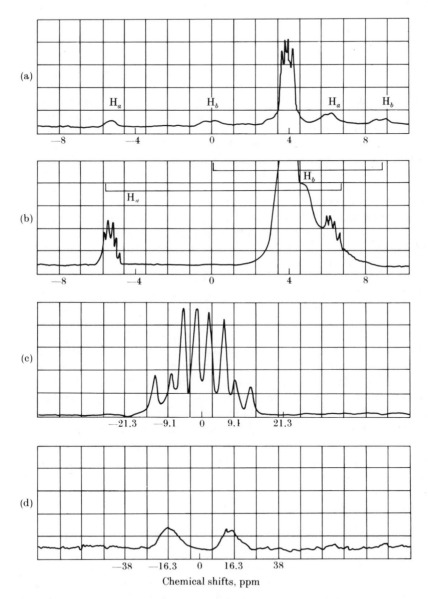

Fig. 19.17 Multiple NMR spectra of the compound $(CH_3)_2PHBH_3$. (a) ^1H spectrum at 30 MHz; (b) ^1H spectrum at 30 MHz while irradiating at the ^{11}B frequency of 9.63 MHz; (c) ^{11}B spectrum at 12.3 MHz; (d) ^{31}P spectrum at 12.3 MHz. [33] (Courtesy of the Faraday Division of the Chemical Society.)

Example The substance $(CH_3)_2PHBH_3$ provides a good illustration of the advantage gained by use of both spin-decoupling and nonproton NMR spectra. [22] A complex proton spectrum results from the extensive spin-spin couplings in the molecule.

Actually, only the two carbon nuclei are nonmagnetic. On the basis of analysis the structure assigned was

$$^aH\!-\!P\!-\!BH_3{}^b$$

with $CH_3{}^c$ groups above and below P.

In Fig. 19.17a the proton spectrum at 30 MHz is shown. The strong resonance at $\delta = 4.0$ is assigned to the c-methyl protons. Since the much weaker resonances at 0.0, 3.0, 6.0, and 9.0 ppm disappear on simultaneous irradiation at the resonance frequency of ^{11}B, as may be seen in Fig. 19.17b, these signals are assigned to the b-protons on boron (with $I = \frac{3}{2}$, it would split the singlet into a quartet). On the other hand, the proton lines at 5.7 and 6.0 ppm become more intense on ^{11}B spin decoupling, suggesting that these lines are traceable to the a-proton, which would give a doublet of such large splitting only if directly bonded to ^{31}P. The extensive fine splitting of each member of the doublet of the a-proton is attributable to spin-spin coupling with the methyl protons.

Figure 19.17c shows the ^{11}B spectrum. The peaks are interpretable as a quartet $(1:3:3:1)$ in which each line is doubled. Splitting by the three b-protons would give the quartet, and its doubling can be traced to splitting by the ^{31}P atom. Figure 19.17d shows the ^{31}P spectrum. The only strong peaks suggest a doublet, interpretable as caused by bonding to the a-proton. This is confirmed by the fact that the value of the coupling constant J_{PH_a} is the same as that observed in the proton spectrum $J_{H_aP} = 350$ Hz. There is also evidence of a great deal of fine structure that should confirm the other assignments, but to be interpretable a mathematical analysis would be necessary. It would be desirable to enhance the details of the fine structure by time averaging.

In general, spectra are taken under slow sweep and small rf field conditions so that saturation can be avoided and the various peak intensities can be obtained by integration. By relating the area of each peak to the total area under all resonances, one can distribute the known number of protons among the different types of resonances observed; this process is often termed proton counting, and will be discussed in the next section. Even if the total number of protons is uncertain, it is possible to establish a calibrating factor for areas of a particular spectrum by unequivocal identification of a resonance. For example, the integrated intensity of a methyl resonance must be equivalent to that of three protons.

19.14 QUANTITATIVE ANALYSIS

Nuclear magnetic resonance spectroscopic techniques are also valuable in quantitative determinations. Both theoretical and practical studies have confirmed a wide variety of applications. Errors connected with saturation, which are the chief ones with which an experimenter contends, can easily be avoided.

As has been discussed in Section 19.6, the theoretical conditions for scanning a spectrum and obtaining resonance lines or multiplets whose total area is directly proportional to the number of nuclei contributing are well known. Sufficient conditions for establishing the relationship are that (a) saturation be avoided and (b) the range of values of T_1 and T_2 be small. Since it is awkward to compute an appropriate rate of scan and rf field strength from measured relaxation times, it is fortunate that calibration techniques are available. [21] Since for a single compound any saturation that occurs generally acts to decrease all the areas, almost all techniques rely on comparison of peak areas.

An effective calibration procedure is to begin at a very low value of H_1 or a very fast sweep rate to be sure that there is no saturation and then gradually increase H_1 or decrease the sweep rate until there is a measurable change in the ratio of areas of two resonances of interest. Since the S/N ratio for integration should be a maximum, a high value of H_1 is desirable. The final conditions will be a compromise and will involve deciding the highest practicable level of H_1.

Example Assume that in the quantitative analysis of a mixture one finds that one peak of substance A and one of substance B are clearly resolved. The areas of the two peaks are compared at several rf power levels to be certain of avoiding saturation effects. Up to an rf field of 0.4 mG the ratio of peak areas A/B is constant; at 1.0 mG it has fallen to 0.9, and at 2.0 mG to 0.8. It is clear that T_1 is greater for the peak of substance A (since this resonance is a saturating factor), and that fields smaller than 1 mG should be used for quantitative analysis.

Quantitative NMR work, of course, has its greatest value where other methods would be less reliable. For example, NMR spectroscopy has a considerable advantage over IR methods. The reason is that intensities of characteristic IR absorptions depend strongly on the whole molecule and not solely on a functional group. With NMR spectroscopy, as suggested above, resonance intensities reflect primarily a given nuclear site as long as the appropriate resonance can be resolved. In addition NMR spectroscopy has the great advantage that mixtures can often be analyzed without the necessity of isolating pure components. It is only necessary that the chemical shifts for the suspected components be reasonably predictable, and that the pattern of the NMR spectrum permits definitive identification of the components. In cases of rare or important samples it is useful that NMR spectroscopy is nondestructive.

Example A study of the reorganization products of $P_2O_3Cl_2F_2$ by NMR spectrometry at different frequencies illustrates the potentialities of the techniques in work with mixtures. [14] The substance, symmetrical diphosphoryl difluoride dichloride, was heated in a sealed NMR tube at 50° for several days, causing "reorganization" products to appear. It was analyzed without opening the tube. ^{31}P spectra were taken at 24.3 and 16.2 MHz and ^{19}F spectra at 40.0 and 24.3 MHz. In this way ^{19}F chemical shifts (from CF_3COOH as external reference) and ^{31}P shifts (from H_3PO_4 as external reference) as well as P–F coupling constants were established, allowing identification of the products. Couplings were verified by spin-decoupling the ^{31}P spectrum while observing the ^{19}F spectrum. The distribution of the phosphorus was found to be approximately as follows:

$$
\begin{array}{lll}
\quad\ \ \text{O} & \quad\ \ \text{O} & \quad\ \ \text{O} \\
\quad\ \ | & \quad\ \ | & \quad\ \ | \\
50\% \text{ in F—P—O groups,} & 25\% \text{ in Cl—P—Cl groups,} & \text{and } 25\% \text{ in O—P—O groups.} \\
\quad\ \ | & \quad\ \ | & \quad\ \ | \\
\quad\ \ \text{Cl} & \quad\ \ \text{F} & \quad\ \ \text{F}
\end{array}
$$

The problem of resolution of resonance peaks is enough of an obstacle for quantitative methods to have become steadily more attractive as NMR has been extended to higher frequencies. For example, applications to proteins and polypeptides are beginning to appear. The considerable effectiveness of frequency in this regard was illustrated in Fig. 19.16, where a proton spectrum of N-sec-butylaniline was shown to be resolved at 220 MHz but not at 60 MHz. Since resolution determines whether peaks necessary to identification can be isolated, it is especially important in a mixture. Another means of improving resolution is to shift an interfering resonance by causing its resonance to move and coalesce with that of an added species with which it is in rapid exchange. [15] Further, dissolving a paramagnetic shift reagent may well resolve overlapping resonances from the different components of a mixture. [21a]

Perhaps the most important quantitative application is that usually described as *proton counting*. All the resonances of a pure substance are integrated and the relative area of each is used to determine the number of protons of that type. If the empirical formula is known, it is straightforward to allot a certain area per proton. When the formula is not known, an ethyl, methyl, or other characteristic resonance can usually be identified for the substance and used to calibrate the integration. If necessary, a known substance of simple spectrum can be quantitatively added. Proton counting has already been cited in connection with assigning correct formulas to substances and examples of its application given in Table 19.7.

Other applications are the analysis of inseparable mixtures whose pure constituents cannot easily be obtained for comparison purposes. The possibility of determining isotopic compositions is also available.

Example The percent substitution of deuterium for hydrogen in a particular position on a molecule can readily be ascertained; this is because, as deuteration progresses, only the resonance peak for the hydrogen being replaced diminishes in intensity, while the others remain constant. A calibration curve can thus be obtained.

Application to polymers. Because of the sensitivity of NMR spectroscopy to the local structure, the technique is a powerful tool for elucidation of polymerization patterns. Whether polymerization proceeds by a head-to-tail joining of monomers, or by a head-to-head or a tail-to-tail arrangement, can usually be determined by NMR spectroscopy at a sufficiently high frequency.

Example The repeating unit in polymers of chloroprene, 2-chlorobutadiene, is $[-CH_2CCl =$
$$\overset{3\quad 4}{CHCH_2-}].$$ This unit can be linked to another in three ways:

1. $-CH_2CCl\overset{3\quad 4}{=CHCH_2}CH_2CCl\overset{3'\; 4'}{=CHCH_2}-$;   3. $-CH_2CCl\overset{3\quad 4}{=CHCH_2}CH_2CH\overset{4'\; 3'}{=CCl}-CH_2-$.

2. $-CH_2CH\overset{4\quad 3}{=CClCH_2}CH_2CCl\overset{3'\; 4'}{=CHCH_2}-$;

At 220 MHz polychloroprene in carbon disulfide yields chemical shift values for the CH_2 resonance in the above types of linkage of 2.35, 2.50, and 2.20, respectively. [17] Quantitative determinations of the relative proportions of each type of linkage produced by polymerization are readily made by comparison of peak areas.

It can be appreciated that NMR spectral techniques are extremely powerful, both in elucidation of polymer repeating units and in determining the stereo-regularity or tacticity, especially for polymers having asymmetric centers in the chain.

As is true of repeating units, quantitative analysis of end-groups and of branches can be made even if their concentration is at levels of 0.01 to 1 %. The monomer ratios in copolymers can also be readily determined. It appears that NMR will find more and more use in the elucidation of biopolymers, especially as resolution is improved still further. Such techniques should be valuable in the quantitative determination of structures of proteins and nucleic acids, and in following their biological interactions.

19.15 PHYSICAL-CHEMICAL APPLICATIONS

The determination of coupling constants for spin-spin interactions has not only furthered molecular determinations by NMR, but has also contributed to quantum-mechanical understandings of bonds. Often it has been possible to elucidate electron distributions in molecules. In a different approach, the determination of relaxation times T_1 and T_2 has made it possible to secure valuable kinetic data, has provided information about certain kinds of molecular motions, and has increased the understanding of exchange phenomena. Complex ion formation has been studied by such procedures.

REFERENCES

Some straightforward general references on an introductory to intermediate level are:

1. L. M. Jackman and S. Sternhell, *Applications of Nuclear Magnetic Resonance Spectroscopy in Organic Chemistry*. 2d ed. New York: Pergamon, 1969
2. R. Lynden-Bell and R. K. Harris, *Nuclear Magnetic Resonance Spectroscopy*. New York: Appleton-Century-Crofts, 1969
3. D. W. Mathieson, ed., *Nuclear Magnetic Resonance for Organic Chemists*. New York: Academic, 1967

A well-written general reference on a more advanced level is:

4. J. A. Pople, W. G. Schneider, and H. J. Bernstein, *High-Resolution Nuclear Magnetic Resonance*. New York: McGraw-Hill, 1959

The principles of nuclear magnetic resonance are treated on an intermediate level in:

5. A. Carrington and A. D. McLachlan, *Introduction to Magnetic Resonance*. New York: Harper and Row, 1967
6. C. P. Slichter, *Principles of Magnetic Resonance*. New York: Harper and Row, 1963

These principles are treated on an advanced level in:

7. A. Abragam, *Principles of Nuclear Magnetism*. Oxford: Oxford University Press, 1961
8. P. L. Corio, *Structure of High-Resolution NMR Spectra*. New York: Academic, 1966

NMR applications, procedures, or instrumentation are emphasized in:

9. Richard R. Ernst, "Sensitivity Enhancement in Magnetic Resonance," in *Advances in Mag-

netic Resonance, Vol. 2, J. S. Waugh, ed. New York: Academic, 1966

10. A. Allerhand, H. S. Gutowsky, J. Jonas, and R. A. Meinzer, "NMR Methods for Determining Chemical-Exchange Rates," *J. Am. Chem. Soc.* **88**, 3185 (1966)

11. W. A. Anderson, "Applications of Modulation Techniques to High-Resolution NMR Spectrometers," *Rev. Sci. Instr.* **33**, 1160 (1962)

12. E. B. Baker and L. W. Burd, "Frequency-Swept and Proton-Stabilized NMR Spectrum for All Nuclei Using a Frequency Synthesizer," *Rev. Sci. Instr.* **34**, 238 (1963)

13. J. D. Baldeschwieler and E. W. Randall, "Chemical Applications of NMR Double Resonance," *Chem. Revs.* **63**, 81 (1963)

14. M. M. Crutchfield, C. F. Callis, and J. R. Van Wazer, "Nuclear Magnetic Resonance Studies of $P_2O_2Cl_2F_2$ and Its Reorganization Products," *Inorg. Chem.* **3**, 280 (1964)

15. R. J. Day and C. N. Reilley, "Analysis by NMR Spectrometry Taking Advantage of the Uncertainty Principle," *Anal. Chem.* **38**, 1323 (1966)

16. R. R. Ernst and W. A. Anderson, "Application of Fourier Transform Spectroscopy to Magnetic Resonance," *Rev. Sci. Instr.* **37**, 93 (1966)

16a. T. C. Farrar, "Pulsed and Fourier Transform NMR Spectroscopy," *Anal. Chem.* **42** (4), 109A (1970)

16b. W. Bremser and H. D. W. Hill, "The Technique of Fourier Transformation in High Resolution NMR Spectroscopy," *Messtechnik* **79**, 14 (1971) [German text]

17. R. C. Ferguson and W. D. Phillips, "High Resolution NMR Spectroscopy," *Science* **157**, 257 (21 July, 1967)

18. J. L. Jungnickel, "Calibration of NMR Chemical Shift Scale," *Anal. Chem.* **35**, 1985 (1963)

19. R. E. Lundin, *et al.*, "Methods and Applications in the Examination of Small Samples by High Resolution NMR," *Appl. Spectr. Rev.* **1**, 131 (1967)

20. J. D. Macomber, "How Does a Crossed-Coil NMR Spectrometer Work?" *Spectroscopy L.* **1**, 131 (1968)

21. P. J. Paulsen and W. D. Cooke, "Quantitative Determination of Hydrogen and Fluorine in Organic Compounds by NMR Spectrometry," *Anal. Chem.* **36**, 1713 (1964)

21a. D. L. Rabenstein, "Applications of Paramagnetic Shift Reagents in (Quantitative) Proton Magnetic Resonance Spectrometry," *Anal. Chem.* **43**, 1599 (1971).

22. J. N. Shoolery, "The Relation of High Resolution Nuclear Magnetic Resonance Spectra to Molecular Structures," *Disc. Faraday Soc.* **19**, 215 (1955)

23. A. L. Van Geet and D. N. Hume, "Measurement of Proton Relaxation Times with a High Resolution Nuclear Magnetic Resonance Spectrometer: Progressive Saturation Method," ". . . Direct Method," *Anal. Chem.* **37**, 979, 983 (1965)

Collections of NMR spectra are offered in:

24. Varian Associates, *Varian Associates High Resolution NMR Spectra Catalogue*, Vol. I, 1962; Vol. II, 1963

25. F. A. Bovey, *NMR Data Tables for Organic Compounds*. New York: Interscience, 1967ff

26. *The Sadtler Standard Spectra*, Philadelphia: Sadtler Research Labs., 1967ff

Effective introductions to structure of organic molecules from NMR spectra may be found in references 41–45, Chapter 16, as well as:

27. R. H. Bible, (a) *Interpretation of NMR Spectra*, 1965; (b) *Guide to the NMR Empirical Method*, 1967. New York: Plenum

EXERCISES

(Answers to certain exercises will be found at the end of the set.)

19.1 On the basis of the 60 MHz spectrum of ethanol in Fig. 19.3,

a) What should be the chemical shift difference between the hydroxyl and methylene peaks of ethanol at 100 MHz in ppm? in hertz?

b) At 100 MHz what should be the splitting of the components of the methylene quartet (in hertz)?

19.2 In methanol there is no coupling between methyl and hydroxyl protons at room temperature because of the rapid rate of exchange of hydroxyl protons between molecules. At $-40\,^{\circ}$C this exchange is slowed sufficiently for coupling to occur.

a) Draw a methanol spectrum as it appears at room temperature. Give approximate δ values.

b) Draw a spectrum as you believe it appears at $-40\,^{\circ}$C.

19.3 In a double-resonance proton magnetic resonance experiment at 60 MHz, a sample of ethanol in $CDCl_3$ is to be irradiated to saturate the methylene resonance while the methyl resonance is viewed.

a) How can the proper irradiating frequency be selected with ease if the NMR spectrum can be viewed on an oscilloscope?

b) According to Fig. 19.3, what audiofrequency should be mixed with the basic 60 MHz signal (relative to TMS) to accomplish the desired saturation?

19.4 Is a single slow scan of an NMR absorption peak as advantageous in terms of signal-to-noise ratio as the averaging of a set of faster scans of the peak requiring the same total time? What conditions must hold for the two processes to yield comparable results?

19.5 The temperature maintained in an unthermostated NMR probe may be determined by observation of the chemical shift of a reference compound whose temperature coefficient is known. Chloroform has a chemical shift of 466.5 Hz downfield relative to TMS at $25\,^{\circ}$C and its shift has a temperature coefficient of 0.20 Hz/deg downfield. What is the temperature of a chloroform sample that shows a chemical shift of 469.3 Hz downfield from TMS?

19.6 NMR spectroscopy has been applied with success to the determination of the relative percentage of branched chain molecules present in hydrocarbon mixtures. Suggest the essentials of a suitable procedure based on determination of methyl groups.

19.7 The method of standard addition is applied to the determination of residual H_2O in high-purity D_2O. The proton resonance due to residual water in a 600 mg D_2O sample is found to have an integrated intensity of 85 units. When 2.0 mg of water are added, the intensity increases to 250 units and when an additional 2.0 mg of water are added, to 415 units. What is the percentage purity of the deuterium oxide?

19.8 Predict an approximate NMR spectrum for the following substance.

$$
\begin{array}{c}
h \\
CH_3 \\
CH_3 \\
g \quad f
\end{array}
\qquad
\begin{array}{l}
a \quad b\,CH_3\,d \\
| \\
CH\!-\!CH_3\ e \\
c
\end{array}
$$

Label the equivalent protons a, b, c, etc., in order of increasing shift downfield and state whether each gives rise to a singlet or multiplet, its approximate chemical shift, and its relative intensity.

19.9 A substance of molecular formula $C_6H_{12}O_2$ has an NMR spectrum with two singlets, one at $\delta = 1.45$ that is more than twice as intense as the other at $\delta = 1.97$. Suggest a probable molecular formula. Is there only one possible structure?

19.10 A chemist decides to learn something of phosphorus NMR spectroscopy by taking the compound trimethyl phosphite $P(OCH)_3$ as a first sample. The value of its magnetogyric ratio is such that its resonances occur at about 24.3 MHz for a field of about 14.1 kG. The phosphorous has a spin number $I = \frac{1}{2}$ and is found to undergo weak spin-spin coupling with the protons in the above compound. What kind of a phosphorus NMR spectrum should be observed? Suggest *very roughly* whether lines should be intense or not. Explain briefly.

19.11 The structure of a compound of molecular formula $C_6H_{13}NO_2$ is to be elucidated by its proton magnetic resonance spectrum if possible. The analysis of a 5% solution in deutero-chloroform yields four resonances (listed in the upfield direction):

Resonance	I	II	III	IV
Intensity	18	17	55	27
Multiplicity	quartet	singlet	singlet	triplet
Chemical shift (δ)	4.2	3.2	2.4	1.3

Propose a structure for the substance and assign the resonances to the sets of protons.

19.12 There is overlap between some of the methylene resonances in the compound

$$\overset{1}{}\ \ \overset{2}{}\ \ \overset{3}{}$$
$$ClCH_2CH_2CH_2Br.$$

For convenience in discussion the carbon atoms have been numbered.

a) How many different sets of equivalent protons are there?
b) Predict roughly the chemical shift and multiplicity of each proton resonance.
c) Which multiplets should overlap? One overlapping resonance is centered at $\delta = 3.57$, the other at $\delta = 3.70$. Since $J_{AB} = 7$ Hz for coupling between methylene protons, sketch the overlap pattern roughly as it would appear at 60 MHz.

19.13 Exchange with D_2O is often employed as a means of identifying the proton NMR resonance due to a hydroxyl proton. What spectral change should be observed after exchange?

ANSWERS TO CHAPTER 19 EXERCISES

19.1a: At 60 MHz the chemical shift is 1.9 ppm or 114 Hz between centers. The splitting is 7 Hz. At 100 MHz the shift is 1.9 ppm or 190 Hz and the spin-spin splitting is still 7 Hz. *19.5*: 39°C. *19.7*: 99.83% by weight. *19.12*: a) There are three different equivalent sets of protons. The resonances in order of increasing shift should be (2), (3), and (1). b) The central methylene group couples to four almost equivalent protons and should be a distorted quintet at $\delta = 1.5$ to 2.5. The outer methylene groups should give triplets on being split by the central pair of hydrogens. c) The triplets due to sets (1) and (3) must overlap. *19.8*: d, e: doublet at $\delta = 1.3$; g, h: singlet at $\delta = 2.5$; c: heptet at $\delta = 2.7$; a, b, f: singlet at $\delta = 6.9$. *19.9*: With so many protons, two singlets can arise only if there are no protons on adjacent carbon atoms. The correct structure is $(CH_3)_3C—OOC—CH_3$. *19.10*: There are nine equivalent protons. A phosphorus resonance multiplet with ten branches should be obtained, with the outermost pair very weak. *19.11*: The structure is

$$\overset{\text{III}}{}\ \ \overset{\text{II}}{}\ \ \ \ \overset{\text{I}}{}\ \overset{\text{IV}}{}$$
$$\Leftarrow (CH_3)_2N—CH_2—COOCH_2CH_3.$$

Resonance assignments are indicated.

Example 2, p. 556:

$$CH_3CH_2—O—\overset{\overset{\textstyle O}{\|}}{C}—CHCl_2.$$

OTHER OPTICAL METHODS

CHAPTER 20

LIGHT SCATTERING PHOTOMETRY

Easily measurable interactions of EM radiation and matter occur over the whole range of known frequencies. Those classifiable as absorption we have already found to apply to a wide variety of analytical and control situations (Chapter 16). The essentially nonabsorptive interactions, such as refraction, polarization, scattering, etc., we now consider. Each has been discussed from a theoretical but qualitative point of view in Chapter 10 and must now be related to appropriate instrumentation and analytical procedures. Most of the nonabsorptive interactions are nonquantized and thus nonspecific for a given molecule or atom. Nevertheless, the interactions are characteristic of particular substances, even though they are very dependent on the conditions of measurement. We may make the following general statement about them collectively: They will prove valuable in analysis to the degree that they can be used

1. To confirm identity or decide between alternative geometric or stereoisometric structures of a pure substance,
2. To determine molecular weights of macromolecules such as polymers, and for large macromolecules, to obtain data on shapes and sizes, or
3. To analyze certain mixtures when the constituents are known.

An exception is the Raman effect, which was taken up in Chapter 18.

20.1 INTRODUCTION

Isolated particles, whether single atoms or molecular aggregates, scatter radiation so long as their major dimension is less than 1 to $1\frac{1}{2}$ wavelengths, as discussed in Section 10.10. Larger particles reflect the radiation. In the UV and visible regions of the spectrum, the scattering particles are those of colloidal size, i.e. from 1 nm to 1 μm in greatest dimension. The scattering of suspended particles is often termed the *Tyndall effect*. At a given wavelength, the scattering pattern in space is symmetrical for suspended particles smaller than $1/10$ to $1/20$ λ and is termed *Rayleigh scattering* and shown in Fig. 10.19. Larger particles scatter much more radiation overall, but relatively less in backward directions. Instrumentally, both the pattern of intensities and the absolute or relative intensity at a given angle are measurable and the basis for analytical determinations.

Turbidity. When a beam of radiation of intensity I_0* passes through a nonabsorbing

---

* Strictly, the turbidity is defined in terms of the irradiance, the radiant energy cm^{-2} s^{-1}. The intensity is the energy per unit solid angle per second.

medium that scatters light, the transmitted intensity I is given by the expression

$$I = I_0 e^{-\tau b}, \tag{20.1}$$

where τ is the turbidity and b the path length in the medium. The quantities τ and I vary with concentration, molecular weight, etc. Frequently, Eq. (20.1) is rearranged to define τ directly:

$$\tau = \frac{2.303}{b} \log_{10} \frac{I_0}{I}. \tag{20.2}$$

When b is in cm, τ has the unit of cm^{-1}. Note that Eq. (20.2) closely resembles Beer's law (Eq. (16.3)).

At very low concentrations of suspended matter, the change in the incident intensity is virtually undetectable, and a measurement of the intensity of the scattered light becomes essential if sensitivity and precision are desired. Whether we make the observation only at 90° to the incident beam or at other angles as well depends on the system and the data sought (Sections 20.3 and 20.4). When we determine scattered intensities, it is ordinarily preferable to work directly with the intensities instead of converting to turbidities. The transformation requires an integration of the intensity over 360° (see footnote on p. 586).

Scattering can serve to establish either concentration or molecular weight, and, if angular scattering data are taken, a good deal about particle shape and size. For the small and very large particles, information obtained by light scattering supplements that available from the more standard molecular weight techniques such as osmometry and electron microscopy. In the intermediate size region (dimensions from 0.03 to 0.10 μm), where none of these approaches gives good information, light scattering is invaluable.

Where concentrations of suspended or dissolved materials are of interest, it is sufficient to determine the intensity of scattering of the system and to read the results from calibration curves for similar systems. This procedure, for example, is customarily used in an inorganic analysis termed *nephelometric* or *turbidimetric* (Section 20.3). A precision of the order of 1 % is attainable. On the other hand, if the molecular weight or shape factors of a macromolecular substance are to be calculated, it is necessary to determine the scattering at several known concentrations and usually at different angles. Calculations then yield an average molecular weight if there is a range of particle sizes, and approximate size and shape information (Section 20.4). We can anticipate that results will be most meaningful for monodisperse systems, that is, those in which all particles are of the same size.

It must be understood that light scattering is a complex phenomenon; the techniques used in measurement are complex, and so is the theory. More so than for many other techniques, the reliability of observation is strongly dependent on proper experimental and measurement procedures. So it is much better adapted to a continuing program of analysis than to an occasional determination.

20.2 INSTRUMENTATION

Since the instrumentation of light scattering photometers is, in general, typical of photometric devices as described in Chapter 17, it is important here to note only special features.

Sources. It is necessary to use sources providing high-intensity monochromatic radiation at as short wavelengths as are usable for efficient light scattering measurements. A mercury arc or a laser, with appropriate filter combinations for isolating one of its emission lines, is undoubtedly the most convenient source (Section 11.3). However, if only a particle count or a determination of the concentration of a particular material is desired, a polychromatic source such as a tungsten lamp is adequate. Even in this case, for best results we should use the blue spectral region; a filter can be used to block other wavelengths.

Detectors. Unless a system is unusually turbid, the intensity of scattering is very small. For that reason photomultiplier tubes are almost universally used. They have the added advantage, of course, of eliminating the need for an amplifier where observations are restricted to systems of moderate and high scattering power.

Rather than attempting to measure the radiation transmitted along the path of the incident beam, an extremely difficult task since the transmitted intensity is perhaps 10^6 times greater, we either fix a detector in orientation to intercept light scattered at 90°, or else mount it on a circular disc that turns to allow measurement at many angles, e.g., at 0° and from 30° to 135°. The outer edge of the disc is usually graduated in degrees and readable from the outside.

Stray radiation, cells. The intense incident beam must somehow be dissipated so that it will not be internally reflected into the detector and completely mask the scattered light. It is not sufficient to rely on regular baffles. Also, since the stray and the scattered radiation are of the same wavelength, filters and monochromators cannot be utilized. A partial solution is to have a long narrow entrance port for the multiplier tube, and to trap the exit beam as described below.

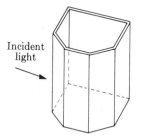

Incident light

Fig. 20.1 Semioctagonal cell for light scattering. The walls not used by either the entering or the exiting beams are ordinarily blackened to absorb light.

Although we can use cells that are mainly cylindrical, they must have flat faces where the entering and exiting beams are to pass. In general, a cell with a rectangular cross-section is preferred. Where measurements are to be made at angles of scattering other than 90°, semioctagonal cells (see Fig. 20.1) are useful. The "octagonal" faces will allow measurements at 45°, 90°, and 135° to the incident beam. Often walls through which light beams are not to pass are painted a dull black to absorb unwanted radiation. In experimental cells, a blackened, curved horn is frequently affixed to the wall directly opposite the entering beam to trap all the beam that is not scattered. Alternatively, we can incorporate a light trap for this purpose in the wall of the chamber in which the cell is located.

Light scattering photometers. A filter photometer can easily be adapted for measurement of scattering at moderate and high intensities (and is convertible for fluorometric and absorption photometric determinations). If provided with a double-beam arrangement, it will be independent of source fluctuations.

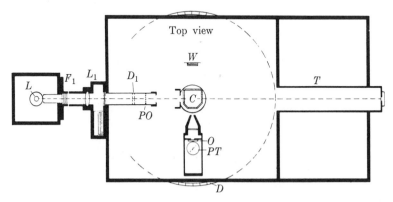

Fig. 20.2 Simplified schematic diagram of a Brice-Phoenix light scattering photometer. C, semi-octagonal cell. D, graduated disc to which deflector is attached. D_1, collimating tube diaphragm. F_1, monochromatic filter. L, mercury lamp. L_1, achromatic lens. O, opal glass depolarizing diffuser. PT, photomultiplier tube. PO, demountable polarizer. T, light-trap tube. W, working standard. (Courtesy of Phoenix Precision Instrument Co.)

Figure 20.2 shows a representative precision light scattering photometer for exact work at low intensities. [9] The multiplier phototube used as a receiver is mounted on a turntable and may be positioned at any desired angle from 0° to 180° relative to the exit beam.

A further modification that provides easy manipulation and access to the cell chamber during a run was suggested by Debye. [10] Here the detector and turntable are in a closed compartment below the cell. Scattered radiation from the cell is intercepted by a small right-angle prism, also attached to the turntable, and reflected downward to the photomultiplier tube whenever a floor shutter is opened.

Measurement of refractive indices. Polymer measurements require a very sensitive refractometer also. To calculate molecular weights, we must know precisely the difference in refractive indices of solvent and solution (see Eq. 20.3), which is ordinarily no larger than 10^{-3} in refractive index. Some type of differential refractometer (Section 21.4) that provides accuracy in the fifth decimal place is indispensable.

20.3 TURBIDIMETRY (AND NEPHELOMETRY)

These terms are meant to designate the measurement of concentrations of particulate matter in a suspension. *Turbidimetric* measurements are those made by transmitted light, and *nephelometric* observations are those made by scattered light. The single term *turbidimetry* will be used here, with the angle of measurement relative to the incident beam specified where necessary.

Measuring the transmitted intensity (0°) allows turbidity readings over a wide range of concentrations but leads to poor sensitivity at low turbidity. It is difficult to detect the small deviations from full illumination caused by low "concentrations." On the other hand, measuring the scattered intensity (from 75 to 135°) gives high sensitivity at low turbidities where the intensity of scattering may be compared with a dark background. However, we cannot reliably determine dense suspensions or high turbidities by scattering (nephelometry), because of the interparticle interference (Section 20.4). Both methods have their range of application. The methods are relative, and data are interpreted by using calibration curves.

The precise duplication of precipitation conditions is critical in this type of analysis. There must be a close control of temperature, amounts and concentrations of samples and reagents, rate of stirring, and length of mixing. Usually a stabilizer, such as gelatin, is added to protect the colloid, that is, to prevent coagulation beyond a certain size. Some sodium benzoate is often used as a preservative. Analyses of this kind are somewhat tedious if performed manually, and automatic devices have been developed for plant stream monitoring. Finally, although there is some overlapping between absorption photometry and turbidimetric methods, colored suspensions are best measured by absorption methods (Section 16.6).

Perhaps the best-known chemical analysis of this type involves the precipitation of barium sulfate under conditions that yield a stable monodisperse suspension. Either sulfur or "sulfate" may be determined by this method.

The concentration of smokes, fogs, aerosols, etc., may be ascertained quite easily by light scattering measurements. Samples are continuously drawn through the scattering cell. In this case calibration curves are obtained with an aerosol of known particle size and physical properties.

Similarly, we can estimate the amount of suspended matter in liquids. For example, the successful makeup of boiler feed water can be monitored by a recording turbidimeter. The idea may also be applied to the analysis of a pair of mutually immiscible liquids if the suspension is reasonably stable. For example, we might estimate the amount of water in a benzene sample and make a correction for the normal solubility.

20.4 SCATTERING BY MACROMOLECULES

Substances of high molecular weight are effective scatterers when dissolved in solvents of sufficiently different refractive index. The scattered intensity of isotropic macromolecules, which we may term the excess scattering of the solution, is in general both angle- and concentration-dependent (Section 10.10). The first type of dependence appears mainly for very large molecules. As the principal dimension of a particle exceeds about one-twentieth the wavelength of the incident radiation, there is *intra*molecular interference between the scattering from different segments of the molecule. The net result is a lessening of intensity in the backward direction ($\theta > 90°$) and the production of an asymmetrical pattern of scattering. The effect of increasing concentration is to cause *inter*molecular interference.

In view of these effects, scattering observations must ordinarily be made as a function both of angle and of concentration if they are to provide a good basis for estimating molecular weights, sizes, and shapes. From theoretical considerations we can show that the molecular weight of an isotropic macromolecule is related directly to the "reduced" scattered intensity I_v (where the subscript v denotes the use of vertically polarized illumination) by the expression

$$\lim_{\substack{c \to 0 \\ \theta \to 0}} \frac{I_v}{c} = \left[\frac{4\pi^2 n_0^2 (\partial n / \partial c)^2}{\lambda_0^4 N_0} \right] M \tag{20.3}$$

$$= K' \cdot M. \tag{20.3a}$$

In the equation, n_0 is the refractive index of the solvent, c the concentration of solute in g ml^{-1}, M its weight-average molecular weight (see below), N_0 Avogadro's number, and λ_0 the vacuum wavelength of the light. The scattering of vertically polarized light is used, since it provides the most reliable measure of molecular weight and size effects. Ordinarily the expression in brackets, which is a constant, is identified as K' (Eq. 20.3a).* In finding the limiting value of I_v/c, the derivative $(\partial n / \partial c)^2$ can be replaced by $[(n - n_0)/c]^2$, where n is the refractive index of the solution. Since the refractive index difference is always small (of the order of 1×10^{-4}) and difficult to determine reliably, this factor often fixes the lower limit of measurement. Best results come from using a differential refractometer (Section 21.4).

The use of the reduced intensity I_v is amply justified in terms of the operations actually carried out in light scattering measurements, as the discussion below shows. By definition,

$$I_v = \frac{i(\theta) r^2}{I_v^0} \tag{20.4}$$

where $i(\theta)$ is the measured excess intensity of scattering at angle θ relative to the incident beam, r is the distance from the center of the scattering solution to the detector, and I_v^0 the incident intensity (of vertically polarized illumination). The value of I_v at 90° we usually term *Rayleigh's ratio* for vertically polarized light. In connection with Eq. (20.3), note that I_v is the only quantity that is a function of θ, and even it is independent of θ if the scattering particles are small compared with the wavelength of the incident light.

If, in addition, the macromolecules are anisotropic, or behave anisotropically through interaction with the solvent, we must allow for the alterations in intensity resulting from the depolarization of the scattered light. Where a correction is necessary it is perhaps simplest to proceed by introducing the Cabannes correction factor for vertically polarized incident illumination into Eq. (20.3a) to give a new constant K, defined as:

$$K = \frac{3 + 3\rho_v}{3 - 4\rho_v} K'. \tag{20.5}$$

The quantity ρ_v is the depolarization ratio for vertically polarized incident light. For

---

* An expression identical in form to Eqs. (20.3) and (20.3a) except that the turbidity τ appears in place of I_v has often been used. Since the turbidity is obtained from the intensity by integrating over the surface of a sphere of radius r, the constant K' in Eq. (20.3a) is multiplied by $8\pi/3$ to give the constant H. The other expression is $\tau = HcM$.

the classes of macromolecules of greatest interest, the linear coiling polymers and the proteins, the correction usually amounts to no more than from 1 to 10%. A thorough discussion of the depolarization of light scattered by large molecules has been given by Doty. [7]

An additional relation, similar to the equation for the osmotic pressure of a solution, gives the dependence of the excess scattered intensity on the concentration in dilute solutions:

$$\frac{Kc}{I_v} = \frac{1}{MP(\theta)} + 2A_2 c. \tag{20.6}$$

Here A_2 is a thermodynamic constant that measures intermolecular interaction at a fixed temperature, and $P(\theta)$ is a probability distribution function relating to the size of the polymer molecule, or more specifically to the distribution of the molecular segments in solution. [8] A detailed treatment of either quantity is beyond the scope of this book. In so far as the use of Eq. (20.6) is concerned, it is fortunate that as θ approaches zero, $P(\theta)$ goes to unity.

Interpretation of data. To determine molecular weights and basic information about size by use of these equations, we take light scattering data at several concentrations (and one or more angles, if necessary) and extrapolate them to $c = 0$ (and to $\theta = 0$, if necessary). In Fig. 20.3 representative extrapolation plots are given. The intercept of the angular extrapolation plot yields the reciprocal of the molecular weight. Under favorable conditions the molecular weights given are accurate to perhaps $\pm 5\%$. If the particles are relatively small, I_v is of course independent of θ, and we take data at a single angle, perhaps 90°, and extrapolate them to infinite dilution.

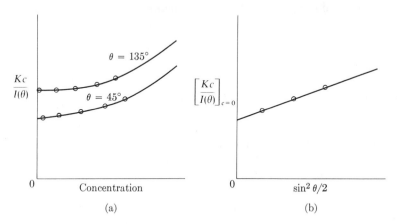

Fig. 20.3   Extrapolation of scattered intensity data for a linear coiling polymer to infinite dilution and zero angle. (a) Concentration extrapolation. (b) Angular extrapolation. In practice, a bilinear extrapolation procedure is more commonly used. [12]

According to Eq. (20.6) an angular extrapolation will also yield some information about particle size. It may be shown that the ratio (initial slope)/(intercept), by virtue of the properties of $P(\theta)$, defines an average radius of gyration $\overline{r^2}$ of a macromolecule independent of its geometry. Figure 20.4 shows the nature of this variable for a mono-disperse (see below) linear coiling polymer, such as polyacrylonitrile.* If the shape of the polymer molecule is known from other measurements, we can use the average radius of gyration to determine a molecular dimension. For example, the average extension of a linear coiling chain or the length of a rigid rod can be calculated easily from it.

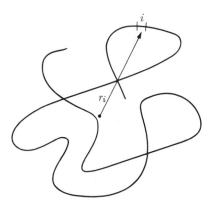

Fig. 20.4 Definition of radius of gyration r^2 for a linear coiling polymer molecule where r_i is the distance from the center of mass of the molecule to the ith segment. The square of r_i must be taken in order that a segment with negative r_i can contribute as well as one with a positive value. Note that each r_i represents a time-average value for that segment; thus r^2 is actually a double average.

Ordinarily the experimental data are not sufficiently precise to warrant an exhaustive interpretation of the angular plot, which, theoretically at least, can also provide some indication of molecular shape as well as of size.

Absolute intensities. Four complications in measurement and interpretation must now be considered.

First, obtaining the reduced intensity I_v by direct measurement is very difficult. The problem is posed by the vast difference between $i(\theta)$ and I_v^0. For the usual dilute polymer solution, $i(\theta)$ is smaller by a factor of from 10^{-4} to 10^{-6} than I_v^0. The precise observation of two intensities of such different magnitude requires good instrumentation and procedures and exceptional care. (In contrast, most measurements in turbidimetry (Section 20.3), which involve a (scattered)/(transmittance) reading of $I_{90°}/I^0$, are not difficult because comparatively turbid solutions are used, i.e. $I_{90°}$ is large.) Actually, in polymer studies it solves the problem to refer scattering intensity measurements to standards, the absolute magnitude of whose scattering has been precisely determined at one or more angles. For example, benzene, clear glass blocks, and solutions of certain samples of polymers have been used. Diffuse reflectors such as blocks of magnesium oxide and magnesium carbonate have also been used.

With the standard in place in the light scattering photometer, we note the response of the instrument at an angle at which the scattering of the standard is known. We can

---

* For a polydisperse system the so-called Z-average radius of gyration is obtained. In this case there has also been an averaging over the intrinsically different sized molecules. [8]

use this reading to calibrate the photometer scale to read in absolute reduced intensity (regardless of angle). An effective way to obtain a simple calibration factor for the scale is to vary the voltage across the photomultiplier tube until a deflection is secured that gives each scale division some absolute value such as 1.00×10^{-4}.

Second, the small volume of scattering solution "observed" by the detector varies with the refractive index of the solution and the angle of observation. Appropriate corrections can be calculated for both potential sources of error. For example, if narrow exit slits are used, I_v should be multiplied by $\sin \theta$ for a cylindrical or semi-octagonal cell to allow for the volume effect. The refractive index correction is appreciable (varying as n_0^2) and is conveniently taken care of when the photometer scale is standardized for absolute intensity readings as described above. The definitive consideration of the general aspects of absolute intensity measurements is by Carr and Zimm. [6]

Third, since only the excess scattered intensity is eventually of interest, we must also measure the solvent scattering and subtract its contribution to the total scattering. For the solutions at the low-concentration end of the extrapolation, the correction may be appreciable; it is customary to take data at increasing dilution until

$$1.5 \leq \frac{I_{v\,\text{solution}}}{I_{v\,\text{solvent}}} \leq 2.0.$$

We define the excess intensity by

$$I_v = J \cdot \sin \theta \cdot [i(\theta)_{\text{solution}} - i(\theta)_{\text{solvent}}], \tag{20.7}$$

where J is the factor needed to convert photometer readings to absolute reduced intensities and the other variables have been defined.

Finally, the scattering caused by foreign particles, like dust, is nearly always the limiting factor in precision measurements. These particles must be scrupulously avoided, since they are relatively quite large and contribute heavily to the scattering (Section 10.10). Filtration through membrane filters or ultrafine sintered glass discs, and in some cases centrifugation, can remove them.

Polydisperse samples. Most polymeric substances contain molecules of many different molecular weights, i.e. they are *polydisperse*. Since the large particles are the best scatterers, the M in Eqs. (20.3) and (20.6) is a *weight-average molecular weight*, defined by the expression

$$\overline{M}_w = \frac{\sum n_i M_i^2}{\sum n_i M_i} \tag{20.8}$$

where n_i is the number of particles possessing molecular weight M_i. Since the molecular weight appears in the numerator as the square, it is apparent that a small percentage of heavier molecules can raise the value of the weight-average molecular weight substantially.

If the degree of polydispersity is of interest, it is common to obtain at least one other experimental measure of the molecular weight to obtain a number-average value, $\overline{M}_n = \sum n_i M_i / \sum n_i$. Osmotic pressure determinations and other observations based on colligative properties give this kind of average. The ratio $\overline{M}_w / \overline{M}_n$ provides a useful index of the degree of polydisperse character. If it is obtained, giving both $\overline{M}_w$ and $\overline{M}_w/\overline{M}_n$ can describe the sample.

REFERENCES

Consult also the appropriate references at the end of Chapter 10.

Light scattering theory and procedures are considered generally in:

1. Manfred J. R. Cantor, ed., *Polymer Fractionation*. New York: Academic, 1967
2. P. Doty and J. T. Edsall, "Light Scattering in Protein Solutions," *Advances in Protein Chem.* **6**, 37 (1951)
3. P. J. Flory, *Principles of Polymer Chemistry*. Ithaca, N.Y.: Cornell University Press, 1953
4. G. Oster, "Light Scattering," in *Physical Methods of Organic Chemistry*. 3d ed., pt 3. A. Weissberger, ed. New York: Interscience, 1960

Theory alone is treated in:

5. Milton Kerker, *The Scattering of Light and Other Electromagnetic Radiation*. New York: Academic, 1969

Some important theoretical papers dealing with light scattering are:

6. C. I. Carr Jr. and B. H. Zimm, "Absolute Intensity of Light Scattering from Pure Liquids and Solutions," *J. Chem. Phys.* **18**, 1616 (1950)
7. P. Doty, "Depolarization of Light Scattered from Dilute Macromolecular Solutions. I. Theoretical Basis," *J. Polymer Sci.* **3**, 750 (1948)
8. B. H. Zimm, "Apparatus and Methods for Measurement and Interpretation of the Angular Variation of Light Scattering; Preliminary Results on Polystyrene Solution," *J. Chem. Phys.* **16**, 1099 (1948)

A few other pertinent references are:

9. B. A. Brice, M. Halwer, and R. Speiser, "Photoelectric Light Scattering Photometer for determining High Molecular Weights," *J. Opt. Soc. Am.* **40**, 768 (1950)
10. P. Debye, "Photoelectric Instrument for Light-Scattering Measurements and a Differential Refractometer," *J. Appl. Phys.* **17**, 392 (1946)
11. E. J. Meehan and W. H. Beattie, "An Absolute Method of Turbidimetric Analysis," *Anal. Chem.* **33**, 632 (1961)
12. P. Outer, C. I. Carr, and B. H. Zimm, "Light Scattering Investigation of the Structure of Polystyrene," *J. Chem. Phys.* **18**, 830 (1950)

EXERCISES

20.1 The absorbance of a cloudy, colored solution is measured in a 1 cm cell as 0.15 without it being realized that some of the light has been scattered. Later the turbidity of the solution is determined to be 0.012. What is the true absorbance of the solution?   [*Ans.*: 0.145]

20.2 Assuming that the molecular weight of a particle is approximately proportional to its volume, what will be the relative scattering effectiveness of two particles (a) when one is 100 times the volume of the other and (b) when both are spherical and one is 100 times the diameter of the other? [*Ans.*: (a) larger particle 100 times better scatterer, (b) larger particle 10^6 times better scatterer.]

20.3 Calculate the values of the weight-average molecular weight M_w and the number-average molecular weight $\overline{M}_n$ for the mixtures obtained from two monodisperse polymers of molecular weights 100,000 and 500,000 when (a) equal numbers of molecules are mixed and (b) equal weights are mixed.   [Ans.: (a) 4.33×10^5, 3.0×10^5, (b) 3.0×10^5, 1.67×10^5.]

20.4 Assuming at low concentrations that Eq. (20.3) gives at least an estimate of the scattering, calculate the I_v expected for the following polymer solution. A solution of $1 \, \mathrm{g} \, \mathrm{l}^{-1}$ of polymer of M_w of 100,000 in carbon tetrachloride ($n = 1.46$) is examined with light of 546.1 nm. By use of a differential refractometer, $n_{\text{soln}} - n_{\text{solvent}} = 1 \times 10^{-3}$. Assume n_{soln} increases nearly linearly with concentration.   [Ans.: 1.8×10^{-8}.]

20.5 It is ordinarily advantageous to make angular measurements of the intensity of scattered light with vertically polarized light rather than with unpolarized light. One reason is that the volume correction for the former is $\sin \theta$, while that for the latter is $1/(1 + \cos^2 \theta)$. If the intensity reading is more accurate than the observation of the angle, show that the $\sin \theta$ correction is preferable. [Hint: calculate the change in each correction factor between $\theta = 45°$ and $\theta = 30°$.]

CHAPTER 21

REFRACTOMETRY

21.1 INTRODUCTION

The refractive index, together with the melting point and the boiling point, is one of the classic physical constants of interest in chemical analysis. Although refraction is a nonspecific property, few substances have identical refractive indices at a given temperature and wavelength. As discussed in Sections 10.5 through 10.7, refraction originates in the optical polarizability of a substance. The greater the polarizability of the molecule or ions, the higher the refractive index. That background material will be assumed familiar in the discussion that follows.

Usually refraction is measured as the refractive index n_2, which is commonly calculated from Eq. (10.8). That expression was

$$\frac{n_2}{n_1} = \frac{\sin \phi}{\sin \phi'}, \qquad (21.1)$$

where n_1 is the index of refraction of the medium through which light is incident at angle ϕ, and ϕ' is the angle of refraction in medium 2 for the radiation of wavelength λ. For purposes of simplification it is convenient to let $n_2 = n_2/n_1$, for the case in which medium 1 is air by assuming $n_{air} = 1$. The conventional refractive index is thus actually a refractive index relative to air.*

The refractive index may be found very precisely. Indeed, the ease and accuracy of observation surpasses that of density determinations. With a critical-angle refractometer (Section 21.3) a precision of 1×10^{-5} units in n is possible, and with a differential gas interferometer with a 100 cm cell, a precision of 3×10^{-8} units in n. These instruments are of simple design, but their optical components must be manufactured and aligned with great care.

The other attractions of refractive index measurements are many. They can be made very simply and rapidly with the majority of the types of refractometers and are nondestructive. In general, they require only small samples. The following list of uses suggests the range of application of refractive index measurements:

1. Confirming the identity of substances,
2. Analyzing mixtures and process streams,

---

* Absolute refractive indices (relative to a vacuum) are found by multiplying the relative n by the refractive index of dry air. At 25 °C and one atmosphere of pressure, $n_{abs} = n_{rel} \times n_{air} = n_{rel} \times 1.00027$.

3. Estimating properties of polymers, such as molecular weight, size, and shape (Section 20.4), and

4. Calculating physical properties, such as reflectivity and optical dispersion.

In the measurement of refractive index precision very much depends on the degree of control of several variables. Chief among these are wavelength and temperature, which are considered below. For gaseous samples the pressure also has to be maintained within narrow limits at a known value. For anisotropic solids (Section 10.13) we must also know the orientation of the sample with respect to the incident radiation. Most crystals are subject to this orientational stipulation, since they are anisotropic. [1, 10] The present discussion is limited to isotropic media, however, since most of the refractometric samples of interest are liquids and gases. In general, samples of this type will be anisotropic only when electrical or magnetic fields are imposed, the phenomenon being known as the *Kerr* or *Faraday* effect, respectively.

21.2 LIGHT SOURCES AND TEMPERATURE CONTROL

The data for water in Table 21.1 give some idea of the dependence of refractive index on temperature and wavelength. Note that the changes in n are nonlinear, although over short intervals we may interpolate linearly with reasonable reliability.

For reasons of instrumental and operating convenience, we commonly obtain refractive indices for analytical purposes in the visible. There the instrumentation is straightforward, and most substances are nonabsorbing. The latter is an advantage, since a strong loss of intensity would cause a detection problem.

Table 21.1 Influence of Wavelength and Temperature on Refractive Index of Water

	Wavelength			n_λ^{20}	Temperature	n_D^t
Color	Fraunhofer symbol	Source element	nm		°C	
Red	C	H	656.3	1.3312	10	1.3337
Yellow	D	Na	589.3	1.3330	20	1.3330
Blue	F	H	486.1	1.3371	30	1.3320
Violet		Hg	435.8	1.3403	40	1.3306
	G'	H	434.0	1.3404	50	1.3290

For a highly precise observation of n, monochromatic radiation must be used. Any source of discrete wavelengths (see Section 11.3) such as an electrical discharge lamp fits the requirement if followed by suitable filters (Section 11.5). The intense sodium doublet (the D-line) at 589.0 and 589.6 nm is the most widely used, but many observations are at mercury, hydrogen, or laser wavelengths. A distinct advantage of a sodium lamp for routine work is that a filter is seldom necessary; even though several other sodium doublets and some neon lines (starter gas) are also present, their intensity is less than 1% that of the D-lines. Furthermore, in critical angle instruments the natural variation of the refractive index with wavelength ensures there will be no loss of precision when wavelengths are separated by more than 10 or 20 nm. The critical ray boundary for each should be distinct and the separation between them great enough so they are easily distinguishable.

If the dispersion of n, that is, its variation with λ, is desired, a mercury lamp (G.E. H-3) with different filters yields four very intense lines at 579.0 (yellow), 546.1 (green), 435.8 (blue), and 404.7 nm (violet). Still more versatile is the type of mercury lamp (G.E. H-4) to which cadmium is added so that there is also the bright red Cd line (at 643.8 nm). Intense continuous sources (see Section 11.2), such as a xenon lamp followed by an appropriate filter or monochromator, are also in use.

Interestingly, white light can also be used for careful refractometry. The obvious deterrent to its use in critical angle instruments is the experimental fact that with it, the critical boundary becomes a wide gray band as a result of dispersion; this reduces the precision with which we can estimate n to perhaps ± 0.005 units. Compensation for the dispersion is imperative. Critical angle instruments that use daylight or tungsten sources have Amici prisms, which can be adjusted to cancel the dispersion. The image displacement type of refractometers use similar compensators when necessary. Amici prisms are discussed in the next section. Finally, in interferometry (Section 21.5), the dispersion produced is not a problem. An interferometric measurement consists merely in aligning two sets of alternating light and dark fringes.

Temperature control.   Most liquids show a decrease in refractive index of about 0.00045 units per degree centigrade rise. Solids are generally less sensitive but do exhibit changes of roughly 0.00001 unit per degree. The decrease in n is linked to a lower bulk polarizability and is thus a direct result of the thermal expansion of substances.

An observation reliable in the fourth decimal place requires thermostating of liquid samples to at least $\pm 0.2\,°\text{C}$. Naturally, for greater precision the control must improve. At high levels of precision the entire refractometer must be thermostated. The ordinary thermostating of liquid samples is by circulating fluid from a constant-temperature bath through a "jacket" surrounding the sample. At least one instrument, the Pulfrich, also provides a thermostated "finger" that may be dipped into the sample. Unless evaporation is also minimized with liquids, the sample temperature will not be uniform.

21.3 CRITICAL ANGLE REFRACTOMETERS

In view of its advantages, it is not surprising that the critical angle principle is common in refractometer design. With rather simple auxiliary devices, such as a monochromatic source and a constant-temperature bath, critical angle refractometers provide sufficient precision of measurement for most liquid and solid samples, cover a broad range of refractive index, and are easily operated.

The critical angle of refraction is defined as the angle of refraction in a medium when radiation is incident on its boundary at *grazing* or 90° incidence. In this case, Eq. (21.1) simplifies to

$$\frac{n_2}{n_1} = \frac{1}{\sin \phi_c}, \qquad (21.2)$$

where ϕ_c is the critical angle at the wavelength used. If we know either n_1 or n_2, we may find the other by a measurement of the critical angle in medium 2. In making an observation, medium 1 is usually the sample, and medium 2 a prism of known n.

As we can deduce from Fig. 21.1, there is a family of angular segments in the refracting prism that is not illuminated by the rays refracted in the sample. All nongrazing rays are refracted at angles smaller than ϕ_c. To form the dark-light boundary, only those rays incident on medium 2 at perhaps from 80 to 90° are of interest. Since these rays may enter medium 2 anywhere along the interface, actually not a single critical ray but an endless set of parallel critical rays is formed. A condensing or focusing lens must be used to coalesce these into the single dark-light boundary viewed through the telescope of the instrument (Fig. 21.1).

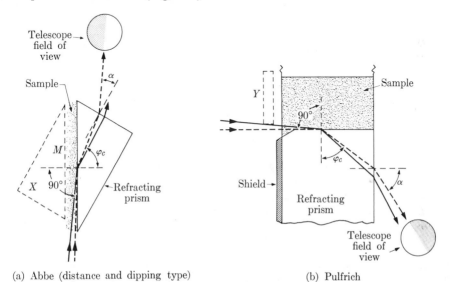

(a) Abbe (distance and dipping type)   (b) Pulfrich

Fig. 21.1 Comparison of the prism arrangements in (a) the Abbe and (b) the Pulfrich refractometers. The critical ray is shown as a broken line. X prism is used only with liquid samples and is an auxiliary prism with a matte surface M that diffuses light. Y is a shutter used to block all rays except those incident near 90°. The thickness of the layer of sample is greatly exaggerated for the Abbe.

The Abbe refractometer.   Figure 21.2 shows one common design for the Abbe type of critical angle refractometer. The very thin layer (1 to 3 drops) of liquid being examined is contained between illuminating prism X and the refracting prism R. The prisms are partially hollowed to allow the circulation of thermostated fluid. Light enters from below, usually being reflected from a mirror. Note two points especially. First, no substance can be examined whose n is greater than that of the refracting prism; total reflection would be the only result. Second, the critical angle *itself* is immeasurable; it is formed *in* prism R. What is determinable is the angle of emergence α of the critical ray (Fig. 21.1).

The angle α may be found by "scanning" the upper edge of the refracting prism R with the telescope. The prism is so mounted that it pivots about a central point on its surface. When the sharp edge of the light-dark boundary has been centered on the cross hairs in the telescope ocular, the reading at the index marker on the calibrated metal or glass scale attached to the instrument is noted.

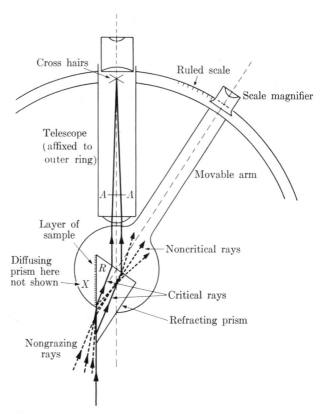

Fig. 21.2 Schematic diagram of an Abbe refractometer. As shown, it is intended for use with monochromatic light. To adapt for use with white light, Amici prisms may be inserted at *AA*.

The standard Abbe scale is graduated directly in n_D to the nearest 0.001 unit. An attached magnifier allows us to estimate the next decimal place. The accuracy is therefore ±0.0001. If we have readings with monochromatic sources other than the sodium *D*-line, graphs are available to correct the readings. [1] Finally, we may determine indices over the considerable range of from 1.30 to 1.70. Only a few substances have *n*'s outside these limits.

For reasons of convenience and cost, a tungsten lamp is a common source for the Abbe in routine work. After the prism and sample have dispersed the white light, the dispersion is largely compensated by a pair of Amici prisms. These are small, direct-vision spectroscopes. The index of refraction of their components is such as to allow the prisms to disperse light without deviating the wavelengths at the *D*-line. Fig. 21.3 shows the combination of prisms termed an *Amici compensator*. We can rotate the prisms in opposite directions by turning an external, beveled, graduated collar. A rough measure of the dispersion of the sample can be obtained by noting the angular setting of the collar in (b) of the figure.

With Amici prisms, we can correct a polychromatic critical ray boundary completely at two wavelengths. Although the boundary appears sharp and reasonably "white," the accuracy of measurement of *n* that is possible with the compensator,

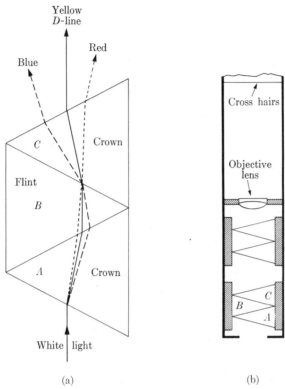

(a)   (b)

Fig. 21.3 An Amici compensator. All wavelengths are deviated except the sodium *D*-line. (a) Detail of dispersion. (b) Position in telescope tube (schematic). The collar which allows the compensator to be rotated is not shown.

regardless of the type of refractometer, is only about 0.0001. A further disadvantage when Amici prisms are used with the Abbe is that we cannot measure the index of refraction at wavelengths other than the *D*-line without making an elaborate reading correction.

The Pulfrich refractometer. In the Pulfrich instrument, the refracting prism is always under the sample. As the schematic partial diagram of the device in Fig. 21.4 shows, the telescope is mounted on a rotatable scale. Not shown is the right-angle prism that reflects the rays emerging from the refracting prism and allows the identification of angle α. The instrument's circular scale is ruled in degrees and fitted with a vernier for estimation to the nearest minute. The value of *n* for different wavelengths of illumination is obtained from tables furnished with the instrument (see Exercise 21.1). The precision and accuracy are about 0.0001 unit in *n* for direct measurements. The usual range of measurement (from 1.33 to 1.60) is extendable from 1.33 to 1.84 by inserting other refracting prisms furnished as interchangeable parts. We may also make differential measurements precisely with the Pulfrich over a range in *n* of about 0.05 by engaging a micrometer drive to position the telescope cross hairs. [1] The accuracy of differences in *n* thus found is ±0.00005 unit.

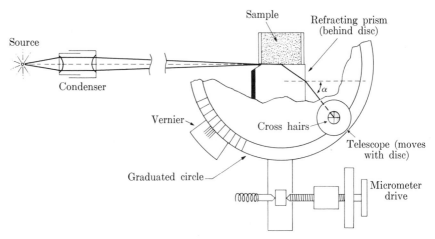

Fig. 21.4 Schematic representation of a Pulfrich refractometer.

Instrumental errors.   The basic differences in the Abbe and Pulfrich types may be high-lighted by a discussion of instrumental errors. In the Abbe, probably the most serious source of error is the cutting off of neargrazing rays, those incident on the refracting prism at very small angles. Fig. 21.1 shows how the standard Abbe refracts only the radiation diffused from the rough or matte surface of prism X into the liquid. Unfor-tunately, this radiation is poor in grazing rays. As a result, the true critical ray boundary may be difficult to perceive, and instead we may select an apparent boundary some-where within the shaded region. The shadow width is often of the order of 1×10^{-4} in n.

This error is absent in the Pulfrich, for the grazing rays may enter along the whole length of its refracting prism. Indeed, the Pulfrich is so designed that radiation may be largely limited to these; besides the condensing lens shown in Fig. 21.4, it has a shutter that can be lowered to block all rays but those incident near 90°. In certain cases, such as the examination of solids, this kind of shielding could also be arranged for the Abbe (Section 21.8).

In either instrument, if the refracting prism or the scale is somehow displaced from its original alignment, this introduces some error into measurements. The Pulfrich is so constructed as to be nearly self-correcting in this regard and the Abbe is not. With the Pulfrich we may redetermine the normal to the surface of the refracting prism at will by reflecting light from the prism surface. [1] We then subtract the zero scale cor-rection from all angular measurements. In contrast, standards of known n must be used with the Abbe to check the alignment. We may then reposition the telescope to give accurate readings. With either device a policy of periodic calibration is desirable (Section 21.7).

Precision Abbe.   In the precision Abbe, the optimum reliability has been improved by a factor of about three. We secure better performance with a bigger and better refracting prism and by using a diffusing prism with a smooth surface. By restricting the illumina-tion as much as possible to grazing incidence, we obtain a greater intensity of grazing rays and a narrower critical ray shadow region. The direct-reading scale of the regular Abbe is replaced by a finely graduated angular scale and a vernier. A table is supplied to convert the readings to refractive indices. Monochromatic light must be used, and tables for other than the *D*-line are available. Table 21.2 compares the precision Abbe with other types.

Dipping refractometer.   The dipping refractometer is quite similar to the regular Abbe. It differs in that it has no auxiliary prism *X* and its telescope tube is affixed rigidly to the refracting prism. For liquid samples, the refracting prism is immersed almost completely. In the telescope the border between light and dark fields impinges on an accurately ruled scale in a *filar micrometer eyepiece*. The exact location of the critical ray is ascertained by moving the scale by means of a micrometer screw device until the nearest division falls on the boundary. Then both scale and micrometer are read, and the readings are converted to refractive indices by reference to a table. Since there is no shielding error, the accuracy is about equal to that of the precision Abbe (Table 21.2).

Necessarily, because of the fixed telescope, the range of refractive index readable with a single prism is restricted to about 0.04 units in *n*. Prisms are easily interchanged. Calibration is sometimes difficult, however, since it must be done with a pure material whose refractive index is in the range of the prism being used.

Process refractometer.   Figure 21.5 is a schematic of a process-stream refractometer in which the sample prism forms a portion of the wall of a transparent sampling pipe. Because of the sensitive optical nulling arrangement used, it permits measurements to ± 0.00003 in *n*.

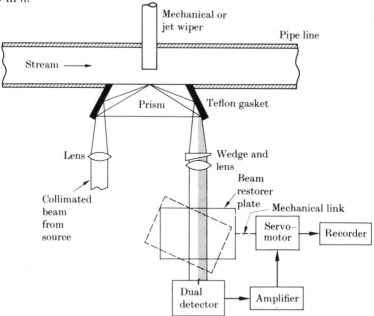

Fig. 21.5 Simplified schematic of an automatic, critical angle refractometer, the Anacon Inline Refractometer. When there is a change in refractive index of the stream, the beam restorer plate is used to return the beam to its original position. Since the instrument relies on total internal reflection with its minute penetration into a sample, the refractometer can be used to monitor the index of highly opaque liquids or suspensions. (Courtesy of Anacon Inc.)

Table 21.2 Characteristics of Refractometers

Operating principle and type	Measurement of refractive index				Liquid sample size, ml	Best use
	Absolute		Differential			
	Range	Precision*	Range	Precision*		
Critical angle						
1. Abbe	1.30 to 1.70	$\pm 1 \times 10^{-4}$	—	—	0.05 to 0.10	Routine analytical
2. Precision Abbe	1.30 to 1.70	$\pm 3 \times 10^{-5}$	—	—	0.05 to 0.10	Precision analytical
3. Pulfrich	1.30 to 1.60	$\pm 1 \times 10^{-4}$	0.05	$\pm 3 \times 10^{-5}$	0.5 to 5	Dispersion and differential measurements
	1.30 to 1.84 (3 prisms)					
4. Dipping	1.325 to 1.367	$\pm 3 \times 10^{-5}$	—	—	5 to 30	Routine precision testing of liquid products
	1.325 to 1.647 (10 prisms)					
Image displacement						
1. Prism spectrometer	No limits	$\pm 1 \times 10^{-6}$	—	—	10 to 25	High-precision absolute measurement
2. Differential	—	—	0.001	$\pm 3 \times 10^{-6}$	5	Precise differential
3. Fisher	1.30 to 1.90	$\pm 2 \times 10^{-3}$	—	—	0.05	Qualitative work
Interference						
1. Interferometer	Liquids $\{$short cell		0.050	$\pm 2 \times 10^{-5}$	0.10	High-precision differential measurements
	long cell		0.0006	$\pm 2 \times 10^{-7}$	8	
	Gas, long cell		0.00005	$\pm 3 \times 10^{-8}$		
2. Interference refractometer (with microscope)			0.002	$\pm 2 \times 10^{-6}$	1	High-precision measurements

* Figures represent ultimate precision realizable.

21.4 IMAGE DISPLACEMENT INSTRUMENTS

In principle, any prism spectroscope or spectrometer is also a refractometer. The angular displacement of the image of the slit is a measure of the index of refraction of the prism at the wavelength being considered. A family of these devices exists in which the prism material is varied and other variables are controlled or measured. Of these, the prism spectrometer is the most versatile and accurate for absolute measurements on liquids and solids.

In design, the precision spectrometer differs little from the spectroscope sketched in Fig. 12.1. If we are to examine a solid, we fashion it into a prism; liquid materials are poured into a hollow prism-shaped vessel. We then seal the sample prism at the center of a large, precisely ruled circle of metal. Exact angular settings of the slit and telescope arms are read off the circle when the refracted slit image has been centered in the telescope field.

Since the image of a slit can be defined very sharply, the optimum precision and accuracy of the spectrometer are extremely good, $\pm 1 \times 10^{-6}$ in units of n. The spectrometer is also very versatile in terms of the possible wavelengths and refractive indices it will handle. For example, if quartz optics are used, UV and near IR observations are possible. There is effectively no measurable limit on the value of n, since any angle of refraction can be determined. As we would expect, very careful manipulation and close temperature control ($\pm 0.002\,°C$ for liquids) are required to obtain optimum accuracy. Because of these factors the instrument is not well suited to routine work.

Differential refractometers. There have been devised a number of image displacement refractometers that respond to the difference between the n of a sample and that of a reference. Many operate automatically (Section 21.6). In each device two hollow prisms set in opposition, as illustrated in Fig. 21.6, are used to hold the liquids. The displacement of the image by one prism tends to offset that by the other. This arrangement keeps the net shift small so that it is precisely measurable with reference to a fixed point. Since differences of the order of 5×10^{-6} in n are sought, monochromatic sources and close temperature control for the sample, reference, and optical components must be provided.

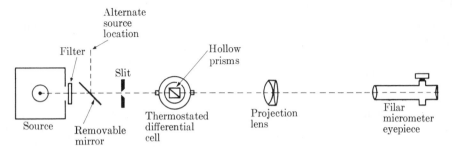

Fig. 21.6 A schematic drawing of the Brice-Phoenix differential refractometer. All components are mounted on an optical bench. The eyepiece is described in Section 21.3. (Courtesy of Phoenix Precision Instrument Co.)

Figure 21.6 is a schematic of a representative differential refractometer for laboratory use. The prism assembly is jacketed for circulation of a thermostating fluid.

In this instrument we measure the actual angular deviation of the slit image on the filar micrometer scale of a stationary telescope. The range of *n* is only about 0.001, but the accuracy approaches that of the precision spectrometer without calling for its delicate manipulations. This type of instrument has widespread use in light scattering photometry (Sections 20.2, 20.4) and in process stream refractometers (Section 21.6).

Schlieren techniques properly fall within this category. [8] They are conventionally used not in measuring refractive indices, but in locating concentration gradients by means of the accompanying refractive index gradients. For example, in protein solutions we may obtain a quantitative estimate of concentration by "Schlieren scanning" of the different layers set up by electrophoresis. Under an electrical field, most of the components of the mixture will migrate in a cell at characteristic rates. As in chromatographic procedures (Chapter 31), each substance tends to occupy a definite zone at the edge of which there is a detectable refractive index gradient.

21.5 THE INTERFEROMETER

By utilizing interference techniques, we can extend the reliability of differential refractive index measurements into the seventh decimal place for liquids and the eighth for gases. Each extension in precision further restricts the difference between the *n* of the standard and that of the sample. This limitation on the range is readily evident in Table 21.2.

In the typical interferometer, the sample and the standard are placed in matched cells of equal length. Rays from a slit illuminated by white or monochromatic light are collimated, directed through the cells and onto a slit at the end of each cell, and then are suitably merged by a lens arrangement. A pattern of interference bands or fringes results. The relative position of the pattern depends on the difference in the two optical path lengths (Section 10.15). In turn, these path lengths are directly related to the refractive indices of the contained gases or liquids. The eye is the sensing device. To avoid counting bands or fringes, we set up a fixed band pattern below the desired pattern, and a variable glass compensator in the sample path is pivoted until the two patterns are in alignment. The Δn is obtained from the reading of the compensator micrometer screw.

Measurements in the IR.   In this range it is convenient to count interference fringes in a regular sealed cell (for liquids). The procedure has been discussed in Section 16.6.

21.6 AUTOMATIC REFRACTOMETERS

Automatic recording refractometers have also been devised. These are usually differential instruments of the image displacement type (Section 21.4). Many use a split photocell detector or dual phototubes. If the light from the slit shifts principally to one photocell as a result of a change in *n*, an unbalance signal appears. It is amplified and fed to a servomotor, which acts to restore balance by inserting a wedge or prism or by turning the sample prism table. In other words, balancing is a "nulling" operation. Figure 21.7 gives a schematic drawing of a photoelectric instrument. The precision of these devices varies from 2×10^{-6} to 1×10^{-4} in *n*. Table 21.2 compares the performance with that of other refractometers.

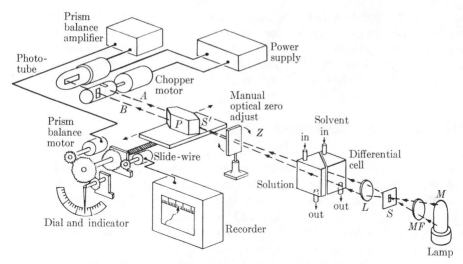

Fig. 21.7 The Phoenix recording differential refractometer. The light from source M is made monochromatic by filter MF. After passing through slit S, the beam is collimated by lens system L. The slit image S', as deviated by the differential cell, falls on the hexagonal prism P, which acts as a beam splitter. Prism P can be moved precisely in a lateral direction until the two beams A and B are of equal intensity. Each beam is alternately interrupted by a synchronous chopper and is diffused before falling on a multiplier phototube. If A and B are not of equal intensity, the amplified unbalance signal is used to drive prism P in the appropriate direction until they are. Thus, it is easy to determine a change in the refractive index of the sample, for it will cause a deviation of the slit position. Both the dial indicator and the recording potentiometer respond to the movements of the prism table and register the refractive index. (Courtesy of Phoenix Precision Instrument Co.)

Automatic differential refractometers are finding increasing application in monitoring chemical streams such as the distillate from an industrial fractionating column or the effluent from a partition chromatograph column. In industrial fractionation we may set the instrument to register deviations from the desired value of n. By connecting the refractometer to an appropriate control unit that will alter an operating variable like the take-off rate, we may usually secure constancy of composition of the output.

21.7 CALIBRATION

Most refractometers present some minor calibration and stability problems. In general, preserving the initial calibration performed by the manufacturer is basically a matter of alignment. For example, the refracting prism of an Abbe must maintain its orientation relative to the scale of indices, or all results will be slightly in error.

Periodic calibrations are desirable, and indeed are indispensable when reliability in and beyond the fourth decimal place is required. They are best made by observations on common pure materials. For example, at 25 °C water ($n_D = 1.33250$), chloroform ($n_D = 1.44293$), and benzene ($n_D = 1.49790$) are good test liquids for the ordinary range of measurements. Almost any substance selected requires some additional purification, like drying and distillation, before it is pure enough to serve as a standard, even if it is purchased as reagent grade stock. (a) We can apply the differences between the observed and standard values of n to subsequent readings as arithmetic corrections, for example,

$n_{act} = n_{obs}$ + correction, or (b) we can adjust the instrument, e.g., for the Abbe when the index is at the proper scale value, we can shift the telescope objective by a key to bring the cross hairs into coincidence with the critical boundary. Since procedural errors can also influence measurements, liquids ought to be used for calibration if most measurements are to be made on liquids, etc. The glass test piece supplied with many Abbe refractometers is also useful in checking the calibration stability.

21.8 ANALYTICAL PROCEDURES

The index of refraction is broadly valuable in *qualitative analysis*. Once we have obtained a substance in a reasonably pure state, determining n immediately narrows the possibilities that should be checked to identify it. For instance, in organic qualitative analysis it is conventional to determine in sequence, for each constituent, the elemental composition, solubility, boiling point, and refractive index. Extensive tables listing compounds according to refractive index are available to facilitate analysis. [18, 19] Where we must examine considerable numbers of unknowns, a systematic physical constant approach is worth while, particularly in conjunction with a technique like IR spectrophotometry. When no value for the refractive index of a compound is available, it may be estimated. The atomic refractions of the substance are added to obtain the molar refraction and then Eq. (21.3) is used to calculate n.

Example An organic substance, liquid at room temperature, is separated by distillation at between 78 and 80 °C from a liquid mixture. Its refractive index n_D at 25° is 1.4980. The compound is definitely not an aliphatic alcohol (n's < 1.48) but may be benzene or some other aromatic compound. Additional physical data are required for an actual identification.

If we know the density of a substance also, plots of n versus density for the various types of organic compounds can provide specific suggestions about the functional groups and the chain length or number of rings. [13, 17]

The dispersion of the refractive index of a substance is another analytically useful physical characteristic in areas where tabulated data are available. It is defined as either $n_F - n_C$ or $n_G - n_D$. The latter is a more recent definition based on the greater availability and ease of use of the mercury and sodium lamps. It has the additional advantage that the dispersion values are about one-third larger. Correlations of dispersion with composition have been fully exploited in petroleum analyses. [14]

Example In gasolines, the aromatic hydrocarbons have $n_F - n_C$ values of the order of 180×10^{-4} and the aliphatics have values close to 99×10^{-4}. The percentages of aromatics may be estimated to 1 % in most cases by obtaining dispersion values accurate to 1×10^{-4}.

Quantitative analysis. Very often the composition of simple, homogeneous liquid or gaseous mixtures can be determined by refractive index measurements after a calibration curve has been prepared. Some criteria for a reliable analysis of a mixture are

1. An instrumental precision that is adequate in comparison with the variation in n that is to be measured,

2. A constant composition except for the constituent of interest, and

3. A nearly linear refractive index-composition curve for the constituent of interest.

Only the last point requires special amplification. The condition of a linear curve is seldom met by liquid mixtures over a broad composition range (from 0 to 50 % or from 0 to 100 %). It is most likely to be satisfied if the constituents are chemically similar. Over small composition ranges, however, we nearly always obtain a linear curve. If the graph shows strong curvature in the composition region of interest, replotting the refractive index data against another concentration parameter may be helpful. Many systems show maxima or minima. For example, the ethanol-water system has a maximum of $n_D = 1.3633$ at 25 °C at about 79.3 weight percent of alcohol. The pure components have values of 1.3594 and 1.3325, respectively. In this case an analysis accurate to 1 % is possible with an Abbe in the range from 0 to 40 % ethanol, but can be no closer than 5 % near the maximum. To analyze gaseous mixtures, very high precision in observation is required, since the refractive index varies very little with composition. This type of mixture is ordinarily analyzed by an interferometer.

Example 1   Pentane-hexane mixtures give a linear plot of refractive index against mole fraction. At 25 °C pentane has an n_D of 1.3530, hexane, one of 1.3732. If an Abbe is used, the composition of a mixture can be determined to about 2 % since $\Delta n = 0.0202$ and the accuracy of the Abbe is ± 0.0001.

It is apparent that a contamination of up to several tenths of one percent of hexane in heptane would probably not even be detected by an Abbe. But with a differential refractometer of precision 3×10^{-6}, as little as

$$\frac{3 \times 10^{-6}}{20200 \times 10^{-6}} \times 100 = 0.015\%$$

could be determined under optimum conditions.

Example 2   The percentage of CO_2 in dry air is to be determined. At standard conditions the refractive indices n_D for air and CO_2 are 1.000292 and 1.000450, respectively, giving a Δn of 15800×10^{-8}. An interferometer with 100 cm cells will allow differences in n as small as 2×10^{-8} to be observed. Accordingly, the concentration of CO_2 may be estimated to about

$$\frac{2 \times 10^{-8}}{15800 \times 10^{-8}} \times 100 = 0.014\%.$$

It is assumed that n varies linearly with composition at constant total pressure.

Isotropic solids.   It is easy to examine large homogeneous pieces of transparent solids. The sample is prepared (if necessary) with two plane, clear faces at about right angles to each other. If we are to use a critical angle instrument the second face need only be clear. We wet the planar face of the sample with a liquid of index of refraction higher than that of the solid and press it tightly against the refracting prism as in Fig. 21.8.

If an Abbe is used, the diffusing prism must be swung back. Uneven pressure on the solid piece must be avoided since the wetting liquid may be formed into a wedge-shaped layer, introducing unexpected refraction. A useful wetting liquid is α-bromo-naphthalene ($n_D^{25} = 1.68$).

When a large crystal or specimen is unavailable, solids can be handled as powders. They are examined by being suspended in a series of liquids of refractive index close to that of the solid. [1] The critical ray boundary will be sharp only if the refractive indices of powder and medium are identical.

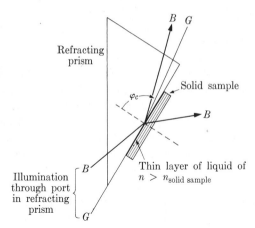

Fig. 21.8 Determination of the refractive index of a solid.

21.9 RESEARCH APPLICATIONS

On a molecular or a molar basis, refraction is an additive function of the atoms and types of bonds in a substance. The refraction per mole, or *molar refraction R*, at a given wavelength is defined as

$$R = \left(\frac{n^2 - 1}{n^2 + 2}\right)\frac{M}{d}, \tag{21.3}$$

where M is the molecular weight and d the density. Since the molar refraction R proves nearly temperature-independent, it is possible to set up a table of the average values of atomic and bond refractions at standard wavelengths. [1]

It is often of structural interest to compare the value of R obtained by adding the usual contributions of atoms and bonds to the refraction with that obtained from Eq. (21.3). If there is a difference, it is suggestive of internal structural complexities. For example, conjugation in a system containing multiple bonds increases the polarizability of a molecule and usually causes an "exaltation" of the molar refraction. Then the value calculated from Eq. (21.3) would be larger than that obtained by addition. We may also obtain information from the molar refraction about external interactions such as intermolecular association. Evidence of this type, though always useful, is largely of corroborative value.

REFERENCES

An intermediate to advanced level discussion of principles, instruments, and techniques is available in:

1. N. Bauer, K. Fajans, and S. L. Lewin, "Refractometry," in *Physical Methods of Organic Chemistry*. 3d ed., vol. 1, pt 2. A. Weissberger, ed. New York: Interscience, 1960
2. J. H. Jaffe, "Critical Angle Refractometry," *J. Opt. Soc. Am.* **47**, 782 (1957); **49**, 1199 (1959)
3. A. M. Taylor, "Studies in Refractive Index," *J. Opt. Soc. Am.* **23**, 206, 263, 308 (1933)

The design, construction, and errors of refractometers are emphasized in:

4. R. Glazebrook, *Dictionary of Applied Physics.* Vol. 4. London: Macmillan, 1923, pp. 760–772.
5. L. C. Martin, *Optical Measuring Instruments, Their Construction, Theory, and Use.* London: Blackie, 1924
6. Ewart Williams, *Applications of Interferometry.* 4th ed. New York: Wiley, 1950
7. B. A. Brice and M. Halwer, "A Differential Refractometer," *J. Opt. Soc. Am.* **41**, 1033 (1951)
8. L. G. Longsworth, "Optical Methods in Electrophoresis," *Ind. Eng. Chem., Anal. Ed.* **18**, 219 (1946)
9. L. W. Tilton and J. K. Taylor, "Refractive Index Measurement," in *Physical Methods in Chemical Analysis*, W. G. Berl, ed. 2d ed., vol. 1. New York: Academic, 1960
10. Ernest E. Wahlstrom, *Optical Crystallography.* 3d ed. New York: Wiley, 1960

Applications and procedures are given emphasis in:

11. S. S. Batsanov, *Refractometry and Chemical Structure.* New York: Consultants Bureau, 1962
12. M. G. Brown, "The Abbe Refractometer and the Use of Dispersion Measurements," *Oil Gas J.* **42**, 42 (1944)
13. E. H. Gilmore, M. Menaul, and V. Schneider, "Use of Physical Constants in Analysis," *Anal. Chem.* **22**, 893 (1950)
14. A. V. Grosse and R. C. Wackher, "Quantitative Determination of Aromatic Hydrocarbons by New Method," *Ind. Eng. Chem., Anal. Ed.* **11**, 614 (1939)
15. D. N. Hanson and Arturo Maimoni, "Gas Analysis by Optical Interferometry," *Anal. Chem.* **31**, 77 (1959)
16. W. Heller, "Remarks on Refractive Index Mixture Rules," *J. Phys. Chem.* **69**, 1123 (1965)
17. H. I. Waterman, *Correlation Between Physical Constants and Chemical Structure.* Amsterdam: Elsevier, 1958

Compilations of refractive index data are available in:

18. S. W. Ferris, *Handbook of Hydrocarbons.* New York: Academic, 1955
19. N. A. Lange, ed., *Handbook of Chemistry.* 9th ed. New York: McGraw-Hill, 1956

EXERCISES

21.1 By means of a sketch, show why a filter passing both the 435.8 and 404.7 nm lines from a mercury lamp source could be used successfully with a critical angle refractometer, assuming adequate visual acuity at these wavelengths. Draw only the sample and refracting prism and show optical paths. Using Table 21.1, estimate the $n_{404.7}$ of water.

21.2 Why must the liquid used as a wetting agent between the glass test piece and the refracting prism of the Abbe have an index of refraction greater than that of the solid? Use a sketch to illustrate.

21.3 A dense flint glass of $n_D = 1.655$ is used for the refracting prism in a Pulfrich. Assuming that the maximum angle of emergence α that can be measured easily is 80°, what is the lower limit of n that can be determined with this prism? (See Exercise 21.6.) [*Ans.*: 1.33.]

21.4 A sample of wet butanol is submitted for analysis. The refractive indices n_D at 25 °C of butanol and water are 1.37226 and 1.33252, respectively. In order to estimate the minimum amount of water detectable, assume a linear relationship between the n of the mixture and the percentage composition. Using in turn a standard Abbe, a differential (image displacement) refractometer, and an interferometer with a long liquid cell, what amounts of water would be detectable by refractometry? [*Ans.*: 0.3 %, 0.01 %, 0.0007 %.]

21.5 Why is it necessary to correct the Abbe refractive index scale when wavelengths other than the D-line are used? Would you expect the correction to be greater for the mercury 546.1 or 404.7 nm line?

21.6 Using Snell's law, show that the formula that must be used to equate the angle of emergence α of the Pulfrich with refractive indices is

$$n = \sqrt{n_p^2 - \sin^2 \alpha},$$

where n is the index of the sample and n_p is the index of the prism.

21.7 A hollow 60° prism of Pyrex is used to hold liquid samples for refractive index measurements with the precision spectrometer. The prism is 4 cm on a side and has 2 mm walls uniformly thick. What correction, if any, will have to be made because the radiation traverses the glass walls as well as the sample?

21.8 The refractive index of a benzene-carbon tetrachloride mixture varies linearly with mole fraction. At 25 °C, a length of Pyrex tubing is found to be invisible in a mixture that is 0.345 mole fraction in benzene. What is the refractive index of Pyrex glass? At 25 °C, the refractive index of carbon tetrachloride is 1.4576, and that of benzene is 1.4979.   [Ans.: 1.472.]

21.9 A refractometer based on the use of fiber optics was developed some years ago. It uses a single uncoated rigid "fiber" of about 1 mm diameter and 25 mm length. Monochromatic light is focused onto a spot at one end of the rod and a photocell is placed at the far end. The rod is positioned in the middle of a liquid cell with opaque walls, i.e. each liquid sample surrounds the rod. (a) Sketch the device and show the paths of reflected and refracted rays in the fiber. (b) Deduce whether the intensity of radiation reaching the detector increases or decreases with increasing n of a sample. (c) For a given sample, predict whether a fiber of closely similar n or greatly different n will give a more accurate measurement.

21.10 Justify the statement: The refractive index of a nonabsorbing substance at a given wavelength can be calculated from a measurement of the transmittance of light of that wavelength. Assume normal incidence on a "rectangular" slab of the substance.

CHAPTER 22

POLARIMETRY AND SPECTROPOLARIMETRY

22.1 INTRODUCTION

A great many substances characteristically rotate the plane of polarized radiation. Although these substances are customarily described as being "optically active," it is more precise to state that they possess *optical rotatory power*. Some theoretical background for this behavior has already been given in Section 10.16.

Optical rotatory power has its origin in structural asymmetry such as exists in any substance that does not have either a plane or a center of symmetry. The asymmetry may be

1. Inherent in the structure of the molecules comprising the substance, as in dextrose,
2. Peculiar to the crystalline form of the substance, as in quartz, and not appear at all in the liquid and gaseous states, and
3. At least in part the result of a particular conformation as in the helical form of a polypeptide.

In the first case it is evidenced in all physical states and in solution; in the second, optical rotatory power is displayed only by the crystal. Figure 22.1 shows three kinds of asymmetrical molecules, as well as one that has a plane of symmetry and is thus optically inactive.

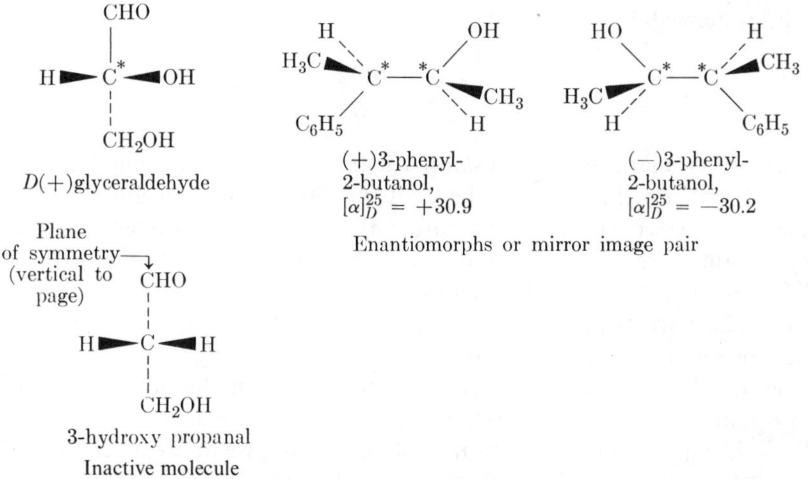

$D(+)$glyceraldehyde

(+)3-phenyl-
2-butanol,
$[\alpha]_D^{25} = +30.9$

(−)3-phenyl-
2-butanol,
$[\alpha]_D^{25} = -30.2$

Enantiomorphs or mirror image pair

Plane of symmetry (vertical to page)

3-hydroxy propanal

Inactive molecule

Fig. 22.1 Optical rotatory power as a function of structure. A heavy bar designates a bond coming out of page, a broken line one going back of page. The asymmetric carbons are starred.

Polarimetry. The instrument selected determines the precision obtainable, and measurements are easily carried through with all types. Of necessity, the analytical applications are limited to the determination of asymmetrical substances. In qualitative analytical studies the optical rotation of a sample at a given wavelength is often a valuable means of identification after the possibilities have been narrowed by use of other data. For a wide variety of complex molecules such as steroids and proteins the optical rotatory dispersion (ORD) curve, i.e. optical rotation measured as a function of wavelength over the VIS and UV regions, is distinctive and is very useful in identification. Both conformational analysis and the determination of absolute conformation of optically active substances are ordinarily carried out by ORD determinations.

In addition, organic mixtures containing one or more optically active substances can often be analyzed quantitatively by polarimetry. For example, the sugar cane content of foodstuffs is routinely determined by this method.

22.2 VARIABLES INFLUENCING OPTICAL ROTATION

Optical rotation depends upon many variables, namely, the wavelength λ, the optical path length b, the temperature t, and the density ρ (or in the case of solutions, the concentration c). There is also a marked dependence upon the magnetic field strength; it must be small even for measurements of ordinary sensitivity unless the field effect itself is of interest. When an appreciable magnetic field is imposed, even optically inactive substances exhibit optical rotation, a phenomenon termed the *Faraday* or *magnetic rotatory effect.* [1] If a substance with optical rotatory power is also anisotropic (Section 10.15), ordinary double refraction is superimposed on the optical rotatory effect. Quartz is an example of such a material. Since the results are difficult to interpret unambiguously unless the beam travels along the optic axis, it is best to analyze these materials by means of other optical properties.

To make the measure of the angular rotation of a substance independent of path length and less dependent on concentration, a *specific rotation* or *specific rotatory power* $[\alpha]$ is defined. It is

$$[\alpha]_\lambda^t = \frac{100\alpha}{lw\rho} \tag{22.1}$$

where α is the angular rotation of a sample in degrees, l is the path length in decimeters (1 dm = 10 cm), w is the weight of the solute in 100 g of solution, and ρ is the density of the solution. The centigrade temperature and the vacuum wavelength at which the value is obtained are specified by the t and λ. For example, most literature values are at 20 °C and 589.3 nm, $[\alpha]_D^{20}$, though measurements at 25 °C and 546.1 nm are also common. The convention adopted to designate the directions of the rotation of the polarization plane and thus the sign of α or $[\alpha]$ is the following: When the polarization plane is rotated clockwise as one faces the emerging beam, the substance is said to be dextrorotatory (+); when the rotation is counterclockwise, levorotatory (−).

Table 22.1 gives an idea of the range of magnitudes we may expect for $[\alpha]$. Values are given at two wavelengths and accompanied by the Drude equation for the substance (Section 10.16), which allows prediction of the α at other wavelengths in the visible. As the Drude equation predicts, we can expect very large rotations (often hundreds of degrees) in the UV region where λ is small. The temperature variation of α is usually linear,

$$[\alpha]_\lambda = [\alpha]_\lambda^0 + nt, \tag{22.2}$$

although the coefficient n varies widely from substance to substance.

Table 22.1 Wavelength Dependence of Optical Rotatory Power

Substance	Solvent	Specific rotation, degrees		Drude equation for rotatory dispersion in visible region $(\lambda, \mu m)$
		589.3 nm	435.8 nm	
Sucrose	H_2O	$+66.5$	$+128.5$	$[\alpha]^{20} = \dfrac{21.648}{\lambda^2 - 0.0213}$
(+)-Octan-2-ol	None	$+9.84$	$+19.2$	$[\alpha]^{20} = \dfrac{3.091}{\lambda^2 - 0.0243}$

Optical rotatory dispersion and circular dichroism.   As Table 22.1 suggests, the optical rotatory power of most substances varies strongly with wavelength, i.e. the substances display optical rotatory dispersion. A knowledge of the dispersion can be a powerful physical tool in many cases. For example, it has important applications to problems of the configuration or structural patterns of molecules such as the steroids and proteins. [3] For studies of this kind, we usually take measurements continuously through the visible and UV regions.

The results may be expressed as specific rotations or, preferably, given in terms of the *molecular rotation* ϕ, which is defined as

$$[\phi] = [\alpha]M/100, \tag{22.3}$$

where $[\alpha]$ is the specific rotation defined earlier and M is the molecular weight of the optically active compound. The use of $[\phi]$ facilitates both comparisons between the rotatory behavior of related compounds, and the addition and subtraction of data. The units of $[\phi]$ are degrees cm^2 per decimole.

As noted in Section 10.16, there is ordinarily a difference in molar absorptivities or absorption coefficients for left-handed and right-handed circularly polarized light. We term this difference circular dichroism in analogy to regular dichroism. Instrumentation that permits its measurement is discussed briefly in Section 22.5.

22.3 INSTRUMENTATION; THE VISUAL POLARIMETER

Figure 22.2 shows a generalized visual device to determine the angle of rotation of the plane of polarization. In its arrangement of components, this type of instrument, a *polarimeter*, bears some resemblance to a single-beam absorption photometer (Section 17.3). Like that device, the polarimeter must, in general, have a radiation source, frequency isolating device, sample cell, and sensing device. Like it also, the basic optical requirements (Chapter 17), such as adequate transparency of components in the spectral range of interest and a housing to minimize stray light, hold for the polarimeter.

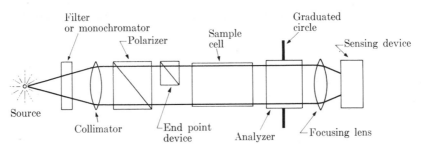

Fig. 22.2 A schematic diagram of a polarimeter.

There are, of course, distinct differences between the polarimeter and the photometer. In the former, polarized radiation must be produced, which requires an analyzer that can be rotated around the polarizer-sample-analyzer axis (Section 10.14). Suppose that the end-point device is omitted for the moment. When the sensing device indicates that the analyzer is set at extinction or minimum intensity, the angular orientation of the analyzer is at right angles to the plane of polarization passed by the sample.

Incorporating the end-point device reduces the measurement to a matching of intensities of sections of the optical field, as is discussed below. By this means the eye becomes a vastly more sensitive detector. In well-designed instruments, we can establish the angle of rotation visually with a precision of from 0.005 to 0.010. It is worth noting that we need not know the magnitude of the transmitted intensity either absolutely or relative to a standard.

Source. If a polarimeter is to measure more than one substance, as is generally the case, a source furnishing monochromatic radiation is necessary. White light can be employed only if the dispersion of the optical rotation of each sample can be compensated for in some way. Perhaps the best example of a polarimeter used with white light is the saccharimeter, a device designed for the quantitative determination of a single substance, cane sugar. The saccharimeter is discussed at the end of this section.

For the typical instrument, an emission source followed by a filter (or monochromator) is the best choice. Sodium and mercury vapor lamps are widely used. In routine studies the emission of the sodium arc lamp is seldom filtered, since 99 % of the intensity is the D-line doublet. Even this doublet with its 0.6 nm difference between lines is often too "impure" a source for really precise studies. For example, for a 1 mm quartz plate the change in α over the interval amounts to 0.25 %. Mercury arc lamps (Section 11.3) have a more even distribution of energy among their several emission lines and do require filters (Section 11.6) to isolate the one desired. Since many discrete lines in the UV and the visible are available, the mercury arc source is frequently the best choice for observing the dispersion of optical rotation.

In the UV a xenon lamp is often used for measurements. A series of filters or a monochromator is indispensable. For work in the IR a Globar or Nernst glower followed by a monochromator is an entirely adequate source.

Polarizer and analyzer. A calcite prism device such as is described in Section 10.14 is the most common polarizing and analyzing device in the visible range. Since its angular field is less than 30°, we may not use it with high convergent or divergent beams, so that at least partial beam collimation is desirable. Some allowance is also necessary for the lateral displacement of a beam on passage through a polarizer, an effect evident in Fig. 10.32.

For studies in the UV, adequate transmission becomes a problem. Since the Canada balsam layer is opaque in that range, an air gap is often substituted. With this modification we may use the polarimeter down to about 230 nm, where calcite begins to absorb strongly. In the IR, transparency of materials is a more severe problem, and polarization is usually by refraction or reflection (Section 10.14). A series of from three to six selenium films or silver chloride plates is placed at the polarizing angle, and the transmitted radiation is from 94 to 99 % linearly polarized or 80 %, respectively.

End-point devices. If the eye is the sensing device, as is customary, it operates inefficiently with a straight analyzer-detector design. The setting for minimum intensity can be located to perhaps half a degree. Even a photoelectric detector lacks sensitivity in the simple extinction type of measurement. The reason is that the rate of change of intensity per degree of rotation is at a minimum at extinction. Figure 22.3 shows the intensity passed by the analyzer at various orientations relative to the incident vibration plane. It can be shown that it varies as $\cos^2 \theta$, where θ is the angle between the plane of incident vibration and that of analyzer extinction (cf. Fig. 10.35).

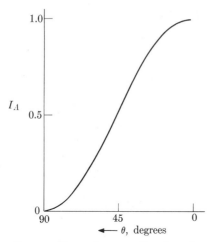

Fig. 22.3 Radiation intensity passed by analyzer as a function of angle θ between plane of incident vibration and orientation of analyzer at extinction.

Several optical end-point devices have been proposed to allow the eye to determine the end point by matching intensities. These are "half-shadow" arrangements in which the end-point device alters the plane of polarization of half or a third of the beam emerging from the polarizer. In effect, the apparatus splits the beam into two or, if two devices are used, three sharply distinct, contiguous portions. The angular difference in the planes of polarization in these adjacent regions is usually of the order of from one to seven degrees. Figure 22.4 shows the vibration angles passed in the half-shadow modification and in the split field seen in the eyepiece. As the analyzer is turned, first one half of the field and then the other becomes blackened. The end point is the setting (2) at which the two halves are of equal intensity. It is thus possible to make visually a reliable location of the plane of polarization of radiation incident on the analyzer. It should be noted that the orientation of the analyzer alone will no longer determine the plane, but that the plane will be different by some constant number of degrees known as the *half-shadow angle*. Where absolute angular rotations are desired, this difference must be taken into account in the design or by calibration.

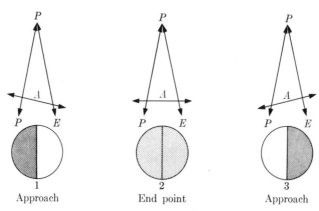

Fig. 22.4 Half-shadow end point.

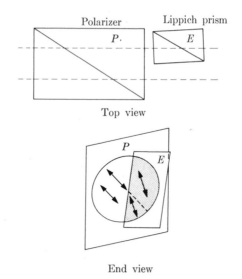

Fig. 22.5 Lippich double-field prism. The Lippich prism is tipped slightly toward the polarizer to obtain a sharply defined boundary between the two fields.

The most flexible and precise end-point device is the Lippich design, illustrated in Fig. 22.5. It consists of a small Nicol prism, which covers half the field of the polarizer and may be rotated with respect to it. Flexibility is achieved, since the greater the angle made by the two prisms, the more light there is admitted at the end point. Even with turbid or absorbing solutions or with low-intensity illumination, it is possible to achieve a balance, although some accuracy is sacrificed in favor of greater sensitivity. A still more sensitive design uses two small Nicol prisms to overlap the upper and lower thirds of the main polarizing prism. The three fields are matched in making a measurement, and since this is possible only if the source of light and the eye are lined up symmetrically with reference to the end-point prisms, all geometric errors are eliminated. With a double-field device the end point depends slightly on alignment of components and the direction of view.

Other end-point devices are sometimes used. Two are the Laurent halfwave plate and the Jellet–Cornu split prism. [1] Although the former has variable sensitivity, it functions only at a single wavelength. The split prism cannot be adjusted for different amounts of transmitted light.

Polarimeter tubes.   Common lengths are 10 and 20 cm. The diameter need only be great enough so that internal reflection of the beams is unlikely. Many tubes are jacketed for circulation of thermostating fluid.

In precision measurements strain and cell positioning can also be sources of error. Strain in optical elements like cell windows introduces birefringence and apparent changes in optical rotation. Thermostating (to 0.1°) and use of strain-free cells, e.g. cells with fused-on windows, annealed if necessary, minimize this source of error. Cells with screw-on captype windows are seldom free from strain birefringence. The position of a cell may be critical with regard to depolarization effects, which usually also appear as changes in optical rotation. For this reason it is wise to choose a stationary cell filled and emptied by syringe.

Detectors.   In the center of the visible region, the eye is quite satisfactory as a sensing device. Sensitivity is greatest if the polarimetry is done in a dark room, after the eye is dark-adapted, and with a wavelength in the green region.

In the UV and IR, photoelectric and photoconductive detection can be substituted. This type of detection also allows the adaptation of a visual instrument for automatic recording. For example, a satisfactory device of this type has a rotating half-shutter followed by a multiplier phototube in place of the telescope in a standard double-field polarimeter. The electrical signal (unbalance) generated when the two halves of the split field differ in intensity is multiplied and fed to a servomotor mechanism to rotate the analyzer to the point of balance. The next section describes a more elegant approach to automatic detection and recording.

Calibration.   At least two avenues of calibration are open. It is often simplest to use a known concentration of an optically active compound. Probably more suitable for precise work is the use of a plate of crystalline quartz that is free of flaws and constant in thickness to better than 100 nm.

The saccharimeter.   It is easy to do analyses of natural products and commercial preparations for sucrose and similar sugars by polarimetric techniques. The frequency of such analyses has led to the development of the saccharimeter, which is a modification of the general polarimeter. It differs from the standard instrument in that it has (a) a fixed half-shade device, (b) an analyzer set at the extinction position or at the position of matching intensities, and (c) a quartz wedge compensator. For sugar analyses the saccharimeter has two advantages over the conventional polarimeter. It may be used with white light and can be calibrated to read sugar concentrations directly.

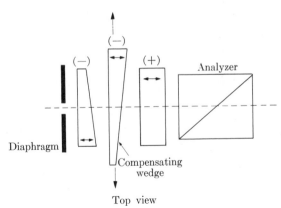

Fig. 22.6 Schematic of the quartz wedge compensator. The compensating wedge moves laterally on a micrometer screw. Direction of optic axis shown by double-headed arrows.

The modifications leading to the saccharimeter are possible because the rotatory dispersion of both the dextro and levo varieties of quartz is nearly identical with that of sucrose. The dispersion the sucrose produces can thus be almost compensated for by the quartz. With concentrated sucrose solutions and with other sugars, differences in dispersion are more pronounced. It then becomes desirable to use a 6% solution of potassium dichromate to filter out the spectral region least compensated.

Figure 22.6 gives a schematic diagram for a standard type of quartz wedge compensator. As noted, two of the pieces are levorotatory, the other dextrorotatory. Since the rotation produced by the sugar is positive, the levo wedge must be pushed upward (in the diagram) to compensate. A calibrated micrometer screw attachment allows a precision setting. Causing the angles of the wedges to oppose each other avoids deviation and dispersion of the beam.

22.4 THE SYMMETRICAL ANGLE POLARIMETER

A simplification in the design of the classic, manual polarimeter that is better adapted to photoelectric detection [8, 10, 12] is based on two ideas:

1. It is possible to measure optical rotation accurately by determining the energy change that accompanies it, and

2. An optically active sample produces a greater change in transmitted intensity when the angle between the planes of polarization in the polarizer and in the analyzer is other than 90°.

The instruments devised are essentially standard absorption photometers to whose cells have been added a polarizer and an analyzer. Provision is made for these elements to be positioned at definite, reproducible angles relative to the polarizer, first at $+\theta$, then at $-\theta$, to remove dependence on an angular setting and simplify interpretation. With the optically active sample in place between the polarizing elements, the power transmitted when the analyzer is set at $+\theta$ is compared with the power when the analyzer is set at $-\theta$. An instrument of this kind is conveniently termed a photoelectric polarimeter.

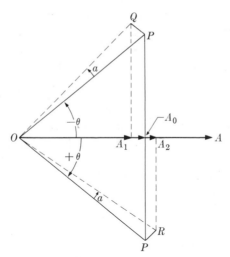

Fig. 22.7 Change in the amplitude of the radiation transmitted by a polarizer-analyzer combination produced by a sample of angular rotation a.

Figure 22.7 shows how photometric measurements of this kind are related to the optical rotation of a sample. P designates the amplitude of vibration of the radiation the polarizer transmits; A that transmitted by the analyzer. Two cases are shown. The first is that in which no sample (or an optically inactive material) is present in the cell, and the angle between the analyzer and polarizer is set alternately at $+\theta$ and $-\theta$. Equal amplitudes of radiation are transmitted at the two settings. The expression for the amplitude is simply $OP \cos\theta$ or OA_0 (cf. Fig. 10.35). The second case shown is one in which an analytical sample of angular rotation $-a$ has been introduced into the cell. Again the transmitted amplitudes for the two orientations of the polarizer-analyzer combination are compared, and this time are found to differ appreciably.

To deduce the optical rotation of the sample, one can proceed as follows. For the angle $+\theta$ the amplitude is $OR \cos(\theta - a) = OA_2$, and for $-\theta$ it is $OQ \cos(-\theta - a) = OA_1$. The power of the transmitted beam in the two cases is the square of the amplitudes, $(OA_2)^2$ and $(OA_1)^2$. Losses in power resulting from absorption, scattering, and reflection reduce both amplitudes by the same factor. If a single cell or a pair of matched cells is used for the comparison, the ratio of the transmitted powers $(OA_2)^2/(OA_1)^2 = R$ does not contain these losses. We can now calculate the angular rotation $-a$ from R, except when stray radiation is present in significant amount (0.5% or more), by using the relation [8]

$$\tan a = \frac{1 - \sqrt{R}}{1 + \sqrt{R}} \cot\theta. \tag{22.3}$$

Calibration charts based on Eq. (22.3) can be prepared through use of solutions of known rotation, like sucrose, to allow conversion of R values to rotations.

According to Eq. (22.3), the larger the value of θ, the greater is the deviation in R from unity ($R = 1$ when $\theta = 0°$) for a given angle of rotation a. Thus, the use of large θ settings should allow a very sensitive determination of rotatory power. Other factors must be considered, however, such as the steady loss in transmitted power as θ increases beyond 45°, and the practical maximum is reached somewhere between 60° and 80°. The best signal-to-noise ratio occurs when $\theta = 45°$.

In a single-channel instrument two measurements are made: first, the intensity transmitted by the sample cell at the desired wavelength with the analyzer set at $+\theta$, then a second measurement at the same wavelength with the analyzer rotated to $-\theta$. The ratio R of intensities is then calculated. With a double-channel spectrophotometer a single measurement suffices, for two identical "rotatory" cells may be used. With the same solution in each, but with the reference cell set for $+\theta$ and the sample cell set at $-\theta$, the measured intensity will be the desired ratio R. Measurements are easily made at different wavelengths to obtain the rotatory dispersion. Measurements precise to the order of 0.002° can be obtained for substances or solutions giving very small angles of rotation.

22.5 AUTOMATIC POLARIMETERS

An optical nulling procedure proves an effective approach to the design of a simple automatic yet sensitive polarimeter. Figure 22.8 shows one type of design in block diagram form. Note that it features the basic polarizer-analyzer combination characteristic of a polarimeter. In order to secure automatic operation and improve the signal-to-noise ratio, the radiation beam is modulated (Section 8.6). The direction of polarization produced by the polarizer is oscillated through a small angle (no more than $\pm 1°$) about an equilibrium value. We can rotate the polarizer itself back and forth a dozen times a second to secure this result. The analyzer is crossed with respect to the polarizer at the equilibrium position. When no sample is present, or when an optically inactive sample is placed in the holder, the detector receives pulses of equal intensity as the polarizer uncrosses in either direction. The pulse frequency is twice that of the modulation frequency.

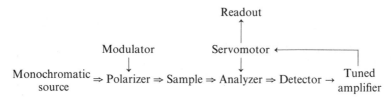

Fig. 22.8 Line block diagram of an automatic polarimeter.

If an optically active sample is placed in the beam, a component of the modulation or basic frequency is also present. An amplifier tuned to that frequency sends energy to the servomotor. We can easily arrange phasing so that it turns the analyzer until a "null" is again attained. The readout is the rotation produced by the servomotor. Reproducibility is of the order of millidegrees.

Since a large light flux would create substantial shot noise at the detector, modulating angles used are seldom large. Yet the rotation must permit sufficient intensity either side of the crossed orientation to maintain a reasonable signal-to-noise ratio even if a sample absorbs at the wavelength(s) used. It is usual to employ discrete sources (Section 11.3) in conjunction with a set of filters to permit measurements at several frequencies. If we are examining highly absorbing solutions, a very intense source, e.g. a laser, can be used with a microcell.

We may also secure modulation electrically by adding Faraday effect (Section 22.1) cells to the arrangement of Fig. 22.8 and removing the servomotor. One cell is placed after the polarizer, the other just before the analyzer. A Faraday cell usually consists of a rod of glass, fused silica, or other isotropic substance that shows a Faraday effect, nestled in a solenoid (hollow coil). Alternating current of the desired modulating frequency applied to the first solenoid induces a varying optical activity in the rod. The direction of polarization is rotated first clockwise and then counterclockwise as current reverses. If the analyzer is crossed with respect to the polarizer, and we insert an optically *inactive* sample, the detector will sense successive pulses of equal amplitude. When we insert an optically active sample, pulse amplitudes will differ.

In this system the optical rotation produced by the sample is compensated by applying a dc voltage to the second Faraday cell. The detector must be followed by a phase-sensitive amplifier (Section 8.7). After filtering, its dc output can be applied to the solenoid around the second rod to cancel or null the optical rotation of the sample. The null position is recognized by a return to pulses of equal amplitude.*

22.6 SPECTROPOLARIMETER

Polarimeters that operate over a wavelength range are termed spectropolarimeters. Most are capable of determining both optical rotation (optical rotatory dispersion or ORD) and circular differential absorption (circular dichroism or CD).

We can construct a spectropolarimeter to determine ORD curves by adding a suitable monochromator and scanning arrangement to an automatic polarimeter. Because determinations are frequently made in absorption regions where the energy of the transmitted beam is very small, stray light must be drastically minimized. As a result, it is customary to use a double monochromator.

Figure 22.9 shows one design of spectropolarimeter. Its double monochromator is unusual in that there are two crystalline quartz prisms P_1 and P_2 and that they are so oriented with respect to the optic axis (Section 10.13) that the first also polarizes the beam and the second analyzes it. A powerful continuous source is used. A pair of Faraday cells secures automatic control. Precision is of the same order of magnitude as indicated earlier even though energy throughput is smaller because monochromators are substituted for filters. It is possible to trace ORD curves from about 700 to 185 nm.

Figure 22.10 shows schematically a spectropolarimeter that can be used either in an ORD or in a CD mode. In the ORD mode the instrument functions like the automatic polarimeter in Fig. 22.8.

The second optical path permits CD measurements. It features a Pockels cell, which utilizes a uniaxial crystal of the dihydrogen phosphate type so oriented that light passes through it along its main or z-axis. The cell contains electrodes that permit an electric field to be applied parallel to the z-axis. Under the field, the crystal becomes

---

* In the null condition the output signal has no component of the modulating frequency. The output is twice the modulating frequency.

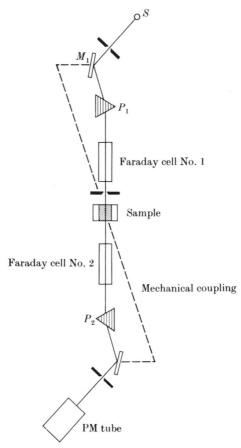

Fig. 22.9 Optical schematic of Bendix-Ericsson Spectropolarimeter. The functions of polarizer and wavelength dispersing device are combined in crystalline quartz prism P_1. An entrance slit (near source S) and scanning mirror M_1 convert P_1 into a scanning monochromator. A second quartz prism P_2, oriented in a crossed position relative to P_1, serves also as the heart of a second, coupled scanning monochromator. Modulation is introduced by energizing the coil of Faraday cell No. 1 with ac of the desired frequency. Sample-induced rotation of the plane of linear polarization is compensated by dc current in the coil of Faraday cell No. 2. (Courtesy of the Bendix Corporation.)

biaxial. If the polarization axis of the polarizer is parallel to the x- or the y-axis of the dihydrogen phosphate crystal, the Pockels cell generates circularly polarized light, either left-handed or right-handed, depending on the field direction. The application of ac of appropriate frequency will provide the desired output to the sample.

If no sample is present, the circularly polarized components are incident on the detector in equal intensity and the detector output is unmodulated dc. If we insert an optically active sample and examine it in a region of an optically active transition, unequal absorption is evident and we obtain an ac output whose phase corresponds to the sign of the circular dichroism and whose magnitude is proportional to the amplitude of the CD. Taking the ratio of ac to dc components and amplifying secures a readout equal to differential absorption. [7, 9]

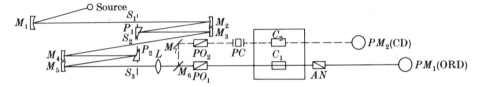

Key:

M_1, M_3, M_5	Focusing mirrors	AN	Analyzer (quartz Rochon prism)
S_1, S_2, S_3	Monochromator slits	PM_1, PM_2	Photomultiplier tubes
M_2, M_4	Collimating mirrors	M_6	Retractable mirror
P_1, P_2	Prisms	M_7	Plane mirror
L	Lens	C_2	CD cell position
PO_1, PO_2	Polarizers (quartz Rochon prisms)	PC	CD modulator (Pockels cell)
C_1	ORD cell position		

Fig. 22.10 Optical schematic of the Durrum-Jasco Recording Spectropolarimeter. A double monochromator using quartz prisms ensures minimal stray light. When used in the ORD mode, mirror M_6 is swung out of the path. The Rochon prism polarizer is mechanically oscillated back and forth through about $\pm 1°$. Nulling is accomplished as in the polarimeter of Fig. 22.8: A servo-motor (not shown) rotates the analyzer. In the CD mode, mirror M_6 is inserted and the mono-chromatic beam passes through a second, stationary Rochon polarizing prism. The emerging linearly polarized light then passes through Pockels cell PC. This device responds to imposed ac by converting the beam to circularly polarized light, first left-handed and then right-handed. The differential absorption of the two types of polarized light is sensed by a detector (not shown). A third optical path (not shown) permits measurement of a conventional transmission curve. (Courtesy of Durrum Instrument Corporation.)

Since most CD peaks relate to particular electronic transitions, circular dichroism measurements are often more attractive than ORD determinations. An ORD curve is more difficult to interpret because optical rotation contains contributions from several transitions. The three-peak CD curve in Fig. 22.11 provides a good illustration of this feature.

REFERENCES

General discussions of optical rotation, polarimeters, and polarimetry on an intermediate level are available in:

1. W. Heller and D. D. Pitts, "Polarimetry," in *Physical Methods of Organic Chemistry.* 3rd ed., Part III. A. Weissberger, ed. New York: Interscience, 1960
2. T. M. Lowry, *Optical Rotatory Power.* New York: Longmans, Green, 1935

Optical rotatory dispersion and circular dichroïsm, their applications, and their instrumentation are considered in:

3. S. Beychok, "*Circular Dichroism of Biological Macromolecules,*" *Science* **154**, 1288 (1966)
4. P. Crabbe, *Optical Rotatory Dispersion and Circular Dichroism in Organic Chemistry.* San Francisco: Holden-Day, 1965
5. Carl Djerassi, *Optical Rotatory Dispersion, Applications to Organic Chemistry.* New York: McGraw-Hill, 1960
6. H. A. O. Hill and P. Day, eds., *Physical Methods in Advanced Inorganic Chemistry.* New York: Interscience, 1968

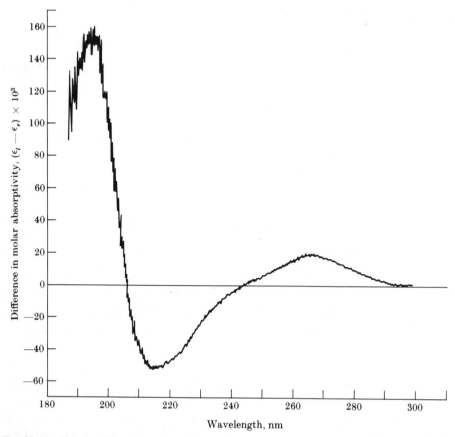

Fig. 22.11 Circular dichroism of bacteriophage f2, a small spherical virus particle in which the major components are a single ribonucleic acid molecule surrounded by approximately 180 identical protein molecules. The concentration of phage particles was 1.4×10^{-8} mol l^{-1}. The positive dichroic absorption band centered at approximately 266 nm is attributable to the nucleic acid component, and the other negative and positive dichroic absorption bands have contributions from both the protein coat and nucleic acid components. (Courtesy of R. W. Henkens and J. L. Middlebrook.)

6a. B. Jirgensons, *Optical Rotatory Dispersion of Proteins and other Macromolecules.* New York: Springer-Verlag, 1969

6b. W. Klyne and A. C. Parker, "Optical Rotatory Dispersion," in *Physical Methods of Organic Chemistry*, 3rd ed., Part III. A. Weissberger, ed. New York: Interscience, 1960

6c. G. Snatzke, "CD and ORD; Principles and Applications to Investigation of Stereochemistry of Natural Products," *Angew. Chem. Int. Ed.* **1**, 14 (1968)

6d. J. T. Yang, "Optical Rotatory Dispersion and Circular Dichroism," in P. Alexander and H. P. Lundgren, eds., *Laboratory Manual of Analytical Methods of Protein Chemistry.* New York: Pergamon, 1969

Emphasis is placed on instrument and design and sources of error in:

7. A. Abu-Shumays and J. J. Duffield, "Circular Dichroism—Theory and Instrumentation," *Anal. Chem.* **38** (7) 29A (1966)

8. Benjamin Carroll, Harold B. Tillem, and Eli S. Freeman, "The Rouy Method for Photo-electric Polarimetry," *Anal. Chem.* **30**, 1099 (1958)

9. H. Cary, R. C. Hawes, P. B. Hooper, J. J. Duffield, and K. P. George, "A Recording Spectro-polarimeter," *Appl. Opt.* **3**, 329 (1964)

10. T. B. Crumpler, W. H. Dyre, and A. Spell, "Simple Photoelectric Polarimeter," *Anal. Chem.* **27**, 1645 (1955)

11. L. C. Martin, *Optical Measuring Instruments.* London: Blackie, 1924

12. Hellmuth Rudolph, "Photoelectric Polarimeter Attachment," *J. Opt. Soc. Am.* **45**, 50 (1955)

13. Auguste L. Rouy and Benjamin Carroll, "The Theoretical Sensitivity and Linearity of Photoelectric Systems for Polarimetry," *Anal. Chem.* **33**, 594 (1961)

EXERCISES

22.1   The specific rotation of dextrose is $+52.5°$ in water solution at $20°$ and 589.3 nm. (a) What will be the rotation of a solution containing 0.0055 g in 100 ml of solution if a 20 cm sample cell is used? (b) Can so dilute a solution be analyzed with 1% accuracy by a polarimeter whose precision is $0.1°$? $0.05°$?

22.2   What is the specific rotation of $(+)$-octan-2-ol at 500 nm? Use the information in Table 22.1.

22.3   A water solution of the sodium salt of an amino acid,

$$NH_2$$
$$|$$
$$NaOOCCH{=}CHCOONa$$

has the following specific rotations at constant temperature but at different wavelengths: 656.3 nm, $-3.54°$; 589.3 nm, $-2.48°$; 516.5 nm, $-1.91°$. Do the data follow a one-term Drude equation? Show your work.

22.4   A water solution of a colorless substance with a specific rotation of $+23°$ is to be examined in a photoelectric polarimeter of the type discussed in Section 22.4. The solution is prepared by dissolving 50 g in 200 ml of solution. A 1 cm sample cell is filled and placed in a spectrophotometer set at 550 nm between Polaroids placed at an angle of $70°$ relative to each other. What will be the ratio of the power transmitted in this case to that transmitted when the angle is changed to $-70°$?

22.5   Assume a standard double-beam spectrophotometer is to be used as a polarimeter without any modification of its optics. Describe the type of sample and reference cell that should be used so that the readout will be the ratio R defined in Section 22.4. Can a reference still be used?

22.6   The Dupont 420 Process Polarimeter is an automatic version of the photoelectric polarimeter discussed in Section 22.4. A linearly polarized beam is sent through the sample cell (a flow cell) and then split into two beams. On the basis of this information, draw a schematic of a possible optical layout that will allow automatic operation.

22.7   The circular dichroism (CD) of a sample is often reported in terms of ellipticity $[\theta]$, where $[\theta] = 3300\ (\epsilon_L - \epsilon_R)$. Calculate the ellipticities of the two peaks and the valley in the CD curve of Fig. 22.11.

SOME
ELECTROANALYTICAL METHODS

CHAPTER 23

THE ELECTROCHEMICAL CELL

The electrochemical properties of solutions form the basis of a major set of chemical measurements. We can observe these properties when a pair of electrodes is inserted in an electrolyte solution and an electrochemical cell is formed. The kind and magnitude of observable phenomena depend on many controllable variables that include the nature, shape, and spacing of electrodes, solution composition, rate of stirring, temperature, and external voltage applied. In response to these variables, electron transfer, ionic migration, and other fundamental processes occur in the cell. Measurement of cell current, voltage and/or time can provide information about the identity and concentration, or activity, of components of the solution. As cell processes have become better understood and possibilities for meaningful measurements have been worked out, a family of electroanalytical techniques has developed.

In this chapter a general background for electroanalytical methods is provided by dealing with the small number of processes involved in cell behavior. Many of these methods are listed in Section 23.5; subsequent chapters deal with individual techniques.

23.1 THE CELL; ELECTRODE POTENTIALS

In the usual line representation of an electrochemical cell we write symbols for the anode (the electrode at which oxidation occurs) and electrolyte surrounding it at the left and symbols for the cathode (the electrode at which reduction occurs) and its surrounding electrolyte at the right. *Galvanic cells*, those producing an electromotive force (emf) spontaneously, and *electrolytic cells*, those to which an external voltage is applied to induce a cell reaction, are so described. For example, a galvanic cell consisting of a saturated calomel electrode (mercury in contact with mercurous chloride paste and saturated KCl solution) and a Cu, Cu^{2+} electrode in $0.1F$ $CuCl_2$ solution is represented as follows:

$$- Hg; Hg_2Cl_2(s), KCl\,(satd.)\,|\,CuCl_2(0.1F); Cu + \qquad (23.1)$$

The semicolons signify phase boundaries across which there is negligible solubility; commas separate two or more solutes in the same solution; and a vertical line marks a liquid-liquid boundary. The identification of the calomel electrode as the anode in cell (23.1) was made on the basis of sound theoretical prediction and will be discussed below. Where such a basis is lacking, an assignment should be made tentatively, and the sign of the cell potential checked experimentally.

In a galvanic cell, the anode is always the more negative electrode. For example, note the electrode signs given for cell (23.1). The situation is opposite for an electrolytic cell, as is seen below. In this type of cell the anode is the more positive electrode.

A liquid junction, such as that between the two electrolyte solutions of cell (23.1) imposes a special requirement. It is evident that the junction must be formed in a manner that permits ions to migrate between electrodes but that prevents mixing of solutions. We meet this need by inserting a porous membrane or a salt bridge. The use of either type of device is shown in cell notation by a double vertical line ||, which symbolizes the one or two new phase boundaries formed. For precise work, additional requirements are imposed on a liquid junction, as discussed in Section 24.1.

An example of a cell without liquid junction is the following:

$$Zn; ZnCl_2(0.1F), AgCl(s); Ag. \tag{23.2}$$

Here a single electrolyte solution contacts both electrodes.

A galvanic cell drives current through an external circuit. If an external voltage of equal magnitude opposes the cell emf there is no current and no net reaction at the cell electrodes. A further increase in the opposing emf, at least in a reversible cell like (23.1) or (23.2), causes the electrode reactions to reverse. For example, in (23.1) the calomel electrode (still negatively charged) becomes the cathode and the Cu, Cu^{2+} electrode, which is still positive, becomes the anode. The cell has become an electrolytic cell. Since only the reversing of a reaction is involved, a general discussion of a cell is applicable to either galvanic or electrolytic operation.

We ordinarily measure both an emf and a current for a cell. As expected, the cell voltage is a sum of potential differences associated with each internal boundary and the voltage drops caused by passage of current through the resistance of the solutions. For example, in cell (23.1) there appear to be boundary potentials at the interfaces between:

1. Liquid mercury* and Hg_2Cl_2 paste;
2. Hg_2Cl_2 paste and saturated KCl solution;
3. Saturated KCl solution and $CuCl_2$ solution; and
4. $CuCl_2$ solution and copper.

It is convenient to sum potentials (1) and (2) as E_{anode}. Now we can express the cell potential E_{cell} as the sum

$$E_{cell} = E_{anode} + E_{cath} + E_{jcn} + iR, \tag{23.3}$$

where E_{jcn} is the liquid junction potential and iR the voltage drop in the bulk electrolyte produced by current flow. A basis for assigning single electrode potentials is described below.

Electrode potentials.   The origin of a potential at an electrode boundary may be traced to a free energy difference between electron levels in the electrode and in any

---

* External contact potentials arise also when leads are attached to electrodes. By convention, pure copper leads are used in measurements in order that potentials between lead wire and electrode will always be reproducible and need not be explicitly known. These potentials are included in the tabulated values of standard potentials.

solution species that interacts electrically at the electrode. By definition, such a species is *electroactive*, i.e. engages in an electron transfer reaction at the electrode. The species is oxidized or reduced.

The isolation of electrode compartments in a cell permits separate consideration of the electron-transfer reactions at each electrode. It is convenient to rely on a generalized representation of the change. As soon as any reaction has occurred at an electrode, both the reduced and oxidized form of the electroactive species must exist. This pair of species is termed an *electrical couple*. With this model in mind, it is possible to represent the two electrode reactions:

$$\text{At the anode: } \text{red}_a - ne^- \rightleftharpoons \text{ox}_a,$$
$$\text{At the cathode: } \text{ox}_c + ne^- \rightleftharpoons \text{red}_c, \tag{23.4}$$

where ox and red are the oxidized and reduced forms of the species, subscripts a and c indicate whether a species is active at the anode or cathode, and n is the number of electrons involved in the transfer. The separate reactions are appropriately labeled half-cell reactions. The overall cell reaction is the sum of the two electrode reactions:

$$\text{red}_a + \text{ox}_c \rightleftharpoons \text{ox}_a + \text{red}_c. \tag{23.5}$$

Example   For cell (23.1) the half-cell reactions are:

$$\text{Anode: } 2Hg(l) + 2Cl^- \rightarrow Hg_2Cl_2(s) + 2e^-$$
$$\text{Cathode: } Cu^{2+} + 2e^- \rightarrow 2Cu(s).$$

As long as there is an external electrical connection between mercury and copper electrodes, each half-cell reaction will proceed as indicated. The overall reaction will be:

$$2Hg + Cu^{2+} + 2Cl^- \rightarrow Hg_2Cl_2 + 2Cu.$$

Under equilibrium conditions, the transfer of electrons occurs reversibly, and it becomes possible to treat cell behavior thermodynamically. The reversible transfer of n moles of electrons through cell potential difference E_{cell} brings about the performance of nFE_{cell} joules of work, where F is the Faraday. This work is accomplished as a result of a decrease in the Gibbs free energy G of the cell, i.e.

$$-\Delta G = nFE_{cell}. \tag{23.6}$$

Equation (23.6) establishes the sign convention for cells. Since reaction occurs spontaneously in a galvanic cell, its free energy change must be negative. Equation (23.6) prescribes that under these conditions the cell emf E must be positive. Practically, this criterion allows a check on the direction of a cell reaction. If half-cell emfs add to a positive sum, the reaction proceeds as hypothesized. If their sum is negative, it proceeds in the direction opposite to that written.

The free energy change of any reversible reaction can be shown to depend on the activities a_i of the species involved. For the general reaction of Eq. (23.5) the free energy change is expressed by the equation

$$\Delta G = \Delta G^0 + RT \ln \frac{a_{ox_a} \cdot a_{red_c}}{a_{red_a} \cdot a_{ox_c}} \tag{23.7}$$

where ΔG^0 is the free energy change for a process in which reactants in their standard states (unit activity) are converted to products in their standard states. Just as an actual cell emf E is related by Eq. (23.6) to the actual free energy change ΔG, it is straightforward to define a standard emf E^0 as the cell potential obtained when reactants and products are present in their standard states. Using Eq. (23.6) and this definition, we can rewrite Eq. (23.7) as

$$E_{cell} = E^0_{cell} - 2.303 \frac{RT}{nF} \log \frac{a_{ox_a} \cdot a_{red_c}}{a_{red_a} \cdot a_{ox_c}}. \tag{23.8}$$

This is the Nernst equation for the cell. In the rewriting, we have made a conversion to common logarithms. Note that Eq. (23.8) does not apply to a cell with liquid junction; for such a case we would need an additional term or terms. [5, Chap. 24]

An important relationship exists between standard electrode potential and the equilibrium constant of a cell reaction. It is obtainable by returning to Eq. (23.7). At equilibrium, $\Delta G = 0$ and the activity fraction (in the logarithmic term) becomes the equilibrium constant K for the cell reaction;

$$0 = \Delta G^0 + RT \ln K. \tag{23.9}$$

According to Eq. (23.6) $\Delta G^0 = -nFE^0_{cell}$ and Eq. (23.9) can be rewritten as

$$nFE^0_{cell} = RT \ln K. \tag{23.10}$$

As implied by Eqs. (23.6) and (23.10), cell potential differences are often measured to obtain the free energy and equilibrium constant of a reaction.

In many instances it is desirable to rewrite Eq. (23.8) in terms of concentrations. The activity and concentration of a species i are related by the expression $a_i = \gamma_i c_i$, where γ_i is the activity coefficient of the species. Activity coefficients have a complex and not well-defined dependence on many solution parameters. They are defined in terms of a standard state in which their value is unity. For ionic species the *standard state* is infinite dilution at 25 °C; nevertheless, $\gamma \simeq 1$ for many ions at concentrations of 10^{-3} M or smaller. For a liquid, solid, or gas, the standard state is the most stable form of a substance at 1 atm and 25 °C.

Unfortunately, experimental activity coefficient data are rather limited for most species. Therefore a method for estimating values is discussed in Section 24.1.

The next step in dealing with a cell is to divide Eq. (23.8) into separate half-cell expressions. The cathode portion, e.g., is

$$E_{cath} = E^0_{cath} + \frac{2.303RT}{nF} \log \frac{a_{ox_c}}{a_{red_c}} \tag{23.11}$$

where E_{cath} and E^0_{cath} are the measured potential and standard potential of the cathode, respectively. A similar equation holds for the anode. A more complete discussion is to be found in Chapter 24. Since the *absolute* potential of a single electrode cannot be determined, a basis for establishing comparative values for electrode standard potentials E^0 has been agreed on by international convention. It is to take $E^0_{cell} = E^0_{half\text{-}cell}$ where the cell is one in which the electrode of interest is the cathode and the anode is a normal hydrogen electrode (unit activity H^+ and H_2 gas, in equilibrium, at a platinized platinum electrode).* This convention establishes standard electrode potentials as associated with reduction reactions.

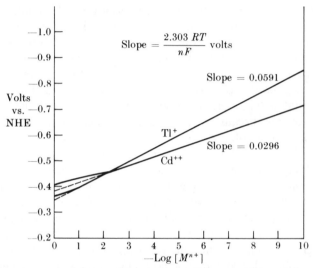

Fig. 23.1 Aqueous electrode potentials (solid curves) as a function of ionic *concentration* at 25 °C. The broken lines represent the potentials predicted by the Nernst equation when activity coefficients *are assumed to be unity*. Actual potentials deviate from the broken lines only above roughly 10^{-3} F. To convert these potentials to values referenced to the saturated calomel electrode, add 0.244 V.

Figure 23.1 illustrates the application of Eq. (23.11) to two simple aqueous electrodes (Tl; Tl$^+$ and Cd; Cd^{2+}). The graph includes actual values of the electrode potential and those calculated by substituting concentrations for activities in the equation. Note that measured potentials deviate only at the higher concentrations where activity coefficients would be expected to depart from unity. As this comparison emphasizes, electrode potential measurements are a standard means of determining activity coefficients.

In addition to this macroscopic or thermodynamic view of a cell, an interpretation on the molecular and electrical level is ultimately essential to extracting maximum information. What effect does a potential at an electrode have on the distribution of

---

* This "Stockholm Convention" of IUPAC is now widely adopted. In the earlier American convention, the normal hydrogen electrode appeared as the cathode. Accordingly, standard electrode potentials were associated with oxidations. Numerical values are identical in the two conventions but differ in sign. For example, the standard potential of the saturated calomel electrode in the Stockholm Convention is +0.2444 V and in the American convention was −0.2444 V. A useful discussion of the conventions is given by T. S. Licht and A. J. de Bethune, *J. Chem. Educ.* **34**, 433 (1957).

ions and solvent near its surface? If the potential of an electrode is suddenly changed, what time interval is required to establish such a distribution? A response to the first query leads to a model of the voltage gradient at an electrode and gives an estimate of where the "bulk" solution begins. An answer to the second question suggests the shortest time required for developing a steady state.

Figure 23.2 shows schematically the potential gradient at a solution electrode. An *electrical double layer* exists near each electrode surface. As we would expect, ions of charge opposite to that on the electrode are strongly attracted not only by the potential gradient but by chemical and other short-range forces. Those ions nearest the surface are essentially unsolvated; beyond this layer exists another narrow region where solvated ions are packed, and still farther out is a wide band with ions of both charges across which the potential falls to its bulk solution value. If several species of like charge are present, those ions most easily desolvated are located near the electrode. It is important to note that molecular double layers exist even in the absence of large concentrations of ions because of the energy of interaction of the electrode and permanent or induced dipoles.

How does cell current relate to this model? If a steady state has been attained, the electrical double layer at each electrode is already formed and we may focus our attention on the *faradaic current* resulting from electron transfer between reduced and oxidized forms of the electroactive species of interest. The nonfaradaic portion of the cell current includes the current due to impurity electrolysis and any *capacitive current*, a component that appears if electrode surface area changes, the voltage across the cell is altered, or solution composition is changed. Capacitive current arises during "charging" or discharging of electrode double layers. An analogy to a capacitor is apt, for the capacitance of the double layer is often large (about $30 \ \mu F \ cm^{-2}$). In the bulk of the solution current is carried by ions.

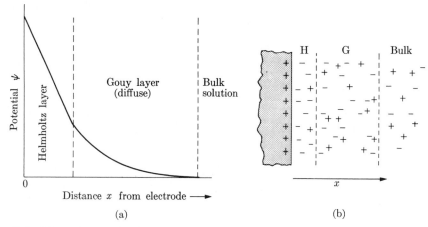

Fig. 23.2 Schematic representation of the electric double layer at an electrode. (a) Potential vs. distance. (b) A model of the double layer.

23.2 CURRENT AND ELECTROLYSIS

When an external voltage E_{app} is applied to a cell and is not equal and opposite to the cell emf, a net chemical reaction takes place. An equivalent number of moles of electrons is transferred at each electrode and ions carry charge across the cell. A cell current exists.

When $E_{app} > E_{cell}$, electrolysis is induced. It is sufficient to consider this case. If cell behavior is reversible, the discussion is also applicable when $E_{app} < E_{cell}$ and the cell functions galvanically. To adapt the treatment to the galvanic case, the sign of current and free energy changes must simply be reversed.

Two types of process occur in the overall scheme of electrolysis:

1. Movement of electroactive material to the electrode from the bulk of the solution, and

2. Reaction of electroactive species at the electrode.

The mass transport mechanisms that govern movement to the electrode are discussed in the next section. Here attention is focused on electrode reactions. They dominate the overall process and their rate determines cell current when we make mass transport sufficiently fast, e.g. by stirring the solution.

During electrolysis much more occurs at an electrode than a simple electron transfer. As chemists picture the situation, the solvated electroactive species appears initially to adsorb on the electrode in some way; subsequently, it may undergo an atomic or electronic rearrangement to a structure more conducive to the impending electron exchange. Then the electron transfer occurs followed by another possible rearrangement. The final product(s) of the electrolysis deposit, or if soluble, diffuse away. Thus the reduction of Fe^{2+} ions at a mercury electrode leads to an amalgam, and iron atoms rapidly diffuse into the interior of the mercury.

The rate of a cell oxidation–reduction reaction will be determined as much by the potential difference applied to a cell as by the activation energy intrinsic to the reaction. We commonly find that electrolysis current increases as a greater potential difference is applied to a cell. Indeed, it is this effect of applied voltage that makes a redox reaction in a cell *electrochemical* and not just chemical.

It is logical to interpret the effect of applied voltage on a cell as resulting from an adjustment of the activation energy barrier for the reaction. To simplify the discussion, consider that only the potential of the cathode is altered when the voltage applied to a cell is changed. For example, we could secure this result if the anode were a reference electrode and the electrolyte concentration were high enough for us to neglect the iR solution voltage drop. The effect of a voltage change in this case would be to alter the free energy barrier for the cathode equilibrium:

$$ox_c + ne^- \rightleftharpoons red_c.$$

Figure 23.3 shows schematically a reaction coordinate for the system. Note the potential energy curves for the oxidized and reduced forms of the species electroactive at the cathode. Figure 23.3a shows the relative position of the curves under equilibrium conditions. Here $E_{app} = E_{eq}$ and the energy barrier to activation is the same for the forward reaction $ox_c + ne^- \rightarrow red_c$ as for the reverse reaction, $red_c \rightarrow ox_c + ne^-$. Rates are equal and $i_{net} = 0$. Note that the electrode potential at which rates are equal has been designated E_{eq}. It will differ from E^0 for the electrode as required by actual concentrations and activity coefficients.

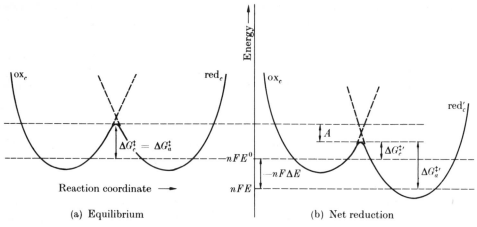

Fig. 23.3 Reaction coordinate diagram for an electron transfer reaction at an electrode. (a) Curves ox_c and red_c are the potential energy curves for the oxidized and reduced forms of the electroactive species at equilibrium, when the cathode voltage equals E_{eq}. Under these conditions the energy barrier to the transfer is equal from either state, $\Delta G_a^\ddagger = \Delta G_c^\ddagger$. (b) The electrode is made more cathodic by ΔE, which effectively lowers the free energy of the reduced form by $nF\Delta E$. The potential energy of the reduced form is now given by curve red_c'. The barrier to reduction is lowered by amount A, where $A = \alpha nF\Delta E$ and α is a constant for the system termed the transfer coefficient.

Figure 23.3b shows the result of making $E_{app} > E_{eq}$* by ΔE volts. Since the anode of the cell is a reference or nonpolarizable electrode, its potential will not alter. The cathode becomes more negative by ΔE volts and its reaction system has a new position of equilibrium. The reduced form is now stabilized by $nF\Delta E$ joules, where n is the number of electrons involved in the rate-controlling process. The figure shows this with a new potential energy curve red_c' whose ground state is just $nF\Delta E$ joules below the original level.

How has the greater negative potential affected activation barriers to forward and reverse reactions at the cathode? Note that activation energy for reduction (the forward process) has fallen and that for oxidation has risen. It can be assumed that some fraction α of the electrochemically induced free energy change $nF\Delta E$ results in lowering the barrier for the forward reaction. The constant α is termed the *transfer coefficient*. Under the altered conditions the activation energy for reduction is

$$\Delta G_{cathodic}^{\ddagger\prime} = \Delta G_{cathodic}^\ddagger - \alpha nF\Delta E. \tag{23.12}$$

The fraction assigned to raising the energy barrier for the reverse reaction is thus $1 - \alpha$, and the activation energy for oxidation is now

$$\Delta G_{anodic}^{\ddagger\prime} = \Delta G_{anodic}^\ddagger + (1 - \alpha)nF\Delta E. \tag{23.12a}$$

Fortunately, the transfer coefficient tends to be constant over a range of potential, for it is basically a measure of the symmetry of the activation barrier.

---

* Recall that the negative terminal of the source of external voltage is connected to the negative cell electrode and the positive terminal to the positive cell electrode.

It is now useful to formulate rate expressions for the forward and reverse reactions. By this means we can relate cell current to applied potential. The following treatment applies for a cathode when the anode is a reference electrode. How to interpret current at the reference electrode, which must equal that at the other electrode, we consider below when we define the exchange current. The symbolism used in treating reaction at the cathode is: forward or cathodic current i_c, forward rate constant k_f, reverse or anodic current i_a, reverse rate constant k_r, current density I (units, A cm^{-2}). At the cathode the rate of reduction R_f is given by

$$R_f = k_f(C_{ox})_e = I_c/nF \tag{23.13}$$

where $(C_{ox})_e$ is the concentration of the oxidized form of the electroactive species at the electrode surface and I_c is the cathodic current density. Similarly, the rate of the reverse reaction is expressed as

$$R_b = k_b(C_{red})_e = I_a/nF. \tag{23.14}$$

We can now formulate expressions for the specific rate constants k_f and k_b. The equations will include an exponential term involving the activation energy. Suffice it here to write these as:

$$k_f = k_0 \exp[-\alpha nF\Delta E/RT] \tag{23.15}$$

and

$$k_b = k_0 \exp[(1 - \alpha)nF\Delta E/RT] \tag{23.16}$$

where k_0 is a rate factor that includes the basic activation energy term $\exp(-\Delta G^{\ddagger}/RT)$.*

Now the cathodic current may be expressed by combining Eqs. (23.13) and (23.15) and multiplying by A, the area of the electrode. The resulting expression is

$$i_c = nFAk_0(C_{ox})_e \exp(-\alpha nF\Delta E/RT). \tag{23.17}$$

We obtain a similar equation for the anodic current. The net cathode current i is the sum of the two opposing currents, i_a and i_c, which have opposite signs,

$$i = i_c + i_a = nFAk_0\{[(C_{ox})_e \exp(-\alpha nF\Delta E/RT) - (C_{red})_e \exp[(1 - \alpha)nF\Delta E/RT]\}. \tag{23.18}$$

This current must, of course, also be the cell current.

It is useful to separate the effect of applied potential at an electrode from that of intrinsic activation energy $\Delta G^{\ddagger}$. This may best be done by letting $E_{app} = E_{eq}$. Then at the cathode $i = 0$ and $i_c = -i_a$: The two current components are of equal magnitude. (A similar description of course holds at the anode.) It is convenient to let either current component be termed the *exchange current* i_0, that is, $i_0 = i_c = -i_a$ when $\Delta E = 0$. To find its value, set $\Delta E = 0$ in Eq. (23.17); then $i_0 = nFAk_0(C_{ox})_e$. The

---

* Usually, the "basic" or chemical activation energy is unknown, and depends not only on the electron transfer but also upon the work function of the metal and other physical quantities. Figure 23.3, and this kinetic treatment, will apply to the rate-determining step in the electron transfer reaction. Should the number of electrons involved in it, n_a, differ from the n in the overall electrode reaction, the value n_a should replace n in the exponentials in Eqs. (23–15) and (23.16), etc.

exchange current proves to be a direct, though ambiguous, measure of the *reversibility* of a reaction. When the exchange current is large, the electrode reaction can be considered reversible; when i_0 is very small, the reaction can be considered irreversible.

A cell current is thus possible only when the potential of its electrodes is forced by a change in the externally applied voltage E_{app} to depart somewhat from the equilibrium value. In other words, only if ΔE in Eq. (23.18) has a value other than zero volts will i_c and $i_a \neq i_0$ at a particular electrode. The difference ΔE is termed the activation overpotential of the electrode and symbolized by η. By definition, $\eta = E_{app} - E_{eq}$.

The larger the exchange current, the smaller the deviation of E_{app} from E_{eq} required for a finite cell current to flow. In general, reversible reactions show an immeasurably small activation overpotential, but the actual value is quite dependent on the conditions under which an electrolysis is carried out. Unfortunately, no unambiguous distinction between reversible and irreversible reactions is possible.

It is essential to distinguish between activation overpotential and what is usually termed *concentration polarization*. The latter is a departure from equilibrium potential due to a depletion of electroactive species at the surface of an electrode. The distinction is that concentration polarization depends upon the rate of mass transport of species to an electrode as well as the rate of electron transfer. Where it is necessary experimentally to distinguish activation overpotential from a depletion effect, we must take exceptional care to insure uniformity in concentration throughout a solution.

What current will we observe if the cathode is at too low a negative potential relative to a reference for the most easily reduced electroactive species to undergo electrolysis? In this range, the difference $E_{app} - E_{eq}$ must be positive for the electrode. The rate of reaction must be minute because of the high activation barrier for the forward reaction. In this range, since the potential of the electrode can be changed at will without a current flowing, the electrode is said to be *polarized*. There will at most

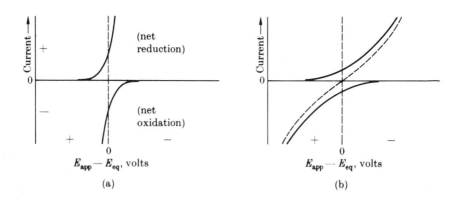

(net reduction)

(net oxidation)

$E_{app} - E_{eq}$, volts

(a)

$E_{app} - E_{eq}$, volts

(b)

Fig. 23.4 Electrolysis curves for an idealized case in which the resistance of the solution is assumed negligible. The movement of ions to the electrodes is therefore infinitely fast. In (a) the electrode reactions are reversible and in (b) they are irreversible. In both (a) and (b) the solid upper curve applies when the electrode is surrounded by the oxidized form of an electroactive species and the lower solid curve applies when it is surrounded by the reduced form of the species. The diagonal broken curve in (b) applies when both oxidized and reduced forms are present initially. The solid curves may also be said to represent i_c and i_a for this case.

be a small *residual current* attributable to impurity electrolysis or electrode charging (Section 25.3). As $E_{app} \rightarrow E_{eq}$, however, and the activation barrier lessens, reduction will begin to occur. The net rate of reduction will increase until limited by the speed with which the species can move to the cathode, as discussed in the next section.

In Fig. 23.4a two current–voltage curves are drawn for a reversible electrode reaction occurring under conditions such that there is very rapid movement of ions in solution. A dashed line designates the equilibrium electrode potential E_{eq}. The upper curve represents the current that flows when only the oxidized form of the electroactive species is present, a case described above. Since a reduction is taking place, the current is regarded by convention as positive. The lower curve depicts the electrolysis when only the reduced form is initially present. A negative current flows, since oxidation is occurring.

Figure 23.4b shows a similar set of curves for the case of a species whose reduction and oxidation are irreversible. Since irreversibility is associated with a slow step in the electron transfer, the slopes of the curves are much smaller. The diagonal (broken) curve shows an additional situation, the current when both oxidized and reduced forms of the electroactive species are present initially. Now when E_{app} is varied, the current goes rapidly from one sign to the other.

23.3 MASS TRANSPORT PROCESSES

In contrast to the idealized curves shown in Fig. 23.4, in actual electrolysis we observe quite finite rates of transport of species. Indeed, control of the modes of mass transport is essential for precise electrochemical measurements. Three types of transport mechanism may be identified,

1. Migration (movement under an electrical gradient);
2. Diffusion (movement under a concentration gradient); and
3. Convection (movement caused by mechanical or thermal agitation).

Migration. Only ions are directly subject to electrical migration, usually simply termed migration. In this mechanism the driving force is the attraction of an electric field set up by a pair of electrodes. If their potential difference is V volts and they are separated by l centimeters, an electrical gradient of V/l volts cm^{-1} will exist between them; the force on an ion of charge q will be qV/l. Neutral species will not be affected directly by the field but may be carried along with ions they solvate. The mobility of an ion (rate of movement in a field of one V cm^{-1}) depends on charge, size, solvation, and other properties. A more detailed examination of migration is inappropriate here; the topic recurs in connection with conductometric methods in Chapter 28, since it is the sole process determining electrolysis current in such measurements.

Interestingly, in most other electrolysis techniques, e.g. polarography, it is desirable to minimize migration for the analytical species. A 50-fold or 100-fold excess of a highly mobile electrolyte, e.g. KCl or KNO_3, that is nonelectrolyzable at the voltage used is added for this purpose. The new electrolyte provides so great a number of charge carriers that its ions carry virtually all the current and migration is of negligible importance for the species of interest. Minority species ions are brought to the electrode mainly by diffusion or convection.

Diffusion. Whenever local differences in concentration of a particular species exist, diffusional processes tend to establish a uniform distribution. These processes are familiar from ordinary experience. They originate in random thermal motion and are most simply described by considering local concentration gradients as the driving force. All factors relating to molecular movement and the nature of a species are collected in a *diffusion coefficient D*.

Example In any given elementary solution volume J, a certain definite fraction of each kind of ions may be considered to move in a given direction. Let this be the x-direction and K be an adjacent elementary volume into which they are moving. This behavior is illustrated in Fig. 23.5. In K, the same *fraction* of each kind of ion may be considered as moving back into the first element J. Since the origin of diffusion is random thermal motion the fraction is essentially independent of the concentration. If the concentration in volume J is twice that in K, there will be two times more ions leaving the first volume and going into the second than are being returned. Each constituent thus diffuses from regions where its concentration is higher to regions where its concentration is lower.

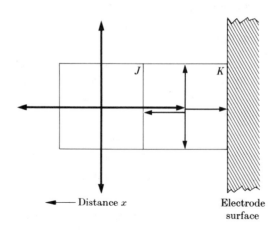

Distance x

Electrode
surface

Fig. 23.5 Front view of diffusion of a single solute from two elementary adjacent cubic volumes of solution at the same temperature. In volume unit J, the constituent is taken as twice as concentrated as it is in K. The fraction of the total number of solute particles moving outward as a result of thermal forces per unit time will be the same for each but because of the concentration difference the number leaving J will be twice as great as from K. As a result, there will be net diffusion from J to K.

How may we express diffusion mathematically? A single case is dealt with explicitly, that of linear diffusion in which movement is in only one direction. An example would be movement of species toward a planar electrode where it is being electrolyzed. Fortunately, this common type is the simplest to treat.

Figure 23.6 represents the situation schematically. An electroactive species present at concentration C_0 in the bulk of the solution is being reduced at the planar electrode at the left. As a result, the species concentration is C_e at the electrode surface. A concentration gradient $(C_0 - C_e)/\delta$ exists across a *diffusion layer* of approximate thickness δ. The layer is taken to extend outward from the electrode surface to the point at which the bulk concentration prevails. Though the outer boundary cannot be defined precisely, the thickness of the layer can be shown to increase with the time of electrolysis. If the electrode is stationary and the solution is stirred, however, the thickness of the layer tends to reach a limiting or steady-state value.

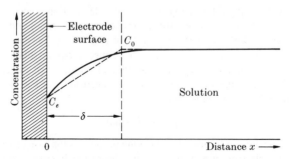

Fig. 23.6 Schematic representation of linear diffusion of an electroactive species to an electrode: C_0, bulk concentration; C_e, steady-state concentration at electrode surface during reduction. Diffusion layer δ extends outward from the electrode. A full line indicates the probable concentration gradient, the broken line an assumed linear gradient.

What is the relationship between the movement of the species and the diffusion layer concentration gradient? It is convenient now to define the *flux* for the diffusing species, the number of moles N that crosses unit area A in unit time dt. At any given distance from the electrode, the flux is proportional to the concentration gradient $\partial C / \partial x$, and is defined by the expression

$$\text{Flux} = \bar{J}_0(x, t) = \frac{1}{A} \frac{dN}{dt} = D \frac{\partial C(x, t)}{\partial x} \tag{23.19}$$

where D is a constant characterizing the species termed the *diffusion coefficient*. Note that for flux to have the proper units, D will ordinarily be expressed in $\text{cm}^2 \ \text{sec}^{-1}$. Both concentration and flux depend upon distance and time. Equation (23.19) is known as *Fick's first law*. If it is valid to approximate the true distribution of electroactive species by a dashed straight line, as in Fig. 23.6, the law reduces to

$$\text{Flux} = D\left(\frac{C_0 - C_e}{\delta}\right). \tag{23.20}$$

Because of the straightforward relation of flux to bulk concentration, there will often be advantages in arranging experimental conditions so that diffusion is the only mechanism by which an electroactive species is transported. If the electron transfer processes are substantially faster than the rate of transport, diffusion will be the rate-controlling step in electrolysis, and then the current can be equated to the flux expressed in Eq. (23.19). To establish the relation, let i be the electrolysis current, A the electrode area, and n the number of electrons involved per species. The current is simply

$$i = nFAD\left(\frac{\partial C}{\partial x}\right)_{x=0} \tag{23.21}$$

where the partial derivative refers to the gradient at the electrode surface. To apply this equation, it remains only to arrange experimental conditions so that the dependence of the partial derivative on time is clearly defined. Before we discuss this further step, an example of the application of Fick's first law is appropriate.

Example Fick's first law provides the basis for a valid description of electrolysis wherever it is possible to keep concentration at the electrode surface negligibly small and to maintain the diffusion layer at constant thickness. Under these conditions the dashed-line model of Fig. 23.6 applies. The dashed line should now be mentally redrawn to connect the point labeled C_0 with the origin. The current attains a maximum, constant value termed the *diffusion current*. As expressed in Eq. (23.20) the gradient is constant outward from the electrode and has the value $(C_0 - C_e)/\delta$. But $C_e \simeq 0$, and the diffusion current i_d is given by

$$i_d = nFADC_0/\delta.$$

When are the requisite conditions attained? One instance is the case of a rapidly stirred solution. Another is that of electrolysis at a rotating microelectrode. In either instance a thin diffusion layer and a steep concentration gradient are present. As a result, in both situations the diffusion current is substantially larger than it would be for diffusion in the absence of stirring or electrode rotation with the same electrode.

In general, diffusion also varies with time and Fick's first law must be extended. How may we express its time dependence? An answer is obtained straightforwardly for the case of linear diffusion when we consider the change in flux in two parallel planes at distances x and $x + dx$ from the electrode surface. It can be shown that this leads to *Fick's second law*. [3]

$$\left[\frac{\partial C(x, t)}{\partial t}\right]_x = D\left[\frac{\partial^2 C(x, t)}{\partial x^2}\right]_t \tag{23.22}$$

where $(\partial C/\partial t)_x$ is the time rate of change of concentration at distance x from the electrode and the second derivative $(\partial^2 C/\partial x^2)_t$ is the rate of variation of the concentration gradient $(\partial C/\partial x)$ with distance at time t.

We can solve Fick's two laws by the usual methods of handling differential equations. For each set of experimental conditions in electrolysis there will be initial conditions as well as boundary conditions. When these conditions are substituted into the appropriate differential equation, an equation defining concentration as the function of distance-time is obtained. Finally, note that these two forms of Fick's equations relate to *linear* diffusion. For example, there are other expressions for diffusion to cylindrical and spherical electrodes.

Example An interesting application of Fick's second law is possible in the case of linear semi-infinite diffusion. Necessary conditions for such an experiment are to apply a large enough potential for electrolysis to immediately deplete the electroactive species at the surface of the electrode. Thus, at the electrode surface, $C_e = 0$ for $t > 0$. That is one boundary condition. A second boundary condition describes the situation at large distances from the electrode. Here the concentration remains essentially undisturbed by diffusion and has the bulk value C_0.

Under these conditions, we can solve Fick's second law to give the result

$$C_{x,t} = \frac{2C_0}{\pi^{1/2}} \int_0^\infty e^{-y^2}\, dy, \tag{23.23}$$

where $y = x/2(Dt)^{1/2}$. The right side of the equation is just the expression known as the error function (erf) when the argument is y. Thus, it is more usual to write Eq. (23.23) as $C_{x,t} = C_0 \,\text{erf}\,[x/2(Dt)^{1/2}]$. In Fig. 23.7 the distribution of the reducible species derived from the equation is shown at three different times. Values of C_x/C_0 are graphed as a function of distance from the electrode surface. Note that the diffusion layer extends further into the bulk of the solution the longer the interval of electrolysis.

It is also possible to find the dependence of current on time. Since the concentration at the electrode surface is essentially zero, we can obtain the current by solving Fick's first law. It is only necessary to differentiate Eq. (23.23) with respect to x and substitute the value in Eq. (23.22). One obtains the relationship known as the Cottrell equation

$$i_t = nFAC_0(D/\pi t)^{1/2}. \tag{23.24}$$

This expression indicates that current falls with time, as we would expect from the broadening of the diffusion layer and the consequent decrease in diffusion rate. The conditions given correspond to those used in the technique *chronoamperometry*.

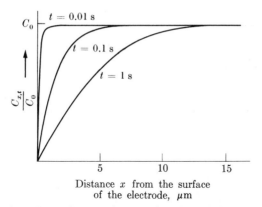

Fig. 23.7 Distribution of reducible species as a function of distance and time of electrolysis. Linear diffusion is occurring in the presence of a large excess of indifferent electrolyte.

Convection. It is also possible to move electroactive species by thermal currents and by stirring, processes grouped under the general term convection. Stirring is a much more effective mechanism than diffusion as a means of bringing a species to an electrode. As noted above, it also acts to stabilize the diffusion layer. Nernst proposed that the stabilizing effect implied a stagnant layer at the electrode-solution interface. This model was pictured in Fig. 23.6. With a diffusion layer of constant thickness, it follows that the current will assume a steady value. The model fails in that the diffusion layer is not of definite thickness, but corresponds more nearly to the full line in Fig. 23.6. Nevertheless, the model is a useful empirical approach. A more exact treatment of convection involves discussion of laminar flow and turbulent flow, as well as a consideration of the geometry of the electrode and surrounding region and is beyond the scope of this book.

Comments about two extremes are worth making. The rate of stirring should be well controlled to secure a constant current. Conversely, in the absence of stirring, solutions that are truly quiet are difficult to maintain. There is an ever-present possibility both of vibrational disturbances and of thermal convection. The upper time limit for a quiet solution is perhaps 100 to 200 s.

23.4 CURRENT–VOLTAGE CURVES

Figure 23.4 showed current–voltage curves for a cell in which mass transport occurs very rapidly and the rate of electron transfer could be varied. Since modes of mass transport have now been examined, it is appropriate to reappraise the curves. They are redrawn in Fig. 23.8 for different rates of mass transport and electron transfer. Since the anodic portions are similar, only the cathodic (reduction) portion of each is repeated. For comparison with the previous figure, a curve for very fast transport is included. What is striking in Fig. 23.8 is that most curves flatten (and one declines) at moderate voltages as mass transport is slowed. As expected, at fast rates of electron transfer the finite rate of mass transport itself limits the current.

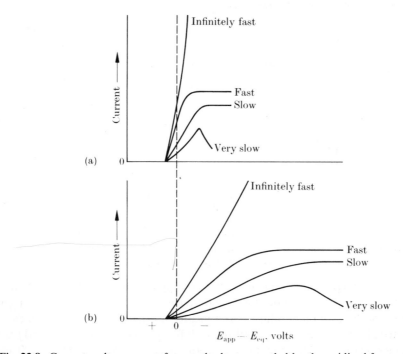

Fig. 23.8 Current–voltage curves for a cathode surrounded by the oxidized form of an electroactive species under conditions of different rates of mass transport and electron transfer. The relative rate of mass transport is indicated beside each curve. In the set of curves designated (a) electron transfer is very fast and in set (b) electron transfer is very slow. For both sets the working electrode is driven steadily more negative relative to a reference electrode.

Under conditions of reversibility that hold for the curves in Fig. 23.8a, electroactive species are reduced as rapidly as they move to the electrode surface. Over the portion of each curve in which current continues to rise linearly with applied voltage, Ohm's law is obeyed. The slope dI/dV of the curve is inversely proportional to the resistance of the cell. For this range Ohm's law can be stated $I = V/R = V\kappa$ where κ is the specific conductance of the solution.

As the voltage applied to the cell increases further, the current "levels off." Its limiting or maximum value is dependent on the rate of transport. At these voltages species are reduced as soon as they reach the electrode. Eventually, the applied potential is sufficient to cause the reduction of other electroreducible substances, often including the solvent, as we see below. Figure 23.8b shows that in an irreversible system, where the electron transfer rate is slow, a much larger applied potential is required to achieve the limiting current. When transport is very slow, as in an unstirred solution in which diffusion is the only mechanism, many current–voltage curves peak at high applied voltages. The rate of transport actually diminishes when the diffusion layer extends far out from the electrode.

For a reversible electrolysis we can relate the potential of an electrode to its standard electrode potential E^0. The connection is most direct when the current has attained half its limiting value; under these conditions equal activities (concentrations) of oxidized and reduced forms of the electroactive species are present at the electrode surface and the potential is usually almost equal to E^0 (Section 25.5). The current rise is called a wave, and the half-height potential, the *half-wave potential* $E_{1/2}$. This situation is illustrated by a curve in Fig. 23.8a. The half-wave potential for the current–voltage curve labeled "fast" coincides with the dashed line that corresponds to $E_{app} = E_{eq}$.

Under conditions of irreversibility (slow electron transfer) the potential at half the limiting current should be the sum of the overpotential and the standard potential, $E_{1/2} = E^0 + \eta$. Similarly, if diffusion is slow, the halfwave potential will be E^0 plus an *apparent* overpotential. This overpotential results from depletion of the electroactive species at the surface of the electrode and is just the concentration polarization discussed earlier.

In the general case several ions and molecules may be electrolyzable at an electrode. These species may be solution components or the solvent itself. For example, under conditions where the potential of an electrode is made steadily more negative or cathodic relative to a reference electrode, one easily reducible species after another may begin to electrolyze as its halfwave potential is approached. This situation is shown in Fig. 23.9 for a stirred solution containing copper and zinc ions. Note that when a new species begins to be reduced, all more easily reduced ones *continue* to be reduced. Eventually a potential sufficiently negative to reduce the solvent is reached and all other electrolyses are obscured.

23.5 SUMMARY OF ELECTROANALYTICAL METHODS

In Table 23.1 most of the common electroanalytical methods are listed and described briefly according to variables controlled and those measured. Each technique calls for direct control of at least one of the three basic variables—current, voltage, and time —and measurement of another. In general, electrical energy is supplied to the electrochemical cell through a control device that determines whether current and/or voltage delivered to the cell are held constant or varied in systematic fashion. Appropriate

Table 23.1 Characteristics of some Electroanalytical Techniques

Technique	Current*	Voltage*	Reagent (volume)*	Time*
Potentiometry				
A. direct‡	driven to zero	prec.	—	—
B. titration‡	driven to zero	mod. prec.	prec.	—
Polarography				
A. dc (classical)	prec.; i_d	slow dc ramp	—	—
B. single sweep	prec.; i_p	fast dc ramp	—	—
C. cyclic voltammetry	prec.; i_p	fast triangular wave	—	—
D. pulse	prec.	square pulses	—	—
E. titration (amperometry)‡	prec.; i_d	selec. const. value	prec.	—
F. ac	prec.	small sine wave + slow dc ramp	—	—
G. ac oscillographic	large sine wave	mod. prec.	—	—
Biamperometric titr.‡	mod. prec.	small, const. value	prec.	—
Chronoamperometry	prec.	selec. const. value	—	prec.
Chronopotentiometry	selec. const. value	prec.	—	prec.
Coulometry				
A. const. pot.‡	prec.	selec. const. value	—	prec.
B. const. cur.‡	selec. prec. value	redox buffer used	—	prec.
Conductometry				
A. direct‡	prec.	small sine wave	—	—
B. titration‡	mod. prec.	small sine wave	prec.	—
Electrogravimetry‡	—	selec. const. value	prec.†	—

* Symbols: full line box ▢ = variable measured (as specified), dashed box ⌐⌐⌐ = variable controlled (as specified); abbreviations: prec., precision; mod., moderate. Thus, e.g., symbol [prec.] indicates that a variable is measured with precision and ⌐dc ramp⌐ indicates that a dc ramp is applied during a measurement.

† Weight of deposit measured precisely.

‡ Solution is stirred.

detection circuitry monitors the output signal, and provides amplification and modification required. Finally the signal information is presented to the readout device.

Note that electroanalytical techniques are usually named with reference to the variable that is measured or controlled. Names therefore customarily refer to the primary variables—potential, current, charge, or time.

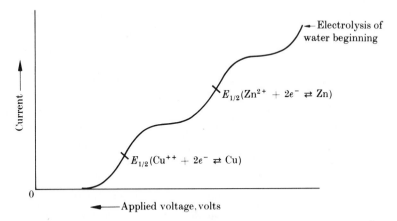

Fig. 23.9 Current–voltage curve for a cell containing Zn^{2+} and Cu^{2+} ions in aqueous solution. The solution is stirred. As the working electrode of the cell is driven steadily more negative relative to a reference electrode, the reduction of Cu^{2+} ions begins. At still more negative potentials Zn^{2+} ions, and finally the solvent, are also reduced.

Example Several illustrations of naming may be helpful. Potentiometry, coulometry, and conductometry are familiar examples of names based on the quantity measured. When a time-dependent response is observed, names properly include reference to time. If electrolysis current is observed in an unstirred solution from the moment a constant voltage is applied, the name chronoamperometry is appropriate. (Polarography can be considered a special case of this technique in which the time dependence is unimportant.) Conversely, if current is controlled in an unstirred solution and the change in voltage with time observed, the label is changed to chronopotentiometry.

In a stirred solution a steady state is obtained almost from the outset. Voltammetry properly applies to this type of method. It may refer to a measurement in which voltage is controlled and current determined, or the reverse: Results are independent of the variable controlled. [5] Cyclic voltammetry provides a final example. In this case the applied voltage is made steadily more negative (cathodic) for a time and then made steadily more positive until the voltage returns to the original value. The solution is not stirred in this case and current is observed.

REFERENCES

References providing a general coverage of electrode processes are:

1. R. N. Adams, *Electrochemistry at Solid Electrodes*. New York: Dekker, 1969
1a. J. O'M. Bockris and A. K. N. Reddy, *Modern Electrochemistry*, 2 vols. New York: Plenum, 1970

2. B. E. Conway, *Theory and Principles of Electrode Processes*. New York: Ronald Press, 1965

3. G. Kortüm, *Treatise on Electrochemistry*. 2d ed. New York: Elsevier, 1965

4. C. N. Reilley and R. W. Murray, "Electroanalytical Principles," a reprint from *Treatise on Analytical Chemistry*. pt I, vol. 4. I. M. Kolthoff and P. J. Elving, eds. New York: Interscience, 1963

A brief but authoritative treatment of major electroanalytical techniques is provided in:

4a. D. R. Browning, ed., *Electrometric Methods*. New York: McGraw-Hill, 1969

All major electroanalytical techniques are discussed comprehensively in:

5. I. M. Kolthoff and P. J. Elving, eds., *Treatise on Analytical Chemistry*, pt I, vol. 4. New York: Interscience, 1963

6. J. J. Lingane, *Electroanalytical Chemistry*. 2d ed. New York: Interscience, 1958

7. A. Weissberger, ed., *Physical Methods of Organic Chemistry*. 3d ed., pt IV. New York: Interscience, 1960

A more advanced treatment of some aspects of electroanalytical chemistry may be found in:

9. Paul Delahay, *Double Layer and Electrode Kinetics*. New York: Interscience, 1965

10. W. H. Reinmuth, "Theory of Electrode Processes", in *Advances in Analytical Chemistry and Instrumentation*. Vol. I. Charles N. Reilley, ed. New York: Interscience, 1960

The physical chemistry of electrolyte solutions is discussed on an advanced level in:

11. Herbert S. Harned and Benton B. Owen, *The Physical Chemistry of Electrolytic Solutions*. 3rd ed. New York: Reinhold, 1958

12. R. A. Robinson and R. H. Stokes, *Electrolyte Solutions*. 2d ed. New York: Academic, 1959

Comprehensive discussions of advances in selected areas of electroanalytical chemistry appear approximately annually in the following continuing series:

13. *Advances in Analytical Chemistry and Instrumentation*. Vol. I (1960), Interscience

14. *Advances in Electrochemistry and Electrochemical Engineering*. Vol. 1 (1961), Interscience

15. *Electroanalytical Chemistry. A Series of Advances*. Vol. 1 (1966), Dekker

EXERCISES

23.1 In an analytical electrolysis cell, solvent electrolysis is likely to occur only at the working electrode. Explain.

23.2 The slope of the reduction wave portion of an electrolysis is nearly constant at $0.1 \ A \ V^{-1}$. What is the resistance of the solution in the cell?

23.3 (a) Contrast the role of the cell in an electroanalytical technique and with that in a spectrophotometric method. (b) To what extent is there a useful analogy between varying the voltage in an electroanalytical technique and the frequency in a spectrophotometric method? (c) An electrodeless cell is also possible in electroanalytical work (Section 28.10). What electrical parameters can be measured when it is used?

23.4 Consider that a cell consisting of a cathode of large exchange current i_0 and an anode of quite small i_0 and items such as a potentiometer, dc power supply regulated to $\pm 1 \ mV$, galvanometer, etc., are available. (a) Draw a schematic circuit diagram for a circuit suitable for applying a known dc voltage to the cell and measuring i_{cell}. Assume E_{cell} is known. (b) If $E_{app} > E_{cell}$, what direction does i_{cell} have? By means of potential energy diagrams, show the barriers to forward and reverse reactions at the anode and cathode. Indicate the magnitude of change in the barriers from the case where $E_{app} = E_{cell}$. At which electrode is i_{cell} essentially determined?

CHAPTER 24

POTENTIOMETRIC METHODS

24.1 INTRODUCTION

Measurements of the difference in potential between the electrodes of a galvanic cell under conditions of zero current are described by the term potentiometry, or sometimes as potentiometry at zero current. Neither current nor time is significant in the technique; it is an equilibrium method. The technique is important because it can provide accurate measurements of (a) free energy changes and equilibrium constants of many solution reactions (Section 23.1) and (b) either activities, concentrations, and/or activity coefficients of many solution species. The latter topic is treated below.

The premises essential to potentiometry were introduced in Section 23.1; that background is assumed familiar in the discussion below. The premises are simply summarized here. They are: that the potential difference between the electrodes of a cell at zero current represents a sum of potential drops: $E_{cell} = E_{anode} + E_{cathode} + E_{jcn}$, where each has its intrinsic sign; that any liquid junction potential E_{jcn} can ordinarily be minimized or held constant; and that the Nernst equation, Eq. (23.8), is separable into expressions for each electrode. The last premise provides a theoretical basis for treating reactions at individual electrodes. If ox and red are the oxidized and reduced forms of the principal species active at an electrode, the electrode potential is given by Eq. (23.11), which is rewritten here in general form:

$$E_{electrode} = E^0_{half\text{-}cell} + \frac{2.303RT}{nF} \log \frac{a_{ox}}{a_{red}}, \qquad (24.1)$$

where $E^0_{hqlf\text{-}cell}$ is the electrode emf under standard conditions, the a's are activities, n is the number of electrons involved in the reaction, and R, T, and F have their usual significance. Equation (24.1) provides a potential relative to the normal hydrogen electrode (Section 23.1).

Example   What is the emf of a Fe^{2+}, Fe^{3+} electrode at 25 °C if ionic activities are 0.01 M and 0.1 M, respectively, and Fe^{3+} is being reduced? If Fe^{2+} is being oxidized?

Solution. If Fe^{2+} and Fe^{3+} are the electroactive species at an inert electrode at 25 °C, the emf of the electrode is given by the equation

$$E = E^0_{half\text{-}cell} + 0.0591 \log [Fe^{3+}]/[Fe^{2+}],$$

where brackets are used to designate activities. From tables, the standard potential E^0 of the electrode is 0.771 V. If reduction is occurring at the electrode, $E^0_{half\text{-}cell} = E^0$, and the electrode emf is

$$E = 0.771 + 0.0591 \log [0.1]/[0.01] = 0.771 + 0.059 = 0.830 \text{ V}.$$

On the other hand, if Fe^{2+} is being oxidized to Fe^{3+}, $E_{half-cell} = -E^0$ and

$$E = -0.771 + 0.0591 \log [0.1]/[0.01] = -0.712 \text{ V}.$$

In a great deal of potentiometry one electrode serves as a *reference electrode*. At a given temperature its potential is independent of cell behavior. Under these conditions, the cell voltage is given by

$$E_{cell} = E_{ind} + E_{ref} + E_{jcn} = E_{ind} + \text{constant}, \tag{24.2}$$

where E_{ind} is the potential of the *indicator electrode* and a_{ox}/a_{red} is the ratio of activities of species electroactive at its surface. Thus, by use of a reference electrode, cell emf becomes essentially a response to the species at one electrode. On this basis we can use E_{cell} to determine a single species directly as in direct potentiometry (Sections 24.3, 24.7, and 24.8). More commonly, however, the arrangement is used to permit E_{cell} to monitor the progress of a titration reaction and determine the equivalence point (Section 24.9 through 24.13).

Estimation of activity coefficients. In many applications of potentiometry the concentration of a species is of interest rather than its activity, which $E_{electrode}$ yields. The conversion to concentration requires a knowledge of activity coefficient values γ to use in the defining relation $a = \gamma C$. There is a problem in that the literature yields few such data except for solutions of single compounds. Fortunately, we can calculate approximate values of activity coefficients for concentrations below about 0.1 M.

To carry out the calculation it should first be recalled that the most important influence on the activity coefficient of an ion is the density of charge in a solution. This density is expressed in terms of the *ionic strength*, μ, defined as $\mu = \frac{1}{2}\Sigma_i C_i z_i^2$, where z_i is the charge of a particular ion and C_i its concentration.* All ions are included in the summation.

The following expression from Debye–Hückel theory enables us to calculate an approximate activity coefficient at low concentrations ($C < 0.1$ M)

$$-\ln \gamma_i = \frac{A z_i^2 \mu^{1/2}}{1 + B d_i \mu^{1/2}} \tag{24.3}$$

in which $A = 1.824 \times 10^6 (DT)^{-3/2}$, $B = 50.29(DT)^{-1/2}$, d_i is the ionic distance of closest approach in centimeters, D is the dielectric constant, and T is the absolute temperature. An average value for d is 4×10^{-8} cm. Note also that at 25 °C in water, $A = 0.509$ and $B = 0.328$.

It is well worth while to estimate activity coefficients in the concentration range 10^{-1} to 10^{-3} M. At concentrations below 10^{-3} M, $\gamma \approx 1$ and it is unnecessary except for highly charged species ($z_i > 2$). At concentrations above 10^{-1} M, estimates based on Eq. (24.3) or other expressions will be substantially in error.

---

* Whatever the units in which concentration is expressed, ionic strength must have the same units. Clearly, the choice of units will affect the magnitude of the activity coefficient. Thus, it is fortunate that activity coefficients in dilute aqueous solution are nearly equal whether molar or molal concentrations are used.

The activity of molecular species also appears in many electrode expressions. For a gaseous substance its partial pressure (in atm) may be substituted for activity, in many cases with no more than 2 % error. For a liquid, $a = 1$ (on a mole fraction scale) unless the solute concentration is appreciable. For example, the activity of water in which a uni-univalent electrolyte is dissolved departs more than one or two percent from unity only when the concentration exceeds about 0.25 M.

Concentration dependence. How sensitively is emf related to activity (concentration)? Now that a means for estimation of activity coefficients is available, the question is unavoidable. It is evident from Eq. (24.1) that the potential of an indicator electrode responds only logarithmically to the activity (concentration) of an electroactive species. As Fig. 23.1 showed, if we graph $\log (a_{ox}/a_{red})$ vs. $E_{electrode}$, a straight line whose slope is $2.303 RT/nF$ results. For $n = 1$ this term has a value of 0.0591 at 25 °C and 0.0661 at 60 °C; thus, the sensitivity of measurement of activity (concentration) increases somewhat with rising temperature. Note also that E is inversely proportional to n: Sensitivity falls in direct proportion to the increase in the number of electrons exchanged.

Example What potential does an Ag indicator electrode have at 25 °C, relative to a saturated calomel electrode (SCE), when the surrounding electrolyte is (a) 0.1 M $AgNO_3$? (b) 0.001 M $AgNO_3$? The question is equivalent to asking, what is the potential of the cell comprising a Ag, Ag^+ electrode and a saturated calomel electrode when first one and then the other electrolyte solution surrounds the silver?

What information is available without calculation? At 25 °C (from tables) $E^0_{Ag, Ag^+} = +0.799$ V, $E^0_{SCE} = +0.244$ V, and $\gamma_{Ag^+} = 0.73$ in 0.1 M $AgNO_3$. Further, γ_{Ag^+} can be safely assumed nearly unity in 10^{-3} M $AgNO_3$.

Considering the reaction at the silver electrode arbitrarily as a reduction, the Nernst equation gives

$$E_{Ag, Ag^+} = E^0 + \frac{2.303RT}{nF} \log \frac{a_{Ag^+}}{a_{Ag}} = E^0 + 0.0591 \log C_{Ag}\gamma_{Ag^+}.$$

Recall that $a_{Ag} = 1$. In 0.1 M $AgNO_3$ the equation becomes

$$E = 0.799 + 0.0591 \log [0.1 \times 0.73] = 0.799 + 0.0591 \times (-1.14) = 0.732 \text{ V}.$$

Relative to SCE,

$$E_{Ag, Ag^+} \text{ is } 0.732 - 0.244 = 0.488 \text{ V}.$$

In 10^{-3} M $AgNO_3$ the silver electrode potential (vs. NHE) is $E = 0.799 - 3 \times 0.0591 = 0.622$ V or $0.622 - 0.244 = 0.378$ V vs. SCE. (Note that the liquid junction potential has been assumed zero.) A 100-fold alteration of silver ion concentration at the silver electrode has caused a 0.11 V drop in response (from 0.488 to 0.378 V).

Liquid junction potential. How much uncertainty was introduced by the neglect of the liquid junction potential in the example above? The question is raised seriously, since in cells of analytical and research interest, a liquid junction is often unavoidable. Indeed, the most common reference electrode, saturated calomel reference, always introduces such a junction at the boundary between its saturated KCl salt bridge and the cell electrolyte solution.

A potential difference arises at a liquid boundary as a result of differences in ionic mobility. Fast ions move across a boundary more quickly than slow ions and a potential difference quickly builds up, as Fig. 24.1 shows. What occurs is that the side of the boundary from which the fast ions originate becomes partially depleted in ions of this sign (positive or negative) while the other side develops a surplus. A steady state is achieved as soon as the developing potential difference equalizes the rates of movement.

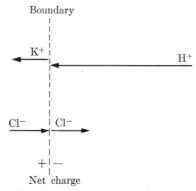

Fig. 24.1 Origin of potential difference at a liquid junction. Equal concentrations of HCl and KCl are assumed present initially. The lengths of arrows represent the relative mobilities of the ions. Since hydrogen ions move faster than potassium ions, the left side of the boundary becomes positive relative to the right side.

Liquid junction potentials present both experimental and theoretical difficulties. These potentials are quite sensitive to the geometry of the area in which they form and their magnitude depends on concentration, temperature, and to a lesser degree on other variables such as pressure. The uncertainties are sufficient that we cannot calculate them accurately and they are seldom known experimentally with reliability. Consequently, whenever possible liquid junctions should be eliminated, or at the very least minimized.

Several steps can be taken. Perhaps the most important is use of a saturated KCl salt bridge. Because of its high concentration, the KCl will perforce carry most of the current at liquid junctions the bridge makes. The choice of K^+ and Cl^- ions, which have nearly equal mobilities, ensures that little charge differential will build up at a junction. If Cl^- cannot be tolerated in the solution, NH_4NO_3 may be substituted.

For minimum potential the junction must also be formed in a region with (a) cylindrical geometry that (b) permits free diffusion and the solution with which it makes contact should also be (c) an aqueous one (d) whose pH is in the range 2–10. Departures from these conditions raise special problems.

In precise work a junction is often formed in a tube by turning a stopcock to bring solutions in contact. Restricted boundaries such as the asbestos fiber type (Fig. 24.2) used in many commercial SCE's are likely to establish a less precise boundary. The pH requirement relating to a junction arises because of the relatively high mobilities of H^+ and OH^- ions (See Table 28.1). This matter is raised again when pH measurements are discussed in Section 24.7.

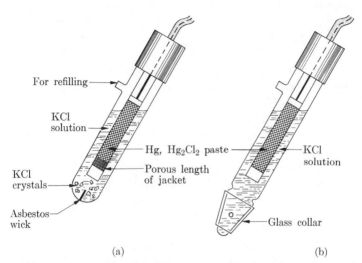

Fig. 24.2 Some common types of calomel electrodes. In (a) an asbestos wick saturated with KCl serves as the salt bridge. In (b) the salt bridge is formed by a rough-ground collar. This type offers lower electrical resistance and is less easily clogged.

In nonaqueous potentiometry junction potentials pose additional questions. Ideally, we should make up the reference electrode and salt bridge with the nonaqueous solvent used in the main part of the cell. [6] This avoids any *medium effect* associated with a nonaqueous–aqueous boundary. The matter will be considered further in Section 24.13.

24.2 ELECTRODES

As used here, the term electrode applies to the conductor and to the surrounding solution with which the conductor is in equilibrium (Section 23.1). In other words, an electrode is considered identical with a half-cell. The following discussion of electrodes is intended to classify them and offer a few criteria for choosing among electrodes.

Reference electrodes. We should keep several factors in mind in selecting a reference electrode. Some of these are the following:

1. Reproducibility without painstaking preparation or assembly,
2. A small temperature coefficient of emf,
3. Reversibility when fairly large currents are drawn,
4. Constancy with time, and
5. Possibility of use with a saturated KCl salt bridge.

So-called electrodes of the second kind are generally the ones that best meet these criteria. These electrodes consist of a core of metal covered by a layer of one of its slightly soluble salts and immersed in a solution of a salt or acid with the same anion.

In the few situations where this solution may also be in contact with the indicator electrode, a liquid junction can be avoided.

In practice, the reference electrodes most often used are the calomel and silver-silver chloride electrodes. These are represented by the symbolism

$$\text{Hg; Hg}_2\text{Cl}_2(\text{s}), \text{KCl soln.} \quad \text{and} \quad \text{Ag; AgCl(s), HCl soln.}$$

respectively. In Fig. 24.2 the construction of two calomel half-cells is illustrated. Concentrations of the KCl solution in the calomel electrode range from saturation (about 4.1 M) down to 0.1 M, while the corresponding standard potentials range from $+0.2444$ to $+0.3356$ V at 25 °C.

Both calomel and silver-silver chloride electrodes are used with an aqueous or agar* salt bridge. This arrangement is satisfactory regardless of the solution around the indicator electrode unless it is strongly acidic or alkaline or of high ionic strength ($\mu > 0.2$). Neither electrode is difficult to assemble. [5]

The silver-silver chloride electrode sometimes allows a liquid junction to be eliminated and is often an attractive alternative to the calomel half-cell. Reproducibility is a greater problem, however, and Ag, AgCl electrodes are usually stored in chloride solutions of about the concentration in which a measurement is to be made.

For either reference electrode the chloride ion is the species that fixes the potential. The Nernst equation gives

$$E_{\text{ref}} = E^0 - \frac{2.303RT}{F} \log a_{\text{Cl}^-} \tag{24.4}$$

with either electrode. Values of E^0 at 25 °C are 0.222 V for the standard AgCl electrode, and 0.268 V for the standard Hg, Hg$_2$Cl$_2$ electrode. Table 24.1 lists values at other temperatures and for nonstandard electrolyte concentrations.

Table 24.1 Potential of the Ag, AgCl and Hg, Hg$_2$Cl$_2$ Electrodes

Temp., °C	$E^0_{\text{Ag, AgCl}}$	$E^0_{\text{Hg, Hg}_2\text{Cl}_2}$ (0.1 M KCl)	(satd. KCl)
0	0.23655		
5	0.23413		
10	0.23142		
15	0.22857	0.3360	0.2508
20	0.22557	0.3358	0.2476
25	0.22234	0.3356	0.2444
30	0.21904	0.3354	0.2417
35	0.21565	0.3353	0.2391
	(unit activity Cl$^-$)		

Indicator electrodes. Table 24.2 lists several types of indicator electrodes. An *electrode-of-the-first-kind* or class, one in which a metal is in contact with its own ions, is usually limited to metals below hydrogen in the electromotive series. We can use

---

* A common recipe calls for 10% KCl, 3% agar, and 87% water.

more active metals to detect their ions if the overvoltage of hydrogen on the metal exceeds their standard oxidation potential.

Table 24.2 Some Types of Indicator Electrodes

Type of Electrode: Design	Interpretive Comments	Representative Example Name and Electrode Line Symbol*	Electrode Reaction
Electrode of first kind: metal, metal ion	Partially selective; also sensitive to all cations more easily reduced	Zinc: $\underline{Zn}$; $\underline{Zn^{2+}}$	$Zn^{2+} + 2e^- \rightarrow Zn$
Redox: inert conductor, $(red)^{a+}$, $(ox)^{(a+n)+}$	Unselective, also responds to other redox couples; ratio of ionic activities detd.	$\underline{Ce^{4+}, Ce^{3+}}$: Pt; Ce^{4+}, Ce^{3+}	$Ce^{4+} + e^- \rightarrow Ce^{3+}$
Gas: inert conductor, gas, gas ion	Unselective	$\underline{Hydrogen}$: Pt; $\underline{H_{2(g)}}$; $\underline{H^+}$	$H^+ + e^- \rightarrow \frac{1}{2} H_2$
Electrode of second kind: metal, ss metal salt, anion of salt	Ion-selective; range: 0.3 M to limit of solubility of ss metal salt	$\underline{Silver\text{-}silver}$ chloride: Ag; AgCl; $\underline{Cl^-}$	$AgCl + e^- \rightarrow Ag + Cl^-$
Membrane	Ion-selective; range: 0.3 M to limit of solubility of substance used†	$\underline{Sodium}$: Ag; AgCl; 0.1 M NaCl; glass membrane of NAS 11–18 glass‡; $\underline{Na^+}$	Na^+ ion exchange at membrane surface

* The electrode name and the species determined by electrode are underlined.

† As usually determined in water. For example, the lower concentration limit of an iodide-selective membrane electrode that incorporates AgI is 10^{-7} M, the molar solubility of AgI.

‡ NAS 11–18 glass has the composition 11% Na_2O, 18% Al_2O_3, 71% SiO_2.

Perhaps the noble metals make the most versatile indicator electrodes. Redox couples in which both the oxidized and reduced members are readily soluble in the solvent give reproducible emf's with platinum or gold. For example, platinum is the usual metal employed in setting up an Fe^{2+}, Fe^{3+} or H_2, H^+ electrode. Electrodes of this type also lend themselves to indirect determinations. An example is the quin-hydrone electrode, which can be used to determine hydrogen ion through the redox reaction

$$\underset{\text{quinone}}{C_6H_4O_2} + 2H^+ + 2e \rightleftarrows \underset{\text{hydroquinone}}{C_6H_4(OH)_2}.$$

Most of the other important indicator electrodes fall into either the membrane or the *electrode-of-the-second-kind* category. Glass electrodes of various types are a major representative of the former class. These and other ion-selective electrodes are so widely used now that they are separately discussed in the next section. Most electrodes of the second kind are of interest because they allow measurement of the anion of a slightly soluble salt.

Interestingly, oxide electrodes of the second kind are responsive to the H^+ ion. For these, hydrogen ions are integral to the chemical change that occurs at the electrode, and the response is direct. The platinum and platinum–10% rhodium electrodes are therefore believed to owe their sensitivity to H^+ ions to a thin layer of platinum oxide. Better known are the Sb, Sb_2O_3 and the Hg, Hg_2O electrodes, which are useful in acid-base titrations in nonaqueous media. For the former, the electrode reaction has been established as $2Sb + 3H_2O \rightleftharpoons Sb_2O_3 + 6H^+ + 6e$.

24.3 ION-SELECTIVE ELECTRODES

Direct potentiometry becomes an attractive method when electrodes responsive mainly to a single ion are available. Even potentiometric titrations benefit from this development. Ideally, a Nernstian response is secured. For example, if an electrode is sensitive to a cation M^+, its response should follow the equation

$$E = \text{const.} + \frac{2.303RT}{nF} \log a_{M^+}, \qquad (24.5)$$

where $n = 1$. The development of a wide variety of such electrodes* became possible when the mechanism of response of the earliest example, the glass electrode, was well understood. All ion-selective electrodes developed to date feature an insoluble membrane or layer of some type as the sensitive element. Included are glass membranes, liquid membranes (a liquid within an inert membrane), crystalline solid-state membranes, precipitate-impregnated silicone rubber layers, and enzymes or other reactive substances in gel layers.

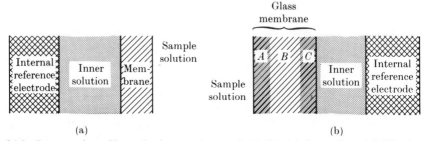

Fig. 24.3 Cross section of ion-selective membrane electrodes. (a) General model. The electrical connection is made to the metal electrode (not shown) in the internal reference. (b) Schematic of glass electrode in aqueous use. Inner and outer membrane layers A and C are hydrated and the center layer B is dry.

In an ion-specific electrode the membrane, crystal, or other discriminating element provides selectivity. Figure 24.3 shows schematically how the electrodes are designed. There are three elements, a sensitive membrane, an inner solution of fixed composition, and an internal reference electrode such as Ag, AgCl. A potential difference develops

---

* The more than 20 ion-selective electrodes commercially available in 1970 included electrodes for some of the alkali, alkaline earth, and heavy metal cations and for many anions.

at both outer and inner surfaces of the membrane but that inside is constant. Where a membrane can swell, as in the glass (membrane) electrode in Fig. 24.4, solvent penetrates and the membrane is solvated like an ion-exchange resin for a short distance in from its boundaries.

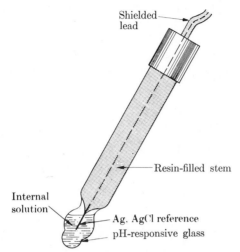

Fig. 24.4 Representative pH electrode. Usually only the membrane at the tip of the electrode bulb is of H^+ ion-selective glass. The high resistivity of the membrane (1 to 1000 MΩ) makes filling the electrode stem with a high-resistance resin desirable to lessen internal surface conductivity.

The mechanism of membrane response seems always to involve a selective ion-exchange process at the solution-membrane boundary. In the case of a homogeneous membrane it may also include differences in rate of diffusion of migration of ions within the membrane. In such a case diffusional processes can either enhance selectivity or reduce it. Since glass membrane electrodes have been best characterized, they will be most fully described below.

Glass membrane electrodes. The basic design is as shown in Fig. 24.4 and indicated schematically in Fig. 24.3b. Ordinarily the membrane is about 50 μm thick and has a resistance of 10^6 to 10^9 Ω.

If placed in an aqueous medium, the outer surface of the membrane hydrates over a period of several hours. The inner surface is permanently hydrated. The thickness of these layers depends on glass composition. The imbibing of water actually leads to a gradual dissolving of the glass; this process essentially determines the useful lifetime of the electrode. Since the membrane mesh is anionic in charge, only cations can penetrate the glass with any facility. As they do, exchange occurs at the boundary. For example, $H^+_{aq} + Na^+_{glass} \rightleftarrows H^+_{glass} + Na^+_{aq}$ and similar exchanges occur. Univalent cations that enter can also diffuse slowly through the hydrated layer; divalent cations that penetrate diffuse scarcely at all. The poor response of a glass membrane to cations of 2+ or 3+ charge is not the result of their exclusion in the exchange step but appears due to their very slow diffusion once they have penetrated. Finally, note that through the dry region of the membrane current is transported mainly by the cation of the lowest charge (other than H^+), in a kind of chain "displacement" process. Glass electrodes also function in other polar solvents such as liquid ammonia, methanol, and molten salts.

The Nernstian response of glass electrodes (especially the pH type) is well known. If Eq. (24.5) is used to describe this behavior, the constant term on the right side is the sum of the potentials of internal reference electrode, inner membrane surface, and any potential that may arise from strain in the membrane (sometimes termed an asymmetry potential).

When two cations of low charge are present in the external solution, e.g. both Na^+ and H^+, we must include a selectivity coefficient in the Nernst equation for it still to be valid. Equation (24.5) takes the form

$$E = \text{const.} + \frac{2.303 n R T}{F} \log \left[a_1^{1/n} + (K_{12}^{pot} a_2)^{1/n} \right] \tag{24.6}$$

where n is a constant for the particular ions and kind of glass, a_1 is the external solution activity of ion 1, the ion for which the electrode is chiefly sensitive, K_{12}^{pot} denotes the overall selectivity coefficient* for ion 2 relative to ion 1, and a_2 is the external activity of ion 2. A fortunate simplification is that n usually has a value near unity.

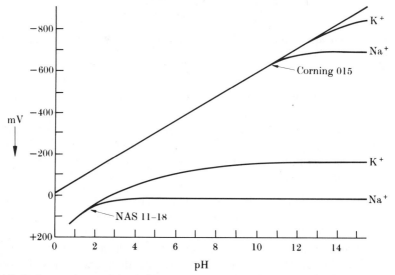

Fig. 24.5 Voltage response of a H^+-selective glass (Corning 015) and a Na^+-selective glass (NAS 11-18) in 0.1 M solutions of the indicated cation. The designation NAS 11-18 signifies composition $Na_2O = 11.0\%$; $Al_2O_3 = 18.0\%$, and $SiO_2 = (100 - 29.0)\%$. Corning 015 glass contains no Al_2O_3.

In Fig. 24.5 the response of two different glasses to H^+ in the presence of 0.1 M Na^+ and K^+ ions is graphed as a function of pH. The regular pH-sensitive glass, Corning

---

* An exact statement of the response of an ion-selective electrode requires that K_{12}^{pot} be considered a product of a diffusion term u_2/u_1, where the u's are mobilities in the membrane, and an ion-exchange selectivity term K_{12} that describes the boundary selectivity. Usually mobilities in these "solid" membranes are unknown and only the overall constant can be given.

015, gives a Nernstian response to H^+ ions to about pH 11, but becomes unusable as a pH electrode about pH 13 in 0.1 M NaOH solution. Its pH error is usually termed the *alkaline error*. By contrast, the Na^+-ion-selective glass (NAS 11–18) responds to H^+ only up to pH 2.* At higher pH values it responds mainly to Na^+. The sodium glass electrode is much less responsive for potassium and other common cations. For example, its relative preference for the Na^+ over K^+ is about 300 at pH 7 and rises to about 3000 at pH 11.

Example   We can apply Eq. (24.6) to the curves of Fig. 24.5. For the Corning 015 membrane K_{12}^{pot} (Na^+ against H^+) $= 10^{-11}$. Assume $n \sim 1$ and that all activity coefficients are unity. What is the value of the log term for (a) $H^+ = 10^{-5}$ M, $Na^+ = 0.1$ M, (b) $H^+ = 10^{-12}$ M, $Na^+ = 0.1$ M, and (c) $H^+ = 10^{-13}$ M, $Na^+ = 0.1$ M?

The log term has the following values for the three sets of conditions cited.

For (a), $\log [10^{-5} + 10^{-11} \times 0.1] = -5$. The response is entirely to the H^+ ion.

For (b), $\log [10^{-12} + 10^{-11} \times 0.1] = -11.7$. The H^+ response is in error by 0.3 pH unit.

For (c), $\log [10^{-13} + 10^{-11} \times 0.1] \simeq -12$. The H^+ response is no longer meaningful.

Glass membranes have so high a resistance that special measurement problems are introduced. If they are to function as a voltage source, the current drawn must be kept smaller than 10^{-11} or 10^{-12} A or response will be in error by more than 1 mV. A further problem is that resistance increases rapidly as temperature decreases. For that reason, the use of a glass electrode at temperatures below those for which it is intended is hazardous.

Where resistance is very high, there are always stray currents, which must be minimized in precise work. Adequate shielding of the glass electrode and its lead can virtually eliminate stray capacitive currents to ground. It is possible to minimize surface conduction along the glass by coating it externally with a water-repellent silicone fluid (it appears not to interfere with the membrane response) and filling most of the interior with a resin or nonconducting fluid. Note that these steps have been taken in the electrode shown in Fig. 24.4.

Precipitate and solid-state electrodes.   Only a few other true membranes appear to possess the selectivity that glasses do. Many sparingly soluble precipitates display surface ion exchange, however, and still show this property when used as crystals or incorporated in silicone rubber matrices. Figure 24.6 shows one electrode design. Note how the layout compares with the schematic model of Fig. 24.3a. Precipitates must also be semiconductors to be suitable for a matrix electrode since the matrix is an insulator. About a 50 weight percent mixture appears to provide the optimum electrical conductivity and a Nernstian response. The most successful electrodes of this type have been for Cl^-, Br^-, and I^- ions. [10] They are quite insensitive to cations, i.e. seem to exchange only anions.

---

* In general, glass membranes are made sensitive to ions other than hydrogen ion by addition of a metal whose coordination number is greater than its oxidation number. For example, aluminum of coordination number 4 and oxidation state 3 serves well.

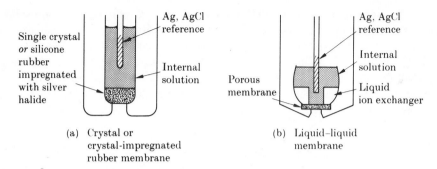

Fig. 24.6 Representative membrane types of ion-selective electrodes. In (a) the membrane is a crystal or impregnated plastic that contains the anion whose detection is sought. Similarly, in (b), the membrane is filled with a liquid ion exchanger that contains the cation for which sensitivity is desired.

Many crystal (solid-state) electrodes have also appeared. For example, a fluoride-ion sensitive electrode that consists of a crystal of lanthanum fluoride doped with europium (II) proves successful for F^- determinations down to 10^{-6} M. A mixed lead sulfide–silver sulfide crystal electrode is sensitive to lead ion.

Either precipitate or crystal electrodes are responsive down to activity levels of anion (or cation) such that the precipitate begins to dissolve. For example, the iodide electrode (based on AgI) can be used down to 10^{-7} M I^-.

One type of enzyme electrode is discussed in Exercise 24.11.

Liquid-membrane electrodes.   Liquid ion exchangers like dinonyl-naphthalene sulfonic acid have been extensively investigated for ion-selective electrodes. As Fig. 24.6b shows, it is possible to arrange a membrane utilizing the liquid ion exchanger. The liquid it is dissolved in must be immobilized but must still be in electrolytic contact with the sample solution. An inert matrix that is porous provides an appropriate permeable barrier. Since contamination of sample also results from diffusion of the internal phase into the sample solution, all possible is done to minimize mixing. Clearly, the ion exchange fluid must be renewed periodically.

Example In a calcium-selective liquid membrane electrode an organo-phosphorous compound serves as the liquid ion exchanger. Contact between the internal and external media occurs in a porous glass frit or other inert matrix. A Nernstian response to calcium can be secured down to about 10^{-5} M over a pH range of 5.5 to 11. Selectivity for calcium ion is high.

Reliability.   To what degree are ion-selective electrodes subject to drift? Fluctuations in response of such electrodes can ideally be kept to about 0.1 mV. Naturally, the temperature and pH of a sample solution under study must be held constant. There is also a considerable drift of electrode response with time and conditions of use so that calibration at frequent intervals is desirable.

Conditioning.   Nearly all ion-specific electrodes seem to provide best results when proper conditioning is employed. If a glass electrode is to be used in aqueous media, it is important that it be soaked one or more hours prior to use in order to develop the hydrated surface layer necessary to ensure adequate response. Measurements made after such a soaking should show no more than a small drift over a period of hours.

Drift seems to be related to gradual structural changes in the surface layer. Thus, for a glass electrode it is in general good practice to keep the electrode tip in distilled water between measurements because of the stress associated with hydration. Other membrane types appear to benefit from standing in moderately dilute solutions of the primary ion.

24.4 THE POTENTIOMETER AND STANDARD CELL

Only if measurements are made at essentially zero current is it possible to determine equilibrium values of cell and electrode potentials. If current is drawn, two effects operate to give a measured emf lower than the equilibrium value. First, an IR drop across the internal resistance of electrodes and solution will oppose the cell emf and cause a low reading. Second, polarization of the electrodes results as current is drawn (Section 23.2) and a low value is observed. It is evident that both effects become more marked with increasing current.

At least two types of voltmeters can measure voltage while drawing minimal current. They differ in magnitude of current required for a response and for that reason tend to be used with different classes of cells. One, the familiar potentiometer, is well known as a comparison or null instrument. As long as the total resistance of a cell is no more than 20 kΩ, the potentiometer can measure its potential difference with high sensitivity and very good accuracy (± 0.01 mV). It proves satisfactory for measurement of the potential of all aqueous cells except those with glass or other membrane electrodes. For a treatment of the potentiometer the reader is referred to the extensive analysis of Section 3.2. The long period of use of this device has given the label "potentiometric" to all methods requring a determination of emf.

When the total resistance of a cell is greater than 20 kΩ, e.g. as would be true for a cell employing an ion-selective electrode or nonaqueous solvent, a pH or ion meter should be used instead. This second type of meter has a very high input impedance and will be discussed in the next section.

Weston standard cell. Nearly all precise measurements of emf are comparisons between an unknown voltage and a reference voltage supplied by a primary standard, the saturated Weston cell. The cell combines two reference electrodes. One, a 12.5% cadmium amalgam, is in contact with crystals of cadmium sulfate and a saturated cadmium sulfate solution; the other is mercury overlaid with a layer of mercurous sulfate, which in turn is in contact with the same saturated cadmium sulfate solution.

An unsaturated version of the Weston cell is also widely employed as a practical secondary standard. It is saturated at 4 °C with no excess salt present, and thus is unsaturated when warmed to room temperature. This cell has a temperature coefficient of emf which is negligible for most purposes (only 10 μV deg^{-1}).

Both kinds of Weston cell are highly reproducible. For best results, the current withdrawn from these cells or any other standard should never amount to more than a small fraction of a milliampere. If the cell is subjected to strenuous service, a few days should be allowed for restoration of the stated voltage. In practice, the emf should be checked yearly.

24.5 pH AND ION METERS

By usage, the term *pH meter* defines a class of voltmeters that is used to measure the potential of very-high-resistance galvanic cells.* In most cases the unusual resistance is attributable to the pH indicator electrode alone. As a variety of additional ion-selective electrodes of high resistance have appeared the designation pH has persisted, though the name pION or ion meter would be more appropriate. The terms pH meter and ion meter will be used interchangeably in this discussion.

There are two basic types of pH meter, potentiometric and direct-reading. The first is essentially a potentiometer with a dc amplifier added to decrease the current required to find the point of balance. It is accurate (a long slidewire can be used) but since it must be balanced at each reading it is inherently slow. Two such instruments are considered in the following examples.

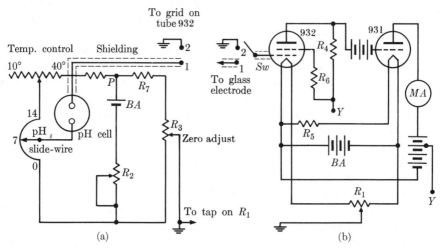

Fig. 24.7 Simplified circuit diagram of a potentiometric pH meter, the Beckman Model G pH meter. (a) Potentiometer circuit as connected for pH measurements. (b) Electron tube circuit for detecting potentiometer unbalance. (Courtesy of Beckman Instruments, Inc.)

Since the input signal is always adjusted to return to the original output, nonlinearity in the amplifier used with a potentiometer is of little consequence. In this arrangement, the amplifier and milliammeter serve only as a null detector. Stability of amplification is vital, however; we achieve it by use of stable components and operation of a circuit at levels of current and voltage well below those allowable. When standardized carefully, a potentiometric pH meter can have an accuracy of about ± 0.01 pH units or ± 0.6 units in V. If a longer, high-precision slidewire is substituted for the regular one, the sensitivity and reproducibility can be extended to ± 0.0025 pH or ± 0.1 mV. In

---

* The classic potentiometer cited in the previous section is not regarded as a pH meter, even though it may occasionally be used for pH measurements, e.g., with a hydrogen or a quinhydrone electrode.

such an instrument the slidewire scale is also graduated in millivolts and the instrument can be calibrated in that mode and so used, if desired. A millivolt readout is
usually preferred for measurement of ions other than H^+.

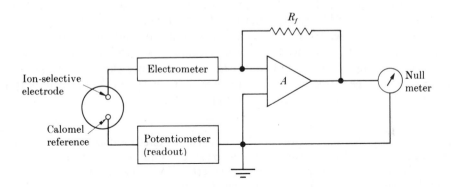

Fig. 24.8 Block diagram of potentiometric type of pH or ion meter that is based on an operational
amplifier of modest $(10^{-8} A)$ input current. An electrometer (a noninverting, unity-gain, high-
input-impedance amplifier) whose input current is only $10^{-13} A$ precedes it. Note that the operational amplifier A serves only to determine the point of balance of the potentiometer. If a high-
input-resistance $(10^{12} \Omega)$ operational amplifier is available, the electrometer is unnecessary.

Example 1   Figure 24.7 shows a simplified version of the circuit of a representative potentiometric pH meter. Coupled to (a) a fairly conventional potentiometric circuit is (b) a two-stage dc
electron-tube amplifier. From the panel of the instrument, one can adjust R_1, R_2, the temperature
control, and the asymmetry or zero adjust control R_3. The milliammeter MA in the plate circuit of
the second stage of the amplifier replaces the galvanometer in a classic potentiometer and serves
as a visual balance indicator during measurement. The necessary steps in making a pH measurement are as follows:

1.   Throw switch Sw to position 2, disconnecting the potentiometer circuit and grounding the
grid of electrometer tube 932. Then vary R_1 until the plate current registered by meter MA has
reached its best operating value (arbitrarily labeled zero). At this point, the amplifier is operating
with optimum sensitivity.

2.   Calibrate the slidewire. Connect to a standard cell (not shown) and by turning a dial set the
temperature compensator to achieve the correct voltage drop per pH unit at the temperature of
measurement; now vary R_2 until MA again reads zero. The proper voltage drop now exists along
the pH slidewire.

3.   Immerse the glass and calomel electrodes in a buffer solution of known pH, set the pH slidewire
to that value, and move the R_3 zero adjust until meter MA once more registers zero. The pH scale
is now calibrated.

4.   When we desire the pH of an unknown solution, we maintain all the other settings and move
the slidewire wiper until MA gives a zero reading.

Example 2   Figure 24.8 shows a block diagram of a potentiometric pH meter employing an
operational amplifier. The potentiometer is connected to the low-impedance portion of the pH cell
where shielding to avoid stray currents is unnecessary. In this design the function of the potentiometer is to apply a voltage of sign opposite to that developed by the pH cell. The electrometer-

operational amplifier pair acts to amplify the unbalance current. When the cell potential is exactly offset by the potentiometer, the output of the amplifier shows the null point has been reached.

The second type of pH or pION meter is simply a high-input-impedance volt-meter that achieves stability by use of negative feedback. It uses an operational ampli-fier like the circuit of Fig. 24.8 but achieves both stability and automatic operation by incorporating the cell in the feedback loop. Accuracy is high and the instrument registers a wide range of pH or millivolt readings as rapidly as its ion-selective elec-trode responds. Indeed, precision of measurement is basically limited by the indicator electrode and the cell rather than by the meter.

Example   Figure 24.9 shows schematically the circuit of a direct-reading type of pH meter. Since the glass or other ion-selective electrode is connected to the inverting input of the high-input-impedance operational amplifier A, only a minute (10^{-12} A or smaller) cell current can flow. The amplifier output current can flow only through R_f and R_{temp}.

In this type of circuit we can secure greater accuracy by increasing amplifier gain and input impedance and using a higher-precision readout device. A taut-band moving-coil meter with a long scale (25 cm) makes a reproducibility of ± 0.005 pH unit possible. With a sufficiently stable amplifier, scale expansion is feasible and even a shorter-scale meter can give readings reproducible to ± 0.002 pH unit. A digital voltmeter readout offers equal precision.

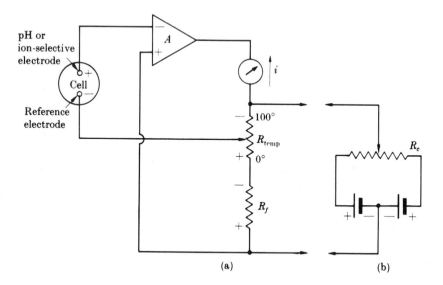

(a)   (b)

Fig. 24.9 Simplified schematic circuit diagram of Beckman Zeromatic SS-3 pH Meter.(a) Basic circuit. The MOSFET type of inputs of operational amplifier A insures a minimal input current. A pH or other ion-selective electrode is connected to the inverting input as shown. The amplifier supplies a current i sufficient to cause a voltage drop in the feedback resistor (R_f + the portion of R_{temp} tapped off) equal to E_{cell}. The variable part of feedback resistor R_{temp} is calibrated in °C to facilitate its adjustment. Detail (b) shows the circuit used to compensate for dc offsets of cell or electronics. The voltage from R_c is applied across R_f. (Courtesy of Beckman Instruments, Inc.)

Errors and calibration. In this section we will consider the calibration procedures that minimize errors peculiar to the pH or ion meter itself. It will be assumed that indicator electrodes of high quality are being used and that their response is not the limiting factor.

When such a meter is used specifically as a pH meter, temperature compensation is a prerequisite. Since the Nernst equation has a factor $2.303\,RT/nF$ as a coefficient of the log of the activity of the species of interest, a scale marked directly in pH units must be restandardized at each operating temperature. For example, the voltage per pH unit changes from 54.2 mV at 0 °C to 70.1 mV at 80 °C. Readings obtained directly in millivolts are not subject to this restandardization, of course.

In a potentiometric type of pH meter, another essential step is the standardization of current through the slidewire. Ordinarily, we accomplish this step by comparing the slidewire voltage drop with the potential of a reference such as a Weston cell or a Zener diode. Besides setting the slidewire current it is necessary to adjust the zero point on the potentiometer scale. We do this by surrounding the indicator and reference electrodes being used with a standard solution that will produce a known emf for the cell. Then the potentiometer zero point is adjusted (Section 3.2) until the meter reads the predicted emf (or pH). The process corresponds to the calibration of the scale. For example, in pH determinations we make the adjustment with a known pH buffer solution in the measuring cell. After calibration, readings on sample solutions are free of error arising from glass membrane strain (asymmetry potential), and when sample and buffer concentrations are similar, also that from junction potential.

In a direct-reading pH meter we need only to set the zero point by observing the response to a standard electrochemical cell. The usual provision of an amplifier gain control as well accommodates a variety of ion-selective electrodes, some of which may have a non-Nernstian response. Making a zero adjustment with a known solution in the measuring cell essentially establishes the intercept of the electrode response curve. Removal of that solution and filling with a second known solution that gives a higher emf reading provides an opportunity to adjust the amplifier gain to the output expected and set the slope of the response curve. This way, an ion meter can be used to register emfs that relate to ion activities even with an ion-selective electrode whose response is linear but non-Nernstian.

24.6 POTENTIOMETRIC TITRATORS

Potentiometric titrations can follow a variety of instrumental procedures. We can add a titrant from a syringe the plunger of which is motor-driven, from a buret, or from a reservoir by pumping. In the first case we know the equivalent volume of titrant from the position of the lead screw at beginning and end of the titration. In the third method, both rate and duration of pumping must be known. Since the degree of involvement of an operator in a titration is a useful basis for classifying instrumentation, we will use it in this discussion of titrators.

Manual titrimeters. We can obtain potentiometric titration curves manually using either a potentiometer (for a cell of resistance less than 20 kΩ) or a pH meter and noting the equilibrium emf after each addition of titrant. In addition, instruments specifically termed *titrimeters* are available. The expense of the manual titrimeter is well justified where certain types of titrations are performed frequently. All these incorporate electronic amplification and can be used with all kinds of electrode and most solvent systems. Usually, burets and a titration vessel are part of the equipment. In these devices there is either a direct-reading meter or a "magic eye" indicator tube so that the end point may be easily detected. The arrangement offers a distinct advantage in replicate titrations. Once the emf at the end point of this type of titration has been measured in a preliminary determination, all later determinations are carried out by titration to the predetermined voltage.* Figure 24.10 shows the general nature of the relationship between cell emf change and the end point.

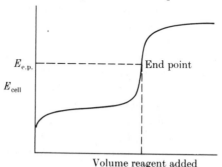

Volume reagent added

Fig. 24.10 Preliminary titration curve used to establish a potentiometric end point. Titrations can subsequently be carried out by titrating until $E_{cell} = E_{e.p.}$, as long as the system and conditions remain constant.

Automatic titrators. The addition of titrant and the detection of a potentiometric end point may be carried out automatically with some additional instrumentation. Two different approaches have been suggested, (a) precise recording of the titration curve at least through the end-point region, and (b) termination of the flow of titrant when the end point is detected. In the former, the operator determines the equivalence point from the curve. In the latter, the operator reads only the initial and final buret volumes, and no curve is recorded. These types may be generalized to give the schematic of an automatic titrator drawn in Fig. 24.11.

Before considering the differences in instruments in any detail, note that they all require nearly the same titration cell arrangement. The titrant is delivered from a carefully positioned capillary tube of very fine bore whose tip is beneath the surface of the solution in the cell and precisely directed. In the first two types of titrimeters listed in Table 24.3, the tube points toward the indicator electrode, in the third, toward the shaft of the stirrer. By virtue of these provisions, volume increments as small as 0.005 ml can be added. Where the tip is directed toward the indicator electrode, the cell overresponds to the freshly added titrant until the reagent can be properly mixed with all the solution. Since the overresponse will be greatest whenever the rate of change of emf with titrant is high, unbalance or end-point anticipation can be provided as discussed below. Moderate flow rates (1 to 5 ml min^{-1}) are used in automatic titration and stirring is very rapid.

---

* If an instrument with a "magic eye" is used, the "eye" can be set to open widest or just close at the end-point voltage.

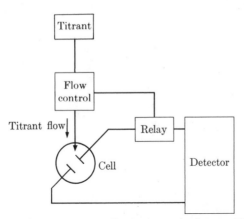

Fig. 24.11 Schematic diagram of a generalized automatic titrator. The basic components and mode of operation used by several varieties of titrators are described in Table 24.3.

In a *curve-recording titrator*, an automatic feed of titrant from a screw-driven syringe seems to work best, since flow must be coordinated with the chart drive of the recording potentiometer. If the self-balancing potentiometer instantaneously lags behind the cell emf by more than a preset amount (5 mV or less), a relay (see Fig. 24.11) is actuated to shut off the titrant. When the potentiometer is again in balance with the cell émf, further titrant is admitted. It is easily possible to obtain titration curves precise to ± 2 mV and ± 0.02 ml or better. An instrument of this type is well adapted both to research on new methods and to routine analyses. It should be noted that only relatively fast reactions can be used as a basis for titrations with this type of titrator.

With an *end-point anticipating titrator*, flow of titrant is cut off when a preset emf is attained during the titration. Adequate anticipation of the end point is achieved by arranging the delivery of titrant for momentary overresponse of the cell as suggested above. Whenever the preset voltage is reached or surpassed, the relay-actuated solenoid valve stops the flow. As further mixing occurs, the cell attains equilibrium, and if the end-point emf has not been reached, more titrant is added. Commerical instruments of this type are well adapted to routine determinations. Fairly slow chemical reactions, as well as fast ones, may be used as a basis for titration with this type of instrument.

With a *second-derivative titrator*, an end point is located automatically by making use of the second derivative of the emf with respect to the volume added. Since the equivalence point ordinarily corresponds to a point of inflection in the titration curve, the first derivative of the emf, dE/dv, will show a maximum there. For the same reason, the second derivative d^2E/dv^2 will be zero at the end point.

Of the three quantities mentioned, only the second derivative behaves in such a way that it can be anticipated without prior information about the system. As the graph in Fig. 24.14 shows, as a variable goes through an inflection point, the second derivative of that variable first goes through a sharp maximum, drops to zero at the inflection point, and then passes through a distinct minimum. If the variable is voltage, as in this case, the differentiation may be carried out electrically with a simple circuit. The sudden drop in voltage as the second derivative falls through zero can easily be

Table 24.3 Components of Three Automatic Titrators

Type	Titrant Supplied From	Flow	Detector	Relay-Actuating Signal	Flow Control*
Curve-recording	Motor-driven syringe	Intermittent near end point	Recording potentiometer	Emf unbalance between cell and potentiometer	Motor driving plunger in syringe
End-point cutoff					
(a) With anticipation	Buret with rubber section	Intermittent near end point and terminated at end point	Self-balancing potentiometer	Emf from cell in excess of preset potentiometer value	Solenoid actuating a clamp
(b) Without anticipation (second-derivative type)	Buret with rubber section	Constant until terminated at end point	Circuit taking second derivative of emf, d^2E/dv^2	Second-derivative pulse	Solenoid actuating a clamp

* See Fig. 24.11.

used to trigger an electronic circuit, which can in turn actuate a solenoid valve on a buret to stop the flow of titrant.

The second-derivative titrator offers the advantages that the titration curve need not be known and that the electrodes need not necessarily give their theoretical response. On the other hand, the titrator responds only when the magnitude of the emf change at the end point is several times the noise level in the system. The noise level tends to rise with the resistance of the cell. For these reasons, second-derivative titrimetry is well suited to titrations in aqueous systems except those involving concentrations below 10^{-3} N and reactions that are only moderately complete (e.g., the titration of a weak acid by a weak base). Slow electrode response, slow reaction, or the small voltage change at the end point precludes many nonaqueous titrations. Almost instantaneous mixing and fast electrode response are essential, since the titrant flow (1 to 5 ml min^{-1}) is not moderated near the end point. Note that we can use a Pt–10% Rh indicator electrode rather than a glass electrode in this type of device for H$^+$ ion detection, to avoid a high-impedance input stage.

Potentiostat. Where a chemical species such as a H$^+$ ion is produced during the course of a slow reaction that is of interest in its own right we employ another type of automatic titrator. In this case titrant is added only as needed to maintain a constant potential of an indicator electrode. If H$^+$ is titrated, the instrument is termed a *pH-stat*.

Example We can study the kinetics of many enzymatic hydrolyses by measuring the hydrogen ion released during reaction. If NaOH titrant is added in sufficient quantity to maintain the pH constant, we know the extent of reaction. Further, carrying the reaction out at constant pH duplicates the buffered condition under which such a change occurs in a physiological system.

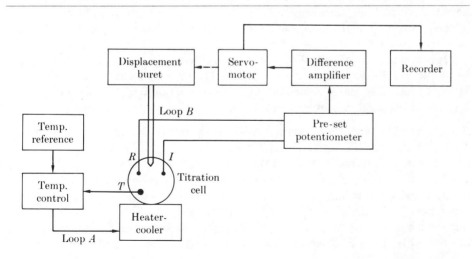

Fig. 24.12 Block diagram of the Sargent Thermostatic Recording pH Stat. Symbol R identifies the reference electrode, I the indicator electrode, and T the temperature sensing device. There are two control loops, A to maintain constant temperature in the titration cell and B to maintain constant pH in the cell by controlled addition of reagent from the buret. The recorder traces a curve of rate of addition of reagent with time. (Courtesy of Sargent-Welch Scientific Co.)

Recording potentiostatic devices that utilize a servo system to control the addition of titrant from a motor-driven displacement buret (syringe) can perform the type of titration described. Figure 24.12 shows a schematic diagram of a pH-stat. When we substitute other ion-selective indicator electrodes the device can determine other species on a constant pION basis.

24.7 PROCEDURE FOR pH MEASUREMENTS

In aqueous solution direct potentiometry determines the hydrogen ion routinely, using a glass electrode-saturated calomel electrode pair and a pH meter. The technique is nondestructive and has the further advantage of very wide concentration range, e.g. 14 pH units in aqueous media at 25 °C, simplicity, and reasonable speed (2 to 30 s response time). Though the precision of most measurements is only moderate, it is adequate for a trace method.

Example Precision may be illustrated by translating pH specifications into activity or concentration units. Measurements reliable to ± 0.1 pH such as might be made with an inexpensive meter yield a H^+ ion concentration accurate to about $\pm 20\%$; those reliable to ± 0.01 pH, concentrations to $\pm 2.5\%$. Under circumstances where conditions are precisely controlled and a very sensitive pH meter is used, accuracies of the order of ± 0.001 pH unit (concentration to $\pm 0.2\%$) become possible.

Electrodes. The common indicator electrode for the H^+ ion is the glass electrode (Section 24.3), although the hydrogen, quinhydrone, antimony, and other electrodes are also used in certain applications. [5]* Sensitivity of a glass electrode to alkali cations, especially Na^+, may reduce its response below the theoretical at pH values above 10; correction charts are available for each glass composition. Electrodes with little Na^+ error up to pH 13 are available. Similarly, in solutions of pH less than 1, low water activities will give rise to error.

It is also important to realize that there is at least one liquid junction in the cell when the usual reference electrode (SCE) is used. This reference incorporates a saturated KCl salt bridge, which establishes the junction with the sample solution. This junction potential is usually unknown, though it may be estimated. [5]

Operational definition of pH. In the case of pH the formal definition $pH = -\log a_{H^+}$ does not lead to a well-prescribed experimental measurement. Two factors are mainly responsible: It is especially difficult to interpret data from a cell with a liquid junction, and, further, it is not possible to obtain from thermodynamics a rigorous definition of the activity coefficient of a single species. We can surmount these difficulties experimentally by devising an appropriate convention. [5] This permits us to assign internally consistent pH values to a number of easily reproducible buffers; then we can relate pH values of other solutions operationally to these standards.

---

* When a pH electrode other than glass is used, an additional requirement is that the oxidizing ability of solutions be about equal to that of the pH buffer used for standardization; otherwise cell emf may depend partly on ions other than the hydrogen ion. The glass electrode is fortunately free of such errors in the range of pH from 1 to 10.

Accordingly, after standardizing the scale of a pH meter with a buffer solution, the pH of any other solution is given by the operational definition

$$pH = pH(B) + \frac{(E - E_B)F}{2.3026RT}. \tag{24.7}$$

Here $pH(B)$ and E_B are the pH and cell emf, respectively, with buffer solution in the cell and pH and E are the values with the sample present.

An important additional advantage of the operational approach is that it provides a basis for circumventing day-to-day instrument and electrode drift, most junction potential error, and changes in E^0 from glass electrode to electrode. Standardizing cell and pH meter compensates these variations.

To what extent does Eq. (24.7) allow us to ignore differences in concentration, constituents, temperature, etc., which might exist between buffer and sample solutions? Also, to what degree does this definition solve the problem of the unknown liquid junction potential? The answers lie in two important assumptions made whenever Eq. (24.7) is used.

First, we assume the liquid junction potential in sample solutions is identical with that in the standardizing buffer. Should this not be true, the pH reading for the sample solution will include the difference between its liquid junction potential and that of the buffer. Fortunately, the use of a saturated KCl bridge minimizes junction potentials, but the greater the difference in ionic strength or pH between sample and buffer, the larger the error, nevertheless. For that reason, buffers of high ionic strength are preferable whenever pH values are to be determined in concentrated solutions, and buffers should if possible be within 2 pH units of a sample.

Second, we assume the buffer and unknown solutions are at the same temperature.* For work at room temperature, this requirement seldom presents any problem; at other temperatures thermostating of all solutions is necessary.

Buffers. Many standard buffers of known composition and defined pH are available commercially or may be prepared easily in the laboratory. Table 24.4 includes five supplied by the National Bureau of Standards.

Procedure. Measurements are rapid if the electrodes have been conditioned in distilled water. Following a calibration of the meter and cell against a buffer solution, we dip the electrodes into the sample, and then balance and read the meter. About 10 ml of sample is adequate in most cases, and with microelectrodes amounts as small as one drop can be used.

Standard pH scale in other media. We can extend the operational definition of pH to media other than water. In a nonaqueous solvent, heavy water, or even a mixed solvent, Eq. (24.7) becomes

$$pH^*(x) = pH^*(B) + \frac{(E_x - E_B)F}{2.3026RT}, \tag{24.8}$$

---

* Strictly speaking, there is little connection between pHs at different temperatures. By definition, the standard potential of the hydrogen electrode is zero at all temperatures. The consequence is that a new pH scale is established at each temperature.

Table 24.4 (a) NBS Primary Standards of pH*

Buffer Solution	pH at 25 °C
Satd. KH tartrate	3.557
0.05 M KH phthalate	4.008
0.025 M KH_2PO_4, 0.025 M Na_2HPO_4 (mixture)	6.865
0.008695 M KH_2PO_4, 0.03043 M Na_2HPO_4	7.413
0.01 M borax	9.180

(b) Secondary and Supplementary Standards†

0.05 M $KH_3(C_2O_4)_2 \cdot H_2O$	1.679
Satd. $Ca(OH)_2$	12.454

* Known pH values are given rather than emfs, since most pH meters are calibrated to read in pH units. In addition, for the user the quotation of a pH value avoids the necessity of his knowing the calomel electrode potential exactly. The advantage results from the fact that the saturated calomel electrode is not readily reproducible in emf. For values at other temperatures see Bates. [5]

† These standards may be used with care outside the intermediate pH range (see [5]).

where the asterisk identifies the pH scale as applying only in the particular medium. Thus, pH*(x) and E_x are values of pH and potential for a sample solution in the medium, and pH*(B) and E_B are values of pH and potential for a pH buffer in the medium. No attempt is made to refer the pH* scale back to water. [5] Scales of this kind that apply uniquely to a given medium have already been devised for alcoholic media and heavy water [16] and seem certain to be extended to other solvents.

24.8 DIRECT POTENTIOMETRY OF IONS

The increasing availability of ion-selective electrodes makes the direct potentiometric measurement of many ions feasible. Any ion M^{n+} for which an indicator electrode is available can be determined at values of pM ($-\log a_{M^{n+}}$) from unity up to the value of pM for the electrode in pure solvent. Since most such electrodes are of the membrane or solid-state type, they have high resistance. Accordingly, a pH or ion meter is the appropriate device for determination of cell potential.

Are activity coefficient problems serious in direct potentiometry? Must we make allowance for the effect of interfering ions on the response of an ion-selective electrode? While the answer to both questions is yes, activity coefficient corrections can usually be estimated (Section 24.1). For univalent ions they are moderate, but they increase with ionic charge. For example, for divalent ions like Cu^{2+} and Ca^{2+}, $\gamma \simeq 0.5$ at 0.1 M ionic strength and approaches unity only at about 10^{-3} to 10^{-4} M. In any event, corrections are usually small for univalent ions below 0.01 M and for divalent ions below 5×10^{-4} M. When activity coefficients are available, we can calculate concentrations from activities.

Interfering ions pose a more complex calculation in direct potentiometry (Section 24.3). For this reason it often proves simplest to prepare empirical calibration curves for a system. We may then secure useful analytical results whenever concentrations of interfering and other ions in an unknown approximate these in the standards. Standard addition methods have also proved a successful way to minimize interferences. Figure 24.13 gives an example of calibration curves for measurement of F^- ion by this type of procedure.

Finally and importantly, direct potentiometry is a valuable procedure for determining activities of ions. For example, equilibrium studies of all kinds and most research investigations require such data.

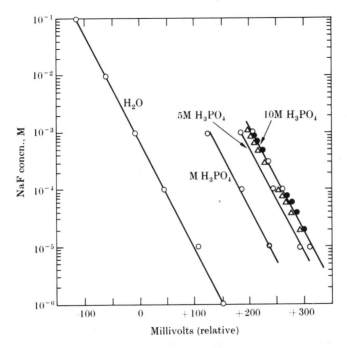

Fig. 24.13 Response of fluoride-selective electrode to sodium fluoride in water and in phosphoric acid. Symbols: ○ no added salts; ●0.015 M Al^{3+}; △0.015 M UO_2^{2+} or Th^{4+}. (E. W. Baumann, *Anal. Chim. Acta.* **42**, 127 (1968); Courtesy of *Anal. Chim. Acta.*)

24.9 POTENTIOMETRIC END POINTS

Potentiometry is used widely as an end-point method. In the concentration range down to 10^{-2} M a potentiometric titration is one of the common precise instrumental techniques for analysis of inorganic samples. Some organic samples are also so analyzable. The reasons are not hard to find. Virtually any "complete" reaction can be followed potentiometrically whether it is a redox change, precipitation, complexation, or acid–base type of reaction. We need only find an indicator electrode that responds to the species of interest, the titrant, or the product. With the availability of increasing numbers of ion-selective electrodes, preparations for titrations should become simpler. Interferences will be less of a problem.

Potentiometric titration also enjoys the advantage that any technique based on observation of a chemical reaction does. It is often possible to alter conditions (solvent, temperature) to increase the completeness or speed of reaction. In short, in potentiometric titration there is a great flexibility in approach to the quantitative determination of a species.*

The precision of a potentiometric titration is closely related to the rate of change of potential of the indicator electrode at the end point. Absolute emf's are unnecessary and while the response of an electrode must be consistent, it need not be precisely reproducible in most cases. The curve of potential vs. titrant volume should have a steep slope in the end-point region to ensure high precision. Note that the logarithmic relation between activity and electrode potential no longer affects the determination. Now, a change in cell emf simply signals the end point; we then calculate a concentration from titration date and not from the emf measurement.

Example   The data below illustrate the variation in cell emf in the end-point regions of two representative titrations in which there are sharp breaks and the end point is established with precision. For each the indicator emf is shown as a function of the fraction f that has been titrated.

A. Titration of 0.01 M HCl with 0.1 M NaOH* B.Titration of 0.01 M $AgNO_3$† with 0.1 M HCl‡

f	pH	E_{ind}, V vs. NHE	f	Ag^+ (M)	E_{ind}, V vs. NHE
0.97	3.52	-0.208	0.97	3×10^{-4}	0.610
0.98	3.70	-0.218	0.98	2×10^{-4}	0.58
0.99	4	-0.236	0.99	1×10^{-4}	0.563
0.999	5	-0.295	0.999	1.6×10^{-5}	0.516
1.00	7	-0.413	1.00	1×10^{-5}	0.504
1.001	9	-0.531	1.001	6.4×10^{-6}	0.492
1.01	10	-0.591	1.01		0.445
1.02	10.30	-0.607	1.02		0.427
1.03	10.48	-0.618	1.03		0.416

* Glass electrode used as indicator electrode.

† Assuming K_{sp} for AgCl $= 10^{-10}$. Values of Ag^+ concentration not calculated for cases in which HCl is in excess and AgCl has become more soluble.

‡ Silver electrode used as indicator electrode.

Sample calculations.   One point on each curve is calculated. Since the titrant is ten times more concentrated than the sample, the change in volume of the solution can be neglected to a first approximation.

Titration A.   For the calculation, assume that 100 ml of 0.01 M HCl is used. At 97 % neutralization of this strong acid, the concentration of acid remaining is 0.03×0.01 M $= 3 \times 10^{-4}$ M. The pH is 3.52 and 9.70 ml of the 0.1 M NaOH has been added. Note that it is possible to neglect the H^+ ion contributed by the ionization of water in this region. The emf of the indicator electrode can then be calculated from Eq. (24.7).

---

* Nearly all titrations can also be followed spectrophotometrically (either without or with an indicator) and amperometrically, some conductometrically. To decide the approach best suited to a given determination, each possibility should be assessed.

Titration B. Assume 100 ml of 0.01 M $AgNO_3$ is used. When 99.9 % of the HCl needed has been added, the concentration of unreacted silver ion is $0.001 \times 0.01 \text{ M} = 1 \times 10^{-5} \text{ M}$. The total concentration of Ag^+ ion is $(1 \times 10^{-5} + x)$ M, where $(1 \times 10^{-5} + x)(x) = K_{sp} = 10^{-10}$. Since $x = 0.6 \times 10^{-5}$ M, $Ag^+ = 1.6 \times 10^{-5}$ M, pAg = 4.80, and the voltage of the silver electrode is $E = E^0 + 0.0591 \log [Ag^+] = 0.799 - 0.283 = 0.516 \text{ V}$ vs. NHE.

Determination of end point. During a potentiometric titration we observe E_{cell} as a function of volume v of titrant added, taking the end point of the reaction to be the point of inflection in the E_{cell} vs. v relation, i.e. the point of steepest slope.

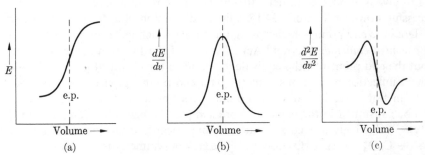

Fig. 24.14 E_{cell} vs. volume of titrant added for the end-point portion of a representative potentiometric titration. (a) Direct plot. (b) First derivative plot. (c) Second derivative plot.

Figure 24.14 shows graphical procedures for identifying this value. If there is a distinct break in a titration curve, it is easy to establish the end point by inspection. For example, in the titration of a strong acid by a strong base (see curve (b) in Fig. 24.15), we can locate the end point visually with a precision of 1 % or better. The majority of titrations yield curves more like that in Fig. 24.14a, however, where the "break" is a long region of moderate slope.

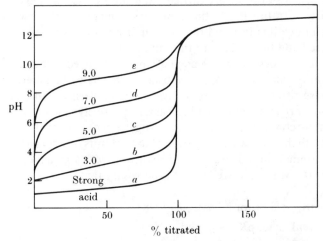

Fig. 24.15 Titration curves of 0.1 M monoprotic acids with 0.1 M NaOH. The pK_a of the acid is indicated on each curve.

Even in these cases, it is easy to locate the inflection point by graphing the first derivative dE/dv vs. v as in Fig. 24.14b. Since the derivative is just the slope of the curve, the maximum corresponds to the point of inflection. We can prepare the graph manually, in which case $\Delta E/\Delta v$ is calculated for several points on either side of the estimated end point and plotted, or automatically, by electronic differentiation of cell emf during the titration (Section 7.5) and recording.

It is possible to locate the end point still more precisely by obtaining the second derivative d^2E/dv^2 and graphing it vs. v as in Fig. 24.14c. Since the rate of change of slope at a point of inflection is zero its value falls to zero at the end point. Usually, since it is tedious to take points sufficiently close for a good calculation, manual procedure fails to give a good second derivative curve. Electronic differentiation is eminently successful, however. Exercise 24.15 calls for discussion of a differentiating circuit.

Does the end point, which was mathematically defined, ever fail to coincide with the *chemical equivalence* point? Actually, only if the titration curve is symmetrical about the end point will the equivalence point of the chemical reaction be identical with the inflection point. For symmetry in the end-point region, the indicator electrode must function reversibly and equal numbers of "molecules" of reactant and titrant must be consumed in the reaction. For example, the neutralization reaction $HCl + NH_3 \rightarrow NH_4Cl$ gives a curve that is symmetrical and the precipitation reaction $2Ag^+ + CrO_4^{2-} \rightarrow Ag_2CrO_4$ does not. The lack of symmetry is seldom serious; agreement between equivalence and inflection points is about 0.01 % for any quite complete reaction. Even if a reaction is only moderately complete, agreement will probably be 0.1 %. Usually this source of error is unimportant, but it may be allowed for if necessary (Section 24.12).

24.10 ACID–BASE TITRATIONS

This section is the first of four devoted to different types of titrations. Most potentiometric titrations of acids or bases are carried out using a glass-calomel electrode pair. If we are running the titration for the first time, we should obtain the whole curve to be sure that no useful detail is lost and that all important variables are under control. Otherwise, we need add titrant only to the end point.

What limits, if any, does the requirement of a precisely detectable end point impose on the concentration and strength of a substance that is to be determined? In an aqueous acid–base titration a precise analysis is possible if (a) an acid or base is appreciably stronger than water (as acid or base, respectively) and (b) the acid or base is substantially more concentrated than the hydrogen ion or (essentially) hydroxyl ions from the water. With these criteria, approximate lower limits on acid and base strength for a reliable determination can be given. To be titrable with adequate precision when 0.1 M titrant and 0.1 M sample are used, it is necessary that:

1. For an acid, $pK_a < 8$ or for a base, $pK_b < 8$;
2. For a salt of weak acid, $pK_a > 4$, and
3. To distinguish a strong and a weak acid or a strong and a weak base $pK_{strong}/pK_{weak} > 10^3$.

In Fig. 24.14 the basis for these limits* is made quite clear.

Example As may be seen from a comparison of curves (c) and (d) in Fig. 24.15 the titration of acetic acid ($pK_a = 4.76$) should yield a much sharper end point than the titration of H_2S ($pK_{a1} = 7.00$) to its first end point. A weak acid reacts incompletely with a strong base, and some unneutralized base is present at the equivalence point. As a result, the pH at this point is greater than 7, and the characteristic end-point region is short.

    If we titrate a very weak acid, e.g. boric acid ($pK_a = 9.23$), we obtain a curve like (e) in Fig. 24.14. There is enough unreacted base at the end point to make the pH nearly that of the strong base titrant. The end point cannot be located with any reliability.

Polyprotic acids (e.g., H_3PO_4 or H_2CO_3) or mixtures of a strong and a weak acid or a strong and a weak base may be titrated if the end-point regions are clearly distinguishable. A quantitative criterion was suggested above. The existence of multiple end points for a polyprotic acid make its determination more flexible, a fact that may often be used to advantage in analyzing mixtures of acids. Thus, malonic acid ($pK_1 = 2.85$ and $pK_2 = 5.66$) may just be potentiometrically titrated in the presence of benzoic acid ($pK_a = 4.20$) by titration to the first end point.

    Clearly, atmospheric CO_2 should be excluded from a basic sample before and during titration. If a strong acid is being titrated, CO_2 does not interfere, since the end point for the strong acid can be distinguished from that of the carbonic acid. On the other hand, CO_2 should be excluded from a weak acid or polyprotic acid sample.

Procedure. The rate of addition of titrant must allow adequate time for mixing and response. Thus, an appropriate rate depends strongly on such factors as the speed of stirring, solution volume, location of the indicator electrode, and nature of the liquid junction. For example, if we use a power stirrer, as in an automatic titrator, the cell emf is erratic unless a reproducible liquid junction is established during the stirring.

    Perhaps a 30 s delay before reading the cell emf is adequate for most manual titrations. A reasonable rule is to wait until the pH reading does not change more than 0.02 pH units per minute.

    It should also be noted that some systems react slowly to the acid or base. Slurries of any kind and some very weak acids fall in this category. In a new system, the rate of response should always be checked.

Qualitative analysis. It is possible to deduce visually from a titration curve the approximate strength of an acid or base. Ordinarily, the pH value at half-neutralization is used, since in aqueous solution it gives the apparent pK_a of a monoprotic acid directly.† Thus, in curve (b) in Fig. 24.15 the half-neutralization pH observed is about 3. For a "monoacidic" base the pOH value at half-neutralization equals pK_b.

---

* If sample concentrations fall below 0.1 M, the first limit is subject to revision in the direction of smaller pK values, and the second to larger pK_a values.

†To obtain the thermodynamic value of pK_a, a correction for activity effects would be needed. Most acid and base dissociation constants are determined potentiometrically.

Such information is particularly helpful in characterizing organic compounds with acidic or basic properties, for it furnishes an index as to which of several kinds of groups is present. For example, information about acid strength would allow sulfonic acid $(pK_a \sim 3)$, carboxyl $(pK_a \sim 5)$, and phenol $(pK_a \sim 10)$ groups to be distinguished. If a substance contains more than one type of acidic or basic group, each half-neutralization pH may be used to establish a rough value of dissociation constant.

24.11 PRECIPITATION AND COMPLEXATION TITRATIONS

Conditions that must be satisfied if an ion is to be determined quantitatively by a potentiometric precipitation or complexation titration are

1. The ion must readily form a salt of low solubility product ($K_{sp} < 10^{-8}$ for a binary compound) or a stable complex of high stability constant.
2. A reliable electrode must be found for one of the ions in the reaction.
3. The reaction must be relatively fast.

If these conditions hold, at the equivalence point the concentration of some reactant or soluble product changes very rapidly with volume of reagent added, and there is a distinct emf break.

Precipitation titrations.   Insoluble salts that meet the requirements given are unfortunately not numerous. They are mainly those containing silver and mercury and less often, copper, zinc, and a few other metals. Anions determined in this way include Cl^-, Br^-, I^-, CN^-, CNS^-, SO_4^{2-}, S^{2-}, and anions of some organic acids. Figure 24.16 graphs three titration curves representing the formation of salts of varying solubility.

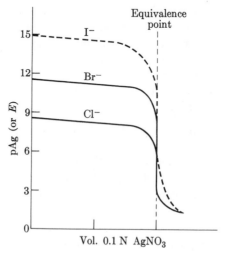

Fig. 24.16 Titration curves for the determination of I^-, Br^-, and Cl^- by titration with $AgNO_3$ solution. A silver indicator electrode is used. Absorption effects cause the "rounding off" of the I^- curve, which is represented by a broken line.

The indicator electrode may be the metal participating in the reaction, a noble metal, an ion-selective electrode, or an electrode of the second kind. For example, in the titration of iodide ion by $AgNO_3$, a silver wire or even a piece of silver-plated platinum may be used. Alternatively, a noble metal like platinum can often be used. (The potential on the platinum electrode would be determined by the iodine-iodide ion couple.) The reference electrode must, of course, be appropriate to the titration but is usually glass, calomel, or a metal electrode. Often a calomel electrode is satisfactory for a brief titration even though a small amount of chloride precipitate may form at the end of the salt bridge in the titration cell.

Example Chloride ion may be determined by titration with standard silver nitrate solution. Two silver wires may be used as the electrodes, one being immersed in the chloride solution, and the second placed in the silver nitrate titrant. Usually the second wire is inserted into the tip of the delivery buret without contact with the sample solution. The tip of the buret, of course, must be kept under the surface of the solution to complete the electrical path. The emf developed is that of a silver concentration cell. Alternatively, a calomel reference electrode can be used.

The occurrence of *coprecipitation, adsorption,* or even *simultaneous precipitation* may lead to uncertainty in the detection of the end point. The first process can result in a very slow attainment of equilibrium. In this case, we might easily appear to have reached the end point too soon. One measure often taken to reduce coprecipitation is to maintain the solution above room temperature. Naturally, this means is feasible only if the accompanying increase in solubility can be tolerated. The second factor, adsorption on the precipitate, we must consider separately for each precipitate, and we cannot eliminate it readily. Figure 24.16 shows its effect on a titration. Simultaneous precipitation, the third undesirable behavior, occurs also in that titration. Since some AgBr precipitates before all the AgI has come out of solution, the effect of simultaneous precipitation is to give a high end point for the I^- ion. A similar situation will exist for the Br^- ion. Where we cannot eliminate these three phenomena, it is often possible to estimate corrections to apply to the actual data by titration of knowns under identical conditions.

Conditions. Mechanical stirring is highly desirable, in order to hasten equilibration. It is advantageous to form the least soluble precipitate of an ion possible to secure a sharp end-point break. For example, titration of silver with iodide ion ($K_{AgI} \sim 10^{-16}$) is preferable to titration with chloride ($K_{AgCl} \sim 10^{-10}$). If only a moderately insoluble precipitate forms, close temperature control is necessary to ensure reproducibility and accuracy. Sometimes, of course, we may add ethanol or methanol and lower the solubility sufficiently to make regulation unnecessary. Indeed, it may be necessary to add nonaqueous solvents if the salt is to be insoluble enough for the titration to be run.

If the titration involves the anion of a weak acid, such as oxalate, pH control is also necessary; otherwise the concentration of the anion varies with acidity, and the solubility is affected. Commonly a noninterfering buffer is added.

Complexation titrations. The avenue to the potentiometric determination of a number of metals has been opened by the possibility of titration using their reaction with polydentate complexing reagents, i.e. chelating agents.* The best known of these is ethylenediaminetetraacetic acid (EDTA) which is used in a partially neutralized form. A typical complexation reaction is of the form

$$M^{2+} + H_2Y^{2-} = MY^{2-} + 2H^+$$

where H_2Y^{2-} represents the anion of the disodium salt of EDTA. Note that a single, well-defined complex is shown as being formed. Stability constants are high except for the alkali metals and a few other metals.

In this type of titration, we can detect the end point with an electrode that is sensitive to the metal ion being complexed. A nonselective platinum-calomel pair has often been used. However, another metal such as mercury (II) that also complexes can sometimes be substituted. It is necessary that the equilibrium constants for the complexes of the two metals differ sufficiently.

Example   Mercury (II) is partially displaced from its EDTA complex by another metal ion M such as Zn^{2+} that is also present. Thus, zinc can be determined potentiometrically with a mercury indicator electrode using EDTA as titrant. As EDTA is added, "free" M^{2+} ions are complexed. At the end point mercury (II) is complexed and the potential jumps.

24.12   REDOX TITRATIONS

The potentiometric method is ideal for monitoring a redox reaction. In such a system, the best indicator electrode is a piece of metal sufficiently noble to be unaffected by the oxidizing agent. Platinum is widely used. Either a short length of wire or a small square is adequate. Noble metals give a somewhat faulty response when both a strong oxidizing agent and F^- ion or Cl^- ion are present in moderate to high concentration. Noble metals are no longer inert when their complex halide ions, e.g., $PtCl_6^{2-}$, may be formed. In redox titrations, we may use a calomel or glass electrode as a reference.

Titration curves.   The calculation of cell emf during a redox titration is simple because only the potential of the indicator electrode will vary. Accordingly, we need calculate only E_{ind}, as given by Eq. (24.1). Then E_{cell} can be found from Eq. (24.2). Consider the system in which reductant red_1 is titrated with oxidant ox_2. The reaction can be represented as

$$red_1 + ox_2 = ox_1 + red_2. \tag{24.9}$$

It is convenient to write the two half-reactions of the system as reductions

$$ox_1 + e = red_1$$

$$ox_2 + e = red_2.$$

When the indicator electrode is in equilibrium with the solution, its potential will be given at 25 °C by the equation

---

* Complexation reactions are probably more widely followed by use of colored indicators.

$$E_{\text{ind}} = E_1^0 + 0.0591 \log \frac{[\text{ox}_1]}{[\text{red}_1]} = E_2^0 + 0.0591 \log \frac{[\text{ox}_2]}{[\text{red}_2]}, \qquad (24.10)$$

where E_1^0 and E_2^0 are the two standard half-cell emfs and brackets denote activities. Note that Eq. (24.10) must follow since the indicator electrode is in equilibrium with both redox couples yet it can have only one potential. How does E_{ind} vary during a titration? Consider again the general reaction given in Eq. (24.9).

Prior to the equivalence point, $[\text{ox}_2] \simeq 0$ and only the redox system associated with the substance titrated, $\text{ox}_1 + e = \text{red}_1$ contributes. If f is the fraction of red_1 titrated,

$$E_{\text{ind}} = E_1^0 + 0.0591 \log f/(1-f) \qquad \text{(when } f < 1\text{).} \qquad (24.11)$$

At the equivalence point, activities of products of the titration will be equal: $[\text{ox}_1] = [\text{red}_2]$. It also follows that $[\text{red}_1] = [\text{ox}_2]$. The solution of Eq. (24.10) for this case proves especially interesting. From Eq. (24.10)

$$E_{\text{ind}} = E_1^0 + 0.0591 \log [\text{ox}_1]/[\text{red}_1]$$

and

$$E_{\text{ind}} = E_2^0 + 0.0591 \log [\text{ox}_2]/[\text{red}_2].$$

Adding the equations and substituting the equalities noted leads to the desired solution. One obtains

$$2E_{\text{ind}} = E_1^0 + E_2^0 + 0.0591 \log \frac{[\text{ox}_1][\text{ox}_2]}{[\text{red}_1][\text{red}_2]}$$

$$= E_1^0 + E_2^0 + 0.0591 \log [1] = E_1^0 + E_2^0$$

and

$$E_{\text{ind}} = (E_1^0 + E_2^0)/2 \qquad \text{(when } f = 1\text{).} \qquad (24.12)$$

In an unsymmetrical titration, Eq. (24.12) becomes

$$E_{\text{ind}} = (n_1 E_1^0 + n_2 E_2^0)/(n_1 + n_2),$$

where n_1 and n_2 are the number of moles of electrons involved in reactions for which the standard potentials are E_1^0 and E_2^0, respectively. It is left to the reader in exercise 24.15 to establish that this equation is valid.

Beyond the equivalence point, $[\text{red}_1] \simeq 0$ and E_{ind} is determined mainly by the second redox system, $\text{ox}_2 + e = \text{red}_2$. Now Eq. (24.10) becomes

$$E_{\text{ind}} = E_2^0 + 0.0591 \log (f-1)/1 \qquad \text{(when } f > 1\text{)} \qquad (24.13)$$

where f is again the fraction of red_1 titrated. In this range $f > 1$.

Formal potentials. Since the ionic strength of solutions in redox titrations is usually high, e.g. 1 M H_2SO_4 may be present, it is impossible to predict activity coefficients of species. A useful empirical approach that still permits calculations of E_{ind} to be made is the use of *formal potentials.* [1] Formal potentials are pseudo-standard electrode emfs measured under conditions close to those normally prevailing in titrations. Equation (24.1) becomes

$$E_{ind} = E^{0'} - 2.303 \frac{RT}{nF} \log \frac{C_{ox}}{C_{red}}, \tag{24.14}$$

where E^0 is the measured formal potential, i.e.,

$$E^{0'} = E^0 + \frac{2.303RT}{nF} \log \frac{\gamma_{ox}}{\gamma_{red}}.$$

Tables of formal potentials as a function of normality of acid are available for many redox systems. [1] As Eq. (24.14) makes clear, when formal potentials are substituted for standard potentials, concentrations may be used to calculate E_{ind}. The use of Eq. (24.14) is restricted to conditions close to those of measurement of a formal potential.

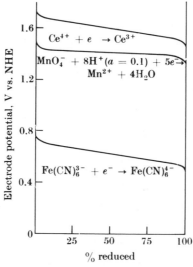

Fig. 24.17   Electrode potential changes during reduction of species shown. The slope of the flat central portion of each curve is determined by n, the number of electrons per mole of reactant involved in the reduction.

To ensure a good break in a titration curve, how strong must an oxidizing or reducing agent be in a given case? Consider the typical emf shift during a redox change. In Fig. 24.17 the variation of electrode potential with fraction reduced is shown for several species that are commonly employed as oxidizing agents. To determine the amount of such substances accurately (to $\pm 0.1\%$) at the conclusion of a reduction the potential must be as small as $E^0 - (2.303 \, RT/nF) \log 1000 = E^0 - 0.18/n$. For the oxidation of the titrant a similar result follows: The final potential must be as large as $E_0 + 0.18/n$. If this be so, how strong a reducing agent must we use as the titrant? The answer is straightforward. If $n = 1$ for both, the standard potentials of oxidant and reductant must differ by 0.36 V; if $n = 2$, by 0.18 V, etc.

Conditions. Most redox reactions are inherently slow because of the complexity of this type of chemical change. For example, the reduction of permanganate ions involves several consecutive reactions. As would be expected, the use of a catalyst and carrying out the titration at a higher temperature often speed up these reactions sufficiently so that they can be followed potentiometrically. Nearly always, we must also maintain the acidity of the solution within limits to avoid incomplete reactions. A particular redox change often occurs only within a restricted pH range. A buffer may be unnecessary; it may suffice to add excess acid or base. A buffer is essential, however, if one or more anions of weak acids are involved in the reaction.

In many instances air (or oxygen) must be excluded from a titration. If good precision is required (better than 1 %) or if very active reductants such as the chromous ion are used, the titrant and the titration vessel should be protected by an atmosphere of an inert gas. In addition, we must remove dissolved oxygen from the sample solution prior to titration by bubbling the inert gas through.

Example   Ferrous ion may be determined quantitatively by titration with permanganate ion in a solution strongly acidified with sulfuric acid (concentration of $H_3O^+ \sim 1$ M). During the titration, the iron is oxidized to the 3+ state, and the manganese reduced to the 2+ state:

$$5Fe^{2+} + 8H^+ + MnO_4^- = 5Fe^{2+} + Mn^{2+} + 4H_2O.$$

Although the reaction involves one permanganate ion for every five ferrous ions and is highly asymmetrical (Section 24.9), the rate of change of emf as titrant is added is so great that no appreciable error results if we take as the end point the point at which the slope has its maximum value.

24.13 ACID–BASE TITRATIONS IN NONAQUEOUS SYSTEMS

Although a great many organic substances possess acidic or basic character, they do so to so slight a degree that they cannot be titrated potentiometrically in water. Water fails as a medium for titrating a very weak acid because of its own weakly acidic character. It will compete with the weak acid of interest on titration with a base and thus diminish the sharpness of the end point. Clearly, substitution of a less acidic solvent like dimethylformamide or an inert one like acetone will correct this situation. Note that the degree of basic character of the nonaqueous solvent is of no consequence.

Just the opposite criterion applies in selection of a nonaqueous solvent suitable for potentiometric titration of a very weak base B: The solvent must be less basic than water. For example, acetic acid is commonly used. What is desired is that the reaction

$$B + H^+_{titrant} = BH^+$$

be essentially complete. In acetic acid completeness is more nearly assured than in water since the competing protonation of solvent SH

$$SH + H^+ = SH_2^+$$

is comparatively slight.

Titration curves obtained in nonaqueous media are similar in shape to those secured in water. The only important difference is that only emf data are available in nonaqueous media.*

Titrants are somewhat standardized. The acid or base used should be as strong as possible so that it will drive the neutralization essentially to completion. Thus, in the titration of weak bases, the very strong acid perchloric acid is preferable to HCl, HNO_3, or HBr. Similarly, the strongest bases are used for titrations of weak acids. These substances include materials such as sodium or potassium methoxide, tetra-butylammonium hydroxide, and sodium aminoethoxide, $NaOCH_2CH_2NH_2$. The titrant is ordinarily dissolved in the solvent to be used. Such reagents are more sensitive to contamination and may be less constant in titer because of high solvent vapor pressure.

Example   Vanillin, a substituted phenol of formula

is a somewhat stronger acid than phenol and may be titrated in ethylenediamine or dimethyl-formamide. A 0.1 M sodium aminoethoxide solution can be used as the titrant and is prepared by dissolving sodium in ethanolamine. Anhydrous solvent must be used. A double set of antimony electrodes can be used, one in the tip of the buret, the other in the solution; these are formed by casting high-grade metal into rods, using glass tubing as a mold. There is a drop of more than 150 mV in the end-point region. (A glass indicator electrode cannot be used with this titrant, apparently because it functions as an ion-selective electrode for sodium.)

Conditions.   In most titrations of weak bases, water can be tolerated in concentrations of up to 3 % of the weight of the original solvent. Greater concentrations lead to poor end points and inaccuracy. Alcohols also interfere because of their basic properties. However, only if the system is free of water is it possible to carry out most titrations of weak acids. The presence of water is the cause of most interferences with very weak acids and bases. Other substances should be checked for possible interference. As examples, (a) CO_2 is readily absorbed by basic solvents unless air is excluded, and (b) most inorganic cations interfere in titrations in acetic acid, since they release hydrogen ions as they form slightly dissociated acetates.

Electrodes.   In nonaqueous titrations in acidic media, the indicator electrode is commonly of glass. To function with any speed, however, its surface layers must be hydrated; presoaking it in water does this.† Minimal dehydration occurs during a regular nonaqueous titration. Electrode response may, however, be sluggish.

---

* A unique pH scale can be established for each solvent (Section 24.7), but there is no theoretical basis on which to relate such "pHs" to aqueous values. [16] One problem is that it is not known how to determine the liquid junction potential between solutions in different solvents.

†The presence of water precludes attaining an absolute value of potential in the medium. Absolute potentials, if needed for activity determinations, may be obtained with a dry-glass electrode providing sufficient time is allowed for equilibration.

Either a calomel electrode reference with an integral sleeve type of salt bridge or a silver-silver chloride reference electrode may be employed. If a regular commercial calomel electrode is used, it may require periodic soaking in water. Since KCl is not as soluble in most nonaqueous solvents as in water, it tends to precipitate from solution at the junction of salt bridge. These crystals will block ionic migration at the boundary unless periodically redissolved.

Unfortunately, the glass electrode does not operate with success in basic titration media. Instead, the hydrogen or antimony-antimonious oxide electrode has been used together with a calomel reference.

Bimetallic electrode systems, i.e. systems employing two identical metal electrodes, are also common. In this case one electrode is inserted in the titrant stream, and the tip of the other is placed in the bulk of the solution. Examples are "double" antimony and "double" platinum electrodes. [18] The analogous "sheltered" reference, in which one electrode of an identical pair is made a reference electrode by inserting it in a small, isolated part of the system being titrated, is used as well.

The measurement of cell emfs in these systems is more difficult because solution resistances tend to be large. As a result, it is essential to employ some type of pH meter (Section 24.5) or titrimeter that can cope with the high resistance. The reproducibility of electrode response tends to be poorer than in aqueous media, and it is generally desirable to obtain the end point from the titration curve rather than by titrating to a preset voltage.

Qualitative analysis. With some experience, it is possible to estimate approximate acid and base strengths from nonaqueous titration curves. The results are relative at best.

REFERENCES

General introductions to potentiometry are available in:

1. N. H. Furman, "Potentiometry", in *Treatise on Analytical Chemistry.* Vol. 4, pt I. I. M. Kolthoff and P. J. Elving, eds. New York: Interscience, 1963
2. I. M. Kolthoff and H. A. Laitinen, *pH and Electro Titrations.* 2d ed. New York: Wiley, 1941
3. J. J. Lingane, *Electroanalytical Chemistry.* 2d ed. New York: Interscience, 1958
4. C. Tanford and S. Wawzanek, "Potentiometry", in *Physical Methods of Organic Chemistry.* 3d ed., pt 4. A. Weissberger, ed. New York: Interscience, 1960

The theory, instrumentation and experimental procedure in determination of pH are set forth in detail in:

5. R. G. Bates, *Determination of pH; Theory and Practice.* New York: Wiley, 1964
6. G. Mattock, *pH Measurement and Titration.* New York: Macmillan, 1961

Glass and other ion-selective electrodes or reference electrodes are treated in:

7. R. A. Durst, ed., *Ion-Selective Electrodes.* Washington: U.S. Govt. Printing Off., 1969
8. George Eisenman, ed., *Glass Electrodes for Hydrogen and Other Cations.* New York: Dekker, 1967
9. D. J. G. Ives and G. J. Janz, eds., *Reference Electrodes—Theory and Practice.* New York: Academic, 1961
10. E. Pungor, "Theory and Application of Anion Selective Membrane Electrodes," *Anal. Chem.* **39** (13) 28A (1967)

The theoretical and phenomenonological aspects of pH and acid-base titrations are treated in:

11. Edward J. King, *Acid-Base Equilibria*. New York: Macmillan, 1965
12. I. M. Kolthoff and Stanley Bruckenstein, "Acid-Bases in Analytical Chemistry," a reprint from *Treatise on Analytical Chemistry*. Vol. I., pt 1. I. M. Kolthoff and P. J. Elving, eds. New York: Interscience, 1959
13. John E. Ricci, *Hydrogen Ion Concentration*. Princeton: Princeton University Press, 1952

A general introduction to titration in nonaqueous solvents is given in:

14. Walter Huber, *Titrations in Nonaqueous Solvents*. New York: Academic, 1967

Various aspects of potentiometric instrumentation are presented in:

15. S. Z. Lewin, "pH Meters," *J. Chem. Educ.* **36**, A595 (1959)

Other papers or chapters of interest that concern specialized aspects of potentiometry are:

16. R. G. Bates, "Standardization of Acidity Measurements," *Anal. Chem.* **40** (6) 28A (1968)
17. D. G. Davis, "Potentiometric Titrations," in *Comprehensive Analytical Chemistry*. Vol. IIA. C. L. Wilson and D. W. Wilson, eds. New York: Elsevier, 1964
18. J. T. Stock and W. C. Purdy, "Potentiometric Electrode Systems in Nonaqueous Titrimetry," *Chem. Rev.* **57**, 1159 (1957)

The basic theory and practice of complexation titrations are treated in:

19. T. S. West, *Complexometry with EDTA and Related Reagents*. 3d ed. Dorset, Eng., BDH Chemicals, 1969
20. G. Schwarzenbach and H. Flaschka, *Complexometric Titrations*. 5th ed. New York: Barnes and Noble, 1969

EXERCISES

24.1 What is the emf of the following cells at 25°? Note any assumptions made.

a) $Zn; Zn^{2+}(a_{Zn^{2+}} = 0.1) \| Cu^{2+}(a_{Cu^{2+}} = 1.0); Cu;$

b) $Hg; Hg_2Cl_2, KCl(satd.) \| Ce^{3+}, Ce^{4+}(a_{Ce^{4+}}/a_{Ce^{3+}} = 10); Pt.$

[*Ans*: (a) 1.129 V, (b) 1.424 V.]

24.2 Show that the half-neutralization pH for a weak acid equals pK_a.

24.3 An acid-base reaction of a weak acid is presumed to extend over the range from 0.1 to 99.9% neutralization ($f = 0.001$ to $f = 0.999$). How does the pH variation over this range relate to the pK_a of the acid?

24.4 Show that the potential of the antimony-antimonious oxide electrode is determined simply by the pH.

24.5 What is the relative error in the determination of the activity of hydrogen ion in a system when the pH is known with an accuracy of 0.05 pH unit?

24.6 A pH meter utilizing the saturated calomel-glass electrode pair is standardized with 0.05 M potassium tetroxalate buffer (pH = 3.56 at 25 °C). (a) What emf does this pH correspond to? (b) An unknown solution gives an emf of 0.564 V. What is its pH?

[*Ans*: (a) 0.210 V; (b) 9.]

24.7 It is desired to have the uncertainty in reading of the potential of an ion-selective electrode be no greater than 0.5 mV. If the total resistance of electrodes and cell is 100 MΩ, what is the maximum tolerable input current to a pH or ION meter used with the electrode?

24.8 A pH-sensitive glass electrode reads low in sodium hydroxide solutions. There is no error in reading in a tetramethyl ammonium hydroxide solution of the same composition. Discuss in terms of the model used to interpret glass electrode behavior.

24.9 Compare direct potentiometry and potentiometric titrations with regard to optimum concentration ranges, precision, and ease of use. Explain the basis for differences.

24.10 A quinhydrone (quinone/hydroquinone) electrode (see page 653) is to be set up for use as a secondary redox potential standard. Solubilities of quinone and hydroquinone are approximately equal and quinhydrone is an equimolar mixture of the two compounds. (a) Write the Nernst equation for the electrode. (b) What items are necessary to set it up? Consider that it will be inserted in solutions. (c) How may its potential be varied precisely without disturbing the organic constituents?

24.11 Enzyme electrodes sensitive to some biologically important molecules have been developed. The electrode consists in part of an enzyme that catalyzes a reaction involving the molecule of interest. One reaction product must be an ion for which an ion-selective electrode is available. The ion-selective electrode is coated with a gel in which the enzyme can be immobilized. In operation the molecule diffuses into the gel and undergoes the selected reaction. A potential proportional to the concentration of the molecule builds up as the ionic product forms.

For example, a urea-sensitive electrode can be developed by immobilizing the enzyme urease on an ammonium-ion sensitive electrode. [See G. G. Guilbault and J. G. Montalvo, *J. Am. Chem. Soc.* **91**, 2164 (1969).]

24.12 What are likely to be the principal errors in determinations made with ion-selective electrodes? Consider use over their acceptable concentration range.

24.13 Describe how the standard-addition method, in which a known volume of a standard solution is added to an unknown solution, can be used with direct potentiometry in a cell without liquid junction to improve the accuracy of determination. Consider factors such as pH, ionic strength, dilution, and interfering species. [See S. E. Manahan, *Anal. Chem.* **42**, 128 (1970).]

24.14 An electrode-solution system is said to be poorly *poised* when electrode potential is strongly influenced by the magnitude of cell current. (a) Will the Pt; Ce^{4+}, Ce^{3+} electrode be poorly poised

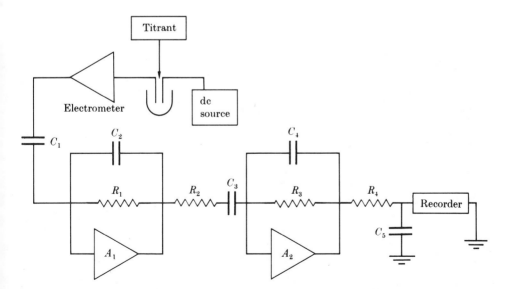

Fig. 24.18 A schematic diagram of a circuit for taking the second derivative of a potentiometric titration curve.

when only Ce^{4+} is present? When only Ce^{3+} is present? When 10^{-3} M Ce^{4+} and 10^{-2} M Ce^{3+} are present? (b) In a given aqueous solution, pH readings that differ by 0.04 pH unit are obtained with a particular glass electrode–SCE pair when the potential difference is read with different pH meters, yet the meters read the pH of standard buffers to within the manufacturer's specification of ± 0.01 pH unit. Buffers are well poised. Explain. [See S. Z. Lewin, *Anal. Chem.* **33** (3) 41A (1961).]

24.15 Show that in an unsymmetrical redox titration the indicator emf at the equivalence point has the value $E_{ind} = (n_1 E_1^0 + n_2 E_2^0)/(n_1 + n_2)$. (See page 679.)

24.16 A schematic diagram of instrumentation for recording the second derivative of a potentiometric titration is shown in Fig. 24.18. (a) Must the electrometer be present for all titrations? Explain. (b) What portion of the circuit comprises the first stage of differentiation? Which resistance and capacitance are necessary to that differentiation? Which resistance and capacitance are added to reduce the response to high frequency noise? (c) What is the role of R_4 and C_5? (d) Draw rough voltage-time plots for a titration signal at the input to the electrometer, in R_2, and in R_4.

CHAPTER 25

POLAROGRAPHY AND AMPEROMETRIC TITRATIONS

25.1 INTRODUCTION

It is usual to group electroanalytical techniques that involve use of a dropping mercury electrode (described in Section 25.3) under the heading polarography. In each the process of interest is electrolysis of a minute fraction of one or more electroactive species. The analyst observes current in an unstirred solution while varying the potential of the dropping electrode systematically. Polarographic techniques include two classical methods, regular or dc polarography and amperometric titrations, which are discussed in this chapter. They also include newer polarographic techniques, some of which —single-sweep or oscillographic polarography, cyclic voltammetry, and pulse polarography—are discussed in the next chapter. It is convenient to defer discussion of this group of techniques because they represent refinements of the classical method. Note, too, at the outset that Chapter 23 presents background essential to an understanding of classical polarography; its contents are assumed familiar in the discussion that follows.

In polarography we observe electrolysis under conditions such that diffusion is the main process effective in bringing an electroactive species to the electrode surface. Other modes of mass transport are suppressed during the intervals of observation: migration, by addition of a 20- to 100-fold excess of inert electrolyte, and convection, by using unstirred solution.* Under these conditions the dropping electrode is polarized and the class of techniques based on the electrode acquires its name.†

Because of the properties of the dropping electrode (Section 25.3) most polarography‡ involves reductions, and discussion will be focused on this type of reaction. When an oxidation at the dropping electrode is of interest, it is only necessary to adjust the potential of the electrode appropriately and to observe an electrolysis current flowing in the opposite direction.

Figure 25.1 shows the essentials of polarographic instrumentation schematically. A representative measurement involves applying a steadily larger potential difference to the polarographic cell by tapping off a portion of the voltage drop produced by battery *BA* in the voltage divider and observing the cell current. The mercury pool

---

* Some stirring occurs as mercury drops fall. As a result, each new drop grows in an essentially virgin solution.
† Microelectrodes other than the dropping mercury electrode are also sometimes used to effect diffusion-limited electrolysis. Solid microelectrodes are discussed briefly in Section 25.13.
‡ Hereafter, when the term polarography or polarographic is used without qualification, it will refer to classical or dc polarography.

electrode serves as an unpolarizable reference electrode (Section 25.2). The voltage applied to the cell thus marks the potential of the dropping mercury electrode relative to that of the reference. We assume there is minimal iR drop across the solution. As the wiper moves along the voltage divider from left to right, the dropping electrode becomes steadily more negative. Voltmeter V, or better a potentiometer, indicates the applied voltage; galvanometer G measures cell current.

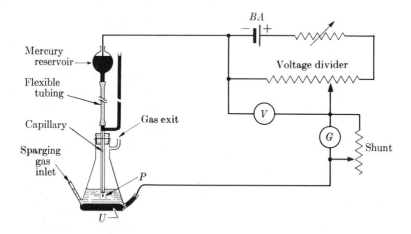

Fig. 25.1 Schematic diagram of a simple polarographic apparatus. P, dropping mercury electrode. U, unpolarizable mercury pool electrode. G, galvanometer. V, voltmeter. Note the sidearm on the dropping electrode to permit measurement of height of mercury column.

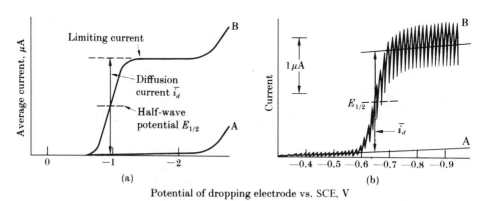

Fig. 25.2 (a) Smoothed current–voltage curves for dc polarography. Curve A, deoxygenated supporting electrolyte alone; curve B, single electroactive species and supporting electrolyte. The diffusion current i_d and half-wave potential $E_{1/2}$ characterize the polarographic wave of the electroactive species. At very negative potentials, there is a further current increase because of reduction of the supporting electrolyte or solvent. (b) A comparable recorded current–voltage curve. The straight lines used to establish the average diffusion current $\bar{i}_d$ are shown as they were drawn by inspection. An accurate value of $i_{d\,max}$, corresponding to the top of the wave, can also be measured if a fast recorder is used, as in this case.

How do the results obtained with such a cell characterize electroactive species in the solution? Figure 25.2 shows two representative polarographic current–voltage curves. When only a supporting electrolyte, e.g., 0.1 KCl, is present, curve *A* is obtained. By contrast, when an electroactive species is also present, curve *B*, termed a *polarogram*, results. It diverges from curve *A* at potentials where reduction of the electroactive species begins. The divergence takes the form of a *wave*, which is the region of almost linear rise in current. Once the electrode voltage is large enough to reduce the electroactive species as rapidly as it diffuses in, the curve levels into a *limiting current* plateau. Though the electrode is made still more negative, no further increase in current is possible until we begin reduction of a new species.

Classical or dc polarography yields two useful data about an electroactive species, diffusion current and half-wave potential. Since concentration is easily calculable from this current, polarography lends itself well to quantitative analysis, as is seen below.

The half-wave potential is a valuable datum for a variety of research studies of complexation, bonding, and equilibrium, as is discussed briefly in Section 25.15. But polarography has little use in qualitative analysis. The half-wave potential of a given species varies considerably with conditions such as pH, ionic strength, supporting electrolyte, and impurities. Further, different species may have nearly the same half-wave potential.

Generally, we may determine any substance (molecular as well as ionic) quantitatively by polarography if we can reduce the substance (or to a lesser degree, oxidize it) at the dropping mercury electrode. Molecules can diffuse as well as ions. To be examined polarographically a substance must be soluble in a solvent appropriate for the reduction (or oxidation). Usually an appropriate supporting electrolyte must also be soluble, though this requirement does not always hold for modified polarographic techniques (Chapter 26).

The largest application of polarography at present is in the analysis of inorganic mixtures. Many metal ions reduce at the dropping mercury electrode to give well-defined waves. For example, under proper conditions, percentages of cobalt, copper, lead, and nickel can be determined successfully in steels; of cadmium, iron, lead, nickel, tin, and zinc in copper alloys; and of dissolved oxygen in many solutions ranging from sea water to physiological fluids. The optimum concentration level is 10^{-3} to 10^{-4} M, but the feasibility of classical polarographic analysis at the level of 10^{-5} M (or even to 10^{-6} M with specialized technique and instrumentation) means it is possible to extend many of these analyses to trace levels.

Polarographic organic analyses are also common, especially for a determination of an individual electroreducible species in a predominately inorganic mixture or for determination of the total concentration of a particular functional group in a mixture. Polarography is also a useful tool in probing the behavior of many systems.

25.2 ELECTROLYSIS CELL AND ELECTRODES

Polarographic techniques center in an electrolysis cell. Its essential elements are evident in Fig. 25.1 but design considerations and the function of parts are not. Clearly, the dropping mercury electrode, which is treated at length in the next section, is the most important part of the cell. It is the *working electrode*, i.e. the electrode at which the electrolysis of interest occurs. It has a role analogous to that of an indicator electrode in a galvanic cell. As the discussion below shows, the rest of the cell exists to complete the electrical circuit and to provide a stable potential base (reference electrode) against which the potential of the working electrode is known.

Working electrodes. In determining the types of electrolysis a working electrode is suited for, the specific properties we must consider are degree of inertness, surface area, and shape. It is of first importance that it be inert over the range of potentials it is to assume. Otherwise, it may undergo dissolution and either preclude a quantitative interpretation of the current–voltage wave or prevent attainment of the desired potential. For example, a mercury electrode of any type cannot act as an anode for the oxidation of bromide ion: Prior to reaching the potential required to oxidize bromide ion, the electrode itself oxidizes ($Hg + 2Br^- \rightarrow Hg_2Br_2 + 2e$).

The most common materials for working electrodes are mercury and platinum. Mercury is eminently satisfactory as a cathode, and platinum is ordinarily usable as either anode or cathode. Since mercury is liquid at room temperature both pool and dropping types see use.

The *dynamic range* of a working electrode also depends on the solvent and supporting electrolyte (if any) used in a cell. Once the working electrode reaches a potential at which it electrolyzes either solvent or supporting electrolyte the electrolysis of an analytical species is completely overwhelmed.

Example In electroanalytical measurements in aqueous solutions a dropping mercury electrode–saturated calomel electrode (SCE) pair is often employed. Relative to the SCE reference electrode at pH 7 in 1 M aqueous KCl supporting electrolyte, a mercury electrode has a dynamic range that extends from $+0.4$ to -1.9 V vs. SCE. The positive boundary is set by its self-oxidation ($Hg \rightarrow Hg^{2+} + 2e$). The negative limit corresponds to the voltage at which the supporting electrolyte is reduced [$K^+ + e \rightarrow K(Hg)$]. Note that the formation of an amalgam greatly lowers the reduction potential of alkali metals.

Figure 25.3 shows applied voltages at which water will be electrolyzed at an inert, nonpolarizable electrode like platinized platinum as a function of pH. With an electrode like mercury on which either hydrogen or oxygen has an overpotential, a still wider voltage range is possible.

Note that the electrolysis of other solvents may also depend on acidity; we may expect this type of dependence whenever a proton or solvent anion appears in the solvent redox reactions.

The electrolysis cell requires, besides a working electrode, a *counter electrode.* This must be nonpolarizable and must also maintain a steady potential. A SCE reference with large liquid junction (Section 24.2) may be satisfactory, or else a mercury pool; both see considerable use. Each has a definite disadvantage: The SCE tends to polarize as currents increase, and the pool does not assume an exactly known potential. For precise work an alternative, three-electrode arrangement is often preferable: working electrode, regular reference electrode, and a current-carrying counter electrode.

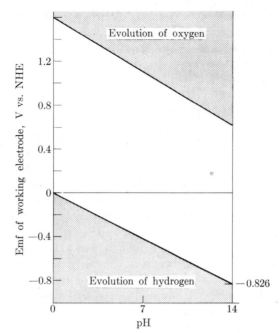

Fig. 25.3 Range of potentials (relative to the normal hydrogen electrode) that may be applied to a working electrode in aqueous solution without electrolyzing water. The overpotential for O_2 or H_2 evolution on a given electrode will increase the voltage range and must be added or subtracted respectively. Further, a correction must be made by use of the Nernst equation for the partial pressure of gas, if other than 1 atm. Potentials relative to the saturated calomel electrode (SCE) can be found by subtracting 0.24 V.

What is at stake is the precision with which it is possible to control the potential of the working electrode independently of cell current. Recall that only the potential across a *pair* of electrodes can be fixed. Accordingly, adequate control depends on making the iR drop either negligible or eliminating it and keeping the potential of the reference electrode constant. If it polarizes, its potential alters. In the following paragraphs useful solutions are suggested for three different experimental conditions.

1.   When the cell current is minute (less than $1\,\mu A$) and the iR drop across the solution is either negligible (no more than 1 mV) or is known, only a regular reference electrode of large surface area is necessary. The essential point is that it must not become polarized.

2.   When the current is larger but the iR drop is still small (the order of 10 mV) only a counter electrode is generally necessary unless it is important to know the potential of the working electrode accurately. (One nearly always can find the applied potential relative to a known half-wave potential.)

The auxiliary electrode serves as a pseudo-reference electrode: It is nonpolarizable and tends to acquire a reasonably constant potential, though not an exactly defined one. For example, since some mercury is oxidized to mercurous chloride, a mercury pool counter anode in a cell with chloride electrolyte maintains an emf close to that of a calomel reference.

3.   Whenever the potential of the working electrode must be precisely known or a large iR drop occurs in the solution, both reference and counter electrodes are needed. It is desirable to place the reference electrode (or tip of its salt bridge, if it has a liquid junction) very close to the working electrode. This arrangement is common in almost all electrochemical studies.

25.3 DROPPING MERCURY ELECTRODE

The electrode consists of a length of fine capillary tubing (0.02 to 0.1 mm diameter bore) attached to an elevated mercury reservoir. A simple version was shown in Fig. 25.1. Mercury drops fall from the end of the capillary at the rate of about 20 per minute. The electrical connection is made through the reservoir. Each drop starts as a hemisphere whose diameter is that of the capillary, becomes nearly spherical, and remains so until it reaches a critical size and breaks away. The electrode is aptly described as an expanding spherical microelectrode.

Since drop time is affected by the potential applied to the electrode and the nature of the solution, adjustment of the height of column to secure the desired drop life should be made under the conditions of usage. Drop lives from 2 s to 7 s are commonly employed. The electrode support should be sturdy since we can obtain reproducible data only if the electrode is free from vibration and the drop time is constant.

Commercial dropping mercury electrodes are readily available. Many feature a mechanical drop dislodger to control drop life. With this precise control it is possible to synchronize the voltage scan with drop life. This correlation is especially important in newer polarographic procedures (Chapter 26).

Perhaps the most severe problem in the use of the dropping electrode is clogging of the capillary. Foreign matter such as dust may enter, but the mercury may also become oxidized or contaminated and build up constricting deposits. It is essential to use pure mercury and to take adequate precautions before storing a dropping electrode.*

Where we desire shorter natural drop times for faster polarography a different electrode design may be desirable. With a regular capillary there is stirring by the falling drop when drop times decrease below 2 s. As a result, diffusion control of current may not be attained. *Smoler* vertical-orifice dropping electrodes avoid this problem even at drop times as short as 0.5 s with mercury flow rates of 5 mg s^{-1}. To prepare a Smoler capillary, a "2 to 5 s" regular capillary is bent in a right angle near its center and broken just beyond the bend to give it an "L" shape.

The qualifications of the dropping mercury electrode for electroanalytical studies are striking. Some of its most desirable characteristics are

1.   A surface that is continuously renewed during each drop;

2.   A surface area calculable from the capillary diameter, elapsed time, and mercury flow rate;

---

* After use, the capillary of the dropping electrode should be thoroughly washed with distilled water with mercury slowly flowing. The reservoir may then be lowered to stop the flow and the electrode stored. An empty flask or beaker may be raised around the capillary as a shield.

3. A continuous expansion into fresh solution as a result of drop growth and the negligible depletion of electroactive species;

4. A high overpotential for the reduction of hydrogen; and

5. The ability to dissolve most other metals.

The last two points require further comment. Even in solutions of pH 3 to 5, hydrogen has such a high overpotential on mercury (about 1.2 V) that the dropping electrode may be used up to at least -1.6 V vs. SCE before water begins to be electrolyzed. In neutral or basic media the cation of the supporting electrolyte is usually reduced first. By using tetraalkylammonium salts (see below) as supporting electrolyte in basic solution we can extend the use of the electrode to about -2.6 V vs. SCE.

The significance of the solubility of metals in mercury is twofold. In the reduction of metal ions, removal of electrolysis products is assured; they dissolve in the mercury drops. A second important aspect is that it is possible to reduce even alkali metal ions in water. With the metallic product soluble in mercury, reduction occurs at a potential as much as 1 V below the standard electrode potential. Even Na^+ and K^+ ions can be polarographically determined if Me_4NBr or Bu_4NBr supporting electrolyte is used.

As already noted, the dropping mercury electrode is quite limited as an anode, for mercury begins to go into solution at potentials of about 0.4 V vs. SCE. For this reason, it is chiefly used to study reductions.

Capacitive current. A peculiarity of any expanding electrode is that it gives rise to a continuous nonfaradaic current. At virtually all applied potentials cell current must flow to develop the electrical double layer that always forms at the surface of an electrode (Section 23.1). The process is analogous to the charging of a capacitor. As long as there is a steady increase in drop area, the charging continues. The average capacitive current is small ($<0.2\ \mu A$), but comprises the irreducible background against which we measure polarographic results.

How does this capacitive current vary during the life of a drop? It is a maximum at the start of a drop when area is increasing rapidly and a minimum near the end of its life when area is changing slowly. The matter is further discussed in Section 26.1.

Electrocapillary maximum. What is at first unexpected is that the magnitude and direction of the dropping electrode's capacitive current vary with potential, solvent, and to a degree with the kind of solutes present. The explanation is to be found in the change of interfacial tension of mercury as electrode potential varies.

When no electrical connection is made, mercury drops exhibit maximum surface tension and appear to have no double layer. If however, we short the electrode to an unpolarizable saturated calomel electrode, it acquires a double layer and a positive charge relative to the solution. The surface tension is now substantially smaller and drop time is shorter than for the "free" electrode. Since each drop now has a positive charge, a capacitive current flows (in the external circuit) from the dropping electrode to the saturated calomel electrode. If we apply voltage to force the dropping electrode potential to a steadily more negative value with respect to SCE, the mercury surface tension rises and reaches a maximum value (identical to the free dropping electrode value) at about -0.5 V vs. SCE. This value is called the electrocapillary maximum.

Drop time is longest, i.e. drops can grow to the largest possible weight, at this potential. There is no capacitive current; it appears there is no double layer. When we make the potential still more negative, however, the dropping electrode current flows again but in the opposite direction. The double layer has changed sign. Figure 25.4 shows the relation of capacitive current to applied potential.

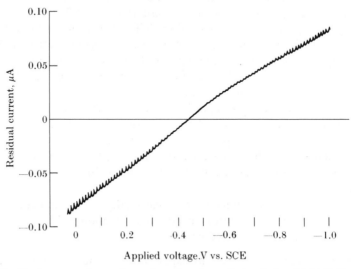

Applied voltage.V vs. SCE

Fig. 25.4 Residual current observed at a dropping electrode in air-free 0.1 M KCl solution. Note that the current falls to zero at the applied voltage corresponding to the electrocapillary maximum of mercury (-0.47 V vs. SCE). This current is mainly a capacitive current.

25.4 FACTORS DETERMINING CELL CURRENT

As suggested in Section 25.1, a distinguishing feature of polarography is that transport processes other than diffusion are minimized for the electroactive species. We virtually eliminate convection by using an unstirred solution; arranging that agitation by falling mercury drops be minimal; reducing vibration from outside; keeping the current minute to reduce heating; and employing a growing electrode that constantly expands into fresh solution. Migration becomes negligible when we swamp out the electrical gradient for the electroactive species through addition of a 50-fold excess of "non-reducible" electrolyte. This *supporting electrolyte* is the principal charge carrier *up to the electrode*. At the electrode, electron transfer completes the process.

Two other physical conditions are necessary to the observation of the electrolysis current under diffusion-limited conditions. First, we must increase the applied potential enough for all the electroactive species of interest to be electrolyzed as soon as it diffuses in. Figure 25.5 depicts the situation. Second, the capacitive current must be small enough for it to be corrected for by subtraction. This condition was well satisfied in the case shown in Fig. 25.2, but will usually not hold for lower concentrations of electroactive species.

Under these conditions what expression for current can we obtain from solving Fick's law of diffusion (Section 23.3)? Does the application of these laws mean the observed linear dependence of diffusion current i_d on concentration is successfully predicted? To make the desired analysis and derive an equation for current, we must adapt Fick's second law for spherical diffusion, which applies in the case of a dropping electrode, and to allow for the gradual expansion of each drop. Ilkovic first carried through a careful analysis and derived the equation for polarographic diffusion current that bears his name. We can restate his formulation many ways. In terms of the average diffusion current $\bar{i}_d$ (see Figs. 25.2 and 25.18 for a method of graphical estimation), the *Ilkovic equation* is

$$\bar{i}_d = 607nD^{1/2}Cm^{2/3}t^{1/6}. \tag{25.1}$$

In terms of maximum current (again see Figs. 25.2 and 25.18), the equation is larger by the factor 7/6, the ratio of maximum to mean current,

$$i_{d\,max} = 708nD^{1/2}Cm^{2/3}t^{1/6}.$$

The quantities on the right side group naturally into three categories. First, the numerical coefficient incorporates constant factors such as the Faraday and conversion factors. There follow the variables that characterize the electroactive species: n, the number of electrons transferred per molecule, D, the diffusion coefficient $(cm^2\,s^{-1})$ and C, the concentration (millimoles per liter). Finally, the product $m^{2/3}t^{1/6}$ identifies the maximum size of mercury drops, where m is the rate of flow of mercury $(mg\,s^{-1})$ and t is the drop life (s).

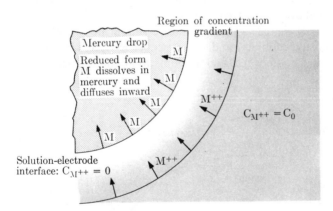

Region of concentration gradient

Mercury drop

Reduced form M dissolves in mercury and diffuses inward

M^{++}

$C_{M^{++}} = C_0$

Solution-electrode interface: $C_{M^{++}} = 0$

M^{++}

Fig. 25.5 Solution behavior at the surface of a polarized dropping mercury electrode during reduction of metallic ion M^{2+}. Its reduced form is assumed soluble in mercury.

The expected direct proportionality between concentration and diffusion current is evident in Eq. (25.1). It is the basis for quantitative polarography, considered at length in Section 25.10. The Ilkovic equation has been found adequate to the majority of polarographic work as long as the drop life is greater than about 2.5 s.

Note that Eq. (25.1) also makes clear that *absolute* quantitative determinations (in contrast to relative analysis based on standard solutions) are difficult. The problem is that an absolute determination requires a knowledge of two electrochemical constants n and D, which are often unknown and difficult to evaluate.

As a result, the Ilkovic equation is only occasionally used to evaluate diffusion coefficients. Where both n and D are unknown we are more likely to calculate a diffusion current constant I^* [6, Chap. 23] instead. It is defined as

$$I^* = \bar{i}_d/Cm^{2/3}t^{1/6} = 607nD^{1/2}.$$

This quantity should be independent of a particular instrument and dropping electrode, and is usually reproducible to $\pm 5\%$. It is more useful than diffusion coefficients in tabulating and comparing electrolysis data for different systems.

There is a more serious difficulty in an absolute use of the Ilkovic equation, however, that arises from an approximation in the original derivation, though it is beyond the scope of this book: Note particularly that for calculation of accurate diffusion constants or use in precise research studies, a correction must be incorporated in Eq. (25.1). [4]

As noted in the preceding section, the interfacial tension of mercury varies with applied potential and directly affects the maximum size mercury drops attain. In terms of the Ilkovic equation this dependence enters through variations in the product $m^{2/3}t^{1/6}$ with applied potential. Figure 25.6 shows the relationship graphically. Both the drop life t and $m^{2/3}t^{1/6}$ go through a maximum at the electrocapillary maximum.

From Fig. 25.6 it appears that diffusion current should decrease somewhat at applied potentials more negative than -1.0 V vs. SCE. Since drop life is shorter, drops will be smaller when they fall. This effect is observable in the downward slope of limiting current at quite negative potentials.

Some mention of the effect of temperature should be included. Because of its influence on viscosity, mobility, and other properties, the temperature coefficient of the diffusion current is positive and amounts to about 1% per degree in aqueous solutions.

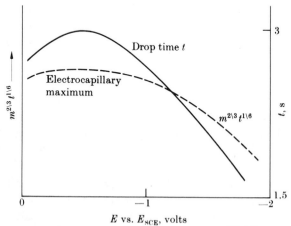

Fig. 25.6 Relative dependence of drop time and the product $m^{2/3}t^{1/6}$ for a dropping mercury electrode on the potential of the electrode.

Finally, how can we check to ensure that a limiting current is basically a diffusion current? The question becomes a pressing one when the actual variety of sources of current is recognized (see below). A straightforward test is whether a linear relationship between diffusion current and product $m^{2/3}t^{1/6}$ is observed as required by Eq. (25.1). Since this product is proportional to $h^{1/2}$, where h is the height of the mercury column, the test really requires only varying column height to see if $i_d \propto h^{1/2}$.

Other currents. Though migration and convection were deliberately minimized to ensure that diffusion alone would determine the current, what assurance is there that there are no other complications? Recall that diffusion control would break down if one or more electrode processes were slow (Section 23.4). Further, it would fail in part if competing electrolyses occurred. While more than a cursory survey of such possibilities is beyond the scope of this book, we cannot ignore them. In practice many instances arise in which currents are "mixed", partly because of diffusion, and partly because of a chemical reaction whose rate is comparable to that of diffusion. We will examine briefly here several types of current that result from such processes. In all such cases the proportionality between current and concentration fails.

Kinetic currents. If either the oxidized or the reduced form of an electroactive species is involved in a dissociation equilibrium or a chemical reaction, the limiting electrolysis current may be complex in form. In the first case, the rate at which the active species appears at the surface of the electrode will be controlled partly by diffusion and partly by its slow formation from a "complex." Since the electrolysis current depends partly on the rate of a nonelectrode reaction, it is called a *kinetic current.* [6]

A kinetic current can be identified by its independence of drop time for a given capillary. The test is best applied at a potential below $E_{1/2}$, since a kinetic current also tends to become diffusion-limited. As stated earlier, diffusion current depends on drop time and varies as the product $m^{2/3}t^{1/6}$.

Example The reduction of formaldehyde gives rise to a kinetic current. Most of the formaldehyde in an aqueous solution is present as a hydrated complex, which is reducible only at voltages higher than those ordinarily used. As a result, the electrolysis current depends on the rate of dissociation of the complex as well as on the rate of diffusion of free formaldehyde.

Catalytic currents. Another source of current arises when an independent reaction rapidly reoxidizes an electrolysis product at the electrode surface. Then the concentration of the electroactive species jumps and we observe an enhanced current wave termed a catalytic wave. It is probable that small quantities of adsorbed catalysts are responsible. Usually they act only over a short range of potential, causing the total current to peak in this region. In general a catalytic current is identifiable by its independence of drop time. Obviously, no diffusion is involved in this case.

Example A catalytic wave is observed when uranyl ions, UO_2^{2+}, are polarographically reduced to uranium (V) in the presence of nitrate ions. Although nitrate ions are not reduced at a dropping mercury electrode at this potential, they are reduced by the uranium (V) ions which return to the (VI) state as a consequence. The freshly formed uranium (VI) ions are then electrically reduced, and the net result is a catalytic wave that represents the simultaneous reduction of uranyl and nitrate ions. The uranium (V) ions catalyze the reduction of the nitrate ions.

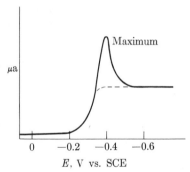

μa

E, V vs. SCE

Fig. 25.7 A representative current maximum obtained in the polarographic observation of a lead (II) solution. The broken line gives the form of the wave when 0.005 % gelatin is added as a maximum suppressor. The curve has been smoothed.

Anomalous currents. Some further sources of current must also be dealt with. They are effects that (a) give rise to current maxima, (b) result in some way from an earlier electrolysis, or (c) arise from adsorption.

In general, a *current maximum* is observed at the top of a polarographic wave. Figure 25.7 shows such a maximum. It may appear as a sharp peak (first-order effect) as in the figure or as a rounded hump (second-order effect). More than one maximum may also occur. Either type of maximum ordinarily tends to obscure the start of the limiting current plateau and makes impossible the determination of a diffusion current in any system that gives closely spaced polarographic waves.

Fortunately, we can eliminate most maxima by adding a minute amount (0.002 to 0.01 %) of almost any nonreducible surface-active agent that will adsorb on mercury. Gelatin is a useful *maximum suppressor* that is effective regardless of the potential or the supporting electrolyte. Triton X-100 is also widely used. Addition of more than a very low concentration of suppressor should be avoided, since it tends to reduce the diffusion current and may even form a complex with the species of interest.

Different models have been advanced for the origin of maxima, but it is clear experimentally that there is a rapid streaming of electrolyte around a mercury drop in the region of a maximum. As a result, convection as well as diffusion is operative in bringing electroactive species to the electrode surface and current is abnormally high. These disturbing effects vanish when the electrode potential is sufficiently negative for its voltage to dominate the situation and set up a steady diffusion layer.

Anomalously low currents may also be observed. An unexpected reaction between some product of a "later" electrolysis and an electroactive species whose reduction began at lower potentials can appear to reduce the height of the later wave. Recall that any wave beyond the first represents the sum of several diffusion currents. If a product generated in a later reduction precipitates or complexes a species* whose reduction began earlier, the contribution of the earlier wave to the total current drops. What is actually observed, however, is that the height of the later wave is smaller than it should be.

---

* Any redox reactions would, of course, fall in the category of kinetic or catalytic currents, which have already been considered.

Example In an unbuffered KCl solution the reduction of iodate ion interferes with that of cadmium ion even though the reduction of cadmium begins at a more positive voltage. The reduction of iodate produces both iodide and hydroxide ions, neither at high concentration. The consequences, however, are immediate: Hydroxide ions precipitate a fraction of the remaining cadmium ions, and the cadmium diffusion current falls. But this decrease occurs only during the iodate wave and might be easily interpreted as due to a small iodate concentration. Buffering the solution at the outset would remedy the difficulty.

Adsorption effects. If an electrolysis product is strongly adsorbed on a dropping electrode, a reduction pre-wave may appear prior to the regularly expected polarographic wave. For example, a pre-wave occurs in the reduction of many organic species. Such an adsorption lowers the activity coefficient of the reduced species far enough for a normal electrolysis wave to be displaced to more positive potentials. Because the magnitude of current is adsorption-controlled, it should be independent of concentration of the species involved, above some threshold value. It should also be independent of the height of the mercury column if drop time is held constant, since the same drop area is covered by the time a drop falls.

25.5 HALF-WAVE POTENTIAL

Earlier it was stated that the half-wave potential $E_{1/2}$ of an electroactive species is nearly equal to its standard electrode potential. These quantities are so important that the relationship should be defined theoretically. Thereby it is possible to base thermodynamic calculations on polarographic half-wave potentials as well as standard cell potentials and factors that cause the two quantities to differ can be classified. To simplify the following discussion, we assume a reduction is occurring. Adapting any of the equations for oxidation will be straightforward.

Even though only the oxidized form of an electroactive species is present initially in a solution, at potentials in the step or wave portion of a current-voltage curve, both reduced and oxidized forms exist at the electrode surface. If the reduction proceeds reversibly, the electrode potential should be described by the Nernst equation.* If the reduced form is soluble in the solution but not in mercury, the defining equation is

$$E_{\text{d.e.}} = E^0_{\text{ox, red}} + \frac{RT}{nF} \ln \frac{f_{\text{ox}}(C_{\text{ox}})_e}{f_{\text{red}}(C_{\text{red}})_e}, \tag{25.2}$$

where the subscript e denotes concentrations at the electrode surface and f_{ox} and f_{red} are activity coefficients of the two forms of the electroactive species.

Though we cannot know concentrations at the electrode surface directly, we can deduce them from the electrolysis current. When diffusion governs the rate of

---

* To apply the Nernst equation during electrolysis requires only that the electrode be in equilibrium with the *immediately adjacent* solution. This assumption is reasonable if the electron transfer occurs reversibly (Section 23.2) and if both oxidized and reduced forms of the species are soluble. For irreversible electrolysis a more elaborate mathematical treatment is required. [6]

electrolysis, the Ilkovic equation can be used to express the difference in concentration in the bulk of the solution and at the electrode surface as:

$$[C_{ox} - (C_{ox})_e]kD_{ox}^{1/2} = i, \tag{25.3}$$

where D_{ox} is the diffusion coefficient of the oxidized form and k is a factor than can be calculated from the Ilkovic equation.* When $i = i_d$, Eq. (25.3) becomes

$$C_{ox}kD_{ox}^{1/2} = i_d.$$

Substituting this value into Eq. (25.3) gives after rearrangement the expression

$$(C_{ox})_e = (i_d - i)/kD_{ox}^{1/2}. \tag{25.4}$$

If none of the reduced form is present initially in the bulk of the solution, but results solely from the reduction,

$$(C_{red})_e = i/kD_{red}^{1/2}, \tag{25.5}$$

where D_{red} is the diffusion constant for the reduced form (in many cases, in mercury). Again k appears. When Eqs. (25.4) and (25.5) are substituted in Eq. (25.2) there results

$$E_{d.e.} = E^0 + \frac{RT}{nF} \ln \frac{i_d - i}{i} + \frac{RT}{nF} \ln \frac{D_{red}^{1/2} f_{ox}}{D_{ox}^{1/2} f_{red}}. \tag{25.6}$$

By definition, the half-wave potential is the value of electrode potential when the current is half the diffusion current. Making this substitution in Eq. (25.6) gives the new expression

$$E_{1/2} = E^0 + \frac{RT}{nF} \ln \frac{D_{red}^{1/2} f_{ox}}{D_{ox}^{1/2} f_{red}}. \tag{25.7}$$

Usually the ratio

$$\frac{D_{red}^{1/2} f_{ox}}{D_{ox}^{1/2} f_{red}}$$

is nearly unity and

$$E_{1/2} \simeq E^0.$$

Only if activity coefficients depart substantially from unity do large differences between halfwave and standard potentials occur.

How is the preceding treatment modified if the reduced form of the species is a metal or other substance soluble in the mercury of the dropping electrode? This behavior will be true of many inorganic species. The electrode reaction is

$$M^{n+} + ne^- + Hg \rightleftharpoons M(Hg),$$

---

* The current is still an average current if Eq. (25.1) is used to find k. The bar will be dropped hereafter to simplify notation. Actually, i could also be taken as the peak current if that from the Ilkovic equation is employed. Whichever form is used, one must be consistent.

where M(Hg) denotes the amalgam formed. For a reversible reaction the potential of the dropping electrode should be given by

$$E_{d.e.} = E_a^0 + \frac{RT}{nF} \ln \frac{(C_{ox})_e f_{ox} a_{Hg}}{(C_{red})_e f_{red}}, \tag{25.8}$$

where E_a^0 is the standard potential of the amalgam electrode, $(C_{red})_e$ and f_{red} are the concentration and the activity coefficient of metal in the amalgam formed at the surface of the mercury drops, and a_{Hg} is the activity of mercury in the amalgam. A treatment parallel to that unfolded in Eqs. (25.3) through (25.6) leads to the expression:

$$E_{1/2} = E_a^0 + \frac{RT}{nF} \ln a_{Hg} + \frac{RT}{nF} \ln \frac{D_{red}^{1/2} f_{ox}}{D_{ox}^{1/2} f_{red}}. \tag{25.9}$$

It can be shown [4] that Eq. (25.9) is well approximated by

$$E_{1/2} = E_{M^{n+}, M}^0 + E_{M^{n+}, M(s)} + \frac{RT}{nF} \ln C_{sat} f_{sat}. \tag{25.10}$$

In this equation $E_{M^{n+}, M}^0$ is the standard potential of the metal, metal ion electrode; $E_{M^{n+}, M(s)}$ is the potential of a cell consisting of a metal, metal ion electrode and a metal ion, saturated (or two-phase) amalgam electrode; C_{sat} and f_{sat} are the concentration and activity coefficient of metal in the *saturated* amalgam (a convenient reference state). What is of particular interest is that for all except very active metals Eq. (25.10) reduces to

$$E_{1/2} \approx E_{M^{n+}, M}^0.$$

Even when the reduced form dissolves in mercury, $E_{1/2}$ nearly equals the standard potential!

Example How well do half-wave and standard potentials agree for common metals? At 25 °C some values of E^0 and $E_{1/2}$ vs. SCE are:

Metal ion	E^0, volts	$E_{1/2}$, volts
Zn^{2+}	-1.01	-1.00
Pb^{2+}	-0.37	-0.39
Tl^+	-0.58	-0.46
Na^+	-2.96	-2.12
K^+	-3.17	-2.14

The preceding discussion treated only a reduction. What differences between reduction and oxidation should be observed? First, for a reversible reaction involving a given electrical couple such as Cu, Cu^{2+}, there should be a single halfwave potential, whether Cu is being oxidized to Cu^{2+} or Cu^{2+} is being reduced to Cu. Second, the processes should differ basically only in terms of the direction of the current. These points are well made in Fig. 25.8. Note that in the figure the current above the abscissa is positive and represents a reduction; current below is negative and represents an oxidation. Half-wave potentials do coincide as expected. Note also that the diffusion current is essentially equal for the three waves since the concentration of the species is identical. Actually, the coincidence of halfwave potentials for oxidation and reduction curves in polarography is a good criterion for reversibility.

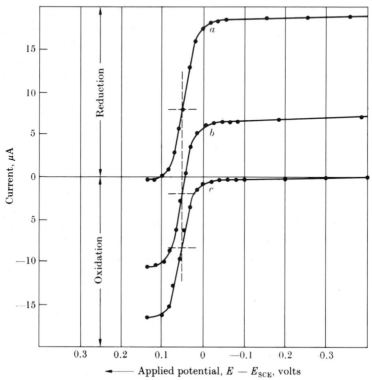

Fig. 25.8 Comparison of reduction and oxidation waves of members of an electrical couple. Polarographic curves obtained for a quinone-hydroquinone couple in a solution buffered at pH 7; (a) quinone, (b) quinone, partly reduced by bubbling hydrogen through it before obtaining polarogram and (c) quinone, fully reduced to hydroquinone by hydrogen gas before obtaining polarogram. (O. H. Müller, *J. Chem. Educ.* **18**, 227 (1941); courtesy of Interscience Publ.)

25.6 BASIC INSTRUMENTATION

The instrumentation for polarographic measurements is outlined in modular form in Fig. 25.9. The electrolysis cell is the heart of a polarograph, for only as the interaction between the working electrode and analytical species is well defined physically is a meaningful measurement of electrolysis current and voltage possible. Electrode combinations and the design of a dropping mercury electrode were described in Sections 25.2 and 25.3, respectively, and attention has been given to the action of electrode and electroactive species under the conditions used in polarography in the preceding two sections.

Two types of cell vessels are shown in Fig. 25.10. Many other types have been developed and are in common use. In the two kinds shown, an external tube leading to the bottom of the vessel is provided so that a solution may be sparged with nitrogen to remove dissolved oxygen before electrolysis is begun. The Erlenmeyer type features a pool counter electrode (mercury is simply poured in to form a 2 to 5 mm layer) to which contact is made by a wire from the outside. The right-hand cell uses a regular SCE reference electrode. It is conveniently placed in a separate arm to avoid the necessity of disturbing it when a new sample solution is introduced.

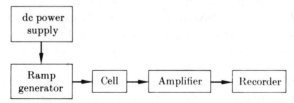

Fig. 25.9 Schematic diagram of a basic polarographic instrument. In some instances the amplifier is omitted and a galvanometer is used for readout. Since an electrical signal is supplied by the cell, no detector-transducer is required.

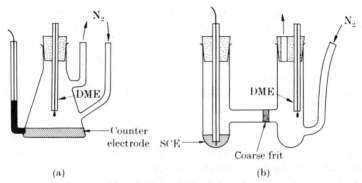

Fig. 25.10 Two types of polarographic cell. The solution being electrolyzed must cover the bottom of the dropping electrode. (a) Erlenmeyer type. (b) H-type.

Yet the application of a potential to a dropping electrode cannot be divorced from a consideration of the distribution of potential drop across a cell. It appears in three regions, at the cathode, at the anode, and in the bulk of the solution (Section 23.1), as indicated by the expression

$$V_{app} = V_{cell} = V_{cathode} + V_{anode} + iR,$$

where algebraic values are added. If the counter electrode is a nonpolarizing reference electrode and the solution resistance is low (less than $100\,\Omega$), iR will be nearly zero and V_{app} will appear as the potential of the dropping electrode vs. the reference.

How well are these conditions met in aqueous polarography with the usual two-electrode (working electrode plus counter electrode) cell? The counter electrode, whether a large-surface-area reference electrode or a mercury pool, does behave as a reference and provides a constant potential.

Example The potential of a mercury pool counter electrode can ordinarily be estimated to within ± 0.03 V. The electrolysis reaction at its surface determines the operative electrical couple.

For example, in a 1 M KCl supporting electrolyte, a mercury pool operating as an anode gives the electrolysis reaction $2Hg + 2Cl^- = Hg_2Cl_2 + 2e$ and the pool acquires the potential of an unsaturated calomel electrode, about $+0.04$ V vs. SCE. Conditions are too variable from cell to cell to permit a closer estimate.

The second condition is met since the voltage drop in the bulk of the solution is usually negligible. A concentrated supporting electrolyte is used and the low solution resistance (below 50 Ω) means an ohmic drop less than 1 mV. Actually, there should be no need to be concerned about an ohmic drop unless we use a fritted agar bridge, a dilute solution, or a nonaqueous solvent. Any of these can easily give rise to a resistance of 1 kΩ or more. Once assured that an applied voltage will be directed to the dropping electrode, we can give our attention to a satisfactory means of imposing a voltage on the cell and measuring the resulting current.

We can set up a simple manual polarograph* easily. As Fig. 25.1 shows, a slide-wire, sensitive galvanometer, working battery, electrodes, and cell are all we basically need. Complexity enters when we desire to achieve one or more of the following: automatic measurement of current and voltage; measurement of current and voltage with greater precision; and photographic measurement in more difficult systems, such as in nonaqueous media or at trace concentrations. Such adaptations are straight-forward if the basic instrumentation has been well thought through. Before considering them, however, we must give special attention to certain aspects of even the simple polarograph.

1. The voltage scan of the dropping electrode must be accurately programmed;
2. The electrolysis current must be determined reliably even though it is fluctuating strongly as mercury drops expand and fall;
3. Small increments in current must be precisely measured under conditions of a relatively large total current.

These aspects are now discussed for basic instrumentation (with the second and third points treated together). In the next section they are reexamined for more sophisticated instrumentation.

Voltage scanning. Most polarography uses a linear voltage scan, termed a *ramp*.† We can generate a ramp simply and reliably by moving a wiper steadily the length of a voltage divider slidewire by hand or by means of a synchronous motor. Figure 25.11 shows this type of design. Good practice calls for use of a slidewire AC whose precision of setting is at least 0.5 % and for arranging that the voltage drop across it be set by adjustment of R_1 to the maximum voltage to be supplied to the cell.

During a scan, wiper B is moved from A to C. Under conditions of relatively small cell current i_{cell}, the applied voltage V_{cell} should be given by

---

* The term is used generically. "Polarograph" is a trademark of E. H. Sargent & Co., but the word has slipped into the common domain.
† For quantitative polarography a voltage just beyond the wave crest might be applied at the outset and the limiting current observed. In practice, this is a satisfactory approach only for routine measurements where the peculiarities of a system are known.

$$V_{\text{cell}} = V_{AB} = \frac{R_{AB}}{R_{AC}} \cdot V_{AC}, \qquad (25.11)$$

where the subscripts refer to lengths of slidewire in Fig. 25.11.

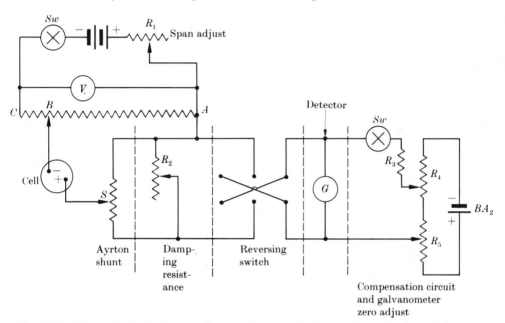

Fig. 25.11 Schematic circuit diagram of a versatile manual polarograph. To obtain a polarogram the wiper or tap is moved along the slidewire from A to C. The galvanometer is overdamped by introduction of resistance R_2. (When Ayrton shunt S is adjusted, R_2 should be oppositely changed.) A compensation circuit may be switched in by closing switch Sw. Current from battery BA_2 will oppose that from the cell. This circuit may be used to compensate an early polarographic wave to permit a later (more cathodic) one to be observed at full sensitivity or to compensate residual current. Resistor R_5 must be large (50 kΩ or larger) to prevent further galvanometer damping or shunting.

Example How closely do we meet the assumption of a relatively small cell current in practice? In most polarography i_{cell} is of the order of 10 μA. Assume a slidewire is used whose resistance is about 100 Ω and that the voltage across it is set to 1.5 V by adjustment of R_1. Then $I_{\text{slidewire}}$ when the cell is not connected is $I_{\text{slidewire}} = 1.5/100 = 15$ mA. Clearly, $I_{\text{slidewire}} > 100 \cdot i_{\text{cell}}$. The uncertainty in voltage V_{cell} should be well below the 0.5% precision of setting of the slidewire.

In studies where we need to know the potential of the dropping electrode to ± 10 mV or better, we must add a reference electrode to the cell, as well as making other changes discussed in the next section.

Current measurement. As Fig. 25.9 shows, no detecter-transducer is required in a polarograph. The cell current simply needs to be "read out." A galvanometer with a sensitivity of at least 0.01 μA mm^{-1} and a period of from 3 to 5 s can ensure the sensitivity and damping characteristics needed. Its range may be easily extended to handle currents as large as 100 μA. For this purpose an Ayrton shunt (S in Fig. 25.11) provides for diversion of a known fraction of the total current around the galvanometer (Section 2.4).

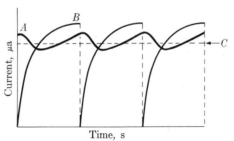

Fig. 25.12 Comparison of observed galvanometer deflections with the actual current fluctuations for a dropping mercury electrode during electrolysis at a constant voltage. A, deflections of galvanometer whose period is long compared with the drop rate. B, actual current fluctuation. C, average current obtained by integration of B.

Will a galvanometer read out an average current or an instantaneous current? The question is an important one. As we may see in Fig. 25.12, the instantaneous current (curve B) fluctuates severely during the growth and fall of mercury drops. The current parallels drop surface area : The current falls essentially to zero as a drop breaks away and rises rapidly again as a new drop grows. All current cycles are identical if solution conditions, voltage, and the rate of flow of mercury are constant and the cell is free of vibration.

Rather than attempt to follow these rapid fluctuations with a galvanometer, which would serve no useful purpose, it is desirable to register a damped version (curve A, Fig. 25.12) from which the average current (curve C) can be deduced visually with ease. If only data like that of curve B are available, we must obtain the average value by calculation. We obtain the desired damping when we use a galvanometer with a long period (4 to 5 s) in a circuit that will overdamp it. For example, in the circuit of Fig. 25.11, overdamping results from use of shunt R_2, and the effective period of the galvanometer increases to 15 s. As the Ayrton shunt S is adjusted, R_2 should be oppositely changed. With this kind of damping, some fluctuations remain (curve A, Fig. 25.12), but it is possible to take the mean by inspection to obtain line C.

Even with damping, the variations registered may be excessive if the diffusion current is large. In this case, the basic circuit may be modified by adding a low-pass RC filter (Section 3.5) to induce further smoothing. Filtering has attendant dangers, however. A careful check should be made to be sure that the waveform and the magnitude of the diffusion current are not altered or at least that allowance can be made for any change that is noted.

Current compensation.   When successive electrolyses are of interest, we can record the first wave at high sensitivity, but we almost always have to lower the galvanometer sensitivity to register the second and any later waves. If the diffusion current for the first wave is much larger than that for the second, it would be preferable to record the second wave with *greater* rather than less sensitivity.

A way around the difficulty is to compensate the diffusion current for the first wave electrically by passing a current equal and opposite to it through the galvanometer while wave 2 is being observed.

Figure 25.11 shows a means of providing compensation. Current from the second battery BA_2 will oppose that from the cell. We can compensate a first wave by adjusting the tap on R_4, then increase the galvanometer sensitivity to spread the next wave over its full deflection range.

In practice, compensation has proved of value mainly for systems that give well-defined waves. A crucial disadvantage is that current fluctuations are always as great as the magnitude of the total diffusion current. When part of the current is compensated, and the rest recorded at high galvanometer sensitivity, the fluctuations can be great enough to cause substantial error in estimating the average current. A further disadvantage is that the increase in sensitivity also causes imperfections in the later wave to be magnified. In sum, although compensation allows perhaps a tenfold enlargement, it provides little gain in precision of measurement. As the next section shows, removing the fluctuations has proved to be a more sophisticated approach.

Calibration. The frequency and elaborateness of calibration of a polarograph naturally depend on the precision desired, the stability of the equipment, and the nature of its use. We can check the uncertainty in both voltage and current readings by appropriate use of a potentiometer of moderate precision (± 0.01 mV or better).

Ordinarily, there are two steps in a voltage calibration. There should be a very occasional determination of the linearity of the slidewire and a somewhat more frequent calibration of the voltmeter. In each case, a simple comparison with the calibrating potentiometer is all that is necessary. The calibration of the voltmeter does not eliminate its inherent uncertainty, and in research studies where halfwave potentials must be observed with precision, the voltage tapped off from the voltage divider is established during each run by comparison with a potentiometer.

We should also check the accuracy of current readings as frequently as experience with a particular instrument indicates. The common procedure is to replace the polarographic cell by a high-precision resistor R, apply a known voltage to it from the polarizing unit, and measure the voltage drop in the resistor with a potentiometer while observing the reading of the readout device. The correct current is easily computed from the voltage drop and the value of R. In photographic recording, the photographic print must be considered to be the presentation device. The accuracy of readings at different sensitivities should also be checked.

25.7 RECORDING AND THREE-ELECTRODE POLAROGRAPHS

We require relatively few modifications to develop an automatic polarograph from the good basic design of Fig. 25.11. The block diagram of Fig. 25.13 shows one logical way to do so. The major alteration is to introduce a precision resistor R as a current detector. Automatic recording is best accomplished with a voltage input. The instantaneous voltage across R is amplified and read out by a fast, modern potentiometric recorder that can follow the fluctuations. To cover a wide current range either we can substitute other precision resistors for R or we can adjust the amplifier range using a precision input attenuator. The other evident difference from the circuit of Fig. 25.11 is that a synchronous motor has been added to perform the voltage scan; it simultaneously advances the chart paper in the recorder.

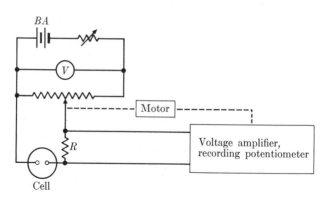

Fig. 25.13 Partial block diagram of an automatic recording polarograph.

How effective is this general design? With a high-input impedance amplifier, we can determine currents as small as 1 nA. A precision of $\pm 0.3\%$ in current determination is secured at ordinary levels (above 0.1 μA). If an accurate applied voltage ($\pm 0.1\%$) is required, we can introduce Zener diode regulation of the dc imposed on the voltage divider. With such a device we can also step up the voltage scanning rate to 0.8 V min^{-1} without loss of precision. Reasonable calibration stability and sensitivity are assured by the null-balance procedure. Finally, if we use a recorder with a fast response (0.5 to 1 s full-scale), we can even record a close approximation to the instantaneous current.

With operational amplifier modules widely available, automatic polarographs of comparable accuracy can be assembled from laboratory modules. Figure 25.14 shows a two-electrode version of this type of polarograph in schematic form (consult Chapter 7 for background). In this design a constant, precisely known input signal V_{B1} is electronically integrated by the circuit of amplifier A_1. The result is a negative-going voltage ramp applied to the dropping electrode. The polarographic cell current is directly amplified by the circuit of amplifier A_2 and converted to a voltage for potentiometric recording.

It is significant that we can make further improvements in the accuracy of measurement only if we can overcome limitations associated with the polarographic cell and the dropping electrode. Four of these limitations are the appreciable iR drops in some solutions, such as nonaqueous ones; the fluctuations in current associated with drop growth; the low resolution secured in the case of nearly overlapping waves; and the large capacitive component of current in the cell current measured at trace concentration levels.

How can we attack these limitations? First, the iR drop in solution can be overcome by introduction of potentiostatic control. In this way it is possible in higher-resistance media to ensure that the potential of the dropping electrode is precisely controlled and thus known.

Second, we can lessen drop-connected current fluctuations by an ingenious approach in which current from successive mercury drops is observed only for an instant near the end of their lives. The result is a series of closely spaced points through which we can draw a smooth current–voltage curve. Alternatively, to secure linear damping of fluctuations, we can introduce RC filters more elaborate than those originally discussed.

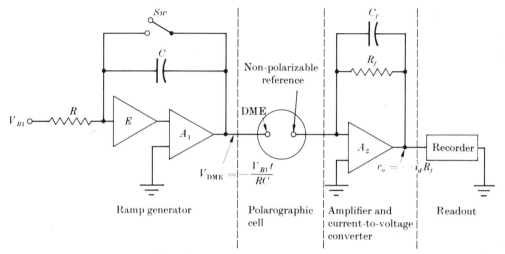

Fig. 25.14 Schematic diagram of an operational amplifier version of a two-electrode polarograph. A voltage ramp is generated by the integrator module based on operational amplifier E and A_1 as a result of its steady input V_{B1}. Electrometer E ensures a high input impedance and accuracy at low ramp slopes. Opening switch Sw starts the generation of the ramp. Current amplifier A_2 plus feedback resistor R_f provides an output voltage proportional to the cell current. Damping of drop-generated fluctuations is provided by shunting capacitor C_f.

Third, we can enhance resolution of close-lying electrolysis waves by electronic differentiation of a smoothed current–voltage curve. An operational amplifier differentiator is the logical choice. Finally, we can make compensation for much of the capacitive current present in a polarographic signal (see below), though major approaches to this problem will be reserved for Chapter 26. The instrumentation for accomplishing the first three steps outlined will now be discussed.

Three-electrode polarograph. A polarographic cell with a third electrode permits the internal iR drop to be minimized. Figure 25.15 shows a standard operational amplifier circuit to accompany it, with both the ramp generator and the current-to-voltage converter (current amplifier) of the previous figure shown only as modules.

The new part of the circuit is a simple *potentiostat*. The central element, amplifier A_2, is used as a voltage follower (Section 7.8) since its entire voltage output to the counter electrode is fed back through SCE to the inverting input. A fraction of the voltage ramp $R_1/(R_1 + R_2)$ is directed to the noninverting input. What are the electrode potentials? The dropping electrode is at virtual ground since it is connected to the inverting input of a grounded amplifier like A_2 in Fig. 25.14.* Because the SCE reference is connected to the noninverting input of amplifier A_3, this electrode must be

---

* Strictly speaking, it is only the lead to the electrode that is at ground. The mercury column of the dropping electrode will have a resistance of about 50 Ω. The *slight iR* drop within the electrode is ordinarily negligible.

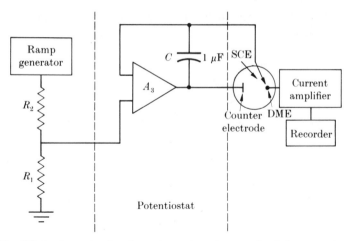

Fig. 25.15 Simplified schematic of a three-electrode polarograph of the operational amplifier type. The SCE reference electrode may be a high-resistance design, but the tip of its salt bridge must be located as near the dropping electrode as possible without being in the current path between dropping electrode and counter electrode.

at the ramp potential applied to the other input. The counter electrode must be at this value plus the iR drop in the solution, and current furnished by A_3 must be exactly that needed to maintain this relationship. Capacitor C bypasses transients that might otherwise lead to instability. There are many more elaborate potentiostat circuits for particular applications.

Tast polarograph. We can eliminate current fluctuations resulting from drop growth by observing current only for a very brief interval near the end of the life of each drop. Since a slow voltage scan is still applied, if we measure the current for each drop at the same point in its life, each drop in effect furnishes one current–voltage point for a curve. In this case, the peak current is plotted. A polarograph of this type would be like any other except in its provision of electronic synchronization of each observation with the growth of a mercury drop. The Tast polarograph (from the German *tasten*, to touch) does just this.* As we would expect, it is more sensitive than an instrument employing a regular readout. The device is also called a strobe polarograph.

Filtering and differentiation. Figure 25.16 shows a part of a circuit devised by Fisher and Kelley [14] that completes this discussion. Such a subcircuit would, e.g., appear between the current amplifier and recorder of Fig. 25.15. Note in Fig. 25.16 two sections of parallel-T filters followed by a low-pass filter of 2 s time constant. With an electrode of 0.5 s drop life, this module successfully rejects the frequencies associated with current fluctuations. The advantage is on the side of this type of efficient linear filter† as contrasted with heavy regular RC damping *or nonlinear* servo recorder

---

* Commercially available from Atlas-Werke AG, West Germany, and Princeton Applied Research. See [2, Chap. 26] for further detail.

† A time lag of about 1 s is introduced, which causes $E_{1/2}$ to be displaced a predictable amount in the direction of the voltage scan. Good waveforms are obtained with the 0.5 s dropping electrode up to scan rates of 0.3 V min^{-1}.

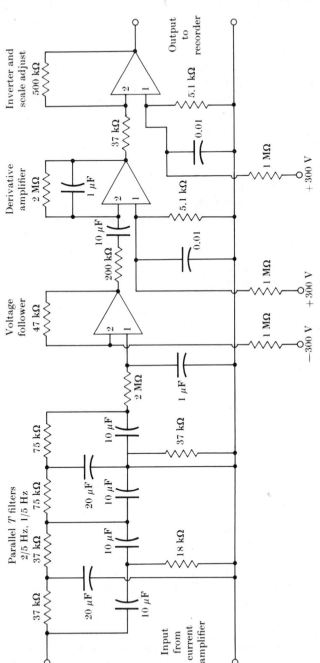

Fig. 25.16 Filter and derivative circuit for a dc polarograph. (Courtesy of McGraw-Hill.)

damping. Here "linear" describes the fact that time required to attain a response to a step input is independent of the height of step. Once the smoothing has been carried out, compensation can be made for much of residual current. A ramp, whose slope is adjusted empirically, is used to cancel this capacitive component. We cannot predict the necessary slope exactly.

Of special interest is the practical differentiator circuit (Section 7.5) that follows the smoothing stages. If we take a first derivative, we can still resolve two species present at equal concentrations when their halfwave potentials are 30 % closer than in a straight polarogram.* Scan rates must be appropriate to the drop life, higher rates being permitted with a faster-dropping electrode.

25.8 RESOLUTION OF WAVES

Whenever two or more electroactive species are present, a successful analysis depends on whether their electrolysis waves are resolvable under some accessible set of conditions. Either Eq. (25.2) or Eq. (25.6) should predict the shape of waves obtained with reversible electrolyzed species. For these equations to hold, the current level is kept minute. In order to generalize the form of electrolysis curves it is desirable to change the ordinate to the relative current i/i_d, which is proportional to $[red]/([ox] + [red])$. Figure 25.17 graphs two generalized electrolysis waves.

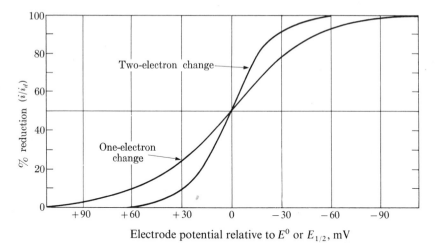

Electrode potential relative to E^0 or $E_{1/2}$, mV

Fig. 25.17 Variation in the potential of a working electrode during electrolysis.

From the figure it appears that a useful criterion for resolution of successive waves must involve at least the parameters n and $E_{1/2}$. This proves to be the case. For the resolution of two waves with no more than 1% overlap,† it can be shown that half-wave

---

* Do not confuse this technique with differential polarography, which requires a double-channel instrument using dual dropping mercury electrodes. The cell in the sample channel may contain a solution with two electrolyzable species one of which is a minor constituent and the other cell a solution that is identical except that the minor constituent is absent. A commercial apparatus based on the technique is available (Davis Differential Cathode Ray Polarograph).
† Height of first wave increased by 1% by contribution from second wave.

potentials must differ by $236/n$ mV. [D. J. Fisher in 10] Note that the criterion fits the curves of Fig. 25.17: The span of a one-electron reduction wave is about 240 mV. The marked decrease in width as n increases is worth emphasizing. Fortunately, many common inorganic species require two electrons for their reduction and thus need only a 118 mV slot per species for good resolution.

What is the effect of concentration? Since $i_d \propto C$ the effect of increasing the concentration of an electroactive species is to raise the height of its wave and therefore increase its slope. Now there is a more severe overlap problem, for the contribution of diffusion current from a second wave to the plateau of an earlier one can become substantial. We discuss this further below.

Irreversibility in an electrolysis spreads a wave out still more. Accordingly, the differences between halfwave potentials of species that give irreversible waves must be greater than $236/n$ mV to secure equally good resolution. We cannot state an exact criterion because of the great differences in degree of irreversibility possible; we have to examine each case individually. Often we cannot obtain adequate resolution.

Supporting electrolyte. Fortunately, it is possible to shift the halfwave potential of species by reaction with substances added as a part of a supporting electrolyte mixture. The major reaction possibilities, in order of decreasing usefulness, are complexing, the formation of a weak acid or base, and redox changes. Since any reagent added will react to a different extent with different species, half-wave potentials will be shifted by varying amounts from their normal values.

Table 25.1 shows the effect of several common supporting electrolytes on the half-wave potentials of some metal ions. When a metal ion is complexed, its halfwave potential is shifted to a more negative value. For example, $E_{1/2}$ for Zn^{2+} shifts 0.35 V when transferred from 1 M NH_3 to water.

Table 25.1 Some Supporting Electrolytes and Half-Wave Potentials*

Metal Ion	Half-Wave Potential, V vs. SCE					
	1 M KCl	1 M KCN	1 M NH_3 1 M NH_4 Cl	1 M NaOH	7.3 M H_3PO_4	1 M Na_3 Cit. 0.1 M NaOH
Cd^{2+}	−0.64	−1.18	−0.81	−0.76	−0.71	−1.46
Co^{2+}	−1.20	−1.45	−1.29	−1.43	−1.20	−1.45
Cu^{2+}	−0.22	NR‡	−0.51	−0.41	−0.09	−0.50
Fe^{2+}			−1.49	−1.46		
Pb^{2+}	−0.44	−0.72		−0.76	−0.53	−0.78
Ni^{2+}	−1.1†	−1.36	−1.10		−1.18	NR
Zn^{2+}	−1.00	NR	−1.35	−1.53	−1.13	−1.43
Sn^{2+}				−1.22	−0.58	−1.12
Tl^+	−0.48		−0.48	−0.46	−0.63	−0.56

* Based on tabulation of Meites [2].
† 0.1 M KCl.
‡ Not reducible.

A quite complete selection of data on half-wave potentials in different supporting electrolytes is given in Meites, [2] and very usable charts of $E_{1/2}$ are presented in Kolthoff and Lingane. [4] Where data are lacking, an estimate of the effect of an unlisted complexing agent is possible if stability constants for its complexes are known. (See Exercise 25.17.) Conversely, such equilibrium constants can be determined polarographically (Section 25.15). The following examples illustrate the utility of varying the supporting electrolyte.

Example 1   A trace concentration (10^{-5} M) of thallium cannot be estimated reliably in an alloy that contains cadmium in considerably greater concentration as long as 1 M KCl is the supporting electrolyte because $\Delta E_{1/2}$ is only 160 mV. According to Table 25.1, if a 1 M NH_3, 1 M NH_4Cl mixture is substituted for KCl, $\Delta E_{1/2}$ for the Tl^+-Cd^{2+} pair increases to 330 mV and thallium can be determined successfully.

Example 2   A small concentration of cobalt is to be measured in a nickel-cobalt mixture. Because of the instrumental problem of measuring the height of a small wave with adequate sensitivity when it follows a high wave (see the discussion of compensation in Section 25.6), the determination would be more reliable if the cobalt reduction occurred first. As Table 25.1 shows, in 1 M KCl, not only is cobalt electrolyzed second, but $\Delta E_{1/2}$ appears about 100 mV.

In this case, oxidation of cobalt to Co(III) may be used advantageously. To effect oxidation at a good potential (below -1.10 V vs. SCE) ethylenediamine is added to the KCl solution; the $E_{1/2}$ for the anodic (oxidation) cobalt wave is then -0.046 V. In ethylenediamine, the nickel reduction wave occurs at -0.8 to -1.0 V without interference.

25.9 READING POLAROGRAPHIC CURVES

With whatever instrument we make a polarographic study of a system, we must trace an entire wave, not just a few points, if precision (± 1 to $\pm 5\%$) is sought in a determination. In securing curves it will be assumed that two kinds of expectations have been met. One kind is chemical, that the system has been deaerated, that current maxima are eliminated, and that impurities are absent. The other type is more nearly instrumental, that the same compensation and damping or filtering procedures have been used with all curves relating to a given constituent and that there is minimum uncertainty in the average current curve. The rationale for securing an entire wave is that in practical systems current does not vary in any precisely predictable fashion with voltage. Irregularities in waves are likely to be important also; these will be missed without the entire curve.

Note that data for equilibrium constants and for structural and physical studies of molecules should be taken only from well-developed waves. Only from such waves is a precision of $\pm 1\%$ obtainable, and then only with replicate measurements.

Figure 25.2 shows a good procedure for reading a polarogram when a single electroactive species is present. We measure the residual current over the potential range of interest using a blank and then subtract it from the limiting current value. When there are multiple electroactive species, it is even more valuable to measure the residual current, for we cannot predict its value accurately by extrapolation. An added advantage is that use of a residual current curve allows automatic correction for unexpected, reducible impurities in the supporting electrolyte. It is likely that the presence of such an impurity might otherwise be overlooked.

In many polarographic determinations the resolution of waves is marginal and waveforms are not ideal. Often we may make a quantitative determination by use of a calibration curve. How should we handle the polarographic data? What we require is the development and use of a systematic procedure for reading polarograms. It should of course be based on a theoretical expectation of slopes and shapes of curves. Suggested steps in such a procedure are: First, we extrapolate the limiting current curve, if necessary, to permit a current value to be read as near the top of a wave as possible. In the case of a plateau with a zero or slightly negative slope, this step becomes especially important. Second, we can assume the point of inflection between successive waves to be the best estimate of the limiting current for the earlier wave. Note how we apply these two principles to the waves in Fig. 25.18. Third, we estimate a half-wave potential by graphical construction. We draw lines representing the residual and diffusion currents through the polarographic curve, or obtain them by extrapolation if necessary. The $E_{1/2}$ is the voltage at which the current has risen to a value halfway between initial and final figures. The figure shows this procedure also. More elaborate graphical procedures have been suggested as well. [2]

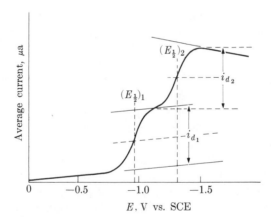

Fig. 25.18 Graphical analysis of polarographic curves. They have been smoothed.

25.10 INORGANIC ANALYSIS

Most quantitative polarographic analysis is by comparative methods.* The objective is to minimize error arising from the inability to control precisely a host of electrolysis variables as well as deviations from the Ilkovic equation. To realize this goal a particular polarograph and dropping mercury electrode are used (under as nearly identical conditions of temperature and head of mercury as possible) to obtain polarograms on the standard and unknown solutions. This type of relative procedure is inherently simple and is capable of good precision.

---

* So-called absolute methods based on use of diffusion current constants and values of m and t for an electrode are used mainly when versatility is more valuable than accuracy, e.g., when a great many different kinds of samples must be analyzed polarographically. [2]

Procedure. An important preliminary step in quantitative polarographic work is the identification of substances in the sample. In a few instances, this process can be carried out polarographically. The next step is to select a supporting electrolyte combination that (a) provides clean separations of all waves of interest, (b) if possible, places any small wave, which represents a trace amount, ahead of high waves, and (c) if necessary, buffers the solution at a particular pH. The discussion of resolution of waves (Section 25.8) is essential background. If elements known to be present at trace levels are of interest, one of the methods to be discussed in Chapter 26 should be explored.

Alkali metal and quaternary ammonium salts are most often used as the supporting or indifferent electrolyte. With KCl, the maximum negative potential attainable with the dropping electrode is about -1.9 V vs. SCE, with Et_4NOH, -2.2 V.

Example Even alkali metals can be successfully analyzed in aqueous solution by polarography by use of tetrabutyl ammonium hydroxide supporting electrolyte. Sample concentrations must be above 5×10^{-4} M, however, because of the large residual currents that flow at very negative potentials. Ethanol may be added (up to 50 to 75 %) to the solution to lower the $E_{1/2}$ somewhat and lessen the residual current.[5]

The chemical purity of the supporting electrolyte is often of critical concern. This is especially true if we must determine a trace constituent. For example, KCl that contains 0.01 % of a reducible foreign contaminant gives a 10^{-4} M solution of that substance if the KCl concentration is 1 M. In this case, either the polarogram shows a diffusion current that is too large or it has spurious detail. We can avoid this type of error by routinely running a polarogram at high sensitivity on each new batch of salt or other reagent that is to be used in a supporting electrolyte. If an impurity wave of significant proportions appears, we can easily remove the foreign material by controlled potential electrolysis. The use of a mercury pool working electrode held at a potential slightly above the step of the impurity wave is recommended for the process (Section 27.7). Usually no more than an hour of electrolysis is required.

If we can find no electrolyte that gives a sufficient separation of a pair of waves of interest, we may explore several possibilities. One is that differentiating the signal may improve the resolution sufficiently. [14] Another is the use of a differential polarographic instrument. A third is that the species reducible at the lower voltage can be separated chemically. Occasionally, it may be chemically reduced and left in solution. The procedure is successful if the interfering substance is much more difficult to reduce from its lower oxidation state than from the upper and if the reducing agent is specific in its action. For example, this method might be effective in nullifying interference from the ferric ion.

A problem unique to the study of oxidations is that the positive voltage necessary to effect electrolysis may be beyond the range of the dropping mercury electrode. If this is the case, we can often substitute for the dropping electrode a microplatinum electrode, of either the stationary or the rotary type. Neither type is nearly as satisfactory as the dropping electrode. With a stationary solid electrode diffusion currents are set up slowly and are not easily reproducible. The surface of either type usually changes as the electrolysis continues. A rotating microelectrode (600 rev/min) is usually preferred, for it offers the advantage of a much larger and more nearly constant diffusion current (Section 25.13).

Once the substances present are identified and the supporting electrolyte (and solvent) selected to optimize the desired determination, analysis can be made. We must dissolve the sample and make any necessary preliminary separation. Either before or at this stage we must dilute an aliquot of the resulting solution by adding supporting electrolyte solution to bring the concentration of as many as possible of the constituents of interest into the favorable 10^{-3} to 10^{-4} M range.

The next step is removal from the solution of dissolved oxygen. It cannot be left in because the reduction of oxygen gives a pronounced diffusion current.* Sparging the solution with a fast flow of purified nitrogen gas for 5 to 10 minutes prior to analysis is usually sufficient. Commerical nitrogen can be used for most sparging; exacting polarography requires commercial nitrogen further purified by passage over copper turnings at 475 °C or through a vanadous salt solution.

The necessary polarograms are then obtained. If time permits, one should be run on a sample of supporting electrolyte solution (after removal of oxygen) to obtain the residual current.

Methods. In the relative methods used in virtually all polarography we use standard solutions in some way. Standards and samples must be equal in concentration of supporting electrolyte, maximum suppressor, and, in most cases, other substances that are present but that are of no analytical interest. Preferably, standards and samples should be run the same day to avoid possible variations in capillary behavior. It is also desirable to watch for evidence of partial clogging of the capillary.

In routine analysis it is probably unnecessary to obtain a polarogram for each sample. Where behavior is known to be reproducible and a species gives a well-defined wave, a single value of current at a voltage well into the limiting plateau should be sufficient. Where this method is used, standards should be run frequently.

How can we use standard samples effectively in polarography? The procedures available are common to many relative instrumental techniques. One is to use a calibration curve of i_d vs. C for each electroactive species of interest. The curves need not be straight. If the diffusion current of a species has been found, its concentration may be read from the calibration curve. Since a calibration line should go through the origin, a simpler but slightly less precise procedure is to match a standard of diffusion current $i_{d(std)}$ against a sample of current $i_{d(x)}$. The concentration of sample is given by the equation $C_x = C_{std}[i_{d(x)}/i_{d(std)}]$.

The *pilot ion* method is still less precise but has the merits of versatility and simplicity. It relies on the fact that the ratio of wave height for two species proves virtually independent of medium, electrodes, and other conditions. Any ion of known concentration can therefore serve as a standard (or pilot ion) for another species. An example best illustrates actual application of the method.

Example A sample to be analysed for zinc by use of lead as a pilot ion is known not to contain lead or another species whose reduction would interfere with the lead wave. Assume it is found

---

* Oxygen gives two waves, one starting at about -0.10 V (product, H_2O_2) and the other beginning at about -0.90 V vs. SCE (product, H_2O or OH^-).

that $i_d(\text{Zn}^{2+})/i_d(\text{Pb}^{2+}) = 1.30$ when their concentrations are equal. In a solution made up from the sample, 0.80 millimoles of lead are added. The zinc diffusion current is found to be 0.75 times that of lead. Let the amount of zinc in the sample be x. Then, $0.75/1.30 = x/0.80$; and $x = 0.46$ millimoles Zn^{2+}.

The *standard addition method* is also used. In it we add a weighed amount of the substance being determined to one of two identical samples of the unknown. We then treat each sample by the same analytical procedure down to the last detail and determine their polarograms consecutively. The weight w_1 of the substance present initially is determined from the expression

$$w_1 = \frac{i_1 x_2}{\Delta i}, \qquad (25.12)$$

where x_2 is the weight of standard added to sample 2, i_1 is the wave height for sample 1 (to which no standard was added), and Δi is the difference in wave heights. The method is precise but somewhat more time-consuming than the other techniques.

25.11 ORGANIC ANALYSIS

We can determine organic substances quantitatively that react in some way at a dropping electrode by polarography. The most important category comprises substances that it is possible to electrolyze directly such as those with a highly polar bond or unsaturation. Table 25.2 lists some electroactive functional groups. Some other minor classes of organic compounds can also be determined. They include substances that react with mercury such as mercaptols, surface-active agents such as detergents, and substances that cause catalytic waves. As we might expect, organic polarography is also attractive for a quantitative functional group analysis.

Table 25.2 Some Organic Functional Groups that are Electroactive*

Group	Approximate $E_{1/2}$ (V vs. SCE)	Group	Approximate $E_{1/2}$ (V vs. SCE)
$-\text{N}{=}\text{O}$	-0.2		
$-\text{OOH}$	-0.5	$-\text{COOH}$	-1.8
$-\text{NO}_2$	-0.9	$>\text{C}{=}\text{O}$	-2.5
$-\text{CHO}$	-1.6	$-\text{NH}_2$	$-0.5\dagger$
$>\text{CX}$	-1.7	$-\text{SH}$	$-0.5\dagger$

* Neutral or basic medium.
† Anodic waves.

In organic polarography water is a favored solvent. To obtain sufficient solubility for organic species at the 10^{-3} to 10^{-4} M level we usually add a second solvent such as methanol or dioxane. Supporting electrolytes are selected mainly for their pH or buffering ability; they are ineffective in shifting halfwave potentials of most molecular substances. The use of potassium and sodium salts or hydroxides as buffer constituents up to potentials of -1.8 V vs. SCE is common. To attain still more negative potentials we substitute quaternary ammonium salts or hydroxides. Close control of pH is nearly always essential, for hydrogen ions are involved in most organic electrolyses. The supporting electrolyte needs to be a strong acid, a strong base, or a well-buffered solution.*

Organic polarography has two serious disadvantages. One is that most polarographic waves are markedly irreversible. Because of their greater voltage spread (see Fig. 23.8), overlapping of waves is unavoidable unless species reduce at widely different potentials or can be separated prior to analysis. The second difficulty is that all substances with a given functional group tend to be reduced over a short range of potentials. For example, most simple alphatic nitro compounds reduce at potentials from -0.60 to -0.72 V vs. SCE. If a single representative of a class is present, it may be determinable in a mixture; if two or more representatives are present only a functional group determination may be feasible.

25.12 MEMBRANE ELECTRODE POLAROGRAPHY

Problems such as a tendency toward current maxima and adsorption make the analysis of gases with a dropping mercury electrode unattractive. Yet if we replace the diffusion layer of an electrode with a semipermeable membrane, polarographic determinations of gases like oxygen become straightforward. The membrane type of polarographic electrode eliminates or minimizes the difficulties. Further, it makes possible the development of a portable instrument.

A membrane electrode is a gold or platinum piece covered with a membrane of polyethylene (if for O_2 and SO_2) or Teflon (if also for halogens). A salt bridge connects the membrane electrode to a reference (usually of an inert metal or carbon). Such a cell can respond either to dissolved gas or to a gaseous mixture. We apply a steady voltage sufficient to achieve a potential on the plateau of the desired polarographic wave (-0.8 V for O_2) and secure a current proportional to the gas concentration. Since ionic and most molecular species are excluded by the membrane, there is reasonable specificity of electrode response to the gas. Sensitivity (0.1 ppm O_2), accuracy ($\pm 1\%$), and response time (10 s for 90% of full scale) are good. Most commercial instruments of this type are portable, determine only oxygen, and provide thermistor compensation for temperature changes.

25.13 AMPEROMETRIC TITRATION

A dropping mercury electrode or other polarized microelectrode may also be used to detect titration end points. A constant voltage is applied and the change in current observed as the titration proceeds. The reaction of interest must also be essentially complete and reasonably fast, as in any titration. As long as reactant, titrant, product, or some combination of them can be reversibly electrolyzed at the polarized electrode, a "polarographic" titration is possible. In accord with modern nomenclature the measurement is termed an amperometric titration with one indicator electrode or

---

* When in excess, a strong acid or base by itself is a buffer. Standard handbooks should be consulted for suitable buffers in the intermediate pH range. Of course, it is essential that a buffer is not reducible and that the equilibria involved in producing or using up hydrogen ion are sufficiently fast to keep the pH at the surface of the dropping mercury electrode constant. This requirement implies that the diffusion rate of the buffer components must also be adequate.

simply an amperometric titration. If both electrodes are polarized during at least part of a titration, the label biamperometric [16] or amperometric titration with two indicator electrodes is applied. We consider this type of titration in the next section.

As in polarography, the limiting current of one or more electroactive species plays a central role in the titration. For this purpose we apply a steady voltage sufficient to charge the indicator electrode (microelectrode) to a potential well into the diffusion-limited range for the electroactive species. During a titration, we take current readings at several points before and after the equivalence point. In general these are graphed and linear portions well removed from the apparent equivalence point are extrapolated to their intersection at the end point.

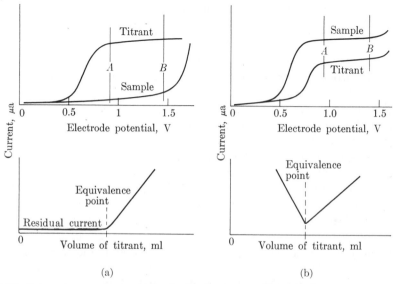

(a)   (b)

Fig. 25.19 Polarograms and amperometric titration curves. The titration curve is that obtained when the microelectrode is at a voltage between A and B. In (a) only the titrant is electroactive. In (b) both the titrant and the substance being analyzed are electroactive.

Figure 25.19 shows the relation between the shape of a titration curve and the character of the species in a titration. If only the titrant is electroactive, no current flows until it is in excess as in the first curve. When titrant and reactant are both electroactive at the applied potential, a "V" curve is obtained like that in Fig. 25.19b. Since we need establish only a sharp change in current by the technique, the precision of an amperometric procedure is superior to that of a straight polarographic determination and is usually $\pm 1\%$ or better. An important general restriction of amperometry is that it is possible to monitor few acid-base titrations; the method is mainly used for precipitation and redox reactions.

Example Lead may be determined by amperometric titration with potassium dichromate, using the dropping mercury-SCE electrode pair. The sample is diluted, if necessary, to bring its lead concentration to about 10^{-2} to 10^{-3} M, potassium nitrate added until it is 0.01 M, and a potential difference of 1 V applied to the cell, with the dropping electrode negative. When 0.05 M $K_2Cr_2O_7$

is used as the tirtrant, both Pb^{2+} and dichromate ion are reduced and a V-shaped titration curve is found. There is no need to remove dissolved oxygen.

If it is necessary to avoid interferences, the titration can be performed instead at zero applied potential if an acetate buffer supporting electrolyte is used. Lead ions are not reduced at this potential but dichromate ions are.

Instrumentation. While we may use the dropping mercury electrode as the indicator electrode, where its extensive negative potential range is not needed, a *rotating platinum microelectrode* is often substituted. This type of electrode is attractive because of its simplicity and ease of construction and use. Its voltage range extends from about 1 V to -1 V vs. SCE. The relatively low hydrogen overvoltage on platinum is responsible for its short negative range. One design is shown in Fig. 25.20. Its rotation is maintained constant at about 600 rev/min.

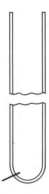

Fig. 25.20   One type of rotating platinum microelectrode. Cracks at the metal-glass seal should be scrupulously avoided, for they are potentially sources of large residual currents. To make electrical contact with the platinum the lower portion of the tube is filled with mercury and a copper wire is inserted. The copper wire remains stationary when the electrode is rotated.

The rotating platinum electrode has three noteworthy advantages over the dropping mercury electrode in titrations: (a) It offers a fixed surface area and thus draws very little capacitive current; (b) it has a very thin diffusion layer as a result of the rapid rotation and gives a larger diffusion current; and (c) it can be used at potentials up to $+1.1$ V vs. SCE. Its greater sensitivity as a detector allows 1 % precision in the titration of certain solutions as dilute as 10^{-4} to 10^{-5} M. The greater potential range means that we may easily carry out oxidations as well as reductions with this electrode. Note that the inherent disadvantages of a solid microelectrode (uncertainty in absolute potential and diffusion current) fail to interfere, since we use a fixed applied potential and only changes in the diffusion current are of concern.

A tall-form 100 ml beaker is an entirely suitable titration cell when closed with a rubber bung through which necessary items can be inserted. Usually an external reference electrode (SCE) is used and is connected to the cell by a salt bridge. This type of reference is preferable to a mercury pool, which may become contaminated during a titration. We may add titrant from a buret or generate it within the cell by a coulometric procedure (Section 27.3).

Procedure.   Preparations for an amperometric titration follow regular polarographic procedure. It is conventional to know the substances present and their halfwave potentials beforehand. Preliminary polarograms or even analyses by other techniques may need to be run. Once we have chosen an appropriate supporting electrolyte and sample dilution, stock supporting electrolyte is added until the volume is about 50 ml.

We can decide the best potential for a titration by reference to polarograms or halfwave potentials of the electroactive species in the system (Fig. 25.19). Naturally, a potential at which a sharp end-point break is secured is the best choice. The titrant should be five or ten times more concentrated than the substance to be analyzed. We can correct for dilution by multiplying the current by the factor $(V_0 + V_{titrant})/V_0$, where V_0 is the initial volume of sample solution.

In many systems before current readings are made we must remove dissolved oxygen because of the relative ease with which it is reduced. In these cases is customary to bubble pure nitrogen through the solution initially and after each addition of titrant to sparge it of oxygen. The procedure provides stirring also.

Like other titration methods amperometric titrations offer the advantages of a graphical procedure. Since linear regions away from the end point are extrapolated to locate the end point, the slight solubility of any precipitate formed, or lack of stability of complexes, etc., is automatically ignored. Such behavior influences the current–voltage curves only in the end-point region. A marked advantage over conductometric titrations is that most foreign salts have no effect on an amperometric titration. The few exceptions are materials reducible in the titration; their presence in even trace amounts will lower the accuracy of an amperometric titration. A particular advantage over photometric titrations is that solutions in amperometric titrations may be highly absorbing or turbid as long as the substances with these properties are not electroactive at the potential chosen. Amperometric end-point procedures are common in titrations.

25.14 BIAMPEROMETRIC TITRATIONS

With some redox systems amperometric titrations can be carried out more simply and accurately using two indicator (polarized) electrodes.* The technique requires use of two stationary platinum electrodes of small surface area. A constant potential difference of the order of 0.01 to 0.1 V is applied and the solution stirred continuously while adding titrant and measuring the current. The low voltage is essential to the method. Currents in the range of from 0 to 100 μA are ordinarily observed. Only a few values near the end point, where the current is essentially zero, need be recorded and graphed (see Fig. 25.21).

For this technique to be applicable to a redox titration one or both of the couples (Section 23.1) in the redox system must undergo an irreversible reaction at the electrodes. This requirement may be better understood by representing a redox titration in general form as:

$$\underset{\text{sample}}{A_1} + \underset{\text{titrant}}{B_2} \rightarrow A_2 + B_1$$

where the subscripts 1 and 2 refer to oxidized and reduced forms of a species respec-

---

* The term dead-stop titration was applied to this technique earlier.

tively. In the reaction substance A_1 is reduced by the titrant B_2. To be developed as a biamperometric method, either couple A_1, A_2 or B_1, B_2 must react irreversibly at the electrodes. For A_1, A_2 to behave this way means that either the reduction of A_1 or the oxidation of A_2 must be a slow reaction. The current through the cell will essentially go to zero whenever the species irreversibly electrolyzed is the only substance that can react at one electrode.

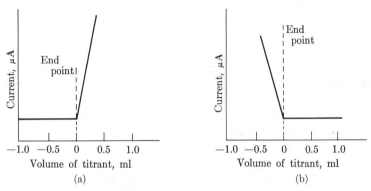

Fig. 25.21 Curves for amperometric titration with two polarized electrodes. (a) Couple A_1, A_2, irreversible; titrant couple B_1, B_2, reversible. (b) Couple A_1, A_2, reversible; titrant couple B_1, B_2, irreversible.

Example 1 The end point in the determination of thiosulfate by titration with iodine is often detected biamperometrically. In the course of the titration iodine is reduced to iodide ion. The I^-, I_2 couple is reversibly electrolyzed, but the thiosulfate, tetrathionate ion couple is not. At the low voltage applied oxidation of thiosulfate ion is not possible at the anode and the reduction of tetrathionate ion is not possible at the cathode.

Figure 25.21a shows the titration curve. Only when I_2 is present in excess (beyond the end point) does electrolysis current exist. Prior to that time, only I^-, which can be reversibly oxidized at the anode, and the irreversible couple are present, and there cannot be electrolysis at both electrodes.

Example 2 The Karl Fischer titration of water provides an especially important application of the biamperometric end-point technique. Stabilized Karl Fischer reagent is a solution of iodine and sulfur dioxide in pyridine (Py) and methyl cellosolve. The essential reaction with water is given by the equation

$$I_2 + SO_2 + H_2O + Py \rightarrow Py \cdot SO_3 + 2Py \cdot HI$$

A second reaction with the cellosolve follows. Only the I_2, I^- couple is reversibly electrolyzed, and a direct titration of water with the reagent gives a curve like that in Fig. 25.21a.

In the titration curves displayed in Fig. 25.21b only the titrant couple behaves irreversibly. Current exists until the end point and then ceases because of polarization of the electrodes. Only the portion of the current curve near the end point is shown. If observed throughout the titration, the current would be found to go through a maximum and then to fall as the sample approached exhaustion.

Instrumentation and procedure. Very simple electrical instrumentation suffices, since the voltage applied is small and constant and need be known only roughly. The fact that we require no reference electrode is an important advantage, especially in anhydrous solution media. We can measure the current with a galvanometer or microammeter or, in the case of nonaqueous media, a pH meter. The voltammetric apparatus, solutions, and procedures are like those in standard amperometric titrations. Stirring is essential.

25.15 RESEARCH APPLICATIONS

From polarographically determined values of half-wave potential we can obtain a great many types of fundamental information. The relationship between such values and standard electrode potentials suggests some of the possibilities. Basically, we are observing an equilibrium involving transition between oxidation states! We can deduce the equilibrium constant for this process itself. But, more important, we can determine equilibrium constants for any rapidly established equilibrium that involves a particular electroactive species by observing the change in halfwave potential as the concentration of one component of the equilibrium system is varied.

It is also possible to study any factor that influences an equilibrium involving an electroactive species such as complex ion formation. For example, halfwave potentials of reversible reductions are ordinarily shifted to more negative values when the electroactive species becomes more strongly bound. Because of such correlations the electronic nature of ligands, stereochemistry, and bonding may all be illuminated.

Similarly, the electroreduction of organic species at a dropping mercury electrode opens whole fields to study. We can investigate the effect of substituents, the nature of bonding near electroactive sites, stereochemical effects, and many other types of interaction. In such a study it is important that the mechanism of the reduction reaction be the same for all systems to be compared so that due allowance can be made for the chemical and electrochemical steps at the dropping mercury electrode.

As might be expected, changing wave heights can be used in the elucidation of kinetic aspects of reactions. We can follow polarographically slowly established equilibria (those requiring 10 s or more) built around an electroactive species. There is an unusual opportunity to study mechanism. Sometimes it has been possible to identify the slow step in a complex reaction polarographically. In the case of multielectron reactions that involve organic molecules, we can elucidate the nature of each step in favorable cases. [8]

REFERENCES

Good introductions to polarography with emphasis on the practical aspects of measurement are provided by:

1. J. Heyrovsky and P. Zuman, *Practical Polarography*. New York: Academic, 1968
2. Louis Meites, *Polarographic Techniques*. 2d ed. New York: Wiley, 1965

Thorough discussions of the principles and techniques of polarography are available in:

4. I. M. Kolthoff and James J. Lingane, *Polarography*. 2d ed., vol. 1. New York: Interscience, 1952.
5. L. Meites, "Voltammetry at the Dropping Mercury Electrode," in *Treatise on Analytical Chemistry*. Pt I, vol. 4. I. M. Kolthoff, P. J. Elving, and E. B. Sandell, eds. New York: Interscience, 1963
6. G. W. C. Milner, *The Principles and Applications of Polarography*. New York: Longmans, Green, 1957
7. O. H. Müller, "Polarography," in *Physical Methods of Organic Chemistry*. 3d ed., Pt IV. A. Weissberger, ed. New York: Interscience, 1960

Some references dealing with specialized aspects of polarography are:

8. Petr Zuman, *Organic Polarographic Analysis*. New York: Macmillan, 1964
9. L. B. Anderson and C. N. Reilley, "Teaching Electroanalytical Chemistry," *J. Chem. Educ.*, **44**, 9 (1967)
10. G. J. Hills, ed., *Polarography 1964*. Vol. 1. New York: Interscience-Wiley, 1966
11. Stal' G. Mairanovskii, *Catalytic and Kinetic Waves in Polarography*. New York: Plenum, 1968
12. J. K. Taylor, "Examination of Absolute and Comparative Methods of Polarographic Analysis," *Anal. Chem.*, **19**, 368 (1947)

Instrumentation is emphasized in:

13. G. L. Booman and W. B. Holbrook, "Electroanalytical Controlled-Potential Instrumentation," *Anal. Chem.*, **35**, 1793 (1963)
14. D. J. Fisher, W. L. Belew, and M. T. Kelley, "A Controlled-Potential and Derivative DC Polarograph . . . ," *Chem. Instr.*, **1**, 181 (1968)
15. S. Z. Lewin, "Electroanalytical Instrumentation," *J. Chem. Educ.*, **39**, A261, A355, A445, A519 (1962)

Amperometric titrations are discussed lucidly in:

16. John T. Stock, *Amperometric Titrations*. New York: Interscience, 1965

EXERCISES

25.1 Give an estimate of the maximum possible percentage depletion of a 10 ml sample of $Zn(NO_3)_2$ solution during 5 min of polarography. Assume that the diffusion current is constant at $10\,\mu A$.

25.2 The overpotential of hydrogen on mercury is 1.2 V. (a) According to Fig. 25.3 at what voltage (vs. normal hydrogen electrode) will water be reduced on mercury at pH = 0 when $p_{H_2} = 1$ atm $(101\ kN\ m^{-2})$? (b) When $p_{H_2} = 0.01$ atm $(1.01\ kN\ m^{-2})$? (c) at pH = 10 and $p_{H_2} = 1$ atm? (d) Give the reduction voltages vs. SCE.

25.3 Describe in detail the components of the cell current for each curve graphed in Fig. 25.8 when the potential is (a) 0.1 V more positive than $E_{1/2}$, (b) equal to $E_{1/2}$, and (c) 0.1 V more negative than $E_{1/2}$.

25.4 (a) Show that the potential of the dropping electrode at an average current $\bar{i}$ is given by

$$E_{DME} = E_{1/2} - \frac{RT}{nF} \ln \left(\frac{\bar{i}}{\bar{i}_d - \bar{i}} \right).$$

(b) Show that the average current $\bar{i}$ is given by

$$\bar{i} = \frac{\bar{i}_d}{1 + \exp\left[nF/RT(E_{1/2} - E) \right]}.$$

25.5 Equation (25.6) is often used as a test of whether a species is electrolyzing reversibly. For this purpose, it is assumed that $(D_{red}/D_{ox})^{1/2} = 1$. (a) How may the equation be plotted as a straight line? (b) Assuming that a straight-line graph is obtained for a species, how may the value of n be obtained from the plot?

25.6 A close approximation to the Ilkovic equation for i_d can be obtained by using the expression for semi-infinite linear diffusion, Eq. (23.23). Show that this is the case. [Consider that the volume of a spherical mercury drop at time t is $Vt = \frac{4}{3}\pi r_t^3$, where V is the volume of mercury flowing (cm^3 s^{-1}) and r_t is the drop radius at time t. Obtain an expression for the area of the sphere $(4\pi r_t^2)$ in terms of the mass rate of flow of mercury (mg s^{-1}) and density ρ that can be substituted in Eq. (23.21).]   [Ans.: $i_t = knD^{1/2}m^{2/3}t^{1/6}C_0$.]

25.7 What will be the error in determining the voltage applied to a polarographic cell if the circuit shown in Fig. 25.11 is used, but slidewire AC has a value of $400\,\Omega$? Assume that the voltage drop across AC is 2 V, the tap is set halfway along its length, and the electrolysis current passed by the cell is $40\,\mu A$.   [Ans.: 0.8%.]

25.8 In the discussion of error in application of cell potential in Section 25.6 the ratio of slidewire current to polarographic cell current was used as a criterion. Can this matter be viewed also as a problem of voltage transfer in which the criterion becomes $R_{cell} \gg R_{slidewire}$? If the latter criterion is used, how should R_{cell} be measured? Discuss briefly.

25.9 A galvanometer with a usable deflection range of 100 mm and a sensitivity of $0.01\,\mu A$ mm^{-1} is used in a polarograph. What reduction in sensitivity is necessary to just register a wave $15\,\mu A$ high? What reduction in sensitivity is necessary if two successive waves of heights 10 and $12\,\mu A$, respectively, are to be observed with maximum precision but without change in setting? Assume that reduction factors of 5, 10, 20, 50, 100, 200, 500, and 1000 are available.   [Ans.: 20; 50.]

25.10 Would $10\,\Omega$ or $1\,k\Omega$ be a more appropriate value for current-measuring resistor R in the circuit of Fig. 25.13 if currents ranging from $1\,\mu A$ to $30\,\mu A$ are to be measured and the dropping electrode potential must be known to ± 5 mV? How does the circuit of Fig. 25.11 avoid this difficulty? At what potential is the reference electrode in the figure?

25.11 Routine polarographic analyses are to be set up for measurements of Cd^{2+} in plating solutions. One type of solution contains no other ions that are electroactive within a few tenths of a volt of $E_{1/2}$ for cadmium. Another type of solution gives several closely spaced reduction waves. Samples must be diluted before polarograms are run. Both a manual polarograph and an automatic polarograph with capability for taking the derivative are available. (a) Which instrument is likely to have the higher signal-to-noise ratio? Why? (b) Which instrument is better suited to each type of determination? Why?

25.12 In the circuit of Fig. 25.14, a scan rate of 300 mV min^{-1} is desired. Values are $R = 1\,M\Omega$, $C = 1\,\mu F$. What must V_{B1} be?

25.13 In the operational amplifier circuit of Fig. 25.14 no provision is made for beginning the scan at other than zero volts. Sketch a simple modification by which a variable bias voltage can be used to initiate the ramp at other desired voltages.

25.14 The following polarographic data were taken from a reversible reduction wave at 25 °C:

E, V vs. SCE	i_{av}, μA
−0.569	0.60
−0.570	1.53
−0.581	2.32
−0.589	3.02
−0.598	3.84
−0.610	4.52
−0.618	4.80

The measured average diffusion current was 4.95 μA. (a) What number of electrons was involved in the electrode reaction? (b) What is the halfwave potential for this reaction? (c) What is the approximate standard electrode potential for the system? State the assumptions made in estimating the last quantity.

25.15 Suggest a procedure for a polarographic analysis of (a) a mixture of Zn^{2+} ion and Co^{2+} ion in about equal concentrations and (b) a trace of Zn^{2+} ion in the presence of a large amount of Co^{2+} ion.

25.16 The usefulness of current compensation in recording a "second" wave is especially marked if the second electroactive species is more dilute than the first to be reduced. Assume equal diffusion coefficients for Cd^{2+} and Zn^{2+} species and use of a current sensitivity of 1/50. Sketch a smoothed polarogram for a mixture of 2×10^{-4} M Cd^{2+} and 5×10^{-5} M Zn^{2+} in 1 M KCl supporting electrolyte (see Table 25.1), assuming a full-scale reading of 20 units is obtained for the sum of the diffusion currents. Draw a second smoothed polarogram under conditions of compensation for the Cd^{2+} wave and recording of the Zn^{2+} wave at a sensitivity of 1/10.

25.17 The halfwave potential of a metallic ion can be shifted by changing to a supporting electrolyte that complexes the ion. Let M and M^{2+} be the reduced and oxidized forms of the metal and X be the ligand with which it complexes (according to the equilibrium $M^{2+} + pX \rightleftharpoons MX_p^{2+}$). (a) Show that the shift in half-wave potential of the metal ion on complexing is given by $(E_{1/2})_{M^{2+}} - (E_{1/2})_{MX_p^{2+}} = 0.059/n \log K[X]^p$ where K is the overall formation constant of the complex ion. (b) Is the alteration in $E_{1/2}$ for Zn^{2+} observed on going from 1 M KCl to 1 M NH_3/1 M NH_4Cl (see Table 25.1) in accord with this relationship? $K_{formation}$ for $Zn(NH_3)_4^{2+}$ is 1.15×10^9. Discuss.

25.18 A lead solution gave a wave whose height was 4.50 μA when the drop time t was 4.00 s and m was 2.35 mg s^{-1}. What diffusion current will be obtained if the mercury column height is decreased so that the drop time becomes 4.40 s? [Hint: The rate of flow of mercury is proportional to the column height, and the drop time is inversely proportional to the column height.]

25.19 The diffusion current of zinc in an unknown solution is 4.15 μA. On addition of 1.00 ml of 5.05×10^{-3} M zinc solution to 25.0 ml of the unknown solution, the zinc wave height increased to 5.32 μA. Calculate the concentration of zinc in the unknown.   [Ans.: 6.0×10^{-4} M.]

25.20   Sketch a cell suitable for a membrane polarographic electrode (Section 25.12). Remember that the reference electrode should not be in contact with the fluid being analyzed. [See G. P. Brierly, *Biochem. Biophys.* **19–4**, 500 (1965).]

25.21   The method of biamperometric titration (two polarized electrodes) is to be used in the determination of ferric sulfate. The titrant is to be titanous sulfate. Sketch the complete titration curve for this analysis from the knowledge that the Fe^{3+}, Fe^{2+} couple is reversible and the Ti^{2+}, Ti^{4+} couple is irreversible. (Since there are no quantitative data, only the general shape of the curve can be indicated.)

25.22   The titration $Ce^{4+} + Fe^{2+} \rightarrow Ce^{3+} + Fe^{3+}$ can be carried out biamperometrically. Two micro platinum electrodes are used with a constant potential ΔV applied across them. Consider the relative concentration of species present at different stages of the titration and possible anode and cathode reactions; then sketch the titration curve that should be obtained. Label regions of the curve according to your analysis.

25.23   For organic substances a cathodic shift (toward more negative potentials) in the reduction of a homologous series indicates increasing difficulty of reduction. Predict the shift for the polarographic reduction (a) of the C—X bond in the halide series R—I, R—Br, R—Cl, R—F; (b) of the first double bond in a series of compounds with increasing conjugation.

25.24   Maleic and fumaric acids, *cis-* and *trans-*isomers, respectively, show single two-electron reduction waves in 1 M NH_3/NH_4Cl supporting electrolyte at 1.40 V and 1.75 V. (a) Write an equation for the reduction occurring. Is the type of supporting electrolyte well chosen? (b) Account for the substantial difference in halfwave potentials.

CHAPTER 26

SINGLE-SWEEP AND PULSE POLAROGRAPHY

26.1 INTRODUCTION

This chapter considers a number of modifications of the classical polarographic technique discussed in Chapter 25. One essentially coulometric technique, stripping analysis, is also taken up since it is related to single-sweep polarography. Each new approach represents an attempt to exploit further the potentialities of the dropping mercury electrode. This device appears at one and the same time to be the electrode best suited to many electrolysis measurements and the source of the major limitations in such measurements. These are (a) fluctuations in current associated with the mercury drop cycle and (b) generation of a capacitive current as an accompaniment to the desired faradaic or electrolysis current. Section 25.7 suggested some ways of dealing with these factors in classical polarography. Each of the techniques presented in this chapter offers another essentially instrumental mode of minimizing the limitations. Other modern polarographic methods might have been included, but were omitted as essentially beyond the scope of the book. Two of the most valuable that fall in this category are ac polarography [2, 8] and oscillographic polarography at controlled alternating currents. [6]

In preparation for a discussion of newer polarographic methods it will be helpful to summarize ideas about the dependence of current in a polarographic cell on the changing area of the dropping mercury electrode.* As described in Section 25.3, the area of each successive mercury drop increases rapidly in the early part of its life. As it continues to grow in size, however, the rate of increase in area falls steadily and there is relatively little change in area during the last moments of drop life.

We can deduce from Fig. 26.1 the effect of drop growth on the faradaic and capacitive components of cell current. The curves shown represent behavior when the potential of the dropping electrode is constant and sufficiently negative to reduce a single species that is present at very low concentration (about 10^{-5} M). Since each drop expands into fresh solution, there is a constant thickness diffusion layer and the faradaic current is directly proportional to drop area (Section 23.2). This component of the total current attains a maximum value at the end of drop life, as Fig. 26.1 shows.

In addition, current unrelated to electron transfer must flow to build up an electrical double layer. Its area will grow rapidly during the early part of drop life but

---

* It is reasonable to assume that the counter electrode of the cell (Section 25.3) is nonpolarizable. Thus, any variations in cell current can be attributed to phenomena occurring at the dropping electrode.

willchange minimally near the end. This capacitive or double-layer charging current
varies in just this fashion. As Fig. 26.1b depicts, i_C is smallest at the end of drop life.

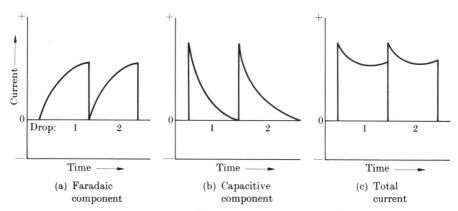

Fig. 26.1 Currents in a cell during reduction of a dilute (10^{-5} M) electroactive species. The dropping mercury electrode is held at a potential more negative than the species' half-wave potential.
Current components are shown over the lifetime of two successive drops.

A useful observation about polarography in quite dilute solutions can now be
made. Consider that the faradaic component of cell current is the desired *signal* and
the capacitive component can be equated to the essentially unknown and uncontrolled
background. To be sure, there is also noise, but it is less important. It is obvious from
Fig. 26.1 that the ratio of signal to background is a maximum near the end of drop life.
For work in dilute solutions, we should measure cell current in this interval. If this is
done in conjunction with use of appropriate electronics, the limit of detection can be
extended by about three orders of magnitude below that of classical polarography.

The techniques presented in this chapter are methods in which a favorable ratio of
signal to background has been realized. As a result, they are useful at trace levels and
with minute samples. Indeed, some of the techniques discussed in this chapter are
competitive in terms of limit of detection with neutron activation and spark-source
mass spectrometry.

Resolution and separability. Possibilities for extending polarography have also been
actively examined in the desire to improve the resolution of close-lying current waves.
The better the resolution possible, the larger the number of different electroactive
species it is possible to determine quantitatively in a single sample. Since resolution
of waves (Section 25.8) depends on differences in half-wave potentials, $\Delta E_{1/2}$, and on
relative concentrations C_1/C_2, different terms are employed to describe each aspect.

In dealing with polarographic curves, the term *resolution* will define the minimum
difference in halfwave potentials necessary for it to be possible to distinguish, at the
$\pm 1\%$ level, current waves of species present at equal concentrations.* The term
separability defines the maximum concentration ratio C_1/C_2 tolerable for two species

---

* As mentioned in Section 25.8, this specification means one wave should not affect the height
of the other by more than 1 %.

(whose halfwave potentials are at least some optimum $\Delta E_{1/2}$ apart) before their current waves are no longer sufficiently well resolved to permit a quantitative calculation of their concentrations. Species 1 is the more easily reduced species. Note that the optimum $\Delta E_{1/2}$ for two species will vary with the nature of the species, the technique, and the mode of signal processing. Note also that the values of resolution and separability are given for each of the newer polarographic techniques listed in Table 26.1. These are most favorable values such as are obtained when signals are differentiated. For comparison purposes, the specifications of the classical procedure under favorable processing are also given.

Example In classical polarography, for two species involving two-electron reductions and no processing of signal the separability is 10:1. A precise (± 1 to $\pm 2\%$) determination of concentration is no longer possible for them when $C_1 > 10C_2$.

Instrumentation. Before examining particular polarographic techniques it is worth while to inspect Fig. 26.2 and the generalized version of modern instrumentation it gives. A careful inspection reveals, as we would expect, that the modules are virtually the same as those required in classical three-electrode polarography. In a classical instrument the waveform generator would be a ramp generator and the signal

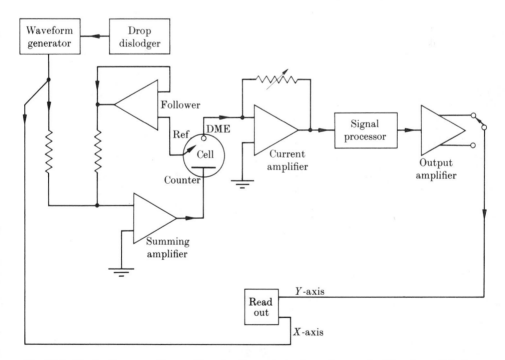

Fig. 26.2 Block diagram of a multimode, three-electrode polarograph. The drop dislodger ensures synchronization of drop life with the measurement sequence. The voltage–time pattern appropriate to each technique is provided by the waveform generator. The signal processor provides control pulses, memory, and other elements necessary to a particular technique.

Table 26.1 Characteristics of Several Electrolysis Techniques Based on the Dropping Mercury Electrode

Name of Technique	Voltage Program	Scan Rate, mV s^{-1}	Analytical Relation of Current to Bulk concn.	Most Favorable Performance		
				Limiting Concentration, M	Resolution, mV	Separability
Classical or dc polarography	Slow linear ramp (over lifetime many drops)	3–5	$i_d \propto C$ mean or peak diffusion current measured	1×10^{-5}	100	10:1
Single-sweep or oscilloscopic polarography	Fast linear ramp (over lifetime single drop)	250–500	$i_p \propto C$	A. Single-channel instrument 3×10^{-7} B. Double-channel instrument 5×10^{-8}	40 40	400:1 1000:1
Cyclic voltammetry	Fast triangular wave (over lifetime single drop)	250–500	$i_p \propto C$	3×10^{-7}	40	400:1

Pulse polarography
normal or integral
mode

A. dc pulses of increasing
amplitude

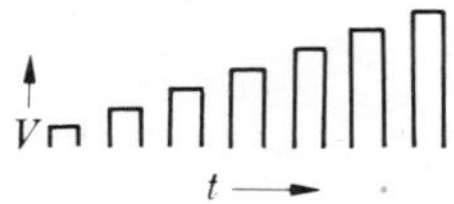

(over lifetime many drops;
one pulse per drop near
end of drop life)

0

$i_p \propto C$
current during
last fraction of
a pulse

1×10^{-7}

40

10,000:1

differential or
derivative mode

(pulse trains of
A type may also
be used)

B. dc pulses of constant
amplitude (20 to
100 mV) on slow
linear ramp

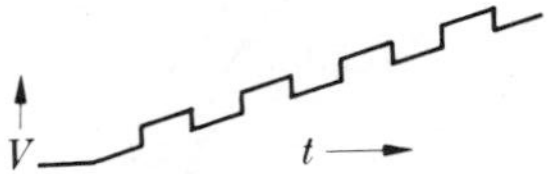

(over lifetime many drops;
one pulse per drop near
end of drop life)

5–15

$\dfrac{\Delta i}{\Delta v}$ measured

1×10^{-8}

30–40

50,000:1

processor would provide damping and compensation (Sections 25.6 and 25.7). The one exception is that a drop dislodger is a necessity in newer methods. It is attached to the electrode and is a precision device that causes a mercury drop to fall and simultaneously provides a "start" signal to the programmer module.

In the newer methods the programmer must be capable of generating a variety of electrical forms such as ramps, triangular waves, and square pulses; the technique chosen determines the appropriate one. The signal processor must be capable of providing functions such as gating (to permit sampling of cell current over the proper time interval) and memory (to compare magnitude of successive current "samples").

As the new polarographic techniques are described, block diagrams are given so that they may be compared with this generalized layout. Finally, note that the diagram of Fig. 26.2 can also be used for a two-electrode instrument by removing the follower module.

26.2 SINGLE-SWEEP POLAROGRAPHY

The distinctive feature of single-sweep polarography is that a voltage range of 0.3 to 0.5 V is scanned linearly during a 0.5 to 2 s interval near the end of the life of one mercury drop. The successive electrolysis contributions of different species are therefore observed under conditions such that capacitive current arising from drop growth is minimal. The rapid scan requires that an oscilloscope be used to display the resulting polarogram. As a result of this readout, an earlier name for the technique, oscilloscopic polarography, is still used occasionally. Other names employed are the precise designation, linear voltage sweep chronoamperometry, and cathode ray polarography.*

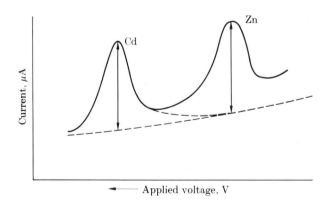

Fig. 26.3 Representative polarogram obtained in single-sweep polarography. Baseline (dashed) gives current in supporting electrolyte alone. Note that the first peak must be extrapolated in some manner to give baseline for measurement of second current peak.

---

* Single-sweep polarography is not to be confused with ac oscillographic polarography in which a 2 V sine-wave signal is imposed across a polarographic cell. [6]   In this method each of the electrodes becomes anode and cathode alternately though only the polarized electrode changes its potential.

Figure 26.3 shows the quite different form of polarogram obtained in single-sweep polarography. Current peaks identify the onset of each new electrolysis. Peaks appear as a result of the speed of the sweep. Once a potential sufficient to start reduction of a species is reached, the fast increase of applied potential causes a rapid reduction of all nearby particles of the species and a relatively large current flows. Then as the region around the drop becomes depleted in the species, the current decreases quickly and begins to approach the baseline asymptotically.

The peak current i_p is proportional to the concentration of a species, as seen below. In order to measure the value, we must establish a baseline. The easiest way is to stop the scan somewhat beyond a peak and watch the current decay visually until the "supporting" electrolyte value is nearly constant. As the potential is increased during a scan this capacitive or background current gradually rises because of the increase in drop area and the rapidity of the scan.

The critical analytical question is how i_p depends on major variables. For a reversible electrolysis that gives soluble products, the Randles–Sevcik equation [2] defines the peak current:

$$i_p = kn^{3/2}m^{2/3}t^{2/3}D^{1/2}v^{1/2}C \tag{26.1}$$

where k is a constant factor, n is the number of electrons per molecule, m is the mercury flow rate (mg s^{-1}), t is the drop life (s), D is the diffusion coefficient, v is the sweep rate (V s^{-1}), and C is the concentration.*

Here we take the peak current as pure faradaic current. What is especially interesting about Eq. (26.1) is the dependence of peak current on the square root of the scan rate. Since i_p is proportional to $v^{1/2}$, a faster scan will increase the faradaic current. Unfortunately, it will also increase capacitive current. It can be shown that $i_c \propto v$. The conclusion is that only at values of v sufficiently small that $v^{1/2} > v$, is the faradaic component favored. In general, the less concentrated a species, the smaller the scan rate must be to ensure that $i_f > i_c$.

Two other types of information about a species, $E_{1/2}$ and n, can often be derived from the polarogram. It can be shown that $E_{peak} = E_{1/2} - 1.1RT/nF$ in the case of a reversible electrolysis. For example, at 25 °C a peak appears at a potential $28/n$ mV more negative than $E_{1/2}$. We can also deduce the value of n for a well-defined peak from the expression $n = 56/(E_{3/4} - E_{1/4})$, where the potentials (in millivolts) are those at which the rising current attains one fourth its peak amplitude and three fourths of that value.

Figure 26.4 shows a block diagram of a single-sweep polarograph. The main modules, the voltage ramp generator, adder-follower, and current amplifier are like those described in Section 25.7. There are two distinctive differences from earlier polarographic circuitry. Readout is made on a storage (long-persistence) oscilloscope and provision is made, as noted earlier, for triggering the voltage sweep at the appro-priate point in the drop life.

In comparison with the classical version, single-sweep polarography features a gain of 10 or more in signal-to-noise ratio at low values of v and gives good results in

---

* For an irreversible reduction $n^{3/2}$ must be replaced by $n(\alpha n_a)^{1/2}$, where α is the transfer coefficient and n_a the number of electrons transferred in the step that determines the reaction.

the 10^{-3} to 10^{-6} M range. Accuracy is about the same, ± 2 to $\pm 3\%$, and depends on the experience of the analyst and the number of replicate samples. There is no net gain in accuracy, since what we achieve in signal-to-noise ratio we lose because of readout on a small oscilloscope screen. Use of a very fast recorder would alter the situation.

Single-sweep polarography also offers better resolution of waves, since there are no current serrations caused by drops, and there are peaks to distinguish instead of waves. Peaks separated by as little as 50 mV can be resolved when species concentrations are comparable. Differentiation of the polarogram will still further improve resolution (to 40 mV). Separability is of the order of 100:1 to 400:1. Single-sweep polarography is fast (about 2 s for a curve after deaeration). A disadvantage is the greater cost of the instrumentation.

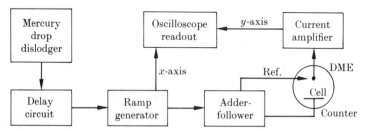

Fig. 26.4 Block diagram of a three-electrode, single-sweep polarograph. When a mercury drop is dislodged at the electrode stand, an electrical pulse is produced simultaneously. The delay circuit retards its arrival at the ramp generator by a precise interval (e.g. about 5 s if a 7 s drop time is used). The voltage ramp output is directed both to the horizontal plates of the oscilloscope and to the follower-adder, where it is added to the potential supplied by the potentiostat (follower) circuit. In this way the reference is swept through exactly the potential range of the ramp. Since the dropping electrode is at a virtual ground, this sweep alters its potential relative to the reference. The cell current is amplified and directed to the vertical oscilloscope plates.

Cyclic voltammetry. Still more can be learned about the behavior of an electroactive species "ox" if it is possible to observe both the forward reaction: ox $+ ne^- \rightarrow$ red, and its reverse: red $\rightarrow$ ox $+ ne^-$. The technique of cyclic voltammetry accomplishes this goal, at least for reasonable reversible reactions. A single cathodic sweep of voltage is followed by an anodic return at the same rate to the starting point. This type of sweep requires a *triangular wave* like that in Table 26.1.

For a reversible system the return sweep in cyclic voltammetry should yield a curve that is an inverted and reversed version of the original polarogram. Figure 26.5 gives an example. A set of oxidation peaks occurs for all species except those reduced irreversibly. For this reason, among others, the method proves an excellent graphic diagnostic device for examination of electrolysis systems. [7] The entire current–voltage curve is sometimes called a cyclic voltammogram.

Where should the negative "leg" of the sweep terminate in cyclic voltammmetry? In general, the working electrode should be swept to a potential sufficiently negative that the concentration C_{ox} falls nearly to zero at the electrode surface.

We can show for a reversible reduction that the difference in voltage between reduction and oxidation peaks is simply $63/n$ mV. Note also that an appreciable increase in scan rate will cause the curves to flatten because capacitive current will increase.

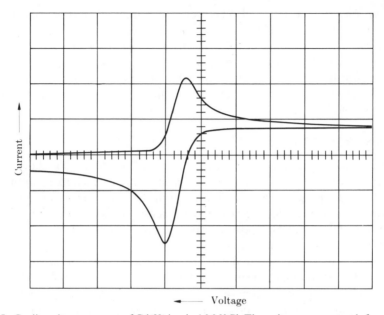

Fig. 26.5 Cyclic voltammogram of Cd(II) ion in 1 M KCl. The voltage scan extends from -0.4 to -0.9 V vs. SCE. The reversibility of the reduction is demonstrated by the "mirror image" appearance of the current curve on the anodic return sweep. (Courtesy of Chemtrix)

Double-channel, single-sweep polarography. Finally, we examine double-channel, single-sweep polarography. This uses a precision dual-channel polarograph employing a pair of identical synchronized dropping mercury electrodes.* One electrode is in a reference cell that contains only supporting electrolyte; the other is in a sample cell that contains electroactive species as well.

The arrangement is attractive because the reference channel provides a capacitive current virtually identical to that in the sample channel. If we subtract the small capacitive current that does flow near the end of drop life by use of the reference channel response, this enhances the limits of detection and separability over those attainable with a single-channel polarograph.

A double-channel instrument is also useful for *differential* single-sweep polarography. In this case, after a trial run, the reference solution is made up with one or more constituents present at a known concentration that is slightly less than that in the sample. A precision of $\pm 1\%$ is possible even at trace levels (see Exercise 26.2).

We can apply the modular system of Fig. 26.2 to a dual-channel procedure with little change. The two polarographic cells operate in parallel, with the output of the reference cell going first to an inverting amplifier which changes the sign of the signal but does not alter its magnitude, and then to the summing point of the current amplifier. The addition: $I_{sample} + (-I_{std})$ at the input of the current amplifier gives the desired difference signal.

---

* Synchronization will be sufficiently close if identical capillaries and electrically triggered drop dislodgers are used.

A *derivative* technique can also be used with a dual-channel instrument. In this case identical solutions are placed in the two cells, but a fixed voltage offset is maintained between the dropping mercury electrodes. The signal produced is $(i_2 - i_1)/(V_2 - V_1) = di/dV$. The *derivative* procedure provides resolution of species whose peaks are only 40 mV apart. If coupled with a stage of electronic differentiation, a second derivative readout is obtained that permits resolution of equal height peaks only 20 mV apart.

26.3 PULSE POLAROGRAPHY

In this technique we apply square voltage pulses of from 40 to 100 ms duration, one per mercury drop, late in drop life. A complex cell current much like that in Fig. 26.1 results. Because a pulse has a long duration, time can be allowed for the capacitive component of current to decay nearly to zero before observing the cell current. For example, with 60 ms pulses a possible decay time might be 40 ms and the current observation time 10 to 15 ms.

In a *normal* or integral pulse polarographic procedure we impose square pulses of successively greater amplitude on a constant starting voltage. Table 26.1 shows this variety of pulse as type A. Each pulse supplies one point on a current–voltage curve. The pulse height plus starting voltage gives the applied potential, and the current is the value observed by averaging the signal measured over the observation or sampling interval. The normal pulse procedure produces an output that is effectively a smoothed classical polarogram with small steps.

Example What duration of pulse and sampling interval should be used for polarography of a sample that contains traces of cadmium? It is known that the faradaic current will be of the order of 10^{-7} A. That being the case, it would be helpful to let the capacitive current decay to about 1×10^{-8} A before observing the cell current.

A rough calculation of an appropriate decay interval can be made by drawing an analogy to the charging of a capacitor (Section 2.5). Here the capacitor C is the electric double layer and it is to be charged to the applied pulse potential through the resistance R of the solution. Assume $C = 5 \mu F$ and $R = 500 \Omega$, a level of resistance higher than is ordinarily encountered even if only a dilute (0.005 M) supporting electrolyte is present. Assume that starting voltage (baseline) is -0.6 V and that the maximum pulse is 100 mV.

The initial charging or capacitive current is $V/R = 100 \times 10^{-3}/500 = 2 \times 10^{-4}$ A. Equation (2.16) defines the capacitive current at time t in this type of series RC circuit as $i_t = i_0 e^{-t/RC}$. By substituting $i_t = 1 \times 10^{-8}$ A, we can find the decay time t. The equation becomes $1 \times 10^{-8} = 2 \times 10^{-4} e^{-t/RC}$ and reduces to $e^{-t/RC} = 5 \times 10^{-5}$. Taking the logarithm of both sides gives $-t/RC = 2.303 \log 5 \times 10^{-5}$. Rearranging and carrying out the arithmetic gives $-t = 500 \times 5 \times 10^{-6} \times 2.303 \times (-4.30)$ and $t \simeq 25$ ms.

Based on this approximate calculation, a reasonable choice of pulse would be one of 50 ms duration in which 30 ms is allowed for decay, followed by current sampling for 15 ms. The last 5 ms would be unused.

In Fig. 26.6 the principal current components associated with pulse polarography are indicated schematically. Note the exponential decay of capacitive current during the pulses (curve A), the gradually increasing cell current associated with drop growth (curve *C*), and the (net) faradaic current during the sampling interval (curve *E*). It is advantageous to integrate the current during the interval to average out fluctuations induced by 60 Hz line voltage as well as general instrumental and electronic noise.

Where we desire very high sensitivity of measurement, we can make a correction for the faradaic and capacitive current increase associated with drop growth. To do so it is necessary (a) to measure the rate of current increase prior to imposing a pulse, (b) to compute the increase anticipated during the current sampling interval, and (c) to subtract the average of this value from the integrated current.

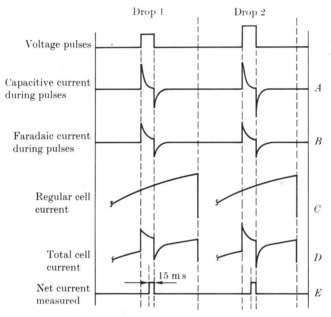

Fig. 26.6 Current waveforms in normal pulse polarography. The current components during the later portion of the life of two successive mercury drops are shown.

Normal-mode* pulse polarography is valuable when solution constituents have well-separated halfwave potentials or have nearly equal concentrations.†

When better resolution or higher separability (Section 26.1) is required, current sampling and processing may be made differentially. In *derivative* or differential mode pulse polarography, differences are taken between current samples from pulses imposed at different voltage levels. The output is then $\Delta i / \Delta V$.

There are two simple ways to secure a differential signal. One is to use the normal train of voltage pulses just described but to process the signal differently. The current

---

* Since a regular polarogram can be considered the integral of a differential curve, the normal mode is often referred to as an integral mode.

† This type of pulse train (type *A* in Table 26.1) offers a distinct advantage when a solid micro-electrode is used. Since pulses are of short duration and the applied voltage returns to the starting value following a pulse, not only does little reduction occur, but reoxidation of the reduced species occurs between pulses. Recall that alteration in the electrode surface is normally a limiting factor in use of solid electrodes.

sampled from a pulse is not read out directly but stored briefly (in a memory or pulse-stretcher circuit). When we sample current from the next higher pulse, we subtract the preceding current. The output is $\Delta i/\Delta V$. The other differential approach calls for addition of low-amplitude square pulses (10 to 30 mV) to a linear voltage ramp as illustrated in Fig. 26.7. One pulse is applied per drop and current is sampled immediately prior to the pulse and again near the end of the pulse. The former value is subtracted from the latter, as in the other method, to give the $\Delta i/\Delta V$ readout. In differential pulse polarography sensitivity is high; resolution improves to 40 mV and separability to 50,000 : 1 !

Should we use a slow (4 to 5 s) or fast (0.5 to 2 s) drop rate in differential pulse polarography? Rapid scanning with long drop times, i.e. use of pulses with large potential differences between them, gives large differential currents and high sensitivity. Quantitative accuracy is high also. The curve is a series of steps, however, and its shape is not well defined. To secure optimum resolution and an accurate curve, we need a slow scan with fast drop times, thus one that gives many points.

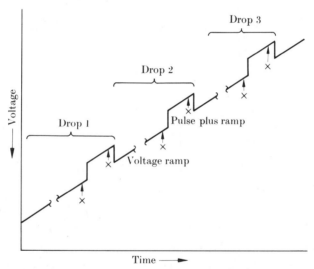

Fig. 26.7 Voltage pattern in differential or derivative pulse polarography. Constant amplitude square pulses are superposed on a linear ramp. One pulse is applied per drop near the end of its life. Current is sampled for a short interval at times marked x. The current measurement preceding a pulse is stored and subtracted electronically from the current measurement near the end of a pulse. The output is proportional to $\Delta i/\Delta v$.

Instrumentation. Figure 26.8 shows a block diagram of a pulse polarograph programmed for differential mode operation. Clever use is made of a 60 Hz synchronous "generator" for gating. The drop time is 2 s. Following a 1.5 s delay from the start of a drop, we activate the 60 Hz generator to start a 100 ms pulse (6 cycles of the generator output). We start a 50 ms pulse simultaneously, which allows us to sample the output (from the differential amplifier) after 50 ms (3 cycles of the 60 Hz generator). A 33 ms pulse generator (2 cycles of 60 Hz) is started after the first 50 ms pulse. When its pulse stops, the current sampling ceases.

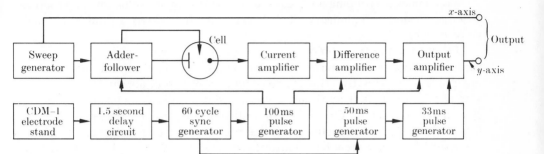

Fig. 26.8 Block diagram of a pulse polarograph operated in a differential mode. All synchronization is accomplished relative to the dislodging of a mercury drop at the electrode stand and the start of a new drop. Several pulse generators are required to provide necessary timing sequences. (Courtesy of Wescan Instruments.)

Little detail is shown for this module marked "output amplifier." It actually may be divided into other modules, one of which is a difference amplifier to respond to the Δi between successive current samplings. Note that the readout must be an $x - y$ recorder and that the ΔV portion of the output derives from the x-axis presentation.

26.4 VOLTAMMETRIC STRIPPING ANALYSIS

Stripping analysis has received an unusual degree of interest, for it appears to be the most sensitive electroanalytical technique presently available. The technique is basically a bulk method like the coulometric procedures discussed in Chapter 27. Yet stripping analysis usually also involves a single-sweep voltage scan at a microelectrode like that discussed earlier in this chapter, and for that reason it has seemed appropriate to treat the method here.

Voltammetric stripping analysis consists of two basic steps:

1. A relatively long electrolysis (up to 30 min) to deposit one or more electroactive species on a microelectrode; and

2. Electrolytic stripping of the deposited species from the microelectrode, usually by application of a slow linear voltage sweep and observation of the resulting current-voltage curve.

In other words, there is a concentration stage (electrodeposition) followed by a single-sweep procedure of the type discussed in Section 26.2. The method is also different from most polarographic procedures in that the electrode is "stationary." It is a hanging mercury drop, a thin film of mercury on a nickel or platinum wire, or a solid microelectrode. Voltammetric stripping analysis is best adapted to determining metals* at the trace level, i.e. in the range 10^{-5} M to 10^{-9} M, though the latter level is reached only in favorable cases. At concentrations above this range a technique utilizing a dropping mercury electrode is preferable.

---

* Some nonmetals such as chlorine can be determined by stripping analysis also. Chloride ions can be oxidized and 'deposited' on a microelectrode as (adsorbed) Cl_2 molecules. A cathodic sweep can be applied to return the molecules to the ionic state.

Voltammetric stripping analysis is also called stripping voltammetry, stripping analysis, inverse voltammetry, and linear potential sweep stripping chromo-amperometry.

Examination of the ratio of signal to capacitive current background plus noise confirms the possibility of meaningful polarographic results even with currents of the order of nanoamperes. By virtue of a constant microelectrode area and a slow voltage scan (2 to 5 mV s^{-1}), there is only a very small capacitive component i_c to the cell current during stripping. Conversely, since stirring minimizes the thickness of the diffusion layer and the electroactive species has been concentrated on the microelectrode, the desired faradaic current i_f is comparatively large (up to 0.1 μA). It is this favorable combination of high i_f and low i_c, even for traces of electroactive species, that makes possible analysis at concentrations at least one order of magnitude below the level usually accessible by pulse polarography and three to four orders of magnitude below that of classical polarography.

During the stripping sweep, we obtain a current-voltage curve generally like the return branch of the cyclic voltammogram of Fig. 26.5. An inverted current peak i_p is observed during the oxidation of a deposited electroactive species. For a hanging mercury drop electrode under controlled conditions the peak can be related to the initial species concentration C_0 by the approximate expression, $i_p \approx 10^{-3}\tau C_0$, where τ is the electrodeposition time (min). Conditions that must be carefully controlled are electrode area A ($i_p \propto A$), scan rate v ($i_p \propto v^{1/2}$), temperature, and rate of stirring. The rate of voltage scan v also affects the peak width, its position relative to $E_{1/2}$, and its symmetry.

Instrumentation.   A suitable vessel for stripping analysis is a 10–15 ml thermostated cell with a removable bottom that has a magnetic impeller for stirring and provides an arrangement for flushing with pure nitrogen. It is desirable to have the appropriate microelectrode and a salt bridge to an external calomel electrode enter through the top. Optimum stirring occurs when one end of the rotating (about 700 rev/min) magnetic impeller is about 7 mm below the tip of the microelectrode. Adsorption on cell walls can be minimized by use of a quartz or polyethylene vessel.

Several types of microelectrodes are in common use. The most appropriate one for a particular analysis depends on the voltage to be applied, the sensitivity desired, and the nature of the electroactive species. A *hanging mercury drop electrode* is the most versatile and widely used. It is formed either by extruding a drop from a micrometer syringe filled with mercury or by transferring one or more drops of mercury from a dropping electrode to a platinum wire stub at the end of a piece of tubing. The main advantage of this electrode is that we may use it for simultaneous analysis of several species, provided each dissolves in the mercury. Their subsequent stripping from a homogeneous amalgam reflects the initial concentration of each in solution.

Some other common types of electrodes are the mercury film electrode (a thin layer of mercury on a nickel or platinum wire), the platinum stub electrode, and the carbon paste electrode. We use platinum and carbon electrodes mainly when we must apply potentials that are too positive for mercury. They give a sensitive response but can be used for analysis of only one species. When we employ a solid electrode in analysis of several species, it is nearly impossible to secure the needed homogenization of the deposited metals prior to stripping.

Electronic modules for stripping voltammetry are like those employed in single-sweep polarography (Section 26.2). If we are to use a slow scan rate, we can employ a classical polarographic apparatus. If we need a rapid scan, we can obtain it through use of operational amplifiers. [3] It is advantageous to incorporate other operational amplifier circuits for reliable measurement of small currents and (if necessary) correction for iR drop in solution.

Procedure. As is true in any trace-analytical work, solvent and supporting electrolyte must be purified. For example, water should be purified by distillation and not by mixed-resin ion exchange that may introduce organic substances. The supporting electrolyte must ordinarily undergo a predeposition purification procedure to remove easily reducible impurities even though they are present only at a very low level of concentration.

In general, it is necessary to develop an individual procedure for each type of sample since current maxima and other considerations characteristic of polarography are not eliminated in stripping voltammetry. Barendrecht references many procedures. [3] Once a procedure and an appropriate electrode are chosen, we renew the electrode by a stripping sweep, introduce sample and solution, add supporting electrolyte, and carry out deaeration. We start stirring and the concentration stage begins with the microelectrode potential set almost 0.3 to 0.4 V more negative than the half-wave potential of the species most difficult to reduce. Thereby we allow for both a greater rate of deposition and some margin of uncertainty. This stage should not last more than 30 min. At longer times impurities may also begin to deposit and some deposited atoms may diffuse too far from the electrode surface to be available during the dissolution steps.

After deposition, we stop stirring for a brief interval (perhaps 30 s) without altering the voltage. During this quiet period convection patterns decay, and with a hanging-drop electrode there is some homogenization within the surface layer of mercury. Electrolysis continues but at a much diminished rate since the diffusion layer widens.

In very occasional cases the medium is changed if thereby resolution of subsequent dissolution peaks may be improved. For example, initial deposition of a metal may be easiest to accomplish in a strongly acid solution to which an organic surfactant has been added. Unless the medium is changed, however, during the stripping process, there will be interference from the surfactants, or from hydrogen evolution. Careful withdrawal of the first solution, and substitution of a neutral, inert salt solution for the stripping step are indicated.

Dissolution during the anodic scan (for metals) should be at a scan rate of 2 to 10 mV s^{-1} for best results.

REFERENCES

Newer developments in polarography are discussed lucidly in:

1. R. C. Rooney, "Modern Analytical Polarography," *Chemistry and Industry*, 875 (1966)
2. Helmut Schmidt and Mark von Stackelberg, *Modern Polarographic Methods.* New York: Academic, 1963

Other references of particular interest are:

3. E. Barendrecht, "Stripping Voltammetry," in *Electroanalytical Chemistry*. Vol. II. A. J. Bard, ed. New York: Dekker, 1967
4. B. Breyer and H. H. Bauer. *Alternating Current Polarography and Tensammetry*. New York: Interscience, 1963
5. D. E. Burge, "Pulse Polarography," *J. Chem. Educ.*, **47**, A81 (1970)
6. R. Kalvoda, *Techniques of Oscillographic Polarography*. 2d ed. New York: Elsevier, 1965
7. I. B. Goldberg and A. J. Bard, "Simultaneous Electrochemical–Electron Spin Resonance Measurements, I." *J. Phys. Chem.* **75**, 3281 (1971), especially pp. 3287–9.
8. D. E. Smith, "AC Polarography and Related Techniques: Theory and Practice," in *Electroanalytical Chemistry*. Vol. I. A. J. Bard, ed. New York: Dekker, 1966

EXERCISES

26.1   Redraw the current–voltage curve of Fig. 26.3 as it would appear for the same system when the technique used is (a) cyclic voltammetry; (b) conventional polarography; (c) voltammetric stripping analysis; (d) derivative pulse polarography.

26.2   A double-channel (differential) single-sweep polarograph offers the possibility of a true differential measurement. Suppose copper and zinc are to be precisely determined in an alloy whose nominal composition is 50% Cu, 20% Ni, and 30% Zn. The supporting electrolyte chosen is $1 M NH_3/1 M NH_4Cl$. (a) From the data in Table 25.1, suggest appropriate voltage scan(s). (b) In a differential determination of copper assume an equal weight of standard Cu-Ni-Zn alloy is to be dissolved in supporting electrolyte to make up a reference solution. Suggest a practical choice of composition for the standard. (c) Repeat for a zinc determination. (d) What advantages does a differential procedure offer?

26.3   In pulse polarography differential measurements can be made by subtracting a given current pulse from the next current pulse. Draw a simplified schematic diagram for a circuit based on a differential amplifier that will achieve the desired subtraction.

26.4   It is desired to carry out a zinc analysis on sea water. Zinc is known to be present at trace levels, partly as "free" ions, partly in complex ions. Which of the techniques discussed in this chapter might be suitable to obtain the concentration of each type of zinc? Explain.

26.5   Early (more anodic) reductions often affect the shape and height of current–voltage curves of later (more cathodic) reductions. Compare their degree of interdependence in (a) dc polarography and single-sweep polarography, (b) dc polarography and derivative pulse polarography.

26.6   Two refinements of chemical polarography, Tast polarography and the filtering compensation procedure of Kelley and coworkers, were described briefly in Section 25.7. Compare these procedures with the newer polarographic methods of this chapter. How well do the Tast and filtering compensation procedures minimize capacitive current?

CHAPTER 27

COULOMETRIC METHODS

27.1 INTRODUCTION

This chapter deals with three procedures based on exhaustive electrolysis—constant-current coulometry, constant-potential coulometry, and electrogravimetry. Contrasting these techniques with classical polarography, we find they not only call for complete reduction of the substance(s) of interest but also require much larger currents and an unpolarized working electrode. They are capable of much higher precision, $\pm 0.1\%$ or better, but are more limited in scope because of the restrictions imposed on the electrolysis process.

The effectiveness of coulometric techniques stems from their basic reliance on electrolysis. Recall that Faraday's laws of electrolysis relate the quantity Q of charge used in electrolysis to the weight W of substance that is electrolyzed by the expression

$$W = \frac{QM}{nF} \tag{27.1}$$

where M is the formula weight, n is the number of electrons required per molecule, and F is the Faraday ($96,487 \text{ C mol}^{-1}$). Charge Q is in coulombs. In a legitimate sense, we can regard a "coulometric" reaction as a titration of an electroxidizable or reducible substance in which electrons are the titrant. Instead of determining the quantity of a titrant, we measure the number of coulombs. With the passage of each Faraday of electricity, one equivalent weight of a substance reacts with electrons.

To make a coulometric analysis feasible, the following basic conditions must be satisfied:

1. The substance of interest must be electrolyzed with 100% current (reaction) efficiency;

2. The number of coulombs (or the weight of product) must be precisely determined.

It is the first condition that essentially limits the range of substances analyzable by coulometric procedures. It is discussed at some length in the following section. The second condition calls for an appropriate instrumental solution. Since the number of coulombs Q is given by $Q = \int i \, dt$, either the integral must be obtained directly or i or t separately determined and then combined. These two approaches have given rise to controlled-potential coulometry, which measures the integral, and constant-current coulometry, which determines the time of electrolysis with a steady current.

Particular advantages of coulometry over other techniques are (a) high accuracy, (b) the possibility of generating and working with reagents like iron(II) that are unstable under ordinary conditions, (c) simplicity of instrumentation, and (d) good sensitivity. High accuracy is possible because of the electrical character of the measurements. Such determinations are intrinsically accurate. It is always possible to determine the number of electrons exchanged by a measurement external to the cell, and no standardization is required. Indeed, precision in coulometry is high enough for the Faraday to have been seriously proposed as the primary chemical standard. Standardization of solution by coulometry is capable of accuracy at least as great as, and probably greater than, by classical wet methods.

The simplicity of much coulometric instrumentation is a great advantage. The end point need only be detected and the circuit broken. Finally, the sensitivity of coulometric measurements is good, for by use of small currents and micro-apparatus, the precision of results is good even at sample concentrations of 10^{-4} M and below.

27.2 COULOMETRIC RELATIONSHIPS

In considering the fundamentals on which coulometry rests it is convenient to limit discussion to reductions though the approach is equally valid for oxidations. To convert from reduction to oxidation sometimes requires a change in the working electrode, e.g. substitution of platinum for mercury in order to achieve sufficiently positive potentials. It also calls for current reversal but this will occur naturally if the potential is altered in an anodic (positive) direction.

The theory of electrode processes and mass transport developed in Sections 23.1 through 23.4 is essential background to this chapter. Two basic questions must be dealt with. In carrying out quantitative coulometry

1. What potential control is necessary to reduce a species of interest with minimal interference?

2. How is it possible to control the system to bring the time of electrolysis down to a half-hour or less?

The questions are relevant both to constant-potential and constant-current coulometry. Other questions will mainly relate to instrumentation and will be treated in the following sections.

Electrode potential change during electrolysis. During an exhaustive reduction, a working cathode becomes steadily more negative (cathodic). How great a change in potential we need to electrolyze a substance quantitatively when a constant, small current flows we may compute from the Nernst equation (Section 23.1). While this situation may appear idealized, it corresponds to the final condition that obtains in constant-potential coulometry. Attention is given later to the effect on potential of the larger currents usually employed in constant-current coulometry.

Let the initial concentration of the oxidized form of the analytical species be C_0. From the Nernst equation, the initial potential E' of the working electrode at 25 °C is given approximately by:

$$E' = E^{0\prime} + \frac{0.0591}{n} \log \frac{C_0}{10^{-3}C_0} = E^{0\prime} + \frac{0.177}{n}. \tag{27.2}$$

Two approximations have been made. Activity coefficients have been neglected since a formal potential (Section 24.12) $E^{0\prime}$ is substituted for the standard potential. $E^{0\prime}$ is the electrode emf in the actual electrolyte medium when equal concentrations of oxidized and reduced form of the electroactive species are present. Also, a meaningful equilibrium potential was assumed first established when the concentration of the reduced form reaches $10^{-3} \times C_0$. After completion of reduction the concentration ratio of the analytical species is reversed giving

$$E' = E^{0\prime} \frac{0.0591}{n} \log \frac{10^{-3}C_0}{C_0} = E^0 - \frac{0.177}{n}. \tag{27.3}$$

The range of voltage ΔE for electrolysis is thus 0.35 V for a one-electron reduction, 0.18 V for a two-electron reduction, and 0.12 V for a three-electron reduction, assuming equal concentrations of each species.

Calculating the final electrode potential that must be reached if an electrolysis is to be quantitative has immediate value in determining whether another reducible species present will interfere. The interference takes the form of a reduction of a small quantity of a second constituent during the determination of the first. How great an error results depends on the difference between their formal potentials (or standard electrode potentials) and on their relative concentrations as indicated in the following example. During coulometry the potential of the working electrode need not be held constant but rather must not be allowed to exceed a value at which reduction of the next most easily reduced species will constitute a serious error.

Example Metal B is to be determined coulometrically in an alloy of metals A and B containing about 95% A and 5% B. Pertinent data are that in 1 M H_2SO_4 $E^{0\prime}$ for $A^{2+} + 2e \rightarrow A$ (Hg) is -0.50 V and $E^{0\prime}$ for $B^{2+} + 2e \rightarrow B$ (Hg) is -0.362 V. What error will be incurred in the determination if the potential of the working electrode is allowed to become as negative as -0.450 vs. SCE during electrolysis?

The potential selected ensures a quantitative determination of B since $E^{0\prime} - E_{final} = 0.088$ V, half the range required for a two-electron reduction. Because the final potential falls close to $E^{0\prime}$ for A, some A will also be reduced. The fraction of A reacting can be deduced from the Nernst equation. Let [ox]/[red] now refer to A only. Then $-0.45 = -0.50 + (0.059/2) \log ([ox]/[red])$, and $\log ([ox]/[red]) = 0.05/0.0296 = 1.7$, or $[ox]/[red] = 50$. About 2% of A was reduced: since its initial concentration was about 5%, that of metal B, the error from this source in determining B is about $0.02 \times 0.05 = 0.001$ or 0.1%.

Current efficiency and redox buffering. When we have to maintain a relatively large current (10 to 500 mA), as in constant-current coulometry, the working electrode swings to a still more extreme voltage than the Nernst equation predicts before an electrolysis is completed. The reason is that we must add activation overpotential (Section 23.2) to the equilibrium voltage of the electrode. As a result, it is common to find toward the end of a determination that electrolysis of a second species has begun and that current efficiency has dropped seriously below 100%.

A good example of this situation is the direct electrolytic oxidation of iron(II) at a platinum anode. The E^0 for the reaction, $Fe^{2+} \rightarrow Fe^{3+} + e$, is $+0.53$ V vs. SCE.

It proves to be the case that the direct electrolysis of ferrous ion cannot be completed without oxidizing some water.*

Example   Current-voltage curves for the coulometric oxidation of iron(II) are graphed in Fig. 27.1. Only curves A and C are applicable unless cerium(III) salt has been added. Further, these are an initial set of curves; as iron is oxidized, curve A sinks steadily nearer the abscissa. When all iron(II) has disappeared, the iron wave vanishes and only curve C remains.

We can now show why it is impossible to complete this direct oxidation with 100% current effciency. If the current is set at the lower dashed line in Fig. 27.1 initially, it is only a matter of time before curve A moves downward enough for the current line to intercept curve C. Then any iron(II) remaining is oxidized simultaneously with water. If this occurs, the value of iron determined is high.

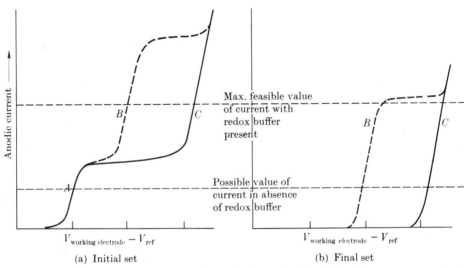

    (a) Initial set   (b) Final set

Fig. 27.1 Current-voltage curves applicable to the determination of Fe^{2+} by aqueous constant-current coulometry. Curve A: Fe^{2+}, Fe^{3+} couple; curve B: Ce^{3+}, Ce^{4+} couple; curve C: H_2O, O_2 couple. As electrolysis of Fe^{2+} proceeds the set of curves, in effect, moves down toward the abscissa. Two cases can be distinguished.

(1) When no Ce^{3+} is added to the system, A-C is the composite current-voltage curve that is applicable. If current is fixed at the value given by the lower broken line, only Fe^{2+} is oxidized at first as in (a) but water is also oxidized before all Fe^{2+} is electrolyzed as in (b).

(2) When Ce^{3+} is added, A-B is the appropriate composite curve. The electrolysis current can now be maintained at the value of the upper broken line without bringing about electrolysis of water.

As a consequence of the nearly certain loss of current efficiency in direct methods, nearly all constant-current methods call for the electrical generation of an intermediate species with 100% current efficiency. It must be capable of quantitative reaction with

---

* It is possible for the oxygen produced to react with remaining ferrous ion but improbable that it will do so rapidly enough to be helpful in this situation.

the analytical species. If an oxidation is sought, the intermediate must be added initially in its reduced form. It is of interest that now the potential of the working electrode remains almost constant. The added redox system is called a *redox buffer* and the overall method now becomes *secondary* constant-current coulometry.

The role of a redox buffer may be clarified by returning to the example of coulometric oxidation of ferrous ions represented in Fig. 27.1. Assume the redox buffer is Ce^{3+}, Ce^{4+}. Then a large concentration of cerous ion Ce^{3+} is added to the solution before beginning the titration. In Fig. 27.1 curve A is now followed by curve B. As current is passed, ceric ion, Ce^{4+}, is electrically generated and easily oxidizes the iron(II) according to the equation, $Ce^{4+} + Fe^{2+} \rightarrow Fe^{3+} + Ce^{3+}$. The current can now be raised to the level of the upper dashed line in the figure. Clearly, the larger the concentration of Ce^{3+} added, the higher this current may be. Not only is the time of electrolysis shortened substantially, but current efficiency remains at 100%. As Fig. 27.1b shows, the working electrode is at all times at a potential below that required to produce oxygen from water. The number of coulombs used in secondary coulometry is, of course, identical to that required in the direct oxidation of iron.

The few exceptions to the use of an intermediate couple in constant-current coulometry are cases in which hydrogen or hydroxyl ions are the generated titrant and there is no concentration polarization. If the substance to be electrolyzed behaves irreversibly at the electrode, it may be necessary to titrate it entirely with generated reagent. Note that precipitation and other types of titrations also call for the generation of a titrant.

In constant-current coulometry, the current must be terminated when the desired electrolysis is complete. The necessary end-point determination is discussed in the next section.

Current change at constant potential. Since it is possible to predict a potential suitable for coulometry of a species, it is also important to consider the current variation if this potential is held throughout. Where a single electrode reaction is occurring, not only is the form of the dependence of current on electrode potential of interest but the factors that determine the magnitude of the current need to be identified. If we know these, we can shorten the electrolysis time. The feasibility of a particular constant-potential coulometric determination often depends on the time required.

When the working electrode is adjusted to a potential at which a single reaction occurs at a fast rate, electrolysis current is diffusion-controlled. With rapid stirring the diffusion layer is thin, and it can be shown that the current i_t at a given time t is given by the equation

$$i_t = i_0 \times 10^{-kt}, \tag{27.4}$$

where i_0 is the initial current and k is a constant defined [4] as

$$k = 0.43 \frac{DA}{v\delta}.$$

Here A is the area of electrode, D is the diffusion coefficient of the species being reduced, v is the solution volume, and δ is the thickness of the diffusion layer. Since the parameters D and δ depend on a great many variables, such as the temperature and rate of stirring, the constant k is best evaluated for each experimental situation. The time required for a quantitatively complete electrolysis can be estimated from Eq. (27.4).

Example It is sought to estimate the length of time required to effect 99.9% completion of a constant-potential electrolysis for which $k = 0.0025$ s^{-1}. A criterion by which the percentage of reaction can be related to the electrolysis current must first be formulated. As discussed in Section 23.3, for a thin diffusion layer the electrolysis current i is proportional to the bulk concentration of the electroactive species if all the active ions are reduced as fast as they arrive. The current at a given time t is then a direct measure of the concentration of the reducible species left in the bulk of the solution at that time, and the current i_0 should be a measure of the original concentration. Then the percentage remaining unelectrolyzed should be given by the ratio i_t/i_0.

The time for 99.9% complete electrolysis corresponds to a value of i_t/i_0 of 0.001. This value can be substituted in Eq. (27.4) and the magnitude of t determined. The substitution yields

$$0.001 = 10^{-0.0025t}, \qquad \text{or } 3 = 0.0025t,$$

and $t = 1200$ s or 20 min. To obtain 99.99% completion, about 27 min would be required, a time which is a third again as long.

From Eq. (27.4) it is apparent that the larger the value of k, the shorter the electrolysis time. Accordingly, for fast electrolysis it is advantageous to use large, closely spaced electrodes. Thus area A is large and volume v is small. Higher temperatures increase D and, up to a point, more rapid stirring reduces δ. Changes in the direction stated shorten an electrolysis. As the above example suggests, a practical criterion for the termination of this type of coulometric determination is that the final current be at least three orders of magnitude less than the initial value.

27.3 CONSTANT-CURRENT INSTRUMENTATION

The essential components for a single-channel, null-balance instrument of this type are a constant-current dc power supply, a means of setting current and a device for measuring it, a timer, an electrolysis cell, and an end-point detection arrangement. During a determination the electrolytic generation of titrant continues unabated until the end point of the desired reaction is sensed by the end-point detector. Then current and timer are stopped. Figure 27.2 shows a representative, constant-current coulometric "titrator" in schematic form. Each of its components must now be considered.

A filtered, regulated dc power supply that furnishes a current of at least 250 mA at a constant voltage of 200 V or more is satisfactory as a dc source. It becomes a constant-current generator when used in series with resistor R_1. The value of R_1, compared with the resistance of the electrochemical cell, must be such that virtually all of the iR drop appears across R_1 and no more than 0.5 to 3 V across the cell. Usually there is a change of 0.2 to 0.4 V in cell voltage during a determination as the working electrode shifts through its potential. Since this represents no more than 0.1 to 0.2% of the output voltage of the power supply, the cell current varies by no more than this figure. If we desire a still greater degree of constancy, it is worth our while to substitute an operational amplifier constant-current generator with booster (Section 7.8).

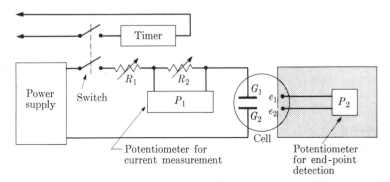

Fig. 27.2 Schematic drawing of instrumentation for coulometry at constant current. Provision is made for potentiometric determination of the end point. G_1 and G_2 are generating and auxiliary electrodes; e_1 and e_2 are monitoring electrodes.

In the simple circuit of Fig. 27.2, R_1 is also varied to set the cell current to the desired level. Ordinarily the current used is smaller than 250 mA to avoid the generation of excessive heat. The voltage drop across the cell is self-adjusting as long as its internal resistance is small ($< 10\,\Omega$) and, within limits, is whatever value is necessary to initiate and maintain electrolysis. If feasible, we select a current that allows the electrolysis of the analytical species to be completed in from 10 to 200 s. If it is possible to adjust the current to values of from 0.1 to 100 mA, it is possible to electro-lyze from 1×10^{-9} to 1×10^{-6} equivalents of a substance per second. The size and concentration of sample that can be accommodated we can quickly estimate on the basis of the time and current restriction. It is clear that the method is particularly well adapted to quite dilute systems. The magnitude of the current is determined by the voltage drop across resistance R_2 as measured by a potentiometer and may also be ascertained to 0.1 %.

As shown in Fig. 27.2, an electrical timer is started and stopped simultaneously with the electrolysis current by throwing a single switch that controls both. Since times as small as 10 s are to be observed, the chronometer should be precise to 0.01 s. Even if the switch is thrown manually, the time can be observed accurately to ± 0.05 s.

A simple dual-transistor, dual-Zener diode current supply constant to $\pm 0.1\%$ was shown in Fig. 4.29b and discussed in Exercise 4.9. More elaborate constant-current supplies based on operational amplifiers were discussed in Section 7.8.

End-point detector. The sensitivity and precision of the end-point device is often crucial to the successful operation of a coulometer. As we have already noted, it is not difficult to maintain and to determine the value of the current to within 0.1 % over a period of many minutes or to observe the elapsed time to within 0.01 s. Unless, however, the end-point device that shuts off the current operates with com-parable precision, the reliability of the other components is wasted. Any standard volumetric end-point detector may be incorporated in a coulometric apparatus, but only potentiometric and amperometric detectors are used to any extent. The reason is that they permit straightforward feedback control of electrolysis current. A potentiometric detector is commonly employed in redox and acidimetric reactions and is the type whose use is illustrated here. Adaptation for amperometric control is straightforward and follows expected lines (Section 25.13). Amperometric detectors are more sensitive and find use especially in more dilute systems.

Precise end-point detection is synonymous with nearly instantaneous detection in coulometers. With the arrangement shown in Fig. 27.2, it is desirable to measure the end-point potential in a preliminary study and then set the potentiometer to this voltage. During an analysis the potentiometer unbalance decreases continuously, and it is easy to locate the end point as occurring at the time at which the galvanometer deflection falls to zero. We can make even manual detection nearly instantaneous by noting the rate of decrease of the deflection and anticipating the appearance of zero deflection. Throughout the procedure, the current between the monitoring electrodes e_1 and e_2 must be kept small; there may be considerable error if the substance being analyzed is electrolyzed to any appreciable extent at these electrodes.

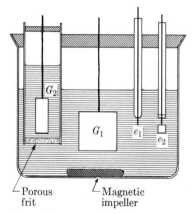

Fig. 27.3 Cell and electrodes for coulometry with potentiometric detection of end points. Electrodes e_1 and e_2 are the pair that monitor the concentration of reactant. G_1 and G_2 are the generating and auxiliary electrodes, respectively.

Cell and generating electrodes. Figure 27.3 presents in more detail a cell for coulometric determination. One of the monitoring electrodes (e_1 or e_2) should be an indicator electrode sensitive to the oxidized or reduced form of the electroactive species, and the other a suitable reference electrode (Section 24.2).

The choice of material and the design of electrodes that carry the electrolysis current must be well considered. Usually a platinum generating electrode is used because of its inertness. Mercury is used occasionally. If halides are being determined, the generating electrode may be silver, and the precipitation of halide ion by silver ion may be the basis for the reaction. In any case, the auxiliary or counter electrode must be carefully shielded from the solution to avoid unnecessary side reactions and any loss of reactant through mechanical trapping. Ordinarily the chamber surrounding the auxiliary electrode is even filled with an electrolyte different from that in the bulk of the solution to isolate it more effectively. Since the generated titrant is often unstable, it is preferable to carry out most of these titrations in a closed vessel. Stirring is essential so that the reactant may have a chance to be completely used. Note the magnetic impeller suggested in Fig. 27.3.

In some instances we cannot maintain 100 % current efficiency with the arrangement shown in Fig. 27.3 because of undesirable side reactions occurring when the titrant is generated in the solution. The best alternative is external generation. In this procedure, the generating electrode is in a capillary tube that extends into the solution. The earliest design (Fig. 27.4) is representative of the type of arrangement commonly used. Most designs deliver only an oxidant *or* a reductant and are better capable of dissipating heat associated with large currents. The generated titrant, as in Fig. 27.4, is moved from the appropriate outlet of the capillary into the analysis flask by a flow of solution, usually by gravity, through the capillary at a constant rate of 0.1 ml min^{-1} or greater. One disadvantage of external generation is that a small amount of unreacted titrant is always in the capillary when the reaction is stopped. It is not difficult to determine the appropriate correction by running a blank, however, and precision can still be good.

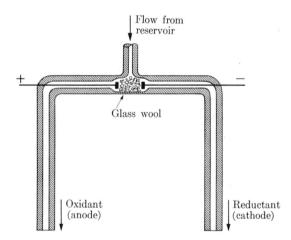

Fig. 27.4 An arrangement for the external generation of reagent. The appropriate outlet is inserted in the titration flask. (D. D. DeFord, J. N. Pitts, Jr., and C. J. Johns, *Proc. Natl. Acad. Sci. U.S.* **36**, 612 (1950); courtesy of U.S. Natl. Acad. Sciences.)

Automatic titrators. The operation of the device in Fig. 27.2 may be made automatic rather simply. If the electrode and other reactions are fast, all that is basically necessary is to add a relay that stops the current and the timer when the potential, as determined by the potentiometer, reaches the end-point value. Note the contrast between this operation and the termination of a titration performed by an automatic potentiometric or photometric titrator. Since the flow of a solution need not be cut off in coulometry, instrumentation can be simpler and more reliable. In effect, the coulometric apparatus has taken the place of the buret and standard solution required in other titrations.

Unfortunately, it is impossible to avoid some additional complexity if a coulo-metric titrator must also cope with reactions in which the reactant is slow to combine with the titrant. To achieve good precision ($\pm$ 0.5 %) with these systems we have to add some sort of anticipation device (Section 24.9). Its function, as in a potentiometric titrator, is to interrupt the generation of titrant briefly when the potential of the indicating electrode e_1 nears its end-point value. When the electrode voltage changes as the result of further reaction, the current is started again, and new titrant is gener-ated. There may be several interruptions before the true end point is attained.

27.4 CONTROLLED-POTENTIAL INSTRUMENTATION

Only with the development in the late 1950s of first-class intrumentation has this technique seen general analytical use. What had previously been lacking were straightforward designs for two modules: a precise current integrator with a wide dynamic range and a precise automatic device to control the potential of the working electrode without interference from other elements in the cell. Good designs for both appeared with the spreading use of the operational amplifier and are now well established.

Current integrator. The operational amplifier integrator discussed in Section 7.6 is the basis for a good coulometric integrator. With a good-quality integrating capacitor (e.g., C_f in the circuit of Fig. 7.14a), adequate shielding of the input lead, and careful control of dc offset of the amplifier, we can obtain precise integration. In coulometry we must give particular attention to sources of error such as faradaic current from electrolysis of impurities and other errors that arise from the electrolysis cell (see Meites and Moros in [4]).

In order to provide the dynamic range needed in a versatile coulometer, a current-divider must be included in the input circuit to reduce the charge the capacitor must store. Figure 27.5 gives a simple schematic version of this type of arrangement.

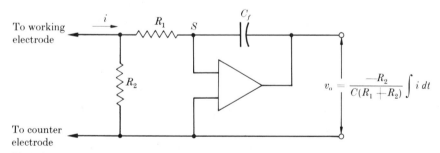

Fig. 27.5 Operational amplifier integrator of wide dynamic range. Point S at the inverting input of the operational amplifier is essentially at ground potential as is the lower end of resistor R_2. Cell current splits with the fraction $iR_2/(R_1 + R_2)$ being stored in C_f. By varying R_1 the range can be changed.

The success of the operational amplifier integrator results from the fact that it keeps point S essentially at the potential of its other input, in this case at ground* by

---

* S is termed a virtual ground.

the negative feedback it maintains through C_f. As a consequence, there is no back voltage at S to interfere with the current in R_1 and the integration is as precise as feedback is capable of maintaining it. Since the level of feedback depends in turn on amplifier gain A, the precision of integration improves as amplifier gain increases. A can easily be as high at 10^7. The lower branch of Fig. 27.6 shows a working version of an integrator; the legend provides an account of the circuit.

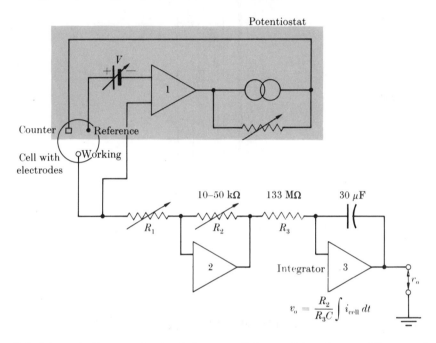

Fig. 27.6 Schematic diagram of a circuit for controlled potential coulometry. The potentiostat (upper circuit reference) maintains the potential of the working electrode at exactly $-$V volts relative to the electrode. The lower circuit amplifies the cell current, isolates the cell (amplifier 2 plus R_1 and R_2 serve these functions), and integrates the varying current with respect to time (amplifier 3 plus R_3 and the capacitor perform this operation). In the upper circuit the overlapping circles symbolize a current source, perhaps a booster amplifier. In the lower circuit the noninverting terminals of amplifiers 2 and 3 are grounded. (G. L. Booman, *Anal. Chem.* **29**, 213 (1957); courtesy of *Analytical Chemistry*.)

Potentiostat. Operational amplifier devices for maintaining a fixed potential were treated in Section 7.8. Figure 27.6 shows the circuit of Booman for a controlled-potential coulometric system. Note that the potentiostat feedback loop (upper branch of circuit) provides the control. In effect, amplifier A provides sufficient current through the counter electrode to maintain electrolysis and keep the potential of the working electrode at $-$ V volts relative to the reference electrode (about at ground potential).

Cells. A cell suitable for controlled-potential coulometry normally holds 10–15 ml of solution. Stirring is usually by means of a magnetic impeller and is vital to minimize electrolysis time. Both counter and reference electrodes are carefully shielded from the turbulence produced, often in the manner shown in Fig. 27.7. Several designs of cells have been developed. [4]

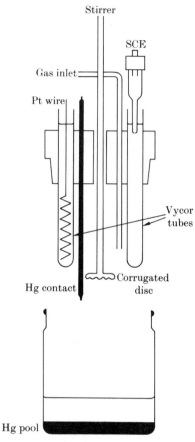

Fig. 27.7 Coulometric titration vessel, Oak Ridge National Laboratory pattern. A platinum gauze can be substituted for the mercury pool. The porous Vycor tubes (Corning) require conditioning and should be restricted to solutions of a given type. (W. D. Shults, *Talanta* **10**, 833 (1963); courtesy of Pergamon Press.)

27.5 COULOMETRIC PROCEDURES

Table 27.1 partially indicates the scope of constant-current coulometry; it lists some electrically generated reagents that have seen a significant amount of use. To perform a particular analysis, it is necessary to select generating electrodes, end-point procedure and electrodes, the value of the electrolysis current, and the sample size or concentration. Since the last two variables are interrelated, some latitude is possible in each. The end-point detection arrangement chosen must provide adequate sensitivity at the concentration level decided on. If a dilute solution or a solution with a large portion of nonaqueous solvent is being analyzed, some electrically indifferent electrolyte such as KCl must be added until the cell resistance is decreased to about 10 Ω. A great many good coulometric procedures have been described by Milner and Lingane. [4, 2] Two brief examples are given here as illustrations of typical procedures.

Table 27.1 Some Electrolytically Generated Titrants

Oxidizing Agents	Reducing Agents	Precipitants	Acidimetric Agents
Br_2	$CuCl_2^-$	Ag^+	OH^-
I_2			
Cl_2	Fe^{2+}	Hg_2^{2+}	H^+
BrO_3^-			
Ce^{4+}	Ti^{3+}	$Fe(CN)_6^{4-}$	
Fe^{3+}			
Ag^+			
Mn^{3+}			

Example 1 The mercaptan content of petroleum stocks may be measured in straightforward fashion by coulometry. (If hydrogen sulfide is also present, additional steps are required.) The hydrocarbon sample is dissolved in a mixture of aqueous methanol and benzene to which ammonia and ammonium nitrate are added to buffer the solution and lower its resistance sufficiently to allow the use of moderate electrolysis currents.

A silver anode generates the titrant, Ag^+ ions, and a platinum electrode immersed in an ammonium nitrate solution serves as an auxiliary or counter electrode. As Ag^+ ions are generated, they precipitate the mercaptide ions quantitatively according to the equation

$$Ag^+ + RS^- \rightarrow AgSR.$$

The end point is located by a silver-silver sulfide, glass electrode pair that sensitively monitors the concentration of Ag^+ ion. The relay is set to terminate the titration. The end point corresponds to an emf of 0.025 V across the monitoring electrodes. When this value is reached, the electrolysis is terminated.

Example 2 The determination of arsenite ion (AsO_3^{3-}) by oxidation to arsenate (AsO_4^{3-}) can be performed coulometrically by generating bromine. In this representative inorganic titration, the supporting electrolyte is an aqueous solution of about 0.1 M in sulfuric acid and 0.2 M in sodium bromide. The titrant Br_2 is produced from the Br^- ions at a platinum anode.

Amperometry with two polarized electrodes (Section 25.14) is often employed to determine the end point in this determination. When this procedure is used, two platinum electrodes of small surface area are used as the amperometric detector, and a steady potential of about 0.1 or 0.2 V is applied across them. The end point is marked by a sudden drop in the current between the two platinum electrodes.

Procedures in controlled-potential coulometry are not essentially different in this chemical aspect. An extensive tabulation of systems available to this type of analysis is given by Milner. [4] In that no end-point detection arrangement is required, operating procedures are less elaborate. Further, no intermediate reagent need by added. Usually with each reference to a method we take care to specify the electrolytes working and reference electrodes, and the potential at which the working electrode must be maintained.

27.6 ELECTROGRAVIMETRY

We can analyze a wide variety of metals whose activity is below that of manganese by *electrodeposition* at controlled potential. This type of analysis was one of the first high-precision methods and is still in common use. As its earlier and less descriptive name, *electroanalysis*, implies, the method measures the amount of substance present by the increase in weight of the working electrode when the analytical substance is quantitatively plated out. A successful electrogravimetric analysis of a given sample is possible if the substance sought can be

1. Plated as an adherent coating when a current density high enough to complete the electrolysis in a "reasonable" time is used (times shorter than one hour are preferred) and

2. Electrolyzed quantitatively at a potential lower than that at which any other species is *plated out*.

Note that current efficiency need *not* be 100%. If any other substance is reduced at the working electrode during the analysis, however, it must not be trapped in the plated layer.

A discussion of factors that control the degree of adherence of an electroplated substance is beyond the scope of this text, although some mention is made of conditions under which we obtain suitable deposits in particular analyses. Given the chemical characteristics of a sample, the possibility of attaining the remaining objectives of this technique depend largely on how closely we can regulate the potential of the working electrode.

Potential control. During an exhaustive reduction, a working cathode becomes steadily more negative or cathodic in potential. How great a change in potential is required to electrolyze a substance quantitatively we may readily compute from the Nernst equation (Section 27.2).

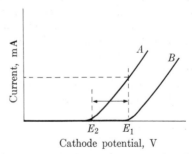

Fig. 27.8 Selective electrolysis by control of potential of working electrode. Substance *A* may be reduced without interference from substance *B* if the cathode potential (relative to a reference electrode) is kept between the values represented by the broken lines.

Such a calculation has immediate value in determining whether other metals interfere. Figure 27.8 shows the minimum difference in electrolysis curves that allows a clean separation of two metals. The potential of the working electrode need not be held constant but must not be allowed to exceed E_1, the value at which electrolysis of the metal that is more difficult to reduce begins. In order to meet the requirements that the time of electrolysis be minimal, the voltage of the electrode is ordinarily set at the most negative value possible without (a) producing interference, e.g. E_1 in the case discussed, or (b) depositing metal too rapidly to give an adherent coating.

Finally in this consideration of potential control, we look at the anode. In certain electrolyses the product of the regular oxidation process at the anode interferes with the desired reduction. The possibilities for such interference are inherent in the open design of the cells used in electrogravimetry (Fig. 27.9) and in the selection of platinum as the most suitable anode material. If chlorine or oxygen is produced at the anode, as often happens in the absence of countermeasures, some of the gas is usually swept to the cathode where it reoxidizes the metal being deposited. We can avoid the production of these oxidizing agents by adding a substance such as hydrazine dihydrochloride, which functions as an *anodic depolarizer*. By definition, such a substance is oxidized at potentials below those required for chlorine or oxygen evolution and yields a product that is chemically inoffensive (hydrazine oxidizes to N_2). The anodic depolarizer acts to stabilize the anode at a low potential.*

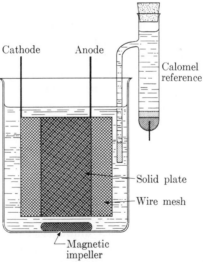

Fig. 27.9 Representative design of a cell for electrogravimetry. The outer cylindrical electrode is conventionally fabricated of gauze or is perforated.

Current and time. If the potential of the working electrode is maintained at a fixed value, as is generally done where close separations are necessary, the electrolysis current decreases continuously with time. Where a single reaction is occurring, the efficiency is, of course, 100%, and the current finally falls nearly to zero. The time needed for any percentage completion of deposition may be calculated by use of Eq. (27.4). In some cases the desired reduction at the working electrode may be

---

* In a real sense, an anodic depolarizer can also be termed a redox buffer (Section 27.2) if its oxidation occurs reversibly at the electrode. Hydrazine does not quite qualify, since it oxidizes irreversibly.

accompanied by the evolution of hydrogen. Then the current decreases to some small value other than zero.

Instrumentation. The apparatus required for an electrogravimetric determination is essentially simple. Cells are designed with a view to maximizing the cathode area, providing efficient stirring, and minimizing iR drop. Figure 27.9 shows an eminently satisfactory design. Platinum is almost always used for the electrodes, since it is inert and such electrodes may be used repeatedly without wear. Before each analysis an electrode is cleaned by stripping off the previous deposit in an appropriate acid. Naturally, it must be dried and weighed before and after each analysis. To achieve the stated objectives, concentric cylindrical electrodes are used, with the outer one the cathode. Since the electrodes are closely spaced, the cathode is either perforated or made of gauze to improve the circulation of the solution. In Fig. 27.9 the stirring is by magnetic stirrer, but in other cell designs it may be by a propeller stirrer or even by rotating the inner cylinder, the anode. There must also be a dc power supply with an adjustable output voltage, or a potentiostat.

Separations. Metal ions that interfere with an electrolysis can often be separated expeditiously by electrochemical means. A mercury cathode with a large, stirred surface has been widely adopted for this purpose. Since the cathode is mercury, the potential required to effect a particular separation can ordinarily be decided by reference to the extensive literature on polarographic half-wave potentials or by performing a preliminary polarographic determination. [2, 4, Chap. 25] The voltage selected should be about 0.15 V more negative than the $E_{1/2}$ of the offending element to give complete separation.

27.7 ELECTROGRAVIMETRIC PROCEDURES

Under optimum conditions, electrogravimetric procedures result in clean separations and deposition with better than 99.99 % completeness. The accuracy of the determinations is generally of the order of 0.1 % but depends on the weight of metal deposited and the sensitivity of weighing. Trace amounts of metals in alloys (concentrations below 0.5 %) can be successfully analyzed with semimicro equipment.

As a preliminary to the actual electrolysis, we must know the constituents of the sample. When little information is available, a qualitative analysis must be run. If we cannot find a suitable electrogravimetric procedure in the literature for the type of sample we have, it is usually well worth our while to run a polarogram under conditions that seem suitable. The result allows a ready estimate of whether a quantitative separation of the substance(s) of interest is possible and may also reveal the presence of unsuspected impurities that can give trouble. If we are to use the half-wave potential data, we must remember that the values for electrolysis on mercury differ slightly from those for deposition on platinum.

If a metal to be determined has a half-wave potential well separated ($\Delta E^0 = 0.5$ V) from that of the next most easily reduced species, we can carry out the analysis with little voltage control. For example, copper(II) ($E^0 = +0.34$ V) can easily be analyzed in the presence of nickel(II) ($E^0 = -0.25$ V). A *constant-total applied potential* in this case ensures precise results. Only when other metals that deposit at potentials close to the favorable potential are present is there a need for potentiostatic control.

Note that the presence of interfering metals need not necessarily preclude analysis by this technique. There are many possibilities for altering the potentials at which substances are electrolyzed by changing the pH or by adding complexing agents (Section 25.8). In other cases, as discussed in the last section, we can make a preliminary quantitative separation of the interfering metal by electrolyzing it at a mercury pool cathode. Only if it is unavoidable do we use a chemical procedure to remove the interfering substance. The objection is mainly the inevitable loss of precision as we add more steps to the analysis.

Example   Copper may be determined in most copper-base alloys by a procedure involving a tartrate medium of pH between 4 and 6. There is a sufficient difference in the stability of the tartrate complexes and the basic deposition potentials that other metals likely to be present do not interfere. The potential of the platinum cathode is set at -0.36 V vs. SCE and maintained by a potentiostat. Hydrazine dihydrochloride is added as an anodic "depolarizer." Metals such as antimony, arsenic, lead, tin, nickel, and zinc are not electrolyzed. If bismuth is present, the pH must be matinained at about 5.2 and the cathode potential set at -0.30 V to avoid interference. (At the higher pH the tartrate complexes are more stable, and the differences among their strengths more pronounced.)

Once the sample has been dissolved, we must arrange any conditions necessary to secure a firmly adherent deposit. Usually these are arrived at empirically. They may include adjustment of pH (by addition of buffer), complexation of the species to be deposited, addition of indifferent electrolyte to lower the resistance, or control of anode potential (by addition of a "depolarizer"). Together with adjustment of initial current density, these variables determine the quality of deposit.

REFERENCES

A comprehensive general coverage of coulometric techniques is provided by:

1. Karl Abresch and Ingeborg Claassen, *Coulometric Analysis*. London: Chapman and Hall, 1965
2. J. J. Lingane, *Electroanalytical Chemistry*. 2d ed. New York: Interscience, 1958
3. L. Meites, "Controlled Potential Analysis," in *Physical Methods of Organic Chemistry*. 3d ed., Part IV. A. Weissberger, ed. New York: Interscience, 1960
4. G. W. C. Milner and G. Phillips, *Coulometry in Analytical Chemistry*. New York: Pergamon, 1967
5. I. Shain, "Coulometric Analysis," in *Treatise on Analytical Chemistry*. Pt I, Vol. 4. I. M. Kolthoff and P. J. Elving, eds. New York: Interscience, 1963
6. N. Tanaka, "Electrodeposition," in *Treatise on Analytical Chemistry*. Pt I, Vol. 4. I. M. Kolthoff and P. J. Elving, eds. New York: Interscience, 1963

EXERCISES

27.1   In an electrogravimetric cell why cannot external control of anode potential be used instead of internal control (achieved by the addition of an anodic depolarizer)? Presumably external control would regulate the anode potential relative to a reference electrode.

27.2 What length of time would be required to titrate 0.15 g methanethiol, CH_3SH, in alkaline solution, using bromine electrolytically generated by a constant current of 100 mA? One mole of bromine oxidizes two moles of thiol.   [*Ans.*: 3010 s.]

27.3 An electric timer reliable to $\pm$ 0.1 s is to be used in constant-current coulometric titrations. Samples of the order of 10^{-4} equivalents are to be electrolyzed. What is the maximum current that can be used if the uncertainty in the determination of the sample is to be no greater than $\pm$ 0.1 %?

27.4 For routine titrations with a constant-current coulometer it is found that currents of either 1 or 10 mA are adequate. A timer graduated to the nearest 0.1 s is used but it is desired to mark its scale so that it is direct-reading in milliequivalents or microequivalents electrolyzed. For the two currents used, what labels should be assigned to the timer scale at the intervals corresponding to 20 s and to 100 s?

27.5 Samples of As_2O_3 are to be determined by reaction with coulometrically generated bromine as outlined on p. 757. Sketch a suitable cell and label all elements clearly. Be sure to include a practicable type of end-point detector. Explain the basis for its choice.

27.6 Show that the output voltage of the integrator of Fig. 27.6 is given by the formula

$$v_0 = \frac{R_2}{R_3 C} \int i_{cell}\, dt.$$

27.7 In the constant-potential coulometric determination of iron (by primary oxidation of iron(II) in acid solution) it was found that the current-time curve followed Eq. (27.4). (a) Show that when the equation holds, a plot of $\log i_t$ vs. t gives a straight line of slope $-k$ and intercept $\log i_0$ *and* that the area under the current vs. time curve is $i_0/2.303k$. (b) The approach implied in part (a) is used in the determination of an iron sample. Current is determined precisely at two known times and the electrolysis is stopped. The data recorded are, when $t = 35.5$ s, $i = 75.3$ mA and when $t = 74.0$ s, $i = 40.5$ mA. Find k and i_0. (c) What weight of iron was present in the sample?   [*Ans.*: (b) $k = 7.00 \times 10^{-3}$ s^{-1}; $i_0 = 135.5$ mA; (c) 4.86 mg.]

CHAPTER 28

CONDUCTOMETRIC METHODS

28.1 INTRODUCTION

For many solutions, electrical conductance is a descriptive property that lends itself readily and usefully to measurement. Simple electrolyte solutions in polar solvents are particularly well adapted to quantitative analysis by conductometric techniques. The range of applications extends from systems of small conductance and very low ionic concentrations, e.g. AgCl in water at 25 °C, to those of high conductance and concentration, e.g. the fused salt mixture KCl-NaCl at 800 °C. Since heretofore few analytical applications of electrical conductance have been made to solids or gases, the present discussion tends to exclude them.

Since conductance is a nonspecific property, it is of little use for identification of solutes or pure substances. Actually, there are few reliable values of specific conductances of pure substances, for conductance is very sensitive to the presence of impurities or structural imperfections (especially in solids). For example, when the conductance is cited for a substance it is usually intended to be more an index of purity than a characteristic constant.

When a single strong electrolyte is present in a dilute solution (in a pure solvent), its concentration can commonly be found directly from a conductance observation. At concentrations above 10^{-3} M, conductance may still be used to measure the concentration if a calibration curve is first determined.

In the usual sample, several electrolytes (some of which are impurities) are present. The conductance due to the species of interest cannot be separated from the measured total in any simple, exact way. Even in this situation, the concentration sought may be determinable conductometrically if the substance can be titrated. It is only required that a titration be found in which there is sufficient variation in conductance at the end point. Most acid–base and many precipitation and complexation titrations do exhibit the required change in conductance. With ordinary care, a precision of about 1 % is possible in a conductometric determination; with precise equipment and control of variables it may be extended to 0.1 %. The titration procedure is readily adaptable to weak acids and bases and to dilute solutions of strong electrolytes down to 10^{-4} M.

28.2 CONDUCTANCE RELATIONSHIPS

Conductance is simply the reciprocal of resistance, a more fundamental property that is a measure of the opposition a substance offers to charge movement. A measured resistance also depends on volume and dimensions. For example, if a sample of regular shape is placed between a pair of parallel electrodes, the resistance measured increases linearly with sample length l and decreases linearly with cross-sectional area A. We remove the dependence on shape and size by defining the *specific resistance* ρ as the resistance of a cube of sample 1 cm on edge. In terms of ρ the measured resistance R of a sample is given by the expression $R = \rho l/A$. Since R is in ohms, ρ must have units Ω cm. The reciprocal of ρ, the *specific conductance* κ, is the quantity of interest here. It is defined by the equation

$$\kappa = 1/\rho = l/AR \qquad (28.1)$$

and has the units Ω^{-1} cm^{-1}. For measurements on solutions the ratio l/A is fixed by the spacing and size of electrodes in the conductance cell (Section 28.4).

In dealing with dissolved electrolytes, it is convenient to define also an equivalent conductance as the conductance associated with one Faraday of charge. This is taken as the conductivity of a slab of solution 1 cm thick and of sufficient breadth and length to hold the volume of solution that contains one equivalent of the electrolyte.* The equivalent conductance Λ is related to specific conductance by the formal expression

$$\Lambda = \frac{1000\kappa}{C}, \qquad (28.2)$$

where C is the normality of the solution. Since both positive and negative ions will share in carrying the current, we can rewrite Eq. (28.2) in terms of the equivalent ionic conductances λ^{+} and λ^{-}

$$\lambda^{-} + \lambda^{+} = \frac{1000\kappa}{C}. \qquad (28.3)$$

Only at infinite dilution are the ionic conductances known precisely. Table 28.1 (p.777) gives a compilation of limiting or infinite-dilution ionic conductances λ_0.

How should we relate conductances to the discussion of mass-transport processes in Section 23.3? As noted there, conductance is the experimental measure of the transport process called migration. When we apply a potential difference across a pair of electrodes, ions first move to set up electrical double layers at the electrode surface (Section 23.1). If the potential is sufficiently large, the oxidation or reduction of electroactive species also begins. As ions are removed by reaction, additional ions move toward the electrodes. Figure 28.1 shows in simplistic terms the mechanism by which conductance occurs.

Mobility. By definition, the mobility u of an ion is its velocity v under an electric field strength E of 1 V cm^{-1}.† The defining equation is

$$v = uE. \qquad (28.4)$$

A force $z_i eE$ acts upon each ion, where z_i is the charge on the ion and e the electron

---

* Experimentally, it might be measured by using planar electrodes 1 cm apart and of sufficient surface area just to contain the required volume of solution.

† E is identical to the electrical gradient in the solution where V volts are applied to plates l centimeters apart.

charge. As a result of the force, an ion accelerates very rapidly until its motion is just offset by the frictional resistance of the solution. Mobility is a measure of its steady-state motion. So rapidly is a limiting velocity attained by ions that in audio-frequency conductance measurements ions may be assumed to travel at a constant velocity, even though the field is reversing a great many times per second.

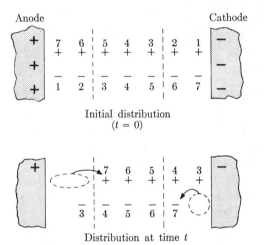

Fig 28.1 Transport of charge by migration. Electrical double layers at electrode surfaces are omitted. At $t = 0$, there are equal numbers of positive and negative ions throughout the bulk solution. In time t, two cations and two anions are discharged by electrolysis. If the cations are assumed to have a mobility twice that of the anions, both cations are replaced at the cathode but only one anion is replaced at the anode. Any ionic species not electrolyzed simply tends to accumulate at the electrodes.

The limiting velocity or mobility of an ionic species is determined by the viscosity of the solvent, the solvated size of the ion, the concentration of the solution, and the potential gradient. It has been found that for ions whose radius is about 0.5 nm (5 Å) or greater, Stokes's law describes approximately the relation between the force on the ion F, bulk viscosity η, and mobility u. The statement of the law is

$$u = \frac{F}{6\pi\eta r}, \tag{28.5}$$

where r is the radius of the ion. Equation (28.5) is of limited validity, but does apply to spherical ions moving in a solvent whose molecules are considerably smaller than the ions.

Remember that most ions are of the same general size as solvent molecules. They therefore share in the general thermal agitation and have at best a randomly directed type of progress. The instantaneous velocity of any ion in a liquid is of the order of 10^4 cm s^{-1}, but its mean free path is so short that its average velocity toward an electrode is no more than 10^{-3} to 10^{-4} cm s^{-1} when the electrical field strength is of the order of 1 V cm^{-1}.

The current through a unit cube of solution may now be expressed in terms of mobilities. Assume for simplicity that a single electrolyte has completely dissociated.

For the positive ions let N_+ be their number per cubic centimeter, u_+ be their mobility, and z_+ be their charge. The related quantities for the negative ions will be denoted by N_-, u_-, and z_-. The total charge arriving at the negative electrode per unit area per second is then $N_+u_+z_+eE$. To convert to cell current, we must include charge arriving at the positive electrode and multiply by electrode area A. The equation obtained is

$$i = (N_+u_+z_+ + N_-u_-z_-)eEA. \tag{28.6}$$

By use of Ohm's law and Eq. (28.1), we can formulate the specific conductance from Eq. (28.6). We obtain

$$\kappa = (N_+u_+z_+ + N_-u_-z_-)e. \tag{28.7}$$

Concentration dependence. At very low concentrations, ions behave essentially independently. Any given ion moves in a medium where other ions are so distant that they fail to influence its velocity or physical behaviour. But from concentrations of the order of $10^{-6}N$ upward ions approach each other sufficiently often that interionic forces are important. In addition many kinds of ions begin to associate. Where such a process occurs, conductance decreases proportionally. It is beyond the scope of this book to treat ion association processes. Two interionic effects are of sufficient importance even where there is no association, however, to warrant a brief description.

Electrophoretic effect. In an electrolyte solution, any ion is surrounded by a sheath of solvent molecules, each held with reasonably strong ion-dipole forces. When an ion moves, its solvation sheath tends to accompany it. In this connection remember there is a continuing interchange between "bound" and "free" solvent in the sheath. Since ions of opposite charge move toward different electrodes, a given ion experiences a drag as solvent "bound" to ions of opposite charge moves past. For example, any negative ion moves through solvent that is not stationary but is actually flowing in the opposite direction since it loosely accompanies positive ions.

Relaxation effect. Another important property of an electrolyte solution that affects ion migration arises from the tendency toward electroneutrality. Any ion may be regarded as surrounded by an atmosphere of ions whose net charge is equal to its charge but opposite in sign. For an ion that is univalent and positive, the essentially spherical atmosphere will include both positive and negative ions but will have an overall charge of -1. The dimensions of an ionic atmosphere can be shown to be inversely proportional to the ionic strength of the solution. At high dilution the radius of the atmosphere is large; in concentrated solutions it may be only a few times the radius of the central ion.

When an ion moves, it tends to leave its atmosphere and a finite time will be required for the thermal and electrical forces to re-establish the randomly arranged atmosphere. Each ion is therefore subjected to a transient restoring force exerted by its old atmosphere as it decays. The opposing force tending to return the central ion to its original location is small at best and because of its time-dependent behavior is termed a relaxation effect. This force also tends to diminish conductance.

According to the general electrostatic theory of electrolytes developed by Fuoss and Onsager, [16] we can represent conductance as a function of concentration C by the following equation

$$\Lambda = \Lambda_0 - SC^{1/2} + EC \log C + JC, \tag{28.8}$$

where Λ_0 is the equivalent conductance at infinite dilution, S is the Onsager coefficient of the limiting conductance law, E is a constant,* and J is a factor dependent on ion size. Appropriate modifications to Eq. (28.8) can be made to cover association of electrolytes. The equation has been shown to hold generally up to concentrations of about 0.1 N.

28.3 ALTERNATING-CURRENT MEASUREMENTS

Because conductance involves the transfer of mass, both solution and electrodes are altered during a measurement. If we impose a dc voltage across a conductance cell there result two immediate, undesirable effects. The electrodes polarize slightly as (a) the solution layer near the electrodes tends to become depleted in the species being oxidized or reduced and (b) the electrode surfaces are altered by the products of electrolysis. The effects are not serious if the current is kept small ($< 10^{-7}$ A), but attention must customarily be given to them. If a larger current flows, a dc conductance measurement may well be invalid.

When an ac voltage of *audio frequency* is applied, the changes described are largely minimized. Because of the frequent reversal of electrolysis, the ionic movement and electrolysis that take place during one half of a cycle can be completely or nearly completely destroyed during the second half of each cycle. Concentrations are maintained essentially constant even though a current exists. The conductance of the solution and the current density at the electrode for a given applied voltage are key variables in arriving at an optimum frequency. If solutions of extremely low conductivity ($\kappa < 10^{-7}$) are being studied or the current density is very low, even dc measurements can be accurate. If the conductance is slightly larger, 60 Hz line current may allow precise measurements. Usually, however, a frequency of about 1000 Hz is preferable. Where great precision is required, we find the conductance at several frequencies in the audio range and extrapolate to infinite frequency. [1]

Note that larger conductance values are usually found at radio frequencies (10^5 to 10^7 Hz). The change is a direct consequence of the increased importance of circuit capacitances and inductances. At radio frequencies, the interpretation must thus be broadened to include the bulk capacitance of the cell as well as the resistance of the solution. Separate consideration will be given to this type of measurement in Section 28.10.

A further aid in the elimination of surface polarization effects is the use of platinized platinum electrodes. [1] These are electrodes on which finely divided platinum has been deposited in a thin, adherent layer by electrolysis. As a result of the greatly increased surface area, the reunion of liberated hydrogen and oxygen appears to be catalyzed. The polarization from this source is thus minimized. The large surface area also eliminates concentration polarization.

Electrical model. A desirable insight into the nature of a conductance measurement

---

* Both S and E are determined by the absolute temperature, dielectric constant and viscosity of the solvent, valence type of the solute, and universal constants. S also includes Λ_0.

is gained by considering an ac circuit that is electrically equivalent to a conductivity cell. Probably the simplest representation is the circuit pictured in bold lines in Fig. 28.2. The bulk of the solution between the electrodes behaves like an ordinary ohmic resistor and is designated R_3. It is this resistance that is of interest. But at each electrode–solution interface there is an ionic double layer (Section 23.1), which must also affect the current. The double layers appear as capacitors of high capacity; without any loss of rigor, these two capacitances may be lumped and labelled C_3. The magnitude of C_3 depends strongly on the amount of platinization of the electrode surface, the extent to which the electrode is polarized, and the time available for the build-up of the ionic layers. For very dilute solutions, that is those whose concentration is of the order of 10^{-4} M or smaller, this simple representation is quite useful.

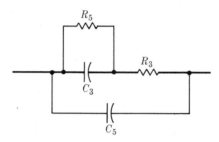

Fig. 28.2 Schematic representation of an ac conductance cell in terms of its equivalent circuit. The simplest equivalent circuit is shown in bold lines. R_3 is the resistance of the bulk solution, C_3 represents the double-layer capacitance at the electrodes, R_5 is the faradaic resistance across the electrode double layer, and C_5 represents the capacitances of the cell electrodes, leads, etc.

We can make the representation more exact and extend it to more concentrated media by including (a) the electrolysis at the metal–solution interfaces, and (b) the cell and lead capacitances. The first appears as an additional resistance R_5 in parallel with the ionic double-layer capacitance C_3. The second may be represented as a capacitance C_5 in parallel with all the other components. Figure 28.2 shows these modifications in light lines. Neither R_5 nor C_5 are major factors in influencing circuit behavior, although they cannot be ignored in very precise observations. Since R_5 is usually of the order of from 0.1 to 1 Ω, the measured cell resistance is nearly equal to R_3. Analogously, C_5 is usually no more than from 10 to 100 pF, about 1000 to 10,000 times smaller than C_3. In Sections 28.4 and 28.5 we use the equivalent circuits in considering cell and bridge design.

28.4 CONDUCTANCE CELLS

The usual envelopes for cells with electrodes are made of hard glass. Where ruggedness is required, e.g. in many field and plant applications, other inert, stable dielectrics such as hard rubber and some of the plastics are also in common use. The electrodes are generally square pieces of stiff platinum foil aligned parallel to each other. It is essential that the electrodes be rigidly supported at the desired spacing; by proper design they may be self-supporting like those shown in Fig. 28.3. If required, the electrodes may be platinized by brief electrolysis in a chloroplatinic acid solution. [6]

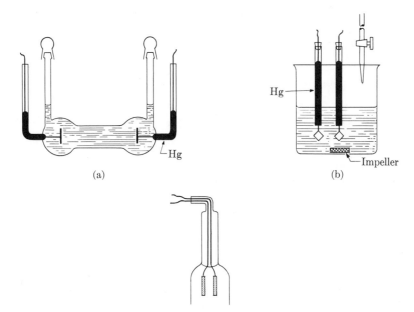

Fig. 28.3 Some types of conductance cells. (a) Jones and Bollinger precision cell. (b) Titration cell (c) Dip-type cell.

Leads. Special attention is always given to the arrangement of the leads to the electrodes, except where an accuracy of from 2 to 5% is adequate. If leads are bare and are brought out close together through the solution, stray electrolytic and capacitive current will pass between them. Accordingly, it is good practice to use insulated lead wires and bring them out of the electrode chamber in opposite directions. Three different designs of conductance cells are illustrated in Fig. 28.3. Note that all obstructed spaces where mixing will not occur readily have been eliminated in the cells of types (a) and (b).

Cell constant. The resistance of a solution between the electrodes of a cell is a function not only of solution specific conductance κ but also of the volume of conducting solution between the electrodes. For a pair of parallel electrodes of area A and spacing l, κ may be obtained by rewriting Eq. (28.1) as

$$R = \frac{l}{A\kappa}. \tag{28.8}$$

In practice we determine the ratio l/A, termed the *cell constant*, for each cell by measuring its resistance when filled with a conductance standard. Solutions of potassium chloride of known concentration are primary standards, their conductances having been accurately determined in cells of known electrode geometry.

For accurate conductance work over a range of concentration it is desirable to use cells of different cell constant. In aqueous work cell constants from about 0.1 to 10 are needed. In nonaqueous media other ranges are called for. The reason is that a bridge of conventional design (Section 28.5) is capable of greatest accuracy if the cell resistance falls in the range from 1 to 30 kΩ.

Example A solution of specific conductance of $10^{-5}\ \Omega^{-1}\ cm^{-1}$ has a resistance of 30,000 Ω or below if its cell constant is 0.3 or smaller.

Thermostating. Control of temperature is indispensable if reliable conductance measurements are sought. The specific conductance of electrolytes increases on the average about 2% per degree Celsius. To reduce the error from this source to 1% therefore requires regulation to $\pm 0.5\,^{\circ}C$; to reduce the error to 0.01% requires regulation to $\pm 0.005\,^{\circ}C$. A constant-temperature bath filled with a light transformer oil is often used to achieve the desired regulation. Water is seldom used as the fluid because of accompanying undesirable capacitance effects between cell and ground.

28.5 THE AC WHEATSTONE BRIDGE

This bridge is the basic instrument for determining conductance. The dc version of the Wheatstone bridge was treated in Sections 3.3 and 3.4; that background is now assumed familiar. In Fig. 28.4a a schematic circuit of the dc bridge has been repeated to permit comparison with the common form of ac Wheatstone bridge shown in Fig. 28.4b. Recall that the condition of balance of the dc bridge is that the potential at points C and D must be equal, yielding the equation

$$\frac{R_1}{R_2} = \frac{R_3}{R_4}. \tag{28.9}$$

Conductance is then obtained by taking the reciprocal of R_3. It is of particular interest that this condition also holds for balance of the ac bridge to within $\pm 0.1\%$. Some variation is to be expected since the ac bridge is properly an *impedance bridge*. Sources of error in the ac bridge will be considered below.

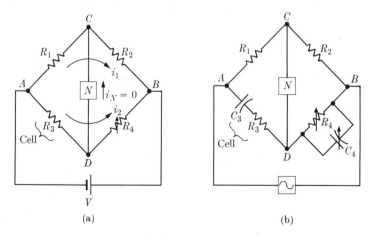

Fig. 28.4 Wheatstone bridge circuit in two versions. In each, R_1 and R_2 are ratio arms and N is a suitable null detector. (a) Simple bridge. (b) Alternating-current conductance bridge. The C_4-R_4 combination provides adequate compensation for both resistance and capacitance of the conductivity cell under most conditions.

Range of measurement. The range of *resistance* measurable may be deduced from Eq. (28.9). If $R_1 = R_2$, unknown resistance R_3 can be measured by the bridges shown in Fig. 28.4 when its value falls within the range $0 < R_3 \leqslant R_4$. Since this span is short, ways to extend it are important. One method is to vary the ratio R_1/R_2 as well as R_4. Bridges offering several set ratios of R_1/R_2 from 0.01 to 100 are common. Range is traded off for accuracy in these bridges; they are accurate at best to about $\pm 1\%$.

Alternatively, range can be extended in conductance measurements by the strategem of use of cells of different cell constant (Section 28.4). This approach permits use of equal values for R_1 and R_2, which is necessary to the construction of precision conductance bridges. If R_1 and R_2 have equal values and have been carefully constructed of stable, low-temperature-coefficient alloy, we can assume their resistances will change in like amount with time and temperature and keep the ratio invariant.

Sources of error. Contact resistance in switches and in leads to the cell, a major potential source of error, can be minimized by keeping every contact possible in series with the power supply (V) or detector (Section 3.3).*

We must now consider certain sources of error peculiar to the use of ac. The resistors that comprise the bridge arms possess distributed inductance and capacitance, and we must regard the cell itself as equivalent to a model like that in Fig. 28.2. Second, there is a considerable number of possible stray current paths in an ac bridge. These are of two types. Any part of the bridge has some capacitance with respect to ground and offers a leakage path. Also, by virtue of the inductance of the resistance coils, there exists the possibility of inductive pickup of stray ac currents from power lines or from the oscillator that supplies the bridge power.

The contribution of error from these sources may be reduced considerably by proper resistance, shielding, and physical arrangement. [8] The resistors should be noninductively wound. The bifilar winding, in which the length of wire required to obtain the desired resistance is doubled back on itself and then wound on the form, is widely used to minimize inductance. It is advantageous to have enough residual capacitance so that the capacitive reactance will nearly cancel the inductive reactance at the operating frequency. The cell capacitance C_5 can be compensated by placing a variable capacitor C_4 in the bridge parallel with resistance R_4, as shown in Fig. 28.4b. Since the problem of eliminating stray leakage paths involves more difficult considerations, it is deferred until the end of this section.

Power sources. Some industrial and field conductivity instruments operate on 60 Hz ac stepped down from a power line. Much better accuracy is generally secured by operation at audio frequencies in the range of from 500 to 4000 Hz. In this case, an electronic oscillator is usually employed as a generator. The output of the oscillator should ideally be of a single frequency (a pure sine wave) and should be variable in amplitude from zero to several volts. If the harmonic content is minimized, a more

---

* In any event, there should be sufficient resistance in the power circuit to ensure that bridge resistors dissipate less than the maximum allowable power.

precise balance can be obtained, for the problem of phase shifts will be simplified (see below). A variable voltage output allows flexibility of operation.

Phase relationships. For a true bridge balance, the ac waves must be in phase at points C and D (Fig. 28.4b). This condition requires either no phase change in either arm or the same phase change in each. Only the latter is a possible solution to the requirement. The capacitance and inductance of the resistors and cell can be minimized but not eliminated.

If accuracies of the order of 1 % are satisfactory we may ignore the phase difference, providing the bridge resistors have been wound with reasonable care. For most nonresearch measurements and conductometric titrations, the phase difference can be neglected. On the other hand, work in which the precision must be 0.1 % or better calls for a careful examination of the phase dependence of the arms. It is customary to simplify the problem by using matched resistors for the ratio arms R_1 and R_2 so that not only are the resistances equal, but the phase behavior is identical. There remains the question of whether the phase difference introduced by the cell in arm 3 will be equal to that caused by the parallel R_4-C_4 combination. A thorough discussion is beyond the scope of this book, but a limiting case can be considered. In general, if the R_4-C_4 combination introduces a phase shift of less than about 10 minutes of arc, R_4 can be taken as equal to the cell resistance R_3 within 0.1 %.

Wagner ground. Finally, the elimination of stray paths for alternating currents must be treated briefly. The problem is solved by (a) electrostatically shielding the resistance arms by enclosing them in electrically grounded metal covers and (b) incorporating a Wagner ground in the circuit. By use of the Wagner device, points C and D of the bridge are brought to ground potential during balancing. This "grounding" operation allows the detector arm to be at ground potential at balance and virtually eliminates stray pickup at a spot where it would cause the greatest error.

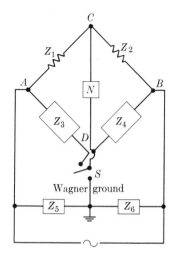

Fig. 28.5 Wagner ground in an ac bridge circuit. It consists of impedances Z_5 and Z_6 and the switch S.

Figure 28.5 gives a schematic of the Wagner ground. The impedances Z_5 and Z_6 are suitable combinations of variable resistors and capacitors. The balancing of the bridge now has some additional steps. A normal balance is first obtained with the Wagner ground out of the circuit. Then the switch S is thrown to the other position. The circuit is rebalanced using the variable elements in the Wagner ground. Next the switch is returned to the "bridge position," and the bridge circuit is rebalanced. Although a measurement requires more time as a result of the additional steps, the presence of the device greatly refines the precision of a conductance observation.

28.6 DETECTORS AND AMPLIFIERS

In selecting a detector to respond to the unbalance signal from a conductance bridge, we must keep several criteria in mind:

1. Adequate sensitivity (too little will lessen the precision of measurement, too much will make balancing a tedious operation),
2. Possibility of amplification,
3. Short response time,
4. Protection against overload, and
5. Ruggedness and stability.

These are not essentially different from the requirements imposed on any detector.

For an audiofrequency ac bridge, a telephone type receiver in conjunction with the human ear is the simplest reliable detector. Although the sensitivity of the ear reaches a maximum in the range of from 1000 to 2000 Hz, reasonably accurate balancing is possible from 500 to 4000 Hz. In general, the sensitivity must be enhanced by use of an amplifier if we desire a precision better than 2%. Furthermore, for highly accurate work, harmonics should be suppressed and a tuned amplifier used. For ac bridges of low sensitivity, we may substitute a rectifying circuit and a dc indicating instrument for the ear.

The electron ray tube, or "magic eye", and cathode ray tube "detectors" are in wider use. Both are electronic devices that give a visual indication of the balance. One or more stages of amplification are essential for other than semiquantitative work. With an electron ray tube, we apply the amplified bridge unbalance signal to the grid of its triode section. As a balance is approached closely, the visible shadow sector widens and at balance reaches its maximum width. With a cathode ray tube, the amplified unbalance signal is usually applied to the vertical deflection plates of the tube. It is usually desirable to spread out the wave pattern to enhance the sensitivity of detection by connecting a sweep circuit to the horizontal plates. The condition of balance is that the signal amplitude be a minimum.

Bridge amplifiers. An amplifier designed to give a logarithmic response offers a definite advantage, for it will produce the greatest response where the signal is smallest, near the point of balance. Some protection against overload must also be provided and is not difficult to incorporate.

Amplifiers inevitably have considerable capacitance to ground. Since the possibility of picking up stray signals is therefore large, electrostatic shielding of the amplifier is essential, and transformer coupling between bridge and amplifier or between stages of the amplifier should be avoided. Where transformers must be used, they should be small and carefully shielded magnetically. It will also relieve the situation considerably if the bridge points C and D can be operated at zero potential by means of a Wagner ground or a similar device.

Figure 28.6 is a block diagram of an ac conductance bridge with amplifier. Many commercial bridges use 60 Hz line voltage in lieu of an audio frequency of 500–1000 Hz such as the oscillator would supply. The null detector may be an electron ray tube (magic eye), oscilloscope, or other suitable device to register the level of ac voltage across the bridge.

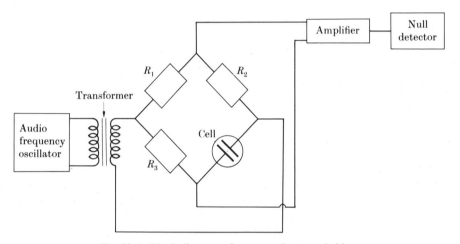

Fig. 28.6 Block diagram of an ac conductance bridge.

Operational amplifier conductometric titrator. Where only changes in conductance and not absolute values are of interest, a Wheatstone bridge is not mandatory. Ohm's law, $V = iR$, suggests that changes in the resistance of a cell might be measured by determining changes in i when a constant voltage V is imposed, i.e. $\Delta i = V/\Delta R$. It is easy to instrument this approach using operational amplifiers, as the block diagram in Fig. 28.7 shows. In the circuit, operational amplifier A serves as a current amplifier (Section 7.7) and provides an output voltage proportional to i.

The instrument in Fig. 28.7 is especially suitable for conductometric titrations, for which we need only relative values of conductance. It is also usual to provide for attenuation in the inverting amplifier (Section 7.4) by adjustments of the ratio of feedback to input resistance (R_f/R_i) that determines the gain of this device. We should estimate in advance the maximum value of conductance expected during a titration and use it as a basis for setting the attenuation to the level to be employed throughout the titration.

28.7 CONDUCTOMETRIC TITRATIONS

In solution, chemical reactions that involve electrolytes are accompanied by a conductance change. If the change is sufficient, we may often determine the end point of

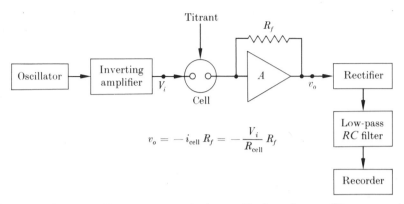

$$v_o = -i_{cell} R_f = -\frac{V_i}{R_{cell}} R_f$$

Fig. 28.7 Operational amplifier conductometric titrator. The inverting amplifier serves to isolate the oscillator and thus avoid loading by the cell, which might otherwise cause changes in voltage V_i as the cell conductance varied. Operational amplifier A is a current amplifier. Its output is directly proportional to the cell conductance as long as its input voltage is constant. The rectifier converts the ac signal to dc plus ripple, following which the RC filter smooths the signal to avoid any spurious dc offset at the recorder.

the reaction simply by monitoring the conductance. We can best understand the origin of the variation by inspection of a representative ionic reaction:

$$A^+B^- + C^+D^- \rightarrow AD + C^+B^-.$$
$$\underset{\text{unknown}}{} \quad \underset{\text{titrant}}{}$$

In the equation, CD is taken as the titrant and we assume AD, one of the products, to be a weakly ionized species. Up to the end point, the equivalents of C^+ ion in the solution at any time are essentially equal to the equivalents of A^+ that have been used up to form species AD. The concentration of B^- ions does not change. The conductance attributable to C^+ ions increases gradually during titration while that of A^+ ions decreases. After the end point, further addition of titrant sends the conductance upward in proportion to the volume added, since the concentration of C^+ and D^- ions in the solution grows steadily.

Example The titration of 0.01 M HCl by 0.1 M NaOH gives the V-shaped conductance curve in Fig. 28.8. As long as rapidly moving hydrogen ions are being replaced by much more slowly moving sodium ions, the conductance falls. After the reaction is complete, further addition of NaOH adds both sodium ions and fast-moving hydroxyl ions and conductance rises sharply and linearly.

In a manual titration we take conductance values periodically after addition of titrant and mixing. Amounts of titrant should be roughly calculated on the basis of estimated end point and the need to obtain four or more points on each branch of the conductometric titration curve well away from the end-point region. We eliminate any appreciable dilution error resulting from the increase in solution values at each point by multiplying the observed conductance by the ratio $(V + V_o)/V_o$, where V_o is the original solution volume and V is the volume of titrant added.* We then plot the data and draw the best straight line through each set of points. As Fig. 28.8 indicates, we should take the point of intersection as the end point.

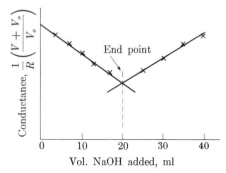

Fig. 28.8 Conductometric titration of 0.01 M HCl by 0.10 M NaOH solution. Note that the ordinate has been corrected for volume change during titration.

With an operational amplifier system like that in Fig. 28.7, we can obtain a titration curve automatically, provided we add titrant slowly and secure complete reaction at all times. Note there is no provision to correct for dilution as the curve is recorded. Linear parts of the curve should be extrapolated to their intersection to locate the end point.

Conductance data near the end point are less valuable since in this region there is little excess of any common ion and reactions may not be complete. For example, near the end point a weak acid or a weak base is more fully dissociated than at other times. Similarly, if a slightly soluble precipitate forms in a titration, it will be more soluble near the end point. Any incomplete reaction leads to curvature in the plot.

Since we can determine an end point by reliance on data far from the end-point region, we can follow conductometrically many reactions that are too incomplete for their end point to be located potentiometrically. For example, phenol, boric acid, and other quite weak acids can be successfully titrated in aqueous solution conductometrically but not potentiometrically. We can also apply the conductometric method to very dilute solutions and to some nonaqueous solutions [11] with good precision if we use sufficiently sensitive bridges and good thermostating. Against these advantages we must set a number of limitations considered later.

In any analysis it is valuable to be able to interpret the form of the characteristic curve obtained. This way we can gain both insight into the behavior of a system and assurance that a reaction is progressing. Since at the concentration levels that usually prevail conductance varies nearly linearly with concentration, it is not difficult to predict behavior in conductometric titrations. To predict a titration curve we also need a listing of relative ionic conductances. Table 28.1 provides such values. Though the data are valid at infinite dilution, they provide a basis for comparison even at

---

* Use of a titrant 10 to 20 times more concentrated than the species being titrated ordinarily allows this correction to be omitted.

ordinary concentrations. The contribution of each ionic species is presumed independent of others. Figure 28.9 shows the result of applying this kind of analysis to the titration system of Fig. 28.8. Figure 28.10 shows the procedure applied again.

Table 28.1 Limiting Equivalent Conductivities of Ions at 25 °C*

Ion	λ_0	Ion	λ_0
H^+	349.8	OH^-	198.6
Li^+	38.7	F^-	55.4
Na^+	50.1	Cl^-	76.4
K^+	73.5	I^-	76.8
NH_4^+	73.5	NO_3^-	71.5
$CH_3NH_3^+$	58.7	ClO_3^-	64.6
Mg^{2+}	53.0	CH_3COO^-	40.9
Ca^{2+}	59.5	SO_4^{2-}	80.0
Ba^{2+}	63.6	CO_3^{2-}	69.3

* Data taken from the compilation of Robinson and Stokes [12, Chap. 23].

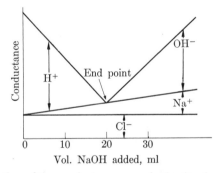

Fig. 28.9 Ionic interpretation of the conductance curve in the titration of 0.01 M HCl by 0.1 M NaOH. The conductance attributable to each species is shown separately. The conductance of the solution at any point in the titration (V-shaped line) is the sum of these contributions.

With bridges like those in Figs. 28.6 and 28.7, we may expect a precision of $\pm 1\%$ or better under favorable circumstances. Where additional refinement in titration and thermostating is possible and we can arrange the use of a high-precision bridge like the Jones bridge manufactured by Leeds and Northrup, reliability can sometimes be of the order of $\pm 0.1\%$.

Limitations and sources of error. We may group the salient "chemical" limitations and sources of error of the conductometric method as follows:

1. An indistinguishable difference in slope of intersecting lines,
2. Curvature in one or more conductance lines beyond end-point region,

3. Volume increase during titration, and

4. Temperature change.

Only the first two points require further discussion. In these comments we assume that a bridge or other instrumentation yielding results accurate to $\pm 1\%$ is used. With better thermostating and more precise instrumentation we may, of course, increase the acceptable range of conductance titrations.

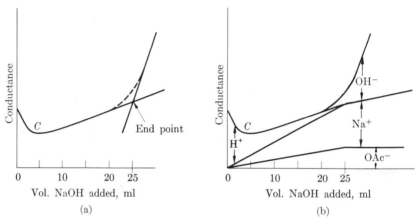

Fig. 28.10 Conductometric titration of 0.01 M acetic acid by 0.1 M NaOH. C is the region in which the suppression of the ionization of weak acid by accumulating acetate ion becomes marked. Curvature at the end point results from hydrolysis of acetate ion. Here the broken line indicates the actual data and the full lines the extrapolation of the linear regions. (a) Titration curve. (b) Ionic contributions to conductance.

The accuracy of locating the end point of a reaction depends significantly on how greatly intersecting conductance curves differ in slope. In this connection, compare the curves in Fig. 28.8 and 28.10a. Accuracy is certain to be smaller in the latter case.

Indeed, if the change in slope is quite small an ionic reaction cannot be followed conductometrically. Usually this difficulty is inherent in a system and may arise for any of several reasons. First, it may be the result of a high concentration of a foreign electrolyte. For example, most redox reactions are ill adapted to conductometric monitoring. Often such solutions must be strongly acidic (as e.g. in dichromate and permanganate oxidations), basic, or contain added salt (as e.g. in many iodometric procedures). In a highly conducting solution a small change in conductance attributable to the desired reaction is difficult to detect precisely. Second, small differences in slope may arise because a sample is dilute. Third, there may be little change in slope because the sample is a very weak electrolyte. Figure 28.10a gives an illustration of this situation. In all such cases, unless instrumentation capable of better than $\pm 1\%$ precision is available, a conductometric titration will not be feasible.

The second source of chemical error, incompleteness of reaction or the occurrence of side reactions, needs only brief comment. If a product of the reaction undergoes substantial hydrolysis, ionization, dissolution, or indeed almost any side reaction, there will be pronounced curvature in the conductance curve and little possibility of determining the end point reliably. Often the disturbing effects may be suppressed.

In aqueous systems it is common to add ethanol to reduce ionization or to lower solubility of a precipitate. When we can no longer locate the linear portion of a curve easily, we can sometimes apply a mathematical method of end-point calculation. [12]

Mixtures of acids or bases.   Often, we may analyze a mixture of a strong and a weak acid (or a strong and a weak base) by conductometric titration. The method is especially attractive when simple photometric and potentiometric methods do not give satisfactory results. In this situation, so long as one acid is strong and pK_a values differ by at least 5, the portion of the conductance curve attributable to each acid is definite. Figure 28.11 shows a curve for the titration of a mixture of acetic and hydrochloric acids. To interpret the graph, we should view the titration as a combination of the separate titrations of HCl and acetic acid already discussed.

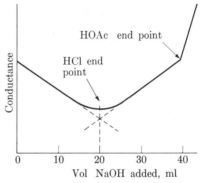

Fig. 28.11   Conductometric titration of an equimolar mixture of 0.01 M HCl and 0.01 M acetic acid. Titrant is 0.1 M NaOH. The slight curvature at the acetic acid end point, resulting from hydrolysis, is not shown.

Precipitation titrations.   Before deciding to follow a precipitation reaction conductometrically, we must study the growth of the crystals and their tendency toward adsorption. Even though there is a sufficient change in conductance during the reaction, the slowness of precipitation, coprecipitation, appreciable solubility, and adsorption effects can greatly increase the uncertainty in the results. There are very favorable instances for the application of precipitation titration, for example in determining some of the alkaline earths, by using sulfates. A particularly good illustration is the titration of solutions containing barium ions, using standard sulfuric acid solutions. The titration curve obtained resembles that in Fig. 28.9. An interesting tabulation of successfully performed titrations is available. [2]

28.8 DIRECT CONCENTRATION DETERMINATIONS

Direct conductance determinations of concentration are most often to determine a single electrolyte.* The determination is possible because, as noted for conductometric titrations, an approximately linear relation is observed between specific conductance

---

* With a weak electrolyte allowance must be made for the effect of one or more equilibria.

and concentration from 10^{-5} to 10^{-1} M. Provision for offsetting the effect of temperature becomes important in industrial determinations, where the temperature of a process stream may vary widely.

Example 1 Specific conductance in aqueous HCl solutions increases linearly with concentration up to about 2% HCl by weight. With a calibration curve, the HCl concentration may be determined by conductance to about 15% by weight.

Example 2 We can study the rate of the following reaction by monitoring the concentration of BH^+ and $CH_3CHNO_2^-$ conductometrically:

$$CH_3CH_2NO_2 + B = CH_3CHNO_2^- + BH^+.$$

Here B is a neutral organic base. Note that the only ionic species present are those formed during the reaction. In calculating the results, we assumed the ions produced did not hydrolize or associate at the concentration level used.

When conductance is used to determine concentrations at trace levels, special care is required. Since the measurement is not selective, we must either first remove foreign conductors or make a correction.* In some instances, limiting ionic conductances can be used to calculate the concentration. More often we prepare a calibration curve in advance.

28.9 RESEARCH APPLICATIONS

Much of the present knowledge of the properties and behavior of electrolyte solutions has been obtained from conductance studies. In particular, there has been intensive investigation of the ionization and association of solutes as a function of dielectric constant and of the acidic or basic character of the solvent. It is interesting to note that precise observations have been made even in very dilute solutions (from 10^{-5} to 10^{-7} M), concentrations beyond the range of many other methods.

The present research interest centers around a microscopic interpretation of solutions. What is sought is a physical model of the molecular arrangement that will reproduce the observed properties. If it is possible to devise a model of general applicability, we can develop a mathematical interpretation that is valid over a large concentration range.

28.10 HIGH-FREQUENCY METHODS

Conductance measurements are also obtained at high audio and at radio frequencies (about 10^5 to 10^7 Hz). Somewhat more involved instrumentation is required, but an advantage gained is that no metal electrodes need be in contact with the solution

---

* When the specific conductance of the solvent becomes as much as 0.5% of the value for the solution, a straight arithmetic correction is made. Since conductance (in dilute solutions, at least) is an additive property,

$$\kappa_{electrolyte} = \kappa_{solution} - \kappa_{solvent}.$$

under investigation. For the measurements it is sufficient to place the glass cell or section of tubing holding the sample solution between the plates of a capacitor (or within the coil of an inductor) that is a part of the resonant circuit of a sine wave oscillator. With this design, the usual electrode effects (possible chemical reaction with an electrode and electrolysis) are eliminated. Since instrumentation differs according to whether measurement is to be on discrete or continuous samples, each will be treated separately.

In instruments that handle separate samples, the oscillator itself serves as a detector since the frequency of its output depends on the conductance and dielectric constant of the solution. The capacitor type of arrangement is the more sensitive of the two means of coupling the solution to the oscillator circuit and has accordingly seen extensive use. Figure 28.12 shows the resonant circuit used in the observation in simple form. Since a parallel LC combination is used, it will act to store energy at its frequency of resonance (Section 2.8) and will cause the coupled oscillator* to generate essentially that frequency. The frequency of resonance in turn is partially determined by the apparent capacitance† of the sample cell. For a conductive sample this capacitance is given by the expression

$$C_{\text{sample cell}} = \frac{C_g(R_s^2\omega^2 C_s^2 + 1)}{R_s^2\omega^2 C_g C_s + R_s^2\omega^2 C_s^2 + 1} \tag{28.10}$$

where ω equals 2π times the frequency f and the other quantities have been identified in connection with Fig. 28.12. From the equation, it is evident that variations in either the capacitance C_s or the resistance R_s of the solution affects the resonance frequency.

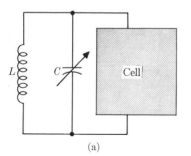
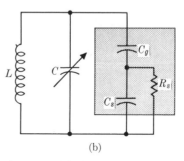

(a)   (b)

Fig. 28.12 Simple version of a resonant circuit in capacitor-type high-frequency measurement of conductance. The circuit is usually coupled to the oscillator through the inductance L (details not shown). (a) Schematic diagram. (b) Equivalent circuit showing details of cell and solution resistances and capacitances. The cell-wall resistance R_g is presumed very large relative to solution resistance R_s and is ignored. The capacitance of the glass walls C_g is small relative to the capacitance of the solution C_s, but is not negligible. The parallel C_s-R_s model of the solution can easily be converted to the series version presented in Fig. 28.2.

---

* A sine wave oscillator is fundamentally an amplifier with strong positive feedback. Such a circuit is frequency-selective (Section 6.4). When put into operation, an oscillator very quickly begins to amplify only the frequency most favored by the circuit, i.e. the one for which the power losses are smallest. If a resonant circuit is present in the base or output circuits, or both, the output frequency of the oscillator will be very nearly the frequency of resonance.

† This quantity is actually the equivalent series capacitance of the filled cell [p. 338 of 16].

One direct result of the complex dependence of the measurements on a combination of capacitance and conductance is the possible loss of sensitivity and accuracy in observations of conductance. [13] Calibrations are difficult to make. There is a degree of compensation in dealing with nonaqueous media, as will be shortly considered: It is possible to examine even poorly conducting media with reliability by this method if there is a possibility of appreciable change in dielectric constant in the analytical range.

A null method of measurement is nearly always used. The result is an instrument that is stable and easy to operate. Several precision capacitors are placed in parallel (thus adding capacitances) with the empty sample cell, and the oscillator is started. When the sample is added to the cell, the capacitance in parallel with it is decreased until the total apparent capacitance returns to the previous figure. The null point is determined by a frequency discriminator, which needs only to register that the initial and final frequencies are identical.

Continuous monitoring. In a radiofrequency conductance device intended for continuous monitoring of a solution two loops or coils of wire couple the solution to the device. They are bound around the pipe carrying the conducting solution and are placed far enough from each other for the solution to provide the only current loop coupling them. The signal induced in the second coil can be amplified and registered directly.

A more precise arrangement is the null circuit shown schematically in Fig. 28.13. The circuit provides for a null-balance readout. The auxiliary loop resistance setting is altered until the detector registers a null reading.

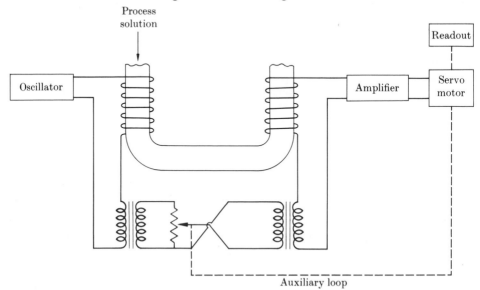

Fig. 28.13 Electrodeless high audiofrequency conductance instrumentation. The solution loop comprises two separated inductive windings around the tubing carrying the electrolyte solution. The coupling of the solution loop is opposed by coupling provided by an auxiliary loop. If they are unequal, the amplified error signal drives a servomotor to alter the auxiliary loop coupling until balance is reattained.

Applications. Electrodeless conductance-capacitance measurements are a useful end-point technique for titrations in which appreciable changes in conductance or dielectric constant occur. They are also useful in monitoring an electrolyte stream. They offer an advantage over conventional electrode conductometry mainly when contact with metal electrodes is undesirable. There are many reasons why electrodes may interfere. They may cause or show undesirable surface polarization effects, a tendency to catalyze reactions (especially troublesome with platinized platinum surfaces in organic systems), a tendency to react with the solution (probable in acidic or basic media or if certain complexing agents are present), or á tendency to obstruct movement of a fluid (likely with slurries).

In aqueous media, these restrictions limit the usefulness of the single-sample method mainly to detection of titration end points. Too great dilution of sample solution must be avoided; best results are secured for concentrations in the range of from 0.001 to 0.01 M. The titrant must be still more concentrated, of course. The volumetric and other experimental details are identical to those for regular conductometric titrations. The precision obtainable in favorable cases is comparable to that in audiofrequency determinations.

It is possible to carry out some nonaqueous titrations with surprising sensitivity. The basic requirement is a change in dielectric constant as a result of the reaction.

Any liquid system in which one component has a markedly different dielectric constant can be quantitatively analyzed with precision. Cells should be used that provide adequate shielding and are insensitive to fluid level when filled beyond a given point. For example, water is often determined in organic fluids by this method, and binary liquid pairs such as ethanol ($\epsilon = 24.3$)-nitrobenzene ($\epsilon = 34.8$) or benzene ($\epsilon = 2.27$)-chlorobenzene ($\epsilon = 5.62$) can be analyzed with precision.

REFERENCES

References that provide a general coverage of conductance and conductometry are:

1. S. Glasstone, *Introduction to Electrochemistry.* New York: Van Nostrand, 1942
2. I. M. Kolthoff and H. A. Laitinen, *pH and Electro Titrations.* New York: Wiley, 1941
3. J. W. Loveland, "Conductometry and Oscillometry," in *Treatise on Analytical Chemistry.* Pt I, Vol. 4. I. M. Kolthoff and P. J. Elving, eds. New York: Interscience, 1963
4. E. Pungor, *Oscillometry and Conductometry.* New York: Pergamon, 1965
5. R. A. Robinson and R. H. Stokes, *Electrolyte Solutions.* 2d ed. New York: Academic, 1959
6. T. Shedlovsky, "Conductometry," in *Physical Methods of Organic Chemistry.* 3d ed., Pt IV. A. Weissberger, ed. New York: Interscience, 1960

Special attention is given to bridges and detectors in:

7. B. Hague, *Alternating Current Bridge Methods.* 5th ed. London: Pitman, 1946
8. Forest K. Harris, *Electrical Measurements.* New York: Wiley, 1952
9. Melville B. Stout, *Basic Electrical Measurements.* New York: Prentice-Hall, 1950

Conductometric and radiofrequency titrations are discussed in:

10. T. S. Burkhalter, "High Frequency Conductometric Titrations," in *Comprehensive Analytical Chemistry.* Vol. IIA. C. L. Wilson and D. W. Wilson, eds. New York: Elsevier, 1964

11. D. G. Davis, "Potentiometric Titrations and Conductometric Titrations," in *Comprehensive Analytical Chemistry*. Vol. IIA. C. L. Wilson and D. W. Wilson, eds. New York: Elsevier, 1964

12. E. Grunwald, "End Point Calculation in Conductometric and Photometric Titrations," *Anal. Chem.* **28**, 1112 (1956)

14. Walter Huber, *Titrations in Nonaqueous Solvents*. New York: Academic, 1967

13. J. L. Hall, J. A. Gibson, H. O. Phillips, and F. E. Critchfield, "Some Evaluations of High-Frequency Titration," *Anal. Chem.* **26**, 1539 (1954)

15. C. N. Reilley, "High Frequency Methods," in *New Instrumental Methods in Electrochemistry* by P. Delahay, ed. New York: Interscience, 1954

Good theoretical treatments of conductance are provided on an intermediate to advanced level in:

16. R. M. Fuoss and F. Accascina, *Electrolytic Conductance*. New York: Interscience, 1959

17. S. Petrucci, ed., *Ionic Interactions*. Vol. I. New York: Academic, 1971

EXERCISES

When appropriate, refer to Table 28.1.

28.1 A cell is found to have a resistance of 4590 Ω when filled at 25 °C with a 0.01 M solution of salt *A* of specific conductance $4.56 \times 10^{-4} \, \Omega^{-1} \, cm^{-1}$. When a 0.001 M solution of salt *B* is placed in the cell and a measurement made at 25 °C, the resistance is found to be 25,230 Ω. Water of conductivity $2.5 \times 10^{-6} \, \Omega^{-1} \, cm^{-1}$ is used. What is the specific conductivity of the second salt?   [*Ans.*: 8.03×10^{-5}.]

28.2 A cell having a cell constant of 0.55 cm^{-1} is filled with a dilute aqueous $NaNO_3$ solution and found to have a resistance of 3210 Ω at 25 °C. If no other electrolyte is present, what is the approximate concentration of the salt? (Use limiting ionic conductances and refer to Section 28.2).   [*Ans.*: 1.4×10^{-3} M.]

28.3 Plot conductometric titration curves for the following systems, ignoring the ionization of any weak electrolyte and the solubility of any precipitate: (a) calcium chloride titrated with silver nitrate, (b) sodium acetate titrated with hydrochloric acid, (c) ammonia titrated with hydrochloric acid, and (d) acetic acid titrated with ammonia. Assume in each case a titrant concentration of 1 M and solution concentrations of 0.01 M. (Calculate the specific conductivity when 0, 0.3, 0.7, 1.2, and 1.5 times the equivalent amount of titrant has been added.)

28.4 In a conductometric titration, the more concentrated the titrant is, the more acute the angle of the conductance curve is, since the excess titrant line rises more steeply. Is the accuracy of the determination affected?

28.5 A precision conductance bridge with ratio arms in the ratio of 1:1 is to be used to measure solutions of specific conductances (a) 1×10^{-2}, (b) 1×10^{-4}, and (c) 1×10^{-6} with equal accuracy. What value of cell constant should be used with each solution?

28.6 An industrial system in which pure water ($R > 1$ MΩ) is furnished is monitored by identical conductivity cells at several points. The conductance of any cell may be checked at will, but ordinarily the cells are connected in parallel between an ac signal source and an indicating meter. Why is this arrangement effective in indicating ionic contamination at any of the check points?

28.7 In order to obtain a continuous record of a conductometric titration it is decided to record the unbalance current from a Wheatstone bridge, after amplification. Assume arm R_3 of the bridge is the titration cell, that arm R_4 is usually varied to obtain an initial balance and that resistances of ratio arms R_1 and R_2 are equal. (a) From one of the methods of analysis of the bridge in Section 3.4, obtain an equation for the dependence of the unbalance current on the titration cell resistance R_3. (b) If R_{cell} is known from other measurements to vary from 200 Ω to 100 Ω and back to 150 Ω should the bridge be balanced at the outset of a titration or come into balance midway if it is desired to obtain highest sensitivity of response to changes in cell conductance? (c) Assume that the bridge is balanced at the beginning of the titration just described. Graph the unbalance current against volume of reagent added.

OTHER METHODS

CHAPTER 29

METHODS USING RADIOISOTOPES

29.1 INTRODUCTION

More than 1000 unstable, that is, radioactive, isotopes are now known. These have nuclei with excess energy and degrade through the process of radioactivity to a lower energy level at a characteristic rate. The excess nuclear energy is usually discharged by the ejection of a highly energetic particle, such as an α- or β-particle. In many cases electromagnetic radiation of the γ-ray type also appears, either accompanying the particle or separately. The instrumental interest in radioactivity centers in the contrast between chemical behavior, which relates to the orbital electrons, and nuclear instability. In so far as the chemical properties are concerned, nuclear instability generally makes very little difference; at the moment of the disintegration of each radioactive atom, however, both its presence and location (within limits) can be instrumentally determined.

As a result of this combination of properties, unstable isotopes play an extremely important role as tracers. They are ordinarily added to a system in the chemical form most suitable to the study. For example, ^{32}P is often added as $(NH_4)_3{}^{32}PO_4$. In what may be called a physical application such as the testing of engine wear, the tagged or labeled material moves with a given phase or substance and serves to establish its location and concentration. In a chemical application such as a study of the mechanism of a reaction, the tagged molecules undergo reactions. In this instance both the level of radioactivity in each product and the molecular location of the radioactive atoms after the change are of interest.

Under favorable conditions, radioactivity may be determined with extreme sensitivity; as few as several thousand radioactive atoms are detectable in many cases. Even under ordinary conditions, radiochemical techniques provide the possibility of analyzing concentrations as low as 10^{-10} to $10^{-14}\,\text{mol ml}^{-1}$. Another consequence of the ease of detection is that no more than a small quantity of radioactive material, which is usually expensive, is required for studies. Since the widely used radioactive isotopes emit β- and γ-radiation, the discussions that follow concentrate on β- and γ-ray techniques.

29.2 ACTIVITY LEVEL AND DECAY RATE

We define the activity or decay rate of a substance in terms of the number of atomic disintegrations occurring in the bulk per second. A *curie* is the quantity of a radioactive substance that gives rise to 3.700×10^{10} disintegrations per second. (Earlier the curie was considered the quantity that gave the same number of disintegrations per second as 1 g of radium.) In practice this unit is inconveniently large and is displaced by the metrically related *milli*curie and *micro*curie. For example, tracer studies are carried out at the μcurie level.

The rate at which radioactive atoms decay is directly proportional to the number n of such atoms present. The rate of disintegration $- dn/dt$ is then defined by the expression

$$-\frac{dn}{dt} = \lambda n, \tag{29.1}$$

where λ is the decay constant for the particular species. For Eq. (29.1) to be valid, we must assume that the number of atoms disintegrating in a unit of time is small compared with the total number of atoms present. According to the equation, λ is just the fraction of the total number of atoms that decay per unit time. Interestingly, the decay constant has been found invariant to all ordinary changes in conditions such as temperature, pressure, electric and magnetic fields, and, of course, even to chemical change.*

When we integrate Eq. (29.1) between n_0, the number of active atoms initially, and n, the number present after the time t, we obtain

$$\ln \frac{n}{n_0} = - \lambda t \quad \text{or} \quad \frac{n}{n_0} = e^{-\lambda t}. \tag{29.2}$$

The activity of a sample falls off exponentially with time.

The number of radioactive atoms left at a particular time is seldom of interest. Likewise, the decay rate is seldom evaluated, although it is well to know the constant λ. Conventionally, the rate of disintegration is given in terms of the *half-life* $t_{1/2}$, the time required for the activity of a sample to be reduced by one half. That is, it is the interval during which half the initial number of radioactive atoms disintegrate. Substituting this condition, $n/n_0 = 1/2$, in Eq. (29.2), we obtain

$$\ln \frac{1}{2} = - \lambda t_{1/2}; \quad t_{1/2} = \frac{\ln 2}{\lambda} = \frac{0.693}{\lambda}.$$

We can observe directly only the activity A. This measured quantity is proportional to λn, but is affected by the efficiency of detection as well as the rate of decay. It is usual to treat activity data by making observations over a period of time and then plotting the logarithm of A versus the time. If we have maintained conditions constant so that the detection efficiency has not varied, we may easily obtain the value of the half-life from this graph by inspection. Then λ can be evaluated as suggested above. Figure 29.1 shows plots of this type, called *decay curves*, for three representative isotopes used in tracer work.

When several independent activities are present, the total activity is the sum of the separate activities $A = A_1 + A_2 + \cdots$. The activity for the mixture may be plotted

---

* Only the type of nuclear decay that results in K-shell electron capture can be influenced. Since an electron outside the nucleus is captured, any chemical alteration that influences the electron density near the nucleus does affect the disintegration rate. This change is an infrequent type of decay.

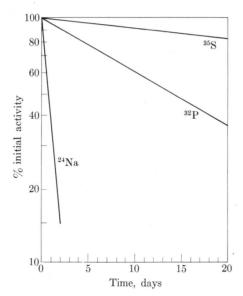

Fig. 29.1 Decay curves for three radioisotopes.

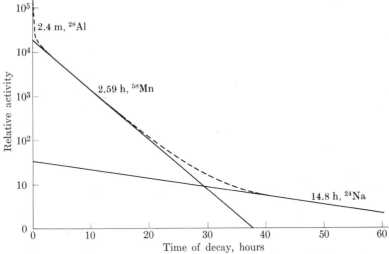

Fig. 29.2 Decay curve (broken line) for mixture of three independently disintegrating activities. The sample is a neutron-activated Mn-Al-Na alloy. The nuclides and half-lives are indicated on the curve. [After G. E. Boyd *et al.*, *Anal. Chem.* **21**, 335 (1949).]

as are the single activities in Fig. 29.1. In this case, we always obtain a curve that is concave upward. The shorter-lived components contribute less to the total disintegration as time passes. After a time equal to several half-lives of the more active components, the longest-lived species predominates, and the curve is a straight line. From the linear region, the half-life of the last substance to decay can be found by inspection. Then if we extrapolate this portion to $t = 0$ and substract it from the original curve, the residual curve should represent the decay of the other components.

The new curve should also display a linear region, allowing the determination of the half-life of the next shorter-lived isotope. In principle, it should then be possible to repeat the process indefinitely. In practice, the resolution is seldom adequate to find $t_{1/2}$ by this procedure for more than three species. Figure 29.2 gives a good illustration of the method.

Decay schemes. Each type of radioactive nucleus (hereafter called a *radioactive nuclide* or simply *radionuclide*) exhibits a distinctive decay pattern. For example, ^{24}Na (see Table 29.3) decays by first emitting a β-particle and then releasing in sequence a 2.76 MeV and a 1.38 MeV γ-photon. Except for the very light nuclei, however, there appear to be few simple disintegration patterns leading from the excited state to the ground state by a mechanism such as a single β-emission. New features of decay schemes have been reported continuously as instrumentation has become more refined.

Beta- or γ-decay or both are the most common types of decay. Alpha-emission is really probable only for the nuclides of elements above lead ($Z > 82$). "Pure" particle emission is a comparatively rare process. For most nuclei, after a particle is ejected there is still excess energy, and one or more γ-photons are also emitted before the nucleus reaches the ground state. It should be noted also that an appreciable number of radioactive species disintegrate to other radionuclides. When this occurs, the activity of the daughter nuclide will also be measured.

29.3 INTERACTION WITH MATTER

Nuclear radiations interact strongly with matter by virtue of their high energies. For example, β-particles are ejected from the common radionuclides with energies ranging from 0.017 to 2 MeV. The interaction can be described by reporting the nature of the process and the distance of travel or penetration before the energy falls to the thermal level. Both aspects suggest methods for the detection and use of radioactivity. The interactions vary with mass, charge, and the energy of the radiation as well as with the same properties of the medium.

For the purpose of detection, ionization is probably the most useful kind of interaction with matter, even though not the most likely primary process. Under the influence of radiation, an electron is ejected from an atom or molecule and a positive fragment left behind: The result is an *ion pair*. The energy of formation of an ion pair in air is about 35 eV on the average. In almost all other gases the figure is smaller, ranging down to about 20 eV. Usually, less than half this energy goes into the actual ionization; the remainder is accounted for by the kinetic energy given to the electron shot out. A small percentage of these secondary electrons have energies greater than the ionization potential of the medium and act to produce further ionization. Indeed, some 60 to 80 % of the total ionization created by α- or β-particles results from the collisions of the energetic secondary electrons.

Though interaction within a solid is not excluded from Table 29.1, it is important to stress the possibility. The energy used by an X-ray in producing an electron-hole pair in germanium is only about 2.9 eV. As a result, ionization in semiconductors is attractive for detection purposes also.

Table 29.1 summarizes the pertinent details of the interaction of α-, β-, γ-, and neutron radiation with atoms of different atomic number Z.

29.4 MEASUREMENT OF RADIATION

The quantitative determination of nuclear radiation depends on the measurement of the ionization or excitation produced during the interaction of the radiation and the bound electrons in a dielectric medium. Since radioactive disintegrations occur in random fashion and vary greatly in rate and energy with the nature of the active substance, any effective measuring device must show

1. Rapid response and recovery and

2. Sensitivity to small amounts of ionization.

While the first must be realized in all stages of an instrument, the second is primarily fixed by the detector.

In gaseous detectors such as the Geiger–Mueller tube, the ion pairs formed by the radiation, which consist of an electron and positive fragment of a molecule, are collected by an electrode system. The response depends on sweeping all the ions and electrons resulting from a single γ-photon or particle to the electrodes of the tube and producing a pulse of electricity at the output. In the scintillation detector, each entering particle triggers the release of many UV or visible photons, which are sensed by a multiplier phototube and likewise converted into a current pulse. Specially prepared photographic emulsions are also used as detectors. For example, very thin emulsions find use in radioautography. In that technique, thin sections of tissue or metal that have taken up radioisotopes are placed in contact with the emulsion in the dark. After developing, the silver deposit provides a "map" of the areas that have become tagged. High resolution is now possible (about 2μm), but the method is not so easily adapted to quantitative determinations. A discussion of the devices used in the study of nuclear energy levels and nuclear reactions is beyond the scope of this book.

In comparing radiation detectors, as they are discussed in the next two sections, we should keep the following criteria in mind:

1. Window or wall thickness (in mg cm^{-2}) and size (the first controls the energy threshold that must be exceeded for radiation to enter, the second is one factor in the geometry of counting),

2. Resolution time, the period during which the detector is insensitive following its response to previous radiation (this factor determines the maximum activity level measurable with precision),

3. Amplification factor, the degree to which the original ionization or excitation is enhanced within the detector,

4. Background counting rate (this factor sets the minimum activity level detectable with precision),

5. Efficiency, which is a measure of the percentage of the energy of the radiation absorbed in the active volume of the detector (this factor determines usefulness in energy spectrometry), and

6. Sensitivity to operating variables such as applied voltage, pressure of the filling gas, operating life, etc.

We may accomplish the task of amplification in one or more ways: by direct

Table 29.1 Characteristics of Four Nuclear Radiations and Their Interaction with Matter

PARTICLE	CHARACTERISTICS			INTERACTION		
	Energy, MeV	*Specific Ionization, ion pairs* cm^{-1}*	*Path*	*Ionization*	*Scattering*	*Other Types*
ALPHA mass 4 charge 2+	5	30,000 to 50,000	Uniform, short	Results from primary collisions, but is more common as result of collisions of secondary electrons	Small amount of scattering by atoms; increases with increasing Z	Electron excitation likely in near collisions
BETA mass 1/2000 charge 1−	0.013 to 2 (electrons from particular isotope have wide range of energies up to characteristic max. value)	100 to 700	Variable in direction, longer	Same as for α-particles	Scattering by electron clouds of atoms; common; increases with increasing Z	X-ray production moderately probable for energies <1 MeV and atoms with Z > 40

GAMMA mass 0 charge 0	0.05 to 3 (all rays from particular isotopic transition have same energy)	1 to 70	direction, long	Results from photoelectric effect, which is most common after γ-rays have lost a large part of their energy	Compton scattering: part of the energy is transferred to an electron in the path of the ray; very common	Pair production (of positron plus electron) occurs occasionally when energy greater than 1.02 MeV
NEUTRON mass 1 charge 0	Variable	Negligible	Very variable in direction	Results only when absorption of neutrons induces radioactivity; all secondarily generated by particles from induced radionuclide	Both elastic and inelastic scattering; common	Absorption by nucleus

*In air.

gaseous amplification, when a gas ionization tube is the detector; by secondary emission from the electrodes of a multiplier phototube when a scintillation detector is used; or by electronic means generally as an adjunct to either of the above or when a proportional counter-detector or ionization chamber is employed.

The output of the detector and amplifier then consists of separate pulses, that we must count or else average over a period of time. Electronic counting (Section 9.5) is used in the first case. Averaging pulses requires a simple resistor-capacitor system and gives a counting rate directly (Section 29.10). Finally, by coupling a detector-amplifier combination that gives a linear relation between radiation energy and pulse size to a pulse height analyzer (Section 29.11), it is possible to determine the energy spectrum of the radiation.

29.5 GAS IONIZATION DETECTORS

The Geiger–Mueller counter, the proportional counter, and the ionization chamber are detectors whose response is based on the ionization of a gas by nuclear radiations. In each case, the filling gas is ionized along the path of the ray or nuclear particle. The total of ion pairs produced ranges, in general, from 100 to 100,000. By applying an electric field across the electrodes of the detector, the electrons and positive ions making up the pairs can be separated and collected at the electrodes. The current obtained is very small, of the order of 10^{-16} to 10^{-13} A, and appears as a number of pulses, one pulse resulting from each radioactive particle.

Example In an experiment, about 50 β-particles per second enter the active volume of an ionization counter. If these are in the range of from 0.05 to 1.0 MeV, about 100 primary ion pairs are formed per centimeter. Assuming a 5 cm active path in the detector, the number of ion pairs collected per second at the electrode is $50 \times 5 \times 100 = 2.5 \times 10^4$. The current is then 2.5×10^4 ion pairs per second $\times 1.6 \times 10^{-19}$ C per ion pair (in the external circuit) $= 4 \times 10^{-15}$ A.

Each pulse of current (which goes to make up the average current just calculated) will be 50 times smaller, or 8×10^{-17} C. Before either the individual pulses or the average current can be registered, the signal must be considerably amplified.

Fundamental circuit. The common detector of the gas ionization type has a cylindrical cathode and an axial wire anode. Ideally, all radioactive particles that penetrate the active volume, that is, the space between the electrodes, are counted. The electrode geometry takes advantage of the fact that the field strength is inversely proportional to the radius of an electrode of circular cross section. Figure 29.3 shows graphically the field set up in such a detector. Near the wire anode, the voltage gradient is perhaps 1 kV cm^{-1}; as a result, electrons are greatly accelerated before collection on the anode. In moving toward the outer cylinder, positive ions experience a much smaller acceleration. Two desirable results are that the positive ions produce a minimum emission of energetic photoelectrons from the cathode and cause negligible damage when they strike the cathode. Both objectives must be realized in good circuit design. Since photoelectron emission would tend to sustain pulses, as discussed under Geiger–Mueller detectors, the former objective is particularly important.

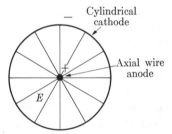

Fig. 29.3 Schematic cross section of a gas ionization detector. Lines of force are drawn to show the very high field strength E near the axial anode. The outer cylinder may be from 1 to 2.5 cm in diameter, the wire from 0.1 to 1 mm in diameter.

Figure 29.4 shows the fundamental associated circuit. The high positive dc voltage needed to charge the anode is supplied indirectly through a large resistor R. If we use a large R even a minute output pulse develops an IR drop sufficiently large to be fed into an amplifier. The capacitance C that appears in the circuit is the small distributed capacitance of the counter and associated circuit. The actual shape of the pulse that appears at the output is, in general, determined by the promptness with which the charged particles produced are removed from the sensitive volume of the tube and by the time constant RC of the external circuit. In most gaseous detectors, electrons are swept to the anode in about 1 or 2 μs and positive ions to the cathode within 100 to 500 μs. If RC is large compared with the ion collection time, a representative pulse is like that pictured in Fig. 29.5. The pulse height and duration also depend, of course, on whether the detector is operating in the ionization, proportional, or Geiger region.

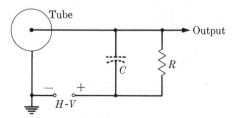

Fig. 29.4 Fundamental circuit for the collection of ions and electrons. R is of the order of 10^9 Ω, and the distributed capacitance C is no more than a few picofarads.

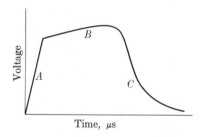

Fig. 29.5 Pulse shape when the time constant RC is large compared with collection time. A, electron collection. B, positive ion collection. C, decay of pulse, at rate determined by time constant RC.

Operating voltage. If a source of monoenergetic radiation is used, several easily distinguishable types of counter action are observable as the potential across the tube is varied. As the voltage is increased from 0 to 350 V the height of the output pulse first becomes larger and then remains constant when all electrons and ions formed are being swept to the electrodes. To interpret these results, we must recall that ion pairs tend to recombine at a definite rate. Therefore, until the voltage applied is sufficient to effect a quick separation of the newly formed ions, only a part of them exists long enough to reach the electrodes. At *saturation*, however, essentially all electrons and ions formed by the entering radiation are being collected. Ionization chambers and electroscopes operate in this range.

As the voltage is further increased, electrons begin to be so strongly accelerated in the high field near the anode that they produce additional ion pairs on collision with gas molecules. The resulting gas amplification spreads only within a small sheath around the path of the nuclear particle. This voltage region is the *region of proportional counting*, so called because under stable conditions the output current pulses from the detector following penetration by radiation are proportional in height to the original number of ion pairs.

At still higher voltages (in most cases 1000 V or more) the photons that result from vigorous electron impacts or recombinations of ion pairs spread the ionization throughout the entire active volume. So great is the resulting degree of amplification in this, the Geiger range, that the size of the output pulse is determined *by conditions in the tube rather than by the energy of the radiation.*

Beyond this region, the counter tube lapses into a series of pulses when each radiation particle arrives and at still higher voltages sustains a continuous discharge. As the Geiger and proportional detectors are discussed below, we consider the ionization processes in more detail.

29.6 GEIGER–MUELLER TUBE

The *Geiger–Mueller tube* or, more simply, the *Geiger tube* has enjoyed general use. It is described first because it is familiar and at the same time the most limited of the three types of gas ionization detectors. In design, the Geiger tube has the coaxial electrode arrangement already discussed. Figure 29.6 shows the construction of a representative type with a window at the end to admit radiation. Depending on the energy of the radiation to be detected, the thickness of the mica end window may be varied from 1 to 4 mg cm^{-2}. Note that a quantity related to the absorbing process rather than to the real thickness is stated. A mica window of 1 mg cm^{-2} will admit all but the lowest-energy β-rays such as those produced by ^{3}H. The cathode is the cylindrical outer wall itself when metal is used. In the majority of Geiger tubes, the wall is a glass cylinder, and the cathode is a metal film deposited by evaporation on the inner surface. If the tube is intended for beta counting, the wall may have a thickness of about 10 mg cm^{-2} so that no end window is necessary. End-window counters average 30 mg cm^{-2} in wall thickness.

Geiger tubes are filled with a gas mixture that consists of about 90 % inert gas such as argon or helium and up to 10 % polyatomic substance, which acts as a quenching agent. Gases such as methane, diethylether, ethanol, and chlorine are widely used.

The total pressure is set at from 0.1 to 1.0 bar, according to the tube design and intended use. Some characteristics of Geiger tubes are summarized in Table 29.2.

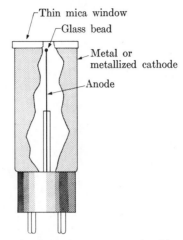

Fig. 29.6 Construction of an end-window Geiger counter. The thin mica window allows ready entrance of nuclear radiation.

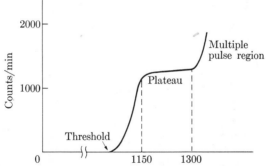

Fig. 29.7 Characteristic counting rate curve for Geiger counter, obtained by observing a given radioactive sample with fixed geometry.

Operation. As suggested in Section 29.5, gas amplification in a Geiger counter is determined by the characteristics of the tube and by the ionic processes in the gas rather than by the energy of the incident radiation. The phenomenon of a widespread ionization avalanche triggered by entrance of radiation begins to be noted in a tube only at high voltages, typically above 1100 V. If all pulses below a certain height characteristic of avalanche ionization are rejected, we may represent the response of a Geiger counter by the curve in Fig. 29.7. To obtain the data, a given radioactive sample was positioned at a fixed distance from a counter. Three features of the response curve should be noted, the distinct threshold voltage, below which no pulses register, the plateau of 100 to 150 V length, and the region beyond the plateau, in which there is a small increase in pulses per unit of time. Most Geiger tubes "plateau" where the counting rate varies only about 1 to 3 % with voltage. The high-voltage power supply

Table 29.2 Characteristics of Some Nuclear Radiation Detectors

Type	Recovery Time, μs	% Efficiency α	β	γ	Usual Threshold Energy* α	β	Lifetime, counts	Operating Conditions Voltage, V	Plateau Length, V	Required Electronic Amplification
Geiger tube										
(a) Halogen-quenched mica window; thickness 1.4 mg cm^{-2}	100 to 300		high	med.	1 cm air†	25 keV	10^{10}	900 to 1200	200	low
(b) Flow (helium-isobutane gas) Mylar film window; thickness 0.7 mg cm^{-2}			high	med.			indef.	1100 to	400	
Scintillation	10^{-3} to 1									medium
(a) ZnS-Ag phosphor		50	0	0						
(b) Liquid scintillator		0	100	5			indef.			
(c) NaI (Tl) crystal		0	0	50			indef.			
Semiconductor Ge (Li) crystal		0	0	low						
Proportional Flow (methane)	1						indef.			high
(a) Metalized Mylar film; thickness 0.15 to 0.9 mg cm^{-2}		high	high	low				3800	500	
(b) Windowless		high	high	low				2800	500	
Ionization Chamber	1 to 10^3	0	low	low			indef.			

* Minimum energy that particle must have to penetrate window.

† Stopping power of window equivalent to 1 cm of air.

need be only moderately well regulated to obtain reproducible readings. The voltage region at the right of the curve is to be avoided, since it is one in which an increasing number of pulses are triggering additional pulses, and the cathode, because it is involved in the process, is likely to be damaged. A continuous discharge begins at potentials slightly higher than those shown.

We can understand the avalanche ionization that occurs in the Geiger region by examining the operative mechanisms in the gas. In the strong electric field near the counter anode, an electron frequently receives enough energy between collisions to produce an ion pair when it collides with a molecule. Although these secondary collisions spread the discharge somewhat, it is the photons of UV radiation released that are mainly responsible for initiating ionization throughout the tube. In the Geiger range a considerable fraction of electron impacts with molecules and recombinations of ion pairs occurs so vigorously as to produce molecules in excited electronic states. Photons of appropriate energy are released when these states decay. Those in the UV range or higher tend to release photoelectrons at points in the counter tube distant from the initial ionizing processes, e.g. at the cathode or from gas molecules having a lower ionization potential than the main gas. As each new photoelectron is accelerated toward the anode, secondary ionization begins along its path. Although the discharge soon spreads throughout the active volume of the counter, it should be noted that most of the amplification still occurs in the region of the anode.   field

As a result of the slow movement of the positive ions, the avalanche is self-terminating. As soon as the electrons have been collected at the anode (in times of the order of 1 μs), a sheath of positive ions is left as a space charge, which lowers the field strength enough to stop further ionization. Not until the positive ions move out of the high-field-strength region near the anode is the tube able to respond to new radioactivity. This time interval is termed the *dead time* and is usually of the order of 50 μs. Actually, it is only a fraction of the period required for the migration of the positive ions to the cathode, which is usually from 100 to 200 μs. After a time equal to the dead time, but before the positive ions have been collected, an entering radioactive particle sometimes triggers a burst of ionization in the counter, but the output pulse is too small to be registered. Thus the recovery time, the total time necessary for the resumption of normal operation by a Geiger counter, is equal to the positive ion migration time.

Quenching. The ionization avalanche in a Geiger tube is self-terminating only under special conditions. This behavior arises from the fact that the positive ion cloud creates so strong a field when it nears the cathode that photoelectrons are released, with the result that a new wave of ionization sweeps through the tube. It is not difficult to arrange internal quenching by adding a small percentage of a polyatomic gas to the "base" inert gas. Although the positive ions formed during the initial avalanche are still largely noble gas ions, these ions have a high probability of transferring their charge to the polyatomic molecules, which have a lower ionization potential, whenever there is a collision. The ions that finally reach the cathode are then nearly all polyatomic gas ions. Upon arrival at the cathode these ions dissociate into free radicals: The time necessary for the dissociation is short compared with that required for the release of photoelectrons. In other words, the internal redistribution of their kinetic energy takes place very quickly. Since no photoelectrons appear, the discharge is terminated, and the tube is said to be self-quenching. Some of the polyatomic gas is used up with each discharge, and the usual tube lifetime is 10^8 or 10^9 counts.

Operating characteristics. Geiger counters respond most sensitively to α- and β-radiation, less so to γ-radiation. If α- or β-particles enter the sensitive volume, about 98 % of their energy is absorbed by the filling gas, in contrast with only 2 % absorption for γ-rays. The type and energy of entering radiation is not distinguished, of course. Nevertheless, since the thickness of the counter window or wall determines the energy threshold for each kind of radiation, there is always some discrimination. For example, the weak β-radiation from ^{14}C is absorbed by all but very thin windows (about 1 mg cm^{-2}), but energetic γ-rays are attenuated only slightly by walls 300 mg cm^{-2} thick, although these walls absorb all ordinary α- and β-radiation. No amplification of the output pulses, which range from 5 to 20 V, is ordinarily supplied.

In spite of their sensitivity and the simplicity of the associated equipment, Geiger tubes are inherently less reproducible, have too long a recovery time for efficient counting at rates above 10,000 counts min^{-1} (Section 29.11), and have little versatility. They are mainly used today for laboratory monitoring and for semiquantitiative studies.

29.7 PROPORTIONAL COUNTERS

The proportional counter or detector is rapidly superseding the Geiger counter as a result of its greater versatility and precision of measurement. These properties are the result of the constancy of its gas amplification and the direct dependence of the amplification on the energy of the entering radiation. The proportional counter is employed both as a closed tube type similar to the Geiger counter and as a windowless or thin-window flow counter. In order to achieve high sensitivity, the latter type is designed with 2π-geometry, i.e. 50 % of the radiation emanating from a thin sample enters the active volume. We achieve this result by a hollow hemispherical cathode and an anode in the form of a small loop of thin wire, which is inserted into the cathode cavity through an insulator. The sample itself is put in position at the center of the base of the hemisphere. Indeed, by placing a second hemispherical detector below, one can obtain 4π-geometry and very reliable counting.

In the windowless or thin-window design of the proportional counter, a continuous stream of counter gas is allowed to flow, and the device is operated at atmospheric pressure or slightly above. Volatile samples such as those containing $^{14}CO_2$ may be carried into the counter on the gas stream. On the other hand, solid or liquid samples are mounted on a slide and introduced either through an airlock (if the counter is windowless) or directly under a thin aluminum or aluminum-coated plastic (e.g. Mylar) film. The flow of gas minimizes the effect of leaks and gives the tube an indefinite lifetime. A commercial flow counter is pictured in Fig. 29.8. The filling gas may be a pure gas such as methane, but is more commonly a mixture such as 90 % argon and 10 % methane.

Since a constant amplification factor is essential in precise work, care is taken in the construction of proportional counters to ensure that the field is uniform along the length of the anode. Usually, the terminals of this electrode are shielded by some sort of guard rings (separate electrodes at the same potential) or a loop of wire is

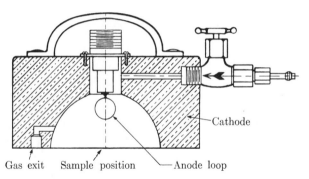

Fig. 29.8 Cross section of the upper half of a windowless flow counter. Note the gas entrance valve, the gas exit at the lower left, and the anode loop in the dome of the chamber. In use, a nearly identical lower half is seated firmly against the section shown to make a counter with 4π-geometry. For a sample placed in the center of such a counting chamber, the counter responds to virtually all radiation emitted.

used to avoid inhomogeneities that would otherwise occur at the ends of the wire.

Operation. In operation, the proportional counter has a high enough operating potential for electrons to cause much additional ionization by collision. Under the conditions of voltage and gas pressure, there is a minimal release of photons and the avalanche of ionization is largely confined to a small cylindrical volume around the radiation track. As a result, only a small fraction of the tube volume is inactivated by the ionization. The recovery time need be no longer than the time necessary to collect the electrons, about 1 μs. Even though the positive ions formed must be dissipated to the cathode, it is unnecessary to wait for this to happen, for the portions of the anode other than those near the radiation track are still sensitive to radiation.

Operating characteristics. Depending on the pressure and the composition of the gas and the potential applied across the electrodes, constant multiplication factors of from 500 to 10,000 are commonly achieved in a proportional counter. We achieve stable operation by selecting a voltage in a range where the counting rate varies no more than from 1 to 2 %. The output pulses are small relative to those from a Geiger detector, and external electronic amplification is necessary to develop pulses of sufficient magnitude to be really usable. Suffice it to repeat here that it is easy to develop a stable amplifier (Chapters 5 and 6).

At a given setting of the amplifier, the heights of α-particle ($\sim$ 5 MeV) pulses will be large compared with β- and γ-particle ($\leq$ 1.5 MeV) pulses. Thus, α- and β-γ-activity levels may easily be distinguished. The counter voltage is simply adjusted so that the type of radiation of interest gives pulses of acceptable height; pulses from radiation in the other category are, of course, either much smaller or larger and can be rejected electronically. For example, a representative proportional flow counter may be stably operated at 900 $\pm$ 50 V and 1300 $\pm$ 50 V for α- and β-γ-counting, respectively. The sensitivity of a proportional counter is high for either very weak radiations or very low activities.

Since the sample may be introduced directly into the active volume of the counter, low-energy radiations of all types may be handled. For example, ^{3}H with its 0.018

MeV β-ray maximum energy is often counted with a proportional device. We can determine very small activities by virtue of the low background. Only those background radiations that fall in the right energy range are registered, with the result that the background count may be about half that for a Geiger detector.

In addition, high activity levels may be handled with a minimum correction of the data. The resolving time of the counter itself is essentially its recovery time, 1 μs. Although electronic amplifiers capable of equally rapid operation are available for use where high precision is required, amplifiers with resolving times of 5 μs are ordinarily used. With either type, several hundred thousand counts per minute can be registered with only a small coincidence loss (less than 2 %).

An especial advantage is the linear correlation between pulse height and the energy of the radiation. By virtue of this property, proportional counters lend themselves readily to analysis of the energy spectrum of a radiation source.

29.8 SCINTILLATION COUNTERS

Together with the proportional counter, the scintillation detector is one of the most generally satisfactory devices for sensing nuclear radiation. In addition to giving an output proportional in magnitude to the energy of the entering radiation, the scintillation detector responds with extreme rapidity (resolution times from 10^{-10} to 10^{-6} s). The counter consists of a scintillator and a multiplier phototube. The scintillator is either a crystalline or a liquid material that interacts with the entering ionizing particles to produce fluorescent radiation. Since the number of photons released per particle is moderate, the output must be amplified to be useful. Accordingly, the scintillator is either attached directly to the photocathode face of a multiplier phototube or connected by a Lucite optical coupler (light pipe) to achieve good optical transmission. The scintillator and phototube face must, of course, be transparent in the optical range of the fluorescence, which is usually in the blue or near UV. Clearly, it is also essential that the volume of the scintillator be large enough to absorb all the energy of the ionizing radiation if its output is to be proportional to energy.

Scintillation phosphors. Alpha-particle detection may best be accomplished by using a very thin (1 mm maximum) layer of transparent phosphor. It has been found satisfactory to use a transparent ZnS screen with silver as an activator.

For β-particle counting liquid scintillation systems are commonly used, though single crystals of anthracene, transstilbene, or NaI (Tl-activated) are also employed. Because the scintillator in liquid systems surrounds a sample, it offers a geometry that is especially advantageous for detection of low-energy beta particles from isotopes such as ^{14}C (0.155 MeV) and ^{3}H (0.018 MeV). The liquid scintillator has two main components, a *solvent* (usually toluene or xylene though dioxane is valuable with aqueous systems) and a *dissolved phosphor*, termed a primary solute or fluor (2,5-diphenyloxazole (PPO) and 2,2-*p*-phenylenebis (5-phenyl-oxazole) (POPOP) are widely used). The particular combination of components is often called a cocktail. The sample is dissolved or suspended in the medium.

Figure 29.9 shows a representative arrangement of modules in a liquid scintillation system. The scintillation system and detectors are mounted in a lighttight, very-low-background-radioactivity housing. By requiring coincidence of pulses from the photomultiplier tubes, much of dark current and noise are blocked from the instrument channel. Discrimination (Section 29.11) further ensures that spurious pulses are rejected.

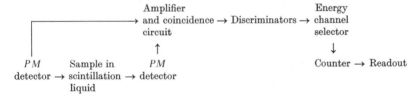

Fig. 29.9 Representative line block diagram for a liquid scintillation counter. PM = photomultiplier tube. The use of two detectors operated in coincidence ensures that dark current pulses or noise pulses arising in the photomultiplier tubes are generally ignored since they tend not to be in coincidence.

Since the fluorescence of an organic molecule is being detected in this process, we must take all reasonable steps to minimize quenching (Section 15.3). Quenching results in a decrease in the amount of light per pulse and in some cases in an entirely radiationless degradation of energy to heat. Since we do not know the exact amount of quenching, we must always determine the counting efficiency of a liquid scintillation counter. The more frequent the standardization the more reliable the results. For a discussion of this topic see the references at the end of the chapter.

In γ-ray detection, NaI crystals activated with about 1% TlI are commonly used as scintillators. This phosphor is very efficient in the absorption of γ-rays, as a result of the high atomic number of I, and gives a large light output. Disadvantages are its hygroscopicity, high refractive index ($n_D \sim 1.8$), and relatively long resolving time (0.3 μs).

In each particular scintillation phosphor, the number of photons released is nearly proportional to the energy absorbed. Since all fluorescence photons, but no stray photons, should reach the phototube, the crystal is usually placed in a lighttight enclosure of aluminum foil, which also serves as a reflector. Care is also taken to see that photons from different regions of the crystal are attenuated as nearly equally as possible. For this purpose the side of the scintillator crystal is often roughened and faced with a diffuse reflector such as MgO. In addition, efficient optical coupling at the scintillator-phototube interface will be hindered by reflection, which increases with increasing refractive index of the scintillator. A thin layer of transparent substance of intermediate refractive index (Section 10.6) lessens the reflection.

Amplification. The multiplier phototube (Section 11.7) produces an amplification of the order of from 10^6 to 10^8. To take advantage of the speed and size of scintillator crystals, tubes are available with large photocathode areas (up to 90 cm^2) and short time spread in the passage of the electrons in one pulse. Additional amplification is ordinarily necessary before the output of a scintillation counter can be fed to a scaler or rate meter.

Operating characteristics. The sensitivity of scintillation counters is high, but considerable precautions must be taken to reduce the background count, which is as much as ten times that of a Geiger counter. Regular shielding is supplemented by special discriminating circuits and by anticoincidence counting arrangements. The scintillator may also be cooled to reduce background.

29.9 SEMICONDUCTOR DETECTORS

The use of semiconductor materials as energy-sensitive radiation detectors is an important development of recent years. Specially prepared diodes of germanium are now widely used in γ-ray spectrometry because they make possible at best ten-fold improvement in resolution. X-ray determinations, nuclear spectrometry, and work with radioisotopes in general have benefited.

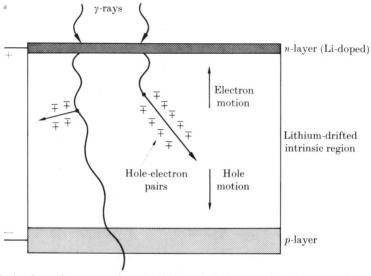

Fig. 29.10 A schematic cross section of a lithium-drifted germanium detector. The n-type layer at the top is about 0.1 mm thick. Hole and electrons formed by ionizing encounters in the central lithium-drifted region are collected by the outer layers. Note that the dc voltage applied reverse-biases the semiconductor. The detector volume (a measure of its ability to absorb all the energy of a γ-ray) is about 5 cm³. (After A. J. Tavendale and G. T. Ewan, *Nucl. Instr. Meth.* **25**, 185 (1963).)

Figure 29.10 shows a schematic cross section of a lithium-drifted germanium detector. It behaves essentially as a solid-state ionization chamber. It operates by collecting holes and electrons formed by ionizing events within its active volume. The device is made from a highly "purified" crystal of p-type germanium (electron-acceptor doping has created an excess of holes). Lithium is vapor-deposited in a layer on one side and then is diffused through much of the germanium slab by raising the temperature and imposing an electric field. In the central portion, since lithium atoms supply electrons to the electron acceptors, leaving mainly bound charges, the diffusion returns the germanium nearly to an "intrinsic" state.

When an electric field is applied as shown, the crystal itself shows minimal conduction. Ionization can be caused within the intrinsic region by γ-rays and the holes and electrons formed are quickly collected as a pulse of current. Since only 2.9 eV of energy is required to produce an electron-hole pair, a γ-ray yields a great many pairs and therefore a large current pulse. A favorable signal-to-noise ratio is implied, but it can be realized only if the crystal temperature is dropped to $-185\,°C$ with liquid nitrogen to reduce severe thermal noise.*

Present Ge(Li) detectors have a relatively small volume. As a consequence, they fail to absorb all the energy of most γ-rays, as is suggested in the illustration, and are relatively inefficient. With a γ-emitter low efficiency is not a severe problem because ordinarily we can use a stronger sample. Nevertheless, the small volume gives trouble when we use a Ge(Li) detector to determine low-energy γ-peaks since Compton scattering† may obscure them. With NaI(Tl) scintillators a much greater volume is possible, leading to stronger γ-peaks and therefore to relatively less pronounced Compton peaks.

29.10 SCALERS AND RATE METERS

When pulses emerge from a Geiger counter or an amplifier associated with one of the other detectors, they are randomly spaced and may occur at rates up to $1000\,s^{-1}$ and more. They cannot, in general, be recorded by mechanical registers, which at best are designed to respond only to 100 evenly spaced pulses per second. An electronic scaling device is always interposed between counter and register. The scaler receives the input pulses, and after each p of them drives the register forward one unit. As a result of the mode of operation of the scaler, p is of the form of either

$$\text{(a)}\ p = 2^m \quad \text{or} \quad \text{(b)}\ p = 10^m \tag{29.3}$$

where m is an integer denoting the number of stages in the scaler. If binary scaling (a) is used, m may range from 6 to 10; if decimal scaling (b) is used, m is usually 2 or 3. By using a scaler, we reduce the number of impulses to which the register must respond, and in addition the impulses are spaced more evenly.

In a binary scaler, the basic electronic unit is a flip-flop oscillator. The unit has two highly stable operating positions. Every input pulse causes the circuit to flip from one position to the other. Only when the circuit returns to its primary status every second pulse is the next scaling stage (or register) activated. A representative unit is discussed in Section 9.4. In decade scalers, glow transfer tubes as well as differently wired flip-flop circuits and other arrangements are used. For binary and decade scaling circuits, the resolving time is about $5\,\mu s$; still faster action can be realized with other arrangements.

Counting rate meter. If we desire only to determine an approximate rate of disintegration, we may use some sort of electronic integrating device. To obtain meaningful rates, it is essential that the incoming pulses be similar in shape and size and of equal duration. Equalizing may be arranged by having the entering pulses drive a circuit (monostable multivibrator) that produces a single square wave pulse of characteristic length when triggered by an incoming pulse (Section 9.4).

---

* Nearly always lithium-drifted germanium detectors must be stored at low temperatures to keep the devices functional. The reduced temperature is necessary to minimize precipitation of the lithium. At room temperature the Li–Ge solid solution is supersaturated.

† See Fig. 13.1.

The monostable multivibrator is followed by an integrating circuit (Section 7.6). Most rate meters are provided with circuits that allow a choice of either of two time constants in the range of from 0.1 to perhaps 10 or 20 s. Ordinarily, the longer the period is, the more precisely the average rate is determined. Instruments of this type are valuable as laboratory monitors.

29.11 PULSE HEIGHT ANALYZERS

The energy spectrum of the emission of a radioisotope is frequently of interest for identification or characterization purposes. Operationally, we find the energy distribution by determining the number of counts per unit time per unit energy interval over the region of measurable activity.

Analysis of a spectrum requires a detector and amplifier that are of high sensitivity and that furnish output pulses proportional in height to the energy of the radiation. Note that we eliminate the Geiger counter as a possible choice. The amplifier output is fed into a pulse height analyzer, which we can adjust to transmit only pulses within a narrow range of voltage amplitudes ΔV, thus radiation in a small energy interval ΔE. (See Section 9.6.)

We set the width of the basic energy interval by means of two electronic discriminator circuits. These are circuits that block any signal pulse from the detector-amplifier that has an amplitude below a set minimum height but that pass all others. For example, we might set a discriminator to pass pulses of amplitude greater than 40 V. Then if a 10 V channel or window is desired, we would set the second discriminator at 50 V. Operating the two discriminators in anticoincidence means the pulses transmitted by the second discriminator are subtracted from those passed by the first, and the output contains only pulses that have an amplitude between 40 and 50 V. Figure 29.11 shows this process schematically.

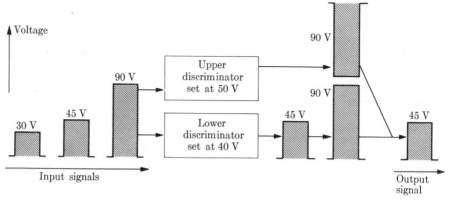

Fig. 29.11 Use of two discriminator circuits to determine an energy channel. The upper and lower discriminators are operated in anticoincidence to establish the channel.

In commercial pulse height analyzers channel widths are usually variable from 1 to 5 V when the total pulse height range of the analyzer is from 0 to 100 V. A high degree of stability is required in the discriminators, the amplifier, and the high-voltage supply to the detector if a spectrum of reasonable accuracy is to be obtained.

Single-channel devices that feature manual or automatic scanning as well as multichannel instruments that provide for the simultaneous determination of the activity in from 50 to 256 energy channels are available commercially. In the former, the window is moved at will over the region of interest. The latter are especially useful for experiments with sort-lived isotopes where we must obtain a maximum flow of energy within a period of seconds or minutes.

29.12 SOURCES OF ERROR

In determining the radioactivity of samples, we must allow for several characteristic types of error: the statistical uncertainty in counting rate, the geometry of counting, errors associated with the physical condition of the sample, and detection errors. Two other possible sources of uncertainty, isotopic exchange and interference from other radioisotopes, are not general problems. Where they do occur, we may often devise special procedures to minimize them.

Statistical uncertainty. Since the disintegration of radionuclides is a random process, counting rates are subject to statistical fluctuation. The rates typically become more precisely established with higher numbers of recorded counts, for the variations average out as they would in most types of measurements. It can be shown that a series of replicate measurements of radioactivity should fall strictly into a binomial distribution.* From the characteristics of the ideal distribution, we can then find the probability of obtaining a certain number of nuclear disintegrations in time t for a sample containing n_0 radioactive atoms and the statistical uncertainty in the measured level of activity derived.

If the number of counts is reasonably large ($N > 100$) and the sample is observed for a time short compared with its half-life, it can be shown that the standard deviation σ_N in the total count is

$$\sigma_N = \sqrt{N} \qquad (29.4)$$

and that the standard deviation in the counting rate is

$$\sigma_r = \frac{\sqrt{N}}{t}. \qquad (29.5)$$

Example Assume that 400 counts have been obtained from a sample over a 10 min period. The standard deviation in the count is $\sqrt{400} = 20$, and the percent standard deviation is $(20 \div 400) \times 100 = 5\%$. Also, the counting rate is 40 min^{-1} and standard deviation in the rate 2 min^{-1}. The results may be expressed as follows: total counts, 400 ± 20; and counting rate, 40 ± 2 counts per minute.

---

* By imposing the restrictions that (a) a large number of active atoms are observed for (b) a time short compared with their half-life and that (c) a large number ($N > 100$) of counts are taken, the Poisson and Gaussian distribution laws may also be used to predict probabilities of disintegration.

Clearly the precision of both the total count and the rate may be improved indefinitely by increasing the time of observation. For example, there will be approximately a 10% uncertainty if 100 counts are recorded but only a 1% uncertainty if 10,000 counts are noted.

To determine the uncertainty in the net counting rate, which is the chief quantity of interest, allowance must likewise be made for the fluctuation in the background level. In Section 1.7 we saw that the uncertainty in a quantity R, which is defined by the expression $R = X - Y$, is related to the standard deviations of X and Y by the expression

$$\sigma_R = \sqrt{\sigma_X^2 + \sigma_Y^2}. \tag{29.6}$$

For the present consideration, let the subscripts R, X, and Y identify the net, total, and background rates, respectively. In practice, experiments where an accuracy of 1% or better is required are designed so that the standard deviation of the total counting rate X is several times the standard deviation of the background rate Y. Inspection of Eq. (29.6) shows that it is not necessary that the background level be known with high precision if this ratio is maintained. In the interest of time, some such arrangement is almost essential, for an unduly long period would be required to obtain 10,000 counts for background, using a well-shielded detector.

Example In a 10 min count on a sample, a total of 1600 disintegrations is registered. The background is counted for 15 min and totals 450 counts. The standard deviation for the total count is $\sqrt{1600} = 40$. For the background it is $\sqrt{450} = 21.2$. The net counting rate is

$$\frac{1600}{10} - \frac{450}{15} = 160 - 30 = 130.$$

The standard deviation in the total is $40/10 = 4$ counts per minute; that of the background is $22/15 = 1.41$, and the standard deviation in the net counting rate is $\sqrt{4^2 + (1.41)^2} = 4.2$. The net counting rate is then 130 ± 4.2 counts per minute.

In a consideration of the normal (Gaussian) distribution it is deduced that the uncertainty in a measurement is less than the standard deviation in about seven measurements out of ten. Expressed somewhat differently, if a counting rate is given as $R \pm \sigma_R$, the confidence level of the data is 70%. The confidence level can be increased by simply allowing (or stating) a larger uncertainty in R. For example, by quoting a counting rate as $R \pm 2\sigma_R$ the confidence level rises to 95%. At this level, only once in twenty times would we expect to obtain a result that deviates from the mean by more than $2\sigma_R$.

Whenever the activity of a sample is very small, the length of time required to obtain a precise count becomes very great. The principal difficulty is that the sample and background activity are nearly the same. The error in the difference between the two, the net rate, is large, according to Eq. (29.6), unless a large number of disintegrations are counted. In this situation, it is imperative that the shielding be excellent and, if feasible, that other circuitry such as a coincidence arrangement be devised to minimize the background rate still further.

Geometry. The sensitive volume of a counter will subtend a certain solid angle with respect to the sample. For example, the end window of a Geiger tube may subtend a solid angle of several degrees with respect to material placed 5 cm from the window. Since the radiation from a sample emanates equally in all directions, we may calculate the percentage of the total that passes through the window into the tube from the angle subtended. Rather descriptively, the calculation is said to be a determination of the geometry of the system.

If we are to compare measurements, the geometry must be reproducible, which means that an arrangement for placing a sample precisely with respect to the detector must be provided. The sample–counter distance may be varied but cannot be less than 1 cm. When samples are very close to a counter window, many rays enter the detector obliquely but pass through so little of the active volume they are not detected. Naturally the sample and detector must be properly shielded from background radiation.

Another factor conveniently considered under geometry is the *back scattering* of radiation from (a) the gas between the sample and the detector and (b) all solid parts. Most of the rays are diverted away from the detector on scattering, but some, such as part of those scattered from the walls of the holder, may be directed toward it. Since the back scattering increases with increasing atomic number Z, counter shields, which are invariably of a heavy metal such as iron ($Z = 26$) or lead ($Z = 82$), are placed several centimeters from the sample to reduce the percentage of scattering into the detector. The dependence on Z suggests that with weak emitters the sensitivity of detection may be much improved if helium is used in the counting chamber instead of air.

Absorption in the gas and in the detector window further reduces the number of ionizing particles or rays. Both absorption and back scattering are often said to reduce the geometry of the system.

Sample preparation errors. In considering radiation losses, we cannot neglect the absorption (and scattering) by the sample itself. Ordinarily, we prepare a sample for counting by spreading a given weight of substance in a planchet (a round, shallow dish of 2 or 3 cm diameter) to give a layer of uniform thickness. Both solids and dissolved solids (after evaporation of solvent) are examined in this fashion. Although relatively thick layers of a substance display a characteristic absorption per unit of weight, with thinner layers the actual absorption varies with thickness and density of packing. This behavior may be understood by assuming that a uniform sample comprises a series of very thin layers of equal thickness. By itself the layer closest to the detector gives a total count independent of thickness and representative of the true activity of the particular material. There is negligible absorption. When a sufficient number of layers have been taken so that all particles emitted from the most distant layer are absorbed within the nearer layers, we again obtain a count independent of thickness. In this case, however, the activity observed is per unit of weight. Samples of intermediate thickness give counting rates that are dependent on thickness and that are difficult to reproduce. We may best avoid errors of this type by preparing samples of definite weight in reproducible fashion.

Coincidence loss. We may trace uncertainty in detection either to coincidence loss or to poor counter efficiency once a particle has entered a properly operating detector. Associated with any counter and its electronic circuitry is a certain pulse resolving time. For example, the Geiger tube has a resolving time of about 200 μs, whereas a scintillation counter with a finer scaler may show a total resolving time of 1 μs. Since the resolving time represents an interval during which a counter and scaler fail to respond to new particles that enter the detector, there will be some coincidence error in general. If the recovery time is τ, the total time during which the unit is insensitive is $R\tau$, where R is the observed counting rate. The number of lost counts per unit of time is just $R' - R\tau$, where R' is the rate we would observe if there were no coincidence loss. To find the true count, note that the number of lost counts is also given by $R'R\tau$. Since the rate at which the count should be observed is R', that rate times the insensitive time $R\tau$ will also express the loss. Using these statements, we find the true rate to be

$$R' = \frac{R}{1 - R\tau}. \tag{29.7}$$

Example A Geiger counting system has a resolving time of 200 μs. At 30,000 counts min^{-1}, which is about 500 counts s^{-1}, the true counting rate is

$$R' = \frac{500}{1 - (500 \times 2 \times 10^{-4})} = 556 \text{ counts s}^{-1}.$$

The error, $556 - 500 = 56$, is 11% of the total number of counts.

Counter efficiency error. Finally, the possibility that error arises from poor or variable counter efficiency must be suggested. Not all particles that enter a detector give up all their energy as is desired even when the detector is capable of responding. Usually poor transfer of energy occurs when radiation traverses a short path in the detector, in terms of the absorbing power of the sensitive volume for that kind of radiation and energy. In pulse height determinations, this type of behavior produces spurious results. Note that in simple activity determinations we must know the detector efficiency to estimate the absolute rate, but we need only know it to be constant to obtain reliable relative measurements. Table 29.2 lists the efficiencies of some representative detectors.

29.13 TRACER TECHNIQUES

When a stable atom in any kind of chemical species (atom, ion, or molecule) is replaced with a radioactive atom, the entity becomes a tracer. In any sort of process (biological, chemical, or physical) its subsequent behavior may then be followed by measurements of its radioactivity. For example, we can find the effectiveness of separation of sodium and potassium ions by ion exchange by "labeling" a fraction of the sodium ions and then continuously observing the level of radioactivity in the effluent washed from the resin column. Both the presence of sodium and its concentration in the effluent are determined at any stage of the process. Under optimum conditions, first the sodium and then the potassium is washed off. In more complex systems, separation procedures are usually called for since the activity in each phase or product must be ascertained. Note that tracer techniques offer advantages over other procedures only in certain types of study; we may best understand these by considering representative applications and some inherent limitations on the use of tracers. Two important areas of application, activation analysis and research, however, are discussed later (Sections 29.14 and 29.16, respectively).

Table 29.3 Characteristics of Some Widely Used Radioisotopes

Nuclide	Half-Life	Maximum β- Energy, MeV	Other Radiation
^{3}H	12.5 years	0.0189	None
^{14}C	5720 years	0.155	None
^{24}Na	14.9 hours	1.39	1.38 and 2.758 MeV γ's
^{32}P	14.3 days	1.712	None
^{35}S	87.1 days	0.166	None
^{45}Ca	152 days	0.254	None
^{55}Fe	2.91 years	None	K X-rays, Auger electrons*
^{60}Co	5.3 years	0.31	1.17 and 1.33 MeV γ's
^{131}I	8 days	0.60 (89%)	0.08 and 0.72 MeV γ's

* When X-rays are emitted because of a K-electron capture, the energy may cause the release of an L or higher-shell electron through a photoelectric process. These ejected electrons are termed *Auger electrons*.

Tracers. Radioisotopes are available from the Oak Ridge National Laboratory and various commercial concerns either in elemental form or in tagged compounds. Table 29.3 lists a few of the isotopes that see considerable use as tracers. Unfortunately, there are no active isotopes of suitable half-life for some of the most common light elements. The most conspicuous absences occur for oxygen and nitrogen, both of which have radioisotopes of such short half-life (at most a few minutes) that they decay too quickly to allow general use. The situation is considerably relieved, however, by the fact that both elements have stable isotopes (^{18}O, ^{17}O, ^{15}N) that can be used in tracer work and detected by the mass spectrograph.

If compounds rather than elements are being studied, radioisotopes must somehow be introduced into the desired position in the compound. Commonly, chemical synthesis is used.

Example A simple, classic synthesis is used to prepare carboxyl-labeled acetic acid, $CH_3{}^{14}COOH$. $Ba^{14}CO_3$, a commercially available starting material is decomposed to $^{14}CO_2$. An excess of the CO_2 is then introduced into the Grignard reaction:

$$CH_3MgBr + {}^{14}CO_2 \rightarrow CH_3{}^{14}COOMgBr \xrightarrow{H_2O} CH_3{}^{14}COOH + Mg(OH)Br.$$

The labeled acetic acid is easily isolated.

Other procedures that are sometimes feasible are biological synthesis, chemical exchange of atoms, and irradiation of the compound to transform one or more stable atoms into radioactive atoms. Where we can use more than one method, the choice is governed by the ease of control of the reaction, its efficiency, the specificity of the position of the radioactive atom, the level of activity obtained in the labeled compound, and the difficulty of the separations. A wide variety of labeled compounds is available commercially.

In a representative tracer study, we use as low a level of activity as possible. The substance to be followed is tagged by adding a small amount of its labeled counterpart. The level of activity must be high enough so that detection difficulties do not arise because of necessary dilutions at any point in the procedure. Then an initial precise assay of activity is made. As the experiment is carried out, the radioactivity of the various phases or substances (after separation) is observed. (The details of such a radioactivity *analysis* are considered in the next section.) If there is no isotope effect, chemical exchange, or other complication (see below), we need only correct the counting rates for dilution and decay before we interpret in terms of concentrations. The decay correction will be significant only if the duration of the study is greater than $0.01 \, t_{1/2}$. Note that we may apply tracer methods to systems where no specific knowledge of the changes occurring is available.

Isotope dilution. Certainly the method of isotope dilution analysis is one of the most valuable tracer procedures. It is used particularly in the analysis of complex inorganic and organic mixtures that are resolvable only with difficulty. For example, vitamin B_{12} can be assayed by isotope dilution in mixture with other intricate organic molecules. The method may be found in the *U.S. Pharmacopoeia*, Supplement XV.

The steps in isotope dilution are as follows: We mix a known weight S of pure labeled compound (chemically identical with the substance of interest) of specific activity A_1 (specific activity is defined as counts per unit of time per gram) thoroughly with the sample, which contains unknown weight x of the sought constituent. We then abstract a small amount of the desired constituent in pure form from the mixture. Whether there is appreciable loss in the separation is unimportant *as long as enough pure substance is isolated for an activity determination.* Let the specific activity of the isolated material be A_2. Then the following relation must hold:

$$\frac{A_1 S}{S + x} = A_2 \qquad \text{or} \qquad x = S\left(\frac{A_1}{A_2} - 1\right). \tag{29.8}$$

Note that we must know the weight isolated to calculate A_2. Depending on the specific activity of the tracer molecules, isotope dilutions may run as high as 1 to 1000 or indeed 1 to 10,000 when a precision of 1 % is sought.

Limitations. We must always design the procedures for using and handling tracers with possible restrictions in mind. The following effects represent potential sources of interference in tracer work: isotope fractionation, chemical exchange (of atoms), radiation from radioactive daughters, and formation of radiocolloids. We should always investigate the chance that one or more of these effects will occur in a study. If we cannot allow for them by calibration or the use of a blank, we may have to abandon the method.

By definition, *isotope fractionation* is the change in isotopic abundances in different parts of a system that results from the carrying out of a process. The effect is negligible except in instances in which there are differences of 10 % or more in the weights of isotopes (in this case, between the mass number of the radioisotope and that of the common stable isotopes). Thus, isotope fractionation is noted for radio-isotopes such as ^{14}C and ^{45}Ca (^{12}C and ^{40}Ca are the common stable isotopes) but is not marked for radioisotope ^{131}I (cf. ^{127}I, which is stable). In general, fractionation is significant only in chemical kinetic studies and in measurements involving equilibria. In kinetics, the effect enters because of the differences in the ease of rupturing bonds. It has been shown by experiment and theoretical treatments that a bond that involves a lighter isotope, for example, a $^{12}C - {}^{12}C$ bond, will break more easily than the same bond with a heavier isotope, for example $^{12}C - {}^{14}C$ or $^{14}C - {}^{14}C$. In equilibria, fractionation may generally be traced either to the same source or to differences in the ease of transporting molecules. For example, the vapor over ordinary water will be richer in ^1H than is the liquid, and somewhat poorer in ^2H. In most analytical measurements with tracers we may neglect the fractionation effect, as it is presumed that quantitative reactions and separation procedures are used. All bonds of one kind are broken or all of a substance is evaporated. If necessary, a calibration may be made to correct for fractionation.

Chemical exchange reactions in which atoms in molecules or ions interchange with chemically identical atoms in other species are often likely and must be allowed for in some tracer studies. For example, bromine exchanges readily between Br_2 and $AsBr_3$ in carbon tetrachloride. It is not necessary that ionization occur for atoms to exchange; the process often proceeds through intermediate states following a collision. Although prediction of the likelihood of exchange in a new system is un-certain, exchange with a sufficient number of compounds and ions has been studied so that the possibilities of exchange in the system under investigation may usually be checked in advance by reference to the literature.

Some interesting problems arise when the daughter atoms formed during the decay of the tracer are also radioactive. Note that a similar situation arises whenever two or more radioisotopes are present in a sample. It is, of course, impossible to admit to the detector only the radiation from one of the radionuclides unless the radiation from the other is much more easily stopped by an absorber. A significant degree of discrimination can often be achieved by the use of a proportional or scintillation counter with a pulse height analyzer. The problem of daughter activity does not arise with most of the commonly used tracers. Where it appears, a delay in counting sufficient to allow the shorter-lived activity to decay is often desirable. When pure radioactive materials are present in solution at very low concentrations (10^{-4} to 10^{-6} M), they tend to form colloids. As a result, this material may be difficult to transfer or collect quantitatively. We may minimize the effect by adding a carrier, as long as the presence of the carrier is unobjectionable. For example, radiostrontium ion may be carried successfully by calcium ion, since the ions behave similarly. At these low concentrations, carriers are also highly desirable to avoid losses from adsorption on glass, filter paper, etc., or by coprecipitation during chemical sep-aration.

29.14 ACTIVATION ANALYSIS

About 56 elements have one or more stable isotopes that may be activated, i.e. made radioactive, by neutron bombardment. Some activations have been accomplished by charged-particle bombardment, although relatively little application of this aproach has been made. The overall nuclear reaction for neutron activation is usually of the (n, γ) type. Each nucleus that absorbs one of the bombarding neutrons becomes unstable, and releases γ-rays to regain stability. Thermal neutrons are used ordinarily, since they are available in large numbers in piles and are readily absorbed. By making use of (a) known differences in neutron activation sensitivity, (b) different levels of neutron flux and (c) different radiation times, we can restrict the activation to one or at most to a few of the elements in a complex sample. There is thus a basis for analysis, since the resulting radioactivity may be observed to determine quantitatively the concentrations of elements.

Activation procedures have wide applications, particularly in the determination of trace quantities. The sensitivity for certain elements is so great that 10^{-14} g of the element can be determined in a milligram of sample. It is convenient to express the sensitivity in terms of the number of grams x of the sought element that must be present in a sample to attain a particular specific activity. This leads to the defining expression

$$x = \frac{AW}{N_0 f\sigma_{at}(1 - e^{-\lambda t})},$$ (29.9)

where A is the activity in disintegrations $\min^{-1}$, W is the atomic weight, N_0 is Avogadro's number, f is the neutron flux in neutrons $cm^{-2} s^{-1}$, σ_{at} is the cross section of the absorbing species (nuclear cross section for activation multiplied by the isotopic abundance of the species), λ is the decay constant, and t is the time of exposure to the neutron flux. We may better understand the significance of the saturation factor, the parenthetical expression, by substituting $0.693 t/t_{1/2}$ for $e^{-\lambda t}$: The degree of saturation with activated nuclei depends on the relative length of the bombardment time t and decay half-life $t_{1/2}$ of the isotope formed. If a given specific activity (proportional to AW/N_0) of a particular element is developed each time, this expression indicates that the number of grams we may detect is inversely proportional to the neutron flux. Large fluxes must be used for greatest sensitivity. Likewise, the number of grams detectable is smaller, the greater the nuclear cross-section of the isotope and the longer the half-life of the nuclide produced.

Figure 29.12 is a table of the elements that we may detect with a sensitivity of 10^{-7} g or less for a moderate nuclear reactor flux. Tables useful in devising activation analyses are provided by Lyon. [14]

Activation procedure. The thermal neutron flux necessary to activate in a period as short as a week (a flux of 10^{11} neutrons $cm^{-2} s^{-1}$ or higher) is ordinarily available only in a nuclear reactor. Levels of 10^{14} neutron $cm^{-2} s^{-1}$ or higher are available at many nuclear reactors. In studies that involve higher concentrations or isotopes that are more easily activated, it is also possible to use sources with fluxes in the range of from 10^6 to 10^{10}, such as Van de Graaff generators and Sb-Be mixtures.

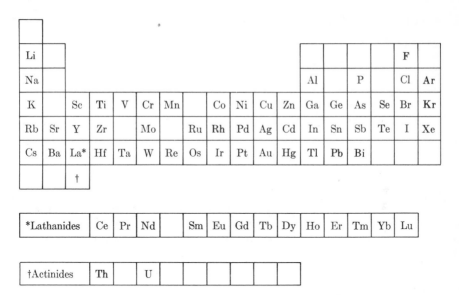

Fig. 29.12 Elements with thermal neutron activation sensitivity of 10^{-7} g or less in a neutron flux of 10^{12} neutrons cm^{-2} s^{-1}. Those elements with an activation sensitivity of 10^{-10} g or less under the same conditions are Dy, Eu, Ho, In, Ir, Lu, Mn, Sm, and Re.

Analytical procedures. Because of the inhomogeneity of the neutron flux in most reactors, the uncertainty in the neutron activation cross-sections, and the difficulty of controlling other variables, it is generally desirable to perform activation analyses on a relative basis. A typical procedure consists of irradiating a standard sample and one or more samples that contain unknown amounts of an element and then comparing the activity produced in each. Since several radioisotopes are usually formed, a chemical separation is ordinarily essential. Its modest goal is that of isolating in pure radioactive form the single nuclide of interest. It is not necessary that the separation be chemically complete. If small amounts of a radioisotope are involved, the addition of a nonradioactive carrier facilitates the operation. Then to be certain that unknown contaminants are not affecting the results, absorption curves (activity versus concentration) for the material isolated from the unknown and for the standard sample ought to be compared. Actually, a simultaneous decay determination may also be desirable. Any differences in the slope of the activity-time curves are indicative of contaminants.

Example The concentration of sodium (all atoms present are ^{23}Na) in aluminum alloys may be determined by activation analysis. Samples are irradiated in standard aluminum sample cans for one week at a flux of 10^{11} neutrons cm^{-2} s^{-1}. The standard in this analysis may conveniently be either sodium bicarbonate or sodium carbonate. After irradiation, a suitable carrier for the radionuclide ^{24}Na is added, and a chemical separation of carrier and ^{24}Na from the rest of the alloy is effected. The activity of the separated material is then determined and compared with that of the standard. A precision of about 1 % is obtained in the range of from 0.01 to 0.04 % sodium.

We may also induce activation by bombardment with other particles. For example, surfaces of materials have been studied with a Van de Graaff generator as a particle source. In the investigations, energetic protons or deuterons beamed at surfaces were found to give reactions of the (n, p) or (d, p) types in general. Sensitivities for individual elements with this technique are in the range of from 10^{-6} to 10^{-8} g cm^{-2}. The method appears particularly useful in studying surface films and corrosion effects. A depth resolution of the order of 0.01 μm can be obtained.

29.15 MISCELLANEOUS METHODS

We can also use the absorption or scattering of nuclear radiation as the basis of measurements. Most techniques involve β-particles, which have moderate penetration yet do not present complex problems. A *collimated source*, one that produces a nearly parallel beam of radiation, is essential for meaningful results, and is placed on one side of the sample, and a detector whose response has been calibrated by the use of standards is placed on the other side.

In addition, many absorption devices that allow determinations of the thickness of a product or its density of packing are in use commercially. Much of the metal and plastic sheeting currently produced is monitored by β-ray gauge to ensure constant thickness.

Procedures have also been developed to use the back scattering (Section 29.12) of β-rays from compounds for the purpose of establishing the identity of materials. Although the methods are nonspecific, if the composition of a substance is known or suspected, we can verify its identity in a few minutes by means of the measurements. For the observation, we locate the source between the sample and the detector but shield it from the detector so that there is no direct penetration of the detector by primary radiation. The shield is so designed, however, as to pass a large percentage of the scattered radiation traveling toward the counter. We can apply the technique to organic or inorganic solids, liquids, and solutions. As long as a volume of sample greater than a determinable minimum is used, the results are independent of density. Since back scattering increases with atomic weight, the precision improves with material of higher Z. For example, chlorinated organic compounds may be identified more easily than fluorinated ones.

29.16 RESEARCH APPLICATIONS

By using radioactive tracers we have gained information about reaction kinetics and mechanisms that we can presently obtain in no other way. The results have been particularly noteworthy in physiology and biochemistry. A good example is the use of ^{14}C in unraveling the complex reaction path by which atmospheric CO_2 is utilized. Although in many reaction rate studies other analytical methods might serve equally well, we can determine the rates under equilibrium conditions only by employing radioisotopes.

Whenever we can measure the exchange between a radioisotope and a stable combined isotope, we can obtain information about stability, bond strength, and to a degree, about bond type. For example, the absence of exchange between the sulfur atoms in sodium thiosulfate certainly indicates the separate chemical character of the two sulfur atoms as well as the stability of the complex. In a somewhat analogous fashion, the path of electron transfer in oxidation-reduction reactions based on complex ions has been investigated. For example, in some oxidations such as $S \rightarrow SO_4^{2-}$ and $NO_2 \rightarrow NO_3^-$, the solvent has been found to supply all or part of the oxygen; in other cases an oxygenated oxidant loses oxygen directly to the nonmetal.

Many physical processes scarcely susceptible to any other approach have been studied with the use of tracer techniques. In particular, we may cite the observation of rates of diffusion in solids and of the self-diffusion of ions in solutions, although the results on the latter have been less conclusive.

29.17 SAFE HANDLING

In carrying out radiochemical processes, there are three types of handling problems:

1. Shielding (to safeguard personnel),
2. Avoiding contamination of equipment, and
3. Disposing of radioactive wastes.

This list should suggest that good procedure is as essential to the attainment of accurate experimental results as it is to the maintenance of healthful conditions for work.

Shielding. In order to ensure the safety of personnel, routine protective measures are highly recommended. Where there is likelihood of regular exposure over a long period, some sort of a health-physics device such as a film badge or pocket (pencil) ionization chamber is recommended. A few commercial sources lease and "read" these devices. Where there is a possibility of sudden exposure to an overdose of radiation, devices that immediately report the level of intensity must be used as well.

The type of routine precautions observed should be formulated in terms of the kind of radiation and the level of activity. To simplify shielding and handling measures, it is desirable to perform all radiochemical operations in a separate area and indeed to use different working areas for different levels of activity. A hood with a good exhaust fan is the preferred site for all manipulations to avoid danger to personnel that might result from any volatilization of radioactive materials.

Arrangements that may be sensible at the millicurie level will appear ridiculous at the microcurie level. If only weak β-emitters such as ^{14}C and ^{35}S are used, the walls of laboratory glassware are thick enough to protect the experimenter even at the millicurie level. More vigorous β-emitters, for example ^{32}P, should be used behind a layer of plastic at the millicurie level. Note that γ-emitters require shielding even at the microcurie level. It is good practice never to handle glassware or other equipment directly, but to wear surgeon's gloves when handling weak emitters at the lowest level and to turn to tongs, beaker holders, remote pipets, etc., at high levels or when the rays are more penetrating.

Contamination. The use of equipment contaminated with radioactivity may easily invalidate the results of a radiochemical experiment. It is necessary to use a separate stock of glassware for different levels of activity and to check all equipment with a portable radiation monitor before use. Any spills of radioactive material should be cleaned up immediately to avoid contaminating other areas as well as endangering personnel. In some cases, special decontamination methods may be advisable. Absorption of activity on glassware is always a problem and should be guarded against.

Disposal. The liquid radioactive waste from most experimentation may be disposed of by diluting the material to a safe level of activity and, if possible, adding carrier before pouring into a drain. The presence of the carrier is desirable where there may be some concentration of the active material either by a physical process or by aquatic organisms. Certain types of solid wastes may be incinerated, but usually solid radioactive material must be stored or buried.

REFERENCES

A general treatment of instrumentation and techniques on an introductory level is available in:
1. D. J. Carswell, *Introduction to Nuclear Chemistry.* New York: American Elsevier, 1967
2. Gerhart Friedlander, Joseph W. Kennedy, and Julian Malcolm Miller, *Nuclear and Radiochemistry.* 2d ed. New York: Wiley, 1964

Special attention is given to detectors in:
3. J. B. Birks, *The Theory and Practice of Scintillation Counting.* New York: Macmillan, 1964
4. G. Dearnaley and D. C. Northrop, *Semiconductor Counters for Nuclear Radiations.* New York: Wiley, 1963
5. William J. Price, *Nuclear Radiation Detection.* New York: McGraw-Hill, 1964
6. Jack Sharp, *Nuclear Radiation Detectors.* 2d ed. New York: Wiley, 1964
7. A. H. Snell, ed., *Nuclear Instruments and Their Uses.* Vol. I. New York: Wiley, 1962

Laboratory techniques in radiochemistry are especially considered in:
8. Grafton D. Chase and Joseph L. Rabinowitz, *Principles of Radioisotope Methodology.* 2d ed. Minneapolis: Burgess, 1962
9. Ralph T. Overman and Herbert M. Clark, *Radioisotope Techniques.* New York: McGraw-Hill, 1960

Nuclear physics is covered on an advanced level in:
10. E. Segre, ed., *Experimental Nuclear Physics.* Vols. I, II, and III. New York: Wiley, 1953, 1959

Specialized methods are treated in:
11. Fay Ajzenberg-Selove, ed., *Nuclear Spectroscopy.* Vols. A and B. New York: Academic, 1960
12. H. J. M. Bowen and D. Gibbons, *Radioactivation Analysis.* Oxford: Clarendon, 1963
13. John R. Catch, *Carbon-14 Compounds.* Washington, D.C.: Butterworths, 1961
14. William S. Lyon, Jr., ed., *Guide to Activation Analysis.* New York: Van Nostrand, 1964

Other references of interest are:
15. E. T. McGuinness and M. C. Cullen, "Continuous Flow Measurement of Beta Radiation Using Suspended Scintillators," *J. Chem. Educ.* **47**, A9 (1970)
16. A. L. Turkevich, J. H. Patterson, and E. J. Franzgrote, "The Chemical Analysis of the Lunar Surface," *Am. Scientist*, **56**, 312 (1968)
17. W. Yang and E. K. C. Lee, "Liquid Scintillation Counting," *J. Chem. Educ.* **46**, 277 (1969)

Tabulations of useful data are:
18. R. C. Koch, *Activation Analysis Handbook.* Vol. 1. New York: Academic, 1960

19. C. M. Lederer, J. M. Hollander, and I. Perlman, *Table of Isotopes*. New York: Wiley, 1967

EXERCISES

29.1   A petroleum crude is to be analyzed for its naphthalene content by isotope dilution. To a 110.0 g sample of the crude is added 0.15 g naphthalene of specific activity 0.10 microcurie g^{-1} (as a result of labeling with ^{14}C). After thorough mixing, 0.250 g of naphthalene is separated in pure form and is found to give 3060 counts min^{-1}. Calculate the percentage of naphthalene in the crude.   [*Ans.*: 2.3%.]

29.2   What is the absolute activity of a 1.00 g sample of ^{35}S, whose half-life is 87 days?
[*Ans.*: 1.59×10^{15} counts s^{-1}.]

29.3   How may an end-window Geiger tube be adapted to count only γ-rays?

29.4   Discuss the use of a wire loop as the anode instead of a straight length of wire in the hemispherical proportional counter.

29.5   It is desired to count only the ^{35}S in a sample that contains both that isotope and an equal activity of ^{38}Cl. If the analysis may be deferred without inconvenience, discuss the factors that would determine how long the material might be held to allow for the decay of the ^{38}Cl. How many days must elapse before the ^{38}Cl activity is only 0.1% of the ^{35}S activity?

29.6   Discuss the relative advantages of the common γ-ray detectors: NaI(Tl) and Ge(Li). What factors restrict the relative efficiency of Ge(Li) detectors? Which detector would probably be chosen for an (n, γ) activation analysis of small, rare samples?

29.7   The degree of exposure of personnel to radioactivity is commonly monitored at present by thermoluminescent dosimeters. The devices contain a phosphor like LiF. When radiation impinges, electrons are excited in the phosphor and a certain fraction are trapped. Subsequent heating of the dosimeter causes the return of these electrons to the ground state and the emission of light. What properties should a phosphor have to be widely useful in this application?

CHAPTER 30

MASS SPECTROMETRY*

30.1 INTRODUCTION

Mass spectrometry is a technique for analysis of materials that relies on conversion of a sample into a gaseous ionic form, followed by separation of the ions according to their mass-to-charge ratios. The term "spectroscopy" is misleading, for no analysis of absorption or emission of radiation is performed. Figure 30.1 shows how the relative amounts of different ions formed in a mass spectrometer under specified conditions produce a "mass spectrum" when they are plotted against the mass-to-charge (m/e) ratio. Spectra are reproducible and contain much specific information; hence

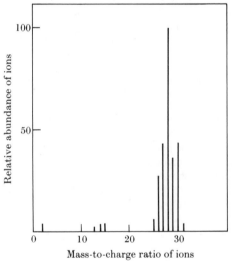

Fig. 30.1 The mass spectrum of ethane. The ion of mass 30 and unit charge has the formula $C_2H_6^+$; that of m/e 28 is $C_2H_4^+$; that of m/e 15 is CH_3^+.

computerized data retrieval and comparison of large numbers of spectra make rapid identification possible. Spectra of mixtures are weighted sums of the spectra of each component; hence analysis of a multicomponent mixture is possible. Spectra generally are the result of gaseous ionic reactions; hence it is possible to put interpretation of spectra, generally from determination of masses of ions and from considerations of bond strengths in molecules, on a rational basis so that we may analyze unknown structures.

---

* By Maurice M. Bursey, Department of Chemistry, University of North Carolina at Chapel Hill, Chapel Hill, North Carolina.

Inlet → Ion source → Mass analyzer → Detector → Recorder

Fig. 30.2 Line block diagram of a mass spectrometer.

As Fig. 30.2 shows, there are several parts in a typical mass spectrometer. In the ion source, the sample is admitted in the gaseous state or converted to a gas by heating and is ionized. In the mass analyzer, the ions produced in the source are sorted into beams of ions of the same m/e ratio. In the detection system, the mass-analyzed ions are detected, either photographically or electronically. Since the sample must be ionized to produce a mass spectrum, the technique is destructive; but only a small sample is required for, say, a structural analysis (about 100 ng of a steroid can produce a satisfactory spectrum), and the information is so specific that structures of new alkaloids have been determined on amounts too small for other methods of analysis.

The most useful applications of mass spectrometry are molecular weight determinations of volatile compounds (up to molecular weights of 2000–3000) and structural analysis from the distribution of peak heights at different m/e ratios, especially for organic compounds with functional groups. For example, the identification of gas chromatographic peaks by mass spectrometry is now routine. For compounds which decompose on heating, the technique sometimes fails: Unprotected biochemical samples cannot be made sufficiently volatile. However, discovery of suitable protecting (or "volatilizing") groups has made progress in mass spectrometric sequencing of oligopeptides and oligosaccharides possible. Quantitative analysis by mass spectrometry is likewise employed for gaseous mixtures and for solid materials.

30.2 RESOLUTION; ISOTOPIC ABUNDANCES

As a rule, the purpose of an instrument governs the required resolution; we must describe this specification before showing how instruments are designed to meet the resolution requirements for a given analysis. The resolution of a mass spectrometer expresses its ability to separate two close-lying peaks in the spectrum and is defined as $m/\Delta m$, where m is the approximate mass of one of the peaks and Δm is its separation in mass units from the other. Focusing problems usually make the actual resolution of a mass spectrometer a function of mass. While the figures quoted for commercial instruments often do not include the mass range for which resolution applies, we can apply them to the separation of ions in the m/e range of 200 to 400 with some confidence. This is the most common range in which resolution is crucial.

While a resolution of 3000 at m/e 300 means that ions of 300.0 and 300.1 are separated, there is no precise definition of the degree of separation expected. Frequently, peaks are called separate if the recorded ion current falls between the peaks to a value 10% of the average of the two peaks, but other values, especially 1% and 50%, have been used.

A low-resolution instrument is one whose resolution is below 1000. Such a device provides integral mass resolution for practically all organic compounds that can be volatilized in a mass spectrometer, except for a few perfluoro compounds of high molecular weight. Almost any commercial instrument can achieve this resolution now; many are guaranteed to a resolution of 3000, and some low-priced ones perform even better.

High-resolution instruments are routinely operated with a resolution of at least 10,000, and resolutions in the 70,000 to 150,000 range are possible. Since the low volatility of high-molecular-weight compounds is a limiting factor in applications, achieving resolution of integral masses at very high m/e ratios is not the purpose of high-resolution instrumentation. The need for high resolution arises when we need to determine accurate masses of organic species of moderate to great complexity. If we can obtain an accurate mass of the molecular ion, the molecular formula of the compound can usually be uniquely determined. This is because nuclear packing fractions for different isotopes of the various elements are each different, and therefore the sums of packing fractions can be used to determine a unique elemental composition. Published tables give exact masses of combinations of isotopes. Table 30.1 lists exact masses of isotopes commonly found in organic compounds.

On the basis that an ion in the spectrum of some compound has the mass 131.0860 if its charge is 1, say, use of Table 30.1 or comparison with other published tables shows that the ion can be $C_{10}H_{11}$. Whether anything else is possible depends on how accurately the mass is known. For example, C_9H_7O has mass 131.0497, and to distinguish between this possibility and the first requires that the mass be determinable within 0.0363 mass unit. If the resolution of the instrument is great enough to separate these two masses (that is, if it exceeds 3600), we can use the instrument to distinguish between possibilities, provided we can find standards with known masses reasonably close to that of the unknown. Unknown masses we determine by comparison with standards rather than by solution of the mass spectrometer equations to be discussed below, since the equations are derived for the ideal instrument with no problems with inhomogeneous fields, uneven scan rates, and the like.

Table 30.1 Some Common Nuclides Found in Organic Compounds*

Isotope	Mass	Relative Abundance†	Isotope	Mass	Relative Abundance†
^1H	1.007825	1.0000	^{18}O	17.99916	0.00204
^2H	2.01410	0.00015	^{19}F	18.99840	1.0000
^{12}C	12.00000	1.0000	^{35}Cl	34.96885	1.0000
^{13}C	13.00335	0.0112	^{37}Cl	36.96590	0.3240
^{14}N	14.00307	1.0000	^{79}Br	78.9183	1.0000
^{15}N	15.00011	0.0037	^{81}Br	80.9163	0.9786
^{16}O	15.99491	1.0000	^{127}I	126.9044	1.0000
^{17}O	16.99914	0.00037			

* Data derived from the *Handbook of Chemistry and Physics*, 49th ed. Cleveland, Ohio: Chemical Rubber Company, 1968.
† Abundance of isotope relative to that of most abundant isotope.

It is in fact frequently the case that an instrument being operated so that it has 10,000 resolution gives mass determinations accurate to one part in 100,000 or more. If peaks are so narrow that resolution is 10,000, then we can read their positions (usually the center of gravity of the peak on the mass scale) accurately by one, sometimes two, orders of magnitude if there is no overlap between peaks.

30.3 SAMPLE ADMISSION

For conventional analysis of organic materials and inorganic gases, the sample must be in the form of a dilute gas before it is ionized; solids can be analyzed by sparking.

It is usual to keep the pressure of the sample in the ion source of an instrument producing conventional mass spectra in the range 10^{-6} to 10^{-7} millibar or torr. Below this range many instruments are not sufficiently sensitive to produce a useful spectrum of an organic compound. Above it, the number of molecules per unit volume in the source is high enough to lead to a moderate probability of collision of ions with these molecules. These collisions can lead to ion-molecule reactions, which are interesting in their own right but can confuse the interpreter of the spectrum, for his initial assignment of the molecular weight would be the m/e ratio of the peak with highest m/e in the spectrum, and this ion might be a product of a collision. Interpretation of a mass spectrum depends heavily on identification of the molecular weight of the compound, and so it is important not to introduce peaks into the spectrum that may confuse assignment.

Table 30.2 Handling of Various Kinds of Samples

Type	Method of Introduction
Gas; liquid with > 2–7 millibar vapor pressure	Gas inlet system; sample withdrawn through leak from 500 ml reservoir (or larger)
Liquid or solid exerting $>$ 2–7 millibar vapor pressure at 250 °C	Heated inlet system; sample withdrawn from reservoir
Solid decomposing at temperature below point where it has 2–7 millibar vapor pressure; solids of low volatility	Direct probe into ion source at temperature where vapor pressure is 10^{-7} to 10^{-6} millibar
Gas chromatographic effluent	Passage through sample enricher that reduces pressure to 10^{-6} millibar and preferentially removes helium
Solids; refractory materials, metals	Inserted as an electrode in spark-source instrument

Various kinds of samples are introduced through different inlet systems (Table 30.2). Gaseous samples are admitted from a bulb through a manifold into a reservoir of at least 500 ml volume; from this the sample leaks through a small aperture into the source at a sufficiently slow rate that an oil diffusion pump (and sometimes additional liquid nitrogen cooling) can maintain the necessary 10^{-6} to 10^{-7} torr or millibar pressure in the source. The depletion rate in the reservoir is then about a few percent an hour, and reproducibility of spectra is not seriously affected by loss of sample (though for mixtures of compounds differing in molecular weight, fractionation because of different rates of effusion through the leak may occur). The reservoir and inlet system connecting it to the ion source are commonly maintained in an oven at temperatures between 180 °C and 300 °C so that a wide range of functionally substituted organic compounds, which may possess a useful vapor pressure only at elevated temperatures, may be introduced into the reservoir (usually through a heated manifold).* Above this temperature range, we do not commonly use glass manifolds for the vacuum system; expansion causes binding of the groundglass valves. In addition, the stability of organic compounds at high temperatures is lowered, and we may obtain the spectrum of a pyrolysis product, not the sample whose spectrum is desired.

To avoid this problem with less stable compounds of low volatility, most instruments now have a direct-insertion probe extending into the ion source. This device makes it possible to bring the sample up to within a few mm of the ionizing beam. A spectrum can be obtained provided the sample achieves a pressure of about 10^{-8} millibar or torr before its decomposition point. For example, the method permits securing spectra of NaCl and decapeptide derivatives. The sample is ionized before thermal equilibration with the walls of the ion source occurs. Especially tricky samples are sometimes run with source and inlet at ambient temperature (some instruments have provision for tap-water cooling of the source, and direct-introduction probes chilled by liquid nitrogen have been designed).

We may also analyze gas chromatographic fractions as they elute from the chromatograph. Since they consist mainly of helium, enrichment in the sample is essential. If a fraction of the effluent is admitted at a tolerable total pressure, too low a sample partial pressure in the source is secured. Consequently, we insert a sample enricher, a device that discards helium more efficiently than organic material, prior to the ion source. A few types of enrichers are described here. We can avoid chromatographic peak broadening with each type.

The Watson–Biemann separator (Fig. 30.3) depends on the fact that helium diffuses through a fritted glass tube much more efficiently than heavier organic molecules. As the chromatographic eluant passes down the tube, helium is preferentially pumped out through the fritted walls, and the enriched sample arrives at the ion source at a total pressure of 10^{-5} millibar or torr. A satisfactory fraction of this eluant, several percent, is the organic sample.

The Ryhage separator achieves the same sort of effect by depending on the fact that the inertia of helium atoms is lower than that of any other species in the same stream. Helium is deflected more easily from the stream than the organic constituents, and lateral pumping in several stages can therefore remove most of the helium but little of the sample.

The Llewellyn separator consists of a silicone rubber diaphragm; this has a low permeability by helium, but organic materials can permeate it readily and can therefore enter the ion source greatly enriched through a membrane of this type.

If we cannot vaporize solids, we may form them into an electrode for sparking

---

* Because pumping is more efficient in the ion source itself, the temperatures there are typically lower than in the inlet system, by up to about 50 °C.

From gas chromatograph

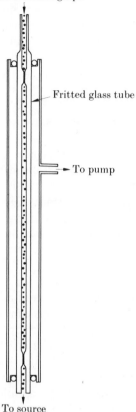

Fritted glass tube

To pump

To source

Fig. 30.3 Schematic diagram of the Watson–Biemann separator.

in the source. Conductors we can form into an electrode by themselves, other materials by mixing with conductors of known composition. Since spark-source mass spectrometry is frequently used for trace analysis, there are limitations on the types of materials usable for electrodes, and there can be problems with the homogeneity of the sample.

30.4 ION FORMATION IN THE ION SOURCE

The usual method of production of ions from a gas is by electron impact. Conventional mass spectra of organic compounds are produced by ionization with electrons emitted from a heated tungsten or rhenium filament and accelerated through a potential difference of 70 to 80 V. The great majority of ions produced under these conditions are positive ions, formed principally by the process

$$A - B + e^- \rightarrow [A - B]^+ + e^- + e^- \tag{30.1}$$

though other processes may be of importance sometimes:

$$A - B + e^- \rightarrow A^+ + B + e^- + e^- \tag{30.2}$$

$$A - B + e^- \rightarrow A^+ + B^- + e^- \tag{30.3}$$

Negative ions are also formed, though the yield of positive to negative ions is in a ratio of about 10^4 for typical organic compounds; the efficiency of production of each kind of ion has a different dependence on voltage (that is, the ionization efficiency curve differs). For negative ions, the principal modes of formation are Eqs. (30.3), (30.4), and (30.5).

$$A - B + e^- \rightarrow [A - B]^- \tag{30.4}$$

$$A - B + e^- \rightarrow A^- + B \tag{30.5}$$

Since almost all analysis is done with positive ions, there will be no further discussion of negative ions.

Collision of 70 V electrons with typical organic compounds would transfer sufficient energy to cause ejection of an electron (occasionally more than one) and the cleavage of several bonds, if the energy transfer were very efficient. It is not. Bond cleavage is not necessarily a consequence of ionization; as a general rule changes in spectra are fairly small above 30 V ionizing energy. The value for ionization in routine spectra, 70 to 80 V, is chosen because the appearance of the spectrum is nearly independent of the voltage of the ionizing electrons in this range, and reproducibility is secured.

We can vary ionization energies, and use an electron-impact technique for the determination of the ionization potentials of atoms and molecules. Because of the thermal spread of the energies of electrons emitted from a filament, we should compare the data obtained generally with data for known substances. These ionization potentials (the energy required to remove an electron from an atom or molecule) are not the same, in general, as those obtained by the interpretation of spectroscopic data, for the ionization process is one that occurs with no nuclear motion since it is fast (10^{-14} s) compared with the period of a molecular vibration. Bond strengths are different in neutral molecules and in the ions corresponding to them. Further equilibrium interatomic distances differ from neutral molecule to ion and the production of ions without change of interatomic distances produces ions in some vibrationally or rotationally excited states. The values of the ionization potential obtained from electron impact studies will therefore be slightly larger than those calculated from spectroscopic data, which actually correspond to ionization to the lowest state of the ion. Figure 30.4 compares the processes.

In addition to the ionization potential of a molecule, we may obtain the appearance potentials of fragment ions by studying the production of these ions at different voltages. The efficiency of production of a fragment ion is frequently dissimilar to the ionization efficiency curve of a standard, and larger errors often occur in these data (see Fig. 30.5). Still, we can gather information about heats of formation and bond strengths in this way. In the absence of activation energies, we may consider the production of an ion A^+ from a molecule $A - B$ by two routes:

$$A - B \rightarrow A - B^+ \rightarrow A^+ + B \tag{30.6}$$

$$A - B \rightarrow A + B \rightarrow A^+ + B \tag{30.7}$$

The first of these is ionization followed by dissociation, the second is dissociation followed by ionization. Calling the dissociation energy d, the ionization potential ip, and the appearance potential ap, we may follow Eq. 30.6 and write

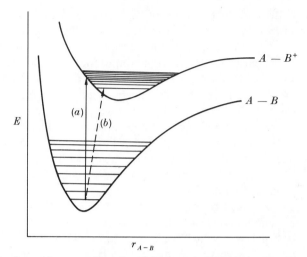

Fig. 30.4 (a) Ionization without motion of nuclei, or vertical ionization. In the molecule $A - B$ illustrated, only excitation to vibrationally excited states of the ion is possible. (b) The hypothetical process of ionization to the lowest state of the ion, or adiabatic ionization.

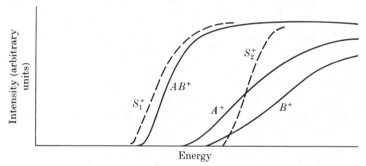

Fig. 30.5 Ionization efficiency curves and fragment production efficiency curves for AB^+ and its daughter ions A^+ and B^+. Note that the ionization efficiency curves of the standards S_1 and S_2 resemble the ionization efficiency curve of AB^+ but that the efficiency of production of fragments can be a less steep function of ionizing energy. These curves are for ionization by electron impact.

$$ap\,(A) = ip\,(A - B) + d\,(A - B^+) \qquad (30.8)$$

or follow Eq. (30.7) and write

$$ap\,(A) = d\,(A - B) + ip\,(A). \qquad (30.9)$$

It would appear that mass spectra of molecules might be predicted from such data. Yet the calculation is not a simple matter. The theory of the production of spectra that has the widest acceptance is the quasi-equilibrium theory. Using this theory, one assumes that the mass spectrum of a compound is the product of a set of competing consecutive unimolecular decompositions of the molecular ion (the ion formed by removal of an electron without fragmentation). Thus, ions of lower mass are produced entirely by fragmentation of molecular ions that have sufficient energy to break apart and the processes of Eqs. (30.2) and (30.3) are not important. Knowing the ionization potential of the molecule and the appearance potentials of all fragments, we can define a dissociation energy for each decomposition process and calculate rates for each process as a function of the energy of the molecular ion. From instrumental considerations, we look upon the rate processes as interrupted after 10^{-5} to 10^{-6} s after ionization when spectral analysis occurs. For many molecules the mass spectrum calculated for a reasonable distribution of ion energies correlates satisfactorily. Disagreement between predicted and observed spectra we can usually correct by refinement of the model. For example, some fragment peaks may result from rearrangements of the molecular ion with cleavage of some bonds and formation of others. In this case we require correction for loss of degrees of freedom in the activated complex.

The chamber where these processes take place is called the *ion source. Electron-impact* ion sources generally have a heater filament to reduce adsorption of samples on the walls. Ionization is performed by electrons emitted from a tungsten or rhenium filament and collimated by slits and magnetic fields so that the region of ionization can be confined to a small fraction of the volume of the entire chamber. Positive ions are removed from the source by repulsion from positively charged repeller plates that drive the ions into the mass analyzer.

Chemical ionization is a second, increasingly important mode of ionization in which a compound to be studied is ionized by reaction with other ions. The most common source of such ions is methane introduced at the relatively high pressure of 1 millibar. By contrast, sample partial pressures are typically 10^{-6} millibar. Electron bombardment of the mixture therefore almost always produces ions from methane. Under these pressure conditions, the molecular ions of methane collide with methane molecules to produce other ions, principally CH_5^+ and $C_2H_5^+$.

As a strong Lewis acid, protonated methane produces ions from the organic compound of interest by proton transfer:

$$CH_5^+ + A - B \rightarrow CH_4 + A - B - H^+ \tag{30.10}$$

The protonated ions frequently have sufficient energy to decompose, and their routes for decomposition are different from those of $A - B^+$. As a result, a study of their fragmentation produces information about the structure of $A - B$ that is complementary to that given by the ordinary electron-impact spectrum.

For chemical ionization, which requires pressures of the order of 1 millibar, pumping on the source and analyzer is not sufficient for operation: 1 millibar is required in the source, yet analyzer pressures much above 10^{-6} millibar cause loss of signal because of deflection of ions on collision. The source must be open to the analyzer to allow the ions to pass into the analyzer, of course. We meet the dilemma by using a very small slit for this aperture and pumping with high-capacity and efficient pumps through very large exit tubes on both sides of the slit.

Field ionization of a molecule, a third technique, results from placing the molecule to be ionized between two closely spaced electrodes. The anode is drawn to a point or an edge (frequently a razor blade) so that a very high electric field gradient (as high as 10 V nm^{-1}) is produced. Ionization by tunnelling is common. There is very little fragmentation of the ion in the absence of electron collisions. Production of the ion in a high electric field reduces the time before analysis from 10^{-6} s to 10^{-9} s, further reducing the chance for fragmentation. Comparatively high amounts of products of reactions between ions and neutral species are observed; these are thought to be the result of intermolecular reactions on the surface of the electrode. This technique has been used to produce spectra of compounds like glucose that ordinarily do not give spectra because they decompose at low temperatures.

For more accurate ionization-potential studies, a *photoionization* process may be used; that is, the reaction

$$A - B + hv \rightarrow A - B^+ + e^- \tag{30.11}$$

produces the ion. Because we can make irradiating light monochromatic, we can determine very accurate values for ionization and appearance potentials. However, the use of photoionization for routine production of mass spectra is not widespread.

Photoionization is commonly accomplished by helium emission lines (^{1}S, 19.81 eV; ^{3}S, 20.61 eV; IP, 24.59 eV). Since no window material transmits photons of these energies, the helium discharge is maintained at a pressure above that acceptable for the ion source, and differential pumping on either side of a slit between discharge tube and source is again used to avoid high pressure in the source.

Another promising method for ionization of gases is *Penning ionization*, which relies on transfer of energy to a molecule from a metastable excited state of some neutral species, commonly argon. Since some organic substances have ionization potentials greater than this metastable state level, these compounds are not ionized; species that can be ionized have exactly 11.6 eV (the value of the excited state level) transferred to them. The sequence of steps is

$$Ar + e^- \rightarrow Ar^* + e^- \tag{30.12}$$

$$Ar^* \, (11.6 \, eV) + A - B \rightarrow Ar + M^+ + e^- \; (\text{for } ip \, (A - B) < 11.6 \, eV) \tag{30.13}$$

In *spark-source analysis* of solids, we place the sample electrode close to an inert electrode. An intermittent voltage sufficient to produce a spark (8000 to 20,000 V) is applied to vaporize and ionize part of the sample without heating the entire sample substantially. For quantitative analysis uniform sampling must be achieved. In trace analysis, where concentrations on the order of 1 ppm will require many sparkings to produce usable ion intensity, uniformity is likely. At higher concentrations, fewer sparkings are required, and the condition of uniformity may not be met. In these cases it is possible to increase the number of sparkings by chopping the ion beam in such a manner that no more than 1 % of the ions reach the detector. Typically, before chopping, analysis calls for 1 to 10^4 sparks per second of about 100 μs duration.

30.5 MASS ANALYZERS

Once ions are produced and removed from the ion source, we may analyze them according to their masses by any of several methods. Perhaps the simplest in principle is *analysis according to time of flight*. Consider a collection of ions produced at some time t_0 and then accelerated in an electric field. Each ion has a kinetic energy eV, where e is its charge and V the electric potential through which it has passed:

$$eV = \tfrac{1}{2}mv^2, \tag{30.14}$$

where m and v represent the mass and velocity of the ion. For ions traveling a distance d between the ion source and the detector, the time of flight t is:

$$t = d \cdot v = d \left(\frac{1}{2V}\right)^{1/2} \cdot \left(\frac{m}{e}\right)^{1/2}. \tag{30.15}$$

The time of arrival of ions produced at t_0 is therefore a function of the m/e ratio of the ion. In a conventional time-of-flight instrument with a flight tube on the order of a few meters and a typical accelerating voltage of about 1000 V, the separation in time of arrival of ions of m/e 300 and 301 is on the order of tens of nanoseconds. Obviously, in order to resolve such peaks, it is necessary that the initial pulse period in which ions are produced be less than this length of time, and it is essential as well that resolution should not deteriorate in the response of the detector electronics.

The most common method of analysis is *analysis by a magnetic field*. A charged particle entering a magnetic field with a given velocity assumes a circular orbit, in which the force acting on the particle, Bev (where B is the magnetic field strength), exactly opposes the centripetal force, mv^2/r (where r is the radius of the orbit of the particle):

$$Bev = mv^2/r. \tag{30.16}$$

Rearranging Eq. (30.16), we obtain

$$\frac{m}{e} = \frac{Br}{v}. \tag{30.17}$$

In the case of ions accelerated through a uniform electrostatic field, Eq. (30.14) applies, and substituting the value of $(2eV/m)^{1/2}$ for v from it into Eq. (30.17) we obtain

$$\frac{m}{e} = \frac{B^2r^2}{2V}. \tag{30.18}$$

Ions accelerated through a uniform electrostatic field and then deflected through a uniform magnetic field will therefore have different radii of curvature of their orbits, as Fig. 30.6 indicates. When they leave the magnetic field, they disperse. The earliest instruments produced a photographic record (a photoplate darkened by the action of ions striking at different positions) from these dispersed ions. It had some resemblance to the appearance of a line spectrum produced by absorbed or emitted light from an atomic source; hence the name "mass spectrum".

Few simple magnetic deflection instruments today rely on photographic plates; instead, they have electrical detectors. This modification requires that a slit with the detector behind it be placed at the end of the magnetic field. Then only ions with orbits of a certain radius (m/e ratio) impinge on the detector; others strike the walls of the analyzer. To scan an entire spectrum, each ion in turn must be given this radius. In other words, ions of different m/e are swept past the detector slit at a known rate and we can prepare a "spectrum" from the intensity of ion current as a function of time. Reference to Eq. (30.19) suggests that we may do this by varying either of two parameters:

1. The accelerating potential V may be decreased while the magnetic field B is held constant. Ions will then be swept by in order of increasing m/e as the accelerating potential decreases.

2. The magnetic field may be increased while the accelerating potential is held constant. Ions are swept by the detector slit in order of increasing m/e as the magnetic field strength increases. This method of analysis is more common now in magnetic-deflection instruments.*

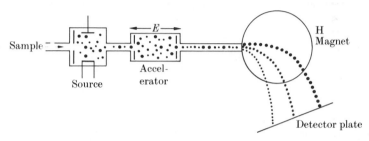

Fig. 30.6 Separation of ions of different m/e in the magnetic field of a magnetic deflection mass spectrometer. Use of a detector plate in this type of unit is of historical interest only.

Instruments that achieve their stated resolution by focusing ions of different m/e in different directions we term *single-focusing* instruments. In a single-focusing instrument there is a lack of uniformity of ion energies, since the accelerating potential experienced by an ion depends upon where in the source it is formed. The resulting spread in ionic energies produces a spread in their radii of curvature in the magnetic field. The result is peak broadening and low to moderate resolution.

To achieve high resolution a mass spectrometer requires double focusing. Its ion beam passes through an energy selector after acceleration but before magnetic analysis. This is done by inserting a unit called an *electrostatic sector*. It consists (Fig. 30.7) of two curved plates across which a uniform potential difference is maintained. Ions entering midway between the plates, and having the proper energy, will describe a circular orbit:

$$\frac{mv^2}{r} = eV'$$

(30.19)

where V' is the potential difference between the plates which form the sides of the sector. The velocity of the particles is determined by their m/e ratio and accelerating potential V, as before (Eq. 30.14). Insertion of the value $(2eV/m)^{1/2}$ for v in the equation for the orbit in the electrostatic sector, Eq. (30.19), yields

$$r = 2V/V'.$$

(30.20)

* The disadvantage of the method of varying the accelerating potential is that some of the accelerating potential "leaks back" into the ion source, leading to altered source conditions. As a result, sensitivity changes as a function of the m/e ratio, and some information is lost in the region of the spectrum where sensitivity is low.

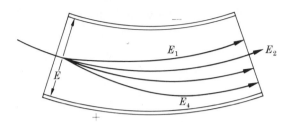

Fig. 30.7 Energy selection of positive ions in an electrostatic analyzer. Only ions previously accelerated by E_2 volts pass through the exit slit at the right.

That is, the location of a slit at the end of the sector defines an orbit that can be achieved only by ions with the total energy imparted by accelerating potential V. We can close the slit down to define ions passing through it very narrowly in energy. Magnetic analysis of the energetically well-defined beam gives high resolution. Ions that reach the detector slit have been focused twice, once in direction and once in velocity.

Different geometrical arrangements of the electrostatic sector and the magnetic sector are in use. In Nier–Johnson geometry (Fig. 30.8), ions are focused at the exit (detector) slit to permit final control of resolution. In Mattauch–Herzog geometry (Fig. 30.9), after magnetic analysis ions are doubly focused at every point along a plane. A slit may be located at any point along this line, or a photographic plate may be placed in the plane. Ions emerging in different directions from the magnetic field are collected simultaneously, which is a distinct advantage with a small sample or one whose characteristics change rapidly, like a gas chromatographic effluent. Slow scanning would give a distorted spectrum in such cases. On the other hand, most single-focusing and Nier–Johnson high-resolution instruments now have provision for rapid scanning of the normal sample mass range (m/e 10 to 300, in 1 to 3 s, for example).

Double-focusing instruments are required when a spark source is used, since ions emerge from such a source with a very wide range of kinetic energies. Very low resolution would result in the absence of energy selection. Again, because the microscopic characteristics of a sample may change very quickly, it is advisable for analysis of samples like alloys, which may be composed of many small crystals of different solid solutions or compounds, to employ photographic recording to secure an integrated reading rather than use a scanning technique that samples a given peak very briefly.

Another type of instrument that enjoys some popularity is the *quadrupole mass filter* (Fig. 30.10). It consists of a set of four parallel rods that sort ions as they pass lengthwise through the set. One diagonally opposite pair of rods is held at $+ V_{dc}$ volts, the other pair at $- V_{dc}$ volts. A radiofrequency oscillator supplies a signal to the first pair of rods and an out-of-phase signal (phase of the rf signal retarded by 180°) to the second pair. The superposed voltages are shown in the figure. At an appropriate ratio of dc to rf potential, and with sufficiently long rods, most ions entering the quadrupole region will oscillate and strike the walls of the instrument. At a given rf potential and frequency it proves to be the case that ions of one m/e ratio can pass through the analyzer and be detected. An entire spectrum can be

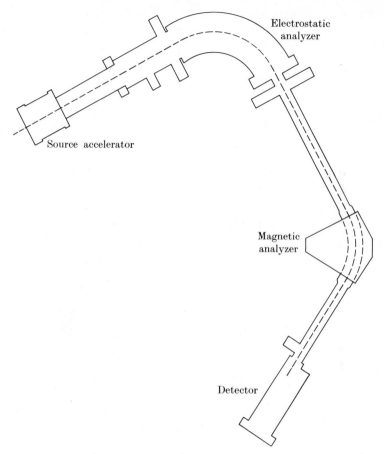

Fig. 30.8 A double-focusing mass spectrometer of Nier–Johnson geometry.

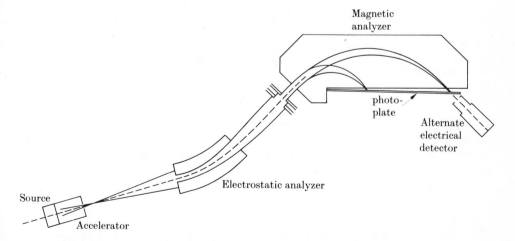

Fig. 30.9 A double-focusing mass spectrometer of Mattauch–Herzog geometry.

produced by varying the rf frequency while the rf and dc potentials remain constant, or by varying the rf potential (and the dc potential simultaneously so that the ratio of potentials remains fixed) while the rf frequency is held constant.

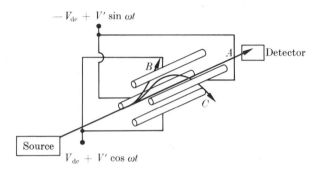

Fig. 30.10 Schematic diagram of the quadrupole mass filter. Ions B and C have improper m/e ratio and are thrown against the walls; A has the correct m/e ratio and is detected at the end of the analyzer.

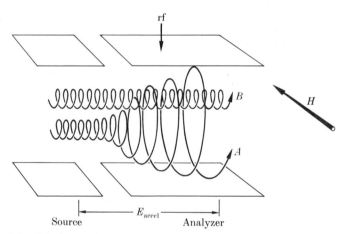

Fig. 30.11 Principle of the ion cyclotron resonance spectrometer. Ion A has the proper m/e, and its frequency corresponds to the rf frequency; it absorbs energy and describes an orbit of increasing radius while maintaining the same frequency. Ion B has a different m/e and does not absorb energy. Ions of the same m/e may have different radii of orbit but must have the same frequency.

In an *ion cyclotron resonance* (ICR) *spectrometer* (Fig. 30.11) advantage is taken of the fact that the frequency of a particle completing a circular orbit in a magnetic field is independent of its velocity but dependent on its m/e ratio (Eq. 30.21). As B changes, since

$$\omega = \frac{eB}{mc} \tag{30.21}$$

the frequency ω associated with a given m/e ratio changes, and ions of different m/e ratios attain a given frequency. If an rf field of frequency ω is applied while an ion has this frequency, the ion absorbs energy from the field. To determine a spectrum, ions are placed in crossed magnetic and rf fields, and the magnetic field is increased while the frequency of the rf field is held constant. Ions of different mass are brought into resonance (that is, attain the frequency of the rf field) as the magnetic field increases, and the absorption of energy is monitored by a sensitive device like a marginal oscillator.

As a mass spectrometer, the ion cyclotron resonance instrument basically offers no advantage over a conventional type. However, the longer residence time of ions in the source and analyzer (about 10^{-3} s) compared to the 10^{-6} s in a conventional instrument, means that collisions of ions with neutral molecules will be about 1000 times more likely. Consequently the instrument is valuable for the study of ion-molecule reactions.

Ion cyclotron double resonance is an especially useful technique for making such studies. Suppose the following ion-molecule reaction

$$A - B + A - B^+ \rightarrow A - B - A^+ + B \tag{30.22}$$

is being investigated by monitoring at ω_{ABA^+}, the frequency corresponding to that of the product ion at a given magnetic field. An rf field of frequency ω_{AB^+}, at this magnetic field strength, is now pulsed on and off. Energy is absorbed by AB^+ ions and the ions react at a different rate with neutral AB molecules to produce ABA^+ ions. The amount of ABA^+ formed in unit time is different from before, causing changed intensity at frequency ω_{ABA^+}. Thus if an ion is produced by the collision of another ion, the process can be detected, provided changing the energy of the reactant ion changes the rate of the production of the second one. This procedure permits processes that produce ions at higher pressures to be identified.

30.6 DETECTORS

After passing through the exit slit of the analyzer of a conventional mass spectro-meter, ions fall on a collector. It is typically a metal electrode in a small cup called a Faraday cage or Faraday cup. The bombardment produces secondary electrons, whose loss would decrease the ion current. A magnetic field or a negatively charged plate forces them back to the collector. We measure the current by the potential drop produced as it flows through a large external resistor.

We may use an electron multiplier if we desire great amplification of the signal, as we normally do in organic analysis. This device was described in Section 11.7.

For precise intensity ratios (mass abundance ratios), such as we require for isotope ratio measurements, the use of a single detector is seldom satisfactory. Small fluctua-tions in source conditions limit the quantitative accuracy. To avoid this problem, a dual collection system is frequently employed. The modified instrument we term an isotope ratio mass spectrometer or an isotope ratiometer. Its dual slit-and-detector units may be placed in appropriate positions for comparison of masses of interest.

As mentioned before, photographic emulsions on glass plates may be used for detection in Mattauch–Herzog double-focusing mass spectrometers. The degree of plate darkening by ion impact can be translated into relative concentrations of ions.

30.7 RECORDING DEVICES

We may display the signal obtained from a scanning mass spectrometer in any of several ways. We can use a pen-and-ink strip-chart recorder if the rate of scan is slow. Faster signals, for example from a time-of-flight instrument, may be displayed by an oscilloscope and recorded photographically. A fast recording oscillograph can also be used; its amplifier output deflects several mirror galvanometers that trace the spectrum on ultraviolet-sensitive paper. The same spectrum is presented at different sensitivities. In this fashion, with four or five galvanometers of different sensitivities, intensities differing by a factor of 10,000 can be read from the same record.

More recently data have been digitized (Section 9.7) and collected on magnetic tape or stored in the memory of a computer for processing.

Example A high-resolution mass spectrum may be collected on-line or on tape. Computer processing of the data may then be used to obtain not only the exact mass of each ion but also to calculate possible empirical formulas for each ion in the spectrum, arrange the ions in a display according to kinds and numbers of atoms present in each ion (a so-called element map, or some modification of such a map), and also assign structural characteristics to the molecule by comparing the differences between empirical formulas to the losses of neutral fragments expected for various functional groups. This last step requires a knowledge of much empirical information about model compounds.

30.8 SPECTRAL INTERPRETATION: AN EXAMPLE

The following example is based on typical methods of spectral interpretation of organic compounds. The spectrum of an unknown was obtained in a single-focusing instrument from a sample introduced through an inlet maintained at 200 °C. The ion source was also at this temperature. High-resolution information was secured on the unknown with a separate instrument whose mass scale was calibrated with a known compound.*

With the unknown, peak matching was used; the technique calls for accurate determination of the ratio of accelerating voltages necessary to bring first a standard peak and then an unknown peak into focus at the detector. The spectrum of the unknown is given in the form of a bar graph (Fig. 30.12). We take the intensity of the largest peak as 100.

As a first guess, we assume reasonably that the intense peak at the high-mass end of the spectrum (at $m/e = 78$) corresponds to a singly-charged ion and thus to the molecular weight M of the unknown compound. We assume further that the small peaks just above this peak in m/e ratio are isotope peaks, i.e. peaks due to the expected content of naturally occurring minor isotopes in the compound. Since

---

* A compound that produces abundant fluorocarbon ions is a suitable standard. The mass defects of its ions are sufficiently different from those of the usual organic ions containing C, H, N, and O that even ions with the same mass number give peaks that can be resolved and measured easily on a high-resolution instrument.

there is no large peak at mass $M + 2$, it is obvious that the compound does not contain Cl or Br (see Table 30.1). We assume then that the $M + 1$ peak is the result of contributions of minor isotopes of C and N, and that the $M + 2$ peak is due to contributions for isotopes of O and C (principally, for the latter, contributions of molecules containing two ^{13}C atoms rather than one ^{14}C atom).

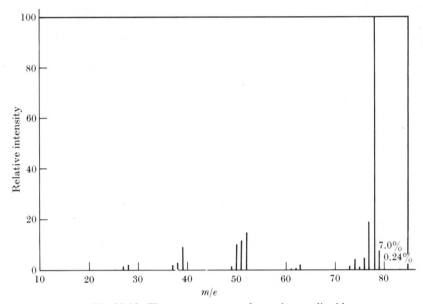

Fig. 30.12 The mass spectrum of an unknown liquid.

Probability laws derived from the binomial theorem state that the intensity of the $M + 1$ peak relative to the intensity of the M peak is given by

$$I_{M+1}/I_M = 0.011 \, (\#C) + 0.0037 \, (\#N), \tag{30.23}$$

where $(\#C)$ and $(\#N)$ are the number of atoms of carbon and nitrogen in the compound. Assuming that the nitrogen content is low,* we neglect it at the start and calculate

$$7.0/100 = 0.070 = 0.011 \, (\# C).$$

The compound apparently contains six carbon atoms; the slight amount of excess intensity over that calculated for six carbons may be a small amount of background material in the instrument, the result of a slight fluctuation in source conditions, or possibly a small amount of protonated species resulting from an ion-molecule reaction in the source. The contribution to the $M + 1$ peak from ^{2}H is not significant.

---

* Since the molecular weight, 78, is even, the number of nitrogen atoms present must be even. This follows from the coincidence that among all the common elements in organic compounds, only N has a principal isotope of even weight and an odd valence. In all other cases, both are even or both are odd.

We calculate the $M + 2$ peak from the formula

$$I_{M+2}/I_M = \frac{[0.011\,(\#\,C)]^2}{2} + 0.0020\,(\#\,O). \qquad (30.24)$$

If we assume that the six carbons alone produce the $M + 2$ peak, we calculate an expected intensity ratio of 0.0022; the observed value is close to this. Carbon atoms account for 72 of the 78 mass units present; the remainder is logically hydrogen, and so the empirical formula of the ion is C_6H_6. A reasonable compound fitting these requirements is benzene, but the spectrum of hexa-1,3-dien-5-yne is similar.

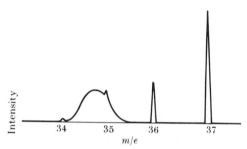

Fig. 30.13 A metastable ion peak at m/e 34.7, with a few low background peaks at integral masses that are useful in interpreting the spectrum.

In addition to the tabulated peaks, there is a broad, triangular peak in the spectrum centered at m/e 34.7 (Fig. 30.13). This is a metastable peak. It is produced by a metastable ion, one whose lifetime is sufficiently long for it not to decompose in the source, but instead to break apart as it passes through the analyzer of the instrument; its lifetime is thus about 10^{-5} to 10^{-6} s. It is accelerated at the heavier mass, that of the precursor ion as it existed in the source, but is deflected at the lighter mass of the final fragment. As this sort of fragment ion enters the magnetic field, it is moving more slowly than normal ions of its mass because it has roughly only the velocity which its precursor had. Hence it is deflected by the magnetic field into an orbit of smaller radius than the orbit of normal fragment ions of its mass. To a first approximation, the radius corresponds to that of an ion of apparent mass m^*, where

$$m^* = \frac{(m_{\text{fragment}})^2}{m_{\text{precursor}}}. \qquad (30.25)$$

The broadening is a result of the possibility of formation of the fragment ion in the fringe of the accelerating field or the fringe of the magnetic field.

We have one equation and two unknowns for determining the nature of m/e 34.7. Though with double-focusing instruments there are alternate ways of studying metastable ions to identify them, we can make use of the general observations that the fragment ion formed in a metastable decomposition is almost always indicated by an intense normal peak, and that the precursor ion is usually indicated by an intense normal peak. While there may be an infinite number of solutions to Eq. (30.25), the most likely one is that for which $m_{fragment}$ and $m_{precursor}$ correspond to large peaks in the spectrum. Trying various combinations of masses suggested by Fig. 30.12, we note that $52^2/78 = 34.7$; it appears that the decomposition $78^+ \rightarrow 52^+ + 26$ explains the metastable peak. Such a fragmentation supports the hypothesis that the unknown is benzene. For further discussion of this spectrum and of qualitative analysis by mass spectrometry, see the references at the end of the chapter.

30.9 QUANTITATIVE ANALYSIS

We frequently use mass spectra for quantitative analysis of organic mixtures. The spectra produced by commercial instruments are reproducible as long as conditions are reproduced and mass peaks from different components are additive. To carry out a precise analysis it is important that the spectra of the components to be analyzed be sufficiently different. For example, it is rarely possible to analyze *cis* and *trans* isomers mass-spectrometrically because of their similar spectra. Further, the efficiency of the instrument in ionizing each component of a mixture must be determined empirically with pure components prior to the analysis. The efficiency of ionization varies from component to component. This preliminary calibration yields a sensitivity factor for each component that is usually expressed in arbitrary chart divisions per micron pressure in the reservoir at the beginning of the analysis. Sensitivity factors vary somewhat from instrument to instrument. In any analysis, of course, we must collect data before significant fractionation occurs by effusion through the leak, an effect noted before.

We cannot analyze most spectra of mixtures by simple correction of each peak intensity by a sensitivity factor, for the total intensities of many peaks are the sums of contributions from the spectra of several components. Simultaneous equations permit us to calculate the contribution to each peak from each component. Consider a three-component mixture of A, B, and C. Choose three peaks in the spectrum of the mixture. The intensity of each peak is the sum of intensities from each component and the corrected intensity per unit pressure; hence the partial pressures of the components can be determined (Eqs. 30.26).

$$I_1 = p_A i_{1A} + p_B i_{1B} + p_C i_{1C}$$
$$I_2 = p_A i_{2A} + p_B i_{2B} + p_C i_{2C} \qquad (30.26)$$
$$I_3 = p_A i_{3A} + p_B i_{3B} + p_C i_{3C}$$

Here I_1, I_2, I_3 are the measured intensities at masses 1, 2, and 3; p_A, p_B, and p_C are the partial pressures of $A, B,$ and C; and $i_{1A}, \ldots, i_{3C}$ are the corrected relative intensities of the peaks at 1, 2, and 3 in the spectra of pure $A, B,$ and C. Since only the partial pressures are unknown, the equations yield their values.

In principle, it is possible to analyze N components in a mixture from N intensities. In practice, more intensities are studied in a spectrum than there are components, simply to serve as a further check on the values of $p_A, \ldots, p_N$ obtained. Obviously, too, if one peak is intense in the spectrum of one constituent but weak in the spectrum of another, this peak is more useful in distinguishing the relative amounts of both present than another peak that is of nearly the same intensity in both spectra. We must therefore exercise some judgment in the choice of peaks to be employed in an analysis.

REFERENCES

General texts emphasizing instrument design are:

1. J. H. Beynon, *Mass Spectrometry and Its Applications to Organic Chemistry.* Amsterdam: Elsevier, 1960
2. R. W. Kiser, *Introduction to Mass Spectrometry and Its Applications.* Englewood Cliffs, N.J.: Prentice-Hall, 1965
3. John Roboz, *Introduction to Mass Spectrometry. Instrumentation and Techniques.* New York: Wiley-Interscience, 1968

Texts emphasizing interpretation of spectra are:

4. Klaus Biemann, *Mass Spectrometry. Organic Chemical Applications.* New York: McGraw-Hill, 1962
5. Herbert Budzikiewicz, Carl Djerassi, and Dudley H. Williams, *Mass Spectrometry of Organic Compounds.* San Francisco: Holden-Day, 1967
6. F. W. McLafferty, *Interpretation of Mass Spectra.* New York: Benjamin, 1966

A chapter on ion cyclotron resonance spectrometry is

7. J. D. Baldeschwieler in *Carbonium Ions.* Vol. 1, G. A. Olah and P. von R. Schleyer, eds. New York: Wiley-Interscience, 1968, p. 413

EXERCISES

30.1 What resolution is required to separate the isotope peak of the molecular ion of benzene at m/e 79 from the molecular ion of pyridine in a mixture of benzene and pyridine?

30.2 One of the ions found in the spectrum of a fluorocarbon standard for high-resolution work is $C_2F_5^+$. How suitable a choice would this be for peak-matching the $C_9H_9^+$ ion? Is it more useful than $C_8H_5O^+$?

30.3 The ionization potential of the methyl radical was found by a photoionization technique to be 9.82 ± 0.04 V. The ionization potential of methane was determined as 12.70 ± 0.01 V, and the appearance potential of CH_3^+ in the spectrum of methane was 14.25 ± 0.02 V. Calculate the strength of the C—H bond broken to produce $\cdot CH_3$ from methane. How does this value compare with the bond strength of the C—H bond quoted in tabulations of data?

If the ionization potential of ethane is 11.52 ± 0.01 V and the appearance potential of CH_3^+ in the spectrum of ethane is 13.6 ± 0.1 V (obtained by another method than photoionization), calculate the C—C bond strength in ethane and compare it with values quoted in other tabulations.

30.4 The major peaks of the mass spectrum of an unknown liquid introduced through the heated inlet at 150 °C are listed below. Identify the compound; no high-resolution data are needed.

m/e:	37	38	50	51	56	73	74	75	76	77	78	112	113	114	115
Intensity:	2.0	5.7	9.6	12	3.9	2.1	4.3	4.6	3.4	45	3.0	100	6.7	33	2.2

30.5 The spectrum of a common natural product introduced as a liquid into the heated inlet system maintained at 185°C is given below. What is the compound?

m/e:	14	15	26	27	28	29	30	31	32	42	43	45	46	47
Intensity:	2.3	4.7	5.2	18	4.5	15	5.3	100	1.1	3.5	11	50	23	0.50

30.6 The principal peaks in the spectrum of toluene have m/e ratios of 39, 50, 51, 63, 65, 89, 91, and 92. There is a broad, triangular peak centered at m/e 46.5. Interpret this peak.

30.7 A mixture of methyl chloride and ethyl chloride was studied by ion cyclotron resonance. Peaks at m/e 79 and 81 in an approximate ratio of 3:1 were observed, and were found to be coupled to the ions of m/e 51 and 53 (ratio again about 3:1) and to m/e 65 and 67 (ratio 3:1) in a way suggested by the following. If the ion of m/e 81 was monitored while those of m/e 65 and 67 were irradiated at their resonant frequencies, the ratio of the double resonance signals was 3:1. If the same ion was observed while those of m/e 51 and 53 were irradiated, the ratio of the double resonance signals was 0:1. The peaks at m/e 79 and 81 were thought to correspond to the structure $CH_3ClC_2H_5^+$. Comment on the origin of the Cl atom in this ion.

30.8 A mixture of 1-hexene, 2-hexene, 4-methyl-1-pentene, and 2-methyl-2-pentene was admitted to the source of a mass spectrometer and intensities of ions found for the mixture as follows:

m/e:	15	26	27	28	29	39	40	41	42	43	53	54	55	56	57	69	84	85
Intensity:	8.6	4.9	50	8.6	21	44	7.9	100	50	56	8.0	4.7	48	53	2.4	45	29	1.9

The 100% peak was 2200 units high on the recorder. Using the tabulation of spectra of pure components (Table 30.3), determine the partial pressures of each component of the mixture.

Table 30.3 Spectra of C_6H_{12} Isomers

m/e	1-hexene	2-hexene	4-me-1-pent	2-me-2-pent
15	7.8	5.0	7.2	7.8
26	6.8	4.6	2.3	2.2
27	68	36	34	23
28	13	7.0	3.9	3.4
29	28	27	6.2	9.2
39	49	29	33	29
40	8.7	4.9	5.7	5.8
41	100	41	72	100
42	75	48	32	9.3
43	60	12	100	5.5
53	7.5	7.8	3.4	8.0
54	6.0	7.3	1.2	1.8
55	59	100	7.9	12
56	86	23	43	7.9
57	3.8	0.93	2.0	0.48
69	19	18	13	92
84	28	29	11	30
85	1.8	1.9	0.7	2.0
Sensitivity of 100% peak, div μm^{-1}	20	29	30	32

CHAPTER 31

CHROMATOGRAPHY*

31.1 INTRODUCTION

Except in rare instances, practical analysis and measurements on substances are complicated by interferences caused by other chemical species present. There are two possible solutions to this problem. The first involves *masking* or immobilizing the interfering species by chemical means. For example, the addition of a complexing agent such as fluoride or phosphate ion renders iron(III) unreactive in the iodometric determination of copper. The second solution requires the *physical separation* of the interfering species from the one in question.

Physical separation can be accomplished in many ways. Mechanical methods like sieving, filtration, and centrifugation generally apply only to cases where species are in different physical states or can be converted to different states. Evaporation, freezing and precipitation are examples of separations based on this approach. By contrast, methods based on the partitioning of a compound between two mutually-immiscible phases, e.g. two liquids or a liquid and a solid, are more generally applicable. Examples are extraction, fractional distillation, and all of the techniques that can be labeled as chromatographic. *Chromatographic* methods are perhaps the most powerful of these techniques, and as a consequence are the most widely used.

This chapter accordingly treats only chromatographic methods and focuses on gas-liquid chromatography. It is beyond the scope of the book to discuss separation methods more extensively.

31.2 THE CHROMATOGRAPHIC PROCESS

The term chromatography (color-writing)† is generally applied to all multiple-stage partitioning processes that lead to individual zones of migration for the components of a multicomponent mixture. Chromatographic processes always involve a *mobile* (or *carrier*) *phase* and a *stationary phase*. The solute (or adsorbate) migrates along the stationary phase at a rate proportional to its relative affinity for the mobile and stationary phases.

What brings about the migration of the solute? Consider the imaginary series of separate liquid-liquid extraction stages shown in Fig. 31.1. A solute is added to the system and dissolved in the lower layer of the first stage. As the two layers of the stage are mixed, the solute will distribute between the immiscible liquids. Let the

---

* By Charles H. Lochmüller, Department of Chemistry, Duke University, Durham, North Carolina.

† The term is a misnomer since uncolored substances may also be separated by chromatographic techniques.

lower layer be the stationary phase and the upper layer be the mobile phase. After equilibrium has been established, the upper layer (phase) is moved into the next stage. Now stage 1 holds a "stationary" phase with dissolved solute and stage 2 holds a "mobile" phase containing solute. New liquid is added to stage 1. Next, both stages 1 and 2 are allowed to equilibrate. Subsequently, the "mobile" phase in each is shifted forward. When the shift is complete, stages 1, 2, and 3 will contain solute with 2 holding the largest total amount. When such a process is carried on again and again, the result is that the solute concentration maximum will move steadily forward and the concentration in stage 1 will approach zero as a limit. In Fig. 31.1 this type of process is followed through four transfers. Note that the distribution of solute among stages follows the binomial coefficients, i.e. $1:1$, $1:2:1$, $1:3:3:1$, etc.

Transfer	Stage	1	2	3	4	5	6
0	Upper	0.5					
0	Lower	0.5	0	0	0	0	0
1	Upper	0.25	0.25				
1	Lower	0.25	0.25	0	0	0	0
2		0.125	0.25	0.125			
2		0.125	0.25	0.125			
3		0.06	0.19	0.19	0.06		
3		0.06	0.19	0.19	0.06	0	0
4		0.03	0.125	0.19	0.125	0.03	
4		0.03	0.125	0.19	0.125	0.03	0

(a)

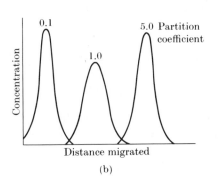

(b)

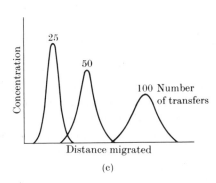

(c)

Fig. 31.1 A multistage extraction scheme. (a) The table shows the relative concentration of solute of partition coefficient 1.00 in the upper (mobile) phase and lower (stationary) phase after n transfers. Equilibrium between phases is assumed attained after each transfer. Transfer is an operation that involves moving each upper phase from left to right one stage. Fresh upper phase (solute-free) is placed in stage 1 after each transfer. (b) The solute distribution along the length of a column (or among stages) after 50 transfers under conditions of different partition coefficient. Note that the larger the coefficient, the farther along the column is the concentration peak. (c) The distribution of solute along a column for a system in which the partition coefficient is 1.00 after n transfers. The value of n is given above each curve.

If there had been two solutes in stage 1, and if they had different distribution coefficients, we would expect their concentration maxima to move through the stages at different rates. After a large number of transfers had been carried out, the two concentration maxima should have migrated apart to such an extent that the solutes will have been separated. This process is not entirely hypothetical. The *Craig* apparatus, which has been used to achieve separation of otherwise labile biological substances, operates in a manner similar to that described.

In chromatography equilibration does not occur in physically distinct stages as in the Craig process. The stationary phase is contained in a tube through which the mobile phase is forced by gravity or a pressure differential. A solute does not remain in a small volume of the tube until it has completely equilibrated; instead the steady movement of the mobile phase spreads equilibrium out over a region.

Several terms developed to describe fractional distillation processes have been carried over to chromatographic procedures with only slight changes in meaning.* A *theoretical plate* is the length of column in which an equilibrium distribution of solute between mobile and stationary phases is established. This length is termed the *height* equivalent to a theoretical plate and the column as a whole is characterized by a *number of theoretical plates.*

31.3 TECHNIQUES OF CHROMATOGRAPHY

Several types of chromatography are in use. We can conveniently divide these techniques into two major classifications: *planar chromatography* and *column chromatography.*†

In planar chromatography, the stationary phase or the medium which *supports* it is spread as a thin film on, for example, a glass plate or cellulose sheet. "Thin-layer" and paper chromatography fall into this classification. While these techniques are unquestionably powerful, they make few if any demands for special instrumentation. Aside from equipment that permits a uniform layer of adsorbent or support to be spread, the only real instrumental emphasis involves the quantitative measurement of the resolved zones. We can use densitometers, spectrometric and radio-metric scanners, etc., for this purpose. The design and use of such instrumentation follows immediately from the discussion of earlier chapters.

All planar techniques have the advantage that zone detection can be accomplished directly on the medium through techniques such as staining, charring with H_2SO_4, or fluorescence excitation. However, planar media can generally be used only once, liquid-liquid chromatography is hard to achieve, and since the rate of flow of the mobile phase is controlled solely by capillary forces, the rate of zone *development* (migration) cannot be conveniently varied.

On the other hand, chromatography in a column (the generally accepted term) or tube can require a great deal of sophisticated instrumentation. This is not to say that the process itself is necessarily complex. Indeed, we can achieve column-chromatographic separations with crude equipment. Nevertheless, column techniques

---

* These terms are also used to describe the Craig method.

† Frontal chromatography, while of thermodynamic significance, is rarely seen in practice and is ignored in this chapter.

require the greatest instrumental emphasis and the rest of this chapter is devoted to them.

Before returning to the theoretical plate concept, a typical column separation should be described. Figure 31.2 shows a representative chromatographic system. It is used as follows. An analyst places a measured amount of sample into the injection port. After a finite time, the recorder registers a response, usually tracing several peaks. This record or trace is a representation of the response of the detector to different concentration zones that pass it as they migrate off or *elute* from the column. Figure 31.3 depicts a representative chromatogram that shows good resolution of components.

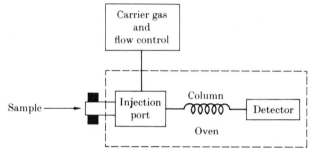

Fig. 31.2 A block diagram of a typical gas chromatograph showing the most important modules. In general, amplifier and readout modules would follow the detector.

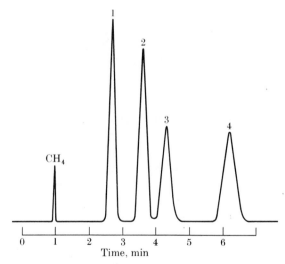

Fig. 31.3 A chromatogram showing the separation of anilines on Chromosorb 103. Compounds separated: 1. aniline; 2. *N*-methylaniline; 3. *N*-ethylaniline; 4. *N*-butylaniline. Column: 120 cm × 4 mm i.d. glass packed with Chromosorb 103 (50/60 mesh). Temperature: 240 °C. Detector: Flame ionization. (Courtesy of Applied Science Laboratories.)

If we require only qualitative and quantitative analytical information (number of zones, their position, relative concentration in solution), this trace or *chromatogram* can be the ultimate goal of the entire process. On the other hand, it is often desirable to collect each component. This process we accomplish most often by collecting *fractions* in a series of individual tubes or traps. We collect when the recorder indicates the elution of a zone.

31.4 FACTORS IMPORTANT IN CHROMATOGRAPHY

In chromatography we are concerned with the rate of migration of a zone (or zones) in a tube of uniform cross-sectional area. The mobile phase flows in this tube. This flow, or better, the *flow rate f* is the volume swept out by a cross section of carrier in a finite time and generally has the units $cm^3 s^{-1}$ or $cm^3 min^{-1}$. The interval that elapses between placing the sample in the system (injection) and the elution of the center of mass of the zone or peak (the maximum of a symmetrical zone) we term the *retention time*. The product of flow rate and retention time is a *retention volume*, v_r. The number of theoretical plates, n, is defined as:

$$n = 16 \, (t_r/\text{base width})^2 \tag{31.1a}$$

or

$$n = 5.54 \, (t_r/\text{full width at half-height})^2, \tag{31.1b}$$

where the widths refer to the peak widths shown in Fig. 31.3 and have the units of t_r. For convenience we will use the symbols w_b for the base width and $w_{1/2}$ for the full width at half-height. A more useful basis for comparison of performance of a column under different conditions or of different columns proves to be the *plate height** (height equivalent to a theoretical plate) H, which is simply:

$$H = L/n, \tag{31.2}$$

where L is the column length (usually in mm). A functional relationship exists between H and flow rate, as Section 31.6 shows.

In chromatography the resolution of components is a function of two parameters, (a) the extent of separation of the centers of mass of the chromatographic zones and (b) the relative widths of the zones themselves. A commonly used measure of the degree of relative zone displacement is the *separation factor*, α, the ratio of the adjusted *retention* volumes, t_r', of the two substances ((1) and (2)) under consideration:

$$\alpha = t_r'(2)/t_r'(1), \tag{31.3}$$

where $t_r'(2) > t_r'(1)$. We define the adjusted retention volume as the difference between the retention time for the substance and the retention time t_m of an "inert" substance:

$$t_r' = t_r - t_m. \tag{31.4}$$

Since an "inert" substance is nonpartitioning, its retention time is a measure of the hold-up of carrier by the column itself.

---

* In light of modern theory, there are numerous objections to the original plate concept as applied to chromatography (Section 31.3). Nevertheless it serves quite well in practical discussions of system performance.

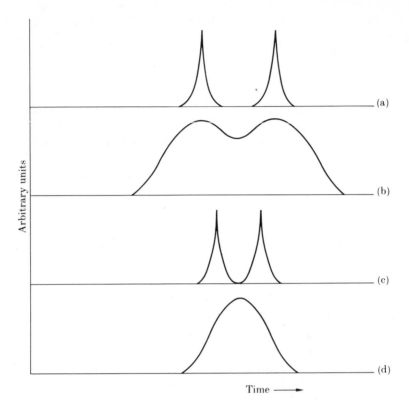

Fig. 31.4 The dependence of the character of a two component chromatogram on the relative values of α and H. (a) high α, high H; (b) high α, low H; (c) low α, high H; (d) low α, low H. Since all peaks are of equal area, amplitudes are exaggerated in (b) and (d).

Example Air or N_2 we can in many cases consider to be nonpartitioning. Chromatographs incorporating thermal conductivity detectors permit the measurement of t_m in this manner. On the other hand methane is used to measure t_m for flame ionization detection. We can also calculate the value of t_m rigorously from the retention behavior of several members of a homologous series, although this is seldom done in practice.

Figure 31.4 shows that the separation factor α is not a practical measure of separation itself. The figure also indicates the interrelation of α, H, and the resolution of bands.

A resolution factor R, which takes into account the peak width can be defined:

$$R = [t'_r(2) - t'_r(1)]/[0.5w_b(1) + 0.5w_b(2)]. \tag{31.5}$$

If $R = 1$, the resolution of two equal-area, symmetrical peaks is about 98% complete and if $R = 1.5$, there is 99.7% complete, base-line separation. We can easily see, then, that an increase in H (a decrease in n) results in a decrease in R.

If the carrier is a gas, then it is possible to speak of a *capacity ratio* in terms of the amount of solute in the mobile phase and in the stationary phase of an equilibrium stage (and in the column):

$$k = C_s V_s / C_m V_m, \tag{31.6}$$

where C_s and C_m are the concentration of solute in the stationary and mobile phases in g ml^{-1} and V_s and V_m are the volumes of the two phases.* Further, the capacity ratio k can be related to the adjusted retention times, or the equivalent volumes, that is, $k = t'_r / t_m$.

The distribution of solute between phases is given by the *partition coefficient K*, which is simply

$$K = C_s / C_m. \tag{31.7}$$

In turn, K is related to the capacity ratio by the parameter β, the volumetric phase ratio of the column ($\beta = V_m / V_s$), by the equation

$$K = \beta k. \tag{31.8}$$

As we can see, the partition coefficient is dependent primarily on the relative affinity of the solute and stationary solvent. The relationship of K and temperature is governed by the same thermodynamic laws as any equilibrium process. A linear relationship between the natural log of K and the reciprocal of the absolute temperature is expected and is experimentally observed (see later). For a given column where the solution process is exothermic, increasing the temperature decreases the partition coefficient and therefore the retention time.

Thus far we have assumed a uniform carrier velocity within the column. In reality we observe an average velocity that depends on the compressibility of the carrier gas in the column, that is in turn a function of the *pressure drop*. The compressibility factor for a uniform column, j, can be expressed as:

$$j = 1.5 (P^2 - 1)/(P^3 - 1), \tag{31.9}$$

where P is defined by $P = p_{\text{inlet}}/p_{\text{outlet}}$. For precise work, we must calculate a corrected retention time t_r^0:

$$t_r^0 = j t_r. \tag{31.10}$$

In any case, for a given column, stationary phase, and temperature, the separation factor is a constant. Under these conditions the experimenter can improve the extent of practical separation only through minimization of H. The magnitude of H can be, and is, affected by the design of the chromatographic system. Let us then begin our examination of the causes of poor efficiency that can be reduced or eliminated by proper design.

---

* When the term "volume of the stationary phase" is referred to, a gas-liquid process is implied. In a gas-solid process the surface area would be substituted.

31.5 THE CONCEPT OF MOMENT IN CHROMATOGRAPHY

Although in practice we measure t_r at the peak maximum, it is really the center of mass of the peak that is of true physical significance. It is at this point in the elution that half the zone has passed the chosen reference point (the detector).

Recall the definition of moment as related to a statistical distribution such as the Gaussian or normal distribution. For an ensemble consisting of $x_1, x_2, x_3 \ldots x_i$, the first moment or arithmetic mean $\bar{x}$ of the ensemble is defined by

$$\bar{x} = \sum_{i=0}^{N} x_i/N, \qquad (31.11)$$

where N is the number of members in the ensemble. This mean is effectively the center of mass of the distribution. In a totally symmetrical distribution, the position of the mean is the position of the maximum. But our immediate concern is with the width of a chromatographic peak, which is related to H. By our acceptance of the simple plate model we have assumed a Gaussian-shaped peak. A well-defined width parameter for such a distribution is the variance σ^2:

$$\sigma^2 = \sum_{i=1}^{N} \frac{(\bar{x} - x_i)^2}{N - 1}. \qquad (31.12)$$

An observed variance is often the total of several independently contributing variances that we can assign to different members of the same ensemble.

$$\sigma^2_{\text{total}} = \sum_{i=1}^{n} \sigma_i^2 \qquad (31.13)$$

where n is the number of sources of variance.

In a chromatographic system, the three major contributors to increased peak variance are the sampling system (injector), the column, and the detector. The variance of a chromatographic peak is related, however, to the zone volume. Since in the ideal the initial zone is infinitesimally narrow, one can write, by analogy with Eq. (31.13), that the observed zone volume v_{total} is the result of a contribution from each component of the chromatographic system:

$$v^2_{\text{total}} = f[v^2_{\text{injector}} + v^2_{\text{column}} + v^2_{\text{detector}}]. \qquad (31.14)$$

Some of the broadening we observe arises from the physicochemical processes that give the desired separation and is practically unavoidable. This is the "active" volume of the chromatograph. The zonal volume arising from various sources that do not contribute to the extent of separation we generally term the "*dead volume*" of a chromatograph. We can minimize the problem of instrumental contributions to H by careful design of each component of a chromatographic system with proper attention to the way all the separate components interact.

31.6 THE RATE THEORY OF COLUMN PERFORMANCE

The column is the heart of a chromatograph. In most cases it consists of a tube filled with a finely divided solid, that may or may not be porous, onto which a liquid stationary phase has been *coated*. The rate theory of van Deemter stands as a milestone in the development of column chromatographic theory. Although its original form has been subject to modification and differing views on the theory of packed columns are not completely resolved, the simplest form of the *van Deemter equation* serves, under normal conditions, to give an account of the physical factors determining H. In this form the theoretical plate height H is expressed as follows

$$H = 2\lambda d_p + \frac{2\gamma D_g}{\bar{u}} + \frac{8d_f^2}{\pi^2 D_l} \cdot \frac{k\bar{u}}{(1 + k)^2}. \tag{31.15}$$

where λ is a constant related to the geometry of the particles with which the column is packed, e.g. whether they are spherical, cubic, etc. and how well the particles are packed; d_p is the average diameter of the support particles; γ is a "tortuosity" factor of the gas flow path; D_g and D_l are the solute diffusion coefficients in gas and liquid phases, respectively; d_f is the liquid film thickness; k is the capacity ratio V_l/V_g; $\bar{u}$ is the average velocity of gas at the column outlet. We can calculate this velocity from the air peak t_{air} of a column. Thus $\bar{u} = L/jt_{air}$, when L is the column length, and j is the compressibility factor. Since $\bar{u}$ is the only variable in Eq. (31.15) for a given column, the character of the equation can be expressed by rewriting it in the form:

$$H = A + B/\bar{u} + C_l\bar{u}. \tag{31.16}$$

Constant A is known as the eddy diffusion term, B as the longitudinal diffusion term, and C_l as the coefficient of mass transfer in the liquid phase.*

The theoretical treatment can be improved by including a consideration of mass transfer in the gas phase. Actually, two terms must be added, $C_g \cdot \bar{u}$, which introduces the diffusion occurring in the moving gas phase, and D, which includes resistance to solute transfer between gas in support particles and the moving gas. The expanded version of Eq. (31.16) is

$$H = A + B/\bar{u} + C_l\bar{u} + C_g\bar{u} + D. \tag{31.17}$$

What does Eq. (31.16) mean in practice? If the theory is correct, we can expect a dependence of H on the controllable factors, carrier velocity $\bar{u}$, liquid film thickness d_f, support particle diameter d_p and shape (included in λ). and column capacity ratio k. We should be able to optimize the design of our chromatographic experiment by an appropriate choice of at least these parameters.

An isothermal plot of observed H vs. $\bar{u}$ for a single solute results in a characteristic hyperbolic curve (see Fig. 31.5). It is evident from this plot that an optimum linear flow rate exists in which diffusional broadening and resistance to mass transfer are balanced. Operation at this flow rate results in the maximum efficiency attainable. Nevertheless, it is not unusual in practical experiments to use $\bar{u}$ values in excess of $\bar{u}_{H\,min}$ in order to save time in analysis.

If we combine the first two terms of the van Deemter expression we obtain the contribution of all longitudinal diffusion terms to peak broadening. If the column is loosely packed or if the particle size distribution is large, paths of various lengths

---

* Some chromatographic scientists take strong exception to a velocity-independent A-term, but further discussion on this point is beyond the scope of this chapter.

are available to gas molecules, and the result is an increase in the flow-rate-indepen-dent A-term. The B-term derives from molecular diffusion in the gas phase which would, of course, occur in any case. This diffusion process is controlled by D_g, the diffusion coefficient for the solute in the gas phase. It proves to be the case that $D_g \propto P^{-1}(M_s M_g)^{-1/2}$, where P is the pressure and M_s and M_g are the solute and carrier gas molecular weights. Since the second term is $B/\bar{u}$, H is reduced by increased carrier velocity and contributions to it from B-terms are minimized at high pressure in tightly packed columns of small particles. Further, the use of a gas of low molecular weight such as H_2 or He as the carrier yields larger H-values than use of Ar or N_2.

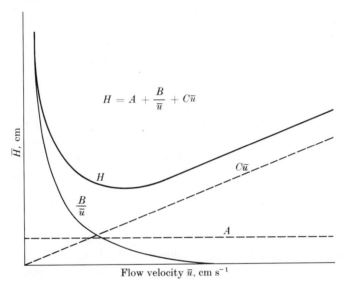

$$H = A + \frac{B}{\bar{u}} + C\bar{u}$$

Flow velocity $\bar{u}$, cm s^{-1}

Fig. 31.5 Plot showing dependence of plate height H on carrier velocity $\bar{u}$. Symbols are from the van Deemter equation; A, eddy diffusion or packing geometry term (multiple path effect), B, longitudinal diffusion term, C or C_l, "resistance to mass transfer" term.

The resistance to mass transfer terms represents several mechanisms including transfer of solute vapor along the following paths: from liquid to gas in the main flow stream, through the liquid; from gas to liquid; from the liquid to the gas in the interparticle spaces; and from gas to gas in the different velocity streams. The liquid phase term is proportional to d_f^2/D_l, and therefore uniform distribution of small amounts of liquid phase of high D_l on the support reduce this contribution to H. High liquid loadings increase capacity but also increase H. The ratio $D_g/D_l \simeq 10^5 - 10^6$ and liquid diffusivity decreases with increasing solute molecular weight in a given solvent. However, the term $k/(1 + k)^2$ predicts that C_l depends on the solute band velocity in the column with a maximum at $k = 1$. H is thus again favored by low liquid loadings. The velocity distribution mechanisms combine with the A-terms to set the maximum obtainable value of H, secured when $k = 0$.

A "good" column therefore has the following characteristics:

1. As light a liquid loading as will satisfy the capacity requirements of the experi-ment,

2. As narrow particle size range and as small particles as is commensurate with an acceptable pressure drop,*

3. As slow a flow rate and one as close to the van Deemter "minimum" as is practicable in terms of required efficiency and analysis time.

Since both retention time and efficiency depend on flow rate and temperature it is important to provide for control of these parameters; flow control can be achieved with simple needle values but true flow regulation requires a more complicated system. [1, 4, 6]

Temperature control. Provision for control of the temperature of the oven or air bath in which the column is located can vary from simple on-off control effected by a bimetallic switch to sophisticated proportional control systems. The latter type of control is used in most of the modern research quality instruments now available.

Temperature conditions are generally established empirically. A good rule of thumb is to maintain the injection port temperature high enough to ensure rapid sample volatilization, the column at about 20–30° above the boiling point of the components and the detector 30–50° above this to insure against condensation.

Proportional control of temperature involves adjustment of heat input (for columns above room temperature, as will ordinarily be the case) to the change in temperature to be effected. The quantity of heat delivered per unit time is regulated. This type of control is generally achieved by incorporating the temperature sensor in a bridge. The bridge imbalance controls the heater circuitry, causing faster delivery of heat as the imbalance increases. Proportional control differs from simple on-off control because:

1. A proportional system is always "on." For this reason the delay between a temperature change and a response is substantially shortened.

2. A response is generated that is tailored to the temperature change needed. In this way temperature "overshoot" is minimized.

Temperature regulation of $\pm 0.2\,°C$ is now commonplace and in certain precision measurements $\pm 0.01\,°C$ has been used.

Example One configuration for a proportional temperature controller is an ac resistance bridge using a phase-sensitive detector. In addition to ratio arms, the other bridge arms consist of two precision resistors, a variable resistor, and a platinum resistance themometer. An operating frequency of about 1 kHz is appropriate. When the bridge is balanced, the output of the phase-sensitive detector is zero. As the temperature changes (generally a cooling trend) the output becomes finite. This signal can be amplified and used to control the output of a silicon controlled rectifier (Section 4.8). The larger the signal, the larger the rectifier current. It is important also that the value of the variable-resistor arm of the bridge, i.e. the set-point, has a finite band width to prevent oscillation of the system. The bandwidth chosen establishes the minimum temperature change that produces a response from the controller.

---

* As a rough approximation, H is proportional to d_p and the pressure drop is proportional to $1/d_p^2$ and the length of the column. Further, a particle size distribution of 80–100 mesh (177 to 149 μm) is the most common compromise with somewhat finer particles used with "high-resolution" columns.

31.7 INLET AND SAMPLING SYSTEMS

Although the end result is the same—a sample is placed on the column—we must make slightly different considerations in the design of inlet devices, depending on whether the mobile phase (or carrier) is a gas or a liquid. Indeed, while the major concern in the design of a chromatographic system is the conservation of H, the physical requirements of gas and liquid differ sufficiently that it will be necessary to discuss each separately.

If a chromatographic experiment is to yield satisfactory qualitative and quantitative information it is essential to use a reproducible sample size. Variations in sample size obviously affect detector response but in some cases a significantly large sample size vs. V_R dependence can also occur. The criteria for judging a chromatographic sampling system are: (a) speed—the faster the sampling the narrower the initial zone width, (b) reproducibility and (c) wide-range applicability to varying sample compositions and physical states.

The most common and most versatile sampling system is the precision, small-volume syringe. These syringes can vary somewhat in design and are available for use with gas, liquid or solid samples and in a range of $1-500$ μl. Figure 31.6 shows all three types. We fill the syringes with the desired sample, pass the needle through a self-sealing septum into the inlet, and "inject" the sample. The use of syringe injection is especially valuable when small amounts of sample are available. The ease with which these syringes can be used must be balanced against several important drawbacks. First, in the measurement of very small volumes a significant negative error can develop from evaporation in the syringe needle during transfer operations. Second, injection times and injection rates vary from one experimenter to another and thus variations in t_r and H are generally observed. Third, post-injection evaporation from the syringe needle in the injection port can further complicate matters. Several attempts have been made to improve the repeatability of this method. It is possible to install small microswitches on the syringe itself that start a clock (t_0) when the plunger is pressed in. The use of a spring-loaded syringe drive can greatly enhance the precision of injection rate. The operator simply presses a button or pulls a trigger.

A significant improvement in sampling precision can be obtained through the use of *sampling valves*. These devices generally fall into one of three basic design categories: (a) the "spool", (b) the sliding plate, and (c) the diaphragm-actuated valve. However, since practically all common sampling valves require a flowing sample stream, their use is limited to experiments where it is permissible or possible to consume larger volumes of sample. The first type, the spool valve (see Fig. 31.7), is applicable to both gases and liquids. The name derives from the undercutting of the plunger or stem that has the shape of a spool. Several of these undercuttings are made along the stem and the direction of flow can be altered by the proper positioning of the spools. Valves of this type have been used successfully at pressures as high as 700 bars. The automation of spool valves is reasonably simple to achieve by means of a pneumatically actuated piston that can be attached to the shaft. These valves do have several drawbacks, however. They are generally slow in their operation (> 100 ms), tend to wear rapidly (especially at the ring seals), and suffer cross-leakage if the sample and carrier streams are not at the same pressure. In general, spool valves

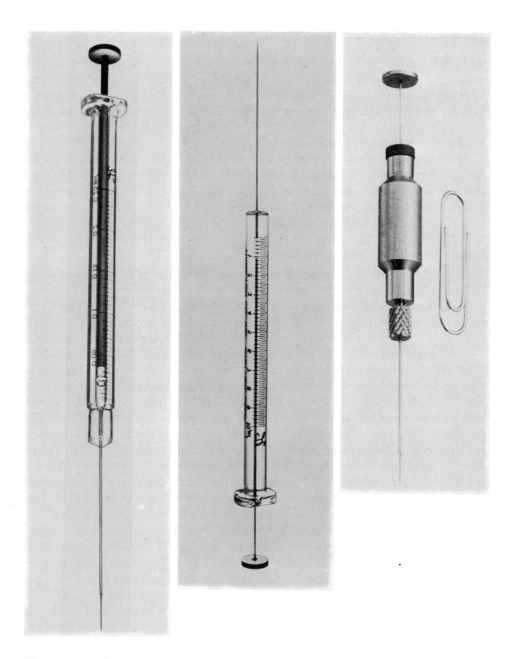

Fig. 31.6 Sampling syringes. (a) A solid-sampling syringe—the solid is placed on the sample tongue of the plunger which is then withdrawn inside the needle. (b) A liquid-sampling syringe with lapped-to-fit metal plunger. (c) A gas-sampling syringe—note Teflon plunger tip which affords a gas-tight seal. (Courtesy of Hamilton Co.)

are limited to about 100 μl minimum sample volume with as large a maximum as is required by the experiment performed.

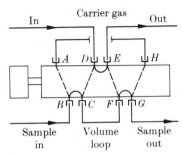

Fig. 31.7 A "spool" valve. Unbroken line: "stem out" position; sample passes through volume loop. Broken line: "stem in" position; sample in volume loop introduced into carrier gas stream, sample stream bypassed through *A-H* bypass. (Courtesy of Loenco Co. Inc.)

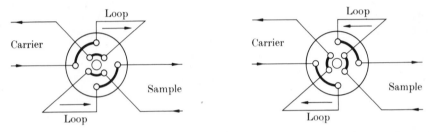

Fig. 31.8 A typical sliding plate valve configuration. The dark lines indicate undercut flow connections and the direction of flow. (Courtesy of Carle Instruments Inc.)

Figure 31.8 illustrates schematically a "sliding-plate" valve of the rotary-motion type. This valve is capable of delivering samples as small as 1 μl and as large as 25 ml or larger. Operation consists of simply sliding two plates, one with drilled holes and one with appropriate undercuts, in such a manner as to change the direction of flow of the carrier and sample loops. In a diaphragm-actuated valve we achieve the same effect through the motion of a steel diaphragm between two plates. The ability to inject 1–5 μl gas samples with either of these valve types greatly enhances the quantitative precision of capillary-column chromatography because the splitter system can be eliminated (see later). Both of these valve types can give fast injection rates (ca. 30 ms) and reproducible injection times.

The best method of reducing or eliminating the *H*-contribution of the inlet system is to eliminate the inlet by simply placing the sample on the column itself. Indeed this can be, and is, done in practice. There are, however, several limitations to the use of this technique. First, if the sample is a liquid and must be volatilized as in gas chromatography then we must make provision to do this rapidly. Second, if the column is flooded by the smallest sample volume that can be placed on it conveniently by syringe or sampling valves (ca. 0.5 μl) then we must somehow provide for dividing the sample between the column and a waste line.

In its simplest form the *injection port* permits the insertion of a syringe needle, through a self-sealing *septum, into the column* without interruption of carrier flow (see Fig. 31.9a). In gas chromatography the volume of the injection port is often increased to allow for sample expansion on volatilization. Gas chromatographic injection ports are also generally quite massive. This guarantees a high heat capacity and therefore rapid volatilization. If the sample volatilizes slowly, the effect is the same as a slow injection rate. In addition, injection of relatively large volumes of liquid directly on the gas chromatographic column eventually leads to "washing off" of the liquid stationary phase for a considerable distance down the column. This can have a deleterious effect on column performance.

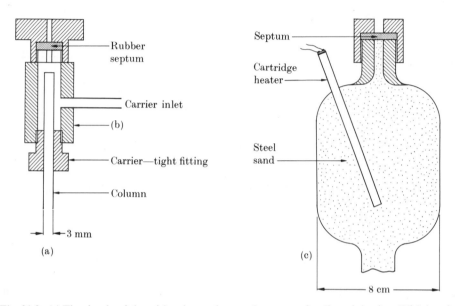

Fig. 31.9 (a) The simplest inlet with column close to the septum for direct injection. Withdrawing the column to the point marked (b) creates an evaporation or flash chamber. (c) A large-scale injection port for "preparative" work. The steel "sand" filling increases the heat capacity and dampens the large pressure pulses arising from the evaporation of large liquid volumes of up to 100 ml or even larger. Type (b) and (c) configurations can include glass lining for sensitive compounds.

In terms of preserving a satisfactory H the most important consideration is to keep the volume—actually dead volume—of the inlet significantly less than that of the column itself. Obviously, it is for the experimenter-designer to decide the compromise between sample size and column efficiency. He generally bases his decision on the actual reason for the chromatographic separation. Very small samples and high-efficiency systems yield good *analytical* results—i.e. the best possible resolution, the largest number of isolated peaks for closely related mixtures, the highest quantitative precision. If we desire sample or component collection, then generally we must inject larger samples unless we are willing to repeat the experiment hundreds or perhaps thousands of times.

The inlet splitter is a device that permits the use of relatively large sample volumes (in the microliter range) with open-tubular or high-resolution columns where nanoliter sample volumes are required. The splitting process is achieved by passing the sample vapor past a needle-like restrictor that connects to the column. Figure 31.10 shows a typical modern inlet splitter. Early splitter designs suffered, in the main, from poor quantitative precision. This was generally because of fractionation of the sample mixture due to poor evaporation rates and poor radial distribution around the needle restrictor due to turbulence. In modern splitter design steps have been taken to eliminate these problems. The splitter in Fig. 31.10 incorporates many of these: (a) an extended split needle and smooth walls around the split-point reduce turbulence and a "suction effect" (due to rapid carrier flow velocity over needle at exit port in older designs), (b) lateral concentration gradients at the split-point have been minimized through carefully computed mixing tube design, (c) viscosity changes at the splitter are also reduced by expansion into a buffer volume rather than directly to the atmosphere, (d) preheating of the carrier gas ensures fast evaporation thus limiting back diffusion at the inlet and, in turn, band spreading. Changing the porous plug restrictor changes the split ratio by changing the gas-velocity ratio at the split point.

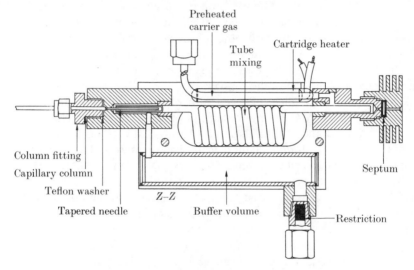

Fig. 31.10 A representative inlet splitter designed for gas chromatography. (Courtesy of Hamilton Co.)

31.8 COLUMN DESIGN

When all is said and done, the column is the only "active" element in the system; upon it depends the extent of separation or lack of it. The novice in the area is often confused by the talk of large-scale columns, "preparative columns," analytical columns, "packed" columns, and open tubular columns. It is important to realize that all "columns" function in the same way. Size, both in terms of length and internal diameter, and whether the column is "packed" with solid or not, are considerations that are made for reasons other than the partitioning processes that give rise to the desired separation. Perhaps the two most important factors are "capacity" (how big a sample can one use effectively) and H. Actually we cannot separate capacity and H, but it is conventional to do so.

We use the terms "preparative" and "large-scale" interchangeably to describe columns with an internal diameter generally greater than 9 mm. Columns 15 cm and larger in diameter have been made and used successfully in gas chromatography. Such columns permit the use of large sample volumes (up to about 100 ml generally) where collection of the separable fractions in large amounts is an important consideration. Such columns are generally inefficient, with H-values of the order of 1–10 mm or so. "Analytical" columns are generally 1.5 mm or 3 mm in diameter and afford H-values in the range of about 0.1 mm or less. Capillary columns have an internal diameter of 0.25 to 0.75 mm. In most cases the term capillary column refers to an open-tubular column in which the stationary phase is coated on the inner walls. The term open-tubular column is perhaps more precise, since packed columns of the same i.d. range can and have been made. Open-tubular columns yield plate heights of about 1 mm but they can be made quite long (generally 30–100 m, although columns in excess of a kilometer have been made). Columns of this type that develop 10^6 plates have been reported.

In the interest of brevity, we will limit our discussions of column technology to packed, "analytical" columns. This type of column is the most generally used and the principles involved apply in most other cases. We will first consider the mechanics of column design and manufacture and then consider the theory and physical processes involved. If you desire more complete information, again consult the appropriate references at the end of the chapter.

A column is, first of all, a tube, generally of circular cross section, that contains the stationary phase. Almost any tubing can be used but certain characteristics are most desirable. First, the material itself must be physically strong. It should not expand and contract significantly with changes in applied pressure and temperature. Second, it should be possible to coil the tubing. This is especially important when long lengths must be used and the oven or thermostatic bath volume is small. Third, the material should be relatively inert. If the surface of the tubing is chromatographically active, then "tailing" of the peak (an unsymmetrical skewing effect) can occur. This effect is important only when the surface area of the tubing represents a significant fraction of the total active column area. Another important consideration is the possibility of sample decomposition or rearrangement due to catalytic activity by the surface.

Glass and stainless steel (Types 304, 316) are reasonably inert materials for tubes but the former is fragile and the latter quite expensive. Aluminum is fairly cheap but can be quite active because of its oxide coating. Nylon, Teflon, and some other plastics are also satisfactory, but not at elevated temperatures. Careful planning is necessary if a satisfactory compromise is to be achieved between these various factors.

The most common form of gas chromatography is gas-liquid and it is the function of the support to "hold" the liquid stationary phase. A large number of materials have been successfully used to perform this task. Which material is the most desirable depends again on the experiment to be performed. The classic gas-chromatographic solid support is crushed firebrick and is available in a pink or in a white form. These materials can, because of their relatively large surface areas, effectively support up to a 30% by weight, liquid loading. Other materials such as Teflon, glass beads and even certain phosphate-based clothes detergents can be used.

A "good" support is inert, not friable, capable of holding a suitable amount of stationary phase, and is easy to pour into the tube itself. As we have seen earlier, a narrow distribution of particle size is also desirable. Inertness can be enhanced in silica-based supports by silanization of the surface-hydroxyl groups. Unfortunately, more inert supports generally have smaller liquid-load capacities. This is especially true of most Teflon-based supports where the situation is further complicated by the ease with which support particles develop an electrostatic charge.

Liquid stationary phases. We generally classify liquid phases as polar, semipolar, and nonpolar, according to their ability to retain and separate compounds that can be grouped into these classes. Thus polar liquids serve for such compounds as alcohols, ketones, amines, and amides while nonpolar liquids serve for hydrocarbons. A differential interaction is desired that can range from differing dispersion forces to differing degrees of stereospecific hydrogen bond formation between solute and solvent molecules. Table 31.1 gives an illustration of varying interactions. After this

Table 31.1 Specific Retention Volumes of Some Solutes in Columns with Nonpolar, Moderately Polar, and Polar Liquid Phases

	Retention Volumes for Different Liquid Phases		
Solute	*n*-Hexedecane	*n*-Hexadecanol	Methoxy-hexadecanol
1-pentene	83.2	85.5	32.0
diethyl ether	89.5	88.3	45.7
ethyl cyanide	87.2	170	99.5
t-butanol	92	200	320

consideration is met, separation of species within homologous series is essentially a boiling point or more properly a molecular size phenomenon. Table 31.2 lists some common stationary phases. The stationary phase itself must have a relatively low vapor pressure at the experimental temperature. This consideration is important both for collection of pure fractions and for consideration of detector sensitivity or response. For this reason liquid columns are generally aged at temperatures slightly higher than the final experimental temperature before use. Maximum operating temperatures are established by the vapor pressure or "bleed rate" of the stationary phase. The methods are varied by which liquids are coated on supports, and the reader should consult the references given at the end of this chapter.

Table 31.2 Some Commonly Used Stationary Phases

Name	Type	Composition	Used for	Max. temp., °C*
SE-30	nonpolar	silicone gum rubber	hydrocarbons	350
SE-52	moderately polar	silicone (methyl phenyl)	steroids, alcohols, pesticides	300
BODPN	polar	β, β-oxydipropionitrile	halogenated compounds	100
Carbowax 20M	polar	polyethylene glycol	alcohols, fatty acids	250

* The maximum operating temperature is quoted for thermal conductivity detection. Flame ionization limits are 30–20 °C lower.

31.9 CHROMATOGRAPHIC DETECTORS

The simplest gas chromatographic detectors are chemical changes we can observe when a component contained in a carrier gas stream is bubbled through a suitable solution (e.g. decoloration of bromine water by unsaturated compounds). A more recent example is the use of gas chromatography followed by thin-layer chromatography where we have allowed the column effluent to collect on a moving thin layer plate as a long, narrow zone. This technique is especially useful for steroids.

The choice of a detector really depends on the use we are to put the chromatographic system to. If the intent is to try to detect very small (ppb) quantities of material, we ordinarily choose a detector that is very *sensitive* (Section 1.6). Such a detector would rarely serve in a system where collection itself is of prime importance and high concentrations of material would be present in the carrier stream. The result would be "saturation" of the detector. After saturating it could make no further response to concentration increases. A nonspecific detector will respond to many different chemical species. On the other hand, there are times when it is very desirable to detect only one class of compounds, e.g. halogenated compounds, phosphorus compounds, sulfur compounds, etc.). Then a very selective detector is desirable. The three most popular detectors (in terms of numbers in actual use) are based on conductivity changes and are discussed in some detail.

It may be worth while to define a few terms as they are used in chromatography. *Response*, as it refers to detectors in chromatography, denotes the minimum time in which a change of concentration will cause a change in detector output. *Sensitivity*, better termed the limit of detection (Section 8.2), refers to the minimum amount (grams, moles, etc.) of some reference material that can be detected. We generally define it as the amount of material that will produce a signal twice the amplitude of the noise generated by and in the detection system.

For trace analysis, it is important that the detector be very sensitive. If the analysis is one involving relatively narrow peaks, response may also be important. Another important factor is the rate at which a given detector *recovers* from an overload. The detector should also have little or no memory, i.e. the response and sensitivity should not depend on the past history of the detector. If large sample concentrations are used as in large-scale gas chromatography, a very sensitive detector is undesirable. A detector that is slower in its response and of lower sensitivity will tend to "iron out" small fluctuations in concentration that we might experience in such an experiment.

Thermal conductivity detectors. Thermal conductivity detectors are perhaps the type most commonly used in gas chromatography. In practice, they consist of a heated resistance wire* in a cell through which the carrier gas flows. If a component elutes from the column and enters the cell and if the component has different heat-conducting properties than the carrier, the heated wire cools or heats. If we make the resistance element to be one arm of a Wheatstone bridge at balance, then a change in *thermal conductivity* in the cell unbalances the bridge. The extent of imbalance is related to the concentration of the component in the cell. Obviously, the widest

---

* Thermistors can also be used but generally at lower operating temperatures than resistance wire elements.

response range is observed when the component and the carrier differ widely in their respective thermal conductivities.

In gas chromatography, it is standard practice to use two cells (or four) machined into a single block of material of high heat capacity (steel, aluminum, etc.). Through one cell flows the output from the column, while through the other flows only carrier gas. We term the former the *sensing* or *sample* cell, the latter the *reference*. Thus a relative measurement is made between the sensing and reference cells in terms of the thermal conductivities of the gases in each. Figure 31.11 shows a schematic for a typical system.

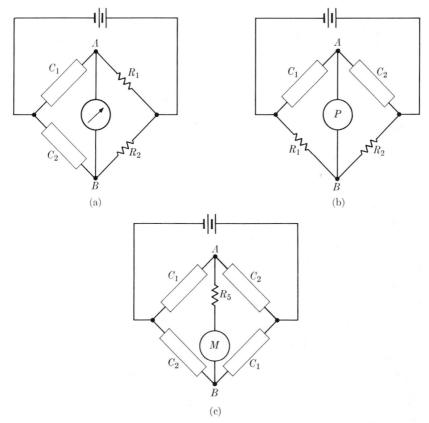

Fig. 31.11 Wheatstone bridge circuits for thermal conductivity cells. (a) Parallel arrangement of two cells. (b) Series arrangement of two cells. (c) Four-cell arrangement. C_1, sample cell. C_2, reference cell. R_1 and R_2, equal-valued resistance "ratio" arms. P, manual or recording potentiometer. M, milliammeter.

In a typical case the output of the detector (the bridge error signal) is fed to a strip chart recorder running at constant speed. Whether the resultant chromatogram is representative of the actual band shapes eluting from the column is to a large extent dependent on the design of the conductivity cell.

There are two basic configurations in thermal conductivity cell design (see Fig. 31.12). The first is the flow-through type in which the gas stream enters at one end of the cell and exits at the other. This type of design affords the fastest response time, making it the choice for analytical experiments. The second type is the so-called "diffusion cell" that can require $20\times$ the time to respond and is often used in large scale experiments. The flow-through type also places much more stringent requirements on the careful control of carrier flow rate than the diffusion type.

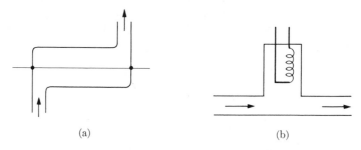

(a)   (b)

Fig. 31.12 Two thermal conductivity cell designs. (a) A flow-through arrangement providing rapid response to changes in composition. It is also sensitive to flow fluctuations. (b) A diffusion type cell providing slow response and relative independence of fluctuations in flow.

Helium or hydrogen* is generally the gas of choice for thermal conductivity measurements because these gases have relatively high thermal conductivities ($k \times 10^7 = 3480$ and 4160, respectively, as compared to 581 for N_2).

The contribution of this type of detector (or any other) to the H of a column is a function of the "cell" volume. Included is the volume of tubing connecting column to detector. In the case of thermal conductivity detectors it is desirable to make the active volume large to permit the highest possible instantaneous concentration in the sensitive area. On the other hand, the "active" detector volume is also system "dead volume" that degrades H. Again, a compromise must be made but a cell designed for 9 mm columns will certainly perform badly with 3 mm columns.

Flame ionization detectors. If the carrier gas is combustible or if it is possible to mix say, hydrogen, with the carrier as it enters the column the possibility of flame ionization detection is established. In principle the detector consists of a small gas burner producing a hydrogen flame, a polarizing voltage source, an ion collector, and a current measuring device (generally an electrometer). Since the combustion of hydrogen produces only a few ions by comparison with an equal amount of carbon, it becomes a relatively simple affair to distinguish the two. Indeed because the background currents are so small (10^{-13} A) a dynamic range of 10^6 is not uncommon. This type of detector offers very high sensitivity to most carbon-containing compounds and is relatively insensitive to the presence of water vapor and air in the carrier gas. In normal use moderate changes in the surrounding temperature and pressure do not affect a detector's performance. Highly halogenated compounds show less than the expected response owing to the efficiency with which halogens capture electrons, thus reducing the observed current. (See Fig. 31.13.)

---

* Hydrogen is frequently used in Europe because of the expense of helium.

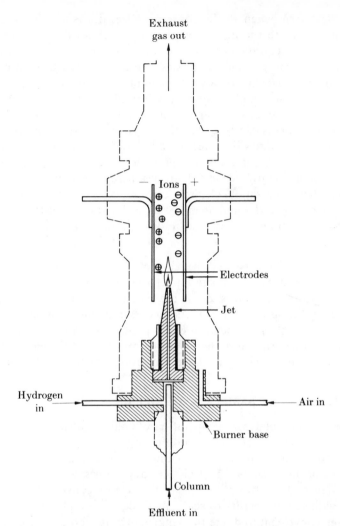

Fig. 31.13 A flame ionization detector. (Courtesy of Beckman Instruments.)

Electron capture detector. If a source of ionizing radiation is used to produce a current then it is possible to follow the *quenching* of this current by such species as oxygen, sulfur, and the halogens. The classic radiation source is tritium gas adsorbed on platinum or palladium foil. This source is limited in its temperature range and is being replaced by ^{63}Ni in nickel foil, which overcomes this problem.

The chamber containing the carrier gas is kept at potential just sufficient to collect all the electrons produced by the source. Molecules of a material having a high electron-capture efficiency, upon entering the chamber, combine with the free electrons, resulting in a reduction of the current observed. To a first approximation the observed current follows the equation

$$I = I_s \exp(-Kcx)$$

where I_s is the current when all electrons are collected, I is the observed current, K is a constant related to the field strength and the electron affinity of the eluting material, c is the concentration of material, and x is a geometry factor for the cell.

Helium and argon provide the highest sensitivity when used as carrier gases. The latter is often mixed with a known amount of methane, which serves to eliminate metastable ions that may confuse the observed results. The use of methane, however, precludes the possibility of simultaneous flame ionization–electron capture experiments. Such experiments can be quite informative since hydrogen and carbon have only small electron affinities. The electron affinity of a molecule depends on the ease with which the hetero-atom is lost by the molecule (assuming a carbon skeleton). Thus ethers capture poorly, while anhydrides, peroxides, etc. are very efficient. In simultaneous flame ionization–electron capture experiments the output of each detector is often recorded simultaneously on a dual-pen recorder. By comparison of the two chromatograms it is possible to distinguish, for example, nonhalogenated from halogenated species.

Other detectors. It is again beyond the scope of this book to cover in detail the many parameters that influence the operation of the three detectors mentioned so far. There are many other detectors. Some are based on a simultaneous flame photometric-flame ionization principle, others involve coulometric measurements. There are detectors that respond to the mass of gas present in them directly. We have tried to present a short description of the operating principles of the most popular types. By far, thermal conductivity and flame ionization are the most commonly used.

31.10 PREPARATION OF SAMPLE AND COLUMN

To improve volatility and permit operation of columns at lower temperatures, we often subject samples to chemical reaction prior to analysis. High-molecular weight compounds possessing active hydrogens can be rendered more volatile by reaction with silylating agents such as $(CH_3)_3SiCl$. Heavy amines, which also exhibit strong tailing due to secondary absorption phenomena, can be converted to volatile amides by reaction with suitable perfluoro acid anhydrides.

It is often convenient to dilute the sample mixture with a solvent prior to injection to prevent overloading. The solvent chosen should show little retention on the column. Unfortunately, the solvent may alter the coating and reduce column performance, an effect that is greatest in open tubular columns. No general rule exists to guide the choice of a suitable solvent but it is clearly advisable to consider the character of the stationary phase and that of the sample when making such a decision.

Coating the support. There are many techniques for coating the liquid (stationary) phase on the support. Three methods of column packing are used most. The "pan" method involves dissolving the stationary phase in an amount of solvent sufficient to cover the support while it is spread in a shallow container. The solvent is allowed to evaporate slowly with occasional, gentle agitation. This method is especially useful with friable supports or those which develop an electrostatic charge. The "rotatory evaporator" method of coating is almost self-explanatory. Its main disadvantage is that abrasion of the support may result during violent tumbling. Both methods give reliable and reproducible percent loading values since the container surface area is small compared with that of the support. The "dynamic" method involves the vacuum filtration of a slurry of support and a solution of the stationary phase. Since no concentration gradients (as might be expected at the surface of an evaporating liquid) exist during the coating process, this method gives the most uniform coatings. However, the percentage liquid loading is less well defined.

Example 1   A commonly used silylating agent is actually a mixture of trimethylchlorosilane and hexamethylidisilizane in dry pyridine. It is generally applied to hydroxy and polyhydroxy compounds. A typical reaction is

$$R-OH + (CH_3)_3SiCl \xrightarrow[\text{pyridine}]{} R-OSi(CH_3)_3 + \text{pyridine hydrochloride.}$$

Example 2   Amines are converted to the perfluoroacyl derivatives quite readily by a reaction such as

$$
\begin{array}{cc}
\overset{\displaystyle CF_3}{\underset{\displaystyle |}{}} & \overset{\displaystyle CF_3}{\underset{\displaystyle |}{}} \\
\end{array}
\qquad
\begin{array}{cc}
H & O \\
| & || \\
\end{array}
\qquad
\begin{array}{c}
O \\
|| \\
\end{array}
$$

$$R-NH_2 + O{=}C{-}O{-}C{=}O \quad \rightarrow \quad R{-}N{-}C{-}CF_3 + CF_3C{-}OH.$$

Methods have been devised that combine the formation of silyl ethers and the perfluoro acylation of amine group. The increase in volatility can be quite large. Heptafloruobutyryl derivatives are often more volatile than the corresponding acetyl derivatives.

Coated supports *should not* be sieved. The abrasion exposes uncoated surface and enhances absorption effects. Drying of the coated support is best achieved by percolating warm gas up through the damp mass. A properly dried support (with the exception of Teflon) should flow freely.

Packing the column. Column preparation is an acquired art. There are, however, some general guidelines to be followed, although not everyone agrees with what is now said. It is best to coil the columns before packing to avoid "bridging" (the creation of voids and lightly compacted zones) and crushing of the support. A standard technique involves placing a glass wool plug at one end of the column, application of a moderate vacuum and addition of small amounts of packing at a time. Tapping and vibration aids in the settling of the bed. Rather, the column should be clamped to a suitable mount that is then vibrated: Care must be taken *not* to tap the column itself. Straight tubes can also be bounced on the sealed end. Since variable flow path lengths are created, segregation of particle sizes in the packing process is undesirable. While this is unavoidable, we obviously minimize it by using narrow particle size ranges. Since the permeability of the column will be reduced (pressure drop will increase), we must also avoid any process leading to the production of "fines".

Curing the column. This process has already been alluded to in Section 31.8 but further explanation may prove worth while. Two processes occur when a column is cured or aged. Stationary phases are often solids or viscous liquids at room temperature. Slow heating of the column serves to spread the coating more evenly on the support. Many stationary phases are also polymers (silicone oils, polyglycols etc.) of a wide molecular weight range. It is desirable to remove the more volatile components prior to column use in order to ensure (a) minimum "bleed" interference in the detector, (b) constant β and hence reproducible retention values for a given temperature and flow rate.

We accomplish curing by *slowly* raising the column temperature to about 30 °C *above* the desired operating range with a reduced carrier flow (ca. 10 % of normal). During this period the column should *not* be connected to the detector! It is impossible to overemphasize the importance of this step in column preparation. Rapid curing can ruin an otherwise well-prepared column and yet curing is often the operation least carefully performed by beginning chromatographers.

Column performance tests. Two column parameters are important, plate height H and capacity ratio k (or t_r for a given flow rate) (Eqs. (31.2) and (31.6)). For any column, H increases slowly and k decreases slowly over a long period of time. This gradual performance loss is inevitable since the stationary phase has a finite vapor pressure and will "bleed off." The support can also catalyze decomposition of the stationary phase. We can guard against unexpected degradation of a given column by routinely following the retention behavior of a reference compound. As retention times become shorter under a given set of conditions, it may need renewal.

Retention indices. How can retention data be compared when different columns are used? One solution is use of retention indices or Kovac indices (named after their inventor). The method calls for chromatographing a homologous series, e.g. C_6–C_{14} hydrocarbons. We then assign an arbitrary value to the retention of each member, viz. $C_6 = 100$, $C_7 = 200$, $C_8 = 300$ etc. A species eluting halfway between C_7 and C_8 then has a retention index of $250/100 = 2.50$. The assumption made is that while absolute retentions of the C_6–C_{14} hydrocarbons may change, their relative retentions will not. To the degree this is true, the index for species referred to these standards will remain constant.

An obvious weakness in this method is that the elution behavior of hydrocarbons bears little or no direct relation to the behavior of other types of compounds such as alcohols. A better procedure is to choose as standards a series of compounds that is chemically related to the compounds indexed. The use of "pure" compounds as stationary phases also improves this technique since, barring decomposition, the average composition is constant.

31.11 ANALYTICAL PROCEDURES

Column chromatographic techniques have made outstanding contributions to *qualitative analysis*. Complex mixtures previously analyzed by tedious fractional distillation methods requiring days to complete are routinely separated chromatographically in hours if not minutes. By direct coupling of a chromatograph to a mass spectrometer, we can identify each individual species "on-the-fly." We can separate, identify, and quantitatively measure nuclear spin isomers, isotopically labeled compounds, positional and geometric isomers, and even enantiomers. The technique is also a source of very pure reference materials for other forms of analysis.

Example We can separate ortho and para hydrogen at liquid nitrogen temperatures using etched glass capillaries. All the possible CH_4 nuclear isomers (^{12}C, ^{13}C, ^1H, ^2H) can be resolved as well under very similar conditions. The enantiomers of chiral perfluoro acyl amides are readily separated on a stationary phase of the ureide of $L(-)$-valine isopropyl ester.

Quantitative analysis. It has already been implied that the peak or peaks in a chromatogram contain quantitative as well as qualitative information. In general, it is advisable to use peak area and not peak height as a concentration measure. The measurement of area can be performed mechanically or electronically. Of the former methods triangulation, cutting and weighing, and planimetry are the most common. The first of these, triangulation, is the simplest since it involves computing the product of peak height times full width at half height. Triangulation is obviously accurate only for symmetrical peaks. Planimetry requires a good deal of practice for good precision to be achieved. Studies of all three methods have been made with the conclusion that the relative error decreases with increase in the area determined. General equations for error propagation and optimum peak shape have also been developed.*

Electronic integration methods for gas-chromatography differ little from those used for peak area measurements with many other techniques (Section 7.6 and 9.8). The digital computer readily performs this operation and is probably the least dependent on an optimum peak profile of all the techniques available.

A word of precaution is warranted with respect to quantitative analysis by relative peak area comparison. This method is valid only if the molar response (area/mole) of the detector is a constant for all the components compared. In practice this is never the case. Thermal conductivity detectors give a relative response to a difference in heat transport properties. We can then predict that the molar response of these detectors will be different for structurally dissimilar molecules. Ionization detectors have a different molar response for different molecules because the number of ions produced in the flame can be characteristic of the structure of each species.

We can overcome this problem in several ways. Perhaps the best way is to use standard mixtures of the compounds to be measured. In this way absolute concentrations can be measured. If the compounds themselves are not available in a pure state, a good compromise may be to use structurally analogous compounds. In this case, the critical assumption is that structurally similar compounds produce similar molar detector responses. There are exceptions to this but it is perhaps more reasonable to compare ketones to ketones and hydrocarbons to hydrocarbons.

31.12 RESEARCH APPLICATIONS

Earlier in this chapter, mention was made of the fact that retention is a thermodynamically controlled process. This fact is of great consequence and deserves to be expanded further.

It is possible to measure the partition coefficient for solution or absorption

---

* D. L. Ball, W. E. Harris, and H. W. Habgood, *Separation Sci.* **2**, 81 (1967).

processes directly by measuring t_r'. As a result we can make direct measurements of ΔG, ΔH, and ΔS by use of two relationships given earlier:

$$k = (t_r - t_m)/t_m$$

$$K = (V_g/V_l)k = \beta k$$

and the standard thermodynamic expressions

$$\Delta G^0 = -RT \ln K$$

$$\frac{d(\ln K)}{dt} = \Delta H^0/R$$

$$\Delta G^0 = \Delta H^0 - T\Delta S^0.$$

It is also possible to measure the differential properties $\Delta(\Delta G^0)$, $\Delta(\Delta H^0)$, and $\Delta(\Delta S^0)$ by measuring α-values for two solutes in the same solvent and applying

$$k_2/k_1 = \alpha$$

$$\ln \alpha = -\frac{\Delta(\Delta H^0)}{RT} + \frac{\Delta(\Delta S^0)}{R}$$

$$\Delta(\Delta G^0) = \Delta(\Delta H^0) - T\Delta(\Delta S^0).$$

Of course, for such measurements to be worth while we must be able to measure retentions accurately and with precision. This requires a chromatographic system of high excellence using digital control of sampling and data acquisition whose performance far exceeds commercial instrumentation presently available. At time of writing the maximum achievable precision in measuring retention times and α-values is in the range of $\pm 0.02\%$ for gas–liquid systems. This corresponds to an error in $\Delta(\Delta G^0)$ of about $\pm 0.1\%$, in $\Delta(\Delta H^0)$ of about $\pm 0.01\%$ and a corresponding error in $\Delta(\Delta S^0)$. Note that these precisions are about one order of magnitude better than the theory used to calculate them at this time and that their significance awaits further developments in chromatographic theory.

It is also possible to measure gas–solid absorption isotherms from the tails of chromatographic peaks. The results are in good agreement with those obtained by more classical static measurements as are the heats of absorption derived from the comparison of isotherms measured by various temperatures. The relative precision for well-behaved systems can be as good as $\pm 2\%$ generally and $\pm 1\%$ for ΔH_s.

Careful measurement of H vs $\bar{u}$ relationships permits measurement of many of the physical constants in the van Deemter equation. Other quantities such as diffusion of solute molecules in liquid–crystal melts and of gas molecules in microporous zeolites can also be investigated in this manner.

31.13 CONCLUSION

For considerations of space many of the interesting details of chromatographic design that are of importance to the specialist have been omitted. For example, we have mentioned more than once the need for flow control, but no lengthy description of the many devices available is presented. For such information consult the chromatographic literature and draw your own conclusions.

The rapidly growing area of high-resolution, high-efficiency, high-speed (so-called modern) liquid chromatography in columns has also been neglected. The reasons for this are at least twofold. First, many of the principles of gas chromatography in columns apply to this technique. The major equipment differences lie, at least at present, in the necessity to contain high pressures (generally in the range of 40 to 140 bars). At this time there is no liquid chromatographic equivalent of the flame ionization detector in terms of carrier independence, response, and sensitivity over a broad range of concentrations. Dead volume considerations are even more important in this technique than in gas chromatography. Second, progress in the area is so rapid that anything that could be said now will be soon outdated.

REFERENCES

Some references providing general coverage in the area of separations are:

1. Erich Heftmann, *Chromatography*. New York: Reinhold, 1967
2. J. C. Giddings, *Advances in Chromatography*. New York: Dekker (a continuing series in treatise form)

Some references to gas chromatography are:

3. O. E. Schupp, "Gas Chromatography," in *Technique of Organic Chemistry*. Vol. XIII. E. S. Perry and A. Weissberger, eds. New York: Interscience, 1968 (theory and practice)
4. J. C. Giddings, *Dynamics of Chromatography*. New York: Dekker, 1965 (theory)
5. H. Purnell, *Gas Chromatography*, New York: Wiley, 1962 (theory, especially thermodynamic aspects)·
6. S. Dal Nogare and R. S. Juvet, *Gas–Liquid Chromatography*. New York: Interscience, 1962
7. L. S. Ettre, *Open Tubular Columns in Gas Chromatography*. New York: Plenum, 1965
8. R. Kaiser, *Gas Phase Chromatography*. Vols. I, II. Washington, D.C.: Butterworths, 1963 (from the practical side)
9. Analabs, *Guide to Stationary Phases for Gas Chromatography*. North Haven, Conn.: Analabs Inc. (an extremely useful little book that is revised annually)

Some references emphasizing physical measurements by gas chromatography are:

10. B. L. Karger, *Anal. Chem.* **39** (8), 24A (1967) (thermodynamics)
11. J. E. Oberholtzer and L. B. Rogers, *Anal. Chem.* **41**, 1234 (1969) (high-precision measurements)
12. J. F. K. Huber and A. I. M. Keulemans in *Gas Chromatography*, 1962. M. Van Swaay, ed. Washington, D.C.: Butterworths, 1962, p. 26 (absorption isotherms)

EXERCISES

31.1 For the case where two adjacent peaks do not differ in concentration, an equation that predicts the minimum number of theoretical plates required to achieve a separation is:

$$n_{\text{req}} = 16[\alpha/(\alpha - 1)]^2 \left[\frac{k_2 + 1}{k_2}\right]^2,$$

where k_2 refers to the second solute. (The student can attempt the derivation of this equation.

Hint: Use the equations that relate peak height, width, and resolution.) It is desired to resolve enantiomorphic pairs where $\alpha = 1.1$. What number of theoretical plates would be required for (a) a packed column where $k = 25$? (b) for an open tubular column where $k = 1.0$?

[*Ans.*: (a) 2788; (b) 2.3×10^5.]

31.2 If for a particular chromatographic system the A, B, C terms of the van Deemter expression are 0.2 cm, 0.40 cm^{2}s^{-1} and 5×10^{-2}s, respectively. Calculate the minimum plate height and the optimum carrier velocity.

31.3 The boiling points of benzene and cyclohexane differ by less than 1 degree (80.1 °C vs. 80.8 °C). Suggest a method by which they can be separated. Give details.

31.4 For a given set of conditions $\alpha = 1.1$ and $H = 1$ mm. Predict the effect of:

a) Lowering the injection port temperature.
b) Shortening the injection time.
c) Doubling column length.
d) Doubling recorder chart speed.
e) Doubling sample size.
f) Halving packing particle size.

31.5 If hydrogen is used as a carrier gas, it is possible to construct a flame ionization detector using the exit tip of the column as a burner. Suggest advantages and disadvantages of this arrangement.

31.6 Given the following data for the chromatographic behavior of 1-methyl-3-cyclohexene and 3-methyl-3-cyclohexene on Carbowax 400.

t °C	α
78.35	1.2297 ± 0.00009
80.30	1.2276 ± 0.00011
80.56	1.2268 ± 0.00007
81.68	1.2244 ± 0.00010
81.98	1.2241 ± 0.00005
84.61	1.2211 ± 0.00008
86.12	1.2189 ± 0.00013
87.18	1.2177 ± 0.00001
89.80	1.2137 ± 0.00010
90.38	1.2133 ± 0.00009

a) Derive an expression relating $\Delta(\Delta H^0)$, $\Delta(\Delta S^0)$, $\Delta(\Delta G^0)$, and α for this process.
b) Graphically or numerically evaluate the thermodynamic quantities from the data supplied.
[*Ans.*: $\Delta(\Delta H^0) = -266.85 \pm 0.02$; $\Delta(\Delta S^0) = -0.350 \pm .001$; $\Delta(\Delta G^0) = -142.00 \pm 0.02$.]

CHARACTERISTICS OF 2N2614 TRANSISTOR

Ge p-n-p alloy-junction type used in small-signal and low-power audio frequency applications. JEDEC TO-1, **Outline** No.1. **Terminals:** 1 - emitter, 2 - base, 3 - collector.

MAXIMUM RATINGS

Collector-to-Base Voltage	V_{CBO}	−40	V
Collector-to-Emitter Voltage ($R_{BE} = 10$ kΩ)	V_{CER}	−35	V
Emitter-to-Base Voltage	V_{EBO}	−25	V
Collector Current	I_C	−50	mA
Emitter Current	I_E	50	mA
Transistor Dissipation:			
$\quad T_A$ up to 55°C	P_T	120	mW
$\quad T_C$ up to 55°C	P_T	300	mW
$\quad T_A$ or T_C above 55°C	P_T	See curve page 116	
Temperature Range:			
$\quad$ Operating (Junction)	T_J(opr)	−65 to 100	°C
$\quad$ Storage	T_{STG}	−65 to 100	°C
Lead-Soldering Temperature (10 s max)	T_L	255	°C

CHARACTERISTICS

Collector-to-Base Breakdown Voltage			
$\quad$ ($I_C = -0.05$ mA, $V_{BE} = 2$ V)	$V_{(BR)CBV}$	−40 min	V
Collector-to-Emitter Breakdown Voltage			
$\quad$ ($I_C = -1$ mA, $R_{BE} = 10$ kΩ)	$V_{(BR)CER}$	−35 min	V
Emitter-to-Base Breakdown Voltage			
$\quad$ ($I_E = -0.05$ mA, $I_C = 0$)	$V_{(BR)EBO}$	−25 min	V
Collector-Cutoff Current ($V_{CB} = -20$ V, $I_E = 0$)	I_{CBO}	−5 max	μA
Emitter-Cutoff Current ($V_{EB} = -20$ V, $I_C = 0$)	I_{EBO}	−7.5 max	μA
Small-Signal Forward-Current Transfer Ratio			
$\quad$ ($V_{CE} = -6$ V, $I_C = -1$ mA, $f = 1$ kHz)	h_{fe}	100 to 250	
Small-Signal Forward-Current Transfer-Ratio Cutoff			
$\quad$ Frequency ($V_{CE} = -6$ V, $I_C = -1$ mA)	f_{hfe}	4 min	MHz
Collector-to-Base Feedback Capacitance			
$\quad$ ($V_{CE} = -6$ V, $I_C = -1$ mA)	$C_{b'c}$	12 max	pF
Intrinsic Base-Spreading Resistance			
$\quad$ ($V_{CE} = -6$ V, $I_C = -1$ mA, $f = 20$ MHz)	$r_{bb'}$	300	Ω

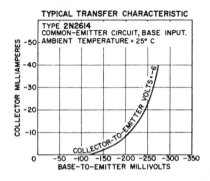

TYPICAL TRANSFER CHARACTERISTIC

TYPE 2N2614
COMMON—EMITTER CIRCUIT, BASE INPUT.
AMBIENT TEMPERATURE = 25° C

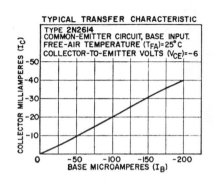

TYPICAL TRANSFER CHARACTERISTIC

TYPE 2N2614
COMMON—EMITTER CIRCUIT, BASE INPUT.
FREE-AIR TEMPERATURE (T_{FA})=25° C
COLLECTOR-TO-EMITTER VOLTS (V_{CE})=−6

---

* The material in Appendix A and Appendix B is reproduced from the *RCA Transistor Manual*, Technical Series SC–13, by kind permission of RCA.

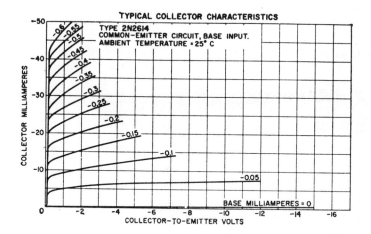

TYPICAL COLLECTOR CHARACTERISTICS

CHARACTERISTICS OF 2N2953 TRANSISTOR

Ge p-n-p alloy-junction type used in af-driver amplifier applications in consumer and industrial equipment. JEDEC TO-1, Outline No.1. Terminals: 1 - emitter, 2 - base, 3 - collector.

MAXIMUM RATINGS

Collector-to-Base Voltage	V_{CBO}	−30	V
Collector-to-Emitter Voltage ($R_{BE} = 10$ kΩ)	V_{CER}	−25	V
Emitter-to-Base Voltage	V_{EBO}	25	V
Collector Current	I_C	−0.15	A
Emitter Current	I_E	0.15	A
Transistor Dissipation:			
T_A up to 55°C	P_T	120	mW
T_C up to 55°C (in an infinite heat sink)	P_T	300	mW
T_C up to 55°C (with practical heat sink,			
$\theta = 50°C/W$)	P_T	225	mW
T_A or T_C (with practical heat sink) above 55°C	P_T	See curve page 116	
Temperature Range:			
Operating (Junction)	T_J (opr)	−65 to 100	°C
Storage	T_{STG}	−65 to 100	°C
Lead-Soldering Temperature (10 s max)	T_L	255	°C

CHARACTERISTICS

Collector-to-Base Breakdown Voltage ($I_C = −0.05$ A,			
$V_{EB} = −2$ V)	$V_{(BR)CBr}$	−30 min	V
Collector-to-Emitter Breakdown Voltage ($I_C = −1$ mA,			
$R_{BE} = 10$ kΩ)	$V_{(BR)CER}$	−25 min	V
Emitter-to-Base Breakdown Voltage ($I_E = −0.05$ mA,			
$I_C = 0$)	$V_{(BR)EBO}$	−25 min	V
Collector-Cutoff Current ($V_{CB} = −20$ V, $I_E = 0$)	I_{CBO}	−5 max	μA
Emitter-Cutoff Current ($V_{EB} = −20$ V, $I_C = 0$)	I_{EBO}	−7.5 max	μA
Small-Signal Forward-Current Transfer Ratio			
($V_{CE} = −10$ V, $I_C = −10$ mA, f = 1 kHz)	h_{fe}	200 min	
Small-Signal Forward-Current Transfer-Ratio Cutoff			
Frequency ($V_{CE} = −12$ V, $I_C = −1$ mA)	f_{hfb}	10	MHz
Intrinsic Base-Spreading Resistance			
($V_{CE} = −10$ V, $I_C = −10$ mA, f = 20 MHz)	r_{bb}'	300	Ω
Collector-to-Base Feedback Capacitance			
($V_{CE} = −12$ V, $I_C = −1$ mA)	$C_{b'c}$	6.5	pF

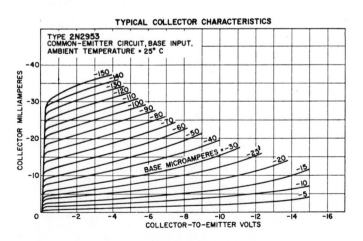

TYPICAL COLLECTOR CHARACTERISTICS

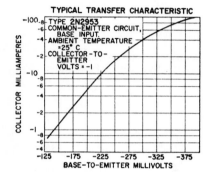

TYPICAL TRANSFER CHARACTERISTIC

TYPE 2N2953
COMMON-EMITTER CIRCUIT, BASE INPUT.
AMBIENT TEMPERATURE =25° C
COLLECTOR-TO-EMITTER VOLTS = -1

COLLECTOR MILLIAMPERES

BASE-TO-EMITTER MILLIVOLTS

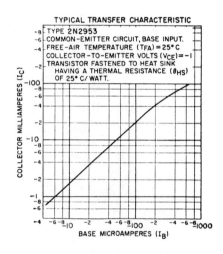

TYPICAL TRANSFER CHARACTERISTIC

TYPE 2N2953
COMMON-EMITTER CIRCUIT, BASE INPUT.
FREE-AIR TEMPERATURE (T_{FA})=25°C
COLLECTOR-TO-EMITTER VOLTS (V_{CE})=-1
TRANSISTOR FASTENED TO HEAT SINK
HAVING A THERMAL RESISTANCE (θ_{HS})
OF 25° C/WATT.

COLLECTOR MILLIAMPERES (I_C)

BASE MICROAMPERES (I_B)

APPENDIX C

SI UNITS

In this text units generally conform to the International System of Units (abbreviated SI for Système Internationale), which is an extension and refinement of the metric system. As a rational, coherent, and comprehensive system it was adopted by the Conférence Genérale des Poids et Mesures in 1960 and is rapidly coming into use around the world. Names, numerical factors, symbols (in parentheses), and definitions of some quantities are given below.*

Exceptions to the use of SI units in the text are made in the case of temperature, which is given in degrees Celsius unless otherwise noted, volumes and concentrations, which are often stated in terms of liters and molarity, gas pressures which are sometimes given in atmospheres, and magnetic quantities (Chapter 19), which are given in emu. There may be occasional other exceptions.

PREFIXES†

Submultiples		Multiples	
10^{-2}	centi (c)	10^3	kilo (k)
10^{-3}	milli (m)	10^6	mega (M)
10^{-6}	micro (μ)	10^9	giga (G)
10^{-9}	nano (n)	10^{12}	tera (T)
10^{-12}	pico (p)		
10^{-15}	femto (f)		
10^{-18}	atto (a)		

SOME SI UNITS

length	meter (m)
mass	kilogram (kg)
time	second (s)
current	ampere (A)
temperature	Kelvin (K)
amount of substance	mole (mol)
luminous intensity	candela (cd)

---

* For more information see G. Socrates and L. J. Sopper, *SI Units and Metrication Conversion Tables*, London: Newnes–Butterworth, 1969; NBS Handbook 102, *ASTM Metric Practice Guide*, Washington, D.C.: U.S. Government Printing Office; M. L. McGlashan, *Physiochemical Quantities and Units*, second edition, London: Royal Institute of Chemistry, 1971.

† Compound prefixes such as mμ should not be used.

DERIVED SI UNITS

Quantity	Name	Definition *	Quantity	Definition
energy	joule (J)	$kg\,m^2s^{-2}$	pressure	newton/meter² $(N\,m^{-2})$
force	newton (N)	$kg\,m\,s^{-2} = J\,m^{-1}$	angular	radian/second
power	watt (W)	$kg\,m^2s^{-3} = J\,s^{-1}$	velocity	$(rad\,s^{-1})$
charge	coulomb (C)	$A\,s$	area	square meter (m^2)
potential difference	volt (V)	$kg\,m^2s^{-3}A^{-1}$ $= J\,A^{-1}s^{-1}$	volume	cubic meter (m^3)
resistance	ohm (Ω)	$kg\,m^2s^{-3}A^{-2}$	velocity	meter/second $(m\,s^{-1})$
frequency	hertz (Hz)	$= J\,A^{-1}s^{-1}$		

SOME OTHER ALLOWED UNITS

volume	liter (l)	$10^{-3}\,m^3$
pressure	bar (bar)	$10^5\,N\,m^{-2}$
mass	tonne (t)	$10^3\,kg = Mg$
energy	electron-volt (eV)	$1.602 \times 10^{-19}\,J$

SOME FUNDAMENTAL CONSTANTS

Avogadro's number (N_0): $6.02 \times 10^{23}\,mol^{-1}$
Planck's constant (h): $6.63 \times 10^{-34}\,J\,s$
Speed of light in vacuum (c): $3.00 \times 10^8\,m\,s^{-1}$
Faraday: $96{,}487\,C\,mol^{-1}$
Gas constant (R): $8.309\,J\,mol^{-1}\,K^{-1}$

CONVERSION FACTORS

energy	$erg = 1 \times 10^{-7}\,J$
	$calorie = 4.1868\,J$
pressure	$atm = 101.3\,kN\,m^{-2} = 1.013\,bar$
	$torr = 133.3\,N\,m^{-2} = 1.333 \times 10^{-3}\,bar$

---

* A space between units indicates that they are multiplied. For example, "m N" means "meter ×
newton" while "mN" means "millinewton."

APPENDIX D

SUPPLEMENTARY REFERENCES

Some valuable articles and books that have appeared too recently to be listed at ends of chapters are collected here. They are grouped according to the chapter(s) of this text most closely related to their topic (the appropriate chapter number is noted at the beginning of each entry). A brief annotation appears at the end of most references.

1. E. L. Bauer, *A Statistical Manual for Chemists,* 2d ed. New York: Academic, 1971. A working manual on an introductory level.

1. G. W. Ewing, ed., *Topics in Chemical Instrumentation.* Easton, Pa.: Chemical Education Publishing Co., 1971. A selection of articles from the *J. Chem. Educ.* column of the same title with updating by the contributing authors.

4. R. S. C. Cobbold, *Theory and Applications of Field-Effect Transistors.* New York: Wiley, 1970. An advanced level presentation.

4, 5, 6. Paul E. Gray and Campbell L. Searle, *Electronic Principles—Physics, Models, and Circuits.* New York: Wiley, 1969. A very good account on an introductory to intermediate level.

5. Lawrence J. Giacoletto, *Differential Amplifiers.* New York: Wiley, 1970. An advanced level presentation.

7. Larry L. Schick, "Linear Circuit Applications of Operational Amplifiers," *IEEE Spectrum* **8** (4), 36 (1971). A clear intermediate-level presentation.

7. G. E. Tobey, J. G. Graeme, and L. P. Huelsman, *Operational Amplifiers—Design and Application.* New York: McGraw-Hill, 1971. A clear, intermediate-level presentation.

8. P. G. Cath and A. M. Peabody, "High Speed Current Measurements," *Anal. Chem.* **43** (11) 91A (1971). An article concerned with minimizing noise.

8. J. D. Ingle, Jr., and S. R. Crouch, "Signal-to-Noise Ratio Comparison of Photomultipliers and Phototubes," *Anal. Chem.* **43**, 1331 (1971).

8. Seymour Letzter and Norman Webster, "Noise in Amplifiers," *IEEE Spectrum* **7** (8) 67 (1970).

9. Lane S. Garrett, "Integrated-Circuit Digital Logic Families," *IEEE Spectrum* **7** (10), 47; (11), 63; (12), 30 (1970). A clear discussion and comparison of integrated circuit logic families.

9. I. Lysyj, P. R. Newton, and W. J. Taylor, "Instrument-Computer System for Analysis of Multicomponent Organic Mixtures," *Anal. Chem.* **43**, 1277 (1971).

9. C. H. Orr and J. A. Norris, eds., *Computers in Analytical Chemistry.* New York: Plenum, 1970. A good intermediate-level account of application of computers to instrumentation.

9. S. P. Perone, "Computer Applications in the Chemistry Laboratory—A Survey," *Anal. Chem.* **43**, 1288 (1971).

10. Joseph W. Simmons and M. J. Guttmann, *States, Waves, and Photons; A Modern Introduction to Light.* Reading, Mass.: Addison-Wesley, 1970. An intermediate-level text on physical optics.

11. B. A. Lengyel, *Lasers*, 2d ed., New York: Wiley-Interscience, 1971. A clear presentation on an intermediate level.

11, 17. James E. Stewart, *Infrared Spectroscopy: Experimental Methods and Techniques.* New York: Dekker, 1970. A good presentation of IR instrumentation and practice on an intermediate to advanced level.

12, 13, 17. P. Bousquet, *Spectroscopy and Its Instrumentation.* London: Adam Hilger, 1971. A clear presentation on an intermediate to advanced level.

13. E. L. Grove, ed., *Analytical Emission Spectroscopy*, Vol. I, Part 1. New York: Dekker, 1971. A presentation of instrumentation and theory.

13. Morris Slavin, *Emission Spectrochemical Analysis.* New York: Wiley-Interscience, 1971. A clear presentation of the experimental side on an introductory to intermediate level.

13, 15, 16, 18, 19. Raymond Chang, *Basic Principles of Spectroscopy.* New York: McGraw-Hill, 1971. A concise, generally clear presentation of theory on an introductory to intermediate level.

14. K. M. Aldous, B. W. Bailey, and J. M. Rankin, "Burning Velocity of the Premixed Nitrous Oxide/Acetylene Flame and Its Influence on Burner Design," *Anal. Chem.* **44**, 191 (1972).

14. G. D. Christian and F. J. Feldman, *Atomic Absorption Spectroscopy: Applications in Agriculture, Biology and Medicine.* New York: Wiley-Interscience, 1970. A clear presentation of theory and practice on an introductory level.

14. J. A. Dean and T. C. Rains, eds., *Flame Emission and Atomic Absorption Spectrometry*, Vol. 2 *Components and Techniques.* New York: Dekker, 1971. A good discussion of instrumentation and practice on an intermediate level.

14. M. B. Denton and H. V. Malmstadt, "Burner and Nebulizer Improvements for Atomic Absorption Spectrometry," *Anal. Chem.* **44**, 241 (1972). A useful article on technical developments.

14. B. V. L'vov, *Atomic Absorption Spectrochemical Analysis.* New York: American Elsevier, 1971. An advanced-level book offering many insights.

14. D. G. Mitchell and A. Johansson, "Simultaneous Multi-element Analysis Using Sequentially Excited Atomic Fluorescence Radiation," *Spectrochim. Acta* **25B**, 175 (1970). An interesting account of a technique.

14, 15. J. D. Winefordner, ed., *Spectrochemical Methods of Analysis: Quantitative Analysis of Atoms and Molecules.* New York: Wiley-Interscience, 1971. A good account on an intermediate level.

15. R. P. Wayne, *Photochemistry.* New York: American Elsevier, 1971. A good account on an introductory to intermediate level.

15, 16, 17, 18. A. Weissberger and B. W. Rossiter, eds., *Physical Methods of Chemistry*, Vol. I,

Part IIIB, *Spectroscopy and Spectrometry in the Infrared, Visible, and Ultraviolet.* New York: Wiley-Interscience, 1972. A clear, experimentally-oriented treatment.

16. L. J. Bellamy, *Advances in Group Frequencies.* London: Methuen, 1968. A supplement to reference 34, Chapter 16.

16. D. F. Boltz, "The Role of Spectrophotometry in Modern Trace Analysis," *Rec. Chem. Progress* **32**, 215 (1971). A valuable discussion of the topic on an intermediate level.

16. E. F. H. Brittain, W. O. George, and C. H. J. Wells, *Introduction to Molecular Spectroscopy.* New York: Academic, 1970. A good introduction to many spectrometric techniques.

16. Norman B. Colthup, *Interpretation of Infrared Spectra.* 5 cassettes and one course manual Washington: Am. Chem. Soc., 1971. A resource for self-instruction.

16. T. J. Porro, "Double-Wavelength Spectroscopy," *Anal. Chem.* **44** (4) 93A (1972). A good account of the uses of the technique in the UV-VIS.

16, 17. Arthur Finch, P. M. Gates, K. Radcliffe, E. N. Dickinson, E. F. Bentley, *Chemical Applications of Far-Infrared Spectroscopy.* New York: Academic, 1970. A well-written volume on an intermediate level.

17. K. D. Moller and W. G. Rothschild, *Far Infrared Spectroscopy.* New York: Wiley, 1971. A good coverage of instrumentation.

17, 19. H. M. Pickett and H. L. Strauss, "Signal-To-Noise Ratio in Fourier Transform Spectrometry," *Anal. Chem.* **44**, 265 (1972). A discussion of interferogram length.

18. P. J. Hendra and C. J. Vear, "Laser Raman Spectroscopy," *Analyst* **95**, 321 (1970).

18. J. Loader, *Basic Laser Raman Spectroscopy.* London: Heyden, 1970. A brief account on an introductory level.

18. M. C. Tobin, *Laser Raman Spectroscopy.* New York: Wiley, 1971. A good account of experimental methods and instrumentation.

19. E. D. Becker, *High Resolution NMR—Theory and Chemical Applications.* New York: Academic, 1969. A well-organized, intermediate-level account.

19. E. D. Becker, "NMR Spectra: Appearance of Patterns from Small Spin Systems," *J. Chem. Educ.* **42**, 591 (1965). A valuable article on analysis of spectra.

19. J. V. Burakevich and J. O'Neill, Jr., "The Determination of Formic Acid by Nuclear Magnetic Resonance Spectroscopy," *Anal. Chim. Acta* **54**, 528 (1971). A good illustration of quantitative analysis by NMR.

19. T. C. Farrar, *Pulse and Fourier Transform NMR. Introduction to Theory and Methods.* New York: Academic, 1971. An intermediate-level account.

19. D. Ziessow and M. Carroll, "Referencing ^{13}C NMR Chemical Shifts," *Ber. Bunsenges. Phys. Chem.* **76**, 61 (1972). A valuable article on criteria for NMR referencing.

19, 20. A. Weissberger and B. W. Rossiter, eds., *Physical Methods of Chemistry,* Vol. I, Part IIA, *Interferometry, Light Scattering, Microscopy, Microwave, and Magnetic Resonance Spectroscopy.* New York: Wiley-Interscience, 1972. A clear, experimentally-oriented presentation.

21. D. J. Caldwell and H. Eyring, *The Theory of Optical Activity.* New York: Wiley-Interscience, 1971. An intermediate to advanced level account.

22. A. Weissberger and B. W. Rossiter, eds., *Physical Methods of Chemistry*, Vol. I, Part IIIC, *Polarimetry*. New York: Wiley-Interscience, 1972. A clear, experimentally-oriented presentation.

23. H. Eyring, D. Henderson, and W. Jost, eds., *Electrochemistry* (Vol. IXA of *Physical Chemistry—An Advanced Treatise*). New York: Academic, 1970. A treatment of selected topics on an advanced level.

23. J. Koryta, J. Dvorak, and V. Bohackova, *Electrochemistry*. London: Methuen, 1970. A balanced treatment on an intermediate level.

23, 24, 25, 26, 27, 28. A. Weissberger and B. W. Rossiter, eds., *Physical Methods of Chemistry*, Vol. I., Part IIA, *Electrochemical Methods*. New York: Wiley-Interscience, 1971. A clear, experimentally-oriented presentation.

24. B. Karlberg, "Nomograph for (Standard) Addition Methods in Analysis with Selective Electrodes," *Anal. Chem.* **43**, 1910 (1971). A useful account.

24. Orest Popovych, "Estimation of Medium Effects for Single Ions in Non-Aqueous Solvents," *Critical Rev. Anal. Chem.* **1**, 73 (1970).

24. E. Pungor and K. Toth, "Ion-Selective Membrane Electrodes," *Analyst* **95**, 625 (1970). A broad review.

24. J. Ruzicka and C. G. Lamm, "Selectrode™—The Universal Ion-Selective Solid-State Electrode," *Anal. Chim. Acta,* **54**, 1 (1971).

25. A. M. Bond and D. R. Canterford, "Comparative Study of a Wide Variety of Polarographic Techniques with Multifunctional Instrumentation," *Anal. Chem.* **44**, 721 (1972).

29. Paul Kruger, *Principles of Activation Analysis*. New York: Wiley, 1971. A good account on an intermediate level.

31. J. J. Kirkland, ed., *Modern Practice of Liquid Chromatography*. New York: Wiley-Interscience, 1971.

31. D. A. Leathard and B. C. Shurlock, *Identification Techniques in Gas Chromatography*. London: Wiley-Interscience, 1971. A good discussion of methods of identifying chromatogram peaks.

INDEX